# Ecological Forest Management

# Ecological Forest Management

**JERRY F. FRANKLIN**
*University of Washington*

**K. NORMAN JOHNSON**
*Oregon State University*

**DEBORA L. JOHNSON**
*Applegate Forestry LLC*

**WAVELAND**

**PRESS, INC.**

Long Grove, Illinois

For information about this book, contact:

Waveland Press, Inc.
4180 IL Route 83, Suite 101
Long Grove, IL 60047-9580
(847) 634-0081
info@waveland.com
www.waveland.com

*Cover:*

*Front, bottom left:* Hardwood landscape in autumn, courtesy of David Foster
*Back left:* Public field review of proposed USFS restoration harvest, courtesy of Deanne Carlson
*Back right:* Red-cockaded woodpecker, courtesy of USFWS

We dedicate this book to our colleague and friend

## ROBERT J. MITCHELL   (October 17, 1955—May 15, 2013)

Bob was a major contributor to and advocate for forest management based on ecological principles. He was a brilliant intellect, untiring in his pursuit of scientific insights regarding the most complex of forest topics, and had only limited patience with those who willfully chose to ignore facts as observed in nature!

Bob led the way in developing the foundational concepts of ecological forestry that we express in this book. When we explain the concept of ecological integrity or describe the economics of ecological forestry, we are, at least in part, relating what Bob has taught us. Thus, his thoughts are still with us.

As satisfying as that might be, it is not quite the same as having Bob here to critique our book. He would have challenged our ideas, helping us to understand and express more deeply the central ideas of ecological forestry. In a good spirited way he would have enriched much of what we say here.

More than anything else, Bob taught us about the wonder and mystery of the natural world and how we should never assume we know something for sure. Rather that we must continue to observe, learn, and think about nature as he did until the day he died.

We miss him.

# About the Authors

*Dr. Jerry Franklin* is professor emeritus of forest ecosystems in the School of Environmental and Forest Sciences at the University of Washington where he has taught ecosystem management and science, silviculture, landscape ecology, and forest ecology. He received his BS and MS in Forest Management from Oregon State University and his PhD in Botany and Soils from Washington State University. He began his career as a research forester at the US Forest Service's Pacific Northwest Research Station where he worked on silvicultural topics, primarily tree regeneration. After a term as a Program Manager in the National Science Foundation, Jerry returned to the USFS PNW Station as a project leader and Chief Plant Ecologist. During this time he was a leader of a scientific team that characterized the ecological nature and importance of old-growth forest ecosystems. He has been an author on over 500 scientific articles and 12 books. Franklin has received numerous honors including honorary doctorate degrees from Lakehead and Simon Fraser Universities, the Barrington Moore Award from the Society of American Foresters, the Eminent Ecologist award from the Ecological Society of America, the LaRoe Award from the Society of Conservation Biology, and the Heinz Award for the Environment. He has served on and has led numerous scientific panels that have advised states, Congress, the White House, and the Province of British Columbia on forestry issues. Over the last decade, much of his time has been spent advising federal, state, Native American, and private landowners on ecological forest management.

*Dr. K. Norman Johnson* is professor emeritus of forest resources in the College of Forestry at Oregon State University where he has taught forest policy, forest management, forest economics, and collaboration. He received his BS in Forestry from the University of California at Berkeley and his PhD in Forest Management from Oregon State University, emphasizing natural resource economics. Norm spent the early part of his career on the theory and practice of timber harvest scheduling and on building forest planning models for large public and private forestry landowners that estimated sustainable harvest levels. He has published numerous articles on these topics and co-authored two books on forest management planning. Over the last 25 years, much of his time, outside of teaching and policy analysis, has been spent advising Oregon's Governors and Congressional Delegation on federal forestry, serving on scientific committees that addressed federal forest issues, and working with Indian tribes on forest planning. Most recently, he has worked with Dr. Franklin to demonstrate ecological forestry principles in the forests of the Pacific Northwest.

*Debora Johnson* received her BS in Forest Management at Oregon State University. She is a Certified Forester (SAF) and Certified GIS Professional (URISA). She specialized in forest inventory, GIS, and forest planning during the 25 years she worked for the Oregon State University College Forests. In that position she also worked on conservation efforts for several threatened and endangered species. She directed the Habitat Restoration Program at the Institute for Applied Ecology where she worked on projects to restore rare prairie habitat. She now runs a consulting company, Applegate Forestry LLC, which is currently assisting the Klamath Tribes on project planning associated with the Tribes' management plan for the Klamath Reservation Forest.

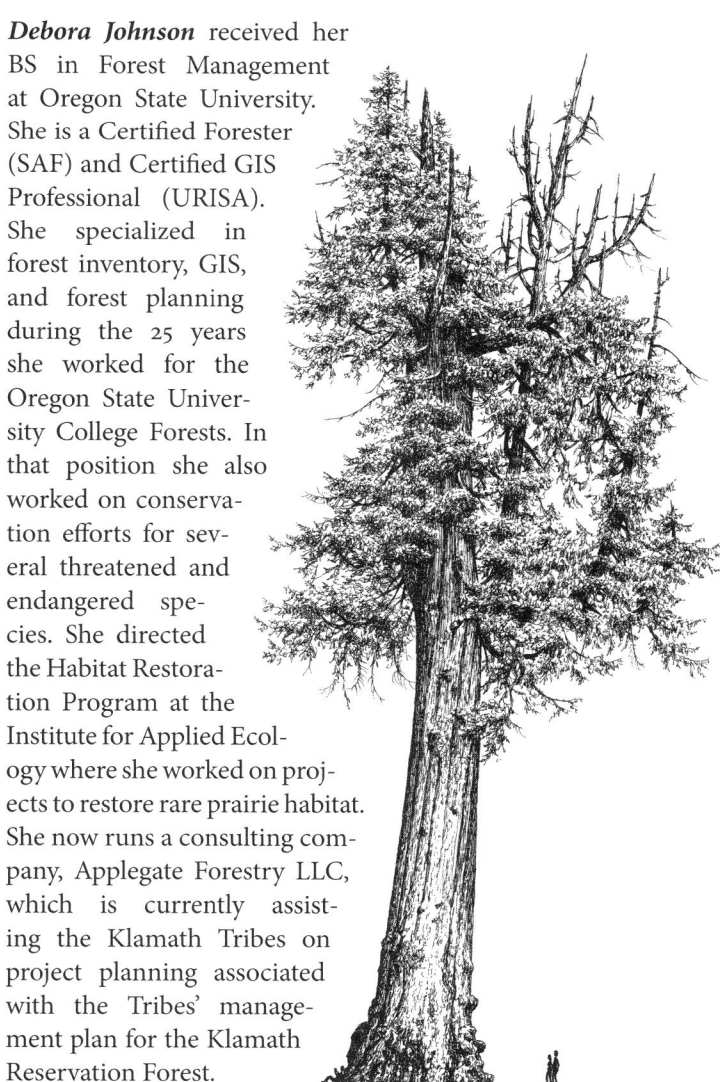

# Contents

# Part II
*Economic and Social Context*    *147*

# Part IV
## Forest Planning

# Part V
## *Summary and Conclusions*    593

# Preface

Collectively we have been engaged in many aspects of forest management over the last 50 years. During this time there have been fundamental changes in all aspects of forestry including the underlying science, underpinning environmental conditions, societal expectations about management of forest ecosystems, and development of a globalized economy.

*Many of our activities have focused on the development and adoption of management practices and policies that would sustain the integrity of forest ecosystems—maintain their essential complement of biota, structures, and functional capacities—while also achieving the goals of the landowners and societies that depend upon them.* These activities have taken us in many directions: advising landowners, states, and conservation groups on forest management; building forest planning models for public and private forests; helping initiate research on old-growth forests; participating in major federal policy analyses; and developing a forest restoration plan for the Klamath Tribes. They have involved collaborations with an ever-expanding community of scientists, academics, students, forestry practitioners, and interested citizens who seek socially inclusive outcomes while sustaining the biodiversity and functionality of forest ecosystems.

Initially, we set out to revise the fourth edition of *Forest Management* (Davis et al., 2001). This book has been in the Davis family for the past 50 years, and one of us (Norm Johnson) coauthored the last two editions (Davis & Johnson, 1985 and Davis et al., 2001). In its time, the various editions of the Davis books were *the* forest management texts used in most forestry schools in the United States. More than anything else, these books dealt with planning the long-term management of forests, with a focus on setting a sustainable timber harvest level and on forests as regulated systems. They covered, and helped define, the essential topics of a forest management book, including timber growth and yield, decision analysis, investment, valuation, methods for determining the allowable cut, and forest planning techniques. With these topics, the several editions attempted to bring together diverse concepts and techniques to assist the forester with the perennial problem of managing forests to provide sustainable supplies of timber and other outputs to meet the needs of both landowners and society.

The most recent editions of *Forest Management* embraced the language and concepts of economics as the foundation upon which to build solutions to forest planning problems. They focused on quantitative decision analysis, systematic development and evaluation of alternatives, consideration of multiple objectives, and trade-off and efficiency analysis to find income-generating or least-cost solutions—all valuable tools in resource planning. However, planning concepts that emulate the development and functioning of natural systems were largely absent or given limited consideration as constraints after the basic planning models had been constructed. While the books acknowledged uncertainties, the overall approach emphasized long planning horizons in the context of a generally stable and predictable future.

In our initial attempt to create a fifth edition of *Forest Management* we ultimately found such an approach to be too limiting. The reasons were many, including increasing social recognition of the importance of maintaining natural ecosystems and the species dependent on them, the diverse ecological goals of many forest landowners, the rapidly changing and increasingly uncertain environmental and social future that we face, and our interests in forest practices based on natural forest models. We also wanted to produce a volume that would engage a much broader spectrum of natural resource students.

Thus, we decided to adopt ecological concepts as the foundation of our forest management text, upon which we would build economic and social considerations. We began with the underlying goal of managing forest ecosystems in ways that would maintain their ecological integrity, as we explored different forest management strategies that emulate the effects of natural disturbances and associated developmental models in prescriptions and management. We gradually became aware that such a radical change in approach required us to go back to fundamentals in order to rethink the philosophical base and principles for this book, which we call *ecological forest management*. We then used these principles in order to once again tackle many of the perennial problems addressed in previous forest management books, with a central focus on managing forests for the array of forest services and products desired by both landowners and society.

## Historical Development of Ecological Forestry Management

Much of the philosophical basis and principles of ecological forestry prove to be not all that new. In the United States, its origins can be found in the writings of silviculturists like Hawley and Toumey in the 1920s; the work begun at Harvard Forest in the 1930s that continues to this day; and the introduction of ecological forestry to the broader forestry community by Spurr and Cline in the 1940s (D'Amato et al., 2017). More recently, Seymour and Hunter (1999) have further developed and advocated use of ecological forestry. Perhaps most importantly, the writings of Aldo Leopold provide a view of the world and the conservation of ecosystems in which ecological forestry can thrive. We also had the advantage, which Leopold did not, of an immense body of scientific and technical knowledge about forest ecosystems that managers and scientists have created over the past 50 years. This knowledge is what makes it possible to translate ecological principles into guides for the practical management of forests.

## Our Goals for This Book

This book is our contribution to an ecologically credible pathway forward for managing the majority of global forestlands, which will be neither preserves nor plantations intensively managed for wood production. We have laid out principles and identified ways in which these principles can be utilized to manage forestlands in real-world situations, with the overriding goal of sustaining the integrity of forest ecosystems while they are managed to provide a diverse array of values, services, and goods to human society.

The book represents an initial exploration of the dimensions of what is useful and possible in ecological forest management. It should not be viewed as a manual of silvicultural practices; a companion volume on silvicultural applications of ecological forest management is in preparation.

We concentrate primarily on temperate forest ecosystems—the region with which we are most familiar. However, we believe that the concepts presented here are adaptable to boreal forests as well as to tropical forests, in at least some of their aspects.

Our personal experiences have shown us that there is a large community of foresters, landowners, scientists, conservationists, and citizens around the world working hard to develop and implement ecologically sound management practices in forest ecosystems. Many of them contributed

to the ideas presented in this book. We acknowledge their creativity and courage, and hope our synthesis informs and empowers them, just as their work has informed and empowered us.

We view this volume as a first approximation of ecological forest management and most certainly not the final word, which we do not expect ever to be written! In that spirit we actively seek feedback from those who attempt to utilize it in terms of additions, clarifications, and corrections; we hope that they will share their experiences in developing and applying ecological forestry with us.

In sum, our goal in writing this book has been to help students, professionals, landowners, and citizens involved in forest management to understand and adopt principles and practices consistent with the goal of maintaining and restoring the integrity of forest ecosystems. *We want to encourage broad adoption of these principles and practices and, conversely, we do not want to discourage or exclude their adoption by insisting on specific practices or standards of performance; every aspect of ecological forest management that is implemented in a forest stand or landscape will contribute to achieving this overall goal.*

## Our Argument for Ecological Forest Management

The experience of writing the book over the past few years has made our belief even stronger that ecological forest management can play a critical role in sustaining the forest ecosystems of the Earth while also providing a multitude of benefits to human society. We believe that ecological forest management is well suited to helping a broad array of people achieve the goals that they have for their forestlands. This seems equally true whether they are family forest owners wishing to provide wildlife habitat while obtaining income from forest products, public land managers committed to providing a complete suite of ecosystem and societal services, or conservationists dedicated to restoring and sustaining natural forests. Ultimately, we view ecological forest management as a conceptual framework embracing all practices that contribute to the integrity of forest ecosystems.

We initiated this project without relating directly to the writings of Aldo Leopold and the ethical perspectives toward the land that he so effectively articulated. However, we found ourselves increasingly drawn to his work, particularly Leopold's classic essay, "The Land Ethic" in *A Sand County Almanac* where he states, "A thing is right when it tends to preserve the integrity, stability, and beauty of the biotic community. It is wrong when it tends otherwise." What better ethical basis for a management approach that sets ecosystem integrity as its goal?

# Acknowledgements

In writing this book, we were fortunate to have the council, contribution, review, and critique of a wide number of people. We wish to especially acknowledge:

- Drs. Christina Eisenberg, Christopher Dunn, and Matthew Thompson for contributing chapters to this book and also Jim Spitz for contributing the section on appraisal.

- Dr. Keala Hagmann for creating the format and cover for the book, and for technical review.

- Dr. Robert Van Pelt for creation of much of the art work and for technical review.

- Drs. Bruce Shindler (public acceptability and trust), Lauren Urgenson (collaboration), Randy Rosenberger (valuation), and Mark Harmon (forest structure and climate change and forests) for important reviews of individual chapters in their early stages.

- Dr. James Johnston, then a graduate student at Oregon State University, who provided considerable assistance in framing the chapters on the drivers of forestry, legal context, and collaboration.

- Deanne Carlson, PhD student at Oregon State University, who helped immensely in integrating economic concepts, such as critical natural capital, into ecological forestry, and made important contributions to chapters on legal context, capital and income, valuation, climate change and forests, and collaboration.

- Dr. Paul Henson for his teachings on integrating forest and wildlife management.

- Susan Jane Brown, Brendan White, Jody Caicco, Sarah Malaby, and Josh Newton for their review of aspects of the legal context for ecological forestry.

- Beth Jacqmain-Palik, Paul Vanderford, Lauren Satterlee, and Brad Kahn for their review of the chapter on certification.

- Chris French, Bill Connelly, and the staff of Ecosystem Management Coordination, US Forest Service for their review of the chapter on national forest planning.

- Drs. Robert Mitchell (deceased), Brian Palik, Antonio D'Amato, Derek Churchill, Andrew Larson, Mark Harmon, James Freund, Mark Swanson, Matthew Betts, Tom Spies, Fred Swanson, James Lutz, and Dale Thornburgh (deceased) for their direct contributions of knowledge and experience helpful in preparation of the ecological and silvicultural sections this book.

- Bill Beese, Robert Williams, and Abe Wheeler who made significant contributions in enriching the ecological and silvicultural concepts covered here by applying them in major real-world applications and sharing their outcomes with us.

- Drs. Jim Sedell (deceased), Gordie Reeves, and Stan Gregory who taught us how to integrate the aquatic ecosystems into the terrestrial.

- Tim Lillebo (deceased) who showed us how to both conserve forests and find collaborative solutions to problems.

- Drs. David Lindenmayer, Gene E. Likens, Andrew Carey, David Foster, John Gordon, and Jack Ward Thomas (deceased) for their significant contributions to the intellectual development of core concepts of ecological forestry as a part of scientific and policy collaborations and extensive writings.

- Cheryl Friesen for all she has taught us about linking science to management of the national forests.

- Laurie Wayburn for her guidance in understanding the California carbon markets.

- Will Hatcher, member of the Klamath Tribes, for helping us understand the dynamics and management priorities in frequent-fire forests.

- Numerous members of Dr. Franklin's Forest Ecosystem Laboratory for their reviews of several versions of many of these chapters (particularly Chapters 2 through 5 and 21), resulting in significant improvements to them.

- The Joseph E. Jones Ecological Research Center and its director, Dr. Lindsay Boring and many staff members, including Drs. Kay Kirkman, Steve Jack, Lora Smith, and Kevin McIntyre, who nurtured ecological forestry during its development and conduct of numerous workshops. The Jones Center also recognized, helped document, and today teaches the ecological approach practiced for decades in longleaf pine by forester Leon Neel.

- Support from the Sitka Center for Arts and the Environment and Frank and Jane Boyden, who provided an environment for much of the critical creative activity leading to this volume.

- Neil Williams, PhD student at Oregon State University, for his review of the chapter on climate change, carbon, and forests.

- Drs. Janean Creighton and Sean Gordon for their insights about structured decision making.

- Forestry and natural resource students at the College of Forestry, Oregon State University who endured reading the early versions of many chapters in Dr. Johnson's senior forest policy course, especially Kyle Stevens who read the entire book and gave thoughtful comments on each chapter and Blaine Kisler who helped with the quantitative planning analysis.

- Support for Jerry Franklin during the preparation of this book by : USDA National Institute of Food and Agriculture, McIntire Stennis Project Accession # 21215889, "Structural Development of Natural forest Stands and Its Relation to Ecosystem Function and Silvicultural Practice", and Accession # 1005426, "Analysis of Spatial Patterning in Natural Douglas-Fir—Western Hemlock Forests and Applications in Restoration of Managed Forests;" and a gift to the University of Washington by Mr. Kenneth L. Fisher.

- The University of Washington's School of Environmental and Forest Science and the Oregon State University's College of Forestry for their support of our opportunity to pursue this project.

Waveland Press provided instrumental assistance, starting with Don Rosso who saw the need for a new approach to writing a forest management text. Jeni Ogilvie was a wonderful editor suggesting reorganizations that improved the flow of the text; questioning vague and inconsistent statements; checking every citation and website; and maintaining a cheery disposition as we missed deadlines. Peter Lilliebridge, compositor, did a masterful job of laying out and putting together the myriad pieces that make up each chapter. For all of this assistance we are very grateful. Finally, we wish to thank Phyllis Franklin for her patience when our dinners and stays together often turned into work sessions for the three of us. Her good humor during our lengthy effort to finish this book has us in awe.

# Tree Drawings
# by Dr. Robert Van Pelt

# Organization and Potential Use of This Book

In the introductory chapter (Chapter 1) we identify and discuss five major themes for our study of forest management in this book. These are:

1. Philosophy and principles of ecological forestry, which are based on natural systems, as contrasted with those of modern production forestry, which are based on managed systems keyed to rate of return on investment;

2. Greatly expanded scientific understanding of forests as complex ecosystems, which provide multiple services and goods;

3. Public policy framework within which forest management occurs;

4. Importance of effective negotiation in forest management, especially (but not exclusively) on public forestlands; and

5. Recognition that strategies for coping with change and uncertainty is a major ingredient in forest management planning in the 21st century.

## The Five Major Parts

Following the introductory chapter, we have organized the book into five parts. Part I consists of four chapters that provide foundational material on forest ecosystems, forest dynamics, silviculture, and landscape ecology. This section reflects our strong belief that everyone interested in ecological forest management—from stakeholders to managing foresters—needs a basic understanding of these concepts. *In a little more than one hundred pages, the ecological foundation on which this book is built is laid out in Part 1. In many ways, the rest of our book is an essay on how these ecological principles can be integrated into, and help structure, approaches to forest management in the 21st century.* Describing forests as ecosystems that provide a multiplicity of functions, exhibit high levels of biological richness, and have complex physical structures is the focus of Chapter 2. Disturbances and their legacies are considered in Chapter 3, followed by sections on forest development and forest archetypes, including recognition of the distinctive nature of frequent-fire forests. This chapter ends with a consideration of climate change and invasive species as major disrupters of forests. Chapter 4 is a primer on the principles that underpin silvicultural activities in ecological forest management and includes numerous examples of real-world applications of ecological forestry in diverse forest types and ownerships. Ecological concepts and management approaches at larger spatial scales (landscapes, drainages, and regions) are the subjects of Chapter 5. Important topics include recognizing environmentally and culturally important areas within managed forest landscapes, such as diverse aquatic habitats, and creating landscapes in which all patches contribute to ecological goals, which we refer to as landscapes that are *shades-of-green*. The last sections of this chapter provide examples of landscape assessment and planning in different ownerships and different regions and discuss landscape considerations in setting patch-level goals.

Part II consists of chapters on the economic and social context in which forest management occurs, emphasizing key factors influencing the use and application of ecological forestry. In Chapter 6, we examine the economic, social, and political drivers of forestry, including ownership, markets, investment strategies, and policy formulation, as well as social perspectives on forest management, including its acceptability. Chapter 7 is centered on environmental policy frameworks for forestry, first considering forest policies in a variety of countries with temperate forests and then examining in detail three major environmental laws in the USA: the National Environmental Policy Act, the Endangered Species Act, and the Clean Water Act. In Chapter 8, we explore the increasingly important role of negotiation in resolving conflicts over forestry, with a focus on collaboration. Principles of mutual gains negotiation are outlined, advice is provided on improving the potential for success, and the crucial role of trust is highlighted. Financial analysis of forest capital is considered in Chapter 9. While classical approaches to investment analysis are presented, we argue for an approach that recognizes the concept of *critical natural capital* and the importance of income to landowners over time in the context of their many goals—vital considerations in long-term sustainability and ecological forestry. Methods for estimating the economic value of forests to humans are discussed in Chapter 10. We consider a variety of approaches, including classical appraisal, as well as recognizing the intrinsic value of ecosystems. Adaptive management is the topic of Chapter 11, the last chapter in this part of the book. We highlight practical approaches that can be used to evaluate the effectiveness of practices and policies and, when indicated, to make needed changes. Also, we emphasize the importance of social processes in enabling these changes to occur.

Part III is composed of five chapters on current issues surrounding management of forests and the potential role that ecological forestry can play in helping to address them. The role of fire in sustaining natural processes is described in Chapter 12, while strategies for managing fire and fuels are addressed in Chapter 13, with an emphasis on issues and approaches in the wildland–urban interface (WUI) and on the necessity for integrating ecological forestry principles into fire and fuels management. The importance and conservation of biological diversity are considered in Chapter 14. Topics include species of special ecological concern and the significance of trophic cascades for ecosystem sustainability. Climate change, carbon, and the complex ways that forests and forest management practices can affect aspects of local and global carbon cycles are addressed in Chapter 15. We explore in-depth the issue of whether forests contribute more to reducing $CO_2$ in the atmosphere by being left to grow or by conversion to wood products on a sustainable basis. Certification of sustainable forest management practices and its potential role in achieving the goals of ecological forestry through market mechanisms is covered in Chapter 16. We emphasize the important role that certification can play by providing society with credible approaches to third-party verification of practices and compare the certification approaches of the Forest Stewardship Council with those of the Sustainable Forestry Initiative.

Part IV consists of four chapters on the topic of forest planning that apply principles of ecological forest management in an uncertain future. We demonstrate how these approaches can be useful for forests ranging from those that are small and privately owned to those that are large and federally controlled. Historical approaches to planning forests to sustain harvest and achieve a regulated forest are covered in Chapter 17, along with a discussion of the relevance of classical decision rules to ecological forestry. Decision making in ecological forestry is the focus of Chapter 18. We recognize two basic approaches: the intuitive, naturalistic approach we use to make day-to-day decisions and the structured approaches that help us to deal with informational and social complexities. Structured decision making, which was introduced in Chapter 18, is employed in Chapter 19 in management planning for a hypothetical family-owned forest. We emphasize the principles of ecological silviculture, multiple goals, the concept of critical natural capital, the embedding of forest planning within a social process, and a view of the future as changing and uncertain. We then use this planning framework in analysis of choices and trade-offs in management of that forest, utilizing an analysis tool called linear programming to simulate least-cost choices. Finally, the history of forest planning for the national forests of the USA is covered in Chapter 20, along with the vision and principles in the recently adopted planning rule for these forests and the potential role of ecological forestry in helping to implement this vision.

Part V consists of a single chapter (Chapter 21) in which we first summarize ecological forest management principles and discuss how ecological forestry can contribute to the resolution of major 21st-century issues in forestry. These issues include the role of forests in combating climate change, the conservation of biological diversity, the challenge of sustaining forest-dependent communities, and the need for understanding that there are many alternatives to the view that forests must be managed as either preserves or plantations. Next, we suggest an overall public policy framework that would encourage ecological forest management and apply this framework to developing forest policies for a region. We close the chapter with a consideration of factors that have delayed the adoption of ecological forestry and suggestions for policy approaches that may help overcome these impediments.

## Intended Audience and Potential Use

We intend for this book to be useful to the broad array of people who have interests in forests and their management, including forest owners, professional foresters, conservationists, policy makers, and the many seriously engaged citizens—forest stakeholders, whether they recognize it or not—who care deeply about forests and their management.

And, of course, we intend this book for the students! This book should prove useful in any college curricula or courses that approach the conservation and management of forests through understanding and emulating the natural processes and functions of forest ecosystems. Thus, the text should be useful in forestry, natural resource management, and applied ecology curricula as well as providing important material for other curricula, such as those related to public policy. It also can provide students enrolled in technical curricula, which are widespread in community colleges, with a deep introduction to the array of forest management topics that underpin forestry in the 21st century.

How might this book be used in a college curriculum? We have prepared it in modular form, which should provide for flexibility in use. After Part I (Ecological Foundations), the chapters are largely self-contained in terms of the material needed to understand them beyond the concepts covered in the early chapters. Thus, beyond the first part, the reader or instructor can pick and choose among chapters based on their specific goals or interests. To help in that assessment, we outline below groups of chapters that cover different forest management topics (Table 1).

Table 1  *Topics covered and parts or chapters where they can be found*

| Topic | Relevant Parts and Chapters |
| --- | --- |
| General introduction to ecological forest management | Chapter 1, Parts I and II, Chapter 21 |
| Forest planning | Chapter 1, Parts I and IV, Chapters 8, 11 |
| Forest policy | Chapter 1, Part I, Chapters 6, 7, 13–16, 20, 21 |
| Current forest management issues | Chapter 1, Parts I and III, Chapters 6, 21 |
| Economic aspects | Chapter 1, Part I, Chapters 6, 9, 10, 16, 19 |
| Social aspects | Chapter 1, Part I, Chapters 6, 8, 11, 18 |

# Some Comments on Terminology

A brief "heads-up" on our use of some terminology in this book.

## Conifers and Hardwoods

The trees we are dealing with are all seed plants belonging to the two major categories of gymnosperms and angiosperms. Gymnosperms are the more ancient group and lack both flowers and enclosed seeds (fruits). All of the gymnosperms that we are going to be dealing with are conifers belonging to the pine, cypress, and yew families (*Pinaceae*, *Cupressaceae*, and *Taxaceae*) and most (but not all) are evergreen, have needle or scale-like leaves, and are often referred to as "softwoods." The general term that we will use for these in the book will be *conifers*. The angiosperms are flowering plants that bear enclosed seeds and have trees from many different families. Trees belonging to this group are mostly broad-leaved, predominantly deciduous in temperate regions, and often referred to as "hardwoods." The general term that we use for this group in the book will be *hardwoods*.

## Stand and Patch

Stand is the term that traditionally has been used in forestry to distinguish areas representing distinctively different forest conditions for management purposes. It has been defined as *"a contiguous group of trees sufficiently uniform in age-class distribution, composition, and structure . . . to be a distinguishable unit"* (Helms 1998, p. 174). There has been a tendency in recent times to equate "stand" with forests of simplified structure and composition, perhaps because of the emphasis in traditional forestry on even-aged management systems. The stand concept is broader than that, however, as can be seen in the above definition.

In ecological forestry we will commonly be dealing with forests that have significant richness in tree age and structure (e.g., uneven-aged forests) and internal heterogeneity (e.g., clustering of trees as well as inclusions of small openings or patches of retained trees). Consequently, in this book *we use the term **stand** in its broadest interpretation* and sometimes apply it to forest areas that incorporate significant heterogeneity in structure, age, composition, and spatial pattern of trees. When describing a general forested area we will often use ***ecosystem*** or ***forest*** instead of stand in order to continually remind the reader and ourselves that the focus in ecological forestry is on the entire ecosystem and not just on the trees, which is implicit in "stand."

The terms ***patch*** and ***patchiness*** are generic descriptors typically used to recognize small areas of relatively homogeneous vegetative conditions, such as a small part of a stand or forest. However, patch has a distinct and central meaning in landscape ecology. Landscapes are approached as networks of patches in many applications of landscape ecology. The nature of that patchwork (i.e., patch classification) will vary with the application, but patches are the fundamental units for stratifying that landscape. Sometimes, landscape patches will be equivalent to stands but not always, as will be explained in Chapter 5. The important point is for the reader to understand that "patch" in landscape ecology has a very specific meaning and represents a spatially large area. We will alert the reader when we are using patch in its landscape application.

*If the land mechanism as a whole is good, then every part is good, whether we understand it or not. If the biota, in the course of eons, has built something we like but do not understand, then who but a fool would discard seemingly useless parts? To keep every cog and wheel is the first precaution of intelligent tinkering.* — ALDO LEOPOLD

CHAPTER 1

# Sustaining Forests and Their Benefits

Forest management books have a rich history of explaining and applying the forestry profession's concepts of sustainability going all the way back to the Middle Ages. By the 17th century, systematic attempts were made to understand the unplanned, often detrimental, consequences of the modifications of forests undertaken for economic reasons. As examples, both John Evelyn's *Silva, or a Discourse on Forest Trees* in 1664 and Colbert's *French Forest Ordinance* in 1669 discuss the negative influence of past utilization practices on forest resources, as well as the needs of future generations for continued use of these resources (Westoby, 1989; Wiersum, 1995).

Further, Wiersum (1995) notes that the concept of sustainability was explicitly formulated in German forestry literature by the 18th century. German forestry lecturer Hartig in 1804 described sustainability as follows: "Every wise forest director has to have evaluated the forest stands without losing time, to utilize them to the greatest possible extent, but still in a way that future generations will have at least as much benefit as the living generation" (Schmutzenhofer, 1992 as quoted in Wiersum, 1995, p. 322). Thus, forestry may be considered one of the first disciplines that explicitly incorporated concerns about safeguarding finite natural resources for future generations (Westoby, 1989; Wiersum, 1995).

In the United States, concerns about forest sustainability helped lead to the forestry profession's birth there in the early 1900s. Timber was needed for houses, railroad ties, fuel, and many other uses, and few laws moderated rapid liquidation of the nation's forests. More and more people became concerned about the possibility of the nation running out of wood—of a coming timber famine. Forestry thus organized around the central theme of ensuring the sustained yield of timber harvest over time. Ideally, timber harvest would be limited to what could be grown. Forests would be protected from fire, and reforestation would occur after harvest. Tax structures would encourage investment

*Jerry Franklin talking to his forest health class on the Fremont-Winema National Forest, Oregon.*

in forests and ensure their continued productivity. Such approaches would both limit the overall harvest that could occur and encourage the growth of a future wood supply (Dana & Fairfax, 1980; Wiersum, 1995).

The *doctrine of sustained yield* became one of professional forestry's guiding principles: "To fulfill our obligations to our descendants and to stabilize our communities, each generation should sustain its resources at a high level and hand them along undiminished. The sustained yield of timber is an aspect of man's most fundamental need: to sustain life itself" (Duerr & Duerr, 1975, p. 36).

Forest management books such as Davis, (1954, 1966) and Davis & Johnson (1987) codified the principles and techniques of sustained yield management, with each book giving a more sophisticated treatment than its predecessor, but still retaining the core idea of sustained yield as the heart of forest sustainability.

The linkage of a sustained yield of timber harvest to forest sustainability became increasingly questioned by the latter part of the 20th century, however. People challenged the idea that all forest values could be protected by such an approach. Legislation elevated the importance of wild areas, wildlife and fish, water, and recreation. Numerous groups outside the forestry profession sought more influence on forest policy and management decisions through protest, litigation, and direct involvement in policy and planning.

In 1987, the World Commission on Environment and Development (widely known as "the Brundtland Commission") (United Nations, 1987) famously defined "sustainable development" as "development that meets the needs of the present without compromising the ability of future generations to meet their own needs." This characterization of

sustainability has been widely accepted throughout the world and has become a guiding principle and benchmark for natural resource policy (Cubbage, O'Laughlin, & Peterson, 2017).

Following the report of the Brundtland Commission, sustainability has been increasingly portrayed as having environmental, economic, and social components. A useful definition of sustainability in this context comes from the US Forest Service (USDA, 2012, p. 21272):

> *Sustainability. The capability to meet the needs of the present generation without compromising the ability of future generations to meet their needs . . . "ecological sustainability" refers to the capability of ecosystems to maintain ecological integrity; "economic sustainability" refers to the capability of society to produce and consume or otherwise benefit from goods and services including contributions to jobs and market and nonmarket benefits; and "social sustainability" refers to the capability of society to support the network of relationships, traditions, culture, and activities that connect people to the land and to one another, and support vibrant communities.*

This definition recognizes that the three components of environmental, societal, and economic sustainability are closely linked. To be truly sustainable, natural resource decisions need to account for all three—"the triple bottom line" (USDA Forest Service, 2011). Schematically, these three components have traditionally been portrayed as separate but partially intersecting components of sustainability (Figure 1.1a), a characterization that emphasizes the limited area where all three components of sustainability are met simultaneously (USDA Forest Service, 2011; Cubbage et al., 2017).

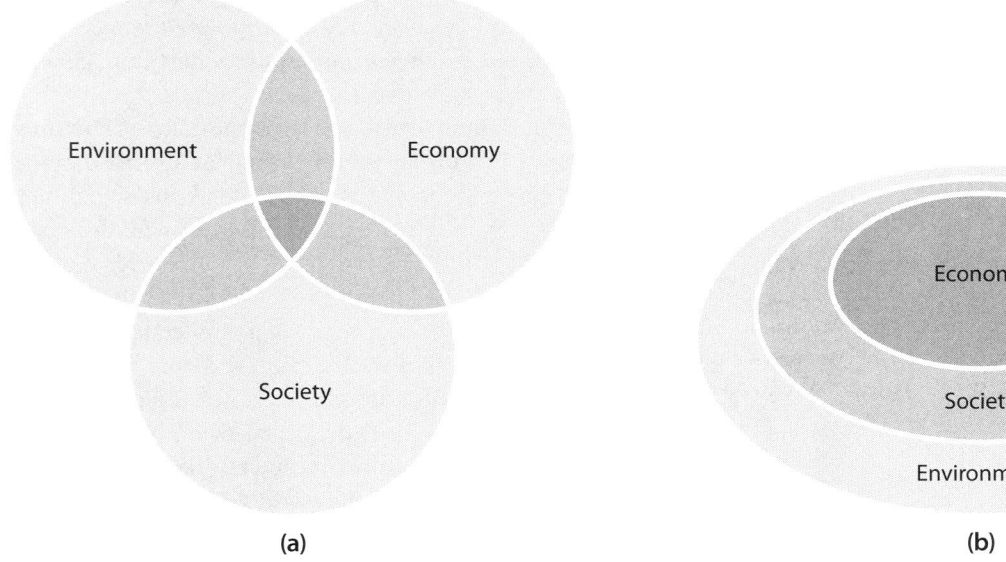

(a)                                          (b)

Figure 1.1 *Two potential relationships of the three components of sustainability (environment, economy, and society): (a) separate but partially intersecting and (b) hierarchical, with economy nested within society, and society nested within the environment. (Source: Adapted from USDA Forest Service, 2011; Cubbage et al., 2017)*

The Millennium Ecosystem Assessment (MEA) (2005) enriched the characterization of sustainability by developing a broad, useful, and widely accepted classification of ecosystem services and their interrelationships. MEA authors introduced these concepts in the preface of the MEA synthesis document (2005, p. v, emphasis added):

*The assessment focuses on the linkages between ecosystems and human well-being and, in particular, on "ecosystem services." An ecosystem is a dynamic complex of plant, animal, and microorganism communities and the non-living environment interacting as a functional unit. . . .* **Ecosystem services are the benefits people obtain from ecosystems.** *These include* **provisioning services** *such as food, water, timber, and fiber;* **regulating services** *that affect climate, floods, disease, wastes, and water quality;* **cultural services** *that provide recreational, aesthetic, and spiritual benefits; and* **supporting services,** *such as soil formation, photosynthesis, and nutrient cycling. . . . The human species, while buffered against environmental changes by culture and technology, is fundamentally dependent on the flow of ecosystem services.*

We will use the MEA classification in this book to describe the goods and services that forests provide humans. They all fall under the mantle of *ecosystem services* as described by the MEA (2005)—the benefits people obtain from ecosystems. [1]

Beyond the importance of ecosystem services to human life on earth, the MEA (2005) stressed the vital nature of regulating and supporting services to the overall functioning of our environment. This characterization coincided with the emerging concept of *critical natural capital* from the discipline of ecological economics—the recognition that many ecosystem processes and services are irreplaceable and nonsubstitutable in providing ecosystem services (Ekins et al., 2003; Farley, 2012; Neumayer, 2013; Turner, 1992).

Thus, thinking about the relationships between the three components of sustainability has evolved, with the realization that they are not merely interconnected but are hierarchical, with economy nested within society, and society nested within the environment (Figure 1.1b) (Cubbage et al., 2017; USDA Forest Service, 2011). This portrayal recognizes that neither societies nor economies can exist without fundamental ecological processes, such as nutrient cycling, water purification, and climate regulation, and that an economic system requires a functioning and accepting society.

This nested characterization, which portrays environmental sustainability as the foundation of the benefits we seek from forests, reflects the philosophical perspective of

this book. In many ways, ecological forestry, as we describe it here, is our attempt to apply this concept to the management of forests.

Given this broader view of forests and their benefits that has evolved over the past few decades, we have stepped back and started over in our quest for a set of concepts and techniques that can be useful as guides to forest sustainability. In this chapter we recognize five themes that provide the framework within which we will address the fundamental question of forest management: How do we sustain forests and the benefits they can provide into an uncertain and unbounded future?

## Five Major Themes

Five central themes underlie our efforts here:

1. Emergence of ecological forestry;
2. Role of scientific knowledge in shaping how professional resource managers and society think about forests and the values they contain;
3. Public policies that limit and direct forest management;
4. Demand by the broader public for participation in decisions that were formerly the purview of professionals; and
5. Recognition of change and uncertainty as an inescapable context for forest management.

A forestry grounded in ecological structures and processes has emerged in the last few decades as people have sought alternatives to the agronomic models that underlie production forestry. Ironically, the increasing use of production forestry to provide the world's industrial wood supply may have contributed to the desire for a different kind of forestry on the world's forests. We present such an alternative model here, which we call *ecological forestry*.

The immense increase in our scientific understanding of trees, forests, and, most profoundly, the recognition of forests as ecosystems has both underpinned and driven the movement toward ecologically based forestry. Early forest research focused on acquiring information related to the silvics of important tree species and development and improvement of techniques for managing stands of trees for the efficient production of wood. Research on the function and structure of forests (as well as other ecosystems) expanded rapidly beginning in the 1960s and now provides us with a comprehensive understanding of forests as ecosystems. This science has deeply altered both the perceptions and the goals of society at large and, consequently, those of resource managers (Skillen, 2015). We understand much more clearly that forests are complex and biologically rich systems that provide many essential services as well as products and are not simply collections of trees! At the

---

1 The provisioning services are sometimes referred to as *products*, a convention we employ, at times, in this book.

same time these altered perspectives and expanded body of knowledge have not been fully incorporated into the established body of forest management education or practice. One goal of this book is to advance that activity.

Public policies now guide and limit forestry around the world. In the United States, for example, a suite of federal environmental laws along with forest practice laws at the state level have created a legal context for the practice of forestry—effectively a wide array of provisions intended to protect environmental resources and ensure resource sustainability. While these laws impact the management of federal forests most of all, very few forests in the United States are beyond their reach to one degree or another. We will repeatedly refer to these laws as a framework within which people, groups, and agencies pursue their goals and discuss how they shape forestry at larger scales.

As forestry lost some of its luster as a trusted keeper of the nation's forests in the latter half of the 20th century, individual citizens and groups became more active in demanding a role in decision making. Also, the suite of environmental laws passed by the United States Congress during the 1970s encourages such a role through their requirements for public participation in federal decisions. Among private companies and groups that own forests, deference to foresters has waned and foresters are increasingly challenged to justify their management proposals. More broadly, contentious national issues, such as the civil rights movement and the Vietnam War in the United States, led to continuing activism on broad fronts. As a result, negotiation has become an element in forestry decision making and is a theme that runs through this book.

Historically, forest management planning generally assumed a stable world, a world with little change over periods long enough to grow crops of trees in regulated forests. However, an idealized stable world is no longer a useful assumption given rapid climate changes, a continu-ing reshuffling of private industrial ownership, globalization of timber markets, and a shifting and still unsolidified role for public forests in many countries. Rather, we need to craft our forest management planning and actions in the context of the changing and uncertain times, which most profoundly includes the consequences of climate and other environmental changes and changing societal agendas. We will return to these thoughts many times in this book.

We discuss each of these themes in more depth below. We will then describe some integrative "coping mechanisms" that will help set a context for the guidance offered in the chapters that follow.

## An Ecological Approach to Forest Management

We will define *ecological forestry* by identifying some of its principles, goals, and practices, and by contrasting it with management designed to optimize efficient production of wood fiber for economic gain, which we will label *production forestry*. We do not intend "production forestry" to be a pejorative label; rather, we use the term to provide a contrast with management that is designed to sustain or restore multiple forest benefits.

Aldo Leopold eloquently captured these contrasting approaches to forestry in his essay called "The Land Ethic" (Box 1.1). At its best, our book is intended for Group B in his classification.

### Ecological Forestry and Production Forestry: A Comparison

We start our comparison with the conceptual foundation of these two approaches to forestry (Franklin & Johnson, 2013):

---

### Box 1.1 Aldo Leopold and ways of valuing forests

In *A Sand County Almanac*, Aldo Leopold (1949, p. 221) observed a common value dichotomy:

*Conservationists are notorious for their dissentions. Superficially these seem to add up to mere confusion, but a more careful scrutiny reveals a single plane of cleavage common to many specialized fields. In each field one group (A) regards the land as soil, and its function as commodity-production; another group (B) regards the land as a biota, and its function as something broader. How much broader is admittedly in a state of doubt and confusion.*

*In my own field, forestry, Group A is quite content to grow trees like cabbages, with cellulose as the basic forest com-modity. It feels no inhibition against violence;[\*] its ideology is agronomic. Group B, on the other hand, sees forestry as fundamentally different from agronomy because it employs natural species, and manages a natural environment rather than creating an artificial one. Group B prefers natural reproduction on principle. It worries on biotic as well as economic grounds about the loss of species like chestnut, and the threatened loss of the white pines. It worries about a whole series of secondary forest functions: wildlife, recreation, watersheds, wilderness areas. To my mind, Group B feels the stirrings of an ecological conscience.*

---

\* Leopold is referring here to the destruction of native ecosystems.

Table 1.1 *Fundamental contrasts between ecological forestry and production forestry*

| Ecological Forestry | Production Forestry |
|---|---|
| Maintains an array of ecosystem structures, functions (processes), and biota at larger spatial scales | Maintains a limited set of ecosystem structures, functions, and biota consistent with economic goals |
| Emphasizes ecosystem diversity and resilience to reduce risks from major ecosystem disruptions | Emphasizes fast-growing species on short rotations to reduce financial risks |
| Tends to increase management and social options | Tends to reduce management and social options |
| Values complexity and heterogeneity | Values simplicity and homogeneity |
| Accommodates landowner and social goals by adjusting the ecological model | Accommodates landowner and social goals by adjusting the economic/agronomic model |

- Ecological forestry utilizes ecological models from natural forest systems as a basis for managing forests. It incorporates principles of natural forest development, including the role of natural disturbances, in the initiation, development, and maintenance of forests and forest landscape mosaics. Most importantly, ecological forestry recognizes that forests are ecosystems with diverse biota, complex structure, and multiple functions, and not simply collections of trees valuable primarily for production of wood. In doing so it seeks to maintain the fundamental capacities (integrity) of the forest ecosystems to which it is applied.

- Production forestry utilizes agronomic and economic models as a basis for managing forests. It combines farming principles with rate of return analysis to find the amount and spatial organization of capital that will best achieve desired economic outcomes. In production forestry the forest, which is generally a plantation, is viewed as a collection of trees that are managed for the economically efficient production of wood. Consideration of other values is limited to what society requires.

These different foundations have profound implications for forestry. In fact, we argue that they lead to fundamentally different ways of thinking about forests and their management. *We present these differences below in their purist forms—without modification by legal constraints or other considerations—so that we can see most clearly their differences.* We recognize that many forest owners may deviate in various degrees from the pure forms of these two approaches to forestry.

First, at the most fundamental level, ecological forestry and production forestry lead to different conclusions about what ecosystem components we wish to conserve, the approach to risk and maintenance of options, the value of complexity and heterogeneity, and the integration of landowner and social goals (Table 1.1).

Second, they result in different ecological, economic, and social consequences (Tables 1.2 to 1.4). Many of the

significant differences between these two types of forestry derive from the different forest structures they seek to create and sustain—the ecological implications of a focus on principles of natural forest development as compared to a focus on forestry as capital management (Table 1.2). It is highly unusual for landowners who manage forests primarily or exclusively for economic rewards to retain an ecologically complex forest; thus production forestry emphasizes that part of the forest ecosystem that contributes directly to achieving the desired rate of return, while trying to minimize the resources devoted to the part that does not provide that return.

In economics terminology, the two types of forestry differ in terms of their assumptions about the substitutability of human-made capital for natural capital. In production forestry, human-made capital is generally treated as substitutable for natural capital. In ecological forestry, an essential physical subset of natural capital must be preserved, because human-made capital cannot substitute for it. This different view about the substitutability of capital carries over into different definitions of sustainability (Box 1.2 and Chapter 9).

Ecological forestry and production forestry, in general, utilize different measures of economic performance, with ecological forestry focused on income (cash flow) over time and the preservation of critical natural capital, and production forestry focused on an acceptable rate of return (Table 1.3). Not surprisingly, higher rates of return on timber capital will generally be calculated for production forestry than for ecological forestry, in part because of the higher levels of forest inventory maintained in ecological forestry and the retention of some slower growing forest. In addition, ecological forestry generally requires greater care and has higher harvest costs due to its more complex prescriptions. Also, though, ecological forestry should be less risky because of its emphasis on diversity and resilience and is generally better positioned for income from other ecosystem services.

Ecological forestry is inherently more amenable to collaborative processes and changing social preferences than

Table 1.2 *Ecological implications of ecological forestry and production forestry*

| Ecological Forestry | Production Forestry |
| --- | --- |
| Provides for continuity in structure, function, and biota between forest generations | Creates discontinuity in structure, function, and biota between forest generations |
| Uses natural stand development models, including effects of disturbances, in developing silvicultural prescriptions | Uses agronomic models in developing silvicultural prescriptions (e.g., plant spacing, use of herbicides, and fertilization) |
| Emphasizes stand-level structural diversity/complexity | Emphasizes stand-level structural simplicity |
| Emphasizes spatial heterogeneity at stand and landscape levels | Emphasizes spatial uniformity at stand and landscape levels |
| Seeks to maintain an array of ecosystem conditions (e.g., successional stages) at larger spatial scales, including older trees and forest and early successional ecosystems | Seeks to maintain age variants of single successional stage (young forest) at larger spatial scales; does not include older trees and forest or early successional ecosystems as management goals |
| Considers and incorporates impacts of natural disturbances | Attempts to eliminate or avoid potential for natural disturbances |

---

Box 1.2  **The substitutability of capital—a key difference between ecological forestry and production forestry**

This dichotomy of characteristics between production forestry and ecological forestry can be traced, in part, to a differing view of the relationship between nature and human well-being, as discussed in the literature of ecological economics. This difference essentially boils down to the belief—or lack of belief—in the ability of human-made forms of capital to act as substitutes for natural capital in the economic calculus of sustainable development.

In the analysis of sustainability and sustainable development, capital is seen as a key factor in maintaining well-being (i.e., sustainability), where capital is "a stock that possesses the capacity of giving rise to flows of goods and/or services" (Ekins, Simon, Deutsch, Folke, & de Groot, 2003, p. 166). Daly and Farley (2011, p. 17) succinctly describe the difference between human-made and natural capital:

> Traditionally economists have defined capital as produced means of production, where "produced" implies "produced by humans." . . . Ecological economists have broadened the definition of capital to include the means of production provided by nature. We define capital as a stock that yields a flow of goods and services into the future. Stocks of manmade capital include our bodies and minds, the artifacts we create, and our social structures. Natural capital is a stock that yields a flow of natural services and tangible natural resources. This includes solar energy, land, minerals, . . . water, living organisms, and the services provided by the interactions of all of these elements in ecological systems.

Some economists and analysts assume that natural capital and other forms of capital are, in general, interchangeable with respect to maintaining human well-being (Ekins et al., 2003; Neumayer, 2013). Production forestry in its pure form reflects this view in management of the forest, with the focus on maintaining the productivity of capital as measured through rate of return on investment in the stands of trees growing there. When a stand's financial performance drops below a specified rate of return, the stand is harvested and the capital moved to an alternative investment. Whether this capital is invested in forests or elsewhere is relatively unimportant. In this view human well-being is related to maintenance of overall capital stocks and their productivity—an idea that has been linked to *weak sustainability*, as we will discuss in more depth in Chapter 9.

Other economists and analysts reject the notion that human-made capital is completely substitutable for natural capital in terms of maintaining human well-being. Scholars that hold this view assert that an essential physical subset of natural capital must be preserved, such as old-growth trees and forest habitat, *because human-made capital cannot fully substitute for this critical natural capital in providing desired ecosystem services* (Ekins et al., 2003; Chiesura & de Groot, 2003)—an idea closely linked to *strong sustainability*.

Ecological forestry takes the view that an essential subset of the forest's natural capital must be preserved and that human forms of capital do not entirely substitute for this critical natural capital. This recognition affects forest planning and management in many ways, and is one of the reasons why the financial analysis of forest capital that drives production forestry has only a limited role in ecological forestry. We will further develop these ideas in Chapters 6 and 9.

Table 1.3 *Economic implications of ecological forestry and production forestry*

| Ecological Forestry | Production Forestry |
| --- | --- |
| Natural capital in forests and human-made capital are *not* considered as completely substitutable | Natural capital in forests and human-made capital are considered substitutable |
| Financial return from management is generally sought, especially cash flow over time, but return on capital is not the primary performance measure | Moderate to high return on capital is the primary performance measure |
| Higher cost per unit of output due to complexity of prescriptions and care needed in management | Lower cost per unit of output due to simplicity of prescriptions |
| May produce significant periodic income from the forest over time, but maintains higher investment level | Producing a periodic income from the forest over time usually secondary consideration to return on capital, considering all investment opportunities |
| Leaves recoverable values (biological legacies) on sites at time of harvest | Minimizes recoverable values left on sites at time of harvest |

production forestry (Table 1.4) because it retains **all the pieces**, as recommended by Aldo Leopold. Thus, it inherently is able to accommodate more interests and perspectives.

Ecological forestry and production forestry lead to very different silvicultural systems and prescriptions (Table 1.5). Most fundamentally, ecological forestry, with its focus on emulating natural forest development and the resulting complexity and heterogeneity, requires different and more complicated prescriptions than does production forestry. Ecological forestry also requires more professional expertise and more time to implement—keeping all the pieces takes extra effort. We have much to learn about implementing ecological forestry and this book represents one of our contributions to that effort.

## Where and How Ecological Forestry Might Be Applied

In their analysis of global forest management options, Lindenmayer et al. (2012) divide each continent into three categories: (1) reserves, (2) plantations, and (3) potential areas for "ecologically sustainable forest management." They point out that most of the global forests are neither formally protected nor in plantations. Given the spatial extent of unprotected forests and ongoing steep declines in forest biodiversity and carbon stocks, they assert it is imperative to find management approaches that will sustain multiple

environmental, economic, and cultural values, and prevent their conversion to other uses. They then suggest that adoption of a retention approach in forests where logging occurs is an essential part of such management—supplementing the protection of large reserves and sensitive areas within forest landscapes, such as aquatic features. This ecological approach to harvesting provides for retention of important selected structures (e.g., trees and decayed logs) to provide for continuity of ecosystem structure, function, and species composition in the post-harvest forest—a crucial element in sustaining forest biodiversity.

Lindenmayer et al. (2012) further argue that their approach supports the integration of environmental, economic, and social values and is broadly applicable to tropical, temperate, and boreal forests, adaptable to different management objectives, and useful in different societal settings. Finally, they argue that widespread adoption of the retention approach would be one of the most significant changes in management practice since the onset of modern high-yield forestry.

We support the view of Lindenmayer et al. (2012) that ecological forestry, which features use of retention approaches, should find broad application on much of the world's forests. While production forestry may supply much of the world's lumber and wood products in the future, this wood supply can be provided by a relatively small portion of the world's forests (Sedjo & Botkin, 1997).

Table 1.4 *Social implications of ecological forestry and production forestry*

| Ecological Forestry | Production Forestry |
| --- | --- |
| Retaining ecosystem components and processes contributes to effectiveness of collaborative efforts | Simplified forests limit potential effectiveness of collaborative efforts |
| Retaining ecosystem components and processes eases ability to respond to changing social goals | Simplified forests limit ability to respond to changing social goals |

Also, reserves, as important as they are, will probably cover only a small portion of these forests. Thus most of the world's forests fall in between the two models (reserves and intensively-managed wood production forests) that have drawn most of the attention in the continuing debate over forests and their future (Bennett, 2015). We have written this book to help define and advance a third model for management of the world's forests.

Lindenmayer et al. (2012) also make the important point that detailed prescriptions of ecological forestry are a function of the forests to which they are applied and to the associated management objectives. *Ecological forestry starts with an ecological model of stand and forest development; its exact application is a function of the forest of interest and the economic and social objectives people have for its conservation and management.* We will illustrate its application in many different settings in this book.

## Relationship of Ecological Forestry to Ecological Restoration

**What Is Ecological Restoration?** In short, ecological restoration attempts to recover degraded forests and landscapes. Some examples of ecological restoration in forests are:

- Thinning forests that have become overgrown because of fire suppression, harvest, and grazing.

- Harvesting small patches of trees to create compositional and spatial heterogeneity in uniform, single-species plantations that developed after harvest of old-growth forests.

- Felling wood into streams to make up for past policies that both removed wood directly from streams and removed trees from beside them.

*More formally, ecological restoration* refers to management activities that contribute to the recovery of ecosystems that have been degraded, damaged, or destroyed. Ecological

Table 1.5 *Characteristics of silvicultural systems and prescriptions of ecological forestry and production forestry*

| Ecological Forestry | Production Forestry |
|---|---|
| Utilizes multi- or uneven-aged management regimes (although multi-aged may be structural mosaics) | Utilizes even-aged management regimes on high-productivity sites and selection (high-grading) on low-productivity sites |
| Focuses on native species and genotypes that provide an array of ecological and other values | Focuses on fast-growing species with desirable financial characteristics, often with tree improvement and genetic engineering |
| Requires lower levels of energy subsidies | Requires higher levels of energy subsidies, such as fertilizers, herbicides, intensive site treatments where justified by rate of return |
| Landscape context of stand-level treatments focuses on maintenance of ecosystem processes and structures | Landscape context of stand-level treatments focuses on efficiency of harvest patch, road, and logging design |
| Utilizes rotation lengths or periodic partial cutting entries that allow expression of forest complexity | Utilizes financially determined rotations on high-productivity sites and opportunistic removals on low-productivity sites |
| Utilizes variable-retention regeneration harvesting practices | Utilizes clearcut regeneration harvesting practices on high-productivity sites |
| Incorporates biological legacies into regeneration harvest treatments, including uneven-aged or selection systems | Incorporating biological legacies is not a goal |
| Keys return intervals for management interventions (e.g., rotations, cutting cycles, frequency of prescribed burning) to ecological criteria | Keys return intervals for management interventions (e.g., rotations) to financial criteria |
| Utilizes variable-density thinning practices | Utilizes uniform-density thinning practices |
| Emphasizes complexity in thinning and, consequently, on modifying understory and midstory conditions as well as overstory conditions | Emphasizes contribution of thinning to financial return and, consequently, on concentrating growing stock on the most efficient growth engines |
| Retains defective trees and structures (e.g., snags, logs, cavities, and brooms) and may create additional such features during treatments | Eliminates defective trees and structures and does not create more |

restoration can also enhance the capacity of an ecosystem to adapt to change. Ecological restoration focuses on reestablishing ecosystem functions by modifying or managing the composition, structure, and spatial arrangement of ecosystem components and by reestablishing processes necessary to make terrestrial and aquatic ecosystems ecologically functional, resilient to disturbance, and adaptive.

Both ecological restoration and ecological forestry are closely linked to three other important ecosystem concepts:

- *Resistance* refers to the capacity of an ecosystem to endure disturbances without undergoing significant change—in effect, to take a hit from fire, wind, drought, or an outbreak of disease or insects without major change, particularly relative to functional capability. For example, fire can burn through a low-density forest dominated by large-diameter trees of fire-tolerant species that has developed under a regime of frequent, low- to moderate-severity fires that consume fuels and create small openings for regeneration. In this example, frequent fire and the resultant structural conditions contribute to the resistance of the forest to more severe fires that could result in significant ecological changes.

- *Resilience* refers to the capacity of an ecosystem to recover to approximately the state that it had before being impacted or modified by a disturbance, particularly with regard to its functional capabilities. In effect, resilience is about the ability of an ecosystem that is significantly altered in its structure, function, or composition (and probably all three!) by a disruptive event to return to a condition that resembles, in appearance and functionality, its original state. For example, a forest subjected to a severe wildfire that killed many or most existing trees, dramatically altering its structure, composition, and function is considered to be resilient if it has the capacity to recover to an approximation of its original condition. Of course, the pattern and rate of recovery (i.e., the way that resilience is expressed) may vary greatly with the ecosystem and disturbance in question.

- *Adaptive capacity* refers to the capacity of an ecosystem to evolve adaptively in response to changing environmental conditions, such as climate change, or to significant modifications in the resident biota, such as losses or additions of species. It is generally expected that forests and landscapes with high levels of native biological diversity and heterogeneity will have adaptive capacities superior to those with reduced levels of native biodiversity and high levels of uniformity.

**How Does Ecological Forestry Relate to Ecological Restoration?**    Ecological forestry can be useful over a wider set of goals and circumstances than ecological restoration. Ecological restoration, in its pure form, is an application of ecological forestry where ecological goals are the sole driver of actions. However, ecological forestry is a broader concept: It utilizes the ecological concepts of restoration but also builds in consideration of economic and social goals of both landowners and society.

To better understand the difference, consider the following examples—the first focused solely on ecological restoration and the others focused more broadly on ecological forestry:

- Thinning overstocked stands in ponderosa pine and mixed-conifer forests in intermountain western North America: Decades of fire exclusion resulting from destruction of tribal cultures, grazing, and fire suppression, combined with overstory harvest and tree planting, have led to a buildup of surface and ladder fuels and small- to medium-sized trees. This buildup of fuels greatly increased the potential for high-severity crown fires compared to historical conditions (Franklin & Johnson, 2012). Reducing fuel loadings by thinning such forests and treating residual slash can greatly increase the resistance of these forests to future wildfires. Sufficient revenue often is created through harvest to pay for the treatments. The thinning used in the harvests is generally socially acceptable, particularly when these treatments retain old and large trees. Ecological restoration can often achieve all goals. We would also call this action an application of ecological forestry, but one in which there is no need to modify the pursuit of ecological goals for other considerations.

- Creating diverse early seral ecosystems through variable-retention harvest in Douglas-fir–western hemlock forests of western Oregon and Washington: Fire suppression and cessation of regeneration harvests on federal lands have created a shortage (compared to historical levels) of the diverse early successional ecosystems that developed on these sites following wildfire. Variable-retention harvest in the plantations that were established after harvesting the old-growth forests, combined with allowing natural post-harvest processes to revegetate the site, can help bring back this missing successional stage. However, a majority of commercial-sized trees may be removed in this harvest, unlike a wildfire in which trees would be retained on site (including the many killed by the fire). Thus, we would not call this action solely ecological restoration, even though it has many attributes of it, because the restorative action has been modified somewhat to consider other goals—production of revenue (economic goal) and employment (cultural and economic goal). We would, however, call this action an application of ecological forestry because it emulates natural processes to a significant degree.

- Maintaining structural (including spatial) complexity during harvests on family forests of the Great Lakes region: Family members inherit a forest that has been subject to many partial harvests over the years, leaving a mixture of size and age classes. They wish to retain their forest's usefulness for the wide variety of wildlife that inhabit it while still obtaining some economic return. After studying the natural history of their forest, they settle on a strategy of harvesting small patches while retaining the remaining old trees and snags. This action might not qualify as ecological restoration, in its pure form, but it does contain many attributes of ecological forestry.

- Managing a property owned by a conservation group in the southeastern USA, covered predominantly by longleaf pine forests to maintain and restore the longleaf pine ecosystem, to provide habitat for a game species (e.g., quail) and for several endangered species (e.g., red-cockaded woodpecker and gopher tortoise), and to produce income to help cover expenses for maintaining the property (e.g., some harvest of merchantable timber): Management activities include regular application of prescribed fire, restoration of tree and understory conditions in areas previously converted to fields or loblolly and slash pine plantations, and timber harvest to provide income. This is another example of ecological forestry that goes beyond pure ecological restoration.

## The Contributions of Expanded Scientific Knowledge

The body of science regarding trees and forests has expanded exponentially during the last half of the 20th century, particularly in our understanding of forests as ecosystems, and this knowledge has significantly altered the views of both professional resource managers and society at large regarding how forests function and the values they contain. Research on trees and forests through the mid-20th century had largely focused on the silvics of commercially important tree species, including their regeneration and growth, and on the management of stands of trees for production of wood and economic returns. Very little research had focused on forests as ecosystems, with the exception of some watershed research, such as at the Coweeta Experimental Forest in North Carolina.

A major expansion in forest ecosystem-based research began in the 1960s, largely stimulated by funding from the National Science Foundation (NSF) but often including significant contributions of sites, data sets, and personnel from the research branch of the US Forest Service; many of the most productive programs were and are collaborations between academic and federal agency scientists. The interdisciplinary watershed-focused program at the Hubbard Brook Experimental Forest in New Hampshire was a prominent early example, which became a model for other programs. The US International Biological Program in 1965–1975 increased funding for ecosystem science, including ecosystem model development, and led to establishment of an Ecosystem Studies program at NSF in 1973 and the Long Term Ecological Research (LTER) program in 1980. Several forest sites are part of the LTER network, resulting in sustained funding of ecosystem-oriented research, including the H. J. Andrews Experimental Forest in Oregon and Harvard Forest in Massachusetts as well as Hubbard Brook and Coweeta. This expansion of ecosystem research in the United States has been paralleled in other developed countries in Europe, Asia, South America, and Australia.

A consequence of these trends has been an immensely expanded understanding of the structure and function of forest ecosystems and the rich array of biota that inhabit them (see Chapter 2). For example, the important roles that dead and down trees play in forests have been recognized, including their importance as critical habitat for many animals. Older forests and trees have been analyzed and recognized for the unique functional roles that they play. The numerous prominent interactions between forests and associated aquatic ecosystems, such as streams and rivers, have been identified and quantified. It has become clear that forests are not simply collections of trees!

Expanded scientific knowledge has proven both a blessing and a burden for the professional forester. When past generations of foresters and other resource professionals focused on maximizing sustained harvests of wood, game, or fish, they may have sensed they were impacting other organisms and functions. However, there was no scientific information to provide them with a context for their activities, even if they had wanted it—i.e., an ecosystem-scale perspective. Now the forester has a greatly expanded knowledge base regarding the forest and its functions and occupants. The information and the insights that it provides are essential in assessing the potential and limitations of the forest and identifying critical elements for consideration in planning and management. On the other hand, a fuller understanding of forest ecosystems introduces complexity and more challenges for resource professionals.

The impact of expanded science, including that of forest ecosystems, has not been limited to resource professionals but has also profoundly affected societal perceptions of the forest and, consequently, their goals and expectations of forest managers. As Aldo Leopold observed, once we learn about something we are likely to begin to care about and value it. Ecological science has documented for society the existence and importance of forest ecosystem services and biota, which, in turn, created a public interest in sustaining those services and organisms. In democratic societies these concerns often are incorporated into laws and regulations, as they have been in the United States (e.g., Skillen, 2015).

Science, then, has been profoundly important in influencing both societal perspectives on forests and their management during the last 50 years. We can expect and hope that it will continue to do so in the current century. With the many challenges associated with environmental and societal change, we will certainly have a significant need for it. Ecological forestry attempts to fully incorporate our understanding of forest ecosystem science into its principles and practices and to utilize practices that enable restoration and maintenance of the multitude of values that people recognize and expect from these ecosystems.

## The Public Policy Framework for Forest Management

Forestry around the world occurs within public policy environments that may include national and state laws and regulations, international trade agreements, and multinational covenants. This policy environment, dynamic and ever changing, is a fact of life in the 21st century. Here we will utilize the policies of the United States as an example of this policy environment to illustrate how it directs and affects forest management. Public forestry policies in other countries each have their own unique framework, as we will note in later chapters.

The United States is first and foremost a nation of laws.[2] Until the 1960s, laws that affected forest management dealt mostly with how to divide up the public domain among settlers, miners, railroads, states, and tribes, along with how much forest to retain in federal ownership. In addition, some legislation provided guidance for management of the national forests (improve and protect the forest, secure favorable conditions of water flows and provide a continuous supply of timber) and for management of national parks that were established.

Beginning with the Wilderness Act of 1964, constraints began to be placed on the discretion of federal foresters to manage federal forestlands as they saw fit. Then came the onslaught of federal environmental laws in the 1970s, which fundamentally changed the way decisions would be made about the national forests, and the priorities for their management. The National Environmental Policy Act, Endangered Species Act, and National Forest Management Act

had perhaps the greatest impact on national forest management; the Endangered Species Act affected management on nonfederal lands, as well, although to a lesser degree. Other federal laws such as the Clean Water Act and the Clean Air Act applied comprehensively to all land ownerships.

Many states adopted forest practice laws governing reforestation, stream pollution, and other considerations. The detailed requirements and process for enforcing the forest practice laws vary substantially from state to state, but they do engage state governments in providing limits and guidance for forest management, to one degree or another.

In sum, the policy environment is a crucial element in directing forest management in the 21st century. It is an inescapable fact of modern life.

## Negotiation: An Essential Element of Forest Management Planning

Forest management planning has historically emphasized decision makers who express their goals, consider choices to achieve them, evaluate trade-offs, and make hard decisions (Davis & Johnson, 1987; Davis et al., 2001). This approach is compatible with and reflective of the ideal of professional foresters who are trusted by firms and society to make decisions in the interests of all. Under such an approach, the importance of negotiation, collaboration, and shared decision making was understandably minimized.

With the decline in confidence that forestry professionals had the "right answer" to forest management problems (Bliss, 2000), many others began to demand a place at the decision table. Now, the notion of shared decision making is more the norm than the exception, particularly on public lands. We illustrate below the important role of negotiation in forestry in the United States today.

### Federal Forestry

It can be argued that the National Environmental Policy Act (NEPA) of 1969—the first major federal environmental law in the United States—ended the unlimited discretion of federal foresters to make decisions without consulting with others (Skillen, 2015). NEPA requires that ecological values be considered by an interdisciplinary team in designing actions and that other agencies and the public are allowed to comment on federal proposals. The Endangered Species Act, passed in 1973, requires that land management agencies consult with regulatory agencies (US Fish and Wildlife Service and National Marine Fisheries) to find actions that will not jeopardize listed species. In addition, the appeal/protest process that has grown up around federal forestry invites negotiated settlements with parties unhappy with decisions, as does the litigation that may follow an unresolved appeal.

---

2 See Dana and Fairfax (1980) for an engrossing history of the development of forest law and policy in the United States and Skillen (2015) for an account of how ecosystem management emerged from the federal environmental laws of the 1970s.

Across the national forests, especially, collaboration has emerged as a mechanism for local groups to find projects on which they agree. Recognizing the need for public support for its actions, the US Forest Service has emphasized public engagement throughout its planning process in a recent revision of regulations to implement the National Forest Management Act (USDA, 2012).

### Private, State, and Tribal Forestry

Negotiation can also be the watchword for private, state, and tribal forestry, although in these contexts it is often done more informally.

Private- and state-lands foresters often must negotiate with neighbors, enforcers of state forest practice laws, and certification groups. In addition, actions of foresters in the forest industry have come under internal scrutiny as never before, as firms strive to become more efficient and competitive.

Family forest management can be a continuous negotiation among siblings and generations as the members of the family sort out their different interests and perspectives for a forest ownership. This negotiation can become especially important when brothers and sisters inherit forests from their parents—such negotiations can determine whether the family continues to hold the property, or sells out and moves on.

Historically, forest management on Indian reservations in the United States has been governed by the commercial focus of federal foresters. With the assent of tribal visions as a guide for forest management on reservations (Gordon et al., 1993, 2003), negotiation among tribal members and tribal governments has become more common.

In sum, communication and negotiation principles and skills are as integral to successful forest management as traditional forest measurement and planning tools. Thus, forestry professionals will need to master them as well.

## Change and Uncertainty: An Enduring Constant in Forest Management

As pointed out by Duerr and Duerr (1975) in their seminal work on the role of culture in sorting through competing values and confronting the unknown, forest managers must cope with significant uncertainties about what the future holds. From the time of the first forest plans many hundreds of years ago, forestry has needed to cope with change and uncertainty; with the long time horizons inherent in the growth cycle of trees, there was no other way to conduct business. The potential for wars, changes in government, economic collapse, changes in social preferences, and natural disturbances (such as wildfires and hurricanes) has always hovered over, and often derailed, the best-laid forest management schemes. While the rate and magnitude of change may be greater now and uncertainties loom larger in our thinking, they have always been a part of forestry—whether explicitly recognized or not. As an example of these uncertainties, who would have predicted the changes in forest management in the Pacific Northwest of the United States since 1990 (Table 1.6)? Such a list certainly does suggest the need for humility in planning for the next 25 years.

Future uncertainties may come from many sources: How will global markets for wood products affect the demand for forest producers in the United States? How will our economic system evolve over time with regard to what people want from forests? What new scientific findings will change the way we understand forest function? What invasive species will attack our forests?

Table 1.6 *Changes in forest management in the Pacific Northwest from 1990 to 2014*

| Private forests | National forests |
|---|---|
| ▪ Rise of globalization and associated questions about the competitiveness of the wood products industry<br>▪ Loss of the vertically integrated forest products firm as the dominant industrial model<br>▪ Rise of the Timber Management Investment Organization (TIMO)<br>▪ Loss of the price premium for large-diameter logs<br>▪ Loss of the expectation of real price rise for timber over time<br>▪ Rise of certification<br>▪ Collapse of the housing market and wood product prices associated with the subprime mortgage crisis<br>▪ Loss of demand for the classical forestry professional: the timber management specialist for large integrated wood products companies | ▪ Rise of conservation of biodiversity as an overarching goal<br>▪ Loss of large, allowable cuts<br>▪ Shift from harvest of overstories to harvest of understories<br>▪ Fire being viewed as a bigger threat to old forests than harvest<br>▪ Logging becoming viewed as forest restoration<br>▪ Major reductions in budget and staffing<br>▪ Shift of the US Forest Service from a wood production agency to a fire-fighting agency<br>▪ Loss of demand for the classical forestry professional: the timber management specialist for the US Forest Service |

**TMEAN (Jan–Dec) 42–50°N, 110–124°W**

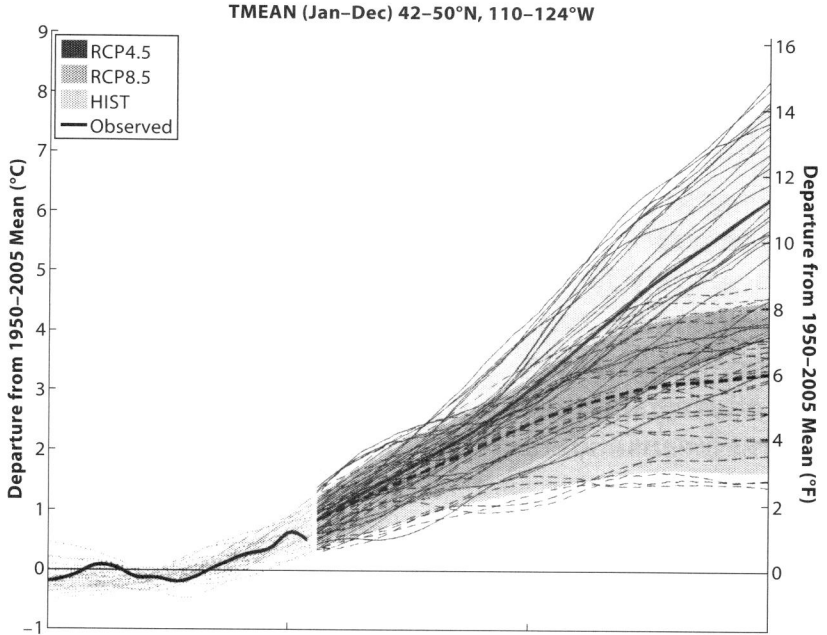

Figure 1.2  *Observed (1950–2011) and simulated (1950–2100) Pacific Northwest mean temperature from selected global models for two scenarios: (1) low-growth in emissions (RCP4.5), due to policy change, and (2) high-growth in emissions (RCP8.5), under business as usual. The broader line under each scenario (dashed for RCP4.5 and solid for RCP8.5) represents the average across the model simulations. (Source:* Climate Change in the Northwest, *edited by Meghan M. Dalton, Philip W. Mote, Amy K. Snover. Copyright © 2013 Oregon Climate Change Research Institute. Reproduced by permission of Island Press, Washington, DC)*

Perhaps our greatest uncertainty is: What future climates can we expect? As an example, climate models for the Pacific Northwest project a wide range of future temperature increases as a function of scientific and policy uncertainty, with the lower temperature projections being possible only if greenhouse gas emissions are significantly reduced (Figure 1.2). Added uncertainties for forestry come from estimating how any level of warming will affect forest growth and associated biodiversity.

With the long time horizons of forest management, uncertainties such as these can easily dominate decisions. This increasing dominance of change and uncertainty suggests that problems cannot be solved primarily through a search for the right data and models. This shift from certainty to uncertainty as the dominant context for problem solving is not unique to forestry and natural resources. Rather, it reflects a broader shift in perspective across science and management.

It might seem that scientific progress should reduce uncertainty. In fact, that view was widespread in the early parts of the last century—scientists were rapidly learning all there was to know, and the prevailing view was uncertainties would soon be reduced to minor issues (Peat, 2002). Many scientists no longer take that view. Rather, the notion of science as a smoothly progressing machine has been replaced by a notion

of science as a beast that lurches from one major idea (paradigm) to another, with the new ideas often replacing (destroying) those which came before them (Kuhn, 1966).

Forestry has gone through a similar shift. For much of the 20th century, young foresters in the United States absorbed the central management concepts of integrated forest products firms utilizing a steady supply of timber from their own land and of the symbiotic relationship between the US Forest Service and a local mill drawing logs from a nearby area. In addition, they were often taught that forestry would be able to control the effects of wildfire, insects, and disease on forests.

These models and views have been seriously challenged. The collapse of the integrated forest products firm (a firm that owns both processing facilities and forests that supply its wood) as the industrial model and the shift from sustained timber production to protection of biodiversity and ecological integrity as the dominant goals for federal forests has surprised and disheartened many foresters. Also, the events of the past decade suggest that large wildfires and insect outbreaks will be a permanent part of our future. These experiences make us less sure of our ability to see and control the future.

Most fundamentally, we realize that Earth has entered an era of rapid climate change without precedent, no matter how far back we look. We may find current forests poorly adapted and susceptible to undesirable changes. Accepting the fact that the future will be different from both the past and the present forces us to manage forests from a very different perspective. Further, although models can estimate a range of potential directions and magnitudes of environmental changes and forest responses in the future, they rarely can predict the future with the level of accuracy and precision desired by resource managers (Pilkey & Pilkey-Jarvis, 2007; Millar, Stephenson, & Stephens, 2007). More than ever, we will manage forests without the kind of roadmap that would make us feel secure in the decisions we make.

Production forestry and ecological forestry have very different strategies for dealing with the uncertainties created by climate and other environmental changes. Production managers will substitute a different species or genotype as evidence emerges that the current tree species or genotype is poorly suited to changing climatic conditions. They also have the option of disposing of the lands and investing their capital elsewhere.

Ecological forestry seeks to create forest ecosystems and landscapes that will be resilient in the face of climate change. Typical approaches involve the creation and maintenance of forest ecosystems and landscapes that are structurally complex, rich in biological diversity, and exhibit redundancy in critical functions—structurally heterogeneous rather than homogeneous and composed of species mixtures rather than monocultures.

This approach of creating more resilient and adaptive forest stands and landscapes is critical for many forest properties, such as where the owners or beneficiaries cannot or do not wish to dispose of their forestlands. This situation probably includes many publicly and tribally owned lands as well as much of the privately owned forestlands. It is also notable that when drastic changes do occur—for example, as a result of climate change—a social priority on many of these lands likely will be to sustain critical ecosystem services, such as the protection of watersheds.

In summary, we believe that managing forests and landscapes based on ecological forestry principles will generally be the most effective strategy to prepare them for climate change where the intent is to maintain forest cover and functional capabilities. We will return to this later in this book.

## Coping Mechanisms: Mysteries, Wickedness, and Tenets

Without a secure roadmap for the future, how will we cope? More specifically: How will professionals give sound advice to landowners and to society about how to conserve and manage forests in a sustainable way that maintains the multitude of benefits these forests now provide? The continued development of scientific information will help, but more is needed. To be effective in such an environment, we will need a variety of "coping mechanisms." We describe three interconnected coping mechanisms below:

1. Viewing forest management as more of a mystery than a puzzle;
2. Expecting *wicked problems* with multiple problem definitions and solutions; and
3. Utilizing a set of "tenets of faith" to help guide us into an uncertain future.

### Seeing Forest Management as More Mystery than Puzzle

Puzzles can be solved, and with their solution comes a sense of satisfaction. Mysteries, on the other hand, have no definitive answers because they are contingent on the future interaction of factors that are known and unknown (Treverton, 2007). Historically, many have looked at forest

management problems as puzzles; that is, we generally saw these problems as a set of puzzles that could be solved once we gathered all the pieces. Science would provide the knowledge needed to identify the pieces and foresters would put them together.

Forestry education has often approached forest management as a puzzle. Early courses in a forestry curriculum provided the pieces of information needed—ecology, silviculture, biometrics, forest economics—leading to capstone courses in which all the pieces were put together and forest management problems were "solved." Only the lack of information prevented a complete solution, and that information was expected to be forthcoming over time. Such an approach was consistent with, and supported by, classical tenets of faith as we highlight below.

The notion of forest management as a puzzle to be solved no longer seems to fit the problems and issues we face in sustaining forests and their benefits. Each of the themes we discuss in this chapter raises questions about the view that forest management is best seen as a puzzle to be solved. The complexities of ecological and geophysical systems suggest that we will forever make decisions without full knowledge of the implications. Public law and policy will continue to intrude, often with little warning. Science will continue to provide new information and, even more important, provide completely new perspectives (epiphanies!). The ongoing negotiations with the outside world so vital to continued social acceptance of forestry do not fit into tidy boxes that need be mastered only once at an institution of higher learning. In addition, the change and uncertainty before us in a warming climate has subtleties we can only begin to understand.

We believe that it is more useful to look at forest management as a mystery, which inherently involves uncertainties and the need for judgment. Puzzles require good information producers. Unraveling mysteries depends on the judgment and critical thinking abilities of the information receivers.

As noted by Gregory Treverton (2007):

*Puzzles can be solved; they have answers. But a mystery offers no such comfort. It poses a question that has no definitive answer because the answer is contingent; it depends on a future interaction of many factors, known and unknown. A mystery cannot be answered; it can only be framed, by identifying the critical factors and applying some sense of how they have interacted in the past and might interact in the future. A mystery is an attempt to define ambiguities.*

*Puzzles may be more satisfying, but the world increasingly offers us mysteries. Treating them as puzzles is like trying to solve the unsolvable—an impossible challenge. But approaching them as mysteries may make us more comfortable with the uncertainties of our age.*

In sum, forestry is more than a board game with set rules and a final solution that we can find if we just look hard enough. Knowledge, while important, does not provide a sufficient guide to forest management. Rather, we will need the ability to work in highly ambiguous environments with patience, reflection, judgment, and continued learning. Thus we see forest management as more mystery than puzzle and reflect this view in the chapters that follow.

## Expecting Wicked Problems with Multiple Problem Definitions and Solutions

Over the last few decades, we have become increasingly aware that forest management problems have multiple definitions and fuzzy boundaries that reflect different ways people view the world, prophesize the future, and value what forests can provide. Thus forest management problems often fall into the category of *wicked problems*:

*Wicked problems share characteristics. Each can be considered as simply a symptom of some higher problem. Selecting a silvicultural regime, for instance, may be seen as a function of growing timber, or the need for sawmill jobs, or visual amenity, or regional development, or some combination of these. The definition is in the mind of the beholder, and how that person chooses to explain the problem determines the scope of the search for a resolution. Furthermore, there is no single correct formulation for a wicked problem, only more or less useful ones. . . . A seemingly innocent local problem [such as shifting from selection cutting to clearcutting to rehabilitate high-graded hardwood stands on the Monongahela National Forest] precipitated the wicked problem of a multilayered power struggle to determine who has a legitimate role in planning the use of the national forests. (Allen & Gould, 1986, p. 22)*

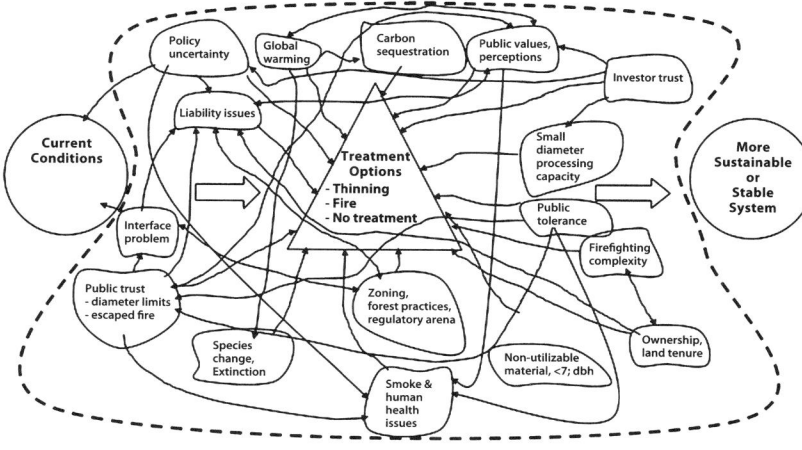

Figure 1.3 *Considerations in fuel treatment options on federal lands—a wicked problem. (Source: Carroll et al., 2007; reproduced by permission of the Society of American Foresters)*

Wicked problems do not fit into the model of rational comprehensive planning problems that have dominated forest management texts of the past. They can be characterized in terms of dynamic conditions, scientific complexity, and multiple participants, each with their own views of problems, solutions, and how the world works (Lachapelle, McCool, & Patterson, 2003). As a result, they lack definitive problem definitions or potential solutions and stopping or finishing points. Ideal solutions are generally not available, only better or worse temporary solutions (Cubbage et al., 2017).

Carroll et al. (2007) point out that this description of a wicked problem fits the difficulties associated with managing the increasing risk of wildland fire in much of the western United States (Figure 1.3). As they describe, causes of the current state of affairs are a complex mix of physical, ecological, economic, and social developments that occurred over more than one hundred years. Proposed steps to improve the current situation involve equally complex dynamics, and the treatment options are more easily defined than implemented. Forest managers must confront difficult scientific and technical questions, as well as social and political ones, if the implementation of treatments is to be regarded as broadly acceptable or successful. Perhaps the thorniest question is that of time scale. Although the forest fuels treatments have potential to mitigate wildfire or "forest health" problems, it may take 50–100 years to treat fire-prone forests and move forest ecosystems to a more sustainable condition—a time scale almost incomprehensible to a political system and public notorious for their impatience. Taken together, Carroll et al. (2007) believe that the interaction of the technical and socio-political issues with the different time scales constitute the wickedness of the "fire problem."

In such an environment, classical approaches to addressing forest management problems in which a problem is defined and then solved, often with the aid of sophisticated planning tools, has only limited value in the world of wicked problems. That does not mean that planning is hopeless, however. Rather, it argues for embedding forest planning in a process that recognizes the social complexity that exists. At the least, expecting multiple problem definitions and solutions, and other characteristics of wicked problems, should help guide how planning might proceed and temper expectations about what can be accomplished. As part of this process, finding ways to think through problems from multiple perspectives will be an important skill of future forest managers.

## Utilizing Tenets of Faith as a Foundation of Decision Making

The appreciation that many, perhaps most, forest management problems are mysteries with a dose of wickedness can be a useful coping mechanism in helping forest managers make decisions. However, forest management problems still may leave managers with a feeling of inadequacy in the face of competing demands and an uncertain future.

Duerr and Duerr (1975) argued that we need faith, a set of tenets constituting a life philosophy, to augment our scientific understanding and our sense of the problems we face. These tenets need to reflect the realities of environment, culture, and economy in which forest management occurs and to give a solid grounding to help us make forest management decisions.

**Forestry's Classical Tenets of Faith**   Professional foresters, like many subculture populations, created a set of tenets that eased forest management decisions and provided ready-made decision rules. The tenets of classical forestry were brought to the United States from Europe at the beginning of the 20th century. They had been developed, refined, and handed down from professional generation to generation in the universities and government bureaus. Duerr and Duerr (1975, p. 36) identified four classical tenets that guided professional forestry for much of the 20th century:

1.  *Recognize the primacy of timber production.*
    "Timber is the chief product of the forest; all else that comes from the forest is by-product, of secondary interest. . . . Wood is, and will always be, a necessity, for it has no true substitutes. . . . In fact, there is going to be a shortage of timber, and the central problem of forest management is the biological and engineering problem of growing more timber."

2.  *Provide for sustained yield.* "To fulfill our obligation to our descendants and to stabilize communities, each generation should sustain its resources at a high level and hand them along undiminished. The sustained yield of timber is an aspect of man's most fundamental need: to sustain life itself."

3.  *Plan for the long run.* "Nature moves and changes slowly; she takes a long time to accomplish such purposes as growing timber. Society must adapt itself to this fact. Be patient. Curb the selfish, short-sighted interests such as those of private enterprise and notably small enterprise. Look to the past. The future will be like the past, and, indeed, should be like the past."

4.  *Obtain absolute standards from the forest.* "The forest is a living thing with its own ends and its means for attaining them under natural law.

The successful manager, regardless of his forest's location or ownership, find his goals and guides in the forest itself, by looking there, and by listening to what the forest tells him. People are not to be trusted in such matters. . . . He [the manager] aims to produce wood of high quality in maximum quantity, and this again is the aim of the forest."

These tenets provided members of the forestry profession with a store of ready-made heuristics that could be used in making decisions quickly and efficiently. In fact, the tenets provided ready-made decisions in themselves. They helped guide foresters through the massive uncertainties that confront all who need to look far into the future and attempt to navigate through competing demands on forests and myriad people and groups who attempt to influence forest management.

**Tenets of Faith for Ecological Forestry**   As Duerr and Duerr further pointed out, one challenge to any profession is to continually refine its tenets to keep in step with society's needs. It can be argued that forestry for too long held to these four tenets without changing or adapting—that foresters employed these tenets in making their decisions after they had ceased to be highly useful in coping with the challenges of managing forests.

Certainly, production forestry as we described it earlier has its own tenets of faith. They include the belief in substantial near-future demand for lumber and other products from fast-grown trees, the ability to outwit climate change with short rotations, the resistance of tree farms to pests that attack intensively managed crops, and the continued social tolerance for this type of forestry.

In preparing this book, we realized that we also rely on a set of tenets to help us integrate our central themes—an ecological forestry approach, the continued expansion in scientific knowledge, a legal framework setting bounds and directions, the collaborative nature of modern forestry, and the recognition of a changing and uncertain world. Here we summarize four key tenets:

1.  *Restore and sustain the integrity of forest and associated ecosystems.* Ecosystems, in all their complexity and variety, are the source of ecosystem services that we seek and upon which we depend. Traditionally we have simplified ecosystems as we undertook their management, whether we only put out wildfires or—more overtly—converted forests to plantations. We simplify at peril, however. Eliminating parts of ecosystems, such as dead wood structures or top predators, can, and often does, come back to haunt us. Therefore, we view restoring and sustaining the basic integrity of ecosystems—their essential

completeness in terms of their biota and capacities—as the foundation of ecological sustainability in forest management (see, e.g., Puettmann, Messier, & Coates, 2008). This is a fundamental principle of ecological forestry. In this book, we will embed the retention of complexity and integrity of ecosystems in our approaches to forest management planning—even while acknowledging the daunting nature of this task.

2. *Develop policies and management practices that consider and sustain a broad array of ecosystem services.* Natural resource management policies have generally tended toward "optimal" approaches, which maximized singular outcomes, such as timber production or revenue generation, but consistently marginalized or eliminated other important services, leading to socially unsustainable outcomes (Gunderson, 1999). In ecological forestry we emphasize policies that perform well in a variety of ecological and social environments rather than attempting to maximize some singular good, service, or income or minimize some cost—policies that provide multiple benefits even if they are "inefficient" in regard to any single benefit.

3. *Be attentive and adaptive to new scientific and technical developments and to changes in societal goals, priorities, and concerns.* Arguably there has never been a more dynamic time in both the scientific and social realms of forestry. Our knowledge of forest and other ecosystems and their interconnectedness has expanded and continues to do so at an exponential rate, forcing us to constantly rethink management goals and approaches. As dynamic as the arena of scientific and technical knowledge is, the social context for forestry is at least as dynamic and unpredictable. The most profound changes in forest policies and practices in the last century were the result of social change—laws and regulations, economic structures (including tax laws), and social interests, such as in the environment—and this will predictably continue to be the case in this century.

Keeping track of changing social perspectives and considering their implications for forestry is critical for managers, as is anticipating the evolving limits of "social acceptability" and the associated legal framework for forestry. Functional forest

management strategies must be developed and implemented within a social context. Forestry is, before anything else, a social science!

4. *Choose management approaches that will reduce risks to forest assets and increase future options.* Change, uncertainty, and surprise will likely dominate the future. Climate change, globalization, changing public tax policies, social movements, and many other environmental, economic, and social changes will affect the future in ways that we can now only dimly imagine. Prudent managers can help prepare for this uncertainty by selecting management approaches that will reduce risks to the forest and increase future options. Reducing risks has to do with identifying potential threats, such as those that might be associated with natural disturbances, climatic change, and invasive species and choosing management alternatives that will reduce the vulnerability of the forest to such threats.

A standard financial response to risk and uncertainty is diversifying investments, such as in a mutual fund with holdings that tend to respond differently to different risks and events. Similarly, ecologists call for heterogeneity at multiple spatial scales, creating redundancy, and increasing resistance and resilience in the face of potential disturbance as ways to survive and adapt in the face of risk and uncertainty. Managing forests to increase options will likely be served by many of the same approaches that are undertaken to reduce risks—e.g., by maintaining structurally and compositionally diverse forests.

These four, interconnected tenets not only provide a mechanism to deal with risk and uncertainty, they also suggest the concepts and tools that will be needed to successfully implement ecological forestry in the modern world. The chapters that follow represent our attempt to provide these concepts and tools. We must acknowledge that these tenets for the 21st century do not provide as much guidance as the classical tenets—they do not attempt to cover the uncertainties all generations face under a set of rigorous decision rules, as did the classical tenets. Rather, they attempt to place management in a framework that will help deal with the inevitable unknowns that we will surely face, leaving more of the decision to our knowledge, analysis, ingenuity, and judgment.

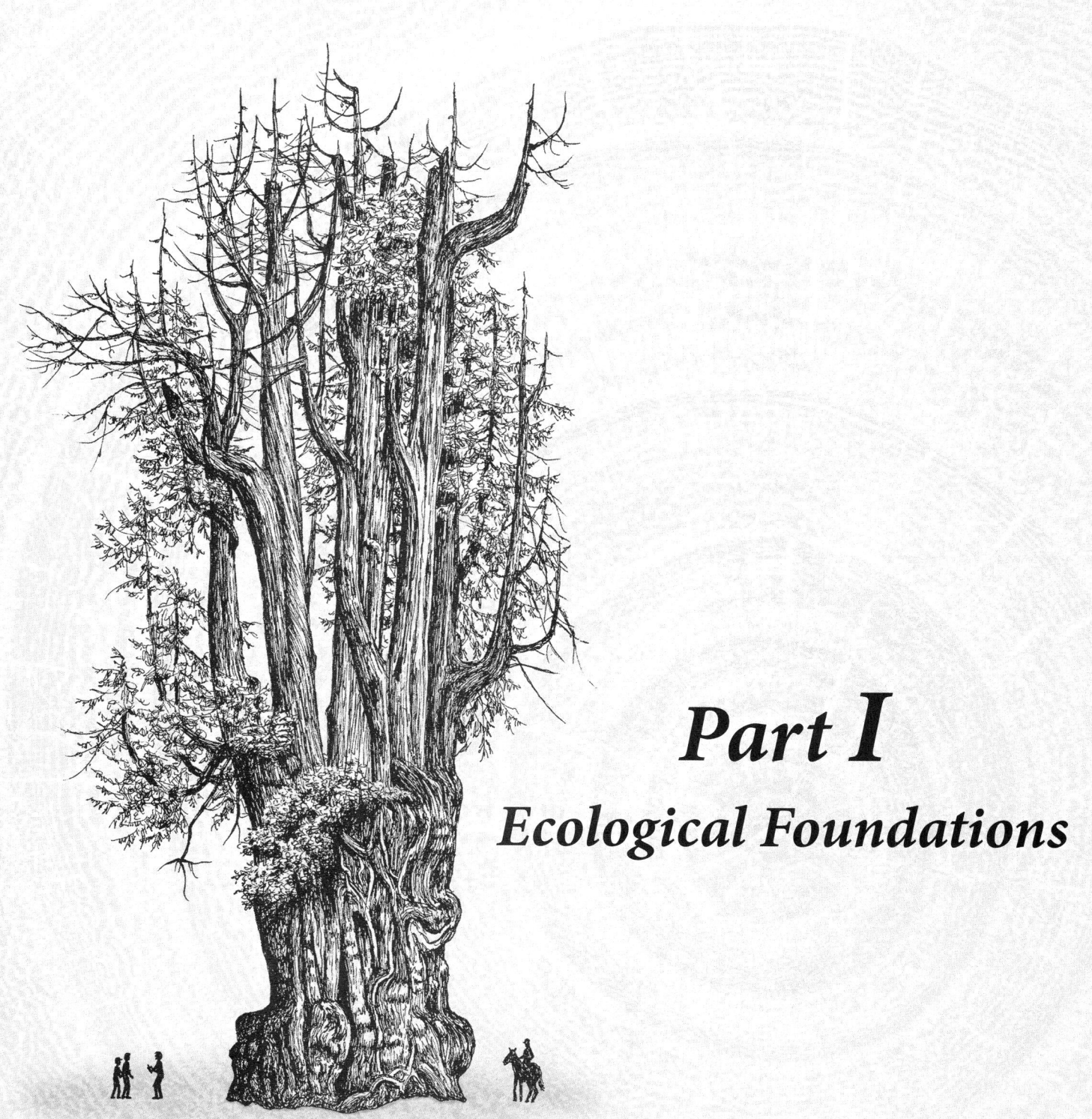

# Part I

## Ecological Foundations

*I bet that the great intellectual insight of the twentieth century . . . will turn out to be ecology, the idea that all things are deeply interconnected.* — BILL McKIBBEN

# CHAPTER 2

# Understanding Forests as Ecosystems

What is a forest? A forest is a highly interactive community of organisms with the tree life form dominating among the energy-capturing green plants. These plants generate the cascade of energy that supports food webs composed of thousands of species, from mammals and birds, through a myriad of insects and other invertebrates, to fungi and microbial organisms. A forest has a complex and often imposing physical structure, which exposes vast surface areas of leaves, branches, and stems to the atmosphere, with which it exchanges gases, water, and particulates. Tree roots penetrate deep into the soil mantle, providing the belowground community with the immense inputs of energy that are required to create and sustain a living soil.

Thus described we can see that a forest is an ecosystem in the fullest sense of the word—it is not simply a collection of trees! As an ecosystem the forest includes all the biota and their complex linkages, the environment in which its branches and roots are embedded and with which it interacts, and certainly the trees—of varied ages and sizes as well as the standing dead trees and down logs.

What do forests do? All forests are working forests, because they all carry out multiple functions that create a broad array of services and products valued by humans—for example, by capturing the sun's energy through photosynthesis and using it to grow and sustain this architectural wonder that sequesters carbon, stabilizes soils, and regulates hydrologic cycles, including moderating the effect of storms. As an ecosystem the forest has many collective attributes. It has *biological richness*, which is not just about species but also very much about the interactions among organisms and the services they provide. It has *structural complexity*, which enables it to provide habitats, to interact physically with the cycles of water and nutrients, and to accumulate wood structures that can be carbon stores or sources of wood.

*The forest ecosystem is dynamic.* It undergoes daily and seasonal cycles. The forest also develops and ages over

*Classic old-growth Douglas-fir–western hemlock forest in the Oregon Coast Range ("Valley of the Giants" on federal land managed by the Bureau of Land Management).*

decades and centuries, undergoing shifts in the presence and abundance of species, in structure, and, most importantly in its functional capabilities. This is sometimes called succession. Much of this long-term evolution is gradual, but disturbances can intrude and punctuate the process; a major disturbance can start it over again albeit (as we will see) with significant organic legacies from the preceding forest.

*Forest ecosystems also have attributes of stability, resistance, and resilience.* Forest ecosystems exhibit significant stability or resistance, which is their ability to tolerate or resist stressors—such as windstorms or drought episodes—without undergoing changes in state. Factors contributing to this include their physical structure and the physiological tolerances of established trees. Resilience, as we discussed in Chapter 1, refers to the ability of the forest to return to an approximation of its original state, particularly with respect to its functional capabilities, when and if it is subjected to a disturbance that causes a significant change in the structure or composition.

*A forest ecosystem has integrity when its major components—biota, structures, and functional capacities are present.* When it lacks important attributes—key organismal groups, essential structures, or critical functional capacities—it can be viewed as being incomplete or lacking integrity. *Sustaining the integrity of the forest is a central tenet of ecological forest management.* We mean by this, sustaining its essential elements and capacities, not necessarily a specific condition or species.

We have begun this chapter by characterizing the forest as an ecosystem because this perspective is central to the goals and philosophy of ecological forest management. This perspective contrasts with a common view of forests as being simply collections of trees. The conceptualization and quantification of forests as ecosystems is unquestionably one of the most important developments in forest science during the last half century (Figure 2.1). The foresters of old certainly intuited that there were aspects and values of a forest beyond just trees and wood production. However, the scientific knowledge that would have allowed an early- or mid-20th century forester—or other resource specialist, such as wildlife or fisheries manager—to comprehend the larger context for their work did not exist. Today that science does exist, and all natural resource managers and serious forest stakeholders need to have a basic understanding of the ecosystems with which they are engaged.

Our goal in this chapter is to introduce the reader to the rich science of forest ecosystems, most of which has been developed during the last half century. At least a rudimentary understanding of the basic elements of a forest ecosystem is a critical underpinning for understanding the philosophy and approaches of ecological forest management. There are several excellent textbooks on forest ecosystems for readers wishing more comprehensive information on the topics covered here and in Chapter 3, including Perry et al.'s (2008) *Forest Ecosystems*, Barnes et al.'s (1998) *Forest Ecology*, and Kimmin's (2004) *Forest Ecology*. A thorough treatment of the ecosystem concept is provided by Likens' (1992) *The Ecosystem Approach: Its Use and Abuse.* Our definition of forest ecosystems explicitly includes aquatic features that are embedded within the forest and are, of course, strongly influenced by it, including streams, rivers, lakes, ponds, and wetlands

*We view humankind as an integral element of forest ecosystems and not separate from them. This includes human influences of both older and modern societies. How could we do anything else in the 21st century!* Furthermore, one of the generic goals of ecological forest management is to sustain a full array of the human values provided by forest ecosystems, including environmental, economic, and social benefits. Although we recognize that many forest ecosystems have been significantly influenced by past and current human activities, we focus largely on attributes of relatively

Figure 2.1 *Our current understanding of natural forests as ecosystems is largely a product of scientific research conducted during the last 60 years, although it is rooted in earlier science and philosophy. Pictured here is an old-growth forest on the H. J. Andrews Experimental Forest in the Cascade Range of Oregon, USA.*

Table 2.1 *Key attributes of forest ecosystems*

| Biodiversity | Biological richness, including species and the numerous interrelationships among the biota, including food webs, mutualisms (e.g., mycorrhizae), and services (e.g., pollination) | |
|---|---|---|
| Function | Work carried out by the ecosystem including | |
| | | Production, including capture, utilization, and cycling of solar energy in the form of energy-rich carbon compounds |
| | | Regulation of the hydrologic cycle |
| | | Regulation of nutrient and other material cycles |
| | | Provision of habitat for biota |
| Structure | Physical structure or architecture of ecosystem including individual structural elements and their spatial arrangements | |
| | | Structures include living trees, standing dead trees, logs, and shrubs |
| | | Structural arrangements include uniform, random, and clustered patterns |

natural (e.g., unmanaged) forest ecosystems in this chapter and the next to help the reader better understand how forest ecosystems are structured, can simultaneously provide a diversity of services and products, and are dynamic in time and space.

## Part 1: Attributes of Forest Ecosystems

*Three important attributes of forest ecosystems are biodiversity, function, and structure. These attributes are a useful way to begin a consideration of forests as ecosystems* (Table 2.1), although ecosystems can be categorized or described in many other ways. Individuals interested in applying ecological forestry need to have a basic understanding of all three of these ecosystem attributes and their interrelationships, as they are highly interlinked.

## Biodiversity of Forest Ecosystems

Biodiversity, which we will use as our shorthand for biological richness, includes the diversity of species or organisms that are present in the ecosystem and their numerous interactions, including trophic relationships (i.e., where they are in the food or energy chain), mutually beneficial relationships (mutualisms, such as mycorrhizae), and services (such as pollination). *The diversity of organisms ("biota") is an important focus in ecological forest management because: (1) organisms are the creative agents that actually generate the ecological services and products that we obtain from forests—the means by which goods and services are generated from the environmental resources (i.e., sunlight, water, nutrients, etc.); and (2) organisms and their interactions are objects of direct and major social interest.*

We equate biological richness to the total biodiversity of the ecosystem, including the numbers and relative abundance of different species (see more on biodiversity in Chapter 14) (Figure 2.2). In natural resource management the focus is often on dominant plant species, such as trees, and on vertebrate animals. Total forest ecosystem species diversity is huge, however, and composed primarily of smaller organisms—insects and other invertebrate animals, fungi, bacteria, and other microbial forms. Much of this diversity is unrecognized or poorly known, despite the many essential roles these smaller but abundant organisms play, such as in the decomposition of dead organic materials and cycling of nutrients.

Food webs or trophic relationships are an important aspect of biodiversity that is about the energetic relationships between organisms. These relationships are often dealt with during discussions of energy flows in ecosystems. Fundamentally food webs identify organisms that are linked through feeding patterns—i.e., who is eating whom—and represent energy flows [see Box 2.1]. However, they are much more than that. We mention food webs here because these linkages are as important to maintaining the biological richness of ecosystems as provision of habitat. A comprehensive understanding of food webs can help us understand why some ecosystems are richer in biological diversity than others and the conditions that are required to maintain that biodiversity. For example, as we will see, dense conifer-dominated forests often have relatively simple food webs based primarily on consumption of dead organic matter or organic debris. In contrast, open shrub- and herb-dominated ecosystems often have more numerous and more complex food webs, which are initiated by organisms that consume plant materials, including leaves, nectar, and fruits. These can be important matters to such biota as songbirds and large grazing animals (e.g., deer and elk). Of course, some food webs are well-known (and even controversial), such as those involving higher order predators (e.g., wolves and grizzly bears), which are discussed in Chapter 14.

## Functions of Forest Ecosystems

*Ecosystem function refers to the processes or activities carried on by ecosystems—i.e., the work that ecosystems do. All forests are working ecosystems in that they carry out ecological functions or processes of value to humankind.* Examples include the capture of the sun's energy through photosynthesis, regulation of the flow of energy, water, nutrients, and other materials, and provision of habitat for other organisms. Traditionally students of ecosystems have categorized the functional attributes of ecosystems primarily in terms of the major flows (sometimes referred to as cycles) of energy or carbon, nutrients, and water. However, in recent years a fourth categorical ecosystem function—provision of habitat that sustains biodiversity—has been added.

**Production Functions**    *The production function of a forest ecosystem begins with the capture of the sun's energy by green plants through photosynthesis and its conversion into energy-rich carbon compounds. These compounds provide*

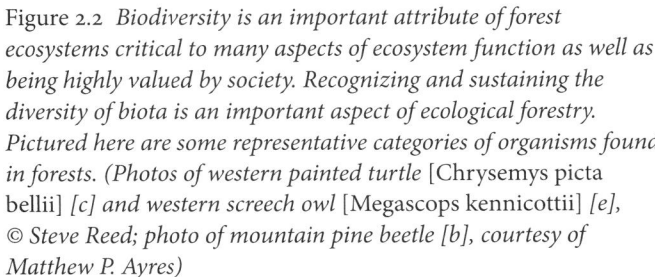

Figure 2.2  *Biodiversity is an important attribute of forest ecosystems critical to many aspects of ecosystem function as well as being highly valued by society. Recognizing and sustaining the diversity of biota is an important aspect of ecological forestry. Pictured here are some representative categories of organisms found in forests. (Photos of western painted turtle [*Chrysemys picta bellii*] [c] and western screech owl [*Megascops kennicottii*] [e], © Steve Reed; photo of mountain pine beetle [b], courtesy of Matthew P. Ayres)*

*the energy to sustain all the organisms and all biological activity occurring within the forest ecosystem (and the world!).* Aspects of the production function are elaborated in Box 2.1. Energy captured through photosynthesis supports the metabolic processes (e.g., respiration) and growth of trees and other green plants, including the production of wood. Ultimately it is the energetic basis for all other nonphotosynthetic organisms in the ecosystem, including animals, fungi, and microbial organisms, through a variety of food webs or trophic pathways. Wood production is only one aspect of forest productivity, although it is an important one, because it is related to the creation of the prominent and complex structures (the trees!) that distinguish forests.

Energy, carbon, and organic matter are all used as metrics to quantify and trace the energy pathways and compartments in ecosystems. Although energy, carbon, and organic matter are all interconvertible metrics, probably the most common measure used in natural resource management is mass or volume per unit area, as exemplified by tonnes/hectare and board feet/acre.

There are many different measures of productivity in forest ecosystems (see Box 2.1). The most fundamental measure is the amount of carbon fixed by photosynthesis per unit area per unit time, but this is difficult to measure directly. Much of the energy of a forest ecosystem goes into sustaining the metabolism and growth of the green plants

---

### Box 2.1  **Production ecology: Capture, transfer, and loss of energy in ecosystems**

Production is about the capture of the sun's energy through photosynthesis, the transformation of that energy into organic matter and its transfer through elements of the ecosystem, and eventual loss through respiration. The basic equation is simple (after Perry, Oren, & Hart, 2008):

$$6\,CO_2 + 6\,H_2O + \text{sun's energy} \leftrightarrow C_6H_{12}O_6 + 6\,O_2$$

Only green plants, through the process of *photosynthesis*, can capture and convert the electromagnetic energy of the sun into the chemical energy of the reduced carbon compounds (variously referred to as carbohydrates or photosynthates). The reverse reaction (from right to left in the equation) is called respiration, which is the metabolic breaking of those carbon bonds by all living organisms for life-sustaining energy and with some loss as heat. *Decomposition* is one form of respiration, which is carried out by organisms that utilize dead organic materials as their energy source.

Green plants are the sun-energy-acquiring organisms and are, consequently, referred to as the *primary producers* of the ecosystem. The plants use this energy to maintain their metabolism (i.e., stay alive) and to grow, adding to and replacing parts of their bodies. Because they provide their own energy they are also called *autotrophs*. Incidentally, not all plants are capable of photosynthesis; some lack chlorophyll and obtain their energy from other plants by developing relationships with green plants, such as by parasitizing them.

All of the other organisms in the ecosystem depend on "hand-me-down" energy from green plants and so they are called *consumers or secondary producers* (for obvious reasons, since they are getting their energy from another source) and, also, *heterotrophs*. There are many categories of consumers or heterotrophs, depending on where they acquire most of their energy. *Herbivores or grazers* directly consume live plant materials, and different herbivores will utilize different plant materials, such as leaves, fruits, and pollen. *Carnivores* obtain their energy by eating other animals. *Omnivores* utilize both plant and animal material. *Detritivores* (also known

as saprotrophs) consume dead organic matter to obtain energy and nutrients. The flow of energy from the plants to and through the rest of the organisms in the ecosystem is known as *trophic pathways or chains or food webs or chains*. We will use food webs as our favored term.

Ecosystem productivity can be defined as the increase in biomass or organic matter (OM) in the ecosystem, and there are two important formulas, which differ only with regard to whether the respiration of living organisms is included:

Gross Primary Productivity (GPP) = Change in OM
+ Respiration

Net Primary Productivity (NPP) = Change in OM
− Respiration

NPP provides a measure of the net exchange in carbon between the forest and atmosphere. If NPP is negative, then the forest is losing carbon to the atmosphere; whereas if NPP is positive, then the forest has been a sink for atmospheric carbon. Hence, ecosystem productivity is ultimately net carbon balance, and wood production is only one element in this equation! It is also important to note that accurately measuring forest ecosystem productivity is very challenging because it fundamentally involves measuring the net flux (inputs and outputs) of carbon between the forest and the atmosphere. This can be and is being done in scientific studies but not as a routine forest measurement.

Biomass is the total weight of organic matter per unit area of an ecosystem. It may be measured in English tons/acre, metric tonnes/hectare, or megagrams of carbon/meter$^2$. Technically this includes all the organic matter, both living and dead. Sometimes biomass is partitioned into live biomass, meaning biomass of living organisms, and dead biomass or necromass, which is not part of living organism. Standing dead trees and logs and other large (e.g., > 5 cm) pieces of wood on the forest floor often represent a significant proportion of the biomass of a forest.

and other organisms that are the base of the food webs. This includes the belowground portions of ecosystems, which in forests typically require disproportionate amounts of the energy captured by green plants; by disproportionate we mean that while the ratio of aboveground/belowground biomass commonly approximates 80/20, much more than 20% of the energy captured by photosynthesis in trees is typically required to maintain the belowground structures. This is a consequence of the high turnover rate of belowground structures, such as fine roots and mycorrhizae, the latter representing the structure formed by the symbiotic relationship between plant roots and many species of fungi.

Forests can have extraordinary productive capacities with their large photosynthetic surfaces (leaves!), and when you combine this with the ability of trees to sequester some of this productivity in large, long-lived structures, massive accumulations of organic matter are possible. The upper boundary of possibilities has been documented in northwestern California, where the old emergent dominant coast redwood with their decay-resistant heartwood have produced forests with a biomass of 5,190 Mg/ha, aboveground carbon stocks of 2,600 Mg/ha, and a leaf area index of 19.4 (i.e., 19.4 m$^2$ of leaves over each m$^2$ of ground) (Van Pelt et al., 2016).

**Edaphic Functions** *Forest ecosystems play important roles in modifying and enriching soils, stabilizing soils and landforms, and participating in nutrient cycles, including conserving nutrients—i.e., preventing nutrients from being leached or otherwise lost from the ecosystem.* Sustaining and, where lost, restoring the desirable chemical, biological, and physical properties of soils are explicit objectives in ecological forestry. The general tendency is for natural ecosystems, including forests and grasslands, to continually improve soil properties by increasing the organic matter content and nutrient stocks in the soil, although there are exceptions. The dependence of the complex, dynamic, and biota-rich life of soils on energy flows provided by trees and other green plants is often overlooked (Perry et al., 2008; Stohr, 2013). The flows of energy into the soil from the canopy of green plants to the roots and associated mycorrhizae are critical to sustaining soils as living entities (more on this later); hence, vegetation and soils have reciprocal dependencies—it is not simply a matter of soils providing trees with nutrients, moisture, and a place to root!

Forests play important roles in the flows or cycles of major nutrients—nitrogen, phosphorus, sulfur, and important bases, such as calcium, potassium, and magnesium. The vegetation itself represents important stocks of these materials. Organic materials produced by the trees and other vegetation contribute directly to nutrient stocks in the soil and to the ability of the soil to retain nutrients, thereby preventing their loss from the ecosystem as a result of such processes as leaching. Vegetation also contributes to the breakdown of soil parent materials.

Biota—including trees—play critical roles in accumulating stocks of biologically available nitrogen. Although elemental nitrogen ($N_2$) is the dominant gas in the atmosphere, most biota (including plants) cannot utilize $N_2$ and require nitrogen in the form of either ammonia ($NH_4^+$) or nitrate ($NO_3^-$). Atmospheric depositions can provide some nitrogen in these forms. However, the most important sources of available N are a small but diverse group of organisms with the ability to convert $N_2$ into $NH_4^+$, a process known as nitrogen fixation (see Box 2.2). These organisms live and do their work in a variety of locales, including as partners in a symbiotic relation with living plants, in dead wood and decayed portions of living trees, and as free-living organisms. A number of woody plant genera are well-known as hosts of N-fixing organisms, including members of the legume family (e.g., *Robinia* and *Acacia*) and the genera *Alnus* (alder) and *Ceanothus* (ceanothus); these organisms typically occupy specialized root structures called nodules. Because biologically available nitrogen is often a limiting factor in forest productivity we have a special interest in plant species that host N fixers.

Forests and other woody plants often play important roles in stabilizing soils on steep slopes or soils developed on highly unstable parent materials, thereby reducing the potential for landslides and other types of landform failures. One important factor contributing to stabiliza-

---

**Box 2.2  Nitrogen fixation**

There is a small but diverse group of organisms that are capable of nitrogen fixation, the conversion of elemental nitrogen, which is so abundant in the atmosphere, to biologically useful forms of nitrogen. These include about 20 genera of nonphotosynthetic bacteria, 15 genera of cyanobacteria (also known as azotobacter), and some actinomycetes. Many of these organisms occur in symbiotic relationships with green plants as nodulated N fixers; examples are bacteria, such as *Rhizobium*, in roots of legumes, or *Frankia* (an actinomycete) in the roots of woody nonleguminous plants. Another common symbiosis is that of cyanobacteria with some lichens, mosses, and ferns. There are also N fixers that live in close association with roots, mycorrhizae, or leaves. Not all N fixers need to be associated with green plants—free-living N fixers include some cyanobacteria, which are capable of carrying on photosynthesis, and some bacteria, which utilize dead organic materials (e.g., wood, litter, and soil organic matter) as energy sources. Hence, nitrogen fixation can occur in a variety of locations including symbiotically with green plants (including lichens), within decaying wood, and as free-living organisms.

tion is the extensive woody root systems developed and sustained by forest and shrub ecosystems. These strong and persistent woody root systems contrast with the root systems developed by grasslands. Woody root systems can continue to bind soils for several years following major disturbances that kill all or most of the trees or shrubs, providing time for newly regenerated vegetation to develop root systems.

Regrowth of vegetation following major disturbances is critical in preventing large nutrient losses following such disturbances. This includes all of the vegetation (e.g., shrubs and herbs) that survives the disturbance as well as any that quickly reestablishes itself; indeed, the rapid vegetative responses of understory shrubs and herbs are likely to be important contributors to retention of nutrients. An experiment in "enforced devegetation" conducted at the Hubbard Brook Experimental Forest in New Hampshire dramatically demonstrated the important role of vegetative regrowth in preventing significant nutrient losses following denudation (Bormann & Likens, 1994). The forest in the treated watershed was cut down (but not removed), and regrowth was suppressed for three growing seasons with herbicides. Losses of nutrients in dissolved form in streamflow were eight times those of a control watershed, and losses of

particulate material (organic and mineral) were ten times higher than the control. While such treatments may seem extreme, they are, in fact, comparable to conditions that can occur in plantations, where all vegetation except for the planted trees has been severely reduced by herbicide treatments; in such circumstances, destruction of the these trees, such as by wildfire, effectively denudes sites until new trees are planted or other vegetation becomes established through natural seeding.

**Hydrologic Functions**    *Forest ecosystems interact in many and important ways with hydrological processes; indeed, it can be argued that the role of forests in watershed protection may be the most important category of ecological service provided by forests in the 21st century* (Figure 2.3). These roles include influences on water balances, water quality, and stabilization of flow regimes associated with both storms and winter snowpacks.

Forests affect water balances through their participation in such processes as interception of precipitation, evapotranspiration, capture of cloud and fog moisture through condensation, hydrological redistribution of soil water, and influences on snow accumulation and melt (Figure 2.3). The structure and composition of the forest and the climatic

Figure 2.3 *One of the most important functional roles of forests in the 21st century will be their role in the protection of watersheds, which facilitates provision of well-regulated flows of high-quality water. Shown here is a stream-gaging station on the H. J. Andrews Experimental Forest in Oregon, USA; watershed researchers were among the first scientists to study forests as ecosystems.*

regime largely determine the qualitative and quantitative roles that forests play in such processes. For example, forests utilize—transpire—large amounts of water in carrying on their metabolic processes during which they remove it from the soil and evaporate it into the atmosphere.[1] Such processes can be at a scale sufficient to actually impact the climate of heavily forested regions, as has been documented for the Amazon Basin (Salati, 1987).

Another important generalization is that evergreen forests will utilize more water than deciduous forests in part because the evergreen trees transpire water year-round. As one example, conversion of a watershed covered with mixed-deciduous hardwood forest to eastern white pine (*Pinus strobus*) in North Carolina reduced total streamflow by about 20% by stand age 15 and 35 to 45% after 25 years (Swank, Swift, & Douglass, 1988).

A second example is provided by a comparison of annual transpiration by quaking aspen (*Populus tremuloides*), lodgepole pine (*Pinus contorta*), subalpine fir (*Abies lasiocarpa*), and Engelmann spruce (*Picea engelmannii*) using a canopy transpiration model (Kaufmann, 1985). Ratios of annual transpiration for stands of equal basal area were 1:1.8:2.1:3.2 in order of aspen, pine, fir, and spruce. Leaf area index and length of transpiration season for the different species were important (but not the only) variables influencing the results.

Another final important generalization is that water use and, conversely, streamflow will vary with the development stage of the forest. For example, in the northwestern North America, dense, young evergreen conifer forests have been found to reduce summer streamflows by about 50% below summer flows in adjacent (paired) watersheds dominated by mature and old forests (Perry & Jones, 2017). As another example, naturally structured and frequently burned longleaf pine (*Pinus taeda*) forests transpire significantly less water than southern pine plantations on comparable sites (Kirkman & Jack, 2017), which is partially explained by lower leaf areas and partially by dominance of old trees in the longleaf forest. When comparisons are made, old trees have usually proven to be more efficient than young trees in their use of water.

Forest structure strongly influences the accumulation and persistence of winter snowpacks. Canopies intercept and hold snow, which can result in some loss of snow to direct evaporation (sublimation). Some intercepted snow ultimately falls to the ground to form snowpacks on the forest floor. In warmer coastal regions, such as those that have transient snowpacks, some intercepted snow will also melt, drip to the ground, and infiltrate the soil. Snow accumulated as a snowpack within a forest is relatively well protected from melting as a result of shading by the canopy and reduced air currents. As a consequence, snow persists later into the spring or summer than snow that has accumulated in open areas. Ideal forest structures for accumulation and persistence of winter snowpacks are forests that have many small- to moderate-sized openings; such forests have less interception of snow than forests with continuous dense canopies but still provide for significant protection of the snowpack from the sun and warm winds. Forests with different canopy structures, such as those in young and old forests, can have highly contrasting effects on snow accumulation and melt in regions of transient or warm snow zones, where rain-on-snow events can cause major flood flows (see Chapter 5).

The large surface areas (including leaves, twigs, and branches) of forest canopies provide immense condensing surfaces for moisture associated with low clouds or fog. Condensation on trees can add significant net precipitation to a site where fog or low clouds are an important environmental feature (Barnes, Zak, Denton, & Spurr, 1998, pp. 168–169), in addition to reducing forest transpiration. For example, condensation from low clouds in an old-growth conifer forest resulted in a net addition of 30" of annual precipitation over that measured in an adjacent opening (Harr, 1982). Kimmins (2004) comments "that water input below forest cover in foggy weather generally exceeds that in the open by 30 to 50%" with highest values on ridge tops. Forests with deep and complex canopies, such as old-growth forests, capture more moisture since they have more extensive canopy surfaces and therefore scavenge a greater volume of air. The large surface areas of forest canopies also make them important precipitating surfaces for aerosols and other air-borne particulates. Incidentally, higher concentrations of dissolved and particulate materials are found in fog and cloud moisture than in ordinary precipitation.

Hydraulic redistribution or lift is an additional hydrological influence of forests. Deep-rooted plants, such as trees, can extract water from deep in soil profiles and release some of it into dry surface soils at night, thereby providing moisture for shallow rooted plants and other soil organisms. Hydraulic redistribution can be a significant factor in forests in arid environments or those subject to seasonal dry periods.

There are numerous additional interactions between forests and surface water bodies located within or adjacent to forest ecosystems, such as streams and rivers. These influences go far beyond the effects of forests on water and nutrient flows discussed above. We will discuss some of these in Chapter 5.

---

1 The contribution of transpiration to global hydrologic fluxes is immense as indicated by the following estimate: "the mean global value for plant transpiration (the water that moves from the soil through plants to the atmosphere) [is estimated] to be 48% of continental precipitation" (Brooks, 2015).

**Habitat Functions**    *Forest ecosystems provide an abundance of habitats or niches for organisms, such as a great variety of structures and microclimatic conditions, in addition to providing the energetic basis for their existence.* As will be seen, one major aspect of the habitat provision function is in the form of critical structures, including trees, snags, and logs. Another aspect of habitat provision is that there is a significant temporal component—that is, forest structures (and the environmental niches they represent) are dynamic due to both internal and external processes (see below and Chapter 3). For example, standing dead trees gradually undergo decay and disintegration; hence,

sustaining important but transient forest structure habitat, such as large snags, can challenge managers.

Trees and other plant structures are important habitat elements of a forest. A diversity of such structures, such as the presence of trees of differing species, sizes, and conditions (e.g., presence of unusual structures, such as cavities and brooms [Figure 2.4]) can provide important habitat or niche diversity. Large trees may be particularly important because of their role as sources of large snags and down boles (see below) or as important structural elements of streams and rivers. Old trees may be important because of the distinctive attributes (niches) they provide (Lindenmayer & Laurance, 2016, and Box 2.3).

Trees are as important as habitat in their dead forms as they are when they are living, and their roles as dead wood continue to evolve as they undergo decay and disintegration (e.g., Harmon et al., 1986; Maser, Tarrant, Trappe, & Franklin, 1988). These dead forms include standing dead trees (snags), down trees or boles on the forest floor (logs), and other dead wood structures, which we will collectively refer to as coarse woody detritus (CWD) in the remainder of this book. There is now an immense body of literature on the importance of CWD to the structure, function, and biodiversity of forests and associated aquatic ecosystems (e.g., Harmon et al., 1986; Maser et al., 1988).

Forest ecosystems provide relatively stable and climatically muted environments for organisms, in addition to providing a system that is structurally complex and niche-rich in comparison with other natural ecosystems. For example, extremes of temperature and wind are highly modulated within closed forests in contrast with contemporaneous conditions found in adjacent nonforested environments. This can make forests important for many organisms either as permanent or temporary refuge habitat (Frey, Hadley, & Betts, 2016a; Frey et al., 2016b).

## Structure of Forest Ecosystems

*Ecosystem structure refers to the architecture of an ecosystem—the physical features or elements of the ecosystem and the spatial patterns in which they are arrayed.* Structure is the most conspicuous feature of forests because of their often massive and complex forms and the volume of space that

Figure 2.4 *Unusual structures such as brooms, which are dense aggregations of branches and twigs, often provide critical or preferred habitat for many organisms, including birds and arborescent mammals. A broom on a Douglas-fir tree stimulated by a dwarf mistletoe infection is illustrated here.*

they occupy (Figure 2.5). Species other than trees, such as shrubs and forbs, also contribute to structural complexity. The tall and decay-resistant tree life form makes much of this structural complexity possible; few other ecosystems exhibit such large, complex, and persistent structures of biological origin, although coral reef ecosystems would be another example.

Of the three major categories of ecosystem attributes (biodiversity, function, and structure), structure has special significance for forest managers and stakeholders for three reasons. First, structures are typically the objects that we manipulate to achieve management objectives. Second,

some of the structures—the trees—are often a major end product of our management, such as logs for harvest. Third, structures are often used as surrogates for processes (e.g., productivity) and species (e.g., habitat) that are difficult to observe or measure directly.

Forest structure is multidimensional—i.e., it includes consideration of (1) the variety and abundance of individual structures, such as trees, snags, and logs as well as (2) the spatial arrangement of the structures and structural conditions within the forest (Table 2.2). Both of these dimensions are important in forest management. In production forestry the focus is exclusively on live trees and uniform

---

### Box 2.3  Ecological significance of old trees

Old trees differ greatly from young trees in some of the roles that they play in forest ecosystems, and this is not just related to their generally larger size, the principle being that *old trees are not simply enlarged versions of younger trees.* Particularly in long-lived species, older trees accumulate significant idiosyncratic features as a result of injuries and infections and responses to those injuries (e.g., reiterated tops) and as a consequence of altered light and temperature conditions (e.g., epicormic branch systems). Even to very old ages, trees commonly retain an ability to grow and repair themselves in response to both damage and improved environmental conditions, although such capacities (and inherent longevity) do vary widely with species.

Large old trees have larger branches, often of both primary and secondary (epicormic) origin, which are important to many canopy organisms and processes. For example, large branches can accumulate massive epiphytic communities and provide essential sites for the nests of large birds, such as eagles, or, alternatively, egg-laying sites for birds that do not create nests, such as marbled murrelet (*Brachyramphus marmoratus*). Older trees have time to develop larger primary branches and to experience stimuli (e.g., breakage) that generate secondary branch systems. Canopies of old trees may also be deep, extending close to the ground—even after undergoing extensive natural pruning as younger trees—as a result of secondary (epicormic) branch development. On the other hand, canopies of old trees in frequent-fire ecosystems are likely to be elevated, reducing the potential for fire to ladder into the crown.

Old trees have larger percentages of heartwood than younger trees of the same species, which results in more durable snags, logs, and other coarse wood structures. Heartwood decays differently than sapwood so it plays different roles as habitat; elements of heartwood may be very persistent in litter and soil systems. Heartwood also behaves differently as a fuel because of its greater content of resinous material.

In many species, older trees develop thick and complex (e.g., furrowed) bark, which create niches for invertebrates that are, of course, potential food sources for other species (e.g., Carey, 2009). Thicker barks make older trees more resis-

tant to wildfire and increase their probability of surviving such events and functioning as foci in ecosystem recovery. Some species may produce masses of loose and stringy bark that are important habitat for invertebrates: e.g., *"Bark streamers provide habitat for a wide array of invertebrates, such as spiders and predatory wingless tree crickets ... [which] are, in turn, prey for several species of marsupials ... and birds"* (Lindenmayer, 2009, p. 75).

The decadent features of older trees are among their most important from the standpoint of habitat for biological diversity. Cavities and other pockets of decay are essential for a wide array of cavity-dependent species (e.g., see (Lindenmayer, 2009; Hunter & Schmiegelow, 2011). Multiple tops provide complex canopies as well as thick vertical branches that are broad, stable platforms, which can accumulate thick mats of organic matter. The epicormic branch systems mentioned earlier may also be the consequence of crown damage and loss. Brooms of various types may also develop as a result of diseases or mistletoes; these can be important nesting, resting, and hiding habitat for birds, mammals, and other animals.

Old trees also represent a distinctive genetic resource, particularly in landscapes that are now dominated by managed forests. These trees not only represent diverse germ banks but also include genotypes that can be viewed as long-term "winners"—i.e., they are trees that have survived diverse climates, attacks by fungi and insects, and possibly intense storms and fires!

Finally, it is important to recognize that large and old trees may continue to accomplish significant net growth. An outstanding example of this has been documented for old coast redwood (*Sequoia sempervirens*) and giant sequoia (*Sequoiadendron giganteum*) trees. After a comprehensive analysis of growth patterns in a large sample of such trees, investigators found no evidence of negative growth–age relationships in either species and concluded that, *"Except for recovery periods following temporary reductions in crown size, annual increments of wood volume and biomass growth increase as redwoods enlarge with age until extrinsic forces cause tree death"* (Sillett et al., 2015, p. 181).

Table 2.2  *Structural elements of forest ecosystems, including individual structures and spatial arrangements of structures*

| Individual structural elements | Exemplary categorizations |
| --- | --- |
| Live trees | Species, size, and condition (e.g., features such as deformities and defects) and densities of each recognized category |
| Standing dead trees | Species, size, and condition (e.g., decay state) and densities of each recognized category. This is often recognized as separate category from other CWD because of the importance of snags as habitat for biodiversity |
| Coarse woody detritus | Down trees, logs, branches, and other coarse wood detritus and/or by species, size, and condition (e.g., decay state) and densities of each recognized category |
| Understory plants | Shrubs, perennial herbs, and other plant life forms and/or coverage by species |
| Root mounds and pits | Density of mounds and pits, depth of pits, and heights of root mounds |
| Organic layers | Type or structure and thickness (mean and variance) |

| Spatial patterns of structures | Exemplary characterizations |
| --- | --- |
| Vertical distribution of foliage/canopy | Single-layered, multilayered, or continuous |
| Horizontal distribution of tree stems | Clustered, uniform, or random; clumped or single |
| Canopy gaps and anti-gaps | Extent (area), sizes, and shapes |
| Unoccupied canopy space | Volume and spatial distribution |

Figure 2.5  *Forests are the most massive and structurally complex terrestrial ecosystems in the world; the existence of the tall and rigid tree life form, including its persistence following death and disintegration, creates the potential for structural complexity and all of the functional and habitat capacities contingent upon this complexity.*

spatial arrangements of these trees in order to optimize the production of harvestable wood. In ecological forestry, we typically seek to sustain a diversity of tree structures, of diverse species and conditions (e.g., decay states), and, often, to create or sustain structural patterns that are non-uniform in their spatial arrangements.

**Individual Forest Structures**    In forest ecosystems the most prominent structural elements are typically trees and their derivatives—standing dead trees and boles and other large pieces of wood on the forest floor (Figure 2.6).

Live trees in natural forest ecosystems typically include a variety of species, sizes, and conditions. Different tree species will produce trees with different growth forms, potential size and longevity, wood qualities (including decay resistance in live and dead forms), forage quality, reproductive structures, etc. The differences between evergreen conifers and deciduous angiosperms (hardwoods) perhaps provide the most striking contrast found among temperate and boreal forests. However, even species that are from the same genera can have significantly different potentials.

Size distributions of trees in forest ecosystems can vary from relatively uniform to highly diverse. Young even-aged forests are typified by relatively uniform tree sizes, whereas many older forests exhibit a wide range of tree sizes. The range or standard deviation of tree sizes is a metric that is sometimes used to distinguish old-growth forests from young stands, as their mean values may be similar but the variance in tree size in old-growth forests is typically much larger than in young forests.

Conditions of live trees in forest ecosystems can vary from sound (lacking decay or damage) and conforming to a structural model[2] to highly altered (some would say deformed) as a result of environmental or biological damage or both. Trees typically accumulate deformities over time, and if they live long enough to become truly old trees, they generally lose their model-conforming form and become highly individualistic structures (e.g., Lindenmayer, 2009; Van Pelt & Sillett, 2008). The deformities that develop include forked boles, broken and multiple tops, root and bole rots, cavities, and brooms. While such conditions are undesirable from the standpoint of wood production, they are often critical in providing habitat important to specific species.

Old trees often accumulate many of these distinctive features as well as having other important features lacking in young trees (Box 2.3, Figure 2.7), which is why retention and maintenance of populations of older as well as larger trees are often objectives in ecological forestry. In general, older forests provide much larger numbers of microhabitats or niches important as habitat for biological diversity than do young forests, and most of this is related to presence of older trees. In one comparison of tree microhabitat structures in Douglas-fir (*Pseudotsuga menziesii*) forests of different stand ages and management histories, *"Recently managed stands had, on average, 115 microhabitats/ha . . . and natural old-growth stands had 745 microhabitats/ha"* (Michel & Winter, 2009); the microhabitats tallied in this study included broken tree tops, bayonet tops, cracks or scars, bark loss, hollow chambers, stem cavities with decay, bark pockets with and without decay, burls, heavy flows of resin, and bark bursts.

Very large trees and the large branches or branch systems that such trees provide represent structural elements that often have unique habitat value. In some trees primary branch systems may provide large branch systems while in other tree species many of the larger branch systems are mainly epicormic branches, which develop from dormant buds laid down as the base of branch and twig systems (Figure 2.8). The development, retention, or restoration of trees with large branches may be a specific structural objective in ecological forestry.

*Live tree populations in forest ecosystems managed under ecological forestry principles most often will be diverse in tree ages, sizes, conditions, and species.* Production forests, on the other hand, will generally consist of trees of relatively uniform size and condition.

Standing and down dead trees, logs, and other CWD are structurally as important to a fully functional forest ecosystem as living trees. The increased emphasis on sustaining wildlife and other elements of forest biodiversity has made incorporation of snags, logs, and other CWD structures a routine but often challenging element in ecological forestry.

Standing dead trees (snags), down dead trees, logs, and other CWD are significant contributors to essentially all of the functional roles carried out by forest ecosystems (Box 2.4, p. 38) (Harmon et al., 1986). Although biologists have been aware of the importance of dead trees and logs for many decades, it has only been recently that many foresters have recognized and accepted the need for sustaining these forest structures. Their best known role is probably provision of habitat critical to the existence of many species, including most vertebrate and many invertebrate animals as well as many fungi and other decomposer organisms.

Regional syntheses of habitat management for forest wildlife (e.g., Thomas, 1979; Johnson & O'Neil, 2001) provide evidence that almost all forest vertebrates make some use of

---

2  Many organisms, including trees, tend to develop following some regular or "model-conforming" pattern. Trees typically follow a common pattern or model of structural development, particularly when they are young. The systematic production of regular whorls of branches and the branching pattern of twigs as branches expand are examples of such "model-conforming" development. Trees may begin to deviate from such model-conforming patterns as a result of damage or limitations in resources, particularly as they grow older and are subject to a history of damage and decay; as a result, they often lose their model-conforming form.

Figure 2.6 *Trees and the snags, logs, and other woody structures derived from them are the most prominent structural elements of forest ecosystems. One of the most important recent changes in our understanding of forest structure is that trees in the dead form (snags, logs, and other coarse wood) are as important to the multiple functions of forest ecosystems as the live trees, such as for carbon sequestration and provision of habitat for biological diversity.*

snags and/or logs as part of their life cycle and daily activities. Many invertebrates have larval stages that are dependent on dead wood. Dead wood also provides substrate for regeneration of trees and other woody plants (the nurse-log phenomenon), often host nitrogen-fixing organisms, and can modify grazing patterns of large herbivores. Large wood structures also have important roles in structuring stream and river ecosystems (see Chapter 5) (Maser et al., 1988; Naiman & Bilby, 1998); indeed, one major objective in maintaining forest buffers on streams and rivers is to provide continuing input of large wood to these aquatic ecosystems.

Snags, logs, and other CWD are typically present in forest ecosystems in a variety of quantities, dimensions (including heights in the case of snags), and conditions (such as their decay state) (e.g., (Maser et al., 1988). All of these variables have important influences on their habitat value. The tree species that produced the wood are also important because of the large differences among species in patterns and rates of wood decay, which are related primarily to the chemical content of the heartwood. In general, wood generated by hardwood trees (angiosperms) decays more rapidly than that of conifers (gymnosperms), although some hardwood forests can have very large quantities of logs and other CWD (Figure 2.9). Some conifers belonging to the cypress family (*Cupressaceae*) are notable for producing heartwood that has extremely slow rates of decay, such as coast redwood and giant sequoia.

*Because of their importance in sustaining the biodiversity and productivity of the forest ecosystem, maintaining appropriate sizes, amounts, and conditions of snags, logs, and other CWD—and restoring this material where it is currently deficient—is a common goal in ecological forest management.*

**Spatial Patterns in Forest Structure**   The spatial arrangement of forest structures can be as important in influencing forest ecosystem functioning as the diversity of individual structures that are present. Important spatial patterns include the horizontal distribution of tree stems or other structural features (e.g., logs) and the vertical distribution of canopy. The nature of unoccupied space within forest canopies—i.e., the amount and spatial pattern of "openness," the reciprocal of space occupied by structures—is also an important structural metric, such as for some birds and other arboreal animals.

Aboveground structures (e.g., tree stems) may have random, clustered or aggregated, or uniform spatial patterns,

Figure 2.7 *Older and larger trees have many distinctive features important as habitat for wildlife and other organisms, such as large branch systems, and decadent features, such as cavities and other deformities (see also the drawings of individual trees by Robert Van Pelt scattered throughout this book).*

Figure 2.8 *Large primary or secondary branch systems represent distinctive structures that are important to a wide variety of biota. The epicormic branch systems, such as on the Douglas-fir shown in these photos, often support complete mini-ecosystems with accumulations of organic soils, epiphytic plants, and invertebrate communities as well as sites utilized by birds, arboreal mammals, and even amphibians. (Photographs from [a] H. J. Andrews Experimental Forest in Oregon, USA and [b] the Wind River Experimental Forest in Washington State)*

and these commonly vary across spatial scales. Relatively uniform spatial patterns are most characteristic of plantations, which are managed following an agronomic model; as an old forestry professor once said, *"There needs to be room to grow but none to waste!"* Natural stands will often show patterns that are clustered or random (e.g., Larson & Churchill, 2008, 2012).

The vertical distribution of canopy or foliage is an important, spatially varying structural attribute. Forest canopies are often characterized as being single layered, multilayered, or continuous from the ground to the top of the crown. Canopy distribution can vary significantly between young and old forests (Figure 2.10) (see Chapter 3). Young forests, including plantations, tend to have high single-layered canopies with relatively little intermediate foliage. Many old forests, on the other hand, have essentially continuous canopies (from the ground to the top of the tallest tree) with the majority of the foliage in the lower part of the canopy (Figure 2.10). Such forests can be described as being ***bottom-loaded*** in contrast to the ***top-loaded*** canopies common in dense young forests.

Figure 2.9 *While coniferous forests are generally viewed as having larger quantities of CWD than hardwood forests, temperate hardwood forests also can have large quantities of decaying logs and other CWD, such as are evident in this old forest of lenga (Nothofagus pumilio) in Tierra del Fuego, Chile.*

## Box 2.4 Important and interesting ecological aspects of coarse woody detritus (CWD)

The importance of standing dead and down trees (snags, logs, and other CWD) has received much attention in terrestrial and aquatic ecosystem studies over the last 35 years creating some challenging issues in forest management, where trees, once dead, were typically not recognized as having significant ecological value. Indeed, snags were historically viewed with great hostility because of valid concerns about the potential danger they posed to forest workers as well as their contributions to wildfire spread.

Functions of CWD in terrestrial forest environments include provision of:

- Habitat for a large variety of organisms including vertebrates, invertebrates, fungi, and a diversity of microbes;
- Long-term sources of carbon (energy) and nutrients;
- Sites where nitrogen fixation can occur;
- Sources of soil organic matter (including forming a unique element in the soil matrix);
- Nurse logs (seedbed) for reproduction of trees and other plants; and
- Structures that can influence geomorphic and hydrologic processes.

Functions of CWD in streams and rivers in forested environments include provision of:

- Structures that can slow movement of water, organic litter, soil, and rock;
- Habitat for biological diversity both directly (wood itself as habitat) and indirectly (by creating different stream habitats, such as debris jams, pools, plunge pools, etc.);
- Sources of carbon and nutrients; and
- Protection of stream banks from erosion by armoring banks and dissipation of energy, such as by creating waterfalls.

Amounts of CWD vary widely with forest type, environmental conditions, site productivity, and forest age, but in typical natural forests CWD often makes up at least 20% of the aboveground organic matter. Major influences of forest type are related to the species that are present because there is wide variability in decay resistance of wood of different species. Temperature and moisture regimes are important environmental variables affecting decay rates, but their effect is not always intuitive. While older forests are typically thought of as having large amounts of CWD (and they do), young forests that develop following a major natural stand-replacement disturbances (not timber harvest) also can have very large amounts of CWD generated by the death (but not consumption or removal) of the pre-disturbance stand (see Chapter 3).

Major processes involved in the decomposition of CWD are respiration, fragmentation, and leaching. Respiration is the process by which organic materials (including CWD) are broken down by decomposer organisms for energy, some of which is lost as heat, causing a gradual decrease in the density of CWD. Fragmentation is the process by which larger pieces of wood are broken into smaller and smaller pieces of wood, which become too small to be counted as part of the CWD pool. This is an important process for snags because gravity is "pulling down" the snags with the help of the animals that are burrowing through it. Fragmentation is also an important process for CWD in streams, because logs are battered as they, rocks, and other materials are moved about. Leaching is the process by which primarily soluble materials are removed by water moving through the woody structure; although little mass is removed, the leached materials are largely high-energy and nutrient rich molecules.

The amount and nature of decay-resistant chemicals in the heartwood is a major factor in determining the decomposition rate of CWD. Heartwood decays at highly variable rates, from rapid to very slow, depending upon its chemical content; it can be highly resistant to decay. All other parts of the tree (sapwood, bark, phloem or inner bark) tend to decay at the same rate regardless of species; sapwood and phloem decay rapidly and bark almost always decomposes very slowly.

Some major differences in rates of decomposition involve:

- *Snag vs. log*—Relative rates of decomposition for snags and logs vary in different environments. In high-rainfall coastal forests of the Pacific Northwest a dead tree of a given size and species will disappear much faster if it is standing than if it is on the forest floor, in part because the log on the forest floor becomes saturated with water and is an anaerobic environment for much of the year. In the pine forests of the intermountain west the snag (provided it remains standing) may last much longer than a comparable dead tree on the ground, which will often undergo relatively rapid and nearly complete decay, due in part to the activity of macroinvertebrates.
- *Terrestrial vs. aquatic*—a log in a terrestrial environment will decay much faster than the similar log in a freshwater stream or pond. Freshwater environments lack animal organisms that can penetrate or "mine" the submerged log; hence, decomposition is generally very slow.
- *Streams/rivers vs. lakes/ponds*—a log in an actively moving body of water will disappear at a much faster rate on average than a comparable log in a still body of water. This is because fragmentation of CWD is occurring in the moving stream or river.

Of course, canopies are actually three-dimensional, and gaps or openings in the canopy (which may be partial or complete) provide important variability as do areas with very dense layers of foliage. These localized conditions can have significant impacts on the understory composition and density (Figure 2.11). Again, we would note the importance of unoccupied or open space within the canopy for many arboreal organisms, such as predatory birds and their prey.

*Because of the significance of structural spatial patterns to ecosystem functioning, ecological forest management is often as concerned with the spatial arrangement of forest structures as it is with the abundance and diversity of the individual structures.* This may be a very major consideration or objective in silvicultural treatments (see Chapter 4).

## Other Structural Aspects

Other important structural aspects of forests include their understories and belowground elements.

**Forest Understories**   Understories are important elements of forest ecosystems that play diverse roles. Understories can be major reservoirs of biodiversity, such as rich mixtures of mosses, herbs, shrubs, and tree regeneration or, on the other hand, be virtually barren in forests with very dense overstory canopies (Figure 2.11b). The understory has been variously referred to as the ground flora, layer, or vegetation and the herbaceous or herb layer or stratum; various height limits have been applied to it, such as from 0.5 to < 2 m (Gilliam & Roberts, 2003). We use the term understory very broadly to include tall shrub and small tree

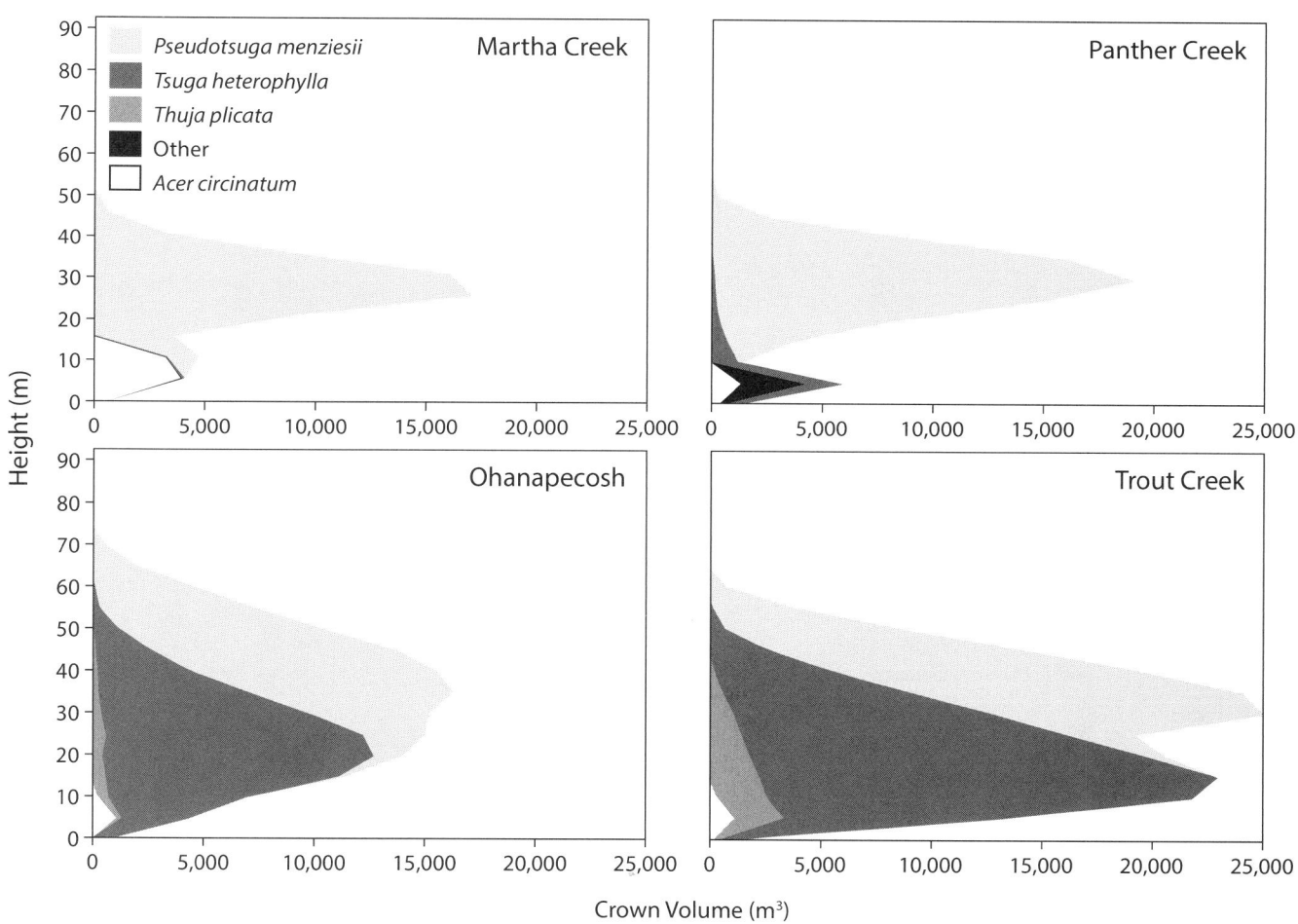

Figure 2.10  *Foliage distribution shifts during stand development from being single-layered and top-loaded in a young forest to being continuous or multi-layered in an old forest as illustrated in this age sequence of Douglas-fir–western hemlock forests. Martha Creek represents a very young stand in which the foliage is predominantly high in the canopy and composed primarily of Douglas-fir. Panther Creek represents a mature forest, which is still predominantly top-loaded but in which an intermediate canopy of shade-tolerant species is beginning to develop. Ohanapecosh represents an old-growth stand early in its development; a well-developed intermediate canopy of western hemlock is present in this forest. Trout Creek represents a more advanced old-growth forest with a large crown volume, including a dense intermediate canopy of western hemlock. (Source: Reprinted from Van Pelt & Nadkarni, 2004, with permission of the Society of American Foresters)*

species that never grow into the overstory canopy as well as the mosses, herbs, ferns, and low shrubs.

Understory species can greatly enrich the biological diversity of the ecosystem both by their presence and by providing critical resources needed to sustain other species, such as forage, nectar, seeds, and fruits. In conifer-dominated forests understory plants may, for example, sustain herbivory-based food webs, which could include lepidoptera (butterflies and moths) and songbirds that feed upon insects. Also, in conifer-dominated forests, understory species may provide seeds or fruits that are important supplemental food sources for rodents that feed primarily on fungi, such as flying squirrels. While the understories of hardwood forests themselves

also contribute such values, the hardwood overstories also provide many of these resources.

Understories may play important roles as surface fuels by influencing the quantity and flammability of those fuels as well as their structure. This is particularly important in forest ecosystems characterized by and dependent upon frequent fire. For example, understories in longleaf pine (*Pinus palustris*) forests (Figure 2.12) not only contribute significantly to the surface fuels but also structure the fuel beds by lofting much of the pine needle litter (Mitchell, Hiers, O'Brien, & Starr, 2009) (see Chapter 3).

Understories need to be considered for their long-term as well as immediate contributions to forest composition and function. Understories can function as reservoirs of tree regeneration or seedling banks, which are available to respond rapidly to unexpected natural disturbances, such as a major windstorm. Further, the composition and abundance of the understory species are likely to be major factors in determining the diversity of the early successional or preforest communities that develop following either a natural disturbance or regeneration harvest (see Chapter 3).

Dense understories of clonal species, such as those composed of dwarf bamboos (*Sasa* spp.), bracken fern (*Pteridium aquilinum*), blackberries (*Rubus* spp.), or other aggressive shrubs or vines, can become major management

Figure 2.11 *Understory vegetation can respond dramatically to development of canopy gaps as illustrated by these two photographs in an old-growth Douglas-fir–western hemlock* (Tsuga heterophylla) *stand. (a) Well-developed and species-diverse understory developed in a canopy gap; (b) Sterile understory found under a very dense overstory; this condition is sometimes referred to as an "antigap." (Photos courtesy of Thomas A. Spies)*

Figure 2.12 *The understory plays important roles in frequent-fire forests by contributing critical fine fuels and by structuring the fuel beds, such as in this longleaf pine forest.*

challenges (Figure 2.13); either native or nonnative species may play such roles. Because such species respond very rapidly to availability of additional light and moisture, they can be significant constraints in designing and implementing thinning treatments. For example, a thinning intended to increase understory diversity in a forest with a well-developed understory dominated by a clonal species may simply result in increasing its dominance. Such understories can also create challenges to tree regeneration following disturbances, including timber harvesting.

*The diversity and structure of forest understories often requires as much attention as that of overstories in ecological forest management.* Silvicultural activities will often include purposeful manipulations of forest overstories to positively influence the composition and structure of understory communities.

**Belowground Ecosystems**  The belowground component or subsystem of forest ecosystems is typically very dynamic (e.g., high rates of productivity and turnover), very rich in biological diversity, and structurally complex (Perry et al., 2008; Stohr, 2013). Despite its importance, the belowground aspects of forest ecosystem structure, function, and composition are relatively poorly understood.

Most of the belowground biological diversity consists of fungi, algae, actinomycetes, bacteria and other microbial organisms and a large variety of invertebrates, including arthropods, nematodes, and protozoa (see Perry et al. [2008] for a comprehensive overview on soil biota). Much of the live biomass consists of vascular plant roots and associated mycorrhizal hyphae (Box 2.5).

Functionally, belowground portions of forest ecosystems are very dynamic, with much higher rates of turnover than occur in aboveground structures (e.g., fine roots vs. leaves). Sustaining this dynamism and associated diversity requires large continuing flows of energy from aboveground portions of green plants into the roots and regions surrounding them (the rhizosphere). The largest component of this dynamism or high turnover is that of the fine roots and mycorrhizae. Although the proportion of above- and belowground live biomass often approximates a ratio of 4:1, the allocation of energy captured by plants through photosynthesis to belowground production is disproportional, particularly on sites that are deficient in moisture or nutrients. Belowground metabolic processes sometimes consume 50 to 75% of the energy captured by the trees through photosynthetic processes. Since belowground portions of forest ecosystems require large energy inputs, greatly reducing or eliminating green plants by removing or killing them can interrupt that flow and quickly cause some soil biota to begin going dormant or dying (see Perry et al., 2008 for examples). When reestablishment of vegetation is delayed, such as by herbicides, there can be significant

Figure 2.13  *Forest understories dominated by clonal species, such as the dwarf bamboo in this subalpine forest in Japan, can be major challenges to aspects of forest management, such as the regeneration of trees or other desirable understory species.*

impacts on soil biota and massive losses of soil nutrients through leaching (Bormann & Likens, 1994).

Structurally, belowground portions of forest ecosystems are as complex as those aboveground, but our knowledge is limited because it is currently difficult to access soil systems without massively altering them. Because live roots and mycorrhizal hyphae are important sources of nutrients and energy, many other elements of the biota, such as bacteria and soil animals, are concentrated in the rhizosphere, which is the area adjacent to the fine roots and hyphae. CWD incorporated into the soil also can be significant and biologically active components of the soil forming additional *biological hotspots*. What can be said with considerable confidence is that there is at least as much spatial patterning in the distribution of biota and functional activity belowground as there is aboveground.

*Sustaining the high flows of energy from green plants into the soil to support the diverse and dynamic belowground subsystem is an important consideration in ecological forest management. Conserving the diversity of fungal species, that can form mycorrhizae is an important part of this goal because significant redundancy is desirable in this important functional group.*

## Interrelationships of Biodiversity, Function, and Structure

Although we have separated our discussion of biodiversity, function, and structure in this section on forest ecosystems, these three attributes are highly inter-related. Biological richness (biodiversity) is obviously strongly dependent upon the physical architecture or structure of the forest ecosystem. Functions, such as production and regulation of the hydrologic flows, are highly related to the biodiversity that is present as well as the structure of the ecosystem. As we will see in the next chapter, all of these attributes undergo change in their dimensions as a forest undergoes development from its birth to old age. We have provided graphic illustrations of these interrelationships and how they change throughout the development of a forest ecosystem in Color Plate 2.1.

---

### Box 2.5 Mycorrhizae—an important tree–fungal association

Mycorrhizae are structures combining vascular plant root and fungal tissue in such a way that both plant and fungus benefit; about 90% of plants form mycorrhizae (Perry et al., 2008) (Figure 2.14). The vascular plant provides the fungus with sugars and other organic molecules and the fungus provides a variety of benefits to the plant, primarily by enhancing the uptake of moisture and nutrients through a hyphal network. Many species of fungi participate as mycorrhizal partners and have varying capabilities and environmental optima. Several different types of mycorrhizae are recognized including: ectomycorrhizae (EM) in which the fungus forms a sheath around the plant root and does not penetrate the root cells and arbuscular mycorrhizae (AM) in which the fungus does penetrate the root cells. AM is the most common type, but EM is the type that occurs on tree species belonging to the pine (*Pinaceae*), oak (*Fagaceae*), myrtle (*Myrtaceae*), and birch (*Betulaceae*) families.

Mycorrhizal hyphae provide an immense belowground network connecting individual plants of the same species as well as connections between different species, such as trees and understory plants. Many mycorrhizal-forming fungal species can form mycorrhizae with many different plant species, which helps them to survive and thrive even when the above-ground plant community (their source of energy) undergoes dramatic changes, such as following timber harvest. For example, many fungi form mycorrhizae (EM) with plant species belonging to both the heather (Ericaceae) and pine families, which provides them with suitable symbionts in both early successional and closed forest stages.

Similarly members of the cypress family share fungal (AM) associates with the majority of flowering plants.

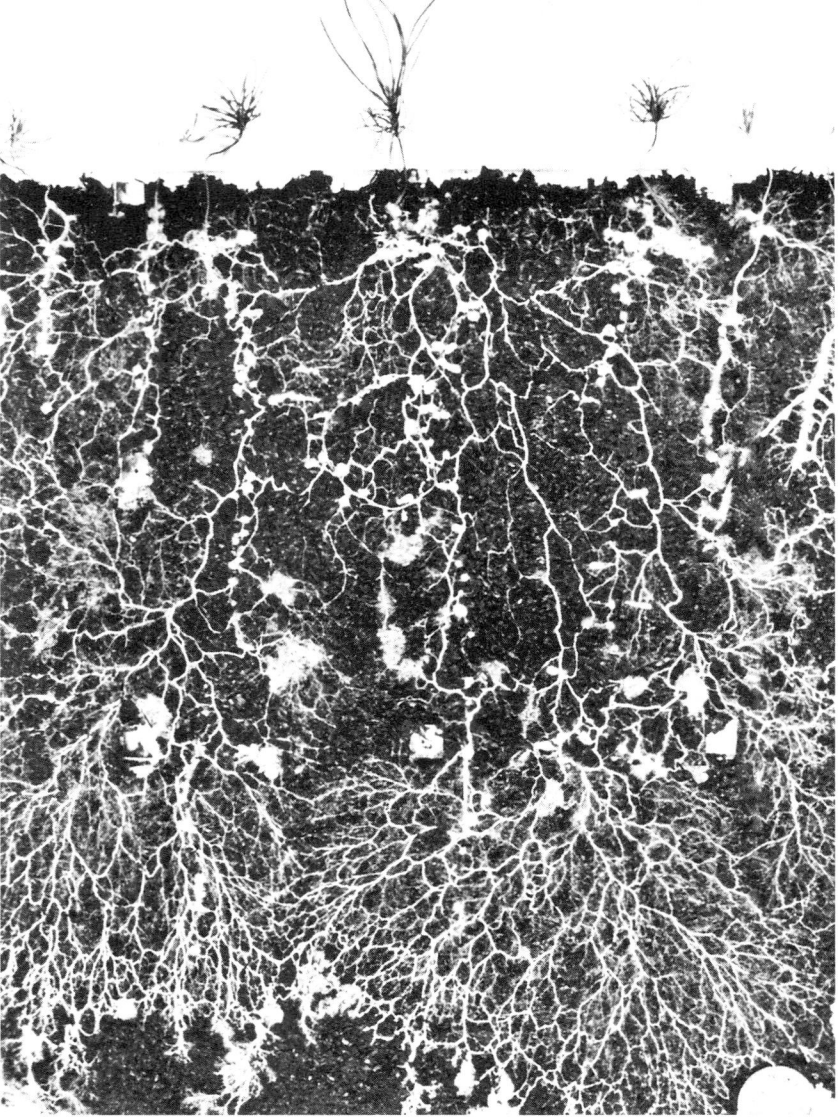

Figure 2.14 *Mycorrhizae are symbiotic structures formed between plant (including tree) roots and fungi that assist in the uptake of moisture and nutrients).* *(Photo courtesy of Sir David Read)*

# Part 2: Forest Ecosystem Development

Established forests are dynamic ecosystems that are constantly changing as a result of both internal processes and external stimuli. These gradual and sometimes subtle changes include those often referred to as succession, although we will wait until Chapter 3 to discuss the more dramatic changes associated with massive (e.g., stand-replacement) disturbances.

Succession is the key ecological concept related to forest ecosystem change, which we define as follows: *Succession is a directional change in the composition or structure of a forest ecosystem or, most commonly, in both composition and structure.* By stipulating directional change, we exclude the seasonal or other cyclic changes that occur in ecosystems. Many ecologists view succession primarily or exclusively as a compositional change in a plant community, such as the gradual replacement of one species by another. An example might be the gradual replacement of a light-demanding pioneer tree species, such as ponderosa pine (*Pinus ponderosa*) or Douglas-fir, by a tree species that is more shade tolerant, such as white fir (*Abies concolor*) or western hemlock (see Box 2.6). However, there are forests—generally those composed of a single tree species—that undergo profound changes in structure over time while undergoing little or no change in composition; an example could be a ponderosa pine forest developing on a site where it is the only tree that can grow. Although less common, we include such circumstances in our definition of succession.

Again, succession in temperate and boreal forests most commonly involves changes in both composition and structure. The structural aspect is often ignored in ecological literature.

Stand development focuses exclusively on changes in the tree component of a forest ecosystem, which is a much more

---

**Box 2.6  Shade tolerance and successional role of tree species**

Shade tolerance and the successional role of tree species are often related but need to be clearly distinguished. Shade tolerance is largely a physiological attribute of a tree species, which is primarily genetically determined, although some phenotypic adjustment is possible (e.g., production of shade vs. sun leaves). The successional role of a tree species is primarily a function of the tree species with which it is associated on the site where the forest is developing.

Shade tolerance references the ability of a tree species to regenerate, survive, and grow in (i.e., to tolerate) low light conditions, such as those that are found in the understory of a forest with a dense overstory. Species that can survive and grow in heavily shaded conditions are called shade tolerant. Examples include beech (*Fagus* spp.) and many species of maple (*Acer* spp.), cedar (*Thuja* and *Chamaecyparis* spp.), hemlock (*Tsuga* spp.), spruce (*Picea* spp.), and true fir (*Abies* spp.). Species that cannot survive and grow in shaded conditions are considered to be shade intolerant. Examples include many species of pine and oak. Of course, there is a continuum in shade tolerance from species that are very tolerant of shade to those that are extremely intolerant of shade. For example, Douglas-fir and many white pines are actually quite capable of tolerating moderate amounts of shade, even though they are often described as being intolerant; i.e., seedlings of these species can get established and survive under the cover of partial shade.

Shade tolerance is primarily a fixed physiological trait of a species and has only limited plasticity. Technically, it is related to the level of light required for a species to reach its compensation point, the point on a gradient of light intensity at which a species can conduct sufficient photosynthesis to fulfill the metabolic needs of a tree seedling—i.e., allow it to survive. Shade tolerance of a species does not change from forest to forest although genotypes may display some variability in this trait.

The successional role of a species depends upon the other tree species that are currently or potentially present on the site—i.e., it is contingent upon the community of tree species with which it is associated. If tree species B is present and is more shade tolerant than tree species A, then species A is likely to eventually be replaced by species B, if no significant disturbance occurs to open up the forest canopy. Species A may be present as a pioneer on the site but subsequently the more shade-tolerant species B will be the one reproducing within the established forest with the potential to eventually replace the nonreproducing species A.

In an example from the real world, the relatively shade-intolerant Douglas-fir typically plays a pioneer or early successional role where it is associated with western hemlock, western redcedar (*Thuja plicata*), or Pacific silver fir (*Abies amabilis*), all of which are much more shade tolerant. However, Douglas-fir may successfully reproduce and persist on sites lacking tree species that are more shade tolerant than it is, such as on hotter drier sites where its only associate is may be ponderosa pine, which is even less shade tolerant than Douglas-fir. On sites where only a single shade-intolerant species—such as ponderosa pine—is present it can play both early- and late-successional roles.

Hence, the successional role of a species is not an attribute of the species but depends upon the array of associated tree species on a particular site. Consequently, the successional role of a tree species can vary from site to site. Relative shade-tolerance will be a major factor in determining successional role where multiple tree species of varied shade tolerances are simultaneously present.

limited perspective on ecosystem change than succession. An example of a major topic in stand development would be changes in the size-class distribution of tree stems, including the relative contribution of different tree species (Oliver & Larson, 1996).

*There are many important processes that contribute to the successional development of an established forest ecosystem (Table 2.3). These can be grouped into three broad categories: (1) development of individual trees or "ontogeny"; (2) competition and other biotic interactions; and (3) small-scale and often chronic disturbances and the legacies that they create.* All three of these categories contribute significantly to forest ecosystem development, including changes in composition, structure, and function. The collective outcome of these processes, in terms of forest demography and structure (including biomass accumulation), will be discussed in Chapter 3. Competition and disturbances are both agents of tree mortality, but we discuss them separately here because of their importance and contrasting impacts on forest development.

## Development of Trees

*The life history or ontogeny of individual trees and the long-term demography of tree populations are important aspects of forest ecosystem development* (Table 2.3). Individual trees are born, grow, undergo changes in form as a result of internal and external processes, and eventually die, thereafter continuing to function as CWD. The pattern and rate of tree growth will be strongly influenced by whether a tree is emerging into an established forest or an opening. Consideration of the entire life history of individual trees has been largely ignored in forestry because of the historical focus in forestry on youthful trees and forests managed for wood production; however, understanding the complete life histories of trees is important in ecological forestry.

Individual trees follow an intrinsic developmental pattern as they grow from seedlings into young, mature, and eventually old trees, assuming they don't die along the way. For example, a seed germinates and becomes an established seedling. It continues to grow into a sapling and eventually a pole-sized individual. The tree eventually reaches sexual maturity and begins producing seeds. Assuming competition from surrounding trees, shaded branches die and

are eventually lost by self-pruning, resulting in an overall "lifting" of the live crown. Surviving individuals continue to grow in diameter and height.

Change continues as a tree reaches maturity. Height growth gradually declines and plateaus around the maximum height the species can achieve on that site. The ratio of heartwood to sapwood in the tree increases. Crowns become more structurally complex, such as by epicormic branch development in response to various stimuli, such as increased light availability or damage to the crown. Canopy depth may be actually be lowered (i.e., deepened) as a result of epicormic branch production. Bark characteristics undergo change, including increased bark thickness and roughness on many species.

Older trees continue to become more unique or individuated and less model-conforming, such as in crown structure (e.g., Van Pelt & Sillett, 2008) (see Box 2.3 for more details). This happens as a result of the unique events expe-

Table 2.3 *Important processes contributing to the compositional and structural development of forests*

| | |
|---|---|
| **Development of individual trees** | Establishment |
| | Growth, including accumulation of mass, volume, and height |
| | Branch death and loss by natural pruning |
| | Production of reproductive structures and seed |
| | Development of decadent features, including cavities, decay pockets, and brooms |
| | Canopy elaboration, including creation of reiterations, epicormic branches and twigs, and large branches |
| | Development of heartwood |
| | Alterations in bark character, such as development of thick, damage-resistant bark |
| | Death and conversion to snags, logs, and other coarse wood structures |
| **Competition and other biotic interactions** | Competition among tree life form and trees of same species (e.g., differential effects on growth and survival of individuals) |
| | Additional effects of competition between trees of different species (e.g., suppression, elimination, or exclusion of one species by another) |
| | Competition between tree life form and other plant life forms (e.g., reduction in cover and diversity of understory shrubs and herbs) |
| | Other biotic interactions including those that involve mutualism or parasitism |
| **Disturbance and legacy creation** | Mortality, breakage, and other mechanical damage to trees from wind, snow, or ice |
| | Creation of pits and mounds by uprooting of trees |
| | Mortality and creation of snags by bark beetles |
| | Reduced growth and mortality of trees by defoliating insects |

rienced by individual trees, including structural damage from wind, ice, and snow and infections of fungi and other pathogens or parasitic organisms, such as dwarf mistletoes. Older trees often develop major canopy reiterations, very large and complex branch systems, and significant amounts of wood decay and cavities. All of these features provide habitat for biota and influence various processes. Eventually trees die, but they continue to play many of the same roles as well as some new ones in the form of snags, logs, and other CWD, as noted earlier. Indeed, the ecological importance of a tree could be viewed as gradually increasing with its age, size, and complexity and then gradually declining following its death (Figure 2.15) (Box 2.7).

In summary, trees undergo major physiological and structural change as they age some of which result from physical and pathological damage and some from intrinsic processes. Trees have distinctive attributes at all ages that determine their contributions to the overall functioning of a forest.

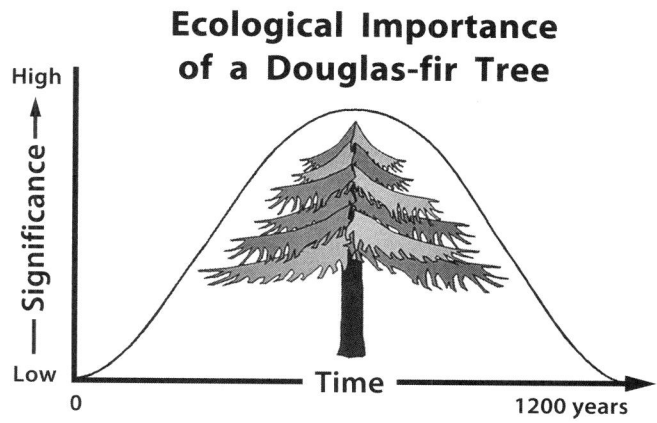

**Ecological Importance of a Douglas-fir Tree**

*Figure 2.15 The ecological importance of a tree—its overall influence on and contribution to the forest ecosystem of which it is a part—can be viewed as gradually increasing over time with its age, size, and complexity and then gradually declining following its death. This reminds us that the tree plays important roles in both live and dead forms and that it persists for significant time periods following its death.*

---

**Box 2.7  Continuity of function between live and dead trees—an example from Australia**

One of the finest illustrations of the continuity of function between living and dead trees is found in the mountain ash (*Eucalyptus regnens*) forests of southeastern Australia. There are many cavity dependent arboreal marsupials and birds in these forests that depend upon cavities living in these forests (Lindenmayer, 2009; Lindenmayer, Blair, McBurney, & Banks, 2015). However, there are no woodpeckers in Australia to create cavities. Instead, cavities in these forests develop very

slowly through wood decay processes and are found only in old trees and the large standing dead trees (or "stags" as they are called in Australia) that the old trees turn into when they die. Consequently, wildlife biologists often do not even bother to distinguish between a tree that is living or dead—simply whether it has abundant cavities, as is evident from their illustrations showing different classes of decay-bearing trees (Figure 2.16).

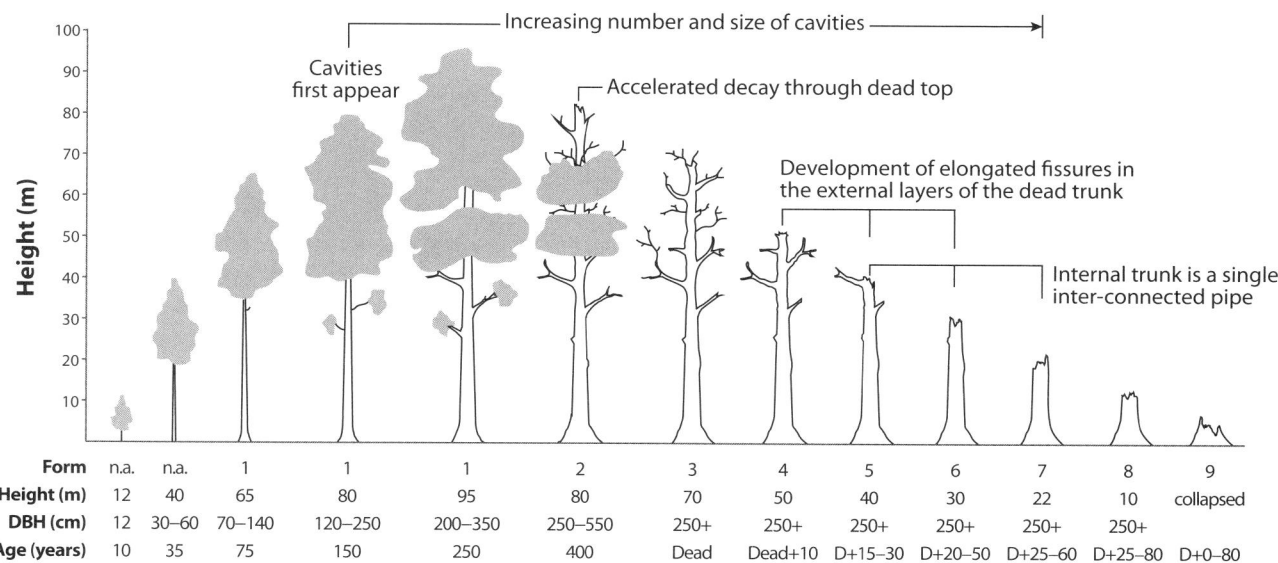

| Form | n.a. | n.a. | 1 | 1 | 1 | 2 | 3 | 4 | 5 | 6 | 7 | 8 | 9 |
|---|---|---|---|---|---|---|---|---|---|---|---|---|---|
| Height (m) | 12 | 40 | 65 | 80 | 95 | 80 | 70 | 50 | 40 | 30 | 22 | 10 | collapsed |
| DBH (cm) | 12 | 30–60 | 70–140 | 120–250 | 200–350 | 250–550 | 250+ | 250+ | 250+ | 250+ | 250+ | 250+ | |
| Age (years) | 10 | 35 | 75 | 150 | 250 | 400 | Dead | Dead+10 | D+15–30 | D+20–50 | D+25–60 | D+25–80 | D+0–80 |

*Figure 2.16 Diagrammatic representation of different forms of trees with cavities or "hollows" in mountain ash forests in southeastern Australia showing the continuity of function between live and dead trees in provision of this important wildlife habitat feature. (Source: Adapted from Lindenmayer, Blair, McBurney, & Banks, 2015; courtesy of David Lindenmayer)*

## Competition

There are many biotic interactions among organisms in the developing forest, and these can be characterized in terms of the balance of benefits and detriments resulting from the interaction:

- Competition: Detriment to both organisms;

- Mutualism: Benefit to both organisms;

- Facilitation: No effect on facilitating organism, benefit to other organism;

- Parasitism: Benefit to the parasitizing organism, detriment to the host organism; and

- Inhibition: No effect on inhibiting organism, detriment to other organism.

We focus here on competitive interactions, but it is important to keep these other important types of biotic interactions in forests in mind. For example, lichens are entities that form a mutualism among several organisms, which always include a fungus and an algal species and, sometimes, an azotobacter, which is an organism capable of fixing nitrogen. Mycorrhizae represent another mutualism between green plants and fungi. Mutualisms can occur among trees, such as among clusters of old trees connected through common root and mycorrhizal systems (Figure 2.17). Indeed, there is increasing experimental evidence of mutualistic networks among groups of trees of the same species but diverse ages and sizes, where trees are not only linked but facilitate survival and growth of small trees (Beiler et al., 2010). Parasitism is well represented by dwarf mistletoes.

Competition is a distinctive and important interaction within tree populations but also includes interactions between trees and other plant life forms. Competition can involve both short and long time periods, such as by affecting both tree regeneration and mortality. Competition is an interaction in which all participants are negatively affected. In a forest, trees and other plants compete with each other for the critical resources of light, water, and nutrients. Competition may occur between individuals of the same species, between different species of the same life form (e.g., two or more tree species), and between plants of different life forms (e.g., trees and herbs). Competition can be measured by effects on plant growth, mortality, and regeneration potential.

Competition in forest ecosystems within even-aged tree cohorts results in distinctive size structures (e.g., diameter distributions) and patterns of mortality. In young forests competitive effects may be most evident in height growth differentiation, which results in the fastest growing individuals moving their canopies to greater heights, thereby suppressing slower growing individuals. This differentiation tends to compound over time—i.e., once a tree undergoes suppression and loss of access to light and moisture, its decline accelerates. Competition in young forests also often produces bell-shaped diameter distributions. Mortality occurs primarily among the smallest trees as a consequence of the reduced light and moisture resources available to them. The intensity of the thinning that takes place is also highly predictable on the basis of the well-documented self-thinning rule or negative 3/2 power law, which defines the maximum density of trees of a particular size (Perry et al., 2008).

Competitively based mortality will tend to move a forest stand toward a more uniform structural condition in terms of both tree size and the spatial distribution of trees. Competition will be most intense in the densest portions of a forest and will be less intense in areas of lower tree density. Consequently, competition creates more spatial uniformity in structure within a forest stand, all portions converging toward the theoretical maximum. The competitive process also contributes to a greater uniformity in tree size as the smallest trees are continuously killed by competition. Competition is essentially the only natural process that moves forests toward greater structural uniformity, which contrasts with effects of agent-based mortality.

Figure 2.17 *Mutualistic relationships can exist among clusters of trees that have grown together for many decades or centuries and share belowground root and mycorrhizal root masses, as exemplified by this cluster of old ponderosa pine. Hence, mutualism may be a more important consideration in silvicultural treatments of such clusters than competition. Cluster of ponderosa pine located in Meeks Table Research Natural Area, Mt. Baker-Snoqualmie National Forest, Washington State, USA.*

Competition for resources also occurs between trees and plants of smaller stature, such as shrubs and herbs. This is evident when a young even-structured forest stand grows up and develops a closed overstory canopy, as described in Chapter 3. The overstory tree canopies intercept most of the light and utilize most of the available soil moisture. Understory plant communities can be virtually eliminated under such circumstances.

Competition is most evident in dense young forests, as discussed in Chapter 3, where it is typically the dominant cause of tree mortality, although other causes may be important (Lutz & Halpern, 2006). However, competition can reappear prominently in older forests that develop canopy gaps as a result of mortality in overstory trees. Dense seedling/sapling tree cohorts can develop in these gaps, which are then subject to intense competitive interactions (Larson et al., 2015; Lutz et al., 2014).

Competition among tree species can also contribute to successional change in forest composition. Effectively, the presence of a dense overstory canopy can prevent successful regeneration of tree species with low shade tolerance. Of course, there will be competition between shade-tolerant and -intolerant species when they occur together as part of an even-aged cohort; often in such cases the shade-intolerant species has an initial growth advantage and will tend to be the more successful of the two. However, competition also plays out over much longer time periods, where the more shade-tolerant species, which had an initial disadvantage, will be able to establish in the forest understory whereas the shade-intolerant species will not. This can lead to the eventual partial or total replacement of one tree species by another in the absence of a major disturbance to the forest overstory. (See Box 2.6). Several examples will be provided in Chapter 3.

## Disturbance and Legacy Creation

Disturbances are events that free resources, such as light, moisture, and nutrients, by killing or damaging existing organisms (Pickett & White, 1985). Forest disturbances occur in an infinite variety of types, sizes, intensities, and effects. The spectacular large and uncommon disturbances are those that come most quickly to mind and are discussed in Chapter 3. However, small chronic disturbance events, such as those causing the death of individual trees or small groups of trees, are most relevant to developmental processes within established forest stands.

Common chronic disturbances within established forest stands are those caused by insects (e.g., bark beetles or defoliators), diseases (e.g., root, butt, and stem rots), wind (e.g., uprooting and stem breakage), and snow and ice (top and stem breakage). Such disturbances create openings in closed forests, thereby freeing up resources, by killing and damaging trees, particularly those in the overstory.

These agents share several important features that make them important in forest development. First, as noted, these agents often kill or damage dominant and codominant trees and not just the smaller trees in the stand, as is the case with competition. Second, agent-based mortality often tends to be spatially aggregated; multiple nearby tree deaths can create significant openings in the overstory canopy. Third, agent-based mortality is highly unpredictable in time and space in contrast with competitively based mortality. Production foresters view both the unpredictability of agent-based mortality and its impacts on overstory trees negatively; those overstory trees are potential crop trees! However, agent-based mortality plays a critical ecological role in creating the structural complexity (gaps and spatial heterogeneity) that is an important attribute of older forests, as we will see in Chapter 3.

Conditions created by disturbance events—including residual biological and physical legacies—are the most important consequence of these events. Although biological legacies are discussed in detail in Chapter 3, we also emphasize here the importance of legacies from the smaller-scale agent-based disturbances characteristic of established forests. Such disturbances create legacies of snags, logs, and other CWD, which structurally enrich the existing stand. Windthrow produces mounds and pits. The pits often provide intermittent pools, which are often important breeding habitat for amphibians, and the mounds sometimes provide plants with refuge from grazing animals (Figure 2.18). Hence, legacies created by small-scale disturbances are important in forest ecosystem development, and are a major factor in creating and sustaining structural complexity in the dynamic but relatively stable, old forest ecosystems. There will be much more about this in Chapter 3.

Figure 2.18 *Tree uprooting creates the pit-and-mound complexity that is an important part of structural heterogeneity in established forests. Tree uprooting does the important work of mixing different layers of soil, itself an important process, and generating logs and other CWD. In addition uprooting creates pits and root mounds. In this forest ecosystem the pits form seasonal ponds, which are important breeding sites for amphibians, and root mounds, which function as refugia for plants that are favored browse species for local ungulates. Douglas-fir uproot in the Quinalt Lake area of Olympic National Forest, Washington State, USA.*

*The most important aspect of a disturbance
is what it leaves behind.* — JERRY FRANKLIN

CHAPTER 3

# Forest Dynamics: Disturbances, Developmental Stages, and Forest Archetypes

Forest ecosystems and landscapes are dynamic systems, a concept that we introduced with the discussion of succession and forest development at the end of Chapter 2. In this chapter we take up several important aspects of forest dynamics. In the first section we address the major disturbances that initiate new forest sequences and the important biological and physical legacies that they generate. A section on forest developmental stages follows; the stages are abstractions of the continuum of change that forests undergo through succession. Three forest archetypes representing major categories of natural forest ecosystems found in temperate zones are described in the third section. In the fourth and final section we review aspects of disruptions to forest ecosystems caused by climate change and invasive species.

## Part 1: Disturbances and Biological Legacies

Disturbances are events that free up resources, such as sunlight, moisture, and nutrients, by killing or damaging the existing organisms using those resources (Pickett & White, 1985). From an ecological perspective, disturbances are viewed as events that modify existing forest ecosystems rather than being categorically viewed as either good or bad. Natural disturbances have been viewed as something to be avoided by foresters focused on wood production because they can significantly disrupt management plans and damage or destroy valuable crop trees. In contrast, ecological foresters need to take a broader view of natural disturbances as events that can be emulated in their silvicultural practices, although at times they also will find them to be disruptive of their plans. Forest disturbances come in a wide variety of types, sizes, intensities, and effects, with the spectacular large and infrequent disturbances coming most immediately to mind and on which we focus in this chapter. However, the small chronic disturbances introduced at the end of Chapter 2, which result in the death of individual trees or small group of trees, are overwhelmingly the most

*Aftermath of the B&B Fire, a high-severity fire in mixed-conifer (near and midview) and subalpine mountain hemlock and true fir forest in the Oregon Cascade Range (Deschutes National Forest).*

common. *The entire spectrum of disturbance types and scales, from the small and frequent to the large and infrequent, provide models for creation and manipulation of forests in ecological forest management.*

Forest disturbances have a variety of sources, many of the most obvious resulting from forces that are outside of the forest ecosystem, such as wildfire, windstorms, epidemics, floods, landslides, volcanoes, and, perhaps, human beings. Drought is a more subtle kind of disturbance with the coup de grace for drought-stressed trees often being delivered by insects, such as bark beetles. Some types of disturbances, such as pathogens (diseases) and some insect pests, might be considered to be endemic or internal to the forest ecosystem, except when major outbreaks occur. Disturbance agents often interact with each other, such as wind uprooting trees weakened by root rots or snapping trees with butt or stem rots; another example would be trees succumbing to pathogens or insects after being damaged in other disturbances, such as a wildfire (Franklin, Shugart & Harmon, 1987).

The majority of disturbance agents (e.g., wind, fire, and insects) are capable of generating disturbances across a wide range of scales depending upon circumstances. For example, some forest types (e.g., ponderosa pine and longleaf pine) historically experienced frequent, low-intensity wildfires that sometimes covered very large areas, but these disturbances typically caused very little mortality of mature trees, and that mortality occurred largely as individuals or small clusters. Other forest types (e.g., Douglas-fir–western

hemlock and lodgepole pine) were primarily influenced by infrequent large disturbances, such as wildfire, which resulted in high levels of (or even complete) mortality of the trees over significant portions of the affected area. Similar to wildfire, wind and insects can be responsible for either frequent small-scale or infrequent large-scale events. We characterize intervals between disturbances as either frequent (chronic disturbances), which are expected at intervals of one year to two to three decades, or infrequent (episodic disturbances), which are generally expected at intervals of a century or more. Disturbances that have intervals between these two can have characteristics of both.

*The conditions created by disturbance events—including the type and abundance of biological and physical legacies that are left behind and the openness that they create—are the most important outcomes of disturbances.* Although we can measure disturbances in many other ways, such as the level and duration of heat in the case of fire or wind strength in the case of windstorm, it is ultimately the outcome or effects of disturbances that are the important determinants of what happens next.

While fire, windstorm, insect epidemics, and other natural disturbances convert trees from a live to a dead state, very little of the biomass contained in these trees is consumed or removed (Figure 3.1). *Biological legacies are significant biologically generated elements of a pre-disturbance ecosystem that persist in some form through even severe natural disturbance events* (Table 3.1; Box 3.1; Color Plate 3.1).

Table 3.1 *Common biological legacies of major disturbances in forest ecosystems; small disturbances—at the scale of an individual tree or a small gap—also generate biological legacies, such as standing dead trees and down logs*

| Living organisms and propagules | Organic matter | Biologically created patterns in soils and sediments |
|---|---|---|
| Sexually mature living trees, shrubs, and herbs | Dead standing trees or snags | Distinctive chemical, physical, and biological patterns in soils created by trees or other plants |
| Live immature trees, such as seedlings and saplings | Downed trees, logs, and other coarse woody structures | Persistent pattern of understory vegetation (e.g., areas that either lack or have an abundance of understory vegetation) developed under influence of pre-disturbance forest |
| Vegetatively reproducing parts of plants (e.g., roots and rhizomes) | Other organic matter, such as fine litter, humus, ash, and charcoal | |
| Soil seed banks, which often include many shrub and herb species and some tree species | Dead root systems | |
| Canopy seed banks, including— but not confined to—to those on serotinous tree species | | |
| Reproductive structures of nonplant biota, such as spores, eggs, etc. | | |
| Living organisms embedded in soils, sediments, or persisting structures, such as decayed logs | | |

Figure 3.1 *Biological legacies produced by major forest-replacing disturbances are composed of varying types of living organisms and dead organic material, as illustrated by (a) wildfire, (b) windstorm, (c) volcanic eruption, and (d) snow avalanche.*

## Box 3.1  Discovering and understanding biological legacies of forest disturbances

Significant elements of the pre-disturbance forest ecosystem persist through most natural disturbance events (Franklin et al., 2002; Franklin, Mitchell & Palik, 2007). Very intense disturbances may kill most or all of the trees and even aboveground animals. However, many organisms—including mature and old trees—typically survive to participate in the development of the post-disturbance ecosystem. *Biological legacies are defined as the organisms (including reproductive structures), organic materials, and biologically derived patterns in soil and vegetation that persist from the pre-disturbance ecosystem into the post-disturbance environment* (Franklin et al., 2000). Biological legacies provide for significant continuity in ecosystem composition, structure, and function between forest generations (Johnstone et al., 2016); this concept is contrary to a traditional view of disturbances as events that create sharp and essentially complete discontinuities between generations.

The biological legacy concept emerged from research following several major natural disturbances, which revealed that such disturbances almost never create a simplified and homogeneous environment. Research at Mount St. Helens after the multiple large and very intense disturbances resulting from the May 1980 eruptions was seminal. Post-disturbance conditions were initially described as a "moonscape" (Franklin & MacMahon, 2000). Subsequent research revealed a diverse array of biological legacies, including living plants and animals (Dale, Swanson, & Crisafulli, 2005). Similar research following other notable disturbance events, such as the Yellowstone Fires of 1988 (Christensen et al., 1989; Wallace, 2004) and Caribbean hurricanes (e.g., Walker, Lodge, Brokaw, & Waide, 1991; Pimm et al., 1994), confirmed the universality of biological legacies and their importance.

### Living Organisms and Propagules

These biological legacies directly perpetuate biota between pre- and post-disturbance forest ecosystems. Living organisms include intact immature and mature plants and animals, perennating plant parts (such as rhizomes and plant parts with sprouting capacity), and propagules, such as seeds, spores, and eggs. Legacies of intense wildfires commonly include live mature trees as individuals or patches of lightly burned or unburned forest. Intense windstorms often leave behind intact forest understory communities, including abundant tree seedlings and saplings (seedling banks).

### Organic Matter and Biologically Derived Structures

Legacies of dead organic matter take many forms and play diverse roles in post-disturbance ecosystems. Some of this organic matter may be in the form of particulates and fine litter. Such materials function as short- and long-term sources of energy and nutrients and enrich and bind soils.

However, in forest landscapes most dead organic matter is left in the form of structural legacies, such as fully or partially intact snags and logs or large pieces of wood (CWD) (Figure 3.1). Such structures, often abundant, massive, and persistent (Harmon et al., 1986), play many important roles in forests and associated aquatic ecosystems, in addition to functioning as long-term energy and nutrient sources. These structures influence geomorphic and hydrologic processes, such as erosion, sediment deposition, and development of channel or bank morphology; provide critical habitat for a large array of living organisms, including provision of substrate, protective cover, nesting sites, and food sources; and ameliorate microclimatic conditions on disturbed sites (Harmon et al., 1986; Maser, Tarrant, Trappe, & Franklin, 1988).

### Biologically Derived Patterns in Soil and Vegetation

These patterns are less obvious and most often encountered in soils or sediments or in understory plant communities. Presence of long-lived plants, such as trees, can generate distinctive patterns in soil chemical, physical, and microbiological properties as a result of the chemical and physical properties of their litter. When the trees are killed or removed, these patterns may persist for decades or even centuries. The disturbance itself can also generate some important patterns in soils and sediments, such as mounds and pits created by tree uprooting.

Biologically generated patterns in soils are common. For example, distinctive radiating patterns in soil properties may be associated with long-lived trees (e.g., Zinke, 1962), as demonstrated by patterns associated with giant sequoia (*Sequoiadendron giganteum*) trees in the Sierra Nevada of California (Zinke & Crocker, 1962). Persistent spatial patterns in soil properties are especially notable where long-lived tree species occur that produce litter with strongly contrasting chemical or physical properties, such as western redcedar and western hemlock (Alban, 1969; Turner & Franz, 1985). Trees or other plants with special functional or physiological capabilities may also create persistent and notable patterns in soil properties, such as species that host nitrogen-fixing organisms.

Forest canopies can produce distinctive and persistent conditions in understory communities by controlling availability of light and moisture. Strong patterning often occurs in forest understory plants in response to variations in overstory canopy density; richer and better developed understories occur under canopy openings (canopy gaps) in contrast with little or no understory in heavily shaded areas (antigaps). Since surviving plants are important sources of post-disturbance vegetative development, pre-disturbance patterns of richness and paucity will tend to perpetuate themselves in the next generation of forest (Franklin & Halpern, 1989).

Table 3.2 *Biological and physical legacies associated with different types of disturbances to established forest ecosystems*

| Legacy | Disturbance agent | | | |
|---|---|---|---|---|
| | *Wind* | *Wildfire*[a] | *Bark beetles* | *Clearcut*[c] |
| *Live, mature trees* | Few/Absent | Few | Species dependent[b] | None |
| *Seedling bank* | Possible | Rare | Possible | None |
| *Intact understory* | Abundant | Rare | Abundant | Very little |
| *Snags* | Few | Abundant | Abundant | None |
| *Logs* | Abundant | Common | None | None |
| *Uproots* | Abundant | None | None | None |
| *Mineral seedbed* | Some (associated with root mounds) | Abundant | None | Abundant |

[a] Fire at the tree and gap scales is largely surface fire that spreads through a stand (with or without crowning) and may kill individual or small groups of trees; we are considering higher severity wildfires in this table.

[b] There may be legacies of live trees depending upon whether there is a nonhost tree species present or if the beetle fails to successfully attack all mature trees of the host species.

[c] Clearcut refers to a classic clearcutting in which all merchantable trees are harvested; i.e., there are no "reserves."

Biological legacies include living organisms and propagules, organic matter and organically derived structures (such as snags and down logs), and organically derived patterns in soils and vegetation. Biological legacies are produced by disturbances at all spatial scales, from the death of an individual tree to forest-replacing disturbances covering thousands of acres.

***Biological legacies are important models for ecological forestry because they exemplify a major way in which natural processes result in continuity in composition, structure, and function between forest generations.*** For example, these legacies can: result in conservation of much of the organic matter, thereby functioning as future sources of energy and nutrients; create large pulses of critical habitat structures (snags and logs); and help maintain micro-environmental conditions that are tolerable for many forest-oriented organisms, allowing them to continue to persist on the disturbed site. Some of these biological legacies also play important roles by influencing geophysical processes, such as erosion and the deposition of sediments. The concept of biological legacies is often utilized in ecological forestry to provide for continuity between forest generations, as illustrated by variable retention harvesting (see Chapter 4).

Disturbances differ significantly in the types and quantities of biological and physical legacies that are left behind (Table 3.2). For example, wildfire tends to kill from below and leaves behind immense legacies of standing dead trees (and often some larger live trees). Fire also generates significant physical legacies of mineral soil and ash seedbeds and provides excellent conditions for regeneration of many shade-intolerant or pioneer tree species. Windstorms, on the other hand, generally kill from above generating large down dead tree and log legacies as well as releasing plants that are in the understory communities, which may be largely intact

and include large numbers of tree seedlings and saplings. Such disturbances actually favor subsequent dominance by shade-tolerant tree species, since it is primarily those species that will have regenerated in forest understories and been released by the disturbance. Significant soil mixing and creation of pit-and-mound topography are also physical legacies of windstorms. Insect outbreaks also tend to kill dominant trees, release understory communities, and create extensive structural legacies in the form of snags. A common human disturbance of forests—clearcutting—contrasts with all of these natural disturbances by leaving few structural legacies, although it does free up resources, such as sunlight, and open up conditions for species that prefer mineral soil seedbeds to organic seedbeds (Table 3.2).

The large legacies of standing dead and down trees created by severe forest-initiating disturbances persist for many decades, functioning as the primary source of CWD for the next generation of forest until it reaches a stage of maturity where it is generating large and durable CWD (Figures 3.2 and 3.3). The persistent nature and critical structural roles of these highly durable and only slowly decaying legacies are often overlooked but are very important considerations in deciding the appropriate management response following major forest disturbances, such as whether to salvage and, if so, what elements of the dead wood legacy to remove and what to leave.

## Part 2: Forest Developmental Stages

Forest ecosystems undergo continuous development following an initiating disturbance in response to internal and external processes. This developmental sequence can be usefully abstracted into a series of stages to better understand the dominant processes that are influencing their development. *The sequence of stages or conditions following an initiating disturbance is called a "sere."* In the case of forests that are subjected to infrequent, high-severity disturbances (such as complete or partial forest replacement

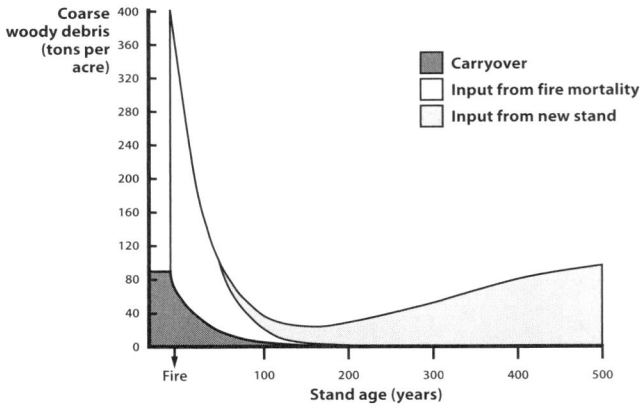

Figure 3.2 *Predicted changes in amounts of coarse wood following a stand-replacement wildfire in a 450-year-old Douglas-fir–western hemlock forest. The fire generates a large pulse of dead wood, which is the major source of coarse wood for the next 100 to 150 years. (Source: Adapted from Spies & Cline, 1988)*

by wildfire or windstorm) these stages typically develop sequentially over time until the forest reaches an old forest stage after one to several centuries or until the sere is terminated by another disturbance. *These stages occur at the scale of the stand or even larger landscapes (e.g., from 10's to 1,000's of acres) depending on the scale of the disturbance.* In the case of forests that are subjected to frequent, low to moderate intensity wildfire, these developmental stages will typically be approximated as elements of a fine-scale spatial mosaic that collectively composes the forest ecosystem (Franklin & Fites-Kaufmann, 1996; Franklin & Van Pelt, 2004). Although the stages may take a somewhat different and more open form in frequent-fire forests (especially in the old forest stage), we believe that they are still a useful construct. A pattern of fine-scale structural mosaics similar to those in frequent-fire forests, which represent different levels of structural development, can also be observed in many chronically wind-disturbed forests.

The developmental sequence is primarily one that consists of gradual changes that take place over long periods of time (e.g., decades), so it can be represented as temporal continuum (e.g., Figure 3.4); however, we break the continuum into stages to provide a simplified model (Table 3.3;

Figure 3.3 *Legacies of highly decay-resistant species can persist for many decades. In this photograph a snag and recently fallen but nearly intact dead tree of western redcedar are still present 110 years after they were killed in a wildfire (1902 Yacolt Burn in southwestern Washington State) that initiated this maturing Douglas-fir forest.*

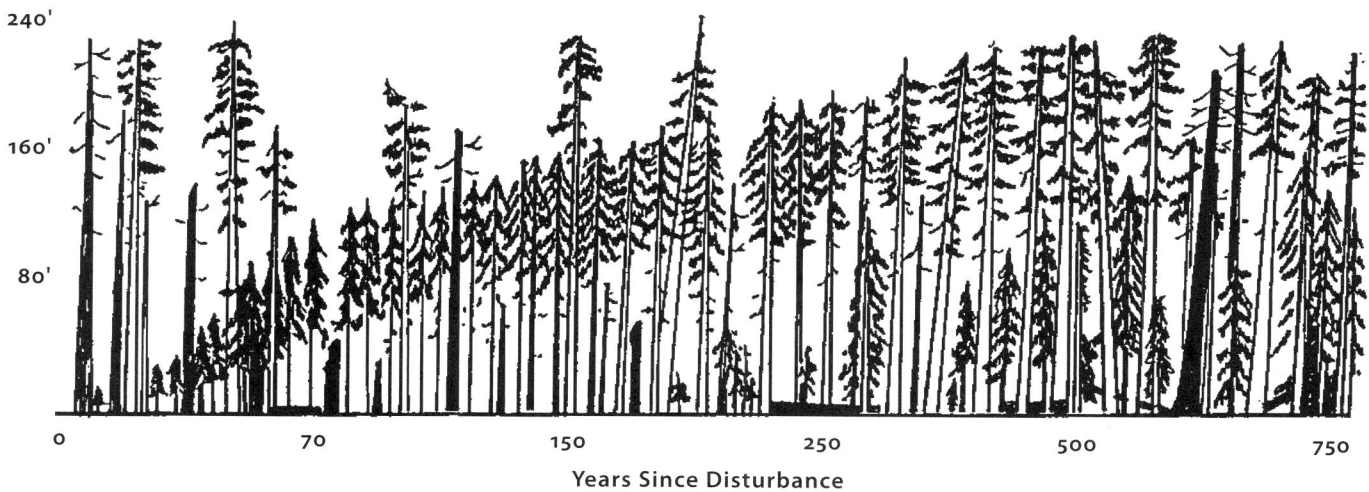

Figure 3.4 *In reality, forest seres are continuous developmental sequences as shown here. In this book we divide them into four stages to better characterize major segments of this time continuum, i.e., as the Preforest, Young Forest, Mature Forest, and Old Forest Stages. (Source: Franklin & Spies, 1991)*

Color Plate 3.2). The developmental sequence begins with an initiating disturbance, which may occur at a relatively large scale (as in infrequently or episodically disturbed forests) or as a relatively small patch (such as a gap in forests subjected to frequent or chronic fire or wind). The disturbance makes available resources by killing existing trees but also leaves a legacy of organisms and structures from the pre-disturbance stand or patch, as previously discussed.

Table 3.3 *Major developmental stages and transitional events in forest ecosystems as presented in this text with a crosswalk to other classifications of forest developmental stages.*

| Classification | | | | | | |
|---|---|---|---|---|---|---|
| *This book* | *Franklin et al.* (2002) | *Oliver & Larson* (1996) | *Spies & Franklin* (1996) | *Carey & Curtis* (1996) | *Bormann & Likens* (1994) | *Frelich* (2002) |
| Disturbance and legacy creation | Disturbance and legacy creation | | | | | |
| (1) Preforest | Cohort establishment | Stand initiation | Establishment phase | Ecosystem initiative | Reorganization phase | Initiation |
| Forest canopy closure | Canopy closure | | | | | |
| (2) Young Forest | Biomass accumulation/ competitive exclusion | Stem exclusion | Thinning phase | Competitive exclusion | Aggradation phase | Stem exclusion |
| (3) Mature Forest | Maturation | Understory reinitiation | Mature phase | Understory reinitiation | Transition phase | Demographic transition |
| | | | | Botanically diverse | | |
| (4) Old Forest | Vertical diversification | Old-growth | Transition phase (early) | Niche diversification | Steady-state | Multiaged |
| | | | | Old-growth | | |
| | Horizontal diversification | | Transition phase (late) | | | |
| | Pioneer cohort loss | | | | | |
| | | | Shifting-gap phase | | | |

We label the developmental stages following the disturbance as the Preforest Stage (PFS), Young Forest Stage (YFS), Mature Forest Stage (MFS), and Old Forest Stage (OFS). These stages are compared with those described in other forest development classifications in Table 3.3. Although the exact nature and duration of each stage varies greatly—both with different forest types and with each sere—a generalized description of each stage and two of the key transitional events (*disturbances and legacy creation* and *tree canopy closure*) follows (Table 3.3). The developmental stages are labeled based on the level of forest maturation (none, young, mature, and old) rather than dominant development processes (e.g., *biomass accumulation* or *competitive exclusion*) as has often been done (Table 3.3). We believe that a maturation-based developmental sequence is more easily adapted to a broad array of forest types than one based on processes, which can vary widely in their expression.

## Disturbance and Legacy Creation Event

The Disturbance and Legacy Creation event (DLC) creates a sufficient opening in an existing forest to initiate a new generation of trees or, if the majority of the existing dominant trees are killed, a sere. Such disturbances leave significant biological and physical legacies, generally including significant numbers of standing and down dead trees, which influence the development of the post-disturbance ecosystem. The amounts and types of legacies will depend upon the type and severity of the disturbance and the nature of the forest that was disturbed, as previously discussed.

## Preforest Stage

The absence of significant tree dominance of the site in the Preforest Stage (PFS) allows other plant life forms to flourish and new cohorts of trees, particularly shade-intolerant species, to become established (Greenberg, Collins & Thompson, III, 2011) (Figures 3.1, 3.5 and Color Plate 3.3). Although other labels, such as *early successional* or *early seral*, have been proposed for this stage, *the most fundamental feature of the PFS is that trees are not the dominant plant life form.* Labeling this stage as *preforest* clearly identifies it as a non-tree-dominated ecosystem but one that is occupying a site that will eventually become forested. It is inappropriate to describe this stage as *young forest* because it is not tree dominated. Other labels applied to this stage, such as the *Stand Initiation* or *Cohort Establishment* Stage (Table 3.3), focus attention on regeneration of a new cohort of trees and, therefore, have a tree-centric bias. In fact, tree regeneration is only one of many important processes that occur in the PFS, and those other labels ignore most of the unique ecological roles of the PFS, which are actually a consequence of the absence of tree dominance.

*The PFS is structurally characterized by its openness or lack of overstory tree dominance and, when the sere arises from natural disturbance of an established forest, a rich structural legacy of snags and logs* (Figure 3.1). While these general features are common to the PFS, the details can vary greatly depending on such variables as the features (e.g., structure and composition) of the preforest stand and the nature of the disturbance. Some large live trees may also survive from the pre-disturbance forest but generally not enough to influence the overall light and moisture environment of the preforest ecosystem following a stand replacement disturbance. After the disturbance, the live plant cover develops gradually from growth of surviving plants, vegetative reproduction of surviving plants, and establishment of new plants from both on-site (e.g., from seed bank and seed produced by surviving trees and other vegetation) and off-site propagules. On many forest sites annual and perennial herbaceous species are important initial dominants but most are transient and replaced in a few years by shrubby species, including legacies (vegetative or seed bank) from the pre-disturbance ecosystem and migrants from outside of the disturbed area. Tree species may be present as legacies in forms ranging from canopy or soil seed banks to seedlings to mature individuals, depending upon the nature of the disturbance and the pre-disturbance forest. Ultimately tree dominance will increase during the PFS, which ends when an overstory tree canopy dominates the majority of the site.

There is relatively rapid recovery of vegetative cover and many ecosystem functions during the PFS, including primary productivity and conservation of nutrients and soil (Color Plate 2.1). Net carbon balance is initially negative (the site is a net source of $CO_2$ release to the atmosphere), due to the abundance of decaying organic matter, warmer temperatures, and reduced leaf area. Accelerated rates of nutrient cycling and increased nitrogen fixation also are characteristic of early seral habitats. The greater diversity of litter inputs and warmer conditions are two factors that contribute to accelerated rates of nutrient release, particularly in forest seres dominated by evergreen conifers. The PFS is also a period when plant species that host nitrogen-fixing organisms typically flourish; these include herbaceous and shrubby members of the legume family (*Leguminosae*, such as lupines, *Lupinus* spp.) and shrubs belonging to such genera as ceanothus and alder.

*The open, plant life-form-diverse, and structurally enhanced PFS often has the highest species diversity of any stage in a forest sere (Swanson et al., 2011) (Color Plate 2.1); this is most profoundly the case with forests dominated by evergreen conifers.* The floristic diversity is derived from a variety of sources, including legacies or survivors from the pre-disturbance forest (some initially present as seed banks) and a variety of weedy invasive species. Animal diversity includes many habitat specialists that find optimal condi-

Figure 3.5 *The Preforest Stage in a forest sere follows an initiating disturbance and is distinguished by a lack of overstory tree dominance, plant communities composed of species of diverse life forms (e.g., mosses, herbs, shrubs, and individual trees), and, often, significant biological legacies (e.g., snags and logs) from the previous forest. PFS persists in the scorch zone of Mount St. Helens, Oregon, USA 20 years after the May 18, 1980, eruption. See also Figure 3.1 and Color Plate 3.3 for other examples of preforest.*

tions primarily or solely in the PFS (Figure 3.6). Among the common groups present as PFS habitat specialists are vertebrates (including many songbirds, reptiles, and ungulates) and many invertebrates, notably including *Lepidoptera* (butterflies and moths) and beetles.

The rich variety of habitat niches and food sources in the PFS is a key factor in the high biotic diversity. Food sources are typically diverse in quality and quantity, which provides for significant numbers and complexity of food webs based on herbivory and consumption of other plant materials, including reproductive parts (e.g., fruits, seeds, and nectar). Many species of vertebrate and invertebrate animals are commonly elements of these food webs. Warmer conditions found in openings are conducive to the development of cold-blooded animals, such as reptiles. Deer, elk and other ungulates find the PFS critical for foraging. Structural legacies (such as snags and logs) also provide a rich array of foraging and resident habitats for vertebrate and invertebrate animals, including larval stages of many invertebrates.

The structure and composition of the PFS undergo continuous change, often moving through periods of dominance by herbs and then shrubs before trees ultimately resume dominance on the site. The duration of the PFS is highly variable depending primarily on the time required for trees to reestablish dominance. In some forest types, such as the mountain ash (*Eucalyptus regnans*) forests of southeastern Australia, this period is so ephemeral as to lack any known habitat specialists that focus upon it, except, for the flame robin (*Petroica phoenicea*); the preforest period is so ephemeral because of the very dense and rapid development of mountain ash reproduction (Lindenmayer, 2009). In other forest types, such as the Douglas-fir–western hemlock forests of northwestern North America, elements of the PFS may persist for several decades, even when tree seed sources are abundant (Freund, Franklin, Larson, & Lutz, 2014; Tepley, Swanson, & Spies, 2014). Many hardwood-dominated forest ecosystems experience a PFS of relatively short duration (e.g., 10–15 years), but the stage still retains ecological significance (see, e.g., Greenberg et al., 2011). On hardwood-dominated sites recovery of tree canopies (leaf area) often occurs very rapidly as a result of vegetative reproduction from damaged trees, such as by sprouting, and advanced regeneration (e.g., Plotkin, Foster, & Carlson, 2013) as well as by rapid growth of new seedlings. Duration of the PFS also commonly varies with disturbance type. For example, the stage is likely to be longer following wildfire, which forces nonsprouting vegetation to establish primarily by from seed, and shorter following windstorms, where understories with abundant advanced regeneration are often left largely intact and subsequent tree canopy recovery is relatively rapid (Figure 3.1).

## Forest Canopy Closure Event

*Forest Canopy Closure (FCC) results in dramatic changes in environmental conditions and biodiversity.* With forest canopy closure, trees resume strong dominance of the site significantly reducing the resources available to other plant life forms. The degree of dominance can vary greatly from nearly complete exclusion of other plant life forms to persistence of significant understory plant species diversity and cover in forests where the overstory is not as dense.

The speed with which canopy closure takes place is extremely variable, although specific forest types or disturbance conditions often have predictable behaviors. For example, FCC in the Australian mountain ash forest typically occurs within five years following wildfire because of abundant canopy seed banks and rapid initial growth rates of seedlings. Tree canopy closure is often rapid on sites disturbed by windstorms due to rapid growth responses by advance tree regeneration and, with many hardwood tree species, by sprouting from damaged trees. In other forest types, complete FCC may take decades, as in the case of Douglas-fir–western hemlock forests in northwestern North America (Freund et al., 2014; Tepley et al., 2014).

Information is lacking on spatial patterns of canopy closure in natural forest seres, but it is likely that there is substantial spatial heterogeneity, particularly where the PFS persists for several decades. Gradual emergence of closed-tree-canopy patches, which eventually merge in episodically disturbed forests, may be a more common pattern

Figure 3.6 *Preforest Stage habitats are generally rich in biological diversity and include many habitat specialists that require the diversity of habitats and food sources that are found there. (Photos of northwestern garter snake* [Thamnophis ordinoides] *[a], orange-crowned warbler* [Vermivora celata] *[b], white-crowned sparrow* [Zonotrichia leucophrys] *[c] © Steve Reed; pale swallowtail* [Papilio eurymedon] *[d] courtesy of David G. James)*

than rapid uniform FCC in these circumstances. More rapid and uniform FCC may be more common in forest ecosystems dominated by hardwoods.

## Young Forest Stage

The Young Forest Stage (YFS) is a period of strong or exclusive dominance by the tree life form following establishment of a closed forest of sufficient height and density to form an overstory canopy. Such forests commonly have simple live tree structures composed of relatively uniformly sized trees (Figure 3.7a and b); however, in most natural seres there will be abundant structural legacies (as snags and logs) from the pre-disturbance forest (Figure 3.7c).

*Biomass accumulation and competition are the dominant developmental processes in the YFS;* hence, this stage has been variously labeled the stem exclusion, competitive exclusion, or biomass accumulation stage (Table 3.3). Biomass accumulation is the most consistent attribute of the YFS, assuming a well-stocked, rapidly growing young forest is present. High rates of primary productivity and biomass accumulation (including wood) are prominent, since essentially all of the site's sunlight, nutrient, and moisture resources are being fully utilized by trees. Considerable litter is generated in the form of competitively killed standing dead trees and branches. Dense forests (particularly of evergreen coni-

fers) transpire large amounts of water, so annual water yields and summer low flows typically decline during the YFS. High levels of nutrient conservation in the ecosystem are characteristic. Nitrogen inputs are minimal unless the site is occupied by a tree or shrub species that hosts nitrogen-fixing organisms. This stage of forest development does not provide the highest levels of tree-sustained soil stability because root systems are not as fully developed as in older forests and the binding strength of the woody root legacies inherited from the pre-disturbance forest are lost in a decade or two.

Competition is another important feature of the YFS. Where tree stem densities are high, intense intertree competition develops. Trees that fall behind in height growth are quickly suppressed. Consequently, mortality is predictably in the smallest diameter classes. Mortality rates are also density dependent so the densest parts of the stand or patch experience the highest rates of competitive-based mortality. The net effect of this intertree competition is to move forest stands toward a more structurally uniform condition during the YFS. Competitive processes also often result in elimination of much or all of the understory vegetation as a result of low light levels. Branch pruning and the gradual elevation of the tree canopies result in the high, single-layered canopies typical of the YFS.

Where the YFS is composed of diverse tree species, such as in many seres dominated by deciduous hardwoods,

Figure 3.7 *The Young Forest Stage (YFS) is often a dense, tree dominated ecosystem with a relatively even-structured live tree component. Denser YFSs may have very little understory (a) whereas less dense YFSs may support significant understories of shrubs and herbs (b). In most natural seres there are abundant structural legacies of dead and down trees from the preceding forest ecosystem as evident in photograph (c).*

physiological characteristics of these species may result in significant compositional as well as structural changes. For example, slower growing species are often overtopped, although they may persist in intermediate canopy positions if they are at least moderately shade tolerant (Oliver & Larson, 1996). Short-lived tree species may play significant early roles in the YFS and subsequently drop out; their positions in the canopy are typically filled by canopy expansion of other canopy trees and by emergence of slower growing trees from the initial cohort, which are often species of intermediate tolerance.

The YFS has the lowest biodiversity of the four developmental stages. Understories in densely shaded forests or patches are sparse with few vascular plant species, so herbivory-based food webs are poorly developed or absent, particularly in forests dominated by conifers. The majority of the biological diversity is associated with detritus-based food webs, since dead organic materials are abundant. Resident animals tend to be either participants in detritus-based food webs, species dependent upon reproductive structures produced by mycorrhizal-forming fungi (e.g., northern flying squirrels [*Glaucomys sabrinus*]), or those that feed primarily on tree seeds (e.g., red and Douglas' squirrels [*Tamiasciurus hudsonicus* and *T. douglasii*]). Higher levels of vertebrate diversity can be expected in the YFS when large legacy structures, such as logs, are present, since vertebrates, such as salamanders and some voles, benefit from such structures. Vertebrates may also use dense young forests for hiding and thermal cover.

There is much variability in the intensity of competitive processes in the YFS as a result of differences in either the density or species composition of the dominant tree canopy or both (Figure 3.7). Naturally regenerated YFSs can have high tree densities but many naturally regenerated young forests fail to experience an intense competitive exclusion period because of lower tree densities; such forests or patches may sustain significant understory plant communities and associated consumer food webs (e.g., Figure 3.7b). These forests also may retain some openings or be subjected to external disturbance processes, such as wind, snow, or ice, which can generate significant openings (e.g., Lutz & Halpern, 2006). In frequent-fire forest landscapes, fire will also be an active and important agent in thinning the YFS. Finally, some tree species (e.g., hemlocks and cedars) produce much denser canopies than others (e.g., pines or Douglas-fir), which can result in extremely depauperate understories.

## Mature Forest Stage

The intense dominance of overstory trees during the YFS eventually eases as tree densities continue to decline as a result of competition and the forest or patch transitions to the Mature Forest Stage (MFS). The forest is still dominated by the initial cohort of trees; however, light and moisture are becoming more available for establishment or expansion of the understory, including reproduction and growth of shade-tolerant trees (Figure 3.8). *The MFS is distinguished from the YFS by (1) aspects of individual tree development, (2) shifts in patterns of mortality in the initial cohort of trees, and (3) initiation of other important processes—such as increased decadence and spatial heterogeneity—that characterize the Old Forest Stage.*

In the MFS the initial cohort of trees lose their youthful appearance and assume more mature features of canopy and bark. Overstory trees will achieve most of their height growth and crown spread during the MFS, although the crowns still tend to conform to classic forms with well-defined apical dominance (see, e.g., Van Pelt & Sillett, 2008). Epicormic or other adventitious branch systems may begin developing on many tree species, sometimes replacing canopy that was lost in natural branch pruning during the YFS. Decadent canopy and bole features, such as rots, brooms, and cavities, also begin to become more abundant. This is also a period when previously present but suppressed tree species may experience some release and enter the overstory canopy. Additional cohorts of shade-tolerant species also are likely to become established.

A major transition occurs in the pattern and dominant causes of tree mortality in the MFS, which significantly increases structural complexity of the stand. Mortality shifts from being primarily competitively based to being largely agent based. Agent-based causes of mortality in the MFS include mortality induced by root and butt rots, bark beetles, and wind (e.g., uprooted and broken trees). These agents kill dominant and codominant trees as well as suppressed and intermediate trees, whereas competition tends to remove only the latter two classes. Agent-based mortality also is often spatially aggregated. The combination of mortality of larger (overstory) trees and contagion generates significant canopy gaps. Creation of these gaps is a key process in the development of spatial heterogeneity or patchiness in structure within the forest ecosystem. The important process of gap creation counteracts the tendency toward uniform tree spacing produced by the competitively based mortality in the YFS.

Understory plant communities reestablish or expand with the increased light and moisture conditions provided by overstory tree mortality and creation of canopy gaps. Depending upon the density of the YFS, some understory plants and tree reproduction may already have been present. However, additional establishment and significant growth of shade-tolerant tree cohorts is a common element during the MFS in episodically disturbed forests. One important consequence of the growth of understory trees is the development of significant intermediate canopy

Figure 3.8  *Well-developed mature Douglas-fir–western hemlock forest in which shade-tolerant hemlocks have now created an intermediate canopy layer and dominant Douglas-fir are achieving most of their height growth and crown spread (H. J. Andrews Experimental Forest, Oregon, USA).*

Development of decadent features accelerates significantly in the MFS. The mass of CWD, including snag and log legacies from the initiating disturbance, has been declining during the YFS and generally reaches its lowest levels early in the MFS (Figure 3.2). The initial CWD legacies have typically undergone extensive decay, and the inputs of small, sapwood-dominated trees dying during the YFS have not made up for these decay losses in the initial legacies. Although legacy CWD may still be evident, much of its mass has been respired or fragmented away except in the case of extremely decay-resistant tree species, if such are present (see Figure 3.3). During the MFS, stocks of CWD begin rebuilding as agent-based mortality in dominant and codominant trees generates larger snags and logs, which include significant heartwood. Other types of decadent features, such as brooms, cavities, and heart rots, also become more prominent and can contribute to mortality.

Transitions from the MFS to the Old Forest Stage are typically gradual and reflect the continued and cumulative effects of processes initiated in the MFS. Only limited information is available on the patterns and rates of these processes, such as development of decadence. Many processes are known to vary with forest productivity (see, e.g., Freund et al., 2014; Larson et al., 2008).

## Old Forest Stage

*The Old Forest Stage (OFS) is typically the most functionally and structurally diverse forest stage in the episodically disturbed forest sere* (Figure 3.9). Structural diversity typically includes an array of live and dead tree sizes and conditions, large old trees of one or more of the dominant tree species, and high levels of spatial heterogeneity in the distribution of stems and canopy. Forests in the OFS typically remain highly functional in terms of productivity and other attributes, such as the ability to influence hydrologic and other material processes, despite what might appear to the casual observer as a decadent and disorderly forest. The OFS has the highest level of biodiversity of the three forested developmental stages, but may be second to the PFS among all four stages in the sere; this diversity includes species that require the unique habitat niches provided by old forests.

The OFS has the greatest structural complexity of any stage in the sere; this complexity includes both individual

between the ground and upper crown (Figure 3.8), which begins moving the canopy toward the vertically continuous canopy that characterizes the Old Forest Stage.

Forests maintain moderate to high levels of productivity in the MFS even though foresters traditionally viewed such forests as being *overmature* because some calculations put them beyond culmination of mean annual increment (CMAI) (see Curtis, 1995, 1997 for a discussion of CMAI and its management relevance). Although CMAI was considered to represent biological maturity, forests reaching the MFS are only just arriving at maturity from an ecological perspective. In fact, high levels of primary productivity generally continue throughout the MFS stage and result in significant additional accumulations of wood, an important consideration in carbon sequestration.

structures and spatial heterogeneity (patchiness). Individual structural elements include a high diversity of live and dead tree structures of widely varying sizes and conditions. Large old trees of one or more dominant species are present, providing a set of unique niches, along with intermediate-sized trees and tree reproduction. Size-class distributions often display the classical inverse-J shape, provided one or more shade-tolerant tree species is present. The large range in tree size is often used as an identifying metric for the OFS.

Decadence is an important and highly evident feature of the OFS. Agent-generated mortality of dominant and codominant as well as intermediate-sized trees is an active process, providing continuing inputs of large snags and logs to the substantial accumulations of CWD already present. These agents include root, butt, and bole rots (fungi), wind (uprooting and tree snapping), and insects (e.g., bark beetles). Competition will also have resumed a significant role, primarily in dense patches of tree reproduction that develop in canopy gaps (Larson et al., 2015). Other decadent features, such as cavities and decay pockets in live trees and brooms developed in response to parasites or pathogens, are typically well represented.

Horizontal heterogeneity is high in the OFS primarily because of continuing gap generation as a result of overstory mortality and subsequent development of dense patches of younger trees within many of the gaps. Outside of gaps, clustered or clumped patterns of tree regeneration are also

characteristic of older forests due to inhibition or creation of growing space by other processes, such as logs, pit mounds, and antigaps. In dense forests clustered patterns are difficult to observe directly but become evident from spatial analyses of tree maps in older forests (e.g., Larson & Franklin, 2006; Larson & Churchill, 2012).

Canopies in the OFS of episodically disturbed forests are typically multilayered or continuous from the ground to the top of the canopy (Figure 3.10). The canopy is also ***bottom loaded*** with the majority of the foliage found lower in the lower half of the profile. This multi-layered and bottom-loaded canopy contrasts sharply with the single-layered and top-loaded canopy characteristic of the YFS. The surfaces of OFS canopies also have a high degree of irregularity or rugosity, as a result of the numerous gaps between large trees (Figure 3.11), again contrasting with the smooth canopy surfaces of dense young forests. [1]

---

1 Canopy structure in the OFS in frequent-fire forest landscapes typically contrasts with that found in episodically disturbed forests to which most of the preceding description applies. Where fire has continued to operate, the OFS on frequent-fire sites predominantly will be a low-density stand of larger-diameter trees that has very little intermediate canopy. If fire is reduced in frequency or effectively eliminated, the OFS typically will develop canopies continuous from ground to the overstory, which greatly increases the potential for uncharacteristic stand-replacement fire. Hence, the concept of continuous canopies from ground to crown expected in the OFS on episodically disturbed sites is not applicable as a dominant condition in frequent-fire forests.

Figure 3.9 *The Old Forest Stage is the most structurally and functionally diverse stage in the development of episodically disturbed forests. Note the diversity of tree sizes and conditions, abundance of dead wood structures, high level of spatial heterogeneity, and vertically continuous canopy in this old-growth forest (Cedar Flats Research Natural Area, Washington State, USA). (Photo courtesy of James Pipkin)*

*Forest ecosystems in the OFS typically continue to have high levels of functionality, including productivity, and significant influences on hydrologic and geomorphic processes.* High levels of gross primary production are typical of the OFS as must always be the case when large leaf areas are present. However, much of the carbon uptake is balanced by losses to respiration and decomposition. Consequently, net productivity—additions to existing carbon stocks (organic matter)—may be relatively modest or even negative. Also, an increasing proportion of the carbon is present as CWD rather than in live trees. In more traditional forestry terms, the old forest typically will have significant gross growth but high mortality and, hence, little or no net additions of wood in live trees. Even so: (1) many trees in old forests are still growing well—including some of the largest and oldest trees; and (2) many (but not all) old forests are still net accumulators of organic matter.

Forests in the OFS continue to strongly influence aspects of the hydrologic cycle, through such processes as interception of precipitation, condensation of cloud and fog moisture, transpiration, and hydraulic redistribution of moisture in soils. Indeed, the earliest scientific studies of old forest function were done by hydrologists who discovered that watersheds vegetated by old forests produced well-regulated flows of high-quality water.

The extensive and deep crowns of the OFS make them highly effective in intercepting precipitation and as condensing and precipitating surfaces for atmospheric moisture and particulates. The structurally complex canopies also can powerfully influence the accumulation and retention of snow because of their complex canopy architecture. For example, OFS canopies include many small openings (gaps), which are favorable for accumulation of deeper snowpacks, while the OFS microclimates will retard snow melting in the spring.

Older forest ecosystems are generally highly retentive of nutrients and effective in stabilization of soils due to their extensive woody root systems. This is a major factor contributing to the high quality of water flowing from watersheds dominated by the OFS, as mentioned above.

Older forest ecosystems are rich in species because they represent a stable environment that is *niche rich.* The OFS commonly has the highest tree species diversity of the sere, particularly if representatives of the shade-intolerant pioneer species are still present. Although many of the vertebrate and invertebrate animals that are present are also present in the young and mature

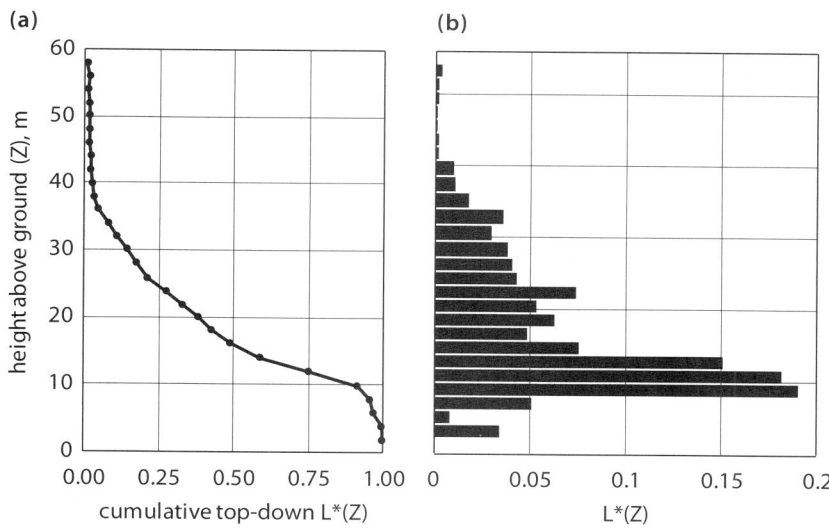

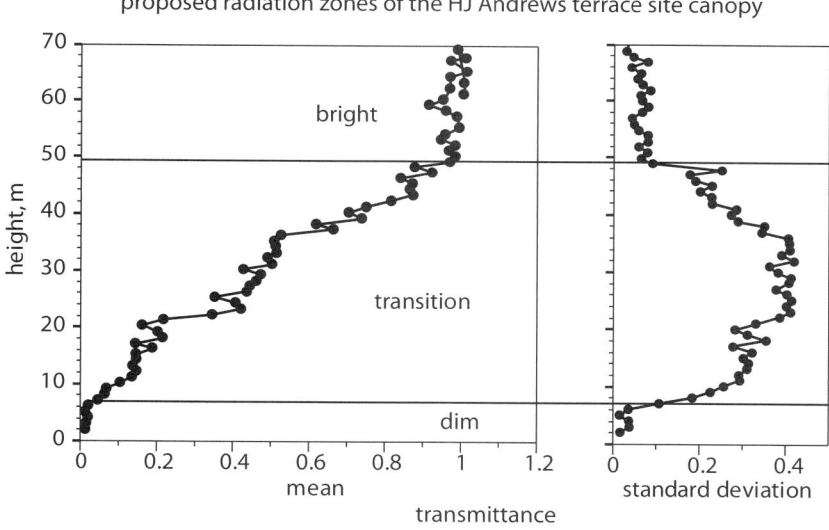

Figure 3.10 *Canopies in episodically disturbed forests achieving the OFS are typically multilayered or continuous from ground to top of crown, have the majority of foliage in the lower half of the canopy (they are bottom loaded), and often display the greatest variation in foliage mass in the midcrown. Illustrative figures for an old Douglas-fir–western hemlock forest canopy of: (a) Cumulative foliage distribution (L = leaf area), (b) Variation in foliage mass by height increments, and (c) Radiation levels and variability in those levels (transmittance = percentage of full sunlight) (Wind River Experimental Forest, Washington State, USA). (Source: Parker, G. C. 1997. Canopy structure and light environment of an old-growth Douglas-fir/western hemlock forest. Northwest Science, 71, 261–270. Reprinted with permission of Northwest Scientific Association)*

*Figure 3.11 Canopy surfaces in forests reaching the OFS typically display a high level of roughness or rugosity as a result of numerous gaps between the dominant trees. This roughness markedly contrasts with the evenness characteristic of YFS canopies. Canopy of Douglas-fir, western hemlock, and western redcedar in OFS at Wind River Experimental Forest, Gifford Pinchot National Forest, Washington State, USA.*

forest stages, there are typically some animals that find conditions in the OFS to be optimal or essential for aspects of their life cycle.

Forest ecosystems that reach the OFS continue to undergo gradual directional changes in structure, function, and composition, albeit at a slower rate than in the previous stages. None of them are static forests as will be seen in subsequent discussions of specific seres, and very few of them will have achieved the status of *climax* forests, from which all representation of shade-intolerant pioneer tree species would, presumably, have been lost.

## Part 3: Important Natural Forest Archetypes

Three natural forest archetypes are conceptualized here to provide the reader with model systems that can assist in understanding the major types of temperate forest ecosystems—their dynamics, similarities, and differences. The archetypes also illustrate how the developmental stages presented in the previous section play out in different forest types.

Although most discussions of forest ecosystems emphasize differences, we emphasize some important similarities. Many forests in the real world will not perfectly fit these models, so they should not be viewed as models that must be directly emulated in management, but elements of the archetypes will be apparent in almost all forests. Our goal here is to help the student, manager, and stakeholder better understand the developmental processes that go on in natural forest seres, which have rarely been emphasized in the forestry literature because of the historical emphasis on the earliest stage of closed forest development (the YFS).

*Disturbance regimes and dominant tree species are used to distinguish the three natural forest archetypes:*

- *Conifer-dominated forests initiated by infrequent (episodic) severe wildfire;*

- *Hardwood-dominated forests initiated by infrequent (episodic) severe windstorms; and*

- *Conifer-dominated forests characterized by frequent (chronic) wildfire.*

The first two archetypes are initiated by severe forest- or landscape-scale disturbances at infrequent intervals (100 years or more), thereby initiating new developmental sequences or seres. In these archetypes, the stages are present at the scale of at least stands and often entire landscapes. The sere begins with a legacy-enriched PFS and eventual establishment and canopy closure by a new tree cohort, which experiences a period of exponential growth (YFS) and maturation (MFS), and eventually arrives at a quasi-equilibrium old-growth stage (OFS). The OFS is rich in a diversity of live and dead tree and log structures and has high levels of spatial heterogeneity. The complexity of the OFS is sustained by frequent, small-scale (tree- and gap-level) disturbances (tree mortality) due to diseases, insects, and wind until a new severe disturbance ends the sere and begins another anew.

Although we have chosen to link the conifer-dominated forest with fire and the hardwood-dominated forest with wind, either forest could experience either type of disturbance as could a mixed forest of conifers and hardwoods. We have picked these examples because they are common and also because they allow us to contrast the response of conifers and hardwoods to stand-replacement disturbances as well as to contrast seres initiated by wildfire and by windstorm.

Forest ecosystems developed on sites that experience frequent fire (the third archetype) are profoundly influenced by a chronic disturbance (fire) that consumes fuels and vegetation (including tree seedlings) at frequent intervals (e.g., one year to several decades). Intense disturbances that eliminate live forest cover over large areas are rare in such forests, which have continued to have frequent fire. Tree mortality occurs primarily as individuals and in small patches, which provide openings for development of understory and midstory vegetation, including tree regeneration, and subsequent stand development. Consequently, in this forest archetype all developmental stages are simultaneously present as elements of a forest mosaic in close proximity to each other (Figure 3.12). The selective pressures of frequent fire tend to produce forests dominated by a low-density population of old and large trees, which have high resistance to low and moderate severity fires. The OFS patches in such forests may be open-savanna-like patches or have more complex structures, such as those described for the episodically disturbed forest. In any case a complete mosaic of patches representing all developmental stages must be present to have a frequent-fire forest ecosystem that is ecologically complete or *fully functional* (Franklin & Van Pelt, 2004). Such a circumstance (a mosaic of different patch types) does not fit the traditional definition of a stand. [2]

Hence, we can see both contrasts and similarities between the episodically and chronically perturbed archetypes. In

the case of the forests initiated by stand-replacement disturbances, the various forest stages are displayed over time as part of a successional sequence. In the case of ecosystems subject to chronic, low severity disturbances, such as frequent fire, the various forest *stages* will be simultaneously present as elements of a complex and often low-contrast spatial mosaic. Interestingly, the OFSs that ultimately develop as the last stage of the episodically disturbed archetypes are also structural mosaics, which are created and maintained by small-scale chronic disturbances (wind, fungi, and insects) operating at the tree and gap levels.

## Natural Forest Archetypes Initiated by Infrequent (Episodic) Severe Disturbances

The vast majority of temperate (as well as boreal) forests in moist regions are characterized by natural disturbance regimes that include infrequent but severe disturbances (most often by wildfire or windstorm) that result in significant areas of complete or near-complete stand-replacement conditions. If the disturbances are large, they are also likely to include areas with low to moderate levels of impact.

**Coniferous Forest Seres Initiated by Severe Wildfire**   *The Douglas-fir–western hemlock (DF–WH) forest of northwestern North America is our primary example of this archetype* (Figure 3.13; Color Plate 3.2). Many attributes of

---

2 The traditional definition of a forest stand is, "a contiguous group of trees sufficiently uniform in age-class distribution, composition, and structure . . . to be a distinguishable unit" (Helms, 1998). This definition does not fit forests that consist of fine-scale structural mosaics. Such forest ecosystems include forests subject to frequent-fire or chronic gap-scale windthrow events as well as some old-growth forests developed on episodically disturbed sites. Fully ecologically functional "stands" in these cases are complex mosaics of patches that differ markedly in structure and sometimes in composition from each other (Franklin & Van Pelt, 2004).

Figure 3.12  *The frequent-fire forest archetype typically has all forest stages represented simultaneously as part of a mosaic of small structural patches, as illustrated by the diverse conditions found in this small area of ponderosa pine forest that has retained much of its historical architecture (Yakama Indian Reservation, Washington State, USA).*

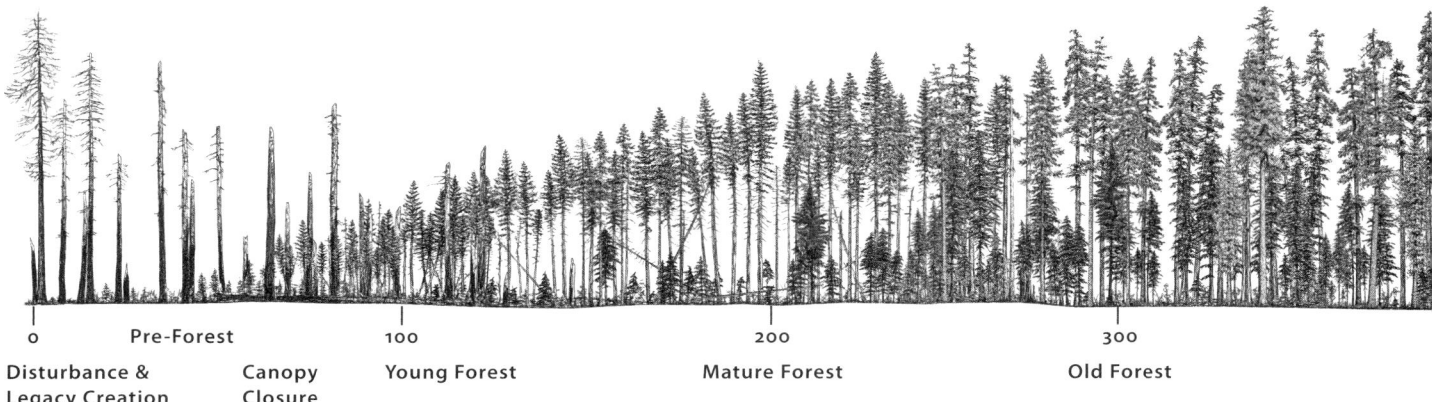

|  |  |  |  |
| --- | --- | --- | --- |
| 0 | 100 | 200 | 300 |
| Pre-Forest | Young Forest | Mature Forest | Old Forest |

Disturbance &          Canopy
Legacy Creation       Closure

Figure 3.13 *Structural representation of a complete Douglas-fir–western hemlock forest sere. The Douglas-fir–western hemlock fire-initiated sere is an outstanding example of a sere that is characterized by: (1) a long-lived shade-intolerant pioneer species that is gradually replaced by more shade-tolerant associates; (2) massive biological legacies from the initiating disturbance; (3) an extended Preforest Stage; (4) development of very high levels of structural complexity in the Mature and Old Forest Stages, including massive accumulations of live and dead organic matter; and (5) several centuries for full development of the sere. Of course, few seres will continue for the eight centuries shown here; seres can be truncated by a major new disturbance at any point. (Illustration by Robert Van Pelt)*

this archetype are well displayed including: (1) initial dominance by a shade-intolerant pioneer species (Douglas-fir), which is gradually replaced by more shade-tolerant associates; (2) high levels of structural legacies (e.g., dead trees and logs) left by the initiating disturbance; (3) an extended and ecologically important Preforest Stage (PFS); (4) high levels of structural complexity and accumulations of live and dead biomass in Mature and Old Forest Stages (MFS and OFS); and (5) a requirement for a long time period (200–400 years) for full development of the OFS. In many respects, the DF–WH sere is a ***bookend*** representation of this archetype because many attributes—such as massiveness of the OFS, the importance of coarse woody detritus (CWD) throughout the sere, and duration and importance of the PFS—are highly developed in the DF–WH sere.

A large and severe wildfire initiates the DF–WH sere (the DLC event). Most wildfires of this type occur during a synoptic weather pattern in which east winds bring hot and very dry air from interior continental regions. These wildfires leave complex mosaics of fire effects (severity) at the stand or larger spatial scales, as they burn through diverse topographic and forest conditions and over many days or weeks. They invariably include significant areas (10's to 100's to 1,000's of acres) of high tree mortality but also can result in areas of intermediate and low overstory tree mortality as well as unburned patches, sometimes of significant extent (e.g., at the scale of stands). Massive legacies of dead trees and logs are left behind that will play important short- and long-term roles in the post-disturbance sere (Figure 3.14). Commonly there are also significant legacies of living trees scattered throughout the burned landscape as individuals,

in clusters, and in larger patches, which persist for varying periods of time.

***The PFS is a persistent and ecologically important stage in the DF–WH sere, because this is the only period***

Figure 3.14 *Massive legacies of standing dead trees and logs are left behind in severely burned portions of wildfires in the Douglas-fir–western hemlock sere. These wood legacies are important structural elements in the Preforest Stage of this sere in part because of their role as critical habitat for many animals, including birds and invertebrates. This photograph was taken on the Warner Creek burn eight growing seasons following the fire (Willamette National Forest, Oregon, USA).*

Years Since Disturbance

*in a potentially multicentury sere that is not dominated by evergreen conifers.* The importance of this stage is a general characteristic of this archetype for the same reason. Elements of the PFS in the DF–WH sere typically persist for four to six decades (Freund et al., 2014; Tepley et al., 2014); this stage has the highest biological diversity of any stage in the sere, in part because of the richness of available habitats and food sources. The PFS persists largely because of the relatively slow rate of conifer tree establishment and growth, which must be from seed provided by surviving sources within the burn or beyond its boundaries. Soil seed banks do not exist for the conifers; under unusual circumstances (e.g., a fall wildfire in the year of a good cone crop) a canopy seed bank may be present following the fire (Larson & Franklin, 2005).

The structure and composition of the PFS undergoes continuous change until it is eventually overtopped by the developing conifer forest. Readily dispersed annual and perennial herbaceous plants dominate initially and are subsequently replaced by shrubs, many of which were present in the pre-disturbance forest either vegetatively or in the seed bank (Figure 3.15). Full development and maturation of shrub species requires several decades.

The YFS is a period of near exclusive dominance by Douglas-fir and other coniferous tree species, which forms dense stands of relatively even age and size (Figure 3.7). Some short-lived hardwood trees, such as bitter cherry (*Prunus emarginata*) and cascara (*Rhamnus purshiana*), are often present but die out after 40 to 80 years. Occasional longer-lived hardwood trees, such as bigleaf maple (*Acer macrophyllum*) and Pacific dogwood (*Cornus nuttallii*) also may be present. The understory in the YFS can be extremely depauperate or have significant herb and shrub cover depending upon the tree density that is present. Many naturally regenerated DF–WH forests appear to have established at relatively low densities so that significant understories are retained (Figure 3.7b) and the amount of competitively-based tree mortality is relatively low in comparison with densely stocked stands.

The Mature Forest Stage (MFS) of the DF–WH sere begins the transformation of the young, competitively driven forest into much more complex older forest (Figure 3.8).

Figure 3.15 *Shrubs and long-lived perennial herbaceous plants typically assume and retain dominance in the Preforest Stage of the Douglas-fir–western hemlock sere. Several different species of shrub are visible in this photo including Pacific rhododendron* (Rhododendron macrophyllum) *and snowbrush* (Ceanothus velutinus) *as well as the perennial herb beargrass* (Xerophyllum tenax). *The rhododendron and beargrass were present in the pre-disturbance forest in vegetative form, whereas the snowbrush was present only in the soil seed bank. Many Douglas-fir and western hemlock seedlings and saplings are intermixed with the shrubs and herbs, and will gradually assume dominance over time. (Variable-retention harvest adjacent to the H. J. Andrews Experimental Forest, Willamette National Forest, Oregon, USA)*

Figure 3.16 *Transect profile of an old-growth Douglas-fir–western hemlock forest at Cedar Flats Research Natural Area (Washington State, USA) illustrating some of the spatial heterogeneity characteristic of the Old Forest Stage. (Illustration by Robert Van Pelt)*

Douglas-fir continues to dominate the overstory and undergoes significant additional growth during its second century of development; Douglas-fir typically has only about 60% of its potential height at an age of 100 years. Typically western hemlock greatly increases its participation in the stand by expanding its occupancy in the lower canopy with some older individuals growing into and creating a midcanopy. Agent-based mortality from wind, root and butt rots, and bark beetles becomes significant during the MFS, resulting in creation of canopy gaps. This, in turn, stimulates additional regeneration and growth of shade-tolerant trees in the understory, which begins to create a midlevel tree canopy. An additional understory tree species—Pacific yew (*Taxus brevifolia*)—may become more evident beginning in this stage. The mortality of larger trees begins the process of restoring larger masses of CWD, as much of the original legacy of dead wood has disappeared due to decay (Figure 3.2).

The Old Forest Stage (OFS) of the DF–WH sere achieves great structural complexity as has been described extensively in the literature and is illustrated in Figure 3.16. It is also the most diverse forest stage in this sere. Notable features of this stage include: (1) presence of large old trees, which often have major epicormic branch systems; (2) diverse tree sizes (mostly western hemlock and other shade-tolerant tree species) displaying the classic reverse J-shaped distribution

Table 3.4 *Tree density (number/acre) and total basal area (ft²/acre) by species and major diameter classes in the 60-acre Wind River Forest Dynamics plot within an approximately 500-year-old Douglas-fir–western hemlock forest at the Wind River Experimental Forest, Washington State, USA*

| Species | Trees/ac dbh (in) | | | | | | | | | | | | | Total | Basal Area/ac (ft²) |
|---|---|---|---|---|---|---|---|---|---|---|---|---|---|---|---|
| | 0–6 | 6–12 | 12–18 | 18–24 | 24–30 | 30–36 | 36–42 | 42–48 | 48–54 | 54–60 | 60–66 | 66–72 | 72–78 | | |
| Western hemlock | 93.92 | 24.23 | 11.59 | 9.12 | 8.69 | 5.96 | 2.32 | 0.63 | 0.06 | | | | | 156.52 | 202.72 |
| Douglas-fir | 0.05 | 0.05 | 0.11 | 0.35 | 0.71 | 1.64 | 2.29 | 1.88 | 1.03 | 0.51 | 0.21 | 0.02 | | 8.85 | 93.74 |
| Pacific silver fir | 62.36 | 5.50 | 1.99 | 0.60 | 0.27 | 0.06 | 0.02 | | | | | | | 70.80 | 23.89 |
| Red cedar | 0.58 | 0.38 | 0.25 | 0.25 | 0.36 | 0.38 | 0.25 | 0.27 | 0.19 | 0.08 | 0.06 | 0.03 | 0.03 | 3.11 | 19.95 |
| Pacific yew | 20.55 | 9.11 | 1.11 | 0.27 | 0.03 | | | | | | | | | 31.07 | 14.14 |
| Grand fir | 0.32 | 0.09 | 0.21 | 0.19 | 0.06 | 0.03 | | | | | | | | 0.90 | 1.63 |
| Noble fir | 0.02 | 0.02 | 0.02 | 0.02 | 0.06 | 0.05 | 0.02 | | | | | | | 0.21 | 0.89 |
| Pacific dogwood | 2.47 | 0.11 | | | | | | | | | | | | 2.58 | 0.57 |
| Western white pine | | | 0.02 | 0.02 | 0.02 | 0.02 | | | | | | | | 0.08 | 0.27 |
| Red alder | 0.08 | 0.05 | 0.02 | | | | | | | | | | | 0.15 | 0.08 |
| **Total** | **180.35** | **39.54** | **15.32** | **10.82** | **10.20** | **8.14** | **4.90** | **2.78** | **1.28** | **0.59** | **0.27** | **0.05** | **0.03** | **274.24** | **357.88** |

*Source:* Data courtesy of James A. Lutz.

(Figure 3.17; Table 3.4); (3) Abundant CWD including large old-tree derived snags and down logs and other decadent features; and (4) Vertically-continuous canopies with the majority of the foliage in the lowest 1/3 of the canopy (Figure 3.10).

*The OFS of the DF–WH forest is best characterized by its structural complexity, which includes a richness of individual structures—such as live trees, snags, and logs—and substantial spatial heterogeneity in their distribution.* The diversity of individual structures is enriched by a variety of sizes and conditions (e.g., decay states). The OFS (e.g., Figure 3.16) can be viewed as a dynamic fine-scale structural patchwork that effectively recapitulates all of the earlier stages in forest development (i.e., PFS, YFS, and MFS) as well as the disturbance and legacy creation and canopy

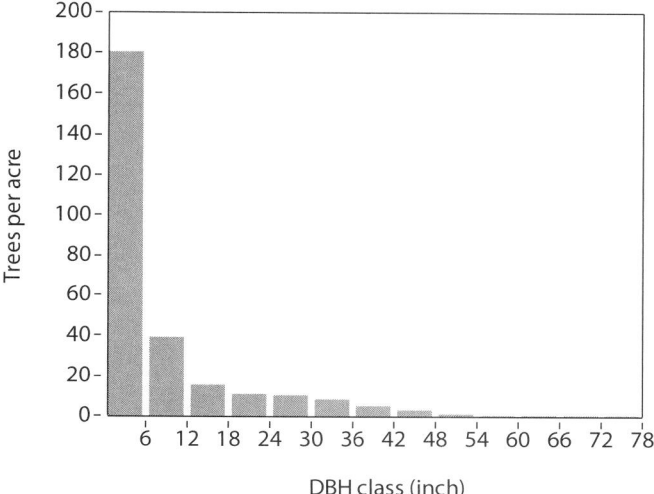

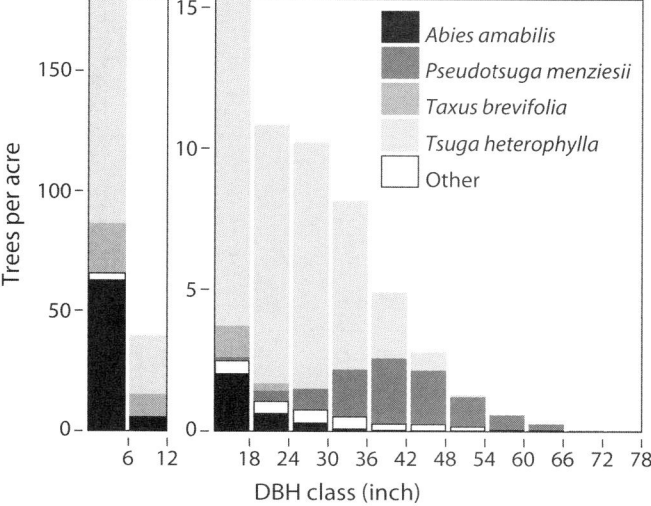

Figure 3.17 *Tree diameter distribution in aggregate (top) and by species (bottom) in the 60-acre Wind River Forest Dynamics plot within an approximately 500-year-old Douglas-fir–western hemlock forest at the Wind River Experimental Forest, Washington State, USA. (Source: Data courtesy of James A. Lutz)*

closure episodes. This dynamic patchwork is sustained by chronic small-scale disturbance events (e.g., insects, disease, and wind) and tree population processes (Lutz et al., 2014; Larson et al., 2015). However, a notable aspect of the OFS is that the gaps present are usually not sufficiently large to allow for successful recruitment of the sere's pioneer species—Douglas-fir!

There is much variability in the structural details of the OFS, some (but not all) of it associated with the age of the forest (Spies & Franklin, 1988; Franklin & Spies, 1991). Although there is great stability and relatively low levels of change in the OFS (see, e.g., Franklin & DeBell, 1988), old forests in the DF–WH sere do continue to undergo directional change over time with consequences for structure, function, and composition as illustrated in Figure 3.13. An earlier treatment of this sere recognized some of this variability or evolution as three separate stages (Table 3.3), which could be viewed as early (Vertical Diversification), mid (Horizontal Diversification), and late (Pioneer Cohort Loss) stages of old-growth DF–WH forest. Theoretically, the eventual loss of Douglas-fir would have major consequences for the structure and function of the ecosystem, particularly if the primary species replacing it was western hemlock, a species of smaller dimension and much less CWD decay resistance; few stands reach such an advanced state, however, before experiencing a major disturbance event that provides the opportunity for Douglas-fir regeneration.

***Variations in the Douglas-fir–Western Hemlock Sere.*** Although the DF–WH archetype is very linear and predictable as presented above, reality is much more diverse. *Large wildfires in DF–WH always included a high severity forest-replacement component. However, portions of such burns suffer low to moderate severity fire as a result of variable burning conditions. The partial stand replacement conditions produced by these less intensely burned areas gives rise to a large set of possible developmental pathways that are alternatives to the one presented above* (Rapp & Spies, 2003; Spies, 2009; Tepley et al., 2013) (Figure 3.18). For example, less intense burns may leave most of the dominant fire-resistant Douglas-firs alive but provide suitable conditions for abundant reproduction of shade-tolerant species, such as western hemlock, resulting in two-aged stands (Tepley et al., 2013). In another case, where the burn is more intense, Douglas-fir may regenerate in the thinned stand. Many other circumstances can create alternative pathways, such as seres that are initiated through disturbances in the YFS or MFS.

Disturbance types other than wildfire can also produce very different outcomes. DF–WH forests sometimes experience massive windstorms, which can eliminate the overstory (Figure 3.1). The largest single forest disturbance event recorded in the Douglas-fir region was the Columbus Day windstorm of 1962. Successional developments following windthrow events follow very different pathways from those following wildfire. Most of the existing understory survives and is released by forest-replacement windthrow events, including tree reproduction. The PFS is much shorter than following wildfire, because advanced tree regeneration is present. Furthermore, the advanced tree regeneration is generally composed of shade-tolerant species, such as western hemlock, western redcedar, and Pacific silver fir. Consequently, the new stand that develops generally will be dominated by shade-tolerant species and not Douglas-fir, in contrast with what happens after wildfire.

***Other Coniferous Forest Seres Initiated by Severe Disturbances.*** There is a wide array of other conifer-dominated forest ecosystems that are initiated by partial or complete stand-replacement wildfire, although few of these seres achieve the same level of age and complexity characteristic of the Douglas-fir–western hemlock forests. Prominent among these are some subalpine forest types, including the lodgepole pine and subalpine fir–Engelmann spruce ecosystems of the Intermountain West. In the Lake States region, forests of jack pine (*Pinus banksiana*) and mixtures of red and eastern white pine (*Pinus resinosa* and *P. strobus*) follow the broad patterns of this archetype.

Lodgepole pine forests that occur at higher elevations in the northern Rocky Mountains, the eastern Cascade Range, and the Sierra Nevada Range exemplify a much shorter-lived and highly simplified version of this archetype (Figure 3.19). These lodgepole pine forests are often growing on low-productivity sites and may be nearly pure lodgepole or, where site conditions are better, include other tree species. Generally they are even-aged forests that regenerated after complete or partial forest-replacement disturbances by wildfire, mountain pine beetle (*Dendroctonus monticolae*) epidemics, or, occasionally, windstorms. Some are multi-aged originating from mixed-severity fire (Heyerdahl et al., 2014). The patches are often very large. The PFS can be relatively short because initial growth of lodgepole pine is rapid, although a PFS of longer duration may occur where seed sources are lacking or on environmentally severe sites. Where dense forests regenerate, development may occur slowly through an intensely competitive YFS.

As lodgepole pine forests mature and thin after a century, lodgepole pine typi-

cally begins reproducing in the understory along with other tree species, such as Engelmann spruce, subalpine fir, or mountain hemlock (*Tsuga mertensiana*) on subalpine forest sites. Over time another major disturbance event (fire, beetles, or storm) will initiate a new sere. While all three of these disturbances kill the overstory of larger old lodgepole pines, wildfire has an additional significant impact because it kills the understory as well as the overstory. Bark beetles

Figure 3.19 *Lodgepole pine is often the only species that can thrive on environmentally challenging sites, such as frost pockets, where it may be found in pure form. This lodgepole pine forest is growing in the pumice-soil region of south-central Oregon on the Fremont-Winema National Forest, USA.*

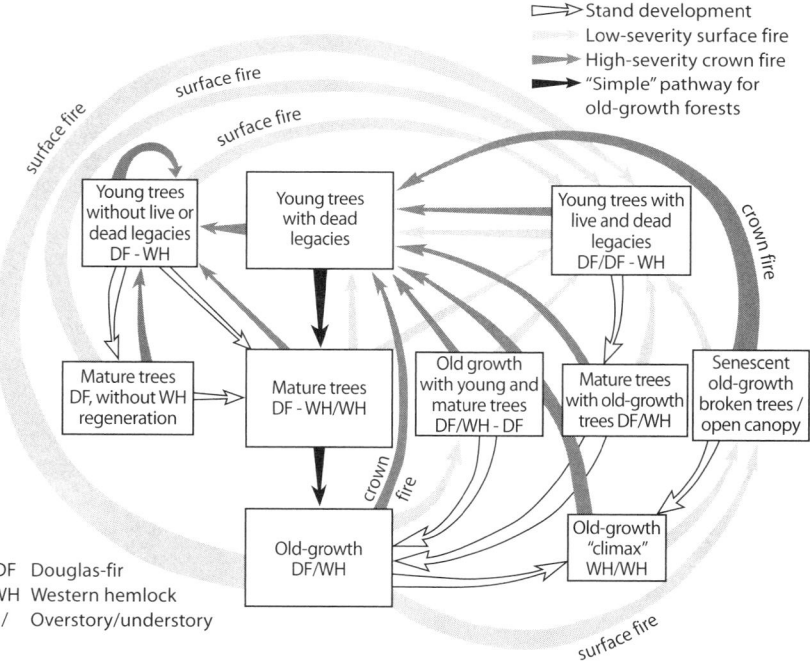

Figure 3.18 *Conceptual model of multiple pathways of Douglas-fir–western hemlock forest development in the Oregon Cascade Range, USA. (Source:* Old Growth in a New World, *edited by Thomas A. Spies and Sally L. Duncan. Copyright © 2009 Island Press. Reproduced by permission of Island Press, Washington, DC)*

and windstorms, on the other hand, kill only the larger of the trees so that most of the tree reproduction survives the disturbance and is released. Where lodgepole pine dominates the regeneration, it generally will again dominate the new stand after beetle attacks or windstorms, but where the reproduction is primarily composed of more shade-tolerant species, such as subalpine fir, Engelmann spruce, and mountain hemlock, then they are likely to dominate the new stand.

### Deciduous Hardwood Forest Seres Initiated by Severe Windstorms

*Deciduous hardwood forests naturally dominated most of the cool moist temperate forest landscapes of the world outside of western North America* (Askins, 2014) in contrast with the conifer-dominated systems of boreal and subalpine regions (Color Plate 3.4). An important general attribute of hardwood trees that distinguishes them from most conifers is their ability to reproduce vegetatively, such as by sprouting. This attribute is highly advantageous since the dominant disturbance regime in these forests is typically wind. Although most wind disturbances occur at the scale of individual trees and gaps, infrequent intense windstorms occur periodically in most regions dominated by deciduous hardwoods, which result in the regeneration of new tree cohorts. The wind events may be ocean generated, such as with hurricanes and typhoons, or locally generated, in the form of tornados or other severe winds associated with thunderstorm events (downbursts, microbursts, and *derechos*, the latter being multiple related downbursts) (Figure 3.20).

Some significant attributes of this archetype following a severe wind disturbance include : (1) live tree legacies that include significant elements of the pre-disturbance stand including broken and partially uprooted trees capable of vegetative regrowth by sprouting, advance regeneration of tree species of intermediate and high shade-tolerance, and soil seed banks; (2) brief PFSs due to rapid vegetative growth from surviving trees and advance regeneration and additional seedling establishment; (3) intensely competitive YFSs commonly composed of diverse tree species, including some short-lived pioneer tree species that drop out during this stage; (4) MFSs in which creation of canopy gaps allows previously suppressed tree species of mid- and highly-shade-tolerant species to move into the overstory; and (5) eventual emergence of uneven-aged, structurally complex OFSs with high tree species diversity due, in part, to continuing formation of gaps. In developing this archetype we have heavily utilized accounts by Frelich (2002) and others in the Lake States, Bormann and Likens (1994) in New Hampshire, and the extensive research at Harvard Forest in central Massachusetts, which includes experimental simulations of hurricanes (Foster et al., 2014).

Severe windstorms, such as those of hurricane-force intensity, leave major legacies of broken and partially or completely uprooted trees (Figure 3.20), standing live trees, significant advance regeneration of species of mid- and high-shade-tolerance, and soil seed banks. Extensive sprouting will occur from root systems, stumps and damaged boles. Uproot mounds and pits resulting from the event are an additional important legacy.

Figure 3.20 *Intense windstorm events are the primary stand-level disturbances in most temperate deciduous forest regions. These may be of either oceanic (hurricanes and typhoons) or local origin (tornados and other severe winds associated with thunderstorms). (a) Forest blown down in the 1938 Hurricane in New England, USA (Photo courtesy of Harvard Forest). (b) Forest of lenga blown down by a tornado-like windstorm in Tierra del Fuego, Argentina. Such "jackpots" of downed trees assist lenga in successfully regenerating by impeding grazing by native herds of guanaco (Lama guanicoe).*

The PFS is generally of short duration because of the aggressive vegetative response of broken but surviving trees and advance tree regeneration as well as growth of new trees developing from seed from seed banks and blown in from outside of the disturbed area (Figure 3.21). Productivity quickly rebounds; at Harvard Forest, litterfall (a measure of productivity) returned to pre-disturbance levels in six years following a simulated hurricane experiment (Plotkin et al., 2013). There is a short period of five to ten years (referred to as "initiation" by Frelich [2002] and "reorganization" by Bormann and Likens [1994]), during which species richness increases. This increase partially results from establishment of herbaceous and shrubby invasive species, such as fireweed (*Epilobium* spp.) and blackberries (*Rubus* spp.). This stage has been described as a "tangle" of herbaceous and woody vegetation, including trees in the form of sprouts, advance regeneration, and seedlings, which include short-lived early seral species, such as pin cherry (*Prunus pennsylvanica*) and aspens (*Populus* spp.). However, with the rapid reestablishment of tree cover, herb and shrub cover declines rapidly.

*The PFS in this archetype is less significant than in the case of the fire-generated conifer-dominated archetype.* This is partly due to its more transient nature and partly due to the fact that the young hardwood forest that replaces it still produces forage, flowers, and fruits that support significant herbivory-based food webs. Even in its abbreviated form the PFS is a valuable resource for vertebrates because of its richness, such as by providing high-quality food patches important to a variety of biota, including birds, bats, and reptiles (Greenberg et al., 2011).

The new cohort of trees in the YFS typically has high density and uniformity (Figure 3.22). A variety of tree species of differing shade tolerances and life spans is also typical. However, intermixed in this cohort may be a legacy of older residual trees that survived the windstorm. Some aggressive, rapidly growing short-lived species, such as pin cherry (*Prunus pennsylvanica*) and quaking and bigtooth aspen (*Populus tremuloides* and *grandidentata*) may assume early dominance in the new cohort but will gradually drop out and be replaced by species with intermediate life spans, such as paper or white birch (*Betula papyrifera*), red maple (*Acer rubrum*), and white ash (*Fraxinus americana*). Twenty years after the hurricane experiment at Harvard Forest, surviving overstory trees (mainly residual oaks) and advance regeneration (primarily sweet or black birch [*Betula lenta*]) dominated the new stand. Pioneer species (black cherry [*Prunus serotina*] and paper birch) initially regenerated abundantly, but few were ultimately recruited into the overstory. It is probable that such pioneers are more important in seres developed following clearcutting or fire.

Intense, density-dependent competitive thinning is the major cause of tree mortality in the YFS, although some mortality is related to the senescence of the short-lived tree species. Overall plant species richness is minimal at this point in the sere. Since the crowns of the dying trees are small, existing trees fill in canopy openings. This stage of development may last for 100 to 150 years (Frelich's [2002] "Stem Exclusion" stage and Bormann & Liken's [1994] "Aggradation Phase").

As in the conifer archetype, the MFS in this sere represents a transitional condition between young and old forest

Figure 3.21 *Although the PFS is of relatively short duration in deciduous hardwood forests, it tends to be rich in species. (a) PFS occupying a large gap in a deciduous hardwood forest in New England, USA. Among the species present are* Rubus *spp., American beech, yellow birch, black cherry, and sugar maple (Photo courtesy of Anthony W. D'Amato). (b) PFS developed following a windthrow event in mature mixed hardwood-pine forest on the Chippewa National Forest (Minnesota, USA). Regenerating trees include quaking aspen, paper birch, northern red oak, red maple, and red pine, all of which were present in the original stand. Red, white, and jack pines have been planted (capped trees). The early seral opportunists include grayleaf red raspberry* (Rubus idaeus *subsp.* strigosus), Bebb willow (Salix bebbiana), *and bracken fern* (Pteridium aquilinum).

Figure 3.22 *Young deciduous hardwood forest of lenga* (Nothofagus pumilio) *on Tierra del Fuego, Argentina.*

Figure 3.23 *Mature deciduous hardwood forest in eastern North America.*

stages (Figure 3.23), and it is so labeled by Frelich (2002) as the "Demographic Transition" stage and by Bormann and Likens (1994) as the "Transition" state. Transition in this case means development of significant canopy openings, recruitment of new age classes of trees into the overstory, development of significant additional decadence (including snags and logs), and additions to the populations of old trees. Most of the legacies (live and dead) from the initiating disturbance are now gone. The MFS in this hardwood-dominated sere may also see reductions in ecosystem biomass and productivity (Bormann & Likens, 1994). The OFS in this sere has high levels of spatial heterogeneity resulting from a history of gap development and filling, which greatly resembles the fine-scale mosaic characteristic of the OFS in the fire-generated conifer-dominated archetype.

The OFS has high levels of structural complexity and species richness (Figures 3.24 and 3.25). All tree ages are represented in the OFS from seedlings and saplings through mature to old trees with their rich array of decadent features; hence, Frelich (2002) labeled the OFS the "Multi-Aged" stage. Diameter distributions typically approximate the inverse J-shaped curve (Figure 3.26). Since large canopy gaps are present, essentially all tree species are likely to find suitable conditions for regeneration and growth; i.e., the composition of OFS "would contain a representation of most species, including some early-successional

species, on a continuing basis" (Bormann & Likens, 1994, p. 175). Common shade-tolerant dominants in the old forest include species such as American beech (*Fagus americana*), sugar maple (*Acer sacharum*), and eastern hemlock (*Tsuga canadensis*), with less tolerant species such as eastern white pine and yellow birch (*Betula alleghaniensis*) successfully reproducing in gaps.

*This species-rich, structurally complex old deciduous forest can persist for a very long period of time, its dynamics being maintained by small tree and gap-scale disturbances generated by pathogens (e.g., root diseases), wind, and insect activity.* Old multiaged stands were the dominant forest condition in model predictions of forest landscape dynamics under the historical disturbance regime in Upper Michigan hemlock-hardwood forests (Frelich, 2002). Bormann and Likens (1994, p. 207) suggest:

*Because of modest levels of exogenous disturbance or long periods between large-scale disturbances, forested regions of the humid, temperate mountains of the northeastern United States might be considered as centers where autogenic development has its highest probability of achieving steady-state conditions, while in almost every direction away from these centers, catastrophic recycling takes on increasing importance.*

Eastern
white pine

Northern
red oak

Sugar
maple

Figure 3.25 *Idealized cross-section of an old-growth deciduous hardwood-dominated forest in the Great Lakes region of the United States illustrating the horizontal and vertical heterogeneity characteristic of such forests. (Illustration by Robert Van Pelt)*

In visualizing this deciduous forest archetype it is important to recognize that it has lost one foundational species (American chestnut, *Castanea dentata*) and is probably in the process of losing another—eastern hemlock. As described by Foster et al. (2014) foundational species are abundant, account for much of the biomass in an ecosystem, are focal points or bases of species networks, such as food webs, and in terms of human perception, fundamentally define an ecosystem (see, also, Chapter 14). American chestnut certainly fulfilled these requirements in large expanses of the pre-20th century eastern deciduous forests of eastern North America before it was effectively eliminated by chestnut blight. It was capable of growing to large size and

Figure 3.24 *Mixed old-growth forest of hardwoods (yellow birch, northern red oak, American beech, and red maple) and conifers (eastern white pine and eastern hemlock) on the Harvard Pisgah Tract near Winchester, New Hampshire, USA in 1930. (Photo courtesy of Harvard Forest)*

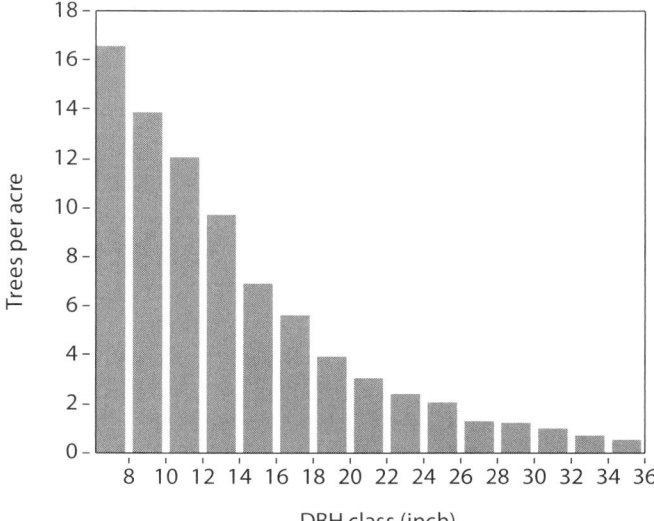

Eastern hemlock    White cedar    American elm    Yellow birch    White ash    American basswood

advanced age compared to most of its associates, produced decay resistant heartwood, which resulted in persistent dead wood structures, and produced large amounts of mast important to wildlife. Similarly, eastern hemlock is a foun-

dational species for *"with no hemlock, there is no distinctive and unique hemlock forest"* (Foster et al., 2014, p. 97), which includes such features as deep shade, evergreen canopy, thick humus, and acid soils.

***Variations in the Deciduous Hardwood Forest Archetype.*** There is an immense amount of variability in a forest type as broadly distributed and rich in species as the hardwood-dominated forests of northeastern North America, let alone the world (Askins, 2014). These include differences in the frequency and type of initiating wind disturbances, diversity of tree species (including short-lived early successional dominants), and the role played by ungulates.

Figure 3.26 *Classic diameter distribution from American beech-birch-maple-hemlock stand in Pennsylvania, USA, showing reverse J-shape; this was developed and used by H. Arthur Meyer, a forestry professor at Pennsylvania State University, to support uneven-aged management approaches in this forest type. (Source: Meyer & Stevenson, 1943)*

Wildfire is an important disturbance element in some deciduous hardwood forests, particularly near the boundaries with prairies and in the transition to boreal regions. In both of these cases, conifers become important components of the stands. Examples would be the mixed hardwood–conifer ecosystems of the Lake States, where red pine and eastern white pine are important conifer associates (Figure 3.27), and, more generally at higher elevations and latitudes, where true firs and spruces become important stand components. However, even where fires occur, crown fires are unusual in hardwood forests due to "relatively (compared with many conifers) high foliar moisture content, low bulk density of the canopy and possibly low content of flammable extractives" (Frelich, 2002, p. 25).

Wildfire does generate developmental patterns that contrast with those from wind disturbance events, since fires tend to kill from below. Consequently, significantly less regeneration from vegetative legacies occurs following wildfire in comparison with windstorm events, whether sprouts from surviving larger trees or advance regeneration. Regeneration following fire in this archetype is much more dependent upon seed dispersed from lightly burned or unburned sites. One consequence of this is that the PFS is likely to be both more species rich and persistent following wildfire than after a windstorm.

The lenga forests found in Tierra del Fuego are a very simplified example of the deciduous hardwood archetype (Figure 3.28); they have few or no other tree species present and low overall higher plant diversity. Lenga is a relatively shade-intolerant species, which has infrequent mast years but usually sustains a seedling bank in the understory. Creation of canopy gaps by wind provides the opportunity for seedlings to develop into dense sapling patches (Figure 3.28), which undergo intense competition but eventually produce individ-

uals that move into the upper canopy. The wind-generated gaps display a classic log-normal distribution with regard to patch size with many small gaps and very few large patches (Rebertus, Kitzberger, Veblen, & Roovers, 1997). Some larger wind events can result in very large patches of windthrow with nearly 100% of the overstory affected. Large amounts of CWD are characteristic of the lenga forests (Figure 2.9), which partially may be a consequence of the dominance of brown-rots in wood decay rather than white-rots, which are more characteristic of deciduous hardwood forests.

## Natural Forest Archetypes Characterized by Frequent Fire

*Forest ecosystems that experience frequent-fire disturbance regimes have highly distinctive structural and compositional features that differ dramatically from the two stand-replacement archetypes that we have just described.* In fact, we are amazed that the profound distinction between frequent-fire and essentially all other temperate forest types has not been more consistently and emphatically recognized by foresters and forest ecologists. In a forest dichotomy the differences between frequent-fire forests and all other closed-canopy temperate and boreal forests are more significant structurally and functionally than the differences between coniferous and hardwood-dominated forests! Perhaps the fundamental uniqueness of the frequent-fire forest has not (in our opinion) been adequately appreciated for several reasons. First, after much initial high-grading and some selective management by landowners, management in the mid-20th century moved toward conversion of such forests to plantations; also, many foresters and stakeholders may not have recognized that fire was an essential feature of a stable and productive forest ecosystem.

Figure 3.27 *There are forest types that regularly experienced significant disturbances from both wind and wildfire, such as this mature red pine-hardwood forest in central Minnesota. Such forests could provide the basis for an additional archetype in which both types of disturbances are interacting to produce unique outcomes from interactions of both types of disturbances and joint dominance by both conifers and hardwoods (Cutfoot Experimental Forests, Chippewa National Forest, Minnesota, USA).*

*Fire is unique among the most common natural disturbances in several features, including its tendency to kill "from below" rather than "from above,"* when it occurs at *low to moderate intensities*; consequently, fire tends to kill smaller trees while the larger dominants and codominants have a high probability of surviving. *Frequent fire also operates selectively in favoring species adapted to survive fire and against species that are easily damaged or killed by fire.* Fire adaptations may relate to structural features of either the reproduction (e.g., seedlings that have fire-resistant features that aid in their survival) or adult trees (e.g., thick fire-resistant bark and pruning of lower branches).

Another unique attribute of fire compared to most other disturbance agents is that humans have the capacity to directly influence this disturbance agent—i.e., either

to limit or eliminate it from a site (for at least a period of time) or to systematically introduce it to sites. Significant changes have occurred in most frequent-fire forest ecosystems as a consequence, most profoundly as a result of the historical and initially very successful efforts to eliminate fire in these ecosystems.

The common natural outcome of the powerful selective force of frequent fire is a predominantly low density forest dominated by larger, older trees (Figure 3.29) regardless of the inherent productivity of the site (e.g., Christensen, 1981, 1988; Glitzenstein, Platt, & Streng, 1995; Hagmann, Franklin, & Johnson, 2013, 2014; Peet & Allard, 1993; Ware, Frost, & Doerr, 1993) (Color Plate 3.5). Frequent fire often overwhelms the influences of other environmental variables, such as productivity. Both of the two primary examples of this archetype that we discuss here—ponderosa pine in western North America and longleaf pine in the southeastern United States—often exhibit classical savanna-like architecture, even though they otherwise occupy very different environments. Ponderosa pine forests are found

Figure 3.28 *Monotypic forests of lenga* (Nothofagus pumilio) *in Tierra del Fuego provide a highly simplified example of a deciduous forest in which wind is the primary exogenous disturbance regime. (a) The forests are relatively simply structured. (b) Canopy gaps are required for successful regeneration as lenga is a relatively shade-intolerant species. Regeneration can be heavily grazed by families of guanaco—a native camelid—but woody debris created by windthrow events confers some protection to the regeneration.*

primarily in seasonally dry climates and often on sites of relatively low productivity due to moisture limitations; hence, they are sometimes referred to as the **dry forests** (Franklin & Johnson, 2012, 2013). Longleaf pine forests, on the other hand, lack a regular dry season and can be highly productive on better soils. Yet, frequent fire produces similar architectures in both types (Figure 3.29).

**Ponderosa Pine Ecosystem**   Frequent-fire forests dominated by ponderosa pine were arguably one of the most extensive forest formations in North America prior to European settlement, but the majority of these forests have been modified by fire suppression and harvesting. Ponderosa pine was the only significant tree species on many sites,

although it often was associated with various species of juniper (*Juniperus* spp.) and oak, Douglas-fir, white or grand fir (*Abies concolor* and *grandis*), lodgepole pine, and western larch (*Larix occidentalis*). Western larch largely replaces ponderosa pine as the major fire-resistant tree dominant in portions of the northern Rocky Mountains. In the Sierra Nevada Range of California, sugar pine (*Pinus lambertiana*), Jeffrey pine (*Pinus jeffreyi*), and incense-cedar (*Calocedrus decurrens*) are significant associates.

*The archetypical ponderosa pine ecosystem is predominantly a fine-scale mosaic of patch types largely reflecting mortality processes (fire and bark beetle) that kill individuals and small clusters of trees* (Figure 3.30). Consequently, the diversity of patch types—openings (PFS) and patches of

Figure 3.29 *Natural forests of ponderosa pine (top) and longleaf pine (bottom) have similar savanna-like architectures despite their significant differences in environment and productivity and in the frequency of fire that is required to sustain these structures. Ponderosa pine forests are often found on dry, low productivity sites and their savanna-like structures can be sustained by fires at relatively long intervals (e.g., 10–25 years). Longleaf pine forests occupy environments that are generally moist throughout the growing season and can be highly productive; sustaining these forests requires fire at relatively short intervals, such as one to three years.*

Figure 3.30 *Profile of a well-developed ponderosa pine forest illustrating the mosaic of conditions, from openings to groves of old trees that are characteristic of such forests. Drawn from transect in Bluejay Springs Research Natural Area, Fremont-Winema National Forests, Oregon, USA. (Illustration by Robert Van Pelt)*

saplings and poles (YFS), mature trees (MFS), and groves dominated by large old trees (OFS)—as well as patches that are mixtures of these conditions are simultaneously present in the mosaic (Franklin & Van Pelt, 2004) (Figure 3.12). While the spatial arrangement of these patches changes over time, the collective forest ecosystem is very stable as long as it continues to experience frequent fire (see Color Plate 3.6). For an ecologically complete forest ecosystem all patch conditions need to be present.

Tree densities in the frequent-fire archetype are typically low with the basal area primarily composed of older, large-diameter trees (Hagmann, Franklin, & Johnson, 2013, 2014; Noss et al., 2006). Diameter distributions are often relatively flat or exhibit bulges in the larger diameter classes; the classic reverse J-shaped diameter distribution found in the stand-replacement archetypes is not characteristic of frequent-fire ecosystems. Tree spatial distributions are often highly clustered rather than uniform (Figure 3.31) (Churchill et al., 2013; Larson & Churchill, 2012). The clumped spatial arrangement of trees has impor-

tant ecological consequences, such as in its effects on the behavior of wildfire and bark beetles and vertebrates' use of the habitat.

Historical ponderosa pine forests also had high levels of landscape continuity; distinct edges or vegetative boundaries were generally encountered only when environmental conditions shifted sufficiently to alter site potentials, such as to grassland or riparian habitat. The lack of traditional "stands" was partially due to the infrequency of extensive high-severity fire events, which would generate distinctive larger patches with well-defined boundaries. Mixed- and high-severity fire behaviors now occur with increasing frequency as the result of the greatly increased intervals between fires.

As moisture conditions improve along environmental (e.g., elevational) gradients ponderosa pine forests shift from nearly pure forests of ponderosa pine to forest ecosystems that include greater mixtures of other species, which are often referred to as mixed-conifer types. In much of the western intermountain North America, species such as

Figure 3.31 *Tree spatial distributions are often highly clumped or clustered in frequent-fire forest ecosystems, which has important consequences in the functioning of these ecosystems, including their response to wildfire and other disturbances.*

Douglas-fir, white or grand fir, and western larch are typical additions. Common associates in the Sierra Nevada mixed-conifer forests are sugar pine, incense-cedar, white fir, Douglas-fir, and California black oak (*Quercus kelloggii*). In the mixed-conifer forests fires can be less frequent, and mixed-severity fires are more common than in the pure ponderosa pine forests.

Although we have used the present tense in these descriptions of the ponderosa pine and mixed-conifer forest ecosystems, most of these forests have been highly modified as a result of Euro-American colonization. Elimination of frequent fire has been the most important change, but this is only one of many disruptions. One of the earliest and nearly universal impacts of Euro-American colonization was grazing by immense herds of cattle and sheep in the second half of the 19th and beginning of the 20th centuries; this eliminated most fine fuels, which were important in sustaining frequent fire, and also competed with tree seedlings. (Noss et al., 2006). Another early and widespread impact was destruction of Native American cultures, many of which had utilized fire. Active fire suppression has been the most important impact during the last 100 years. Finally, logging has dramatically altered many of these forests such as by selective logging of larger trees, clearcutting, and establishment of plantations.

The outcome of all of these impacts has been the conversion of the majority of frequent-fire forests to dense, fuel-rich stands dominated by species intolerant of fire and drought (Figure 3.32) with the further consequence that large, uncharacteristic stand-replacement wildfires are now the dominant disturbance regime (Figure 3.33). Unexpectedly, the impacts of fire elimination generally have been much greater in the mixed-conifer forests than in the pure ponderosa pine forests. Factors responsible for this faster response of mixed-conifer forests to elimination of fire are related to their significantly greater productivity (more available moisture) and the regeneration and rapid growth of species, such as white fir, which produce highly flammable fuel ladders. This more rapid shift in forest fuels on mixed-conifer sites is often overlooked because it usually involves many fewer "missed" fire intervals than on drier sites. There are significant efforts underway to restore many of the pine and mixed-conifer forests to more resistant conditions (see Chapter 4).

**Longleaf Pine Ecosystem**    In order to maintain its composition and structure, the longleaf pine ecosystem requires fire at very frequent intervals (one to three years), which makes it the "bookend" ecosystem of the frequent-fire forests. At longer fire intervals competing hardwoods become established and have the potential to increase their dominance, eliminating the potential for frequent fire and successful reproduction of longleaf pine. *The longleaf pine ecosystem is the most finely tuned to its disturbance regime of any forest ecosystem we know.*

A second exceptional attribute of the longleaf pine ecosystem is its very high biodiversity, which is composed of both plant and animal species; in fact, *we believe that the longleaf pine ecosystem is the most biologically rich temperate forest ecosystem in the world.* Understories in longleaf pine ecosystems may include 300–400 vascular plant species. The bunchgrasses, such as the widespread wiregrass (*Aristida stricta*), make critical contributions to the quantity and structure of surface fuels required to support the very frequent fires (Mitchell, Hiers, O'Brien, & Starr, 2009). The rich vertebrate diversity includes birds, amphibians, reptiles, and mammals; notable species include gopher tortoises (*Gopherus polyphemus*) and red-cockaded woodpeckers (*Picoides borealis*) (Figure 3.34). A comprehensive treatment of the longleaf pine ecosystem and its management is provided in *Ecological Restoration and Management of Longleaf Pine Forests* (Kirkman & Jack, 2017).

The architecture of the archetypical longleaf pine ecosystem is very similar structurally to that of ponderosa pine (Figure 3.29). Savannas dominated by larger-diameter trees are characteristic. Lightning fires generate openings in the forest where patches of longleaf pine reproduction can

Figure 3.32 *Many ponderosa pine and mixed-conifer forests have undergone dramatic change with the removal of fire, including increased densities, dominance of fire- and drought-intolerant trees, and greatly increased fuel loadings, including abundant ladder fuels. Old ponderosa pine are now surrounded by young and mature Douglas-fir and grand fir that have grown up around it as a result of fire suppression (land managed by the Washington Department of Natural Resources near Ellensberg, Washington State, USA).*

develop (Figure 3.35), but regeneration is not necessarily confined to openings. Diameter distributions are relatively flat under the frequent-fire regimes.

Longleaf pine forests once covered 80 million acres in a crescent extending from Virginia across the Southeast to eastern Texas. Today only about 3% of these forests remain and much of that is on federal military reservations. Some of the original longleaf pine acreage has been converted to agricultural and other domestic uses. Of the area remaining in forest cover, the vast majority of the longleaf pine has been converted into plantations of other southern pines, such as loblolly and slash pine, which are more amenable to intensive forest management. Interest in restoration and management of longleaf pine is increasing, however, with much of it based on ecological forestry approaches (see Chapter 4). Social concerns over smoke from prescribed burns are one of the major challenges to sustaining this ecosystem in the future.

**Other Frequent-Fire Forest Ecosystems**    The pitch pine–hardwood forests found in New Jersey (known as the Pine Barrens) are a distinctive type of frequent-fire forest (see Chapter 4). Pitch pine (*Pinus rigida*) is capable of reproducing vegetatively after being subjected to severe wildfire. The hardwoods associated with it, which include several species of oak, also are capable of regenerating themselves

vegetatively. Hence, forests composed of pitch pine and hardwoods are capable of experiencing a severe canopy-consuming wildfire, but many of the trees, including the dominants, will survive such events by abundant sprouting.

Frequent-fire forest ecosystems composed of pine or mixtures of pine and oak species are widespread in North America and the world (O'Brien et al., 2008).

## Applying Principles from the Forest Archetypes

So, what is the value of these archetypes? Do they represent the real world of the natural forest? Is this what we are likely to see when we visit unmanaged forest landscapes? Are they what we are trying to emulate in ecological forestry practice?

The archetypes that we have presented here are simplified models of how forest ecosystem development may proceed in unmanaged forest landscapes. As we have presented them, the two episodically disturbed landscapes are linear, segmented, and predictable, and the frequent-fire archetype does not experience a stand-replacement disturbance event! Of course, the natural (or seminatural) world is never that simple!

The complexity of the real world begins with the complexity and stochastic nature of disturbances themselves.

Figure 3.33 *Large, uncharacteristic stand-replacement fires are now common in many frequent-fire forest landscapes of the western United States; the fore- and mid-ground areas in this photo of part of the B&B fire of 2008 are examples. More distant high-elevation areas (subalpine forests) are portions of the landscape characterized historically by stand-replacement fires (Deschutes National Forest, Oregon, USA).*

The disturbances that initiate seres rarely act uniformly over very large areas. For example, in the Douglas-fir–western hemlock ecosystem, as much or more of the area of a large wildfire may have burned at low to moderate severity levels as burned at a high severity level. Large disturbances in these landscapes rarely burn at high severity throughout, killing essentially all of the dominants of the pre-disturbance forest, although significant portions of them may exhibit that severity. The areas of intermediate disturbance exhibit highly varied levels of legacies and openness across the burned landscape. The resulting forest landscapes are complex mosaics, including patches of diverse tree ages and structural conditions.

The nature of the seres initiated by these complex disturbances will also vary in species composition, rates of development, and intensity of processes, such as competition. Spatial patterns in the types and amounts of legacies will vary depending on the localized severity of a particular disturbance. Some of the variables, such as availability of seed sources, are highly stochastic but can be very important. However, patterns, such as in the dominance of pioneer species, can be predicted on a probabilistic basis. Of course, many seres will be truncated long before running their course by succeeding disturbance events, producing diverse starting points (e.g., legacies) along the developmental sequence.

Forests generated and maintained under frequent-fire regimes would appear to be extraordinarily stable as an ecosystem—at least so long as their fire regime is maintained! As presented in the archetype these

forests would rarely undergo a forest-replacement disturbance; rather, dynamics occur at the level of the individual patches that make up the forest mosaic.

However, fire behaviors do vary and extensive areas of the western North American landscape have fire regimes, particularly in moister portions of frequent-fire landscapes, that are sufficiently variable that "mixed" behaviors are encountered, which means that sometimes significant portions of these forests can burn at moderate to high severity. These forests are often composed of mixtures of species that are not as resistant to fire and drought as ponderosa pine. Conditions in these mixed-conifer forest landscapes can fluctuate between the stable, frequent-fire model and the

Figure 3.35 *Longleaf pine forests under frequent-fire regimes exhibit extensive open areas where natural regeneration can become established and light-loving elements of the understory can be sustained.*

Figure 3.34 *Gopher tortoises (a) and red-cockaded woodpeckers (b) are found in the species-rich longleaf pine ecosystem (Gopher tortoise photo courtesy of Lora L. Smith; red-cockaded woodpecker photo courtesy of USFWS)*

episodically disturbed model. Many stakeholders and managers view this mixed behavior as a problem rather than seeing the opportunity that it provides, which is the option of moving management in these mixed-conifer regions toward either of the frequent-fire or episodic models.

*So, given the complexity of the real world, why have we presented these simple archetypes? First, we created them to help students (in the broadest sense) of forest ecosystems see as clearly as possible some of the internal or endogenous processes that are at work in the progressive natural development of forest ecosystems.* Equally important is to understand that the product of these developmental processes is not just structural or compositional changes but, most profoundly, changes in the functionality of the forest. *Different forest stages have very different functional capabilities!* This is well demonstrated in Color Plate 2.1. Of course, structural change always has been at the core of forestry, but structure has been far too narrowly focused on the living tree and the young forest. In this century, a student of forests must be thinking about the array of conditions and capabilities provided by an entire sere and equally the live and dead tree components. We believe that the development and maturation of the forest ecosystem is most easily grasped in the form of temporal stages rather than as a continuum of constant and endless change.

*The second major value of these archetypes in the highly variable real world is to help us understand how we can develop approaches to forest management that will sustain arrays of services and goods similar to those provided by natural forest ecosystems.* For example, biological legacies exemplify ways in which structural, compositional, and, most importantly, functional attributes can be sustained through multiple generations of forest. Natural forest seres rarely started from "scratch" after a disturbance. The legacies and extensive areas of mixed-severity disturbance that are associated with large severe disturbances demonstrate ways that an array of organisms and functions can be sustained, such as by partial cutting regimes. Even-aged rotations requiring several centuries are not needed!

The tree and gap-level dynamics of old forests demonstrate the tendency of forests—in the absence of major exogenous disturbances—to evolve toward species-rich and structurally complex ecosystems that are sustained over long periods of time by small-scale chronic disturbance regimes. Forest conditions dominated by chronic disturbances—the frequent-fire forest ecosystems and the old forest stages of the episodically disturbed forests—appear to be the most stable of forest states under their natural disturbance regimes.

Nothing that we have presented here can substitute for natural resource professionals developing a deep personal knowledge of the forest ecosystems for which they are responsible. Professionals must develop a thorough knowl-edge of the natural and social history of the ecosystems for which they are responsible in order to be able to develop appropriate management plans and silvicultural prescriptions. Hopefully, models and archetypes such as we have provided will be of assistance, but their interpretation depends upon knowledge of the local ecosystem. Resource professionals must always recognize that, regardless of their specialty, comprehensive understanding of the ecosystem is critical not only in prescribing and carrying out activities but also in their important role as the primary representatives of these ecosystems to human society.

In Chapter 4 we will see how patterns and processes associated with natural forest development provide us with a set of principles that we can use as the basis for silvicultural prescriptions for ecological forest management.

## Part 4: Disruptions Associated with Climate Change and Invasive Organisms

*Climate change and invasive organisms* are and will continue to be major disrupters of forest ecosystems, and the disruptions that they create can have very different consequences than the historical natural disturbances discussed earlier in this chapter. They *have the potential to cause permanent changes in composition, structure, and function of existing forest ecosystems and even cause their conversion to nonforested ecosystems.* From at least some perspectives, invasive organisms probably are more threatening than climate change, because they have the potential to effectively eliminate species, including foundational species. While climate change may displace species and disrupt forest ecosystems, altering the biodiversity, structure, and function of existing ecosystems, the potential generally exists for displaced species to migrate or be moved to more suitable locations and for forest ecosystems to adjust to the altered environment. Invasive species, on the other hand, can extirpate native species and permanently alter the fundamental nature—structure, function, and disturbance regimes—of forest ecosystems, as we will see.

This section has been included to help remind ecological forest managers and stakeholders of these two risks and the need to manage forests with consideration of these potentially system-changing agents.

### Climate Change

Influences of climate change on forest ecosystems will be many and varied, from effects on individual plant and animal organisms to major alterations in the character (type, frequency, severity, and extent) of stand- and landscape-level disturbances. Although the unknowns of climate change are immense, we can make some inferences about what some of the impacts will be, which we will review in this section. Other aspects of climate change are discussed in Chapter 15.

Environmental variables that are being affected by climate change include temperature, total and seasonal distribution of precipitation, moisture deficits and drought, and snowpack. Increased temperatures are a certainty, although the amount of increase is uncertain and will vary widely in different regions and even locally within different parts of the same landscape. There will also be variability in the relative amount of warming in different seasons and between day and night; night temperatures are of particular interest because of their impact on tree and other green plant respiration. Changing precipitation regimes will interact with increasing temperatures to influence such variables as seasonal moisture deficits.

Climate change is reducing the depth and duration of winter snowpacks with impacts on a wide variety of forest regions. The winter snowpack is critical for many mountain forests, particularly where the majority of precipitation occurs as snow during the winter (Mote, Hamlet, Clark, & Lettenmaier, 2005). This includes the pine and mixed-conifer forests of western intermountain North America and the Sierra Nevada Range of California, where decreases in the duration, extent, and depth of winter snowpack are affecting water stress during the growing season and influencing nutrient cycling and erosion (e.g., Ryan et al., 2014). Reduced winter snowpacks have been implicated in extensive mortality of Alaska cedar in coastal Alaska, which has resulted in increased freezing of shallow root systems with resulting death of trees over significant areas (Hennon, D'Amore, Schaberg, Wittwer, & Shanley, 2012). Reduced winter snowpacks have also increased the freezing of surface soils in the Appalachian Mountains of New England. Reductions in winter snowpacks are predicted to continue.

Climate change has both direct and indirect effects on ecosystem structure, function, and composition (Figure 3.36). The direct effects include alterations in the metabolism and population dynamics of organisms, including potential invertebrate pests and pathogens, as well as trees and all of their associated symbionts, such as mycorrhizal fungi. The indirect effects of climate change are primarily a result of altered disturbance regimes. *Although it is an indirect effect, the climate-change-induced modifications of disturbance regimes are likely to produce the most rapid and extensive alterations in forests, disrupting established trees and forests and forcing them to undergo a regeneration cycle.*

## Direct Effects of Climate Change

Effects of climate change on the distribution and growth of tree species is a major concern of foresters. Climate change can result in environmental conditions to which current species or genotypes are not well adapted resulting in

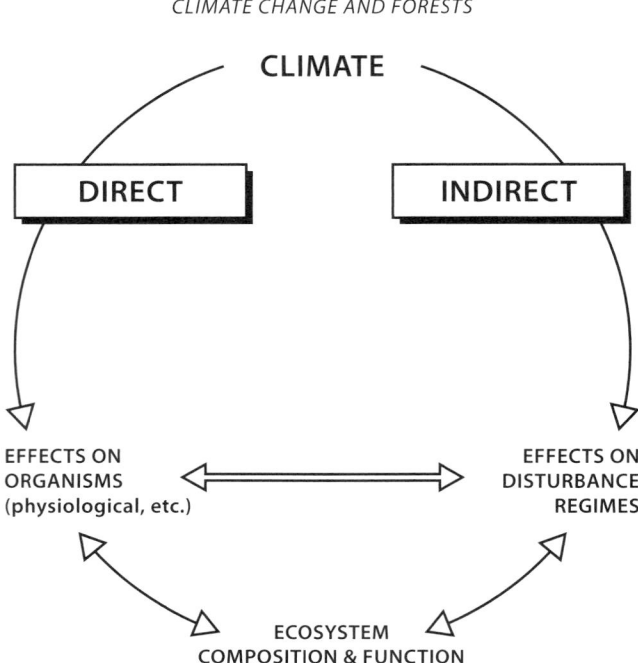

*CLIMATE CHANGE AND FORESTS*

Figure 3.36 *Climate change has both direct and indirect effects on ecosystem structure, function, and composition. Direct effects include influences on the metabolism and population dynamics of individual organisms, including potential invertebrate pests and pathogens. Indirect effects include alterations in disturbance regimes, which are likely to produce the most rapid and extensive alterations in forests. (Franklin et al., 1991)*

decreased vigor, growth, and competitiveness. While established trees may have considerable tolerance of the altered environment, the same tree species may have difficulty or fail to regenerate itself on the climatically modified site.

Climate change will cause system-level changes in the composition, function, and structure of intact forest ecosystems. Obviously, loss of an important tree species, such as an emergent dominant or a species with decay-resistant wood, would result in significant reductions of functional richness and structural complexity. For example, green plant (primary) productivity might be expected to increase in response to higher levels of $CO_2$, since $CO_2$ is one of the limiting components in photosynthesis. However, there are constraints on such increases associated with limitations of water and nitrogen (Ryan et al.,2014). Increased $CO_2$ concentrations have been found to increase net productivity of forest ecosystems in some ecosystem-scale studies known as Free Air $CO_2$ Exchange (FACE) experiments, but it is not clear whether carbon is sequestered in a form that lasts or if it is simply more rapidly cycled between the forest and atmosphere (Birdsey, Jenkins, & Johnston, 2007). Other metabolic processes, such as respiration, also accelerate with higher temperatures. Increased temperatures and altered moisture regimes could significantly alter decomposition rates, most often resulting in decreased stocks of dead organic materials. For example, warmer and drier summers predictably would accelerate decomposition of logs and other CWD on the forest floor in Douglas-fir–western hemlock forests in northwestern North America.

Climate change will also impact the physiology and population dynamics of nonplant organisms that are part of the ecosystem including important symbionts, such as mycorrhizal-forming fungi, and insect pests and pathogens. Fortunately, most forests have a diversity of fungal species that form mycorrhizae that vary in their environmental optima and thereby provide significant redundancy that will help sustain this important symbiosis. Overall warmer growing-season and winter temperatures will increase the virulence of at least some pests and pathogens, as will be discussed below.

## Climate-Induced Changes in Disturbance Regimes

Climate change is expected to significantly alter the disturbance regimes impacting forest ecosystems and almost certainly has already begun to do so as suggested in examples discussed below. Many scientists believe that climate change will be most conspicuously experienced as severe stand-disrupting disturbances by such agents as wildfire, windstorms of both oceanic and continental origin, and outbreaks of insects and diseases (Franklin & Spies, 1991; Spies et al., 2010). Established forest ecosystems have considerable ability to tolerate significant environmental change. However, severe disturbances disrupt these established forests and force the ecosystem to undergo a cycle of tree regeneration; establishment of a new generation of trees is the stage in forest development most vulnerable to adverse environmental conditions. This is especially true for tree species that have to regenerate from seed, which is the case for most coniferous species; it is not as challenging for trees that can regenerate vegetatively (e.g., from root or stump sprouts), as is the case for most hardwoods. This is also one of the major reasons why hardwoods are fundamentally better adapted to impacts of climate change than conifers.

*Wildfire.* Climate change is expected to result in significantly more wildfire than has been the case historically. Part of this is the direct result of higher temperatures and increased moisture deficits, particularly in areas that already experience relatively dry seasons. Other factors may include the more frequent and extended droughts, potential for increased lightning ignitions, and more frequent synoptic weather patterns that create extraordinary burning conditions, such as those associated with strong hot and dry winds. General aspects of wildfire are dis-

cussed in Chapters 12 and 13. It is uncertain whether the unusual burning conditions and wildfires of recent fire seasons (including 2015) in western North America are climate change–related, but they may exemplify the new "normal." Some scientists have concluded that fire seasons are now longer as a result of climate change (Westerling, Hidalgo, Cayan, & Swetnam, 2006).

*Windstorms.* Climate change is very likely to result in greater atmospheric turbulence if for no other reason than a warmer Earth has more energy. Warming oceans might be expected to produce storms with both greater energy and water content and at greater frequency. Ocean-generated storms, such as hurricanes and typhoons, have always been important sources of forest disturbance and are, in many forest regions, the defining episodic disturbance. Hotter continents might also be expected to generate more frequent and severe storms, which can produce high wind events, such as tornados and derechos. Lightning storms are particularly significant in some regions, such as western North America, where they provide the primary source of wildfire ignitions. This paragraph is speculative on our part as there is no current scientific consensus on how climate change will affect the frequency, intensity, and location of intensive storm systems, but it is a reasonable possibility that it will do so. This is currently an active area of research and we should know more about the linkage in the near future, which is significant, given the historical importance of major storm events in the disturbance history of forest regions.

*Pests and Pathogens.* Climate change can influence outbreaks of pests and pathogens directly through their influence on the biology of either the pest organisms (e.g., metabolism or population dynamics) or the host tree species (e.g., reduced vigor as a result of moisture stress) or both. Forest conditions can also be very important in influencing the potential for massive outbreaks, such as the availability of extensive populations of the vulnerable stage of a host tree species.

Insect outbreaks provide us with some of the most conspicuous examples to date of what are believed to be disturbances caused or intensified by altered climatic conditions. The massive outbreaks of mountain pine beetle populations in forests dominated by lodgepole pine in the Canadian provinces of British Columbia and Alberta are one well-known example. These outbreaks are believed to be at least partially the result of warming temperatures (one to two degrees C) that allowed for high survival of overwintering beetles and shorter developmental periods (Raffa et al., 2008, p. 511): *"Collectively, reduced beetle mortality, a shortened life cycle, and the increased area and connectivity of climatically and demographically susceptible forests"* produced the outbreak. Similar large-scale outbreaks of mountain pine beetle have occurred in lodgepole-dominated forests in the northern and central Rocky Mountains and on the eastern slopes of the Cascade Range, although the role of climate change is not so clear in these cases, since the majority of lodgepole pine forests are fundamentally "boom-and-bust" ecosystems that undergo stand replacement events.

The pinyon ips beetle (*Ips confusus*) decimated pinyon pine (*Pinus edulis* and *monophylla*) populations in the southwestern United States following a drought with high temperatures during 2002 and 2003. This attack was not confined to areas near the lower forest line but, rather, was widely distributed throughout the pinyon–juniper woodland type and included attacks on all sizes and ages of trees (Raffa et al., 2008). Although droughts are expected in these woodlands, *"the abnormally high temperatures that exacerbated host stress—and may have increased the annual number of beetle generations—are probably a product of ongoing warming due to anthropogenic emissions* (Breshears et al., 2005)" (Raffa et al., 2008, p. 511).

Insects that defoliate trees tend to have cycles that are influenced by populations of pathogens and pests that prey upon them (Dwyer, Dushoff, & Yee, 2004). Much less is known about how climate patterns influence populations of defoliators (Ayres et al., 2014). In the case of the western spruce budworm (*Choristoneura occidentalis*), an important western North American defoliator, outbreaks in conifer forests of western intermountain North America have been responding to climatic variability over the past 300 years and are projected to increase over the coming century in response to warmer, drier, and more variable conditions.

Other types of insects may show more aggressive behaviors as a result of climate change, increasing their intensity of attack and expanding their range. For example, the balsam woolly aphid, an introduced sucking insect, has been limited in its impacts by cold temperatures in high-elevation stands of subalpine fir in much of western North America. The intensity of infestations and damage and mortality to subalpine fir is increasing in the subalpine parklands of the Cascade Range and Olympic Mountains, which is almost certainly due to warming temperature regimes.

Climate change can also have significant impacts on behavior of pathogens and the susceptibility of host species (e.g., Kliejunas et al., 2009). Pathogens may be particularly responsive since they have short life cycles (including rapid reproduction potential and genetic evolution) and mobility. However, fungal responses to climate are complicated and not well understood (Allen et al., 2010). One western North American tree pathogen that is expected to benefit from climate change is Swiss needle cast (*Phaeocryptopus gaeumannii*), which causes premature needle loss in Douglas-fir in both its native range and in Europe. Although part of the Swiss needle cast problem

in northwestern North America is the result of excessive planting of Douglas-fir near the Pacific Ocean, predicted warmer winter temperatures as a result of climate change may increase the severity and range of needle cast infections (Stone, Coop, & Manger, 2008).

These examples, as well as others that could be cited, mostly involve *novel* behaviors of native pests and pathogens, a term we use to identify behaviors that we have not previously observed and that could also be referred to as *regime shifts* (Raffa et al., 2008). We can expect to experience many novel behaviors—some of them on very large scales—as a consequence of climate change and its impacts on both pathogens and hosts. Human activities, such as fire suppression, have certainly contributed to the creation of large and connected areas of vulnerable host conditions (Raffa et al., 2008).

## Invasive Organisms

*Invasive organisms (hereafter called "invasives") we judge to be an even greater potential threat to the integrity of forest ecosystems than climate change, second only to the impacts of conversion of forests to nonforest conditions*, such as housing developments and agricultural land. Invasives are invertebrate animals (e.g., insects), pathogens, plants, and vertebrate animals that arrive from distant locations (usually other continents) and become established in existing ecosystems, weakening, killing, and replacing existing species, including those that are foundational or keystone, critical to the structure and function of the existing forest ecosystems. *The activities of invasives can cause major changes in forest ecosystem composition or structure or both with significant consequences to the functional capabilities of that ecosystem and its vulnerabilities to other natural disturbances.* There are numerous significant examples to illustrate the potential negative impacts of invasives, some of which we describe below.

Humans invariably facilitate the arrival of these invasives either directly or indirectly, both accidentally and intentionally. Humans also contribute to the problem by creating conditions that facilitate the establishment and spread of the invasives, including serving as the vector for their spread. Invasives invariably degrade at least some of the attributes of the affected ecosystem, including its stability. In addition to their direct disruptive effects on ecosystems some invasives also end up altering the natural disturbance regime of an ecosystem, as illustrated by the effect of cheatgrass (*Bromus tectorum*) on the fire regimes of the grasslands it has infested.

Introduced pests and pathogens have had tremendous impacts on the forests of North America. We have repeatedly seen that these introduced organisms have—practically, if not literally—eliminated important forest species.

There are no better examples than those of the chestnut blight (*Cryphonectria parasitica*) on the American chestnut and hemlock woolly adelgid (*Adelges tsugae*) on eastern hemlock (Foster et al., 2014). American chestnut was perhaps the most important single hardwood tree species in eastern North America for many reasons including the abundance and quality of its wood, its decay resistance, and the production of mast for wildlife. Chestnut blight was introduced on imported chestnut seedlings in 1900 and in 40 years effectively extirpated the species as a tree throughout its range (Edmonds et al., 2011). Eastern hemlock, which Foster et al. (2014) convincingly identify as a foundational species, has been effectively eliminated from much of its range by the hemlock woolly adelgid and possibly could be eliminated from the rest of it, particularly with warming temperatures (Edmonds et al., 2011).

The list of the invasive forest pests and pathogens in North America is long and continually growing; the primary source of these invasives has been Eurasia, and *importation of live nursery stock has been a consistently important mechanism for introductions.* Virtually every important tree species in eastern North America is now affected by a seriously damaging invasive. White pine blister rust (*Cronartium ribicola*) was an early introduction on nursery stock that now affects all of the white pine species throughout North America (Box 3.2). Dutch elm disease (*Ophiostoma ulmi*) reached North America in 1930 and has decimated multiple species of elms. Sudden oak death is a relatively recent introduction, which has been repeatedly introduced on imported nursery stock from Europe despite efforts to prevent it.

This history with invasive insects parallels that of the pathogens. Gypsy moth (*Lymantria dispar*) was an early intentional (1869) introduction to North America, where it was intended to become the basis for a silkworm industry. Beech scale (*Cryptococcus fagisuga*) was introduced from Europe in 1890 and facilitates the entrance of the fungus *Nectria coccinea* var. *faginata*, resulting in the decline and death of American beech. Balsam woolly aphid (*Adelges piceae*), is an extremely damaging pest on many species of true fir (*Abies* spp.). Other recent introductions include the Asian long-horned beetle (*Anolophora glabripennis*) and emerald ash borer (*Agrilus planipennis*), the latter with the potential to effectively eliminate all North American species of ash (*Fraxinus* spp.).

Introduced pathogens and pests can significantly impact animals as well as plants. We will not attempt to review this topic other than to note that these pathogens can affect entire groups of organisms and not just individual species. An excellent example of this are two fungi, *Batrachochytrium salamandrivorans* (*Bsal*) and *B. dendrobatidis* (*Bd*), both of which cause the deadly skin disease chytridiomycosis in amphibians. *Bd* has contributed significantly to major declines and extinctions in amphibian species around the globe, including North America. Currently major efforts are underway to prevent the introduction of *Bsal* to the United States. The threats from such organisms can be to entire organismal groups (amphibians in this case), which play important functional roles in ecosystems, such as in control of disease-spreading mosquitoes.

Invasive plants typically have traits that allow them to outcompete native species for resources. Disturbed and degraded ecosystems provide outstanding opportunities for them to get established and spread, although some are quite capable of invading intact ecosystems. An outstanding example in western North America that we already mentioned is cheatgrass, which has infested rangelands and dry forests (Mack, 1981); once established it is highly resistant to displacement by native species. There are literally hundreds of examples of invasive plants that we could offer, but we will discuss just two that are spreading through southeastern North America: cogongrass (*Imperata cylindrical*) and kudzu (*Pueraria montana*). Cogongrass is a perennial rhizomatous grass native to Asia. It is a serious threat to longleaf pine forests where it forms monotypic stands that smother the incredibly species-rich herbaceous understories found in these forests. Worse yet, cogongrass burns much hotter than native species, resulting in significant fire-caused mortality and species shifts (Jose, Cox, Miller, Donn, & Merritt, 2002). Although cold temperatures limit the spread of cogongrass, climate warming is expected to increase its already extensive range (Ayres et al., 2014). Kudzu is a perennial vine native to Asia that smothers and kills vegetation. Like cogongrass, the spread of kudzu has been limited by killing frosts, but it is expected to expand northward; it could become an invasive problem in coastal Oregon and Washington (Bradley, Wilcove, & Oppenheimer, 2010). Kudzu has also been shown to release sequestered soil carbon (Tamura & Tharayil, 2014).

Invasive vertebrate animals close out our categories of invasive species. Human beings are probably the common vector for introduction of invasive vertebrates. Introductions often have been intentional, although there are also many examples of species that "hitched rides" to new continents. The impacts of invasive vertebrate animals is a very large topic with a massive literature that we cannot begin to review here. Our major point is to remind readers that invasive vertebrate animal species can significantly impact forest ecosystems in diverse ways. One common example is by altering food webs resulting in the displacement, death, and potential extirpation of native vertebrate species.

Invasive vertebrates may also be capable of directly killing trees and altering the basic nature of ecosystems and landscapes. North American beaver (*Castor canadensis*) have significant abilities to modify forests and stream ecosystems through their engineering activities, and their effects are often (but not always) considered to be ecologically beneficial within North America. About 70 years ago they were introduced to the large island of Tierra del Fuego to provide the basis for a fur industry, but this industry never materialized. The beaver found the environment greatly to their liking, however, and spread to stream and river ecosystems throughout the island, totally altering the structure of these aquatic ecosystems (Figure 3.37) and destroying significant forest areas. There are no predators on the beaver in the native fauna of the island. In the initial population explosion they occupied habitat that could not sustain beaver activity, such as timberline forests, departing after the food source (*Nothofagus* spp.) was exhausted (Figure 3.37). Beaver have escaped the island and are now established on the mainland of South America.

*We have included this material on invasives because forest managers and stakeholders need to be aware of the continuing risk and immense consequences of introductions of virulent invasive organisms. Indeed, if anything, the rate of these introductions may have accelerated as a result of the volume and rapidity of intercontinental commerce.* From an ecological perspective the problem of invasive organisms has a parallel with the potential of infectious diseases to human health—except that we appear to be much more passive about invasives that do not directly infest us!

## Interactions between Climate Change and Invasive Organisms

Interactions can be expected between climate change and invasive organisms. We can, for example, hypothesize that climate-stressed trees are going to be more susceptible to exotic as well as native pests, pathogens, consumers, and predators. We have provided several examples of these interactions in the preceding section. Some of these interactions may play out very quickly while others may require a long period to be realized, as in the case of whitebark pine (*Pinus albicaulis*) (Box 3.2 and Figure 3.38).

## Conclusions

We will consider how ecological foresters can prepare for and respond to the challenges of climate change and invasive species in Chapters 4 and 5 through creating and maintaining biologically diverse and heterogeneous ecosystems and landscapes. Also, we come back to these themes in Chapter 21. As has been repeatedly and recently noted (e.g., Pace, Carpenter, & Cole, 2016), the impacts will often appear with little or no advance warning, which emphasizes the need for managing ecosystems in ways that enhance their resilience. Despite current efforts to prevent introductions of invasives, the introductions continue, including imports of live nursery stock (probably the most important single source of invasive pathogens) and exotic animals. Greater efforts to prevent such activities, intentional and accidental, deserve the attention of foresters and stakeholders.

These challenges are important for both ecological and production foresters. Although production foresters have options to terminate existing stands and shift to other genotypes, species, or even crops, the financial impacts of

Figure 3.37 *North American beaver* (Castor canadensis) *were intentionally introduced to Tierra del Fuego to provide the basis for a fur industry. The island proved to be highly suitable habitat for beaver, however, and populations boomed resulting in massive alterations to stream and river environments and significant destruction of native forests.*

invasive pests or reduced fitness of crop trees can be expensive. Furthermore, the conditions created by production forestry—extensive areas occupied exclusively by potential host trees—are vulnerable to outbreaks of both native and introduced pests and pathogens. Properties managed under ecological forestry principles, on the other hand, are inherently less vulnerable because of the diversity of species and stand conditions that are present. However, most owners, managers, and stakeholders engaged in ecological forestry approaches are also committed to their forests for the long run and so lack the option of liquidating the forest and investing in alternatives, which is possible in production forestry (see Chapter 1). Hence, ecological forest managers have an intense interest in creating forest conditions that reduce the risks of catastrophic impacts from climate change and invasive species.

---

**Box 3.2  Effects of white pine blister rust and climate change on whitebark pine**

Whitebark pine is a tree species that plays an important ecological role in the high-elevation forests and timberline regions of western North America (Bockino & Tinker, 2012). Whitebark pine produces large, nutrient-rich seeds that are an important food source for many bird and small mammal species, as well as grizzly and black bears (*Ursus arctos horribilis* and *Ursus americanus*, respectively). The wingless seeds are dispersed primarily by Clark's nutcrackers (*Nucifraga columbiana*), but trees have to be quite old before they begin to produce seed (> 50 years). Colonization by whitebark pine aids in ecosystem development on harsh sites after fire and other disturbances and may shelter the establishment of other less hardy vegetation. Whitebark pine also helps regulate snow cover and reduce soil erosion (Keane et al., 2012).

Whitebark pine is in serious decline throughout much the northern Rocky Mountains and Cascade Ranges because of

mountain pine beetle outbreaks exacerbated by warming temperatures and the introduced pathogen, white pine blister rust (Figure 3.38). Mountain pine beetles attack all western pines, spending the majority of their life cycle under the bark of host trees except when adults emerge and fly in search of new host trees. Although large-scale outbreaks of this native bark beetle have been common in lodgepole pine, attacks on whitebark pine are believed to have been uncommon based on dendrological studies, probably because of cold winter temperatures in these subalpine habitats (Bockino & Tinker, 2012). Warmer temperatures have allowed increased winter survival of all life stages and completion of entire life cycles within a single year (Logan, Macfarlane, & Wilcox, 2010).

White pine blister rust infects whitebark pine with spores that penetrate leaf stomata and produce mycelia that grow through the cambial tissue of the twigs, branches, and eventually the main trunk. This gradually weakens the tree and, when the infection reaches the main trunk, kills it. Trees with heavy blister rust infections tend to be preferentially selected for attack by mountain pine beetles.

The consequence of the warmth-stimulated mountain pine beetle attacks combined with white pine blister rust infections has been to decimate whitebark pine populations, making it impossible for it to fulfill its critical foundational roles in most portions of its range, including the Greater Yellowstone Ecosystem. The potential for at least localized extinction of white bark pine populations is also possible because even young reproductive seedlings and saplings can be infected and killed by the blister rust.

*Figure 3.38  Whitebark pine are being killed by a combination of the introduced disease, white pine blister rust, and attacks by mountain pine beetle. Whitebark pine is an important tree in high-elevation forests and timberline areas of western North America. It is undergoing catastrophic population declines due to combined effects of introduced blister rust and mountain pine beetle infestations, with the latter believed to be at least partially a consequence of warming climates. The pine is viewed as a foundational species because of the importance of its seed as a food source, such as for grizzly bears. (Photo courtesy of Bruce Andre for* Washington State Magazine*)*

*It is generally recognized that . . . silvicultural treatments should follow nature as far as possible. In practice, however, this maxim often has been forgotten or otherwise violated.* — STEPHEN H. SPURR AND A. C. CLINE

# CHAPTER 4

# Silvicultural Principles for Ecological Forestry

Application of ecological forestry principles to silvicultural treatments of forest stands and landscapes is the subject of this chapter. Our goal is to lay out principles that underpin ecological silviculture and use examples to show how these principles are applied to meet varied goals in diverse forest ecosystems. This chapter begins to provide guidance for development and implementation of specific silvicultural practices and prescriptions; a companion volume on silvicultural approaches in ecological forest management is under preparation.

We begin the chapter with an introduction to silviculture and a quick review of the general goals for which we manipulate forest structure and composition. Next we identify some broad ecological principles derived from studies of forest ecosystems, seres, and landscapes that are fundamental to silvicultural practices in ecological forestry. Finally, we provide real-world examples of silvicultural applications of ecological forestry principles. These cover all categories of silvicultural activities used in ecological forestry, such as thinning and partial cutting of forest stands, creation of openings, and species enrichment using examples that represent all three of the forest archetypes presented in Chapter 3.

We limit our use of traditional forestry terminology in this chapter. Traditional terminology often fails to convey clearly the treatments that are being done, because over time, these terms have been used in many diverse ways. Consequently, we will generally describe the specifics of our silvicultural treatments, including their spatial and structural elements.

Some general silvicultural references that readers may find beneficial include the following: Puettman, Coates, and Messier's valuable review of the history of silviculture and contrasting perspectives of forest silviculturalists and ecologists in *A Critique of Silviculture: Managing for Complexity* (2009); Kevin O'Hara's *Multiaged Silviculture: Managing for Complex Forest Stand Structures* (2014) offers

*Simulation of a variable retention harvest in the Oregon Coast Range that retained one-third of the stand mostly in aggregates. (Courtesy of Laura Hardin)*

useful variety of perspectives relevant to ecological forestry; R. D. Nyland et al.'s *Silviculture Concepts and Applications* (2007) and Smith, Larson, Kelty, and Ashton's *The Practice of Silviculture: Applied Forest Ecology* (1997) provide broad reviews of topics basic to silvicultural practices. Andrew B. Carey's book, *AIMing for Healthy Forests: Active, Intentional Management for Multiple Values* (2007) contains useful information and many practical perspectives relevant to ecological forest management.

## Goals and Categories of Silvicultural Activities in Ecological Forestry

Silviculture is defined as the *"art and science of controlling the establishment, growth, composition, health, and quality of forests and woodlands to meet the diverse needs and values of landowners and society on a sustainable basis"* (Helms, 1998, p. 167). Smith et al. (1997) emphasize that, *"Silvicultural practice consists of the various treatments applied to forests to maintain and enhance their utility for any purpose"* (p. 3) and add that, *"The production of timber . . . is neither the only nor necessarily the dominant [objective]"* (p. 4). We might be inclined to substitute "influencing" for "controlling" in Helms' definition to better recognize human limitations. We would also add to these definitions that silvicultural activities in ecological forestry applications emphasize use of natural forest models as their basis rather than agronomic models (see the principles below).

Silviculture carries the implication of active rather than passive human participation in the initiation and development of forest ecosystems. This has probably never been more appropriate than in the 21st century when humankind has altered so many of the fundamental conditions under which forest ecosystems have evolved. We believe forests in this century will often require human participation to assist them in their continued adaptation to shifting environments and disturbance regimes, and we will say more about this later. In that regard, we follow the fundamental philosophy of Aldo Leopold who understood the imperative of human participation in management and restoration of the "land" or, as we would put it, the ecosystem.

What are the goals of ecological foresters when applying silvicultural treatments to forest ecosystems and landscapes? As stated in the definition of silviculture given above, the goal is to "meet the diverse needs and values of landowners and society on a sustainable basis." Thus, the mix of ecosystem services sought by particular prescriptions will depend on the forests being managed and the desires of both the landowners and society. In the language of the Millennium Ecosystem Assessment (MEA) (2005 p. v), this mix may include *"provisioning services* [often called *products*] such as food, water, timber, and fiber; *regulating services* that affect climate, floods, disease, wastes, and water quality; *cultural services* that provide recreational, aesthetic, and spiritual benefits; and *supporting services,* such as soil formation, photosynthesis, and nutrient cycling." While the mix may vary by forest and landowner, the basic approach does not. Rather, the ecological forester will utilize ecological models from natural forest systems as a basis for managing forests, incorporating principles of natural forest development, including the role of natural disturbances, in the initiation, development, and maintenance of forests and forest landscape mosaics.

What are some of the silvicultural activities or interventions that are undertaken in ecological forestry and for what reasons? They include:

- Creation of forest openings to provide non-tree-dominated habitats in forested landscapes, which are needed to support early successional biota and ecosystem processes as well as to provide conditions for the regeneration of desired shade-intolerant tree species. Openings were important elements of almost all natural forest landscapes and are fundamental to sustaining the full array of forest biota and functions.

- Modifying existing forests in order to direct forest development (structure, composition, and functionality) toward diverse outcomes, including creation of conditions that are resistant and resilient to disturbances, provision of habitat for desired species, and production and harvesting of economically important forest products.

- Enriching forest complexity by sustaining and, where necessary, restoring ecologically important structures, such as snags, logs, and large and old trees.

- Modifying forest composition—such as by adding desirable species or constraining or eliminating undesirable species—to improve economic and social values, ecological functions, and/or forest resilience.

We will provide a number of examples of how goals and treatments in ecological forestry vary by landowner later in this chapter.

## Principles Underlying Silvicultural Activities in Ecological Forestry

*A small set of ecological principles underpin the design of silvicultural activities in ecological forestry.* Three principles that operate at the stand or harvest-unit level are providing for:

- *Continuity in forest structure, function, and biota between pre- and post-harvest ecosystems;*

- *Creation and maintenance of structural complexity and biological richness, including spatial heterogeneity at multiple spatial scales; and*

- *Silvicultural activities at times that reflect ecological processes.*

A fourth principle involves the integration of stand-level silvicultural activities at larger spatial scales:

- *Planning and implementing silvicultural activities in the context of plans developed at larger (landscape) spatial scales.*

All four of these principles contribute to the overriding objective we have of sustaining the integrity of the forest ecosystems that are being managed (Chapter 2).

A final, fifth principle provides an overarching social goal:

- *Emphasizing silvicultural activities that are expected to reduce risks to important forest values and to increase future societal options in the management and use of the forest.*

## Continuity in Forest Structure, Function, and Composition

*In ecological forestry silvicultural activities in forests, such as those associated with timber harvest, provide for significant continuity in forest structure, function, and composition between the pre- and post-harvest stands.*

Most natural disturbances leave significant biological legacies from the pre-disturbance forest in the form of living organisms, structures, dead organic matter, and soil and vegetative patterns, as we described in Chapter 3. These legacies provide for continuity in elements of structure, function, and composition between the pre-disturbance and post-disturbance ecosystems. *Note that this principle includes the regeneration of new tree cohorts.*

Ecological forestry emulates that process through the recognition and retention of biological legacies in all silvicultural treatments, although not necessarily at the same levels of those legacies provided by natural disturbances. The silvicultural goal is to provide for significant continuity in structural, functional, and compositional elements between forest generations. This is in contrast to traditional even-aged management systems, which effectively eliminate most elements of the pre-harvest forest, thereby creating significant discontinuities between forest generations.

A common application of this principle in ecological forestry is the selective retention of structures and organisms at the time of forest harvests, sometimes referred to as variable-retention harvesting (Franklin, Berg, Thornburg, & Tappeiner, 1997; Franklin, Mitchell, & Palik, 2007).

Variable-retention harvesting has been widely adopted in many parts of the world (Gustafsson et al., 2012), in part because of the demonstrated ability of retention to mitigate many ecological impacts of traditional even-aged harvest systems (e.g., Mori & Kitagawa, 2014; Fedrowitz et al., 2014) (Box 4.1).

Variable-retention harvesting is readily adapted to a broad array of forest types and management objectives. Retention can be focused on individual structures, such as large live and dead trees (snags) and down logs on the forest floor, or on small patches or islands of intact forest. It can also be focused on retention of specific species in the overstory or understory or on broad functional groups (e.g., conifers or hardwoods). Retention may be either distributed widely through the harvest unit (dispersed retention) or concentrated in intact forest patches (aggregated retention) (Figure 4.2). Each approach has its ecological, economic, and social advantages (Table 4.1, p. 96), so silvicultural prescriptions will often include elements of both (Figure 4.2d).

The philosophy and some specific goals of variable-retention harvesting are detailed in Franklin et al. (1997) and in Chapter 8 of Lindenmayer and Franklin (2002, pp. 163–195), and these relate to both continuity between forest generations and more rapid restoration of biodiversity and functional capacities in the post-harvest ecosystem. Specific goals of variable-retention harvesting include: (1) sustaining or "lifeboating" species and processes; (2) structurally enriching the post-harvest forest both immediately following harvest and over the long term; and (3) improving connectivity for biota in the post-harvest forest. The lifeboating goal is accomplished in multiple ways including the provision of critical structures for biota, alteration of the microclimate of the harvested area, and sustaining the flow of energy-rich carbohydrates to belowground biota (see Chapter 2). Critical structures typically include live trees, snags, and logs but also may include patches of shrubs or, in conifer-dominated forests, hardwoods and intact forest floors. The presence of live and dead tree structures is also important in modifying the microclimate of the harvested area, reducing extremes of temperature and moisture as well as providing protective cover, which is related to the third goal of improving connectivity for biota.

The structural enrichment of the post-harvest stand has long-term consequences in addition to its role in lifeboating. It can help to ensure that there will be a diversity of structures (and, thereby, habitats or niches) in the post-harvest stand. Some of these structures will host a variety of other organisms, such as epiphytes (plants, such as mosses and lichens, growing on other plants), and will provide the inoculum for the developing younger forest elements with these organisms. These structures are also important in stabilizing soils and retaining soil nutrients, as mentioned in Chapter 2. Of course, structural enrichment of the post-harvest stand

## Box 4.1  Potential of silvicultural practices that incorporate retention and multiaged forest ecosystems

Even-aged silvicultural systems were a dominant form of forest management by the mid-20th century and used regeneration harvest practices—such as clearcutting—that intentionally retained few aboveground legacies from the pre-harvest stand. Indeed, a traditional measure of good forest practice was the absence of any significant forest residues—a "clean" harvest unit! Consequently, forest harvest practices were generally at the removal end of the retention/removal continuum (Figure 4.1); i.e., they were harvest systems designed to generate even-aged and even-structured young forests. Modifications were sometimes made to these systems to mitigate impacts on nontimber values, but the context and intent of even-aged forest terminology and practices were retained.

*The most productive arena for creating silvicultural systems that effectively integrate ecological, economic, and cultural objectives is application of silvicultural practices in the central range of the retention/removal continuum.* Such practices result in the creation and maintenance of forest ecosystems of

Figure 4.1 *Variable retention harvesting takes advantage of the continuum of potential forest harvest possibilities (a), which has been largely ignored in traditional even-aged and uneven-aged forest practices (b). Silvicultural practices that take advantage of the central range of the continuum of harvest possibilities result in the creation and maintenance of mixed-age and structure stands in which multiple management objectives (e.g., ecological and economic) can be achieved. (Source: Conserving Forest Biodiversity, by David B. Lindenmayer and Jerry F. Franklin. Copyright © 2002 by the authors. Reproduced by permission of Island Press, Washington, DC)*

mixed age and complex structure, as has been advocated by O'Hara (2014). Approaches that focus on prescriptions at either the very low or very high ranges of retention are likely to be significantly less effective at integrating multiple objectives.

Unfortunately, North American forestry has no significant tradition of creating and sustaining forest ecosystems using harvest approaches in the central range of the retention/removal continuum, nor is there a generally accepted terminology to describe such approaches, although multiaged silviculture provides some models for such practices (O'Hara, 2014).

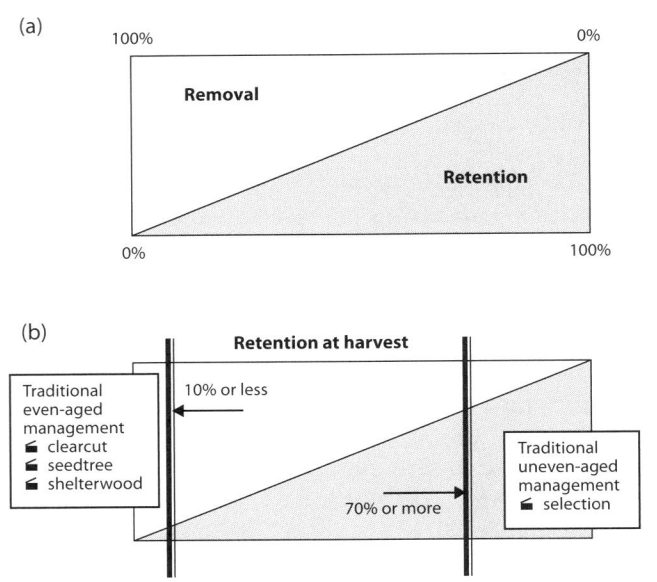

represents a major contribution to development of the structurally complex forests; for example, that legacy can include old trees, large snags, and large down logs, which would otherwise take centuries to replace. This legacy is likely to result in more rapid return of some displaced species (such as raptors) that require such structures.

Finally, connectivity for the majority of forest biota will be better in areas harvested with significant structural retention than in areas lacking legacies. One way the retention does this is by providing significant hiding cover. When large areas (landscapes) are being subjected to harvest the use of retention can result in much better connectivity at those scales, as well (see Chapter 5).

Providing continuity between forest generations through retention is broadly applicable in ecological forestry, regardless of harvest intensity. The most obvious applications of retention harvesting are where large portions of a stand are being opened up by harvest. However, retention is equally applicable to more selective types of forest harvest, such as those where individual trees or groups of trees are being harvested. For example, an individual tree selection harvest

in which old and decadent trees, snags, and logs are explicitly retained to achieve ecological goals would exemplify application of the retention principle, since such structures would not typically have been retained in traditional selection harvests. Similarly, selective harvest of groups or small patches of trees with retention of scattered live trees and snags would qualify as retention.

Retention is a valuable way to create and sustain structures and stand conditions that could not otherwise be developed within the selected management cycle or rotation. These may be individual structures, such as large, old trees, which provide unique habitats and sources of large snags and logs. Retention can also be used to create and sustain biologically diverse and structurally complex forest conditions similar to those found in older forest stages in forest landscapes managed on rotations much shorter than the natural sere. For example, Andrew Carey (Carey, Lippke, & Sessions, 1999) developed a management approach called, "biodiversity pathways," which combined structural retention at regeneration harvests and periodic thinning to produce forests with high levels of structural complexity and vertebrate diversity.

Note that old tree structures can be incorporated into managed stands without having to grow an entire old-growth forest by using retention-based approaches because individual structures (such as old trees) can be retained or developed over multiple rotations.

Retention levels also have a significant influence on the question of appropriate harvest unit patch size. Harvest unit patch size is often an important and controversial topic in areas where even-aged management regimes are being used. For example, the size of clearcut patches is often an important social issue, which, while public objections may be based on visual criteria, is also important in terms of impacts on various ecological processes and biota. Even modest levels of well-distributed retention (e.g., 10–15%) can significantly reduce visual and ecological impacts of timber harvest. The importance of harvest unit patch

Figure 4.2 *Variable-retention harvesting in which significant structural and compositional elements of the pre-harvest forest are retained for inclusion in the post-harvest ecosystem can take many forms in terms of the specific biotic elements (e.g., trees, snags, logs, shrubs) and amounts of them that are retained as well as in the spatial patterns for the retention. Illustrated here are several examples of different patterns of retention: (a) Uniformly dispersed retention of dominant trees ("dispersed" retention); retention of patches of intact forest ("aggregated" retention) with either sharp (b) or fuzzy (c) boundaries; and (d) a retention harvest that includes both dispersed and aggregated retention.*

size decreases as the levels of retention are increased and becomes practically irrelevant in areas harvested with high levels of retention. An important consequence is that large harvest units can be incorporated into management practices where significant retention is practiced, which may result in units that are both more efficient and more consistent in size and content with the forest patches created by natural disturbances (Figure 4.3).

Traditional forest practices have generally not intentionally retained elements of harvested stands, particularly where even-aged management systems are being applied (Smith et al., 1997). Since at least the mid-20th century, management goals using such systems have emphasized high levels of wood utilization, intensive site preparation (e.g., slash disposal and herbicide treatments), and rapid reestablishment of tree cover by planting (see Box 4.1). Classic seed-tree and shelterwood systems initially do retain some trees but only until regeneration is established, after which the retained trees will be removed.

Table 4.1 *Comparison of ecological, operational, and social aspects of dispersed and aggregated approaches to structural retention*

| Characteristic or objective | Spatial pattern of retention | |
| --- | --- | --- |
| | *Dispersed* | *Aggregated* |
| Microclimate modification | Less intense but generalized over harvest area | More intense but only within a localized area within the harvest area |
| Influence on geohydrological processes | Same as above | Same as above |
| Maintenance of root strength | Same as above | Same as above |
| Retention of diverse tree sizes, species, and conditions | Low probability | High probability |
| Retention of large-diameter trees | More emphasis | Less emphasis |
| Retention of multiple vegetation layers | Low probability | High probability |
| Retention of snags | More challenging to accomplish | More readily accomplished |
| Retention of areas with minimal forest floor and understory disturbance | Not possible | Possible |
| Retention of structurally intact forest habitat patches | Not possible | Possible |
| Distributed sources of coarse woody debris | Yes | No |
| Distributed sources of arboreal energy to maintain belowground processes | Yes | No |
| Windthrow hazard of residual trees | Average wind firmness greater (strong dominants), but trees are isolated | Average wind firmness less, but trees have mutual support |
| Residual tree damage | High probability | Low probability |
| Tree form and geometry | Uniform | Variable |
| Distribution of fine fuels | Uniform | Variable |
| Growth of tree regeneration (intolerant species) | Lower (harvested areas retain significant overhead canopy) | Higher (harvested areas are open to full sunlight) |
| Growth of tree regeneration (tolerant species) | Higher (some protective forest cover) | Varied—could be outcompeted in harvested areas by intolerant species |
| Probability of providing conditions suitable for development of preforest communities | Lower because of distributed overstory canopy, which may limit preforest ecosystem development | Higher because harvested areas are open to full sunlight |
| Management flexibility in treating young stands (e.g., helicopter use) | Less | More |
| Harvest costs (e.g., layout and logging) | More | Less |
| Safety issues | Generally more | Generally fewer |
| Social acceptability of harvested area (e.g., aesthetics) | Generally better | Generally poorer |

## Managing for Structural Complexity and Compositional Richness in Forest Management Units/Patches

*In ecological forestry silvicultural activities manipulate established stands to create, restore, and/or sustain structural complexity and biological diversity. This is most often accomplished by some treatment that can be characterized broadly as thinning or partial cutting.* Other tools that may be utilized include fire, planting, artificial creation of habitat (e.g., creating cavities or killing trees to provide snags or logs), pruning, and selective use of herbicides to combat invasive or noxious species. *Snags, logs, decadent features of living trees, and old trees are critical elements of forest complexity in ecological forestry.*

The ecological forester manages forest stands to develop and sustain structurally, compositionally, and functionally diverse conditions. Structural complexity within forest stands typically will involve an array of individual structures including live trees of differing species, sizes, conditions, and ages as well as a diversity of snags, logs, and other woody structures. *An emphasis on dead wood structures as well as live trees is one of the distinctive features of ecological forestry approaches.*

Patterns of structural complexity differ among forest types, particularly between forests characterized by frequent-fire regimes and forests characterized by episodic partial or complete stand-replacement regimes. In the case of frequent-fire forests, dense forest stands—particularly those with continuous or multilayered canopies—are highly vulnerable to stand-replacement wildfire. Hence, in these forest ecosystems much of the structural complexity (e.g., multiple canopy layers) occurs as part of a patch mosaic rather than being found within a single patch, as explained and illustrated in Figures 3.12, 3.30, and 3.31; see also Figures 4.4, 4.5, and Color Plate 3.6.

Creation and maintenance of heterogeneous—nonuniform—spatial patterns is an additional and important

Figure 4.3 *Harvest unit patch size loses much of its ecological and social significance as an increasing percentage of the pre-harvest forest is retained. With higher levels of retention both the visual and environmental impacts of harvest are dramatically reduced as illustrated here.*

Figure 4.4 *Frequent-fire forest ecosystems typically display much of their structural complexity as a mosaic or patchwork of small (e.g., 0.1–0.25 acre) patches as illustrated in this profile of a mixed-conifer forest in the Sierra Nevada Range, Yosemite National Park, California, USA. (Illustration by Robert Van Pelt)*

element in structurally complex forests. Essentially all natural forest ecosystems exhibit aspects of heterogeneity—for example, in the clustered patterns of tree stem distribution (see Chapter 2). Heterogeneous patterns have important influences on forest function, such as provision of habitat for fauna, and on impacts of disturbances, such as wildfire and bark beetles (e.g., see Churchill et al., 2013). Hence, one of the goals in ecological forestry is to restore patterns of stand heterogeneity that are modeled on natural forest stands.

Forest ecosystems that exhibit both a diversity of individual structures and complex spatial arrangements of those structures can be viewed as *niche rich*. They provide the diversity of conditions, such as structures and microclimates, needed to sustain high species and functional diversity. These conditions obviously offer a significant contrast to the highly simplified forest conditions created in production forestry. The development of plantations of uniformly spaced and relatively even-sized trees creates optimal conditions for efficient production of wood but marginalizes or eliminates many other forest values.

Selectively reducing tree densities in forest ecosystems is one of the primary tools used in ecological forestry. Often such treatments are referred to as *thinning*, but thinning is defined primarily as a "cultural treatment to reduce . . . [tree density] . . . primarily to improve growth, enhance forest health, or recover potential mortality" (Helms, 1998, p. 185). From an ecological forestry perspective, this definition of thinning does not adequately describe treatment goals. *Partial cutting* is a more generic term but also is historically associated with high-grading of forests. We use the term "thinning" but often with modifiers, such as ecological or restoration thinning, to distinguish it from more traditional production thinning practices.

Creation of spatially heterogeneous outcomes is a common objective in ecological thinning; hence such thinning often includes prescriptions that specifically vary the

Figure 4.5 *Sierran mixed-conifer stands are typically fine-scale structural mosaics that include patches of large-diameter trees and openings; such small-scale mosaics are typical of frequent-fire ecosystems (Lassen National Forest, California, USA).*

intensity of the thinning, which are commonly described as *variable-density* prescriptions (Figure 4.6). These can take a variety of forms including the incorporation of unthinned

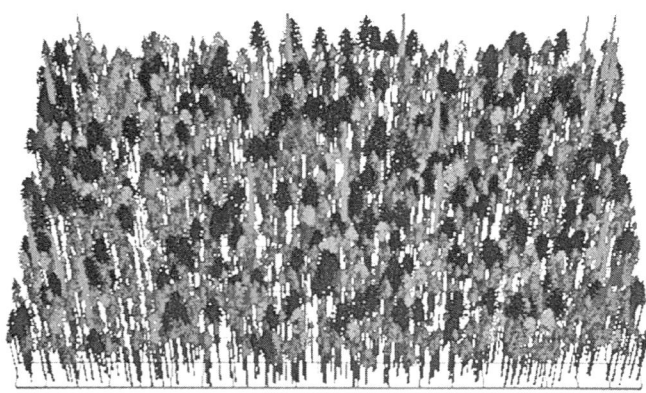

Clavicle 301, S 1/2, Unthinned

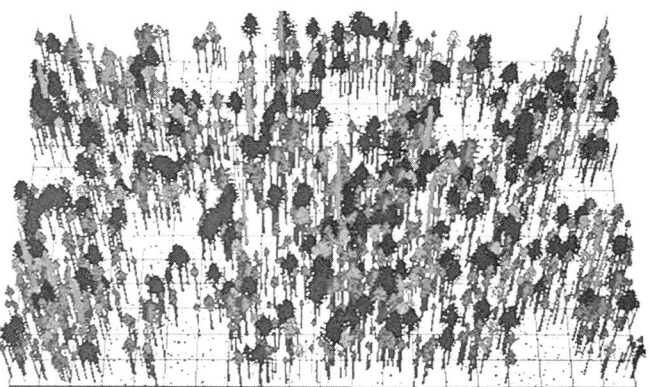

Clavicle 301, S 1/2, Thinned

Figure 4.6 *Variable-density thinning (VDT) prescriptions produce spatially heterogeneous outcomes, as illustrated in this simulated VDT thinning of a Douglas-fir forest in the Pacific Northwest, USA. The initial stand is on the left and the projected stand following a variable-density thinning is on the right. (Source: USDA Forest Service)*

areas (*skips*) and heavily thinned areas or openings (*gaps*). Thinning based on cluster- or clump-based algorithms, such as the *ICO-approach* (ICO = individuals, clusters, and openings) of Churchill et al. (2013) can provide predictably heterogeneous outcomes based on natural models appropriate to the forest type. In many cases, these approaches can be combined with other prescriptive elements (e.g., intense thinning around selected trees) to enhance rapid development of trees of larger diameter; this approach can also be used to develop larger branch systems, which may be a wildlife-related objective.

Ecologically based thinnings almost invariably have more diverse goals than simply stimulating growth of overstory dominant and codominant trees and, consequently, may require some overstory tree removal. These associated goals may include stimulating development of trees in subordinate positions, including seedlings or saplings in the understory, or trees occupying intermediate positions in the canopy. A common example of that in conifer forests might be partial release of hardwood trees that are being overtopped or suppressed. Enhancing understory herb and shrub diversity and productivity may be another important objective in ecological thinning. As noted, achieving such goals as release of mid- or understory elements may involve removal or modification of overstory trees or *thinning from above*, in contrast to focusing only on small and intermediate tree removal (*thinning from below*) as is typical in production forest thinning. Creation of openings in the overstory—removal of some dominant and codominant trees—is almost certain to be necessary if the stand currently has a closed canopy and the treatment goals include providing additional sunlight, moisture, and nutrients to suppressed elements of the forest.

We conclude this section by again emphasizing some contrasts between thinning as practiced in production forestry and thinning as generally applied in ecological forestry. *Thinnings with primarily ecological objectives will often require silvicultural prescriptions that provide for spatially varying outcomes (heterogeneity) and for benefits to biota other than dominant or crop trees.* While ecological and production thinnings often have related goals, such as reduction of stand densities and development of some larger-diameter trees, ecological thinning inevitably incorporates much broader objectives related to enhancing the structural complexity (including spatial heterogeneity) and biological richness of treated stands.

## Silvicultural Activities Keyed to Ecologically Based Intervals

*In ecological forestry, silvicultural activities occur at intervals reflective of ecological processes.* This is a broad concept that includes not only recovery of forest

ecosystem structure and function following a major treatment (i.e., some minimal time interval that is required) but also relates to maximum intervals between activities (e.g., prescribed burning).

Time intervals for silvicultural activities have typically focused on determining the intervals between regeneration harvests (e.g., rotation age) and appropriate ages for thinning, including precommercial thinning (PCT). Biological measures, such as culmination of mean annual increment (CMAI), are frequently used to determine rotation ages on public lands on the basis that harvest at CMAI maximizes forest productivity, despite the difficulty of identifying a particular age at which CMAI occurs. Economic criteria are typically used in areas managed under production forestry approaches, where the goal is to maximize return on investment; such criteria generally lead to rotations shorter than CMAI.

Determining time intervals for silvicultural activities is often more complex in ecological forestry because considerations are not limited to wood production or financial returns. For example, in setting intervals between regeneration harvests ecological foresters need to consider both the time needed for specific structural elements and functional attributes to recover to a desired level and the time period over which it is expected to be at that desired level. For example, a structural goal might include development of a population of larger-diameter trees or large well-decayed snags that was reduced by previous harvests. Another example might be the reestablishment of a mature forest that will be effective at moderating impacts of intense rain-on-snow events. Not only are long time intervals required to develop such structures or forest conditions but, once created, that structure or condition may need to be maintained for a significant time period before again undergoing harvest.

Fortunately retention harvesting approaches enable the ecological forester to create and retain such structures for multiple rotations, rather than having to create them afresh following each harvest as would be necessary under strict, even-aged silvicultural systems. In fact, retention or partial-cutting approaches greatly reduce concerns over rotation length needed to achieve desired structures, since significant elements of the pre-harvest forest are partially or fully retained. *Retention approaches allow for more flexibility in setting rotations while sustaining desired structures or functions, as they can dramatically reduce the time required to reestablish desired structural conditions. In effect, retention can partially substitute for time.*

In fact, retention harvesting (as well as ecological thinning) is key to creating or restoring the structural complexity and functionality typical of older forest stages of development. This is particularly the case for forest types growing on sites where long time periods are required to develop complex older forests following stand-replacement disturbance events, such as the Douglas-fir–western hemlock forests described in Chapter 3. Few forestland managers are likely to have the time and space to consider managing forests on the rotations of 250+ years, which would be required to develop old-growth forests following a clearcut harvest in the Douglas-fir region. Creating approximations of such forests in much shorter periods is possible using retention harvesting—that is, using a partial stand-replacement type of disturbance.

Intervals in ecological thinning of stands are likely to be much more varied in timing under management systems based on ecological forestry than under production forestry systems—just as the types of activities are much more varied in content and application. This is because of the greater diversity of elements—trees, CWD, etc.—and processes that are management foci in ecological forestry, many of which do not lend themselves to a classic crop-based management systems.

Maximal intervals between silvicultural activities sometimes need to be considered. An excellent example of this is the maximal interval between prescribed burns in specific forests consistent with maintaining desired structures and processes. Longleaf pine forests, as an example, require prescribed burning at very frequent intervals (one to three years) because of the aggressiveness of potential competing hardwoods on the sites that longleaf pine occupy. Return

intervals for prescribed fire or mechanical treatment can be significantly longer in the less productive frequent-fire forests found in western North America, such as those dominated by ponderosa pine.

## Planning and Implementing Silvicultural Activities at Larger Spatial Scales

It is essential to plan and implement silvicultural activities at larger spatial scales when ecological forestry is being practiced on larger ownerships. Silvicultural treatment of forest stands should not be considered in isolation! Much of this involves issues that will be covered in Chapter 5, so we will only briefly review some key points here.

Spatial heterogeneity is an important aspect of landscape-level silvicultural planning. One of the goals commonly will be creation of diverse stand conditions at the landscape level. This diversity usually will include preforest patches— areas not dominated by the tree life-form—at spatial scales appropriate to the forest type being managed and biota under consideration (Box 4.2) (Figure 4.7). While this is particularly relevant in forest regions where episodic forest-replacement disturbance regimes dominate, it also is relevant to landscapes characterized by frequent fire.

The spatial heterogeneity sought on larger landscapes managed according to ecological forestry principles generally will include a diversity of forest developmental stages

---

**Box 4.2  Openings free of dominance by trees are essential elements of forest landscapes managed under ecological forestry principles**

Essentially all natural temperate forest landscapes include areas that are not currently dominated by the tree life-form, although these historically may have varied widely in nature and extent with the forest region and disturbance regime. These openings are ecologically important landscape patches because the shrub- and herb-dominated early successional ecosystems that occupy them are needed by many native organisms for all or part of their life cycles (see Chapter 3). They are also key sites for important ecosystem processes, such as nitrogen fixation. Provision of such openings at appropriate spatial and temporal scales is important on larger and probably many smaller forest properties managed according to ecological forestry principles. The natural pattern of forest openings in the forest type being managed should be an important consideration. Possible approaches to providing for openings include purposeful creation of such areas by harvest or fire or both, management of harvested forest areas to allow for greater duration and/or complexity of the preforest period, and reliance on natural disturbances to create such areas, none of which are mutually exclusive.

Figure 4.7 *Openings free of dominance by live trees are essential elements of most temperate forest landscapes because of the important roles they play as sites for key ecological functions and as critical habitat for many biota characteristic of those landscapes.*

from openings occupied by preforest or early successional vegetation to mature and old forest ecosystems of diverse composition and structural complexity. Disturbances of either human or natural origin are necessary to initiate the sequential developmental stages characteristic of forest ecosystems subject to partial or complete forest-replacement disturbances (see Chapter 3). *At an appropriate spatial scale, "We need the whole sere!" in order to sustain the full array of structural conditions, functions, and biota.* We would note that this type of diversity is not provided by landscapes composed of multiple age-classes of young, structurally simplified monotypic forest plantations! However, we would note again that it is much easier to maintain structurally complex older forests with disturbances (harvest regimes) that only remove a part of a forest. This approach is very consistent with natural models of forest-replacement disturbances, as illustrated by the multiple developmental pathways noted for Douglas-fir–western hemlock forests in Chapter 3.

Patch heterogeneity is also needed to provide a diversity of developmental stages in fire-frequent landscapes. Forest landscapes subject to frequent fire typically consisted of large contiguous areas occupied by complex spatial mosaics of small patches of low to moderate contrast, which included openings (see Chapter 3). These landscapes also generally included sites that were fire refugia—areas that burned less frequently than the majority of the landscape and provided some larger patches of denser forest. In existing frequent-fire forest landscapes, areas of denser forest now are quite common and extensive as a result of many decades of fire suppression. These denser forest patches often provide expanded areas of important habitat for notable species, such as raptors and squirrels. Consequently, sustaining larger patches of denser forest habitat may be required in ecologically based restoration programs in frequent-fire landscapes.

## Reducing Risks and Increasing Societal Options

*Emphasize silvicultural activities that reduce risks to important forest values and increase future societal options in the management and use of the forest.*

This final principle relates to our vision of an appropriate mind-set for forest managers and stakeholders in an extraordinarily uncertain 21st century. How should a prudent ecological forester approach the development of goals and prescriptions of forest treatments? The future has always been unknowable, but the levels of uncertainty about both future environmental and social

conditions are extraordinary in this century. Historically the forester could be relatively certain about the environmental conditions under which the forest would develop. There were unlikely to be major changes in climate, soil conditions, and commercial tree species. Market forces were at work but primarily at local and national levels rather than at global levels. Changes in societal perspectives on forests and forest management—both environmental and economic—have powerfully altered forest policy and management in recent decades and certainly will continue to do so in unpredictable ways in this century.

We suggest that ecological foresters can respond to this uncertainty by seeking to manage forest properties in ways that will both (1) reduce risks of damage or loss to the forest and (2) increase management options for future generations. Reducing risk is about increasing the resilience of the forest property being managed, such as by increasing compositional and structural diversity. Increasing options involves creating forest conditions that can be the basis for alternative developmental pathways and shifts in emphasis among desired ecosystem services.

Decreasing risk and increasing options in management will sometimes involve setting goals that have much shorter time lines than traditional forest rotations. For example, creating a more resistant and resilient forest condition in the next several decades may well take precedence over a longer-term focus on creation of some hypothetical desired future condition. This certainly would be a useful approach in the forest regions of western North America where extensive areas of dense forest that are at high risk of stand-replacement wildfire are currently present. In such situations, silvicultural treatments to increase the resistance of these stands and landscapes in the near term would seem to have priority over other long-term management goals (Figure 4.8).

Figure 4.8 *Silvicultural treatments to restore forest conditions that are more resistant to wildfire, drought, and insects have a very high priority in the frequent-fire forests of western North America because of their risk of being subject to events that will eliminate irreplaceable elements of such forests, such as killing old trees, as in this mixed-conifer stand that has developed immense fuel loadings as a result of fire suppression (Fremont-Winema National Forests, Oregon, USA).*

*Ecological forestry is highly suited to creating management approaches that will improve the ability of forest stands and landscapes to cope with both major environmental (including climate) changes and invasive species.* Creating and maintaining biologically diverse and heterogeneous ecosystems and landscapes is, in fact, a generic prescription for improving both the resistance and resilience of forests as well as meeting the goals of reducing risk and increasing options! Tree species richness is very important to these goals as tree monocultures are notoriously vulnerable to disturbances. However, creating diversity in other functionally important groups of species, such as mycorrhizal-forming fungi, is also important. This diversity provides redundancy so that the ecosystem is less likely to lose important functional capabilities. Spatial patterning—heterogeneity—is important at multiple scales, from the stand to the landscape. For example, it is increasingly clear that landscape-level heterogeneity may be one of the only ways to deal with outbreaks of native bark beetles (Raffa et al., 2008). We will have more to say about landscape-scale heterogeneity in Chapter 5.

Ecologically based approaches to management can be particularly important in the case of fire-frequent forest ecosystems and landscapes, so many of which are in unnatural states that are highly vulnerable to disturbances as a result of past management (see Figure 4.8 and Chapter 3). Ecologically based restoration of the forests to a more resistant state will not only dramatically reduce their vulnerability to current disturbance regimes but prepare them for the predicted increases in fire and moisture stress predicted under climate change. We clearly understand the generic forest structure that is highly resistant to fire and related disturbances in these landscapes, and we know how to restore those forests to that more resilient state using silvicultural treatments.

## Developing Silvicultural Prescriptions in Ecological Forestry

*In ecological forestry development of silvicultural prescriptions begins with knowledge of the forest ecosystem that is to be managed and its constituent species.* This knowledge is necessary since the primary directive in ecological forestry is to model management on structures and rhythms characteristic of the natural forest. By doing so, ecological foresters seek to retain aspects of structure, function, and composition characteristic of natural forests. Toward that end, ecological foresters need an understanding of the of the ecology, disturbance regimes, and developmental processes of the forest they manage, including the habitat requirements of plant or animal species of special interest or concern (Box 4.3).

*A set of management goals is also needed to provide the context for the management of specific stands.* Such

---

**Box 4.3  Suggestions for developing a thorough knowledge of the forest ecosystems of a region**

How do you go about developing the knowledge base critical to the practice of ecological forestry? Personal experience is one of our favored approaches—spending extensive time in the local forests observing and learning, with generous use of such instruments as increment borers, diameter tapes, and laser range finders and important informational materials, such as field guides to flora, fauna, and plant communities. Visit examples of natural forests, including forests representing varying development stages and sites representing diverse growing conditions. Familiarize yourself with the forest community or habitat type classification for your geographical region—almost all forest areas in the US and Canada have this information in some form or another. Visit areas recently subjected to disturbances, such as wind or fire (or even volcanoes or landslides), which will provide valuable insights. Learn about the environmental gradients in the region, including gradients in soil conditions (catenas). Examine forest understories to understand successional trends as well as environmental conditions, noting the reproductive status of different tree species as well as plant species that are important environmental indicators.

Talk to people who know and use the forests. Pick the brains of resource professionals with extensive experience in the region and cover a diversity of topics, including forests, wildlife, fisheries, geology and geomorphology, soils, and climate. Explore the views of stakeholders with a diversity of perspectives on forest values in the region. Look for special sources of expertise in academic institutions, extension organizations, and organizations of forest users. Seek out and visit locations that are knowledge rich as a result of a history of study, such as experimental forests or locations with long-term permanent sample plots or studies and talk with individuals who have been involved in these areas or studies.

Pursue traditional sources of knowledge: books, articles, archives with historical records, historical maps, and relevant museums. Seek out historical accounts, photos, and management plans for forest areas. And, of course, make full use of sources of knowledge found on the Internet.

And, to repeat our admonition at the beginning—above all, spend time visiting and observing forests representing a diversity of management conditions including, but not confined to, the best examples that you can find of the natural forests, which will provide the models that can be used in developing ecologically based forest management approaches!

goal setting is often a complex social process involving many technical, economic, and value-based issues, a process discussed elsewhere in this book (see Chapter 6 and Chapters 18–20). Even with defined goals, the process of designing silvicultural treatments in ecological forestry will be challenging and involve social as well as scientific and technical elements because of diverse and sometimes conflicting objectives. However, ecologically based silvicultural treatments will rarely seek to optimize a single outcome, although some objectives may receive more emphasis than others in balancing environmental, economic, and social goals; silvicultural treatments that are designed to maximize a singular outcome, such as wood production or habitat for a single species of wildlife, invariably result in marginalization or elimination of other important forest ecosystem functions.

*A thorough assessment of conditions (structure, species composition, etc.) is important for development of goals and silvicultural prescriptions in ecological forestry, including on-the-ground examinations.* While much relevant information can be gathered using a variety of traditional and nontraditional (e.g., LiDAR [light detection and ranging] imagery) tools, field-based examinations are critical to fully assess the opportunities and limitations provided by existing forest stands (see Box 4.4). For example, in variable-retention harvesting it is important to identify and capitalize on localized stand conditions that are desirable locations for retention patches; these may be, for example, areas with concentrations of older trees and/or snags and logs and areas of unique specialized habitat conditions, such as seeps and rock outcrops. Similarly, it is important to identify and retain more biologically diverse portions of stands that are proposed for variable-density thinning. Taking advantage of opportunities provided by stands that are the focus of proposed silvicultural treatments can most fully be accomplished by on-the-ground examinations of

that forest (see Box 4.4). We are not alone in these views. O'Hara (2014), for example, notes that multiaged silviculture requires a higher level of management investment and forester skills; he likens it to a more "artful" approach but one that is required in order to acquire the social license needed to manage many forest properties; such examinations are also needed to fully realize the ecological potential of the stands.

Some of the background knowledge and steps associated with development of silvicultural prescriptions are exemplified in development of a variable-retention harvest prescription in Box 4.5.

## Exemplary Applications of Ecological Forestry Principles

In the sections that follow we provide examples of how the principles of ecological forestry are being applied in the real world. They represent only a very small sample of the many applications that have occurred during the last several decades or are currently underway. We have selected them from both episodically and chronically disturbed forests to provide a broad array of forest types, geographies, and management objectives. In each we provide brief background on the natural history and management goals and describe how ecological forestry principles help link these two elements.

### Managing Lake States National Wildlife Refuges Using Ecological Forestry

The National Wildlife Refuge System managed by the US Fish and Wildlife Service covers over 60 million ha of land in the United States and its territories. Management of these properties is directed to restoration of fish, wildlife, and plant populations. Historically management focused

---

**Box 4.4 Assessments of conditions and opportunities in existing stands: an example**

The thorough examination of a forest stand proposed for an ecologically based silvicultural treatment is critically important to ensure that the opportunities and limitations that it offers are fully assessed. These may be many and diverse including important tree structures, such as old trees and snags, and microsites, such as seeps and rock outcrops. Forester Abe Wheeler, who works for the US Bureau of Land Management in Oregon, has developed a successful approach in which he leads multidisciplinary teams into a proposed project area, asking each specialist to view and record the GPS location of elements of the ecosystem that they view as important. They then share their observations to create a collective view of the important features that

need to be considered as a part of the silvicultural prescription. Ultimately the team produces an integrated project plan that recognizes and incorporates the array of values present on the site.

While not everyone has an interdisciplinary team at their disposal, carefully walking and observing the stand of interest before harvest can do wonders for understanding the unique characteristics of the stand as a guide to harvest and retention. With some background on what to look for, much of this discovery can be done by an individual forester or by a family who owns the forest. While perhaps not perfect, such an effort will undoubtedly reveal important features to conserve.

Box 4.5 **Elements in development of a silvicultural prescription for a variable retention harvest**

*As we discussed at the beginning of this section, silvicultural prescriptions begin with a thorough knowledge of the forest ecosystem that is to be managed and its constituent species.* This knowledge provides the basis for modeling management on structures and rhythms characteristic of the natural forest.

The ecological forester will also need to know general management goals for the property and for the project. Once provided with those goals, it is important to assess the spatial and temporal context for the stand to be treated. What is the nature of the ownership and landscape in which it is embedded and what are the ecological roles that the stand is intended to play in the longer-term conservation of that ownership or landscape? How does it relate to and interact with surrounding stands?

Examination of the forest stand or stands in the project area is the next step. Some of this involves traditional assessments of stand conditions, such as the composition and dimensions of the trees—tree species, densities, basal areas, volumes, and such. However, a careful examination is required to assess the opportunities existing within the stand(s) that would result in ecologically richer outcomes from the treatment. For example, what kind of variability exists within the stand in composition (e.g., patches with diverse understories or composed of less common trees species), structure (e.g., areas with concentrations of logs and CWD on the forest floor), or environmental diversity (e.g., areas with seeps or rock outcrops), which may be important as specialized habitat. In Box 4.4 we provided an example of how one forester used interdisciplinary teams to assess the ecologically significant conditions within a stand. However, individuals carefully walking and observing their forest can also discover many special places to guide placement of retention patches This inventory provides the ecological forester with valuable insights into opportunities within the stand, including locations of structures and features that should receive either a modified treatment or become a part of the retention.

Key elements in the variable-retention harvest treatment are: (1) what to retain; (2) how much to retain; and (3) the spatial pattern for the retention—in patches or dispersed throughout the harvest unit. These questions may have already been partially answered in the overall management plan. This may not always be the case, however. The question of "what to retain" can be quite simple (as it was in early applications in the Douglas-fir region)—retain some live trees, large snags, and large down logs. Today the question of what to retain can involve a diversity of structures, species, and environmental niches. In our earlier example (Box 4.4), the stand survey provided some critical insights into what to retain and where it is.

Answering the question of how much to retain can be challenging if an approximate answer has not already been provided by management (as in our example). Conceptually it is simple enough—retain enough to achieve the management objectives that are the rationale for the retention. Quantifying ecological benefits from various levels and patterns of retention is difficult, however, and quantitative scientific information that can support such decisions is typically scarce. Hence, the "expert opinion" of scientists or other respected professionals is often used to develop guidelines for levels of retention. There is a social element, as well—i.e., the retention needs to be sufficient to satisfy various stakeholders that it is meaningful—for example, that what is being done is different from a clearcut! We describe the retention levels in a number of examples of variable-retention harvest in the next section.

In this discussion, we will assume that the project area has been previously managed. We will also assume that the retention goal on this property is to retain approximately 1/3 of the stand with the majority of the retention in the form of aggregates and embedded riparian buffers but with a scattering of mature live trees, snags, and logs throughout the harvested two-thirds of the stand. However, this should be seen as the average retention goal across the forest, with higher levels applied in a stand with many special features and lower levels in stands with fewer of these features.

As we introduced above, potential features on which to anchor aggregated retention patches include clumps of old trees, large snags you wish to protect, concentrations of large down logs from past harvests, seeps and springs, and unique biological or cultural features. Features to key on for dispersed retention might include large, old trees with cavities, large branches, or broken tops, rare trees, or trees that would be a valued seed source.

The pattern of the retention is a complex and important element in the silvicultural prescription. As noted earlier in this chapter, dispersed and aggregated patterns of retention provide different ecological benefits (Table 4.1), which is why both types of retention patterns often are utilized on a harvest unit. For example, dispersed retention provides a broadly distributed benefit over a harvest unit. Aggregated retention, in contrast, provides a relatively undisturbed forest patch rather than individual or small clusters of isolated structures. Thus aggregated retention allows for greater diversity of structural conditions and a more moderate microclimate than does dispersed retention—albeit its influence is highly localized within the harvest unit.

Retention does need to be well distributed in the harvest unit, regardless of the amount or pattern that is chosen. Retention has relatively little ecological benefit if it is all on the edges or boundaries of the harvest unit. Recall the goals of retention—lifeboating organisms, providing inoculum for recolonization, and structurally enriching the post-harvest forest. If the retention is just around the edges or in one patch in a far corner of the harvest unit, it will make little or no contribution to those goals. When the government of British Columbia (BC) adopted a legal definition of variable-retention harvesting (necessary so that the BC Forest Service could issue harvesting permits for the practice) it included a spatial component: more than half of the harvest unit had to be within one tree height of the base of a tree or group of trees (Lindenmayer & Franklin, 2002, p. 179). This is only one approach to assuring that the retention is reasonably well distributed over the harvest unit, but the BC example illustrates the importance of ensuring that the retention is well distributed.

largely on providing for highly specific habitat needs of single species, but in recent years the focus has broadened to ecosystem conservation and provision of more general habitat needs important to multiple species. In a recent survey, refuge managers in portions of the Midwest and Northeast found ecological forestry approaches well suited to an array of management goals (Corace, Goebel, Hix, Casselman, & Seefelt, 2009). Forest management was an important aspect of present-day activities on 70% of the refuges, and this included the goal of promoting ecological integrity on the majority (56%) of them; forest management to produce focal species habitat was also a primary goal on 37% of the refuges surveyed.

Because of their focus on creating and sustaining habitat for a diversity of species, some of the most innovative silviculture in North America currently is done by the foresters working for the US Fish and Wildlife Service. Traditional production-based silvicultural approaches have not proven to be well suited to their goals, stimulating them to incorporate emerging forest ecosystem science into silvicultural practices.

Applications in four Lake States refuges incorporate three principles underlying silvicultural activities in ecological forestry (Corace et al., 2009; Corace & Goebel, 2010): biological legacies, development of structural complexity, and treatments at appropriate time intervals. In mixed-pine (red, eastern white, and jack pine) forests ecological forestry approaches are being used to restore historical conditions. These mixed pine forests were historically subject to frequent non-stand-replacing fires but have developed higher homogeneous fuel loadings and a higher percentage of fire-intolerant tree species, such as red maple and aspen, due to harvest and fire suppression. Restoration begins with mechanical treatments to reduce fuels, create structural complexity, including a larger population of snags, and increase the proportion of red and eastern white pine, followed by prescribed fire.

An important aspect of management in northern hardwood forests is treatments to improve habitat in stands that are being impacted by decline of American beech, due to beech-bark disease (Figure 4.9). There is no harvest of beech in these treatments in order to conserve any individuals that may be disease resistant. Trees adjacent to mature yellow birch and eastern hemlock are thinned in order to stimulate seed production and regeneration by these species. Sapling stands are also being thinned to favor yellow birch and eastern hemlock and to reduce the representation of red maple.

Management of jack pine forests, which focused initially on providing habitat for the Kirtland's warbler (*Setophaga kirtlandii*), is being broadened using ecological principles. Creation of large areas of dense jack pine plantations incorporating some small openings for heterogeneity has been the primary approach (Figure 4.10). While this has provided habitat for the Kirtland's warbler it has not done as well at providing for other biota that are part of the jack pine ecosystem. First, an entire suite of birds is of interest, which include several species identified as having "significant conservation priority"; meeting the needs of this suite requires the entire sere including preforest habitat (0–5 years), young forest (5–23 years), and mature forest (>23 years). For example, the upland sandpiper, along with other fauna and flora, requires the open stage following harvest, which traditionally has been truncated by intensive reforestation. The rose-breasted grosbeak and other species require the mature forest stage. The planta-

Figure 4.9 *Mature hardwood forest on Seney National Wildlife Refuge (upper Michigan, USA) that has been thinned to accelerate the development of improved forest conditions for a variety of bird and mammal species. American beech are being retained in this stand, despite the presence of beech bark disease, to conserve any resistant beech that are present.*

tion model does not provide these conditions. Second, heterogeneity provided in the plantation model is quite unlike that provided when jack pine stands are regenerated by fire (Figure 4.10). Finally, the plantation model does not provide for sufficient CWD, snags, and larger-diameter trees needed by elements of the biota. As summarized by Tucker et al. (2016, abstract), "Landscape metrics suggest the current landscape is younger and more fragmented than the pre-European landscape. These changes indicate restriction of the historic range of age variability, largely due to conversion of older jack pine stands to young KW (Kirtland warbler) habitat plantations."

Ecologically based approaches that incorporate significant biological legacies (including snags and large trees) extend the preforest stage by use of natural regeneration or less intense planting. These approaches will also provide for more mature forest and greater use of fire to regenerate jack pine stands. Overall they will substantially expand the ability of the jack pine management regime to accommodate the full array of biota and processes.

## Stoddard-Neel System for Management of Longleaf Pine

Figure 4.10 *Jack pine forest regenerated using prescribed fire (center) compared with traditional plantation management for Kirtland's warbler (surrounding the prescribed fire area). The openings obvious in the plantation are to provide foraging habitat for the warbler, which nests in the plantations. The fire-generated forest has much greater heterogeneity and provides habitat for a greater variety of species than the plantation-based approach, while also successfully providing habitat needed by the Kirtland's warbler. This illustrates an important principle: when managing to create habitat for species of high conservation concern, it is preferable to use approaches that enhance overall ecosystem and landscape functionality in contrast to creating highly artificial habitats that have limited value for other species and for maintaining ecosystem integrity.*

Millions of acres in the southeastern United States were historically open forests dominated by longleaf pine. We view longleaf pine forests as the "bookend" frequent-fire forest (see Chapter 3) because longleaf pine forests require fire at very frequent (one- to three-year) intervals; we know of no other temperate forest ecosystem that is so finely tuned to its disturbance regime. Longleaf pine forests support extraordinary diverse flora and fauna; indeed, these forests support the highest biodiversity of any temperate forest type so far as we know. Natural forest understories in longleaf pine typically include hundreds of vascular plant species, primarily grasses and forbs. Reptiles, amphibians, mammals, and birds provide a rich fauna that includes several threatened species, such as the red-cockaded woodpecker and gopher tortoise. Major initiatives are underway to retain existing longleaf pine forests and significantly expand the existing acreage of longleaf-dominated forests.

Although greatly reduced in extent, longleaf forests are where an early ecologically based approach to forest management—the Stoddard-Neel system—evolved (Neel, 2010; Way, 2011) and is continuing to evolve and be used with

adaptations that reflect current ecosystem science, such as sustaining snags, logs, and old trees.

The goal of the Stoddard-Neel approach is to obtain ecological and economic benefits by emulating the small-scale disturbance regime characteristic of longleaf pine; this goal explicitly includes providing for both game and nongame wildlife. Stoddard-Neel creates small openings and gradually expands them by harvesting individual trees and conducting prescribed burns at frequent (one- to three-year) intervals. Trees of poor form that have significant value for wildlife (known as *character trees*) are retained. Longleaf pine regeneration is established, often by burning just before ripening of seed crops and skipping the burn in the following year. Gaps are kept small so that there is sufficient pine needle fall to sustain prescribed burns. Sustaining the diverse ground cover, which typically includes hundreds of species (Figure 4.11), is a primary management objective; Neel (2010, p. 116) has described this rich community as the "biological heart of the longleaf pine forest." Grasses, such as wiregrass, contribute structure as well as content to the surface fuels (Mitchell et al., 2009).

Major initiatives are underway to restore longleaf pine to landscapes currently dominated by plantations of other southern pines. One common approach used in national forests has been to clearcut existing slash or loblolly pine plantations and plant longleaf pine seedlings. This approach violates the continuity principle of ecological forestry, however. The Joseph E. Jones Ecological Research Center (Ichauway Plantation) has pioneered an alternative approach to longleaf pine restoration by gradually removing plantation pine overstories, rather than clearcutting them, and underplanting longleaf pine (Figure 4.12) (Kirkman, Mitchell, Kaeser, Pecot, & Coffey, 2007). Important processes are sustained in this approach, such as continued availability of the pine needle litter needed as fuel for prescribed burns and retention of larger tree and snag habitats during the conversion. Variations of this management approach are being widely utilized on a variety of ownerships in the southeastern United States to restore

and manage existing longleaf pine stands and convert other stands, such as on military reservations and in wildlife refuges.

## Variable-Retention Harvesting in Pacific Northwest Temperate Conifer Forests

The conifer-dominated temperate forests found along the Pacific Coast of North America, from northern California to Alaska, are notable for their productivity and the massiveness and complexity of the older forest stages (see Chapter 3). The dominant historical disturbance regime in these forests was highly infrequent, episodic disturbance (fire or wind) that included areas of high-severity, stand-replacement mortality (see Chapter 3). These forests have historically been managed using even-aged systems of clearcutting followed by planting. However, this approach became increasingly unacceptable in the late 20th century

Figure 4.11 *The understory of longleaf pine stands has been described as the "biological heart of the longleaf pine forest" and includes hundreds of species, such as wiregrass, which contribute essential structure and content to the surface fuels needed to support the nearly annual fires that are required to sustain the ecosystem against hardwood encroachment.*

Figure 4.12 *View of slash pine plantation being gradually converted over to a dominance of longleaf pine at Ichauway Plantation, Georgia, USA. Some overstory slash pine was retained to provide continuity in large tree structure and pine needle litter (surface fuel) during the transition. Longleaf pine has been planted in the openings created through harvest. (Photo courtesy of Joseph E. Jones Ecological Research Center)*

on many forest properties, such as governmentally owned and managed lands, due to its negative impacts on multiple social and environmental values. On such lands harvest systems that retain significant structural elements of the pre-harvest stand (e.g., live trees, snags, and intact forest patches) have largely replaced clearcutting. This approach to harvesting was labeled *variable retention* and legally adopted as an approved harvest practice by the British Columbia (Canada) government following the recommendations of the Clayoquot Sound Science Panel in 1995 (Lindenmayer & Franklin, 2002); legal standing was necessary to allow the BC Forest Service to issue harvesting permits based on retention harvesting.

Our example is focused on application of variable-retention harvesting in moist temperate forests on federal forestlands in the northwestern United States (Franklin & Johnson, 2012). Regeneration harvests in these forests virtually ceased in the early 21st century due to social objections and litigation. Resumption of variable-retention harvest-ing is proposed in younger, previously harvested forests to (1) create early seral habitat and regenerate shade-intolerant species, and (2) produce timber, while (3) sustaining most forest structures, functions, and organisms (Franklin & Johnson, 2012).

For federal forests, we have recently suggested a generalized variable-retention prescription in which approximately one-third of each harvest unit is retained as intact forest patches (Figure 4.13), which includes riparian buffers that intrude into the harvest unit. Additional retention of individual trees, small tree clusters, snags, and down wood is required within the harvested areas (Figure 4.13). Any older trees (generally over 150 years of age) that occur within the harvest unit are also retained.

An ecological objective of these variable-retention harvests is to create a structurally complex and species-rich preforest developmental stage and sustain elements of it for several decades. Hence, measures that would inhibit development or speed its loss by stand closure, such as intensive

Figure 4.13 *Oblique and overhead views of a simulation of the generic variable-retention silvicultural prescription proposed for use primarily in plantations and other younger forest ecosystems on moist federal forestlands in the Pacific Northwest, USA. The prescription provides for approximately 1/3 of the forest, including riparian buffers that intrude into the harvest unit, to be retained in aggregates of various sizes distributed throughout the management unit and approximately 2/3 to be harvested with retention of scattered individual and clustered trees, snags, and logs. One of the ecological goals is creation of high-quality early successional habitat. (Simulation courtesy of Laura Hardin)*

Figure 4.14 *Application of a variable-retention prescription on the Buck Rising Timber Sale on federal forestlands managed by the Bureau of Land Management in southwestern Oregon, USA. Note the use of both aggregated and dispersed retention. A private forest tract being managed using production forestry principles, including multiple applications of herbicides, occupies the upper-right portion of the photograph. (Photo courtesy of the Douglas Forest Protective Association)*

Figure 4.15 *Variable-retention harvest prescriptions are widely utilized in the management of trust lands by Washington State's Department of Natural Resources. This harvest unit utilizes both dispersed and aggregated retention; aggregates are visible to the left of center and on the right. While retention levels vary considerably with management objectives, typical levels of retention are in the range of 10–15%, not counting riparian buffers. (Photo courtesy of the Washington Department of Natural Resources)*

site preparation, broadcast spraying of herbicides, or aggressive tree regeneration efforts, are inconsistent with creating and maintaining this complex, species-rich stage.

This approach is being utilized on federal forestlands managed by the Bureau of Land Management in southwestern Oregon, USA (Figure 4.14) (Wheeler, 2012).

Variable-retention harvesting is being widely applied in the coastal temperate forests by a variety of agencies and organizations. The Washington Department of Natural Resources utilizes both aggregated and dispersed retention in its forest harvesting programs (Figure 4.15), in part to meet obligations under a Habitat Conservation Plan negotiated with the US Fish and Wildlife Service. Weyerhaeuser Corporation made skilled use of variable-retention prescriptions when it owned and managed forestlands on Vancouver Island in coastal British Columbia (Bunnell & Dunsworth, 2010) (Figure 4.16). The Weyerhaeuser activity was the continuation of a complete transition from clearcutting to variable-retention harvests that was initiated by MacMillan-Bloedel Corporation. Western Forest Products is the current manager of the portion of those lands that were crown lands managed under tree farm licenses from the BC government and has continued to use variable-retention harvesting; during 2011 to 2015 61% of the harvesting was done using variable-retention prescriptions with an average of 29% retention on the variable-retention units.

The archetype in all of these examples is the episodically fire-disturbed conifer-dominated forest (Chapter 3). The goal in all cases includes providing for continuity in structure, function, and composition between generations in order to simultaneously achieve ecological objectives, such as conserving important species, and economic objectives, including providing wood fiber to support local industries and communities.

## Ecological Forestry in the Pinelands National Reserve

Pitch and shortleaf pine, which dominate the forests of the Pinelands National Reserve in southern New Jersey, are well adapted to fire (Figure 4.17). Persistence of these forests has historically been associated with frequent, low-intensity fire events although they are also adapted to less frequent, partial stand-replacement fire events. An ecologically based forest management approach that recognizes the role of fire is needed to sustain these forests and associated ecosystems and biodiversity (Christensen, 2000).

To help sustain these unique ecosystems the US Congress created the 1.1-million-acre Pinelands National Reserve (PNR) in 1979. Within a year, the State of New Jersey passed the Pinelands Protection Act, which chartered a Pinelands Commission with the power to regulate use of both public and private lands within the PNR. The commission was responsible for the development of the Comprehensive Management Plan (CMP), which governs land management within the PNR.

Forest management is a permitted use under the CMP. However, any planned forest management must sustain the ecological integrity of the land and the Pineland's native forest types. In addition, it must be demonstrated that planned forest management activity will not result in irreversible adverse impact to any of the more than 80 at-risk plant or animal species found within the PNR.

These standards were adopted with the understanding that human disturbances and severe wildfires over the last 400 years have shaped the unique forest structure and plant communities that are found in the PNR. Further, these standards recognize that continued disturbance would be needed

Figure 4.16 *Variable-retention silvicultural approaches have been widely applied on Crown lands and on private lands in coastal British Columbia. This area was harvested by Weyerhaeuser Corporation using an aggregated-retention approach when it owned and managed forestlands on Vancouver Island, British Columbia. The average level of retention after an initial five-year period of transition from clearcutting to variable-retention harvesting (begun under MacMillan Bloedel ownership) was 22%.*

as part of the long-term management in order to perpetuate the unique biodiversity on this regional landscape.

It became increasingly obvious that sustaining these fire-dependent ecosystems would require active management involving manipulation of the vegetation and fire. However, the first concern in such active management would have to be the maintenance of the ecological integrity of the PNR; the objective of commercial timber harvest, which was encouraged by the CMP, would have to be a secondary objective. This would require a different approach to forest

Figure 4.17 *Frequent-fire forests of pitch and shortleaf pine are a dominant ecosystem type in the Pinelands National Reserve in New Jersey, USA; active management is required to sustain this ecosystem and its associated biodiversity, including many species of special interest. Untreated stand is pictured on left and treated on the right. (Photos courtesy of Bob Williams)*

Figure 4.18 *Silvicultural treatments based on ecological forestry principles have benefited many of the specialized biota in the Pinelands National Reserve, such as the pine snake* (Pituophis melanoleucus). *(Photo courtesy of John Parke)*

management than the traditional approach of clearcutting. Hence the requirement emerged for an ecologically based approach to forest management that could help restore and maintain ecological integrity. The presence of one or more of the many listed threatened and/or endangered plants or animals (Figure 4.18) on or near a given forest drives the regulatory process, and forest harvest plans will be approved or disapproved based upon the biological needs of these threatened and/or endangered species.

Initially, ecological standards were largely based on passive management, making it difficult for the approval of active forest management. Tree cutting was perceived to be bad for native biota. However, by the early 1990s many people were realizing that the lack of disturbance and elimination of fire were having an adverse impact on most native forest types and associated biodiversity. The decline of many rare plant species, as well as habitat suitability for many animal species, suggested the need for a different approach.

Some foresters, who understood the natural functioning of these fire-dependent forest ecosystems, began planning silvicultural treatments that would harvest timber in a way that would produce desirable ecological outcomes. Ecological forestry principles, such as providing for continuity of structure and function, provided guidance as did the specific approaches historically used in the Stoddard-Neel System (see longleaf pine example). Silvicultural treatments

included the retention or creation of tree groups, snags, down wood, and older trees. These approaches have been used and shown how habitat suitability for key elements of biodiversity can be enhanced or restored (Figure 4.18). They have also increased opportunities to utilize both more frequent and more intense fire, further restoring the ecological integrity of this special forest.

Ecological forest management approaches have shown that ecologically beneficial management can be carried out while allowing for economically viable extraction of wood products. Positive economic return has been essential; without the management subsidy that the return provides it would have been difficult to accomplish any of the needed management activities within the PNR.

In summary, an ecological forest management approach in the PNR has demonstrated an ability to meet the twin standards of ecological restoration and economic viability. In all cases ecologically based management placed a much greater emphasis on what was being left following the harvests than on what was being removed. Typically the treatments have provided forest structures needed to perpetuate many of the threatened and endangered populations. As demonstrated here, the ecological forestry approach does not simply avoid adverse impacts but actually seeks to enhance the long-term ecological integrity of the diverse forest types found across the PNR landscape.

## Restoring Resistance to Frequent-Fire Forests in Eastern Oregon

Ponderosa pine and dry mixed-conifer forests in eastern Oregon have been dramatically altered by grazing, logging, and, most profoundly, the elimination of fire as is the case throughout much of western intermountain North America (see Chapter 3). These forests have become much denser with greatly increased fuel loadings and a shift in dominance from fire- and drought-tolerant tree species (e.g., ponderosa pine and western larch) to fire- and drought-intolerant species (e.g., grand and white fir). Populations of large old trees, which historically dominated most of these forests and provided the structural backbone of this ecosystem, have also been greatly reduced and are at risk (Figure 4.19) or completely lost.

Ecologically based approaches are being utilized to restore these frequent-fire forests and landscapes to structural and compositional conditions that are more resistant and resilient to fire, drought, and insect attack, as well as to restore old tree populations (Figure 4.20). The restoration strategy was initially developed by the Klamath Tribes for use on the historical Klamath Reservation (Johnson, Franklin, & Johnson, 2008) and subsequently expanded into a general manual, *Restoration of Dry Forests in Eastern Oregon. A Field Guide* (Franklin et al., 2013).

The silvicultural goal of this restoration is to restore resistance of the dry forests, including restoration of the old tree populations. Basic elements of the prescription include the following:

- Retain all older trees and remove fuels and competing vegetation from their neighborhood;

- Develop silvicultural prescription and marking guide for remaining stand that will:

  ○ Reduce stand density;

  ○ Increase mean diameter of the residual stand;

  ○ Shift composition to more fire- and drought-tolerant species; and

  ○ Create spatially heterogeneous outcome.

- Provide for retention of appropriate levels of snags and down wood;

- Provide for treatment of fuels created by the silvicultural activity; and

- Plan and implement activities at larger spatial scales, including retention of some larger untreated patches of denser forest needed by specific wildlife.

Retaining and enhancing the continued survival of existing older trees is a high priority objective in this restoration strategy (Figure 4.19) because it is the older trees that are the structural keystone of these dry forests, including having the greatest resistance to fire. Survival enhancement is accomplished by removing surface and ladder fuels and younger competing trees from the vicinity, which is prescribed as being twice the drip line of the old tree crowns. Of course, desirable younger trees, such as vigorous pine saplings and poles, can be selectively retained.

Ecological thinning in the remainder of the stand has four objectives, which need to be prioritized as it is often difficult to optimize the first three simultaneously: (1) Reducing stand density is fundamental to reducing fuel loadings and competition for limited moisture and nutrient resources; it is targeted either in terms of residual trees-per-acre or basal area. (2) Increasing the mean diameter of the residual stand helps achieve the goal of developing a stand that is not only of lower density but composed predominantly of trees of larger diameter, which will be better able to resist fire, drought, and insects. (3) Shifting composition of the stand back toward dominance by species of greater fire and drought tolerance, such as ponderosa pine, and away from species of low fire and drought tolerance, such as grand or white fir, will also help increase the stand's survivability. As already noted, foresters must decide the relative priority among these three objectives; for example, it may be necessary to retain more white fir than desirable to meet a target

Figure 4.19 *Retaining and enhancing the survival of old trees is the first element in a silvicultural treatment to restore ponderosa pine and mixed-conifer forests to a more resistant condition. The old pine trees in this photograph are surrounded by dense, young white fir that create ladder fuels and compete with the old pines for moisture and nutrients. Enhancing the survival of the old pines is achieved by removing major surface and ladder fuels and competing vegetation from around them (Fremont-Winema National Forests, Oregon, USA).*

basal area, or conversely, it may be necessary to accept a lower basal area in order to remove a larger percentage of white fir.

The fourth stand prescriptive objective of restoring higher levels of spatial heterogeneity can be done without modifying the first three objectives. It involves how the stand is marked rather than what is marked. The primary approach used to achieve desirable patterns of spatial heterogeneity during restoration thinning is use of the ICO technique described earlier in this chapter. The ICO-based approach, which involves marking tree clusters of various sizes as well as individual trees, produces heterogeneity that is modeled on that observed in natural stands, is replicable, and is easily taught to marking crews (Churchill et al., 2013).

Approximations of this silvicultural approach are in wide use in eastern Oregon and eastern Washington, including the Fremont-Winema, Malheur, and Okanogan-Wenatchee National Forests.

All of the silvicultural principles described earlier in this chapter are incorporated into this restoration treatment in pine and mixed-conifer forests. These include continuity between generations and treatment of established stands to produce desired structural and compositional conditions. The concept of appropriate time intervals between treatments emerges in the follow-up treatments, whether by mechanical treatment or fire, that are needed to sustain or further enhance the resistant condition created by the initial treatment; some form of continued management is imperative in frequent-fire forests to sustain the desired level of resistance.

## Northern Hardwood Ecological Forestry

Mesic northern hardwood forests of the western Great Lakes region are the most productive and species-rich forest ecosystems in the region. The natural disturbance regime of this forest is characterized by chronic small-scale to mesoscale wind events that remove trees individually or in small groups and in patches of up 0.5 ha. The resultant structure consists of multicohort forests with heterogeneous canopy cover, a wide range of tree diameters and ages (including very large and old individuals), and a diverse mixture of canopy tree species that range from moderately light demanding to shade tolerant.

Because of their productive capacity and tree diversity, these forests have been widely managed for sawtimber and veneer logs. However, the silvicultural approaches used have often been disconnected from the natural dynamics and resultant structural and compositional characteristics of northern hardwood forest ecosystems. Traditionally, these forests have been managed using even-aged systems of clearcutting, with little attention to continuity across forest generations, or single-tree selection and diameter-limit cutting, which drives stands toward homogenous structure, loss of mature trees, and near-monospecific composition. Under both approaches, little consideration often is given to timing activities to ecologically appropriate time intervals or varying harvest severity to approximate the range of canopy gap sizes created under historical disturbance regimes.

The Aitkin County Land Department (ACLD, Minnesota, USA) has been an early adopter of ecologically grounded management of northern hardwoods that runs

Figure 4.20 *These pictures illustrate the basic elements of the restoration prescription for a ponderosa pine stand: retain all older trees and remove fuels and competing vegetation, reduce stand density, increase mean diameter, and create spatially heterogeneous conditions. The pretreatment condition is on the top and the posttreatment condition is on the bottom (Deschutes National Forest, Oregon, USA). (Photos courtesy of the USDA Forest Service)*

counter to the traditional, region-wide approaches described above (Figure 4.21). The impetus for doing this is reflected in the land stewardship goal of the ACLD, which includes providing timber and fiber for industry, offering recreational opportunities for residents and visitors, and sustaining the ecological integrity of the land and forests. It also allowed these lands to be among the first publicly managed forestlands in the USA to be certified by the Forest Stewardship Council. The northern hardwood resource managed by the ACLD includes Northern Mesic Hardwoods on well-drained to moderately well-drained loamy soils dominated by sugar maple, northern red oak (*Quercus rubra*), and basswood (*Tilia* spp.), with lesser amounts of paper birch and quaking aspen, and Northern Rich Mesic Hardwoods on well-drained to poorly drained loamy soils dominated by sugar maple, with lesser amounts of basswood, yellow birch, paper birch, black ash (*Fraxinus nigra*), northern red oak, and ironwood (*Ostrya virginiana*). Many of these stands originated following heavy, exploitive cutting in the region at the turn of the 20th century and are greatly simplified in structure and composition relative to the natural systems preceding them.

Broad management goals for these forests include fostering development of mature forest stages with heterogeneous structure, maintaining large forest patch sizes and interior forest habitat, and managing for long-lived (and large-sized) midtolerant to tolerant tree species. Specific silvicultural actions reflect consideration of the three main principles of ecological forestry (continuity, structural complexity between generations and biological richness, and ecologically grounded intervention intervals) and serve to link the natural dynamics of these forests to the broad management goals. For example, uneven-aged regeneration systems incorporate a combination of single-tree and group selection, implemented using a variable-density thinning (VDT) approach, which generates small-scale to mesoscale openings. This approach fosters the development of multiple-age cohorts, maintains forest continuity at the stand scale over time, and also creates structural

Figure 4.21 *Exemplary partial cutting in northern hardwood stand on lands managed by the Aitkin County (Minnesota, USA) Land Department, which had the goal of improving both the structure and species composition of this forest, while providing a commercial harvest. (Photo courtesy of Mark Jacobs)*

Figure 4.22 *Large-scale long-term experiment in harvesting of mixed pine–hardwood forest using small gaps and thinning of intervening forest areas. Experiment designed by the Northern Forest Experiment Station of the US Forest Service and implemented by the Chippewa National Forest, Minnesota, USA.*

heterogeneity over space, allowing establishment of diverse tree species that vary in shade tolerance. Moreover, when larger opening sizes are cut in these forests, legacy patches are retained within openings to lifeboat species and structures, such as large, cavity-bearing trees, in newly regenerating openings. Finally, rotation ages for patches created with mesoscale gap cutting are set up to 120% of the normal rotation age for the forest, fostering the development of larger and older trees. Beyond the ecological benefits provided by the VDT approach applied on the Aitkin County land base, the local logging community has found this approach more operable than some of the traditional approaches to northern hardwoods in the region (single-tree selection and uniform thinning), highlighting the economic viability of this management system.

Much experimentation as well as project-level management using ecological forestry approaches are underway in the northern hardwood and mixed pine-hardwood stands of the Lake States (Figure 4.22).

## Applications of Ecological Silviculture on Other Continents

Although the examples of ecologically based silvicultural practices that we have provided here are confined to North America, such approaches are being undertaken in temperate and even subtropical regions throughout the world. For example, retention-based timber harvesting is being applied in forests in Europe, Australia (Figure 4.23), Asia, and South America (Gustafsson et al., 2012) and has been shown to have had positive effects in conservation of biodiversity (Fedrowitz et al., 2014).

Figure 4.23 *Aggregated retention in wet eucalypt forests in Tasmania; a major challenge in applying retention in this forest type has been the need for high intensity fire to create conditions for reproduction of the eucalypts—hence, the use of aggregates. (Photo courtesy of Forestry Tasmania)*

*The whole is greater than the sum of its parts.* — ARISTOTLE

CHAPTER 5

# Larger Spatial-Scale Concerns: Landscapes and Regions

Ecological forest management will often be applied to large land areas that incorporate significant diversity in forests and other environmental features, and social complexities, such as multiple ownerships. Comprehensive spatial and temporal planning will help integrate and sustain environmental, economic, and social values. While these plans typically will be implemented at smaller scales, such as stands and stream reaches, developing these plans at the larger or landscape scale helps to ensure that the collective effects of the activities will have the desired landscape-level outcomes.

In classic forest planning, larger forested properties were organized for the sustained production of wood (see Chapter 17 for a thorough exposition on this topic). The larger spatial-scale goal was achievement of a "fully regulated forest"—a forest divided into stands or compartments such that harvest equaled growth and the same volume could be harvested in perpetuity. Silvicultural prescriptions were developed and implemented at the stand level but at a rate such that they would create age classes of equal productivity, thus enabling a constant harvest from period to period.

Today scientists and managers realize forest management is dominated by issues that are best addressed at landscape and regional scales even though projects involving management are typically going to be implemented at smaller scales, such as a stand or a small collection of stands. Some examples include:

- Wildlife—provision of habitat for wide-ranging species and landscape connectivity (e.g., issues related to fragmentation).

- Watershed—concerns for water quality, flow regulation, provision of wood and sediment inputs, and connectivity for aquatic biota (e.g., issues related to cumulative effects).

- Wildfire—consideration of how the spatial organization of fuels affects fire flow through a landscape.

*The landscape of Harvard Forest, Petersham, Massachusetts.*

Emergent properties also occur at larger spatial scales—e.g., watersheds, forest landscapes, and ecoregions exhibit attributes/behaviors that are not observed at the scale of a stream reach or a forest stand, such as cumulative effects on watersheds from activities distributed throughout different parts of that watershed. Thus, either many environmental issues need consideration at larger spatial scales or dysfunctional and often unacceptable outcomes may result.

Fortunately, relevant bodies of science and critical technologies have emerged that make it possible for managers and stakeholders to better understand the ecological consequences of activities at larger spatial scales, most notably (but not exclusively) landscape ecology. In this chapter we move from the scale of the stand to a consideration of landscapes and the ecological issues associated with management of forests at that scale. In Part 1 we review some basic concepts and principles related to landscape ecology, which is the source of much of the relevant science. Conservation of important environmental and cultural resources within a managed landscape is the main topic in Part 2. Planning management activities at the landscape scale is the focus of Part 3, which includes a vision for ecological forest management at the landscape scale, along with exemplary efforts at creating this type of landscape on individual ownerships. Then, we consider approaches to regional, multi-owner assessment and planning, and finally, we discuss some landscape considerations in setting patch-level goals. Our goal throughout the chapter is to focus on larger spatial-scale concepts, issues, and approaches that we believe are important in ecological forest management.

## Part 1: Some Basic Concepts and Principles of Landscape Ecology

Spatial ecology is the subset of ecology that focuses on the effects of spatial patterns on ecological processes, and landscape ecology is the application of spatial ecology at large spatial scales. In North America this subset of ecological science emerged as a major arena for research and application in resource management in the 1980s, although it has had a much longer history in Europe. Much of the interest in North America was stimulated by recognition of issues having large spatial dimensions—the scale of landscape ecology. One early issue was related to sustaining landscapes of sufficient size and diversity to provide for the needs of megafauna, such as grizzly bear,

Rocky Mountain elk, and wolves, as exemplified by the emergence of the Greater Yellowstone Ecosystem concept.

The passage of the National Environmental Policy Act (NEPA), which requires environmental analyses of federal actions in the United States, brought other large spatial-area concerns to the fore, especially those related to cumulative effects of federal activities. Cumulative effects measure the collective consequences of many activities that as individual actions might be relatively unimportant environmentally but collectively produce damaging consequences (see Chapter 7 for a discussion of NEPA and cumulative effects). Another emergent concern at larger spatial scales was fragmentation of habitats required for sustaining native biological diversity. Fragmentation involves overall loss of forest cover and reduced sizes and increased isolation of the residual forest patches (Figure 5.1). We will talk more about these landscape-level dysfunctions later in this chapter.

Fortunately the development of landscape ecology was greatly facilitated by the emergence of previously unavailable but critical technological capabilities. High-capacity computers became available along with software for management and manipulation of spatially explicit data sets

Figure 5.1 *Fragmentation of forest habitats by timber harvesting was an early focus in landscape ecology, a condition created by the dispersed-patch clearcutting approach adopted on federal forests in the Pacific Northwest (Mt. Hood National Forest, Oregon, USA, in the early 1980s).*

(geographic information systems or GIS). General availability of Global Positioning Systems (GPS) made it possible to acquire and reference spatially explicit location data. New remote-imaging technologies, such as LiDAR, emerged. Collectively, these developments enabled rapid expansion in both the science and application of landscape ecology from the early 1980s until the present.

Landscape ecology is primarily the subset of spatial ecology that deals with large spatial scales—i.e., ecological patterns at the scale of thousands or millions of acres, entire watersheds or drainage basins, mountain ranges, and even entire regions. There are numerous and comprehensive references on the science and application of landscape ecology for those wishing to expand beyond our brief introduction, including: Richard T. Forman's several books, particularly *Land Mosaics: The Ecology of Landscapes and Regions* (Forman, 1995); the textbook, *Landscape Ecology in Theory and Practice. Pattern and Process* by Turner, Gardner, and O'Neill (2001), and *Conserving Forest Biodiversity* (Lindenmayer & Franklin, 2002).

Our treatment of landscape ecology involves brief discussions of key organizing elements in landscape ecology: patchworks, networks, and gradients. In addition we will briefly consider the concept and importance of edges (boundaries between patches) and the attribute of landscape connectivity or permeability.

## Patchworks

Landscapes are viewed as collections of patches of different types in much of the literature of landscape ecology (Figure 5.2). Patches are distinguishable areas of certain types that differ from other patches in size, shape, and conditions, including different vegetative cover or ecosystem types, such as forests, meadows, bare rock, and lakes. A dominant patch type, called the matrix, is sometimes recognized in the landscape. The matrix may be defined as the most extensive or the most connected patch type in the landscape or simply as the most important patch type in influencing landscape processes. Another generic patch type that is sometimes recognized is the corridor, which is usually a long and narrow patch, often further defined as connecting two patches of similar type.

Patches are the building blocks in most applications of landscape ecology—i.e., they are the most common approach used to divide up or stratify a landscape. Patches help bring order to the complexity that is typically present in the landscapes in the real world. A specific goal in creating order is recognizing areas that differ in current conditions and underlying characteristics relevant to particular management interests, so that we can assess, plan, and project. Hence, landscape patches are important conceptually and practically in ecological forestry.

Patches have attributes of size, shape, content, boundary, distribution, frequency, and persistence. Patch content will largely determine the level of contrast with adjacent patches and, as we will understand later, the functionality of the landscape. Persistence relates to whether patches are essentially permanent because of their physical nature (e.g., lakes and rock outcrops), semipermanent because of management intent (e.g., reserved forest areas), or transient (e.g., harvest areas). In landscape analyses there generally will be some minimal size of patch that is recognized, most commonly for practical reasons. Many, if not most, patches in forest landscapes managed with ecological forestry will also exhibit internal heterogeneity or "patchiness" at spatial scales smaller than the minimum patch size; examples are tree clumps and small openings.

The patch classification developed for a particular problem—i.e., the criteria for recognizing patches—will depend upon the specific application or focus of interest in that landscape. There is no universal or "natural" pattern of patches on a landscape relevant to all analytical or management questions. The production forester, hydrologist, landscape ecologist, conservation biologist, and economist may all choose different sets of criteria for recognizing patches and describing the landscape.

An ecological forester and a production forester have significantly different landscape visions. A production forester's

Figure 5.2 *Landscapes are often viewed as interacting systems of patches of contrasting conditions, often with the repetition of similar patches over large areas. Patches of forest, agricultural lands, and built areas are present in this rural landscape (Clark County in southwestern Washington State, USA).*

idealized landscape will be one in which the landscape is composed of multiple ages of plantations (Figure 5.3). The patches themselves (sizes, shapes, etc.) are determined primarily by economic and technical considerations (e.g., issues related to access and logging methods) and are considered to be permanent, in the sense that it is the intent that repeated tree crops will be grown within the same boundaries, with the rotation age rising and falling as the desired rate of return, logging and wood processing technology, and wood product price forecasts change. The content of the patches is homogeneous structurally and compositionally, keyed to the types and spacing of trees that will provide the desired financial return.

The ecological forester's ideal landscape is more complex. Natural landscapes, or at least ecologically relevant issues, provide models for appropriate patch sizes, shapes, and boundaries, although technical, economic, or social issues also may be significant considerations. Some patches are essentially permanent because of their nature (e.g., lakes, rock outcrops, riparian vegetation, and meadows) or semipermanent because of management intent (e.g., riparian buffers). However, most patches recognized in ecological forestry are likely to be transient, because the patchwork will be undergoing change as the result of management, other disturbances, and successional processes. Effectively, most patches will undergo segmentation and recombination into new patchworks over time. This probably will be common, for example, in landscapes that are undergoing restoration, where patch sizes that were initially selected turn out to be inappropriate from the standpoint of ecological objectives. However, division and recombination of patches through disturbance or management also will be characteristic of many forest properties. Finally, but very importantly, patches created through the practice of ecological forestry will generally incorporate internal spatial heterogeneity—i.e., patches will not be structurally and/or compositionally uniform internally.

Given its currency in landscape ecology, *patch* is the primary term often used to describe landscape units that are viewed as important building blocks for planning and managing forests ecologically. These landscape patches are sometimes equivalent to *stands*, which in our broader use of the term includes areas that may exhibit considerable internal heterogeneity. However, these landscape patches also can contain multiple stands or cut across stands, as when they occur in a home range of a bird or when a riparian buffer is delineated.

Figure 5.3 *Typical production forestry landscape with multiple age-classes of managed forests or plantations. In such a landscape, stands are composed of homogeneous even-aged forest patches, as is the case in this landscape occupied by plantations of Monterey pine* (Pinus radiata) *in New Zealand.*

**Edges** Edges, or the boundaries between landscape patches, are an important topic in landscape ecology because they can influence many ecological processes, particularly if the adjacent patches are highly contrasting in structure or composition. Edge phenomena include the reciprocal influences of adjacent patches on each other as well as the unique conditions (i.e., habitat) provided by the edge itself. The reciprocal influences on physical and biological conditions between adjacent patches are often referred to as *edge effects*, and these are typically most intense at edges where the contrast between adjacent patches is very high, such as between a recent clearcut and an old-growth forest (Figure 5.4). Edges are typically easy to define and measure, but it is edge effects—the type and extent of the mutual influences of adjacent patches on each other—that are often of most interest, and these can be difficult to measure and to evaluate. The extent of edge effects or area of edge influence depends upon the parameter, process, or organism of interest—there is no single measure of edge effect applicable to all edge-related ecological phenomena.

The boundaries or edges between patches in landscapes have multiple attributes including shape (straight or convoluted), contrast (structural and/or compositional between the adjacent patches), breadth (narrow or diffuse), and structure (open, such as in the case of recent harvest boundaries, or closed, such as by vegetative growth). Edges have many significant impacts on ecological processes in landscapes, including influencing conditions within patches (edge effects), providing locations where resources of two contrasting patch types are available (specialized habitats needed by some biota), and creating locations more prone to certain kinds of disturbances.

*Edge effects, or the areas of edge influence, relate to the reciprocal influences of adjacent patches on each other with respect to some parameter, process, or organism.* While edges generally can be easily observed and measured, edge effects are conditional and depend upon the parameter (e.g., microclimatic variable), organism, or process (e.g., parasitism or windthrow potential) of interest, among other variables. This can be seen readily by comparing the influence of a clearcut-forest boundary on different microclimatic parameters in the forest patch (Figure 5.5); in this example the area of edge influence is less or relatively *shallow* for soil temperature and radiation and more or relatively *deep* for relative humidity and wind. Many other variables can influence the area of microclimatic edge influences, including season, time of day, overall weather conditions, slope, and aspect (e.g., north or south). Extreme conditions or worse-case scenarios are often emphasized in evaluating edge influences, because it is often extreme conditions (e.g., such as those that occur on very hot and dry days) that can control species distributions or processes, such as fire behavior.

Edges can have significant influences on ecosystem processes, including disturbances. Productivity will be higher along a forest edge adjacent to an opening due to availability of additional light and other resources. Tree mortality and reproduction of plant species is commonly affected by edges (e.g., Chen, Franklin, & Spies, 1992). Edges can have profound influences on disturbances by either bounding or limiting their spread or by producing conditions that are highly susceptible to disturbances, such as windthrow (e.g., Franklin & Forman, 1987).

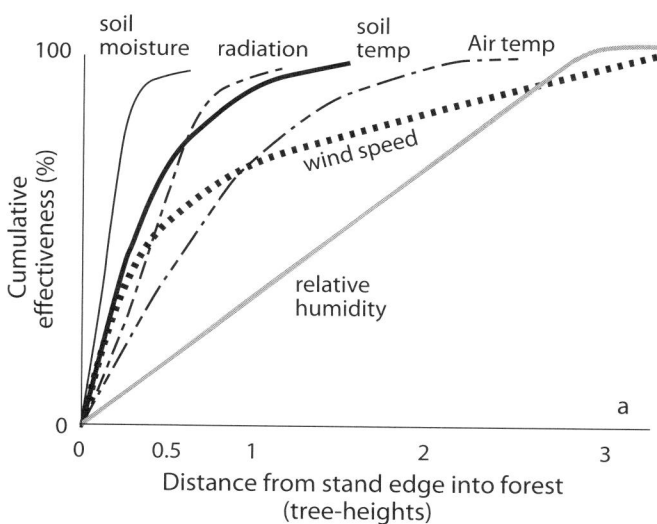

Figure 5.5 *Extent of edge influences varies dramatically with the parameter of interest (as well as many other factors). This is apparent in this generalized representation of the extent of edge influences on different microclimatic variables within an old-growth forest patch adjacent to a clearcut patch. (Adapted from Forest Ecosystem Management Assessment Team, 1993)*

Edges have both positive and negative impacts on biota. Wildlife specialists typically focus on edges as distinct and desirable habitat for many game species. Their concept of edge is usually broad, incorporating large areas, such as those utilized by species that feed in openings while using the forest side of edges as hiding and thermal cover (Hunter & Schmiegelow, 2011). However, many biota react negatively to edges to varying degrees, such as species dependent upon the *interior* environment of a large intact forest patch or opening; the adverse effects of edges on such species may be due to any of several factors, including altered microclimatic conditions (e.g., forest lichens and mosses), predation, or nest parasitism. In general, biodiversity in terms of species numbers is predicted to be high at edges, although this is not always the case.

Figure 5.4 *Edges, the boundaries between adjacent patches, are important landscape features because of the reciprocal influences (edge effects) that adjacent patches have on each other and the unique habitat present at edges, where the resources of two different patch types are adjacent. Edge effects are generally most significant when high contrasts exist between the vegetation in adjacent patches, as illustrated by this edge between an old forest and a clearcut. Edge habitat will be important for some organisms, such as elk and deer, which require the contrasting conditions present in the two different patches, such as forage and hiding cover. Edges can have negative impacts on other biota, as some species (e.g., forest interior species) may react negatively to edges.*

We reiterate that edge effects are reciprocal so that biota and processes in openings are also significantly influenced by adjacent forest patches and, as with forest biota, some species utilizing open areas may be negatively impacted by the influences of adjacent forest patches.

**Connectivity/Permeability**   Connectivity (or permeability) is an important attribute of patchworks within landscapes. This relates to the ability of organisms or materials to move through a landscape. Landscapes that consist of highly contrasting patchworks are often viewed as having low connectivity, but connectivity actually depends upon the organism or process of interest. For example, roads can be barriers to movements of many animals. However, other animals use roads as routes to enter and move through landscapes.

The literature of conservation biology typically emphasizes habitat corridors as the essential means of providing connectivity for organisms. Yet this is only one way—and often not the most effective way—of creating permeable landscapes, as many organisms do not respond to or utilize corridors, such as is the case with the northern spotted owl (Thomas et al., 1990). As described later in this chapter, *in ecological forestry we are interested in creating landscapes that have high permeability or connectivity for the full array of organisms, and we do this primarily by creating landscapes that have lower patch contrast.*

## Networks

Networks offer a contrasting way to patchworks of thinking about landscapes and their effects on ecological processes. Many important landscape features, such as stream systems and transportation systems, are not easily represented as patchworks (Figure 5.6). The most important natural network in forest landscapes is generally the riverine network or drainage system, which is composed of streams and rivers. Riverine networks are generally viewed as being highly connected because of their continuity with the dominance of flows following the energy gradient from the first order (smallest perennial streams) to higher order reaches. However, some flows of nutrients and energy, such as those associated with anadromous fish, are reversed. Connectivity is generally viewed as being high in the riverine network, but connectivity between headwater streams may be very poor for some aquatic organisms, because of the great distances that they may have to travel (down one stream ecosystem and up another) between headwaters.

The most important human-created networks are typically transportation systems, such as road networks. Natural (mostly dendritic) and human-created (often rectilinear) networks contrast significantly in their attributes. The frequent intersections between road and stream networks can create major management challenges. For example, road sys-

tems alter drainage patterns (Figure 5.7), create barriers to movement of aquatic organisms, and destabilize hill slopes and stream channels. Since many human-created networks, such as roads, railroads, pipelines, and transmission lines, frequently intersect stream and river networks and other topographic features at sharp angles, managers must be aware of their potential impacts on natural flows of materials (e.g., water and sediment) and organisms. Issues associated with road networks are considered in more detail in Box 5.1.

## Gradients

Gradients add an additional important perspective on landscapes to those of patchworks and networks, particularly when viewing large and environmentally varied landscapes or regions. Environmental gradients are most characteristic and profound in mountainous regions, such as western North America, but are typically present in all landscapes. Gradients involve systematic changes in environmental attributes, such as in precipitation, temperature, wind, and soil conditions, which occur as one travels along elevational, topographic, edaphic, latitudinal, or longitudinal gradients. Along the coast of western North America,

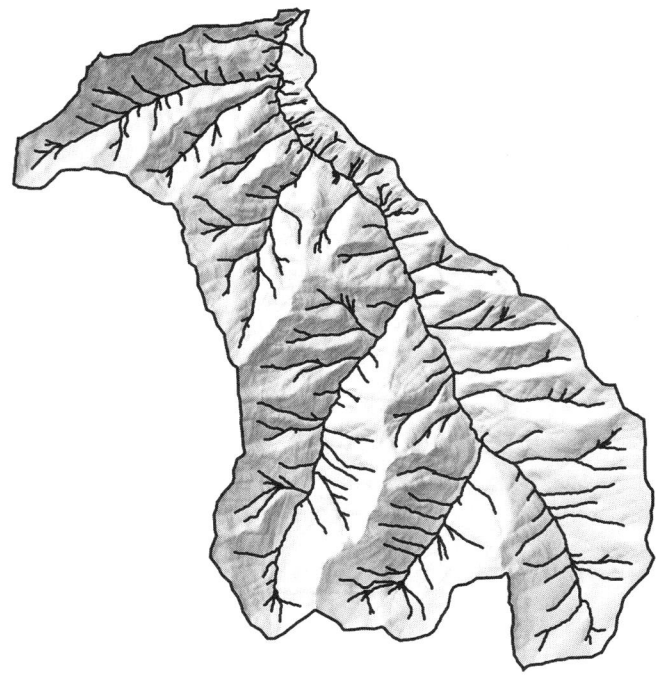

Figure 5.6 *Stream and river networks are the most extensive natural networks in most landscapes. This network is dendritic (a branching system) and has energy and material flows that are predominantly unidirectional (downstream), although there are important exceptions, such as the upstream flow of anadromous fish. Illustrated is a stream network in a small drainage in the Cascade Range of Oregon. (Adapted from Forest Ecosystem Management Assessment Team, 1993)*

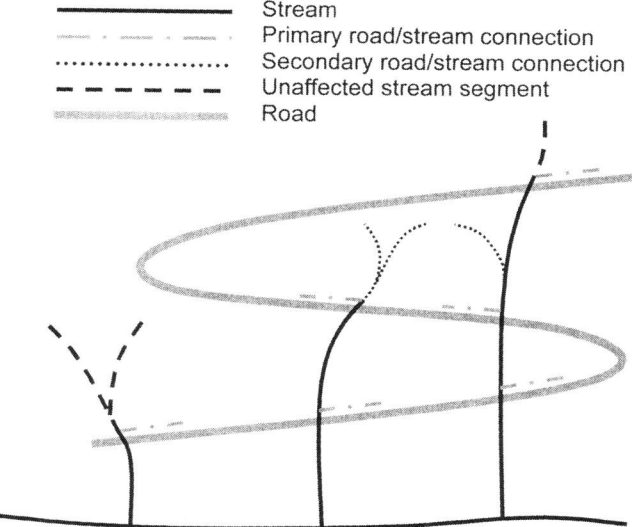

———————  Stream
— · —— · —— · —  Primary road/stream connection
··················  Secondary road/stream connection
— — — — —  Unaffected stream segment
▬▬▬▬▬  Road

*Figure 5.7  There are numerous and important interactions between road and stream networks in mountainous landscapes, which can include significant modifications of hydrologic flows as illustrated here. (Source: Conserving Forest Biodiversity, by David B. Lindenmayer and Jerry F. Franklin. Copyright © 2002 by the authors. Reproduced by permission of Island Press, Washington, DC)*

for example, major environmental gradients are associated with the predominant westerly air flows and weather systems that move onto the continent, ascend coastal mountain ranges, descend into interior valleys, and ascend up additional mountain ranges. Similar environmental gradients are present in almost all regions. Major gradients

in soil conditions are also characteristic of many regions, often resulting from gradients in soil-forming processes, such as in deposition of wind-carried (aeolian) materials or by the recession of continental glaciers. All of these gradients produce systematic but often only gradual changes in the nature of the patchwork that is present.

Important gradients in human-created landscape features, such as in the density of human dwellings and percentage of forestlands, are also present, such as when one moves from metropolitan to urban to rural to semi-wild and wild landscapes. These are often associated with environmental gradients but may also be independent of natural environmental gradients, particularly in regions where environmental gradients are subdued. Some of these gradients are recognized in forest management, as in the case of the *wildland–urban interface* (WUI).

## Part 2: Areas of Special Environmental or Cultural Significance

Identifying areas of exceptional environmental and cultural significance is an essential first step in developing a landscape-level management plan based on ecological forestry principles (Lindenmayer & Franklin, 2003). Such areas need to be spatially identified and assessed to determine the management approach necessary to sustain those values.

### Large Ecological Reserves and Protected Areas

Large ecological reserves and protected areas are important to a global forest conservation strategy (Figure 5.8).

---

### Box 5.1  Management issues related to road networks

Roads can have many negative impacts on terrestrial and aquatic environments (Gucinski, Furniss, Ziemer, & Brookes, 2001; Lindenmayer & Franklin, 2002; Trombulak & Frissell, 2000). In the case of terrestrial organisms, roads can function as major barriers to movement, alter the behavior of animals, and directly and indirectly cause significant mortality. They can also facilitate the dispersal of undesirable organisms, such as weeds, pathogens, and animal pests. Roads fragment and modify terrestrial physical environments, such as by generating edge effects, which can result in modified disturbance regimes.

Impacts of roads on aquatic environments, such as stream and river networks, can be profound and permanently alter the functioning of the riverine network, including its role as habitat for aquatic organisms. Roads can significantly alter the hydrological regime, including peak or flood flow responses; this results from roads extending the surface channel network (the road ditches) and intersecting and redirecting groundwater flows into surface channels

(Figure 5.7). Roads can negatively impact water quality, such as by increasing sediment loads, which can result in chronic alterations of aquatic ecosystems. Roads can also destabilize landforms and stream channels, which can result in episodic events, such as landslides and debris flows. Road–stream crossings with inadequate culverts commonly create conditions for initiation of such events. Finally, roads can be major barriers to the upstream movement of aquatic organisms, such as fish, if stream culverts are installed in ways that create difficult or impossible steps at the outfalls.

In applying ecological forestry it is important to reduce the negative impacts of road networks on terrestrial and aquatic ecosystems and organisms during the development of such networks and, more commonly, by modifying existing road systems and adopting maintenance practices that reduce potential problems. When new roads are required, road location and construction practices are the most important considerations, with special attention paid to road network drainage and stream and river crossings.

These are generally areas that are managed in ways that minimize intrusive human activities, particularly those associated with the extraction of natural resources. The large protected areas are important in many ways. For example, they are important in providing us with baselines in which larger spatial-scale processes are allowed to work, including those associated with disturbances, such as wildfire. They also provide locations where we can observe the consequences of climate change when no overt human efforts are made to mitigate its impacts on ecosystems. To a degree and, again, if left alone, large protected areas provide locales where ecosystems and biota are allowed to evolve on their own, without overt human intercession. Such reserves are also critical habitat for fauna that require large areas with little or no permanent human occupancy.

Consequently, identification of larger ecological reserves or protected areas and their conservation is an essential component of regional, national, and international efforts in conservation. The selection of such areas and their designation as preserves or protected areas is typically facilitated or mandated by government policies and processes that are largely political and influenced by nongovernmental organizations. For example, in Australia the identification of a series of reserves for important forest types was mandated at the federal level with the states given responsibility for fulfilling this mandate. In the United States, many of the larger conservation areas have been established on federal lands as national parks, national monuments, and wilderness. Large conservation organizations, such as The Nature Conservancy and World Wildlife Fund, have also played important roles. Conservation scientists have developed theoretical approaches to the design of such systems and systematic approaches to identifying gaps in protected area networks (see Chapter 7 in Lindenmayer & Franklin, 2002).

Active management does sometimes occur in large ecological reserves and parks, but it is generally directed strictly to conservation and recreational objectives. In such cases the principles of ecologically based management outlined in this book may be highly relevant if active management is undertaken, such as for purposes of restoration.

Despite the important role that large ecological reserves play in global conservation, ecological reserves are unlikely to ever be sufficient in extent and representativeness to sustain the majority of global biodiversity, let alone the important array of ecological processes upon which human life depends. Hence, management approaches (like ecological

Figure 5.8 *Large ecological reserves play important roles in global and national conservation strategies such as by providing wild baselines for the effects of climate change and other human activities and providing areas where large spatial-scale and long temporal-scale processes are allowed to play out free of major human efforts to modify or direct these processes. They also provide the landscapes required by species that do poorly in areas with significant permanent human occupancy (Upper Suiattle River drainage and Ten Peaks Range in the Glacier Peak Wilderness, Washington State, USA).*

forestry) that conserve biodiversity and critical ecological processes are imperative for the landscapes managed and settled by humans, which occupy the majority of the temperate forest regions of the world. A major development in the United States toward that end has been the delineation of habitat networks to help recover metapopulations of at-risk species identified through the Endangered Species Act. This work is generally accomplished through administrative processes involving scientists and resource professionals as well as citizens. These habitat networks can make important contributions to the conservation frameworks for entire bioregions, as we see with the red-cockaded woodpecker and the northern spotted owl.

## Mesoscale Areas of Conservation Concern

Most of the areas of special conservation concern in actively managed landscapes (as opposed to preserves) are going to be at the midspatial scale or what Hunter (2005) describes as the **mesoscale**. While we envision that such areas will generally involve management strategies different from those used for the forest landscape as a whole, they should not be viewed as reserves or *no management* areas. Some of them will actually require highly focused active management, particularly when there is a need to restore or sustain important structures or processes.

Categories of mesoscale areas of exceptional or special importance that should be considered in ecological forestry include:

- *Aquatic and semiaquatic ecosystems*, including streams, rivers, ponds, lakes, wetlands, and swamps.

- *Specialized habitats*, such as cliffs, rocky outcrops, caves, thermal features, vernal features, and meadows.

- *Biological hotspots*, such as "ordinary" appearing portions of terrestrial or aquatic environments that actually have special significance for specific organisms (e.g., as calving or spawning habitat) or processes (e.g., as source areas for coarse woody detritus).

- *Refugia and relictual vegetation* (e.g., old-growth remnants).

- *Biological pathways*, such as "corridors" in the broadest sense, which may be either obvious or subtle.

- *Important cultural sites* for indigenous or modern cultures, including spiritual, historical, recreational, and natural resource gathering sites (e.g., food or medicinal plants).

We have included only a brief review of these very diverse mesoscale and important areas in this book. For a more comprehensive discussion we encourage readers to consult Chapter 6 of Lindenmayer and Franklin (2002).

**Aquatic and Semiaquatic Ecosystems**  Aquatic and semi-aquatic ecosystems represent the largest and most universal category of forest landscape elements that require special management consideration. This is because of their (1) frequent presence and extent in forest landscapes and (2) ecological significance, in terms of both biota and ecological processes. Included here is a broad array of aquatic and semiaquatic features that may be embedded in forested landscapes. Springs and seeps, intermittent and permanent streams, rivers, ponds, lakes, wetlands of various types including fens, bogs, and depressional wetlands, swamps, and vernal pools (Figure 5.9), are among these features. Recognition of the importance of aquatic features and of the obligations that landowners and forest managers have toward them

Figure 5.9 *Aquatic and semiaquatic ecosystems are critical hydrological elements of most forest landscapes and are rich in biological diversity; sustaining the composition, structure, and function of these ecosystems is an essential element of ecological forestry. Examples illustrated here include streams (a), rivers (b), lakes and ponds (c), and wetlands (d).*

## Box 5.2 Important influences of forests on stream and river ecosystems

Near-stream forest ecosystems profoundly influence small- to medium-sized streams by:

- Modifying key environmental variables, such as light and temperature, with their canopies.

- Providing most of the energy and nutrient base in heavily shaded streams in the form of litter inputs (allochthonous materials); variability in source (e.g., conifer and hardwood, herbaceous and woody) and timing (e.g., distributed over longer rather than shorter periods of the year) of litter inputs is highly desirable.

- Providing logs and other CWD (Figure 5.10), which increases the ability of the stream to:
  - Retain organic materials and detain water flows.
  - Dissipate energy.

- Creating habitat diversity directly in the form of logs and log jams and indirectly by producing sediment accumulations (bars) and plunge pools.

- Stabilizing streambanks with their root systems and protective cover.

Larger streams and rivers interact with adjacent forests differently than with small streams because:

- Forest cover no longer dominates the physical environment (microclimate) of the aquatic ecosystem (river) (Figure 5.11a).

- Much of the energetic input (allochthonous material) has been processed and is fine particulate material.

- Large streams and rivers can float and rearrange the large logs and other CWD (Figure 5.11b).

- Large streams and rivers recruit logs and other CWD from the forest by bank cutting and by inputs of CWD in the form of debris flows from tributaries.

- Logs and other CWD create much of the complexity or habitat diversity in larger streams and rivers (Figure 5.11b), such as by influencing deposition of sediments and creation of islands, creation of off-channel habitat, and hydrologic excavation of deep holes.

Aquatic and semiaquatic ecosystems are viewed as intrinsic elements of the forest ecosystem in ecological forestry, which recognizes their contributions to and dependencies upon the forest. Management is undertaken to sustain and, where necessary, restore those values.

Figure 5.10 *The physical and biological properties of small streams are strongly influenced by the forest ecosystems in which they are embedded. Forest canopy cover largely determines the light and temperature environment of these streams. Much of the energy and nutrient base of the stream is provided by the terrestrial environment as inputs of litter and other organic debris. Logs and other woody debris from the forest provide much of the structural complexity and retentive structure of the stream channel.*

Figure 5.11 *(a) Large pieces of wood are important structural components of large river ecosystems, which access much of their CWD by bank cutting and move it about in subsequent fluvial activities (Tongass National Forest, Alaska, USA). (b) Rivers have the capacity to float even the largest logs and rearrange the aggregate logs in ways that modify fluvial processes and channel structure (South Fork Hoh River, Olympic National Park, Washington).*

Figure 5.12 *Forested buffers are a common approach to sustaining critical forest–stream interactions, such as provision of shade for and delivery of large logs to small streams (Olympic Peninsula, Washington State, USA).*

have increased dramatically in the last half century as a result of both increased scientific knowledge and legal regulations. Aquatic and semiaquatic ecosystems and their essential linkages to the surrounding terrestrial ecosystems should be fully recognized in ecological forestry practices.

As noted in Chapter 2 one of the most important functional roles of forests involves watershed protection, including maintenance of high-quality, well-regulated flows of water and provision of habitat for aquatic organisms. Addressing these important protective functions begins with informed and conservative management of aquatic features present on the landscape. Hence, stewardship of these aquatic features is an obligation assumed when management of forest landscapes is undertaken in ecological forestry.

Aquatic and semiaquatic ecosystems are important management concerns because of their widespread occurrence and the numerous and critical interactions between terrestrial and aquatic portions of forested landscapes. They are also critical habitat for a rich array of biota, including fish, amphibians, invertebrate communities of such diverse forms as mollusks and insects, vascular plants, algae, fungi, and an array of microbial organisms.

Aquatic and semiaquatic ecosystems have significant reciprocal influences on conditions and biota in adjacent forest and other terrestrial ecosystems. An important and often overlooked role is that of providing sources of water, food, and nutrients for terrestrial organisms. Aquatic ecosystems are significant sources of invertebrates, which emerge as adults to function as food sources for terrestrial animals particularly, but not exclusively, in near-stream (riparian) habitats (see Fausch, 2015). Migratory (anadromous) organisms, such as salmon and other fish that return from the ocean to streams and rivers to spawn, provide energy and nutrient subsidies to the terrestrial system and biota. Aquatic eco-

systems also modify microclimates of adjacent terrestrial ecosystems, creating distinctive riparian or *littoral habitats*; these microclimatic influences and the presence of elevated water tables further increase the biological diversity within these specialized habitats.

Aquatic and semiaquatic ecosystems are highly influenced by forests and other terrestrial systems in many important ways, some of which are elaborated for stream and river ecosystems in Box 5.2 and illustrated in Figures 5.10 and 5.11. Terrestrial vegetation stabilizes streambanks and shorelines. Terrestrial ecosystems provide large inputs of living and dead organic material to aquatic ecosystems, which are important sources of energy and nutrients for aquatic organisms; these inputs of organic materials or *allochthonous inputs*[1] are the primary source of energy and nutrients in small forested streams, particularly those that flow through dense shady forests. Inputs of logs and other CWD provide critical structures that not only contribute to habitat complexity but play important physical roles, such as by increasing the retentiveness of stream ecosystems. Without such structures, allochthonous materials would be flushed downstream before they could be utilized as energy and nutrient sources in the local ecosystem. Wood-related structures also assist in detention of water during major storm events.

An immense body of scientific and management literature now exists on the science and management of the interactions between forests and aquatic ecosystems, which would require another book to do it justice. The following are some useful sources of additional information on forest–aquatic interactions: *Riparia: Ecology, Conservation, and Management of Streamside Communities* (Naiman, Decamps, & McClain, 2010); *River Ecology and Management: Lessons from the Pacific Coastal Ecoregion* (Naiman & Bilby, 1998); and *Fishes and Forestry: Worldwide Watershed Interactions and Management* (Northcote & Hartman, 2008). The short book, *For the Love of Rivers: A Scientist's Journey* (Fausch, 2015), provides an engaging personalized perspective on some of the ecological interactions between small streams and forests.

Creation of buffers or protective zones along edges of aquatic and semiaquatic features, such as riparian buffers along streams and rivers, is a common approach to sustaining critical forest–stream interactions in managed landscapes (Figure 5.12). Although riparian buffers are often

---

1 Allochthonous inputs refer to all of the live and dead organic materials (including leaf litter and live and dead insects) falling into the aquatic ecosystem from the surrounding environment, such as the forest. Allochthonous materials contrast with autochthonous organic materials, which are produced by green plants within the aquatic ecosystem. In small, shaded stream systems the vast majority of the energy base (often >80–95%) will be provided by the allochthonous inputs, which become the basis for extensive food webs by being processed by microbial organisms and invertebrates within the stream.

primarily thought of as protective zones, such buffers may need to be managed. For example, management may be needed to restore structure and function, where it has been lost, and then to sustain the important forest influences on the aquatic ecosystem. These influences include provision of energy and nutrient-rich allochthonous inputs, provision of large CWD, shading, and stabilization of banks.

*Several important principles should guide efforts to create and manage riparian buffers:*

- *First, all the functional roles of riparian buffers need to be considered even though some may have a higher priority at a given place and time.* For example, the potential for stream temperatures lethal to anadromous fish was a major concern when stream buffers were first proposed in the Pacific Northwest; hence, the shading function had high importance. Currently, provision of large, decay-resistant CWD is often a restoration emphasis because many streams have lost much or all of their historic wood structure as a result of past management.

- *Second, structural and compositional diversity is important in riparian habitats.* For example, the uniform, heavily shaded conditions provided by dense young conifer forests dramatically limit the quality, amount, and timing of allochthonous inputs as well as reduce the potential for primary productivity (photosynthesis by algae and other plants) within the stream itself. High-quality riparian habitat typically has significant heterogeneity in vegetational and environmental conditions (e.g., mixtures of open and shaded conditions) along its length. The vegetational diversity should include hardwood trees and shrubs.

- *Last but not least, it is always important to remember that riparian and littoral areas are unique and important habitats in and of themselves and not just for what they are providing to the aquatic ecosystem.* These habitats have specialized communities of plants and animals that occupy them and other creatures that use them to meet their needs. Protection of such habitats is warranted by their unique features as well as for their contributions to the aquatic system.

Larger spatial-scale aspects of stream and river ecosystems are challenging because each reach is part of a highly interconnected linear network in which the majority of energy and materials flows from headwaters to outlet. Hence, impacts to one area can ramify through the system. Similarly, sources and sinks for materials, such as CWD and sediment, may be widely separated in time and space. CWD, which comes from somewhere upstream, ultimately is needed in the estuary, though it may take decades or even centuries to get there.

Figure 5.13 *Large river systems interact strongly with adjacent forest ecosystems, although they are largely free of the influence of direct forest cover. Such rivers are capable of capturing large amounts of wood through bank cutting and moving it, where concentrations may contribute to sediment deposition and formation of river bars and islands.*

Related to this point, although rivers and streams in forested watersheds may recruit significant quantities of CWD through bank erosion (Figure 5.13), the delivery of CWD and sediments from steep headwater channels to main stems by debris flows is crucial to geomorphic and ecological processes in some streams and rivers. For example, high-quality spawning and rearing habitat for Pacific salmon (*Oncorhynchus* spp.) in many streams and rivers of coastal northwestern North America is dependent on episodic debris flows from their tributaries (Figure 5.14) (Benda et al., 2004; Reeves et al., 2003). The spatially and temporally variable input of large wood, organic material, and sediments from such events results in the creation of a mosaic of complex in-stream and off-channel habitats to which Pacific salmon are adapted (Reeves et al., 1995; Waples et al., 2009). Hence, in such river systems it is important to manage headwater forests of key tributaries to ensure that when headwater areas fail, the resulting debris flows incorporate significant quantities of large trees and logs. Spatial analysis can identify which headwater areas are most important for maintaining these disturbance processes, considering the probability of slope failure, ecological sensitivity, spatial architecture of the stream system, and other factors (Reeves et al., 2016).

Although so far we have focused on streams and rivers, surrounding forest conditions are also important to other aquatic features that are embedded in forest landscapes, such as lakes, ponds, swamps, fens, and bogs. Forests along the shores of lakes and ponds (the littoral zone) play many of the same roles as they do for streams and rivers. They provide inputs of energy and nutrients in the form of allochthonous materials, including logs and other coarse woody debris that provide structures, stabilize shorelines, and provide habitat for amphibians and emerging invertebrates. Of course, the importance of some of these roles will be greater in small ponds than in large lakes. Near-lake forests are also important in regulating water quality in streams that are tributary to ponds, lakes, and wetlands.

Some aquatic features, such as many swamps, actually incorporate significant tree and CWD components, which are critical structural and functional elements of those systems. The bald cypress (*Taxodium distichum*) and tupelo (*Nyssa* spp.) swamps of the southeastern United States provide an outstanding and widespread example.

Many of these features are *isolated wetlands*, which means that they lack persistent surface water connections, such as with rivers, but invariably they have hydrologic and biogeochemical connectivity, such as through ground water (Cohen et al., 2016). Such wetlands are often biological hotspots of high diversity and productivity. They are also critical landscape elements that not only provide important habitat for many species, including reptiles and amphibians, but also facilitate the biological movement of many species. Such wetlands are notable features of pine woodlands in the southeastern United States (Kirkman & Jack, 2017).

**Other Areas of Special Ecological Significance**   Forested landscapes often have a variety of features that have special ecological significance because of their particular ecological functions, such as providing specialized habitat for some biota (Lindenmayer & Franklin, 2002). All of these represent special environments that biologically enrich forested landscapes as well as providing essential habitat for species of commercial, legal, and ecological importance. Hence, it is important to identify such areas and adjust their management to sustain their special values.

Distinctive physical features are easily recognized areas of special ecological significance. Rock promontories, cliffs, and rockslides are examples; they can be critical sites for biodiversity, such as nesting sites for birds, habitat for other vertebrate and invertebrate animals, escape sites (e.g., for sheep and goats), and habitat for populations of rare plant species or communities (Figure 5.15). Caves can be roosting and wintering habitat for bats and locales for cave-evolved animal species.

Unusual geological formations, such as those dominated by serpentine and other ultramafic rocks or limestone outcrops, often host unusual or rare plant species and communities (Figure 5.15). Serpentines, which develop soils with unusual chemical properties, are one of the best known examples (Kruckeberg, 1967). Compositionally and structurally distinct communities are characteristic of serpentine sites and commonly include rare plants that are not found on areas of normal soil. Cedar glades and sand barrens provide other examples of habitats distinctive in structure and composition in deciduous forest regions in eastern North America. Cedar glades are grassy islands with abundant eastern red cedar

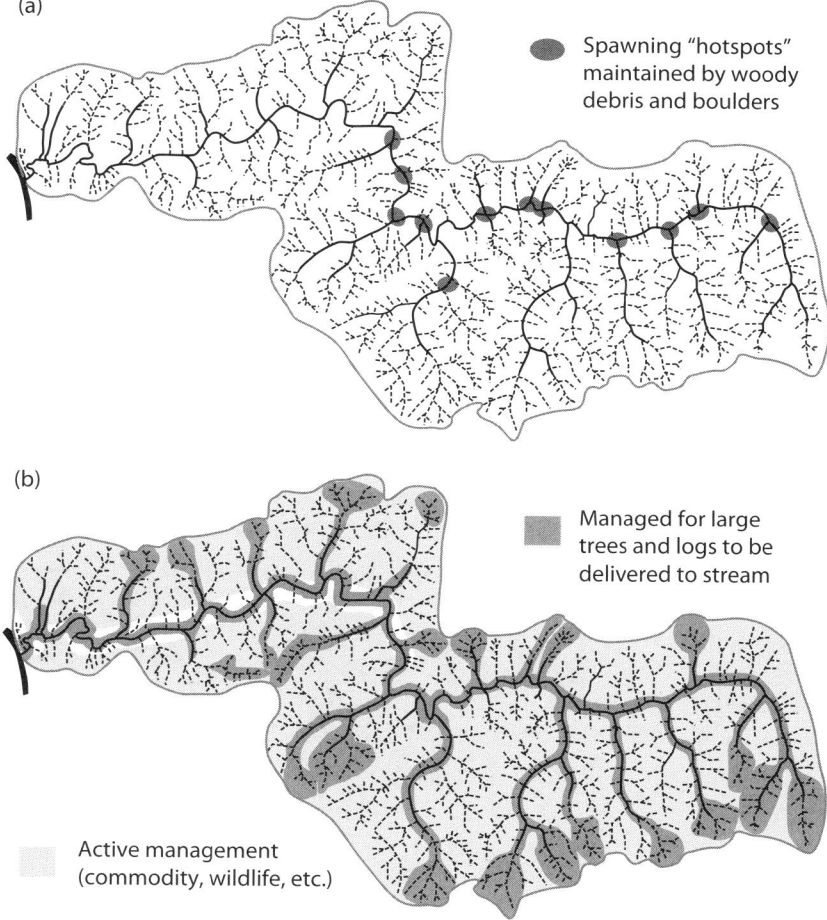

(a)

Spawning "hotspots" maintained by woody debris and boulders

(b)

Managed for large trees and logs to be delivered to stream

Active management (commodity, wildlife, etc.)

Figure 5.14 *Headwater portions of some river drainages need to be managed so as to ensure that periodic landslides and debris torrents contain the large quantities of CWD that are needed to sustain debris dams in the main stem, which are the primary locations of fish spawning habitat. (a) Locations of high-quality fish-spawning habitat in the Knowles Creek drainage in the Oregon Coast Range; note that most of these areas are at high angle intersections between a tributary and the main stem. (b) Source areas (headwaters) for debris jam materials, which need to be managed to sustain forest patches that provide significant amounts of large wood when they fail. (Adapted from Lindenmayer & Franklin (2002) by Kathryn Ronnenberg, US Forest Service PNW Research Station)*

(*Juniperus virginiana*) developed on thin-bedded dolomitic limestone outcrops. Deep deposits of sand also may support distinctive flora and fauna.

Seasonally ponded areas can be important habitats and may not be readily recognized as being aquatic features. Vernal pools are perhaps the best known example of such features. These areas are wet and biologically productive during the spring and early summer and are usually populated by dependent plant and animal life forms. Their size varies from very small (a few square feet) to many acres.

Meadows, shrub fields, and other natural nonforested openings are a very diverse but easily recognized category of special feature (Figure 5.15). Such ecosystems bring significant diversity to forested landscapes because of the contrast they provide with forests in terms of structure, function, and composition. Such nontree-dominated ecosystems are likely to support species that are not found in adjacent forest-dominated areas. They may also provide critical habitat for species, such as deer and elk, which utilize forested areas for cover and meadows and other open areas in the foraging.

***Biological hot spots*** are habitats that have unusual ecological importance in the life histories of important animal species but may not be obvious to an untrained eye. Calving areas for Roosevelt elk (*Cervus canadensis roosevelti*) in forested landscapes are an example. Pregnant elk seek somewhat isolated and protected sites with good forage and water availability for the birth of their young. In a particular river drainage, suitable calving sites may be limited in extent but can be readily identified by wildlife biologists. Similarly, not all portions of stream and river systems are of equal value as spawning habitat for fish. Some reaches have optimal conditions for spawning and initial survival of fry. This is the case with the coastal river systems in Oregon mentioned earlier in which the complex aquatic environments created by wood-rich debris avalanches are the primary locales for spawning. Other types of biological hotspots include foraging areas that provide rare but important food resources and overwintering habitats for large populations of particular organisms, such as caves for bats (Lindenmayer & Franklin, 2002).

Corridors, particularly those used by animals for their seasonal movements or migration, are areas of special ecological significance. We will have more to say about landscape connectivity later in this chapter. However, areas that historically have been used for major animal movements need to be recognized and managed to accommodate their continued functioning as travel routes. These corridors will often be related to specific topographic features, such as valleys that connect major habitat segments or prominent passes on key travel routes.

Remnant patches of natural vegetation, such as areas of old or unusual forest or trees or uncut primeval forest, are the last category of ecologically important areas that we will consider. These may have many worthwhile values, including provision of habitat for species dependent upon such

Figure 5.15 *Recognizing and appropriately managing distinctive physical and vegetative features can be extremely important in sustaining the biological diversity of forested landscapes and often provide critical habitat for specific plant and animal species. Such areas need to be identified and management needs carefully assessed. Some examples are: (a) rock slides, rock outcrops, and cliffs; (b) unusual geological formations, such as areas of serpentine and other ultramafic rocks; and (c) meadows.*

conditions, as reference sites for scientific and management studies, and as sources of genotypes for species that have been otherwise eliminated from or highly modified in the local landscape.

## Areas of Cultural or Other Social Significance

Managed forest landscapes often contain culturally and socially significant sites. These can be of either historical or modern significance or both. They can be sites that have major recreational, inspirational, religious, or patriotic significance. They can also be sites that provide culturally important products, such as foods, medicines, or construction materials. *Identifying and acknowledging such sites is important and can be critical to acquiring and sustaining societal support for management activities.*

Cultural sites are most often identified with indigenous peoples, such as Native Americans (USA) or First Nations (Canada), although they certainly are not confined to indigenous peoples. Sites of cultural significance include

areas used for spiritual quests or other religious activities, for gathering plants used for food, medicine, or construction materials, such as those used in basket weaving, and sources of wood for construction of canoes, houses, and poles. Burial sites are very important. Trees that have been modified as a result of past indigenous activities (*culturally modified trees*) are often viewed as significant cultural objects. One of the challenges in protecting these cultural resources can be the reluctance of indigenous societies to divulge the location of such resources. Finally, there may be areas that were the locales of settlements or cultivated lands in historic or older times.

Maintaining some cultural features, such as food plants, may require active management. Huckleberries (*Vaccinium* spp.) provide a good example and are found in many forested regions of North America. Huckleberry fields provide a food resource that is historically and currently important to Native American tribes and is also valued by other rural and urban populations (see, e.g., Richards & Alexander, 2006) (Figure 5.16). Many of these huckleberry fields are persistent early successional communities that typically were created and sustained on potentially forested sites by fire of both natural and anthropogenic origin. Periodic disturbance, such as fire or tree removal, is required to prevent forests from dominating such sites, which would greatly reduce huckleberry production.

## Part 3: Planning Management Activities at the Landscape Level

We begin this section of the landscape ecology chapter by reminding readers that ecological forestry is about managing forest properties in ways that will sustain multiple ecological, economic, and social values. Ecological forestry is not just about restoring forests and forested landscapes to high levels of ecological functionality, although this is certainly one of its important applications. Ecological forestry is also about managing forest landscapes for flows of economically important products and services to provide the landowner with income, the manager with financial resources for stewardship, and communities with raw materials and other ecosystem services—and doing all of this while sustaining structurally complex ecosystems, multifunctional landscapes, and native biota!

It is at landscape and regional levels where the ultimate consequences of the many deci-

Figure 5.16 *Huckleberry fields are shrub-dominated ecosystems that are important culturally as food sources for Native American societies as well as for local rural and urban populations. These are typically communities that are created and maintained by fire and other periodic disturbances, which are required to prevent trees from taking over the sites and suppressing the berry bushes (Sawtooth Huckleberry Field, Gifford Pinchot National Forest, Washington State, USA).*

sions made at smaller scales, such as for individual forest patches, are experienced. Hence, assessing the aggregate implications of these decisions from many different perspectives is often the focus of landscape planning. Providing for heterogeneity—a diversity of patch types and conditions at larger spatial scales—is likely to be one important element in this assessment, but the challenge remains of determining what kind of landscape patches are needed and how they are to be distributed in time and space. As described previously in this chapter, recognizing areas in the landscape that have special significance environmentally or culturally is a major and early element in the overall task.

This section begins with an exploration of what an idealized landscape managed according to ecological forestry principles might look like, which we call *shades-of-green* landscape. We focus here on landscapes being actively managed for multiple objectives because we believe that managed landscapes, rather than protected landscapes, are the most challenging for landscape goal setting. As part of this discussion, we compare this idealized landscape to others often advocated by different groups. Next we highlight some exemplary efforts at creating shades-of-green landscapes on individual ownerships. Then, we consider approaches to regional, multi-owner assessment and planning, utilizing case studies of the Oregon Coast Range and New England in the US. Finally, we discuss some landscape considerations in setting patch-level goals, including distributing harvest activities across the landscape, providing habitat in time and space, avoiding cumulative effects, and prioritizing actions.

## Creating Landscapes that Are Shades-of-Green

The idealized ecological forestry landscape is one in which essentially all of the patches in the landscape are making some contribution to the goals of maintaining multiple ecosystem functions and sustaining biological diversity. We are talking here about managed landscapes containing lands with different goals and stages of development, including harvested areas. We can expect that the constituent patches will vary significantly in the extent to which ecological values are emphasized, such as their level of structural richness. However, we assume all patches that will be harvested will be managed so they also make a contribution to ecological capacity, such as by retaining live trees, snags, and logs.

We describe such idealized landscapes as shades-of-green because all patches are consciously managed to sustain elements of structure, function, and biodiversity (see Color Plate 5.1). Such landscapes will differ significantly in both appearance and functionality from more traditionally managed forest landscapes that typically are partitioned into (1) areas devoted to intensive wood production, and (2) areas devoted to sustaining biological diversity and other ecological values (Figure 5.17 and Color Plate 5.1).

With ecological forestry, the creation of landscapes that are shades-of-green is accomplished through several types of actions:

- Recognizing areas within the landscape that have special ecological value and requiring management to conserve those values, as discussed earlier in this chapter. Aquatic features and the areas adjacent

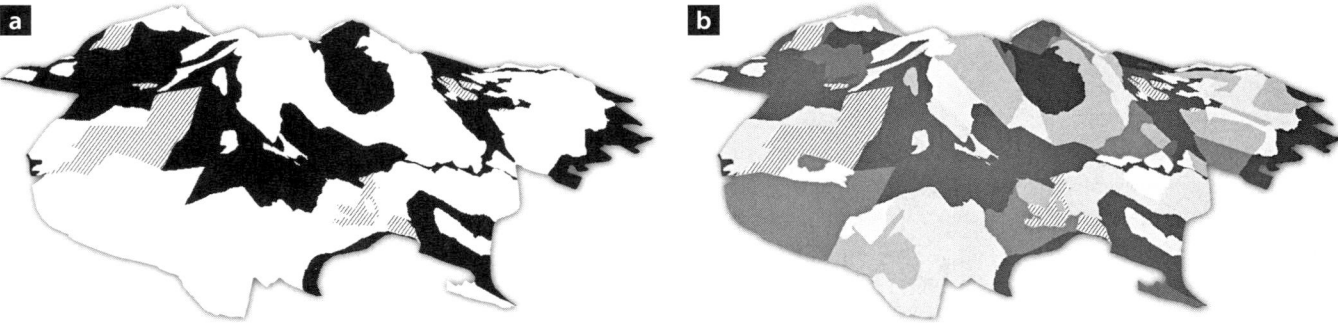

Figure 5.17 *Two contrasting visions of managed forest landscapes. (a) A traditional view of a forest landscape in which reserved areas (shown here as black) are embedded in a matrix, which is managed without significant consideration of ecological values (shown here as white). The reserved areas are intended to provide any habitat needed to sustain forest biodiversity. This landscape vision encourages management decisions that will tend to create a black-and-white reality, since there is neither a plan nor an expectation for harvested areas to help sustain biodiversity and diverse ecological functions. (b) A landscape managed according to ecological forestry principles in which all landscape patches are managed to sustain at least some elements of habitat and ecological functionality. This landscape can be viewed as a patchwork that is "shades-of-green" (although it is portrayed here as shades-of-gray). Essentially all patches in this landscape retain significant ecological content (e.g., organisms, structures, and moderated microclimates) and thereby contribute to goals of maintaining ecological functions and biodiversity, even immediately following a timber harvest. The ecological contribution of the light green patches (shown as light gray here) may come primarily from retention of live trees, logs, and snags during harvest. Dark green patches (shown as dark gray here) could include mesoscale areas of ecological emphasis, ecological reserves, and natural and near-natural structurally rich young, mature and old forest, and preforest conditions. Nonforest is shown as patches with diagonal lines.*

to them are the most extensive and ecologically important example in most forests, so stewardship of these elements will generally be a high priority in ecological forestry. Of course, this includes recognition of any formally reserved areas located within the landscape under consideration.

- Creating the diversity and proportions of patch types needed in the landscape to maintain or restore ecological integrity and help achieve social objectives. The mesoscale areas of ecological emphasis identified initially (see previous bullet) contribute to the diversity of patch types. Consideration of desired patch-size distribution is also a part of this step; for example, patch sizes must provide for the habitat needs of specialized biota.

- Developing and applying silvicultural prescriptions in managed patches that maintain significant ecological content, such as complex structure and environmental niches. Retaining significant structural elements in harvested patches within an actively managed forest is one of the most important ways that this can be accomplished (see Chapter 4).

Actively managed shades-of-green landscapes are expected to provide a broad range of patch conditions. In heavily harvested patches, their ecological contribution may come primarily from retention of logs, snags, and live trees, providing the light green patches (Color Plate 5.1) or light gray (Figure 5.17). Other patches, such as the mesoscale areas of ecological emphasis, ecological reserves, or other natural or near-natural structurally rich young, mature or old forest or preforest, provide the dark green patches (Color Plate 5.1) or dark gray (Figure 5.17).

Creating landscapes that are shades-of-green effectively eliminates numerous problems that emerge in landscapes managed as black-and-white patchworks. For example, problems associated with connectivity for biota will be greatly reduced, since there will be few, if any, large areas completely lacking in cover. Extensive areas of hostile habitat, created through complete forest clearing, will be rare or absent in such a landscape. Instead there will be structure and hiding cover throughout. Similarly, areas of high-contrast edges will be limited along with the significant adverse edge effects that they create. In fact, special attention may need to be paid to ensure that sufficient areas of well-defined edge are present for biota that require them.

Smaller forest ownerships are not likely to face the full array of landscape issues encountered on larger forest properties. There will certainly be smaller versions of many of these issues, however, that will need to be addressed in developing management plans for these ownerships (see Chapter 19). Many of these issues may focus on ecologically

sensitive areas, including riparian zones, and the need for a diversity of patch conditions. Also smaller ownerships may have to deal with size and distribution of patches.

Forest stakeholders have widely varying views regarding the ideal forest landscape, but these have rarely included managed landscapes that could be described as shades-of-green. Some landowners are focused on short-term financial rewards—achieving a certain level of return on capital—with the only ecological constraints being those imposed by the productivity of the land and by laws and regulations. Their idealized landscape is one of continuous tree farms with fast-growing stands of different ages interspersed with recently harvested lands (Figure 5.3). Many conservation-oriented stakeholders have generally favored dividing forests into two categories—*natural* forests in reserved or protected areas, which have significant ecological and inspirational value, and *managed* forests, which they assume will be managed following production forestry philosophies and, consequently, have little or no ecological value. Indeed, this notion of a bipolar landscape (preserves and plantations) has had wide currency in forest policy debates (Bennett, 2015).

In conservation biology, the application of the theory of island biogeography to forest and other terrestrial landscapes can be interpreted as a black-and-white dichotomy in which terrestrial landscapes are viewed as consisting of islands of protected areas or *habitat* embedded in a matrix of managed areas, which are viewed as *not habitat*, an ecologically empty and potentially hostile *ocean*. In this interpretation, protected areas are the parts of the landscape devoted to sustaining biodiversity, and managed areas are viewed as contributing little or nothing to the ecological goals or, even worse, as largely hostile to the presence and passage of biota. This also relates to the emphasis by many conservation biologists on providing corridors of suitable habitat to connect the protected areas.

Serious problems arise when black-and-white views of local and regional landscapes become the primary basis for policy or management. If the working premise in policy is that only protected areas are expected to provide habitat to sustain biodiversity and no significant contributions are expected from the surrounding matrix or managed landscape, then the resulting management will likely produce that outcome—i.e., *if your vision of the world is black-and-white, then you are likely to manage the world in ways that will produce that outcome!*

It is important to remember that many powerful interest groups at both ends of the conservation continuum may actually prefer black-and-white solutions and differ only in their views as to which condition (black or white) should predominate! They seek to pursue their particular value set, whether it is preservation or dollars, without the compromises that are inherent in integrated management solutions.

Achieving an ecologically perfect landscape condition in the real world may not be very realistic, but the vision of landscapes that are *shades-of-green* can move things in that direction. Sustaining the richness of ecological processes and biota in the forested *matrix*—the managed majority of the forest landscapes—is imperative in our view. The importance of this richness has been demonstrated repeatedly (see, e.g., Prugh et al., 2008). Otherwise, we will fail to sustain both the array of ecological services we expect from most forest properties and the majority of forest biodiversity. Neither of these goals can be accomplished with the small percentage of temperate forestlands that can and will be exclusively dedicated to protected areas, even assuming that such areas are optimal for such a task. *As important as preserved lands are to conservation, preserves cannot conserve the majority of global biological diversity. This can only be accomplished by incorporating conservation of biodiversity into management of the majority of global forests.*

## Exemplary Efforts at Creating Shades-of-Green Landscapes

There are numerous real-world examples where forest management is being implemented in ways that, either intentionally or fortuitously, produce landscapes that are approximate shades-of-green. Many of these are smaller forest properties, such as those owned and managed by families or individuals, conservation organizations, community and other local governmental organizations, and Native American tribes. These efforts may be more common in eastern North America—in both the deciduous hardwood forests of the Northeast and the frequent-fire forests of the Southeast—than in western North America. The diversity of the eastern deciduous forests and dominance of family forest ownership are probably factors that have encouraged such approaches. There has also been a broader tradition of uneven-aged management in eastern North America, as exemplified by properties like the Pioneer Forest (Guldin, Iffrig, & Flader, 2008).

A lack of supportive science and exemplary forest management models may have hobbled development and application of such approaches more broadly, since individuals or organizations using them are criticized as deviating from mainstream or "accepted" forest practices. Innovative mechanisms are being developed to assist landowners in landscapes that are primarily collections of small ownerships, in producing shades-of-green outcomes. We will provide an example from New England later in this chapter.

Many larger forest properties are being managed under ecological forestry principles resulting in landscapes that are effectively shades-of-green. We provide examples of such management approaches by private, state, and federal organizations in the following paragraphs, along with some examples of related approaches.

Green Diamond Corporation provides an example of landscape-level ecological forest management on its properties in the coast redwood region of northern California (Figure 5.18). Green Diamond grows second-growth redwood that it sells to manufacturing facilities that process the logs into Forest Stewardship Council (FSC)-certified wood products. Consequently, management of their lands must be and is certified by FSC (see Chapter 16 for a discussion of FSC certification goals and standards). All regeneration harvesting done on Green Diamond Lands includes significant structural retention (Figure 5.18) and consideration of biological diversity, including northern spotted owls.

Figure 5.18 *All harvesting of second-growth redwood forests on Green Diamond lands in the redwood region of northwestern California is done using variable-retention harvest prescriptions; clearcutting is not used. Regenerating, growing, and harvesting second-growth coast redwood is the primary management goal on these lands, but with the additional goal of sustaining other elements of native biodiversity besides the redwood tree itself. Management practices on these corporate lands are certified by the Forest Stewardship Council (northwestern California, USA).*

Figure 5.19 *Native Americans have major challenges in managing their Reservation lands since they often depend upon them for economic, cultural, and environmental values. Many forested Reservations provide excellent examples of forest landscapes that are successfully managed to provide this full array of values. Pictured here is a mixed-conifer forest stand that has been restored to a more resistant state as a part of a landscape-level restoration effort on the Flathead Reservation (Montana, USA).*

Figure 5.20 *Aerial view of a harvested area on trust lands managed by the Washington State Department of Natural Resources; the level of retained forest patches and structures is typical of these lands and includes significant buffering of riparian habitat. (Photo courtesy of Washington State Department of Natural Resources)*

Many forested reservations owned and managed by Native Americans provide excellent examples of forest landscapes that are shades-of-green. Tribes typically need to manage these lands for multiple values including income, space for sustenance and living, and cultural and spiritual values. Some excel at this activity, such as on the Menominee Tribe in Wisconsin, which has managed their Reservation for more than a century using approaches that provide for diverse forest stands and continuous forest cover (Mausel, Waupochick, & Pecore, 2017). The Confederated Salish and Kootenai Tribes of the Flathead Nation provide another good example in their management of their Reservation in western Montana, where widespread efforts to restore frequent-fire forest landscapes have been underway for nearly two decades (Figure 5.19).

The Washington State Department of Natural Resources (WADNR) manages 2.4 million acres of forestlands, much of it to produce income for trusts, using ecologically based approaches that allow them to integrate economic, social, and environmental goals. Their approach was developed in 1997 as part of an agreement (Habitat Conservation Plan) with the US Fish and Wildlife Service to protect federally listed threatened and endangered species. Recognition and conservative management of ecologically and culturally important areas are a significant element of the WADNR program. For example, protection of aquatic features includes the use of significant riparian buffers, an activity that has its own mandate in a consensus-generated Fish Forests and Agreement applicable to all nonfederal forestlands in the state and formally adopted by legislative and executive actions. Various forms of retention harvesting are utilized on trust lands (Figure 5.20) to sustain biological diversity, structurally enrich the next generation of forest stands, and improve the permeability of the landscape. In moist coastal forest regions, the remaining old-growth forests have been removed from harvest consideration. In the interior dry (frequent-fire) forest region, significant retention of old trees occurs in timber-harvest programs and restoration projects. The Habitat Conservation Plan was influenced by a concept called *biodiversity pathways*, developed under the leadership of Andrew B. Carey (Carey & Curtis, 1996). Although never implemented in its entirety, a modeled analysis of Carey's approach provides evidence that high levels of both ecological outputs and income are possible (Carey, Lippke, & Sessions, 1999).

US Forest Service management of the national forests, under the agency's laws and regulations, will generally result in a shades-of-green landscape with an emphasis on the darker shades (Chapter 20). Perhaps the movement toward ecologically based landscape-scale approaches is most evident in the moist temperate forests in northwestern North America, which was historically characterized by even-aged management and clearcutting. The Northwest Forest Plan (NWFP) (USDA Forest Service and USDI BLM, 1994) was a landmark effort to shift management approaches on over 24 million acres of federal forestlands within the range of

the northern spotted owl. It provided for sustaining significant ecological content (structure and biota) on harvested areas through mandated minimum retention levels of 15% of the pre-harvest forest measured either by area (in the case of aggregated retention) or live-tree basal area (in the case of dispersed retention). However, as originally constructed the NWFP would still have resulted in landscapes with strong patch contrasts between preserved and managed areas. This led to conceptual development of an alternative approach (the Blue River strategy) that would have produced a broader gradient of patch conditions (Figure 5.21); this approach patterned its cutting cycles (rotations) and retention levels on historical fire regimes in the central Oregon Cascade Range. Although this strategy was not formally adopted, we have included it here to illustrate yet another innovative and science-based model for creating managed landscapes that are shades-of-green.

## Fire Regime Areas

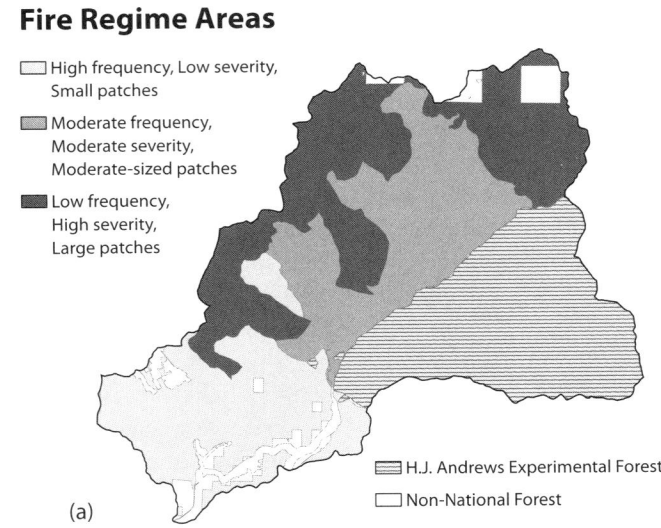

(a)

*Figure 5.21 The Blue River landscape management strategy was developed for a 23,908-acre drainage in the Cascade Range of western Oregon and utilized a management model based upon natural disturbance regimes. Harvesting regimes varied depending upon the natural fire regime in terms of rotation age (100, 180, and 260 years), harvest size (small, medium, and large), and retention (50, 30, and 15% crown cover retained). Illustrated here are: (a) division of the landscape into different fire regimes; (b) management areas based on land allocations of NWFP, including Matrix (harvest with 15% retention), Riparian Reserves and Special Area Reserves; and (c) Blue River landscape plan with management areas subject to different harvest regimes (Areas 1, 2, and 3), Special Area Reserves, and Aquatic Reserves. The NWFP approach results in a high-contrast landscape of old growth (reserves) and young forest (matrix). The Blue River Plan provides for a much greater diversity of forest conditions and a carefully designed set of aquatic reserves. (Source: Adapted from Cissel et al., 1999)*

## NWFP Management Areas

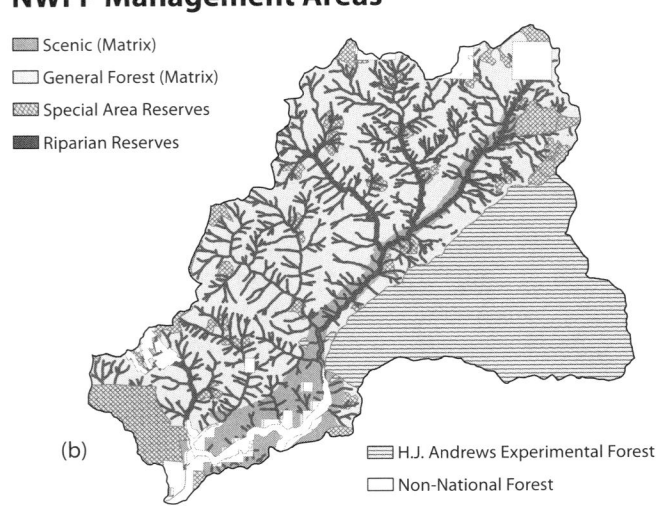

(b)

## Landscape Plan Management Areas

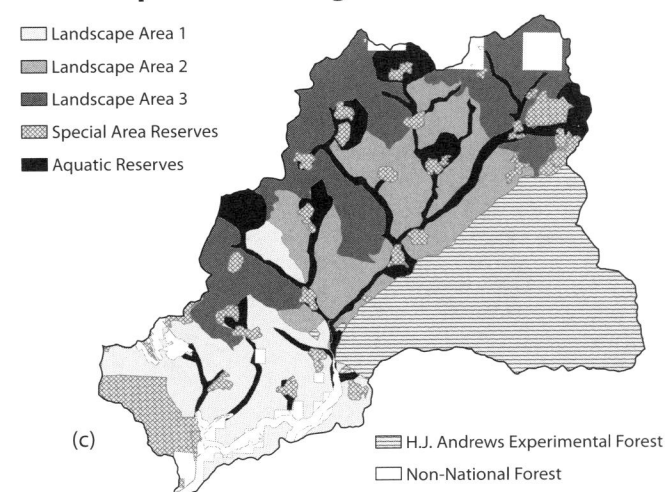

(c)

Creating and maintaining fire-frequent landscapes consistent with a shades-of-green strategy is conceptually fairly straightforward. Such a strategy is consistent with the natural model of frequent, low- to moderate-severity disturbances, which generate and maintain landscapes that are mosaics of forest patches of varied structure, including occasional small openings. An example of an existing private longleaf pine landscape managed in this way (the Joseph E. Jones Ecological Research Center) is provided in Chapter 4, Figure 4.12. Large contiguous areas of longleaf pine forest have been maintained on many other private properties in the southeastern United States for quail hunting, using prescribed fire—albeit such management has not always been ecologically optimal.

There are many current examples of efforts to restore frequent-fire landscapes on public lands in western North America (e.g., Figure 4.20), but there are also significant challenges. These include (1) an initial need for intensive and sometimes expensive treatments to create more resistant forest conditions on many sites and (2) a continuing need to sustain the more resistant forest conditions, such as through regular application (by man or nature) of fire. Fortunately some of these restoration treatments can help pay for themselves through the sale of forest products. In addition, there are significant social issues associated with both restoration and the continued use of fire, including health-related concerns associated with smoke from prescribed burning (Franklin, Hagmann, & Urgenson, 2014).

## Ecoregional Assessments in Multi-owner Landscapes: Pursuing Shades-of-Green

Societies are increasingly challenged to develop approaches for sustaining biodiversity and ecosystem processes at very large spatial scales—the scale of entire ecological regions or provinces. This is driven by various motivations but most basically by the fact that many environmental issues can be dealt with only at these larger scales. Interestingly, efforts to conserve individual species, such as the greater sage-grouse (*Centrocercus urophasianus*) and northern spotted owl, made apparent the need for such a large-landscape perspective and ultimately resulted in development of regional strategies. The challenges are immense, however, because such efforts inevitably involve multiple ownerships (often with a dominance of private rather than public owners) and an array of land uses and political entities. Earlier in this chapter we provided a vision for creating forest landscapes that are shades-of-green, owned and managed by individual owners. How, though, do we move toward such a goal at large scales and across diverse ownerships?

One way to achieve ecological and social goals in multi-owner landscapes might be to use a planning and harvest scheduling approach in which owners coordinate their activities across the landscape (Davis & Liu, 1998). In much of the United States, corporations own and manage a large amount of highly productive forestland, and these forests often are crucial to the success of regional ecosystem planning. However, antitrust laws, such as the Sherman Antitrust Act of 1890, may limit the industry's ability to participate in such a planning effort because competing firms are restricted in their ability to coordinate activities. Consequently, the real and perceived threats of antitrust litigation create serious disincentives to the forest industry's participation in large-scale ecosystem management (Thompson et al., 2004). In addition, such approaches have an element of compulsion and socialized planning that is largely antithetical to traditions of private property rights and economic freedom, certainly in the United States.

Some recent efforts at ecoregional assessment and planning have taken a different approach. These assessments describe current conditions and issues in forest conservation. Often there is a special focus on potential or expected future changes in land use, such as conversion of forests to housing and other developments or conversion of forests to intensively managed plantations. In these assessments, analysts project likely trends in land use and forest condition through time. The description of current conditions and projections of future trends provide the context for consideration of policy changes by policy makers, stakeholder groups, and individuals. These policy revisions can be suggested and accomplished incrementally, as a focus on a particular problem emerges, or comprehensively.

We will illustrate this conditions/issues/trends/policy response approach to ecoregional assessment and planning through applications in two contrasting ecoregions: (1) Coastal Oregon (Box 5.3) and (2) New England (Box 5.4). Very different policy issues emerge in these two examples, with the former focused on biodiversity issues related to loss of forest structural stages and the latter focused on loss of forestlands to development.

## Some Landscape Considerations in Setting Patch-Level Goals

Plans for landscapes managed using ecological forestry approaches will typically have general goals for the amounts, sizes, and distributions of patches of different forest conditions. Landscape-level goals may be as simple as general plans to maintain desired amounts and distributions of forests representing specific structural conditions (e.g., developmental stages). In some ways this resembles the planning for the classical regulated forest where a distribution of stand conditions (usually age classes) was sought that would provide a perpetual sustained harvest as the foundation of forest sustainability (see Chapter 17). However, we now

*(continued on page 142)*

## Box 5.3  Landscape assessment and planning in the Oregon Coast Range

The Oregon Coast Range Province is a multi-owner region dominated by productive conifer forests, steep mountainous topography, and abundant rainfall covering approximately two million hectares (Color Plate 5.2). Conifer, hardwood, and mixed forest cover approximately three-fourths of the area. Urban and rural residential development is concentrated on the western and eastern margins of the study area and along major rivers, with dairy farming along the western edge and agriculture and woodlands along the eastern edge (Spies et al., 2007). A checkerboard of federal and private lands covers much of the landscape.

Historically wildfire was the dominant natural disturbance in the Oregon Coast Range Province. Wildfires tended to be large and include extensive areas of high severity; wildfires occurred at return intervals that ranged from 100 years near the eastern (valley) margin to more than 200 years near the Pacific Ocean. Windstorms are also important and frequently blow down forests on headlands and other areas close to the Pacific Ocean, although wind is less of an issue further from the coast. Landslides and debris flows are relatively common in steeper areas and have influenced stream habitats throughout the Oregon Coast Range Province (Spies et al., 2007).

Climate change is anticipated to have only a moderate effect on these forests because of their proximity to the Pacific Ocean where marine influences are expected to partially offset effects of increasing temperature. However, the relatively dry summer period is expected to lengthen and increase in intensity (levels of moisture deficit), which will result in somewhat longer and more severe fire seasons.

Settlement by Euro-Americans began in the mid-1800s, pushing the aboriginal peoples into reservations. In the last 100 years, human activities have become the major forest disturbance. Logging began in the late 1800s on private lands and after World War II on public lands, creating a vast network of roads that caused excessive stream sedimentation. In the 1800s and early 1900s, wildfires set by settlers and loggers burned large areas of the region. Old-growth forests were systematically liquidated, followed by natural regeneration and later planting that maintained the forest cover. Also extensive coastal wetlands were ditched and drained for dairy farms and other livestock production (Spies et al., 2007).

In the late 1980s, litigation over conservation of the northern spotted owl and concerns about other species associated with mature and old-growth forests, such as the marbled murrelet (Brachyramphus marmoratus), led to a reexamination of forest policy for federal lands in this province. Concerns over declining salmon stocks added to the policy issues.

Resulting studies, which were commissioned by federal agencies and the United States Congress in the early 1990s, documented that levels of mature and old forests in the province had fallen far below historical levels due to extensive harvests across all ownerships. Further, continued implementation of federal forest plans (where most of the mature and old forests remained) would further deplete them (Johnson, Franklin, Thomas, & Gordon, 1991; Forest Ecosystem Management Assessment Team, 1993).

Federal policy makers directed scientists to construct plans for management of the federal lands throughout the range of the northern spotted owl that assumed state and private landowners would meet Oregon Forest Practice Act regulations but assume no additional contributions to biodiversity conservation beyond that (Forest Ecosystem Management Assessment Team, 1993). Consequently, federal lands would need to provide any late successional habitat (mature and old forests) and additional aquatic conservation measures. The resulting Northwest Forest Plan (NWFP) (USDA and USDI BLM, 1994) represented a major shift in management of the federal lands, which was particularly evident in this province where federal forestlands are a minority of the forest. Here, the NWFP changed the management focus from timber production to biodiversity protection on federal lands, with over 80% of federal forests placed in ecological reserves to maintain and increase the area of mature and old-growth forests and protect riparian areas.

The NWFP was followed by a Coastal Landscape Analysis and Modeling Study (CLAMS), which focused on systematically understanding the implications of the multitude of policies for the Oregon Coast Range Province then in place for protection of biodiversity, control of timber harvest, and related issues (Spies et al., 2007; Johnson et al., 2007). First the probable conversion of forest to other uses (such as agriculture and rural residential and urban development) was projected for many decades into the future. The CLAMS analysis started with the knowledge that very little wildland forest (forest areas with few dwellings) had been lost in Oregon over the previous several decades due to Oregon's restrictive land-use laws (see Lettman et al., 2013 for more detail on Oregon's land-use laws and their effect on wildland forest conservation). However, those laws do allow for a gradual expansion in the **urban growth boundary** around cities and towns as population increases. CLAMS projections of urban/suburban expansion suggested that almost all development would occur on agricultural and family forestlands on the eastern edge of the province (Johnson et al., 2007). For the foreseeable future, these limited expansions would leave the remainder of the Oregon Coast Range Province as one of the most extensive areas of mixed-ownership wildland forest in the western United States.

CLAMS scientists assessed the current representation of different structural stages, using imagery and nearest-neighbor techniques (Ohman & Gregory, 2002). Comparing their results to a sophisticated simulation of historical conditions and range of variability over time (Figure 5.22) (Wimberly, 2002), they confirmed that the province had much lower levels of mature and old forest than it did in the past. Also, the combination of clearcutting and intensive management,

Table 5.1 *Historical structural class proportions generated from 250 simulated landscapes, based on fire regimes characteristic of the Oregon Coast Range over the 1,000 years prior to Euro-American colonization (Wimberly, 2002) and recent structural class proportions (Johnson et al., 2007; Spies et al., 2007). Historical includes mean and range, where range includes all values in the 5 and 95% quantiles (includes all values except those in the lowest 5% or the highest 5% of the observations)*

| Structural Class | Historical Mean (Range) | Recent (1996)* |
|---|---|---|
| Old | 44 (29–52) | 2 |
| Mature | 17 (12–28) | 14 |
| Young | 21 (15–31) | 65 |
| Preforest[†] | 18 (12–28) | 3 |

\* Also, 16% was classified as "open"—most are recently clearcut corporate lands with a dense complement of conifer seedlings, but with few structural legacies and a low diversity and density of diverse early seral plants due to suppression of this vegetation. This category does not have a historical analog.

† Called "early successional" in Wimberly (2002)

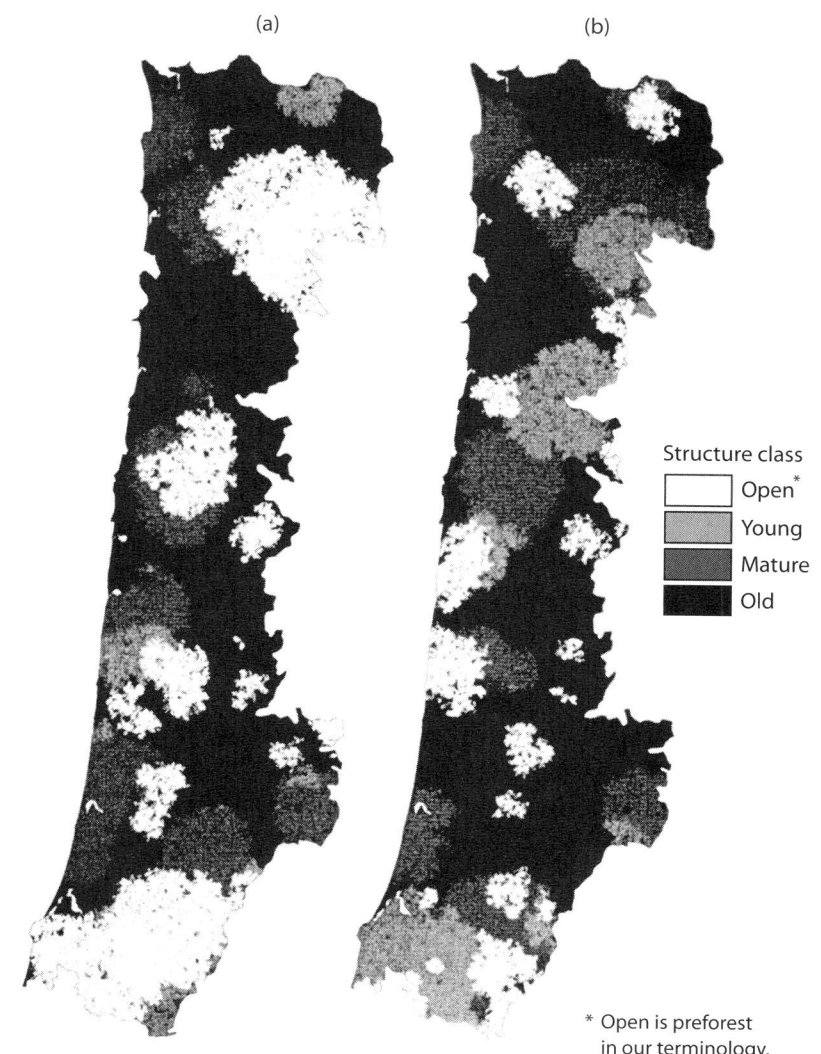

(a)                    (b)

Structure class

□ Open*
▨ Young
▩ Mature
■ Old

\* Open is preforest in our terminology.

along with effective fire suppression had largely eliminated the rich and complex preforest ecosystems that were present historically. On the other hand, the region has an abundance of structurally and biologically simplified plantations (much of the young forest and open in Table 5.1), which were established following the clearcutting of the historical forests.

To put it another way, the levels of old and preforest were far below the ***Historical Range of Variability*** (HRV), while the young forests were far above that range (Table 5.1). The HRV is an estimate of the variation in physical and biological conditions in some period of the past as a function of natural climatic fluctuations and disturbance regimes, and is often used as a benchmark for conditions that describe functional ecosystems (Davis, Johnson, Bettinger, & Howard, 2001; Keane, Hessburg, Landres, & Swanson, 2009; Landres, Morgan, & Swanson, 1999; Morgan et al., 1994). While any assessment that utilizes the HRV must also consider future, expected climate change and other changes from the past (Millar, Stephenson, & Stephens, 2007), the HRV can still provide useful information on how much a contemporary landscape diverges from one in which biota survived and evolved. Compared to the HRV estimated by Wimberly (2002), the contemporary landscape in the Oregon Coastal Province was outside the range that it had experienced historically in terms of the proportion of forest in the old, young, and preforest structural conditions (Table 5.1)—a signal that the ecosystems of the Oregon Coastal Province might not be able to continue the ecological benefits and habitats that they had historically provided.

Wimberly (2002) also measured the patch size of openings created by historical fires in the Oregon Coast Range Province and that were subsequently occupied by biologically rich preforest communities

Figure 5.22 *Two simulated landscapes from Wimberly (2000) spatial simulation of the historical fire regimes over time and their landscape effects in the Oregon Coast Range Province: (a) a resulting landscape pattern and (b) the landscape pattern after 80 more years of disturbance and succession. (Source: Davis et al., 2001)*

(continued)

(Table 5.2). Almost 80% of the patches were over 100 ha, and in fact, patches over 1,000 ha contributed most of the area, upon which the preforest communities could develop. These findings suggest that historical wildfire disturbances in the Coast Range provided large complex openings, which almost certainly had extensive biological legacies, including a high diversity of animals and plants! Current policies for private lands, the location of most harvests that create openings, promote the opposite results: they constrain all landowners to a harvest opening size of less than 100 ha; they require the retention of very few legacies; and they require that shrubs do not overtop commercial seedlings.

Scientists working on CLAMS next projected forest management into the future under the policies currently in place on the different ownerships: simulations of likely forest practices by private forest owners based on legal requirements, assumed landowner goals, and recent actions and simulations of federal and state forest plan implementation. The scientists projected that over two-thirds of future harvest would come from corporate forests utilizing production forestry techniques, with only modest levels from other owners. They also projected that mature and old forests would gradually increase, but that biologically rich and structurally complex preforest ecosystems would continue at very low levels (far below HRV), while structurally simplified plantations would continue to dominate much of the landscape (Figure 5.23).

This analysis sets the stage for a discussion of further policy revisions, such as those that would encourage an increase in biologically rich and structurally complex preforest on private forestlands in the Oregon Coast Range Province. Such an adjustment could help address the large array of early seral habitat specialists (e.g., birds and butterflies) that are in decline. In addition, the CLAMS' projection suggested that riparian protection in the province as a whole would be much less than that on federal lands, especially on headwater streams. Since federal and private lands share watersheds with federally listed threatened fish stocks, policy revision on private lands may be needed for riparian protection as well. We will cover some possible revisions in Oregon forest practices in Chapter 21 when we illustrate how ecological forestry could be encouraged across this ecoregion.

Table 5.2 *Historical patch-size distributions of openings generated from 250 simulated landscapes, based on fire regimes characteristic of the Oregon Coast Range over the 1,000 years prior to Euro-American colonization (from Wimberly, 2002)*

| Hectare range[*] | Proportion of patches | Proportion of area |
|---|---|---|
| 0–11 | 5 | <1 |
| 10–100 | 18 | <1 |
| 100–1,000 | 37 | 3 |
| 1,000–10,000 | 30 | 22 |
| 10,000–100,000 | 7 | 51 |
| 100,000+ | 3 | 24 |

[*] A hectare equals approximately 2.47 acres.

Figure 5.23 *Corporate forest landscape in the Oregon Coast Province, containing plantations grown on short, 35–45-year rotations. (Photo courtesy of Deanne Carlson)*

## Box 5.4  Landscape assessment and planning in New England

Before European settlement, the New England region of the northeastern USA supported ancient and varied forests, with pitch pine, oak, hickory, and chestnut in the south, white pine, hemlock, birch, beech, and maple in the central and northern uplands, and spruce, fir, and paper birch in the north. Almost 400 years ago, arriving colonists began to displace the aboriginal people and transform the land. Forests were cleared for farms over much of the region and remaining forests were used for many purposes. Logging removed most of the old-growth trees, especially the white pine, while hunting, trapping, and habitat degradation decimated many native species and deforestation associated with land clearing opened the forest up for early successional plants and animals. As farming peaked in the late 19th century and people headed to the Midwest, the agrarian landscape began to return to forest. This process acceler-

Figure 5.24  *Housing development in New England forest.*

ated in the 20th century as New England farmers found it increasingly difficult to compete with other food producers. As a result, forest once again covers much of New England (Foster et al., 2010) (Color Plate 5.3a).

Recently a group of scientists, policy makers, and administrators, led by David Foster of Harvard Forest (Foster et al., 2010) reviewed the current status and future trends of forest cover in New England. They expressed alarm at the expected land use changes that they and others foresaw in the next few decades in New England (Foster et al., 2010, p. 9):

*The incredible ecological, social, and economic opportunities in New England's forested landscape are accompanied by threats of equal magnitude (Kittredge, 2009). For the first time since agricultural abandonment in the mid-1800s, all six New England states are experiencing a decline in forest cover that is projected to continue into the future. This second wave of deforestation poses far greater challenges than the previous episode. The permanent development and landscape fragmentation of today, often involving asphalt, concrete, and steel, are much harder to reverse than the historic clearing of land for farms and pasture.*

While noting that climate change and "adverse harvest practices" would negatively affect these forests to some degree, Foster et al. (2010) focused on land-use change as the biggest threat to forests (Color Plate 5.3b). They recognized three types of land-use change:

- **Deforestation and development.** Historical clearing for agriculture comprised a "soft" deforestation; abandoned farms readily reverted to forest. In contrast, today's developments cause a "hard" deforestation for commercial complexes, ski resorts, and single-family and multiunit residential dwellings that converts land forever (Figure 5.24).

- **Perforation.** The subtle infiltration of houses and human activities into natural landscapes is more widespread than development and also can be disruptive to ecosystems, hydrology, wildlife, and recreation (Figure 5.25).

- **Parcelization.** Across New England, the age and number of landowners is increasing, tract sizes are decreasing, and more owners are absentee. As an example, the vast industrial forests in Northern Maine, long owned by a few families and timber companies, have been sold to real estate companies, investment firms, and developers. These changes can hinder conservation efforts, set the stage for deforestation, and threaten the long tradition of public access to private forests.

In the face of these current and future threats, Foster et al. (2010, p. 10) concluded that "the single most important action that we can take is to maintain forested landscapes on a scale that allows natural and human communities to flourish." Toward that end, they propose retaining most of the existing forest either as woodland, where timber harvest and many other forest uses can occur, or wildland, where natural processes will be emphasized (Color Plate 5.3c).

In many ways, their proposal for the 33 million acres of New England is similar to the goals of Oregon's land-use laws. The Oregon laws passed in the 1970s covered the 30 million acres of nonfederal land in Oregon and, among other goals, were designed to protect prime forest and farmlands from

*(continued)*

Figure 5.25 *New England landscape perforated with homes. (Photo courtesy of David Foster)*

- **Pioneer new conservation mechanisms to ensure that lands remain permanently forested** such as conservation aggregation—the process of working with multiple landowners to advance conservation across many individual parcels of land simultaneously.

- **Continue and advance innovative financing strategies.** As mentioned above, New England already has sizeable tracts protected from development. Many of these are nationally recognizable, such as the White Mountain National Forest, Acadia National Forest, and Baxter State Park. In recent decades, though, concern about the "breakup" of traditional ownerships spurred the purchase of **conservation easements** from major forest landowners in Maine and Northern New Hampshire. These easements limit development, through funding provided by various groups and governments. The funding for these easements can be quite creative: conservation groups obtained a conservation easement for the forest around Moosehead Lake in Maine by working with the timber company that owned the land around the lake on zoning changes that would allow some carefully planned development (Box 10.5). Other helpful financial tools could come from enhancing income tax and property tax incentives for forest protection, expanding mitigation programs, and targeting philanthropic investment. Further, as pointed out by D'Amato, Catanzaro, Demery, Kittredge, and Ferrare (2010) (Box 6.1), combining revenue streams from forest conservation and use, whether from timber products, floral products, or carbon storage, with other financial incentives is critical to the long-term economic viability of forest ownerships in New England.

conversion to other uses. As with the Oregon land-use laws, Foster et al. (2010) wish to "shepherd sensible development." However, they recognize that passage of statewide land-use laws—like those in Oregon—is not likely to occur in New England for many reasons. Rather, *they embrace a suite of policy proposals to double the rate of forest protection*, building on the network of forests already protected from development (Color Plate 5.3d) and recognizing the challenges of engaging the hundreds of thousands of forest landowners of New England:

- **Increase engagement with landowners though regional conservation partnerships that work across political boundaries and landscapes** to improve management and ensure permanent conservation of forests through a collaborative effort.

- **Utilize planning and policy tools to carefully guide development.** As Foster et al. (2010) pointed out, current zoning in many communities may accelerate forest loss, such as by requiring dispersed versus clustered housing. In general, they recommend revising land use policies to make more efficient use of land, reduce cost of public services, and provide fair housing to meet community needs.

realize that providing a multitude of ecosystem services from the forest is more complicated than regulating a set of age classes, and also realize that actually attaining such an idealized landscape in our uncertain future is unlikely!

**Spatial Distribution of Harvest Activities** Implementation of timber harvesting activities across the landscape in ways that emulate natural models and sustain ecological values include considerations of patch (harvest unit) size and internal content (e.g., biological legacies) as well as their distribution (e.g., concentrated of dispersed). Patch

size and content are likely to be strongly related, particularly in episodically disturbed forest types where the natural disturbance patches were often very large but also incorporated large and spatially varied levels of biological legacies. Both the ecological merit and social acceptability of larger harvest units are likely to be much greater when higher levels of biological legacies are retained. Large harvest units with low levels of biological legacies are not likely to fulfill either ecological or social needs.

Distribution of the harvesting activities over the landscape is also an important consideration—should they be concentrated in some portion of the landscape over a given time period or widely dispersed? Much of past timber harvesting activity on public lands has chosen to disperse activities, essentially assuming that work will occur in all parts of the landscape all of the time. Of course, harvesting was also primarily by clearcutting (few or no legacies) and often adopted patch sizes that were not consistent with natural models or habitat needs of native biota. Under such circumstances, dispersed approaches could and did result in creation of landscapes highly susceptible to disturbances and lacking in habitat for native biota (Box 5.5).

**Providing Habitat across Space and Time**   Landscapes managed using ecological forestry approaches often will include a goal of providing habitat conditions required by specific biota. These desired conditions can vary from simply providing for a specific type of habitat patch scattered through a landscape managed for other objectives (Box 5.6), to maintaining a distribution of patch sizes through time (Hessburg et al., 2007), to managing areas to sustain intricate patterns of cover and forage patches over time (see Chapter 19 for discussion of planning for dynamic spatial relationships over time.).

**Avoiding Cumulative Effects**   Cumulative effects are generally defined as the aggregate consequences of human activities (e.g., clearcutting or road building) in an area. Unacceptable cumulative effects are those occurring over a time period insufficient to allow for recovery, which results in some landscape-level dysfunctional response, such as enhanced flood flows following storms (see Chapter 7 for more discussion of cumulative effects in a legal context). One way of dealing with such phenomena is to limit the amount of activity that is allowed over a particular time period with the goal of reducing either the probability or intensity of a dysfunctional effect. These limitations can be expressed through a landscape-level threshold for some specific patch types or conditions that contribute to the dysfunction. A real-world example of a landscape-level threshold to control the effect of harvest on rain-on-snow flood events along the Pacific Coast of northwestern North America is provided in Box 5.7.

**Prioritizing Treatments in Federal Frequent-Fire Landscapes**   Many factors are important in setting treatment priorities at the landscape level, including ecological, economic, and social considerations. Some of these will be obvious depending upon the circumstances, particularly where restoration is a primary objective.

In frequent-fire forests that are part of the WUI, fuel treatments would be of high priority, because of the desire to protect human life and developments, with the actions often coordinated with those of adjacent communities. Even here, though, principles of ecological forestry can be integrated into the treatments. Elsewhere in frequent-fire landscapes, treatments that involve spatial strategies to constrain fire movement may take priority, especially where it is not possible to treat large areas for either logistical or economic reasons. Areas having high ecological value, such as forests that still contain significant numbers of large old trees, would have priority for treatment from an environmental perspective.

Setting priorities for restoring frequent-fire landscapes generally will require consideration of many factors, including where major resource values are at risk, logistical concerns (accessibility), and economics. Moister—more productive portions of the landscape—will often have a high priority because such sites develop dense, fuel-loaded forests much more rapidly than drier sites (Franklin, Hagmann, & Urgenson, 2014). Prioritizing restoration of such areas is further indicated when residual large old trees are present, since these are keystone structures that are essentially irreplaceable—hence the need to restore those areas to decrease the risk that they will be lost. Prioritizing restoration based upon the number of missed fire-return intervals is probably not helpful if such sites represent low productivity habitats that accumulate fuels at a lower rate than more productive sites. Another consideration in restoring frequent-fire landscapes may be to match up areas where restoration can provide a positive economic return with those that cannot, allowing restoration to be extended to a larger proportion of the landscape (see Chapters 4, 12, and 13 for more discussion on the points in this section).

## Box 5.5  Distributing management patches across a landscape

The distribution of management activities, such as timber harvesting, can have profound ecological consequences at the level of the landscape. For example, should managers choose to concentrate or disperse their activities across their landscape? On public lands the decision has often been made to disperse activities rather than to concentrate them, perhaps in the belief that dispersing them over a larger area will reduce their impacts. This is often not the case, however, with regards to impacts on hydrologic regimes and fisheries (e.g., Reeves & Spies, 2017, p. 215–216), where choosing to concentrate activities at the level of a watershed at a moment in time may be superior to dispersing the same level of activity over several watersheds.

Dispersed patch clearcutting provides a classic example of the potential consequences of dispersing activities at an ecologically inappropriate patch size. This dispersed approach to harvesting was adopted in converting the old-growth Douglas-fir forests in northwestern North America to managed forests. Franklin and Forman (1987) utilized a simple **checkerboard model** to explore the consequences of dispersing small (e.g., 10 ha) clearcuts through a hypothetical old-growth forest landscape of 1,000 ha (Figure 5.26). In their theoretical exercise they dispersed these small clearcuts as regularly as possible through a 1,000 ha model landscape and examined how this affected landscape attributes (patch size, edge, interior forest area) and potential for various kinds of disturbances (wind, fire, pests and pathogens) (Figure 5.26).

Rapid changes in landscape metrics and significant thresholds were evident from the analysis. Dispersing clearcut units resulted in a threshold about 1/3 of the way into the harvest cycle at which residual forest patch size underwent a rapid reduction (Figure 5.27a). A rapid increase

in the amount of edge between residual forest patches and cutover areas was associated with harvest entries, peaking at the 50% cutover level (Figure 5.27b). Interior forest conditions were completely eliminated by the 50% cutover point even though half the forest area still remained (Figure 5.27c). Data collected from national forest landscapes harvested using dispersed patch clearcutting provided empirical support as did mathematical analyses using percolation models. Such rapid changes in landscape metrics had not been anticipated when the approach was adopted.

The emerging landscape structure from dispersed patch clearcutting created favorable conditions for major disturbances, such as high potential for windthrow and fire in residual forest patches. Edges between forest and cutover patches have a high potential for windthrow (such as Gratkowski, 1956, and Alexander, 1964), and hence, risk of windthrow in residual patches increased rapidly as the cutting progressed, peaked early in the cutting cycle, and remained high until the last forest patch was cut (Figure 5.27d). Similarly the potential for fire ignitions increased rapidly as a result of early development of the road system, and the potential for fire spread into residual forest patches increased with the increasing exposure of the patch interiors to microclimatic influence of adjacent cutovers (Figure 5.27e). Effects of the cutting pattern on pests and pathogens varied depending upon how it influenced their access to their host species and age classes (Figure 5.27f).

Several lessons are apparent from this analysis. Most profoundly, fragmentation of the residual forest occurs very rapidly using a dispersed patch clearcutting approach. One consequence is that dispersing activities in space greatly increases the potential for several major kinds of disturbances as the harvest cycle progresses, as was the case with

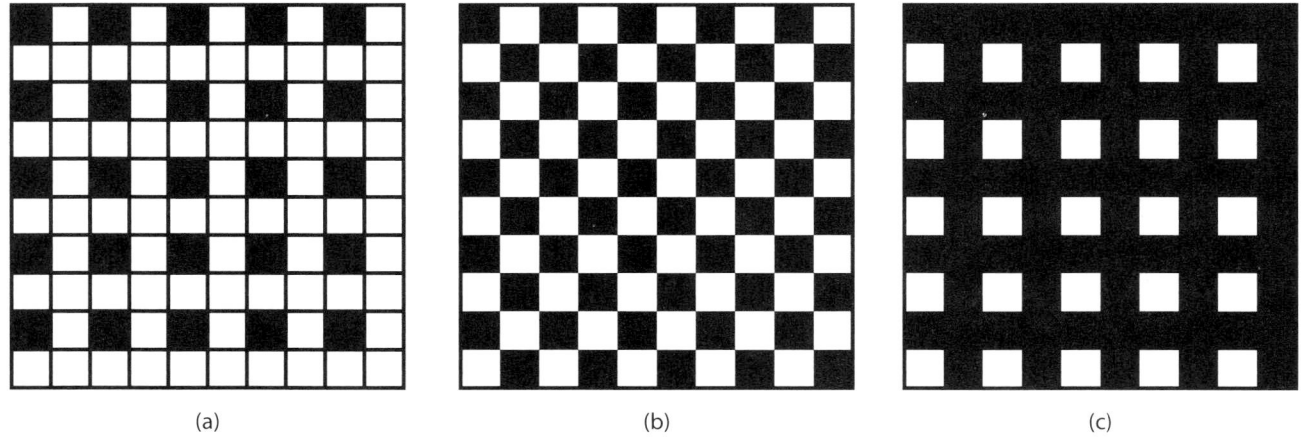

(a)                          (b)                          (c)

Figure 5.26 *Checkerboard model illustrating progression of a harvest cycle through a theoretical 1,000 ha landscape in which 10 ha clearcuts are progressively taken with the goal of maximum dispersion of these harvest units. Shown in this progression are the 25, 50, and 75 percent cutover points in such a model. (Republished with permission of Springer-Verlag Dordrecht from Franklin & Forman, 1987; permission conveyed through Copyright Clearance Center, Inc.)*

windthrow in the Bull Run watershed (Sinton et al., 2000). Another lesson is that the selection of harvest unit patch size can be critical; the patch size of 40 to 60 acres that was chosen for federal lands in the Douglas-fir region was far too small to provide for residual forest patches free of major edge effects (documented in many subsequent studies e.g., Chen, Franklin, & Spies, 1993, 1995) and was inconsistent with forest patch sizes needed by many of the biota (Franklin & Forman, 1987). More attention to natural models of primeval Douglas-fir landscapes (e.g., studying the characteristic forest patch sizes and their internal structure) would have been helpful.

Restoring landscapes to more appropriate patch mosaics (size and condition of patches)—stitching the landscape back together—may be an important objective in ecological forestry treatments. In many forest types, an effort of this type would likely require an increase in the size of treated patches, which would also require a shift in policies to allow for these larger units. Of course, increases in harvest unit patch size would need to be accompanied by ecological forestry prescriptions that provide for retention of significant biological legacies, so the ecological and social effects of the increase in harvest unit patch size would be much less than with clearcutting.

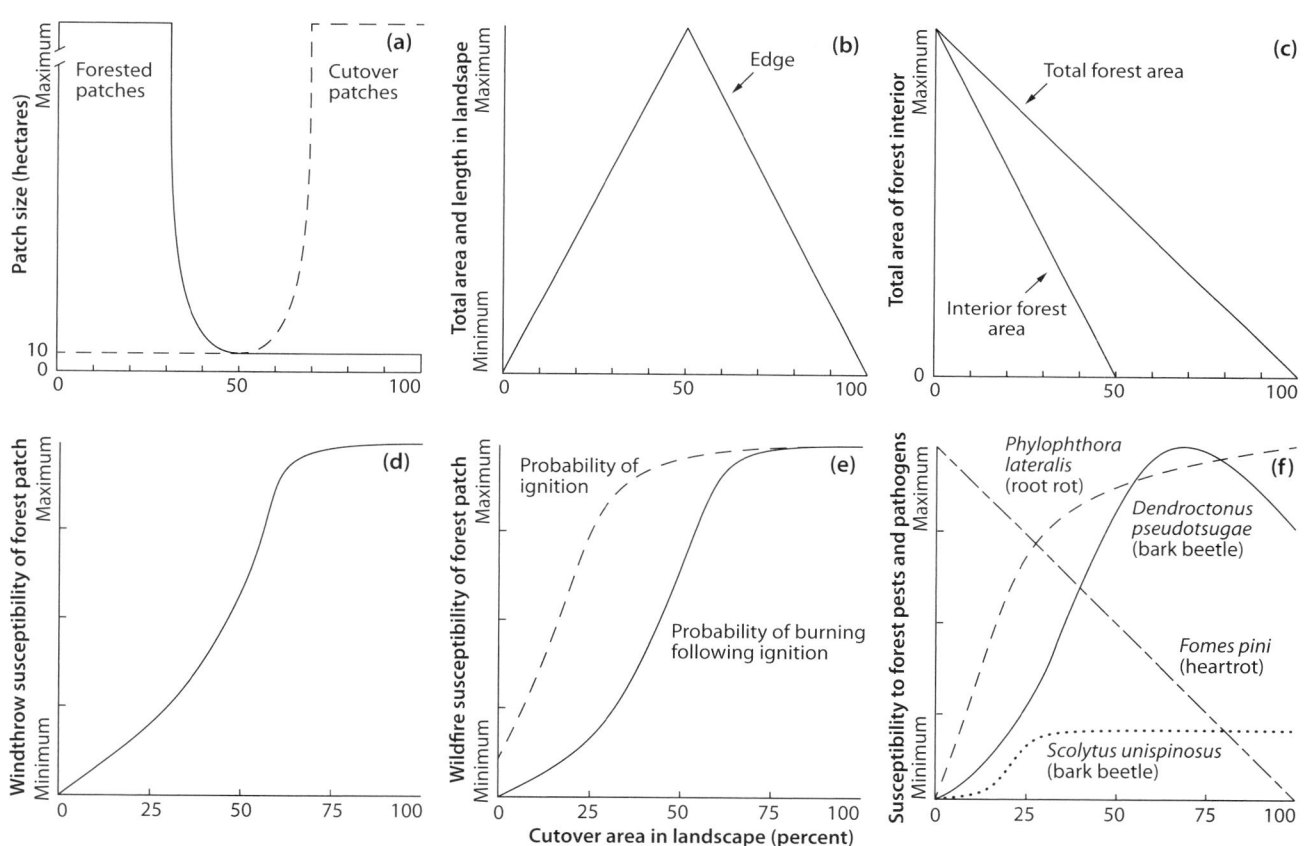

Figure 5.27 *Responses of landscape-level parameters to progressive timber harvests in a hypothetical 1,000 ha primeval Douglas-fir forest landscape following the principle of maximum dispersion of each succeeding series of 10 ha clearcuts: (a) Average size of forest and cutover patches; (b) Amount of edge or border between residual forest patches and cutovers; (c) Area of residual forest and of interior forest habitat, the latter calculated assuming edge effects that extend 140 m (approximately 2 tree heights) into a forest from a clearcut edge; (d) Potential for windthrow in residual forest patches, which increases with the amount of edge and length of wind fetches between harvest units; (e) Potential for wildfire in residual forest patches, where ignition potential increases rapidly with development of the road system and potential for spread within the forest patches increases with altered microclimate influences of adjacent clearcuts; and (f) Potential for insect and fungus infections in residual forest patches, which is highly species specific—i.e., the potential reflects the interactions of pest/pathogen life histories and environment (including dispersal mechanisms) and the distribution of susceptible stages of the host species (see Franklin and Forman 1987 for more details). (Republished with permission of Springer-Verlag Dordrecht from Franklin & Forman, 1987; permission conveyed through Copyright Clearance Center, Inc.)*

## Box 5.6  Maintaining dense forest habitat while restoring resiliency to frequent-fire landscapes

Restoration programs are being undertaken over large areas in many regions of western North America, where suppression of wildfire resulted in development of large contiguous areas of dense forest that are now potentially subject to high-severity wildfires (see Chapters 3, 12, and 13). A primary goal in these restoration efforts is to increase the resistance and adaptive capacity of forests and landscapes in the face of future fire and drought. However, these restoration programs often need to include plans for retention of dense and structurally complex forest patches as part of the restored landscape in order to provide important habitat for species needing denser forests. A common example in western pine and mixed-conifer forests are raptors, such as goshawks and owls, which may need the denser forest patches for nesting, roosting, and foraging. Of course, in all probability an ecological forester would be retaining some denser forest areas based simply on the principles of providing for landscape heterogeneity.

A real-world example of this need is the northern spotted owl (Strix occidentalis caurina), which requires relatively dense forest patches when inhabiting landscapes historically characterized by frequent fire. These dense forest patches are most characteristically dominated by mature Douglas-fir and/or true firs and provide nesting and roosting habitat. The dense forest patches also provide the type of habitat needed by the northern spotted owl's primary prey species, the northern flying squirrel (Glaucomus sabrinus). Hence, programs to restore frequent-fire landscapes within the range of the northern spotted owl also need to incorporate retention or restoration of appropriate sizes and distributions of denser forest patches of suitable character as well as a plan for replacement of such patches when they burn. The northern goshawk (Accipiter gentilis) is a much more widespread example of a raptor found in frequent-fire forest landscapes in western North America that also requires denser forest patches.

The red-cockaded woodpecker (Picoides borealis) is another example of a focal species that occupies frequent-fire forest landscapes and requires a landscape-level approach for providing critical nesting and foraging habitat. However, its requirements are fully consistent with the open conditions provided in mature longleaf pine forests managed with frequent prescribed fire.

## Box 5.7  A landscape threshold: limitations on recently harvested conditions in landscapes potentially subject to rain-on-snow events

Rain-on-snow storms are a primary source of major floods in streams and rivers in many of the coastal mountain regions of northwestern North America from northern California to the Gulf of Alaska. These events are a consequence of the transient or warm snow zones that span broad elevational bands in coastal mountains. During cold periods in the winter, significant snowpacks can accumulate at middle to low elevations in these mountains. When such periods are followed by one or more weather systems that bring strong flows of warm, moist tropical air to the region (locally known as the "Pineapple Express"), rain-on-snow storm events occur. The flooding is a combined consequence of heavy rains and rapidly melting snow because of the warm air temperatures.

Mature and old conifer forests in this region have rigid canopies with large and strong branch systems, which can intercept much of the snowfall. There are several paths for this intercepted snow: some melts, drips to the ground, and enters the soil; most of the remainder ultimately falls to forest floor ending up as snowpack in the shaded and largely wind-free forest understories. In contrast, snow accumulates on the ground in recent cutovers and young forests developing on earlier clearcuts. Little of the snow melts and infiltrates into the soil. This large mass of snow is fully exposed to the warm winds that arrive with the tropical air masses resulting in rapid melting. The combination of melting snow and rain produces major flood events. Because of the large snow accumulations and open exposed conditions, the contribution of recent cutovers and young forests to flood flows is much higher than that of mature and old forests.

Flood events cause significant downstream damage so there are significant incentives to avoid exacerbating these flood events. Consequently, public agencies managing lands in the transient snow zones have developed thresholds regarding the percentages of the stream drainages that can be in conditions (such as recent clearcuts and young forests) that could significantly intensify rain-on-snow flood events. For example, Washington State Department of Natural Resources has developed thresholds for maximal amounts of these conditions allowed in drainages on lands that it manages within transient snow zones. Some national forests, such as the Mt. Baker-Snoqualmie National Forest, also incorporated such thresholds in their management plans.

# Part II

*Economic and
Social Context*

*The son-of-a-bitch who invented checkerboards*
*ought to be sitting in hell on coals roasting.*
*For a very long time. . . . Let's face it: ecological*
*systems don't come in squares.* — JACK WARD THOMAS

# CHAPTER 6

# Economic, Social, and Political Drivers of Forestry

In this chapter, we outline five major economic, social, and political drivers of forest conservation and management in the United States and many other parts of the world:

- *Ownership* plays a role in determining forest management goals and environmental responsibilities.

- *Markets* are important drivers of forest conservation and use, both in terms of which lands stay in forests and the management strategies used.

- *Investment and income strategies* can greatly influence landowner evaluation of forest conservation alternatives.

- *Policy formation processes* are a political vehicle by which society expresses its wishes for forest management.

- *Social acceptability* of forestry directs and limits the roles that forest management can play in achieving landowner and public goals for forests.

We will utilize the example of the United States here but will broaden the discussion to other countries in the next chapter. At the end of each major section, we will summarize the implications of our analysis and findings for the potential and shape of ecological forestry in the future.

## Ownership

The conterminous United States is approximately one-third forested (Oswalt, Smith, Miles, & Pugh, 2014) (Figure 6.1), and forest ownership is a key to the use of forestland there. Landowner goals and public expectations vary with different types of ownership, a theme we will come back to throughout this chapter and the next. To help recognize these differing goals and expectations, we will break the discussion about ownership into public and private landowners and then into subcategories.

*A checkerboard of private industrial forest and Bureau of Land Management (BLM) forest in western Oregon, with most of the intact forest on BLM lands.*

We will focus on how the type of ownership influences the kind of forestry that might be practiced and on the potential interest in ecological forestry. The spatial arrangement of these ownerships also influences this potential. Land disposal policies in the early history of the United States left large areas of the West in a checkerboard pattern of landownership, with alternating sections of federal and private (often corporate) lands (Dana & Fairfax, 1980; Nie, 2008), as shown in the opening photo of this chapter and in Color Plate 5.2. This *crazy quilt* of landownership can greatly complicate ecological forestry at the landscape scale.

## Private Forests

Almost 60% of forests in the United States are in private ownership, with these forests concentrated in the north and south (Butler, 2008) (Figure 6.1; Figure 6.2). Most private forests are *family forests* (Figure 6.2). Family forest owners are defined as "families, individuals, trusts, estates, and family partnerships that own forest land" (Butler, 2016a, p. 11). Most of the remaining private land is in the hands of corporate landowners who are primarily located in Maine, Oregon, Washington, and the southeastern USA. We used to call corporate owners the *forest industry*, when this land was to provide a wood supply for saw, plywood, and pulp mills. Now, much of the corporate forest is owned by various kinds of investment companies who manage the financial resources of retirement funds, insurance companies, universities, and wealthy individuals.

Private forestland makes a substantial contribution to timber harvest, accounting for more than 80% of all timber harvested in the United States in 2011 (Oswalt et al., 2014). Most of the remaining harvest comes from national forests and state forests.

**Landowner Objectives**   *Corporate landowners are generally presumed to maximize profits from their forestlands, within governmental constraints.* Historically, forest products firms held large tracts of forestlands as a hedge against price swings for wood fiber on the open market, or other disruptions of supply. Many of these forests in the United States, though, have been sold or transferred to Timber Investment Management Organizations (TIMOs), Real Estate Investment Trusts (REITs), or pension funds. These organizations focus on optimizing return on capital for their investors; investments in timber compete with other investment alternatives for a place in their portfolio. Thus, more than ever, corporate forest landowners focus primarily on achieving a competitive rate of return (Binkley, Raper, & Washburn, 1996; Cubbage, Snider, Abt, & Moulton, 2003). Such an approach epitomizes the production forestry model described in Chapter 1, in which forests are seen as fungible capital assets to manage or

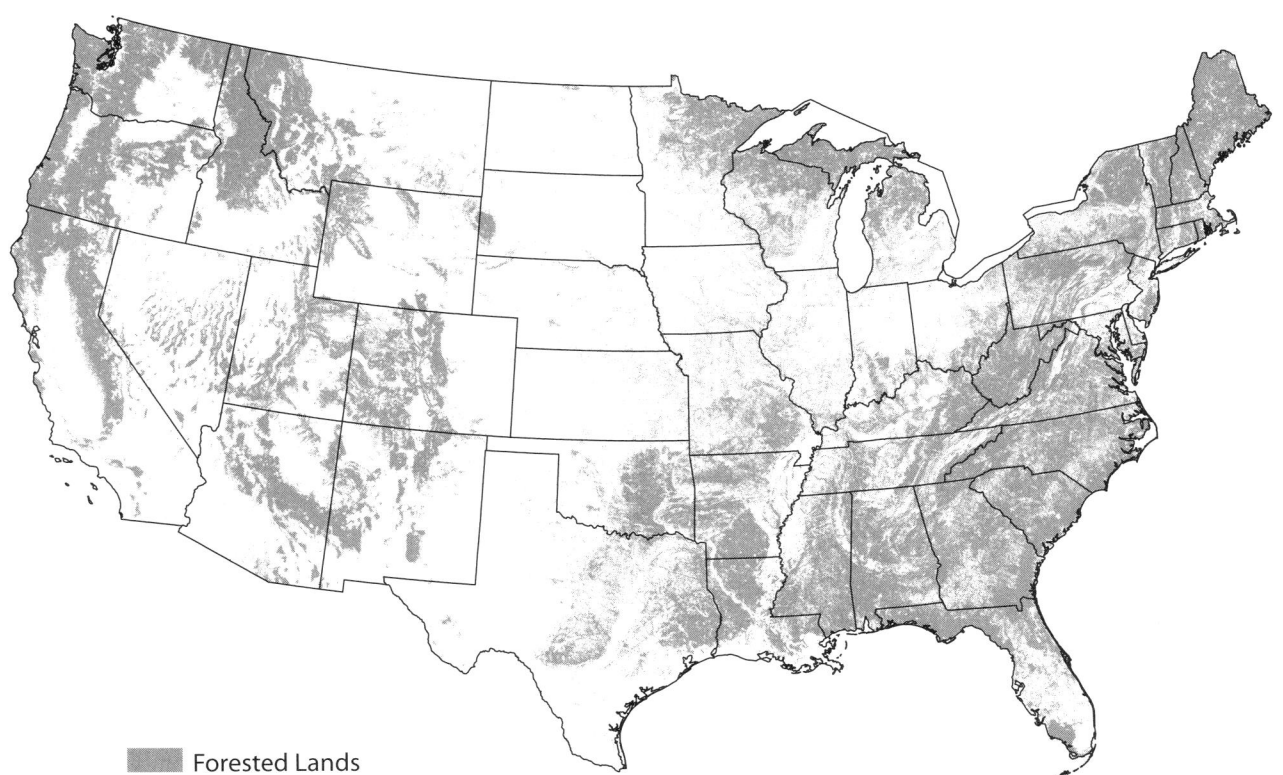

Forested Lands

Figure 6.1 *Forests of the conterminous United States.*

sell as needed to meet financial goals. We will discuss rate of return analysis in more depth in Chapter 9.

*Family forest landowners generally have a much more complicated and diverse set of goals.* The objectives and motivations of family forest landowners throughout the world have been examined in a variety of studies. A national study of family forest landowners in the United States found that beauty/scenery, protecting and improving wildlife habitat, passing land to their heirs, privacy, protecting biodiversity, and protecting water were the most important reasons for owning forest (Figure 6.3) (Butler et al., 2016b). Other studies, such as Birch (1996) and Bliss and McNabb (1992) have documented similar goals families have for their forests. These studies substantiate that *financial return from timber production is not the sole goal, or perhaps even a major goal, for many family forest landowners. Rather, they have a multiplicity of goals into which timber production and harvest must fit.* As stated by Butler (2011, p. 88):

*Despite what some of us might have learned in forestry school, timber production is not the primary reason that families own land. . . . Rather the most important reasons for*

land ownership are related to the aesthetics and privacy the land provides and its importance as part of their families' legacy. "Aesthetics" is shorthand for the enjoyment owners get from many facets of the land—the trees, the wildlife, everything about it. Many owners have a primary or secondary residence on the land and greatly value the privacy and solitude the forests provide. "Legacy" is their ability to pass the land on to the next generation: many owners have inherited the land from their parents or other relatives and would like to do the same for future generations.

*The goals of family forest landowners have important implications for management schemes that might be useful to them. They also raise serious doubts about the appropriateness of rate of return analysis as a primary decision-making criterion* for these landowners as is typically assumed for corporate landowners.

**Forest Conservation Challenges** Private forest conservation in the United States faces a number of challenges in the 21st century. We highlight three here: (1) conversion to other uses, (2) at-risk species, and (3) wildfire risk.

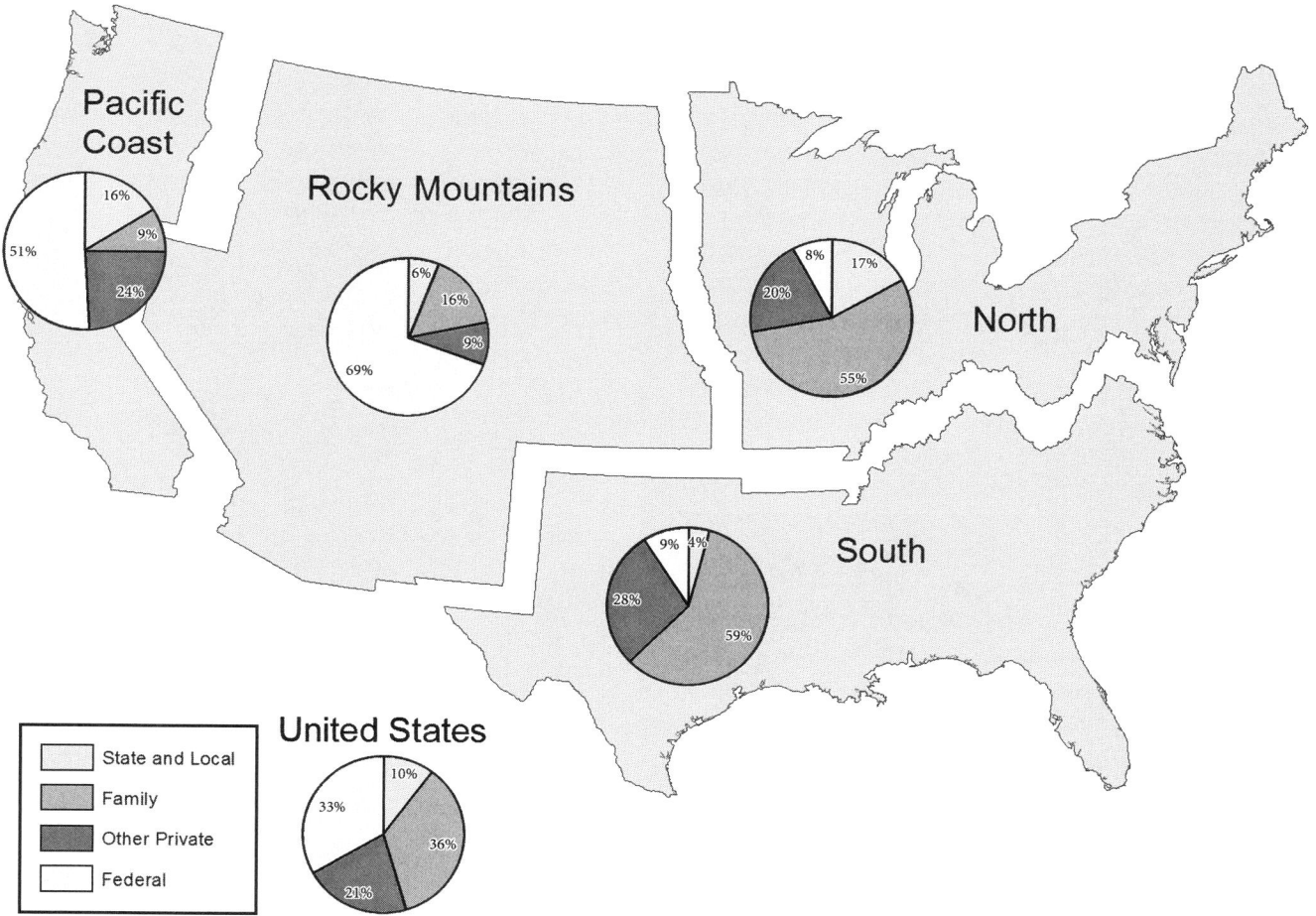

Figure 6.2 *Forest landowners by region in the conterminous United States.* (*Source: Butler et al., 2008*)

*Expected conversion of family and corporate forests into homes, subdivisions, and shopping malls will further fragment private forests* in many parts of the United States and reduce their ability to provide forest-related ecosystem services.[1] Stein et al. (2009) projected that this increase in housing density, and associated developments, will be especially concentrated along the East Coast and in the mid-South, Florida, and Michigan (Figure 6.4). Also, pockets of forest near major cities will be affected in the West, although public lands there may buffer the effects. Research by Wear and Coulston (2015) suggest that this development can significantly reduce the ability of the forests of the East and South to continue to function as important carbon sinks.

As Stein et al. (2009, p. 24, emphasis added) pointed out citing Robles et al. (2008):

Approximately 60% of 'at-risk' . . . vertebrate and invertebrate animals and plants in the conterminous United States are associated with private forests, *and two-thirds of the watersheds in the conterminous United States that include private forests have been identified as having at-risk species. . . . In most watersheds identified as having the greatest number of at-risk species, at least one species is found only on private land, and these forests are often isolated and particularly vulnerable to development.*[2]

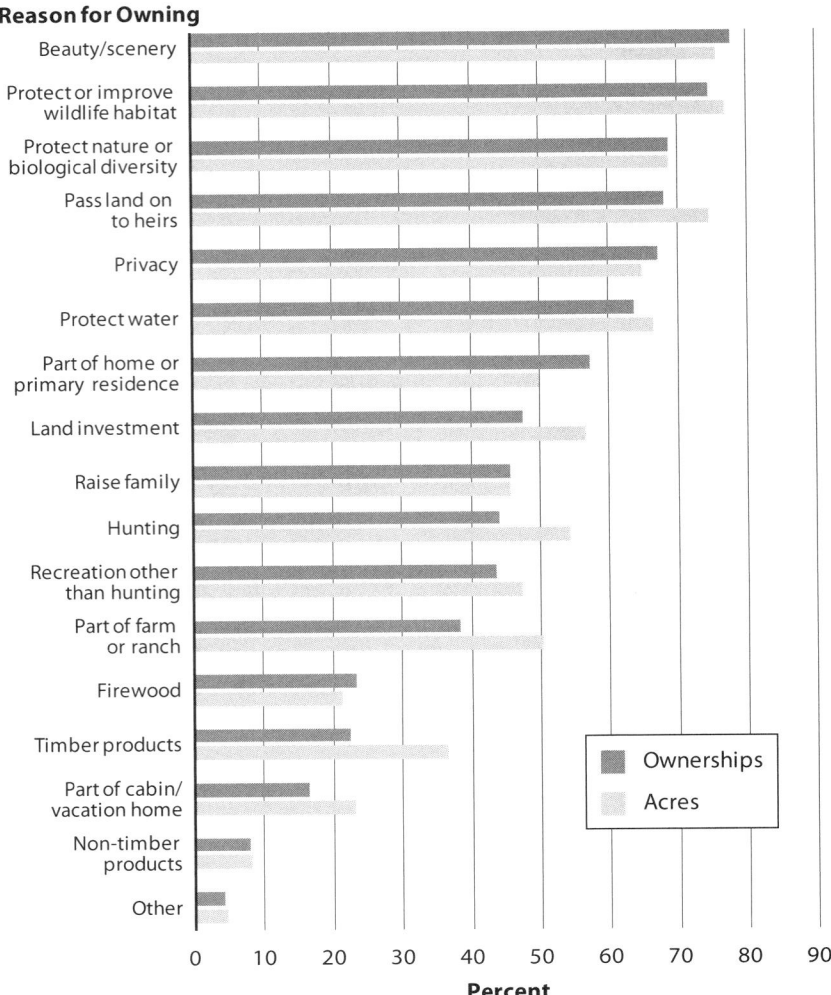

**Reason for Owning**

Figure 6.3 *Why families own forests (percentage of family forestland and ownerships greater than 10 acres that rated an objective as "important" or "very important" on a five-point Likert scale). (Source: Adapted from Butler et al., 2016b; data available online at: www.fia.fs.fed.us/nwos)*

Especially watersheds in the South and parts of California have large numbers of at-risk species on private forests (Figure 6.5).

As Stein et al. (2009, p. 24) further pointed out, again citing Robles et al. (2008): "Private forests are especially critical for wide-ranging animals that cross patchworks of public and private lands at different seasons or life stages, such as the endangered Florida panther (*Puma concolor coryi*)" (Figure 6.6). Private lands are also critical for species such as Leona's little blue butterfly (*Philotiella leona*) and Nelso's checkermallow (*Sidalcea nelsoniana*), as these lands cover much of their historical range (Figure 6.7).

By one estimate, land use conversion owing to development had contributed to the decline of approximately 35% of all imperiled species nationwide by the late 1990s (Wilcove, Rothstein, Dubow, Phillips, & Lasos, 2000). Further development will most probably continue that downward trend. At some point, it is likely that private development trends (discussed above) will substantially conflict with the national commitment in the Endangered Species Act to protect threatened and endangered species. We will discuss private landowner responsibilities under that act in the next chapter.

1 As we discussed in Chapter 1, the Millennium Ecosystem Assessment (MEA) (2005, p. v.) developed a comprehensive classification of ecosystem services that we use here: "These include *provisioning services* [often called products] such as food, water, timber, and fiber; *regulating services* that affect climate, floods, disease, wastes, and water quality; *cultural services* that provide recreational, aesthetic, and spiritual benefits; and *supporting services*, such as soil formation, photosynthesis, and nutrient cycling."

2 As defined by Stein et al. (2009, p. 24), "at-risk species include those plants and animals that are listed under the Endangered Species Act or are designated as critically imperiled, imperiled, or vulnerable according to the NatureServe Conservation Status Ranking system."

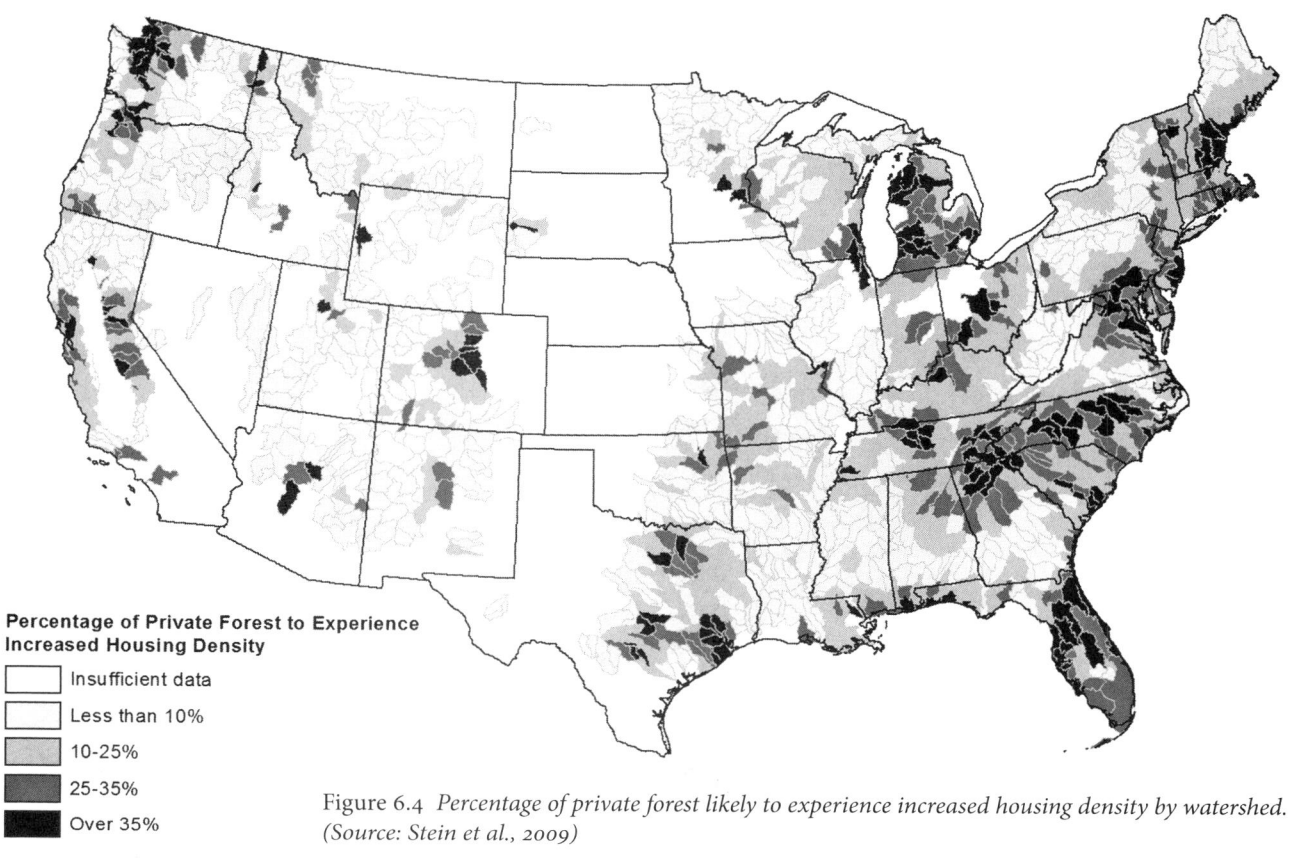

**Percentage of Private Forest to Experience Increased Housing Density**

| | |
|---|---|
| | Insufficient data |
| | Less than 10% |
| | 10-25% |
| | 25-35% |
| | Over 35% |

Figure 6.4  *Percentage of private forest likely to experience increased housing density by watershed.*
*(Source: Stein et al., 2009)*

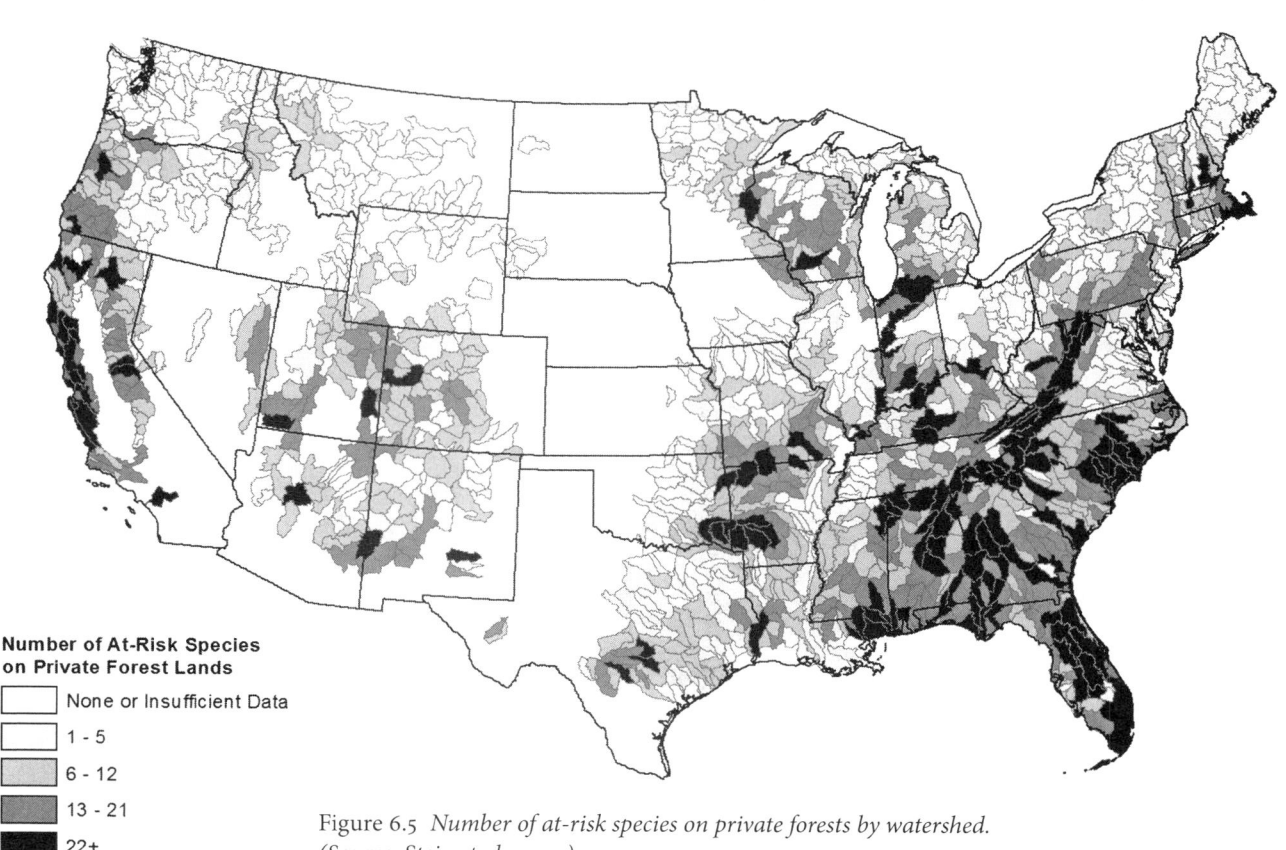

**Number of At-Risk Species on Private Forest Lands**

| | |
|---|---|
| | None or Insufficient Data |
| | 1 - 5 |
| | 6 - 12 |
| | 13 - 21 |
| | 22+ |

Figure 6.5  *Number of at-risk species on private forests by watershed.*
*(Source: Stein et al., 2009)*

Figure 6.6  *The Florida panther, one of the most endangered carnivores in the world, ranges over a mixture of public and private lands. (Photo credit: Animals Animals © Lynn Stone)*

Figure 6.7  *Examples of at-risk species where private lands cover most or all of their historical range: (a) Leona's little blue butterfly (photo courtesy of David G. James) and (b) Nelson's checkermallow (photo courtesy of Steve Gisler).*

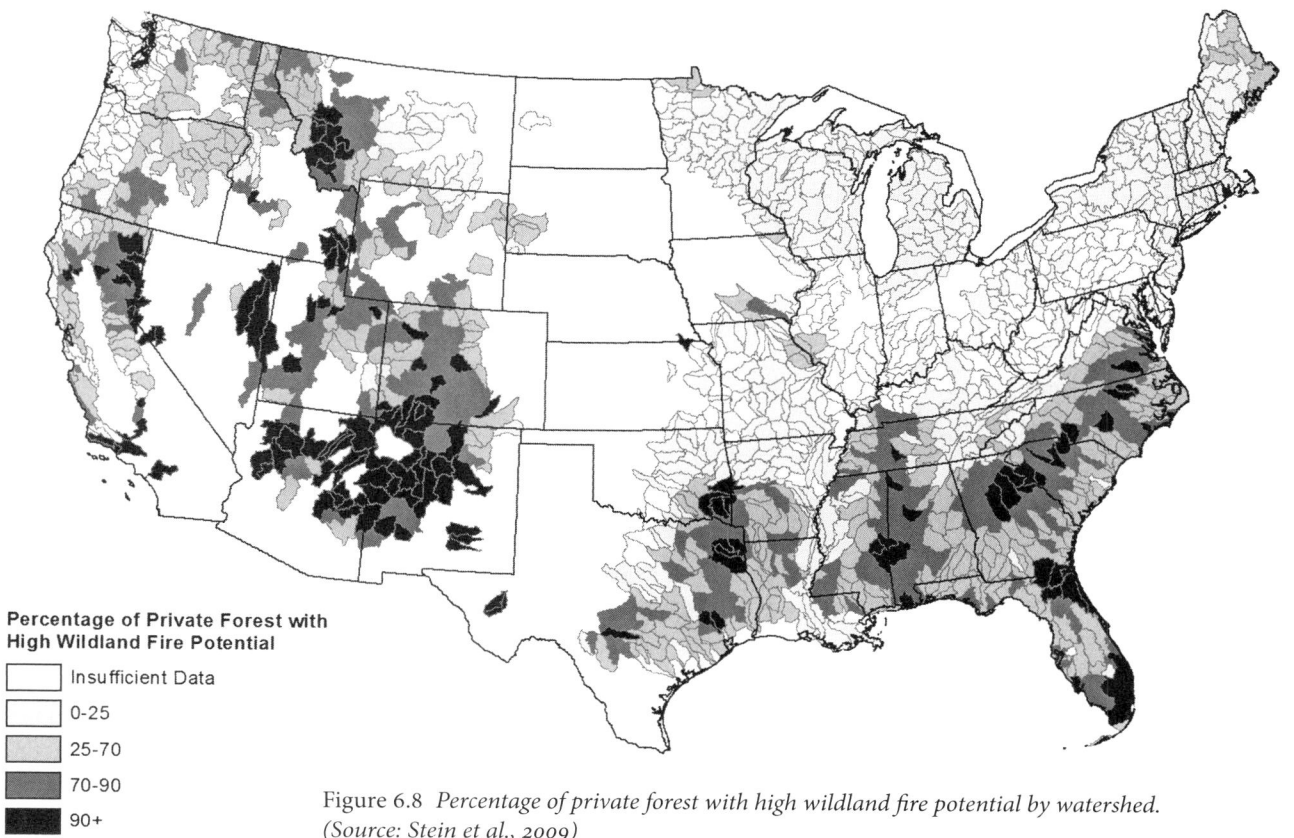

Percentage of Private Forest with
High Wildland Fire Potential

Insufficient Data
0-25
25-70
70-90
90+

Figure 6.8  *Percentage of private forest with high wildland fire potential by watershed. (Source: Stein et al., 2009)*

Figure 6.9  *The intrusion of housing developments into forests and shrublands of the West create very complex fuel hazard and fire protection issues. Aftermath of the Waldo Canyon fire in Colorado showing blocks of homes burned by the fire (especially in the lower center of the photo). (Photo credit: Kari Greer, US Forest Service)*

Watersheds can also be depicted relative to their potential for wildfire on private forests (Figure 6.8).[3] ***Large areas of the interior West and the South have more than 70% of private forest classified as having high fire potential.*** Communities in these watersheds that are within or next to national forests face especially complex fuel hazard conditions (Figure 6.9), which we will discuss in Chapters 12 and 13. Comparing Figures 6.4 and 6.8, we see that a number of watersheds where significant development is expected over the next few decades, especially in the mid-South, also have much of their private land in the higher wildfire potential categories.

3 The rankings are derived from the Wildland Fire Potential Model produced by the Forest Service's Fire Modeling Institute (http://www.fs.fed.us/fmi/).

## Public Forests

*National forests* control the largest portion of publicly owned forest in the United States, with most of those lands in the West (Figure 6.2). *They have increasingly shouldered responsibilities for conservation of biodiversity and watershed protection and have become the foundation of regional plans for conservation of threatened and endangered species.* Toward that end, harvest has greatly declined on those lands, as they shift their focus to protection of biodiversity and ecological restoration. We will discuss federal conservation responsibilities more fully in the next chapter when we discuss the Endangered Species Act and other federal laws and again in Chapter 20 when we focus specifically on national forest planning goals and procedures.

Most *other public forests* in the United States are state trust forests, such as those of Washington, Pennsylvania, Minnesota, and Wisconsin. In many cases, state trust forests are managed under sustained yield with a primary purpose to produce revenue for schools and other purposes. However, they must balance their obligations to their direct beneficiaries with those to the general public. In addition, state forests are highly visible to federal regulators enforcing federal environmental laws like the Endangered Species Act. The dual obligations and greater visibility often result in management strategies between those of private landowners and those of the national forests (Souder & Fairfax, 1996).

All told, public forests produce less than 20% of the national harvest (Oswalt et al., 2014). Still, harvest from public lands is important to local community economic vitality, especially in parts of the West.

## Tribal Forests

Forests on Indian reservations in the United States are held in trust by the Bureau of Indian Affairs (BIA) in the Department of Interior. Until recently, foresters in the BIA managed much of these forests as if their highest goal was to produce commercial timber revenue on a sustained yield basis for tribes within each reservation. Now, tribal visions, which generally consider a wide variety of goals much like family forests, play an important role in guiding forest management (Gordon et al., 1993; Gordon et al., 2013). Furthermore, many tribes have now taken over responsibility for management of reservation forests from BIA foresters.

## Conservation Responsibilities: Different Roles for Different Landowners

The policy framework at any time reflects the policy battles that preceded it. In the United States, these past battles and past policy choices have left asymmetric environmental policy conditions: *laws, regulations, and public expectations placed the greatest responsibility for environmental protection on federal forests, then on state forests, and lastly on private forests.*

**Federal Forests**   Federal forests, especially the national forests, have a complicated mandate: they are faced with a multitude of conservation responsibilities and a national constituency with diverse and conflicting desires. In the 1990s, federal forest management went through the biggest shift in management in the 100-year history of these lands. The emphasis on economic development, which dominated the first 75 years of their history, gave way to an emphasis on environmental protection and provision of biodiversity (Skillen, 2015). While we can argue whether this came about because of a changing social consensus, changing policy problems, passage of environmental laws, interest group tactics, activist federal judges, or new scientific findings, there can be no doubt that major changes occurred.

Thus, federal forests have become the first stop in assigning environmental responsibilities among the different landowners, as we noted in the discussion of ecoregional planning in the Oregon Coast Range Province (Chapter 5). This has led to increased emphasis on management of these forests to conserve ecosystem services such as water quality, endangered species, and biodiversity. It has also changed the broader decision-making environment on these lands. Proposals for cutting trees must clear a number of procedural and substantive hurdles before they are accepted, creating great frustration on the part of some and heartfelt thanks on the part of others.

While it is hard to generalize as to the basis for action on federal forests, a few questions often dominate the policy discussion:

1. Are the proposed actions intended to achieve some environmental goal? Achieving an economic goal is, in general, no longer a sufficient reason for action by itself.

2. Is there evidence that the actions will produce the desired environmental effect?

**State Forests**   The goals of state forests vary from state to state, but many have a primary responsibility to produce revenue for the state in which they reside, especially for schools. They also generally have environmental responsibilities beyond those of private lands for three interrelated reasons:

1. Specific mandates for some state forests to take a broader view of forest values than a sole focus on revenue creation. As an example, the state forests of northwestern Oregon must be managed to achieve the *highest permanent value* which has been interpreted as broader than financial return from timber harvest.

2. Social pressures to take a broader view, especially from urban dwellers.

3. Their visibility to federal regulators relative to enforcement of the Endangered Species Act and other laws. State forests are often large contiguous ownerships making their actions—especially the cumulative effect of their actions—easier to see and evaluate. Also, enforcement of these laws on state forests does not single out individuals or companies for regulation, actions that can be politically explosive.

Thus, in actual practice, state forests fall between private and federal forests in terms of conservation responsibilities; they play an especially important conservation role in landscapes without much federal land, such as New England.

**Private Forests**    A series of legal tests and political struggles in the early decades of the 20th century resulted in leaving regulation of private forests to the states while focusing federal legislation on cooperative federal–state–private fire protection and various federal programs to purchase forestland or subsidize forest activities (Ellefson, 2000). Protection of public values in private forests through state regulation generally occurs in two major ways: (1) direct state regulation of private forest practices, such as limiting logging near streams and requiring regeneration of commercial trees after harvest, and (2) land-use restrictions to encourage retention of forests. These regulations vary greatly from state to state. The discussion on ecoregional planning in the Oregon Coast Range Province at the end of Chapter 5 illustrates both of these approaches. We will discuss the types of forest practices regulated in more detail in the next chapter.

Also, as we will see in the next chapter, many federal laws also impact private forest management. The Endangered Species Act has specific limitations on private actions to prevent harm to threatened and endangered species. In addition a number of federal laws require development and application of forestry ***best management practices*** (BMPs)—specific practices or actions used to reduce or control impacts to water bodies from nonpoint-source pollution. BMPs may be mandatory, such as built into state forest practice regulations, or may be voluntary. Even states that do not have legally required BMPs often have water quality laws that can be used to enforce BMP compliance (Cubbage, O'Laughlin, & Peterson, 2017). We will discuss BMPs again in the next chapter under nonpoint-source pollution controls of the Clean Water Act. Overall, various studies have shown a relatively high rate of compliance by private landowners with forestry BMPs (Cubbage et al., 2017), although standards vary state to state.

State forest-practice laws and land-use laws fall under the general umbrella of public regulation of private landowner activities. Private land ownership in the United States, as derived from English common law,[4] has traditionally been considered as a bundle of rights regarding acquisition, use, and disposal of land and its products. A private owner holds exclusive but not absolute rights. These are always limited and conditioned by the overall interests of society as administered by the state; early state court decisions clearly established that state legislatures could exercise police power to achieve a natural resource objective that is in the general public interest (Cubbage & Siegel, 1985).

Federal regulation came into the picture with the passage of federal environmental laws in the 1970s, especially the Endangered Species Act, Clean Water Act, and Clean Air Act. All of these acts potentially restrict private activities and have been a continuous source of court tests and political arguments. Some, like the Clean Water Act, which we will review in the next chapter, are generally administered by the states as a way to reduce federal intrusion into the lives of citizens.

Public taking of private property without just compensation is proscribed by the Fifth Amendment to the Constitution and its state counterparts. Generally, the courts have been unwilling to consider regulating private property for a recognized public purpose a *taking*, unless the value of the property is totally (or almost totally) extinguished—something close to condemnation. Prohibiting removal of some value, requiring reinvestment, or delaying removal of some value generally has not been sufficient to be interpreted as a taking (Cubbage & Siegel, 1985). In summarizing recent court decisions on takings, a topic of continual court refinement, Cubbage et al. (2017, p. 337) state: "In short, one might conclude that environmental regulation must have very substantial negative impacts on land or other property values before it is considered a taking."

This inability of private landowners to receive payment for limitations on forest use to protect the environment ensures that every proposed state and federal regulation that might constrict private forest management will evoke a major political battle. It also ensures that private landowners will continually try to find some way to shift the cost of these policies to the public itself.

While it is hard to generalize the basis for regulating private forests to achieve environmental goals, a few questions will often dominate the policy discussion of private forest regulation:

1. Can the environmental goals be met on federal forests? If they can be met there, it is highly

4 The United States has two types of law: written and common. Written law includes constitutions, statutes, regulations, executive orders, and court decisions interpreting these documents. Common law, adopted from England, includes law created by courts as they decide disputes in the absence of written law (Cubbage & Siegel, 1985).

likely that attention will shift to those forests and adjustments made to their management.

2. If they cannot be met on federal forests, can these goals be met on state forests? If they can be met there, attention will shift to those lands. However, given the goals of state lands, as discussed above, the outcome of the public deliberations here is less clear.

3. If federal and state lands are not sufficient, is there evidence that restriction of private forest activities will achieve the desired outcome? Thus, the *burden of proof* is placed, to a significant degree, on those (states or federal government) who want to restrict private activities.

4. If federal and state forests cannot fill the void, and proof of environmental effects is strong, will state regulation of private land help forestall federal regulation? In many cases, private landowners greatly prefer state regulation to direct federal regulation, feeling they will have more influence in the development and implementation of regulations in their own state. We have seen such an approach to stream and lake protection, where state forest practice laws and state implementation of the federal Clean Water Act have been the primary regulatory mechanisms. (The Clean Water Act, and the states' role in its implementation, is discussed in Chapter 7.)

### Implications for Ecological Forestry

Timber harvest volume in the United States, especially softwood volume, may increasingly come from the production forests of corporate owners. Currently, we would expect that these landowners will have little interest in ecological forestry. Future interest will most likely depend on two developments: (1) whether ecological forestry can help meet federal and state requirements for conservation of at-risk species, and (2) whether elements of ecological forestry are needed for market access (we will discuss more about this issue in Chapter 16 on certification).

Family forest landowners control most of the private forestland in the United States, especially in the East and South. They own a very high percentage of the private land where land development is likely to occur over the next few decades, where significant numbers of at-risk species occur, and where wildfire risk is high. With the well-documented multiple values of these landowners, ecological forestry would seem a good fit for those lands where forestry will be practiced, potentially helping to forestall land conversion in some cases. We will come back to this theme numerous times in later chapters.

A number of state forests, such as in Washington, Minnesota, and Pennsylvania, already practice variations on ecological forestry, and we expect them to continue to lead in innovations, as will many tribal forests.

National forests have a myriad of problems that ecological forestry can help address, from maintaining resilient ecosystems to recovering at-risk species, while also providing revenue to do these good works as we discuss in Chapter 20. The biggest issue for national forest management, though, may be whether the public in the United States considers commercial timber harvest from these lands, on a continuing basis, to be permissible.

## Markets

Markets are social constructs connecting willing buyers and willing sellers for the purpose of exchanging some good or service for a price (Duerr, 1960). Neoclassical economists by the end of the 19th century had proven that, in theory, a price-based economic system can efficiently allocate resources (Cubbage, O'Laughlin, & Bullock, 1993; Randall, 1981). By efficiency, we mean producing the greatest economic value of goods or services with a given set of inputs, or producing a given output at lowest cost. Economic efficiency in natural resource management is desirable in that it minimizes the waste of natural and human-made resources and allows more benefit from any level of resource use (Cubbage et al., 2017).

Relying on consumer sovereignty and entrepreneurship to create markets that determine how resources should be allocated and the goods and services that should be produced has become an increasingly powerful force around the world. In the United States, it is often said that we live in a *capitalistic society* with a *market economy*, meaning that we rely on the investments of entrepreneurs and market allocations to determine what is produced and who gains from that production. Thus, historically, we have often turned to private individuals driven by price signals from markets to decide what is produced from our natural resources and who is rewarded.

While a myriad of political and social forces affect forest conservation and management, markets for ecosystem services provided by forests play a role, either directly or indirectly, in forest management of most ownerships in the United States and in many other countries around the world. Unfortunately, *markets have been successfully developed for only a few of these ecosystem services, such as timber, substantially limiting landowner interest and ability in producing other forest benefits.* Markets for many other essential services provided by forests, such as watershed protection and provision of wildlife habitat, are generally absent.

Why don't we utilize markets for more ecosystem services from the forest? In some cases, this result comes from institutional or political reluctance to charge for the good or service in question, such as the use of lakes for fishing and swimming on the national forests in the USA. In other cases, which we will discuss here, the ecosystem services have characteristics that make attainment of economic efficiency through markets difficult or impossible, resulting in *market failure.*

Natural resource characteristics affect the appropriateness of markets to best allocate and protect these resources. Goods and services may be classified into four categories based on their properties of consumption (rivalry) and exclusion. A rival good or service is one for which the use of one unit by one person precludes the use of that unit at the same time by another person (goods or services are consumed individually). Conversely, a nonrival good is a good or service where one person has an insignificant impact on the quantity or quality of a good or service available for another person to use (goods or services can be consumed jointly). Exclusivity is an institutional construct that allows a person to protect his or her property. Exclusivity implies that anyone wishing to use the resource must have permission of the owner; that is, the owner has the right and the ability to exclude other potential users (Daly & Farley, 2011; Cubbage et al., 2017).

Relative to these two properties, we will examine four types of goods and services, following Cubbage et al. (2017): (1) private, (2) toll, (3) common pool, and (4) collective. The potential for market failure is especially high with common pool and collective goods and services, resulting in overexploitation or inadequate provision, respectively, and a call for government intervention. We will describe each of these types below, along with examples of ecosystem services that fit into each of the categories.

*Private goods and services*, consumed individually and exclusively, are most amenable to production and trade in markets. Examples of forest ecosystem services that may fit this description include timber, firewood, and floral products.

*Toll goods and services*, consumed jointly and where exclusion is possible, are also amenable to production and trade through markets. An example of an ecosystem service that fits this description is a use of a park where many can enjoy the scenery at the same time but admission can be charged.

*Common pool goods and services* are consumed individually, but exclusion is difficult since property rights are either nonexistent, poorly defined, or poorly enforced. An example of an ecosystem service that fits the common pool category historically in the United States was forage for cattle grazing on public domain range lands where grazing was not controlled (Dana & Fairfax, 1980). Common pool resources are often overused or destroyed as each resource user maximizes his or her own gain from the resource (Ostrom, 1998; Randall, 1981). Incentives to conserve can be weak because each person is not assured the benefits of such conservation, since they do not own the resource. Rather the incentive to overconsume common pool resources can be strong as the benefits of overconsumption accrue to the

individual, while the costs of overconsumption are borne by all users of the resource. With each user following the logic of self-interest, the resource will be depleted, leading to the *tragedy of the commons* (Hardin, 1968). When fishermen compete to catch the most fish from the ocean or grazers compete to stock the most cattle on the rangeland, damage to or destruction of the resource often results. In general, common pool resources will be inefficiently used, overused, or destroyed if markets are relied on to allocate these resources.

Some argue that establishing property rights (ownership) to common pool resources can overcome problems associated with their inefficient use or overuse when allocated by markets (Stroup & Baden, 1973). Successful examples of this solution are found in some fisheries in which an individual transferable quota to catch a certain amount of fish is assigned or sold to fishermen, who can then buy and sell them as they see fit (Newell, Sanchirico, & Kerr, 2005). As another example, hunting leases give lessees access rights, with the result that the lessees usually can be counted on to help the landowner protect the resource (Cubbage et al., 2017).

*Collective goods and services* are consumed jointly, and exclusion is infeasible; if such goods or services are available to one, they are available to all. As an example, when a species is saved from extinction, all who care about that species will benefit whether they contribute to saving it or not. Other examples are control of wildland forest fires and provision for carbon storage to counter climate change. In some sense, these goods or services are consumed by many and owned by none, making a direct payment requirement for such benefits difficult or impossible (Cubbage et al., 2017). Thus, collective goods and services will generally be underprovided through markets.

Beyond the inadequacies of markets to allocate some goods and services efficiently, theoretical claims of market efficiency do not address the equity of the distribution of income that drives them. As an example, it can be argued that the rights to fish and swim in lakes on national forests in the USA are given away (not allocated through markets) because there is a desire to make those activities available to all whether or not they have sufficient income to pay for them. As another example, societies may not like the provision for the welfare of future generations made through markets, that is, they are concerned that unfettered markets will leave future generations with a depleted resource base.

*When markets fail to adequately provide ecosystem services from the forest we often turn to government policy and action*, whether it be to establish property rights, regulate markets, supplement markets, take over production, or institute other programs. We will cover a number of these governmental policies and actions in the next chapter and throughout this book.

*However, markets are still an important social mechanism in determining what is produced in forests and how landowners are financially rewarded,* and we will discuss some of them here. We will first look at the market for land conversion—one of the major challenges to forest permanence on private lands in the United States as highlighted in Figure 6.4. Then, we will briefly discuss markets for two forest ecosystem services, timber and carbon sequestration. Finally, we will note the role of forest certification in achieving forest sustainability through markets.

## Market-driven Forest Conversion

Forestry usually is one of the lower-valued uses of private forests—a residual use for land not demanded for cities, rural residences, and high-valued agriculture (Duerr, 1960). Thus forest management is often relegated to the less productive or steeper forests. We expect that development trend to continue in the future in the United States as people spread out across the forested landscape (Figure 6.4). This demand for more forest for settlement derives from many sources including increasing population, a desire to own a home (or a second home) in the country, and government fiscal and tax policy that encourages home ownership, such as low interest rates and homeowner interest deductions on federal income taxes.

*Development pressures play out differently in different parts of the United States, depending on the institutional arrangements in each state or local district, guiding and restricting land development.* Where these land use laws are generally malleable, as they are in much of the United States, economic pressures will result in a continuing conversion of farm and forest, as rural ranchettes, housing developments, and associated services spread throughout the countryside.

It is certainly true that this development goes in fits and starts based on broader economic and social conditions, with many booms and busts in rural land development in the past and more to come in the future. As an example, the general economic recession in 2008 associated with difficulties in the housing markets slowed development for a while. Still the expansion of settlement into farm and forest is projected to continue, especially in the eastern United States (Figure 6.4), reversing the historical concentration of population that occurred during much of the 20th century.

Some states or localities, such as Oregon, tightly control this development. In the 1970s, Oregon's legislature passed land-use laws at the demand of then Governor Tom McCall. One major goal of these laws was to protect prime farm and forestland. The zoning that followed makes it difficult to develop farm or forestland unless it is part of slowly expanding cities and towns (Figure 6.10). Various citizen initiatives to loosen these laws have had minimal effect. Thus development has been concentrated around settled areas, and gradual expansion of this development is projected to continue. Very little private forest has been lost to development in Oregon over the last 30 years. Assuming these land-use laws continue, the next decades will see a gradual build-out from urban and rural cores, leaving much of the forest largely unfragmented (Lettman, 2013). Also, lands classified as Exclusive Farm Use or Forest Conservation have much lower annual property tax rates than other lands, with much of the property tax on timber turned into a yield tax paid as a percentage of the value of timber when it is harvested.

As we saw in the ecoregional assessment case study in New England, discussed in Chapter 5, other states have much looser controls on development and allow significant market-driven land conversion. This can be especially difficult when the forest is appraised at its value for development and taxed accordingly. In those cases, significant policy shifts may be needed to retain the land in forest (Box 6.1).

Sometimes the land is cleared for houses and yards; other times houses are built inside forests. Even in the latter case, the remaining forest around the houses can have

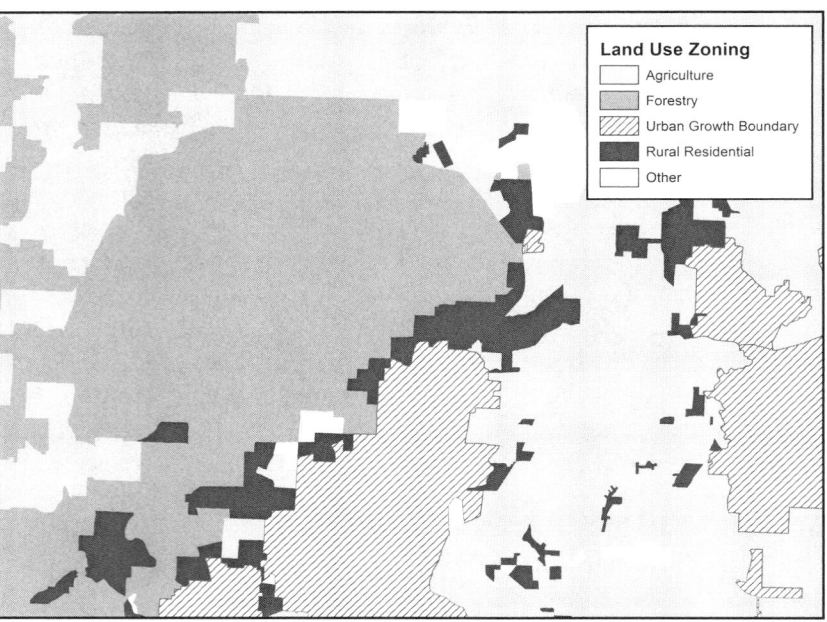

Figure 6.10  *Land-use zoning near Corvallis, Oregon. It is very difficult to shift land zoned as Agriculture or Forestry into another zoning category that will allow development. To accommodate population growth, the Urban Growth Boundary will gradually expand.*

greatly diminished value for both protection of biodiversity or commercial timber production. In addition, there can be a substantial indirect effect on these two ecosystem services from the intervening forestlands between houses and settlements. As an example, Wear, Liu, Foreman, and Sheffield, (1999) documented that increased settlement density in the state of Virginia decreased the probability that forest in the area would be utilized as commercial timberland. Less of a signal of these effects has been found in Oregon (Kline, Azuma, & Alig, 2004).

## Markets for Ecosystem Services of the Forest

Forests provide a multitude of ecosystem services (Figure 6.11). Unfortunately for landowners in the United States, markets exist for only a few of these services where landowners can be compensated for their production, with timber markets being the most widespread. Some local markets exist for mushrooms, floral products, hunting, recreation, and other ecosystem services, but they generally remain much more limited than timber markets. We will

---

### Box 6.1 Keeping land in forest with rising land values and property taxes: A case study in Massachusetts

While family forests represent the largest proportion of forestland within the United States, forest conversion, fragmentation, and parcelization can greatly impede the ability of families to manage these lands for the variety of ecosystem services they can produce (see New England case study in Chapter 5). D'Amato, Catanzaro, Damery, Kittredge, and Ferrare (2010) suggest that a factor driving this trend is the inability of landowners to meet the property tax burden on their lands. To test this hypothesis, they evaluated the effectiveness of three approaches commonly suggested for meeting the financial demand of property taxes: (1) financial returns from timber management, (2) enrollment in a *current-use tax program* in which the forest is assessed in terms of its value as timberlands, rather than its development value, and (3) sale of a conservation easement that precludes development.

For this case study, they focused on the Massachusetts section of the Deerfield River Watershed (DRW) because of the significant amount of forest cover in this region and the presence of regionally common forest types and ownership patterns representative of many regions in the Northeast. The most important result from their hypothetical but realistic analyses is that revenue from periodic timber harvests cannot keep pace with the annual property tax expenses of landownership in the DRW, the most rural region of Massachusetts, with its rising land values and property taxes. Relative to the two tools they examined to increase the flow of revenue to the forest owner who keeps the land in forest, they found somewhat different results.

The current-use tax program did help reduce the tax burden somewhat. However, relatively few landowners apply for it. In Massachusetts, forestland of 10 or more contiguous acres that is used for timber production and has a state-approved forest management plan is eligible for this program. One possible reason for low enrollment in the Massachusetts current-use program might be its misalignment with landowner objectives. Landowners whose primary ownership objectives are privacy, aesthetic values, and a place to raise their family (Butler et al., 2016b) are satisfied with the benefits that their land provides without active management or management planning. Landowner objectives are often being met by doing nothing on these ownerships or by conducting

only sporadic management activities, while many ecosystem services are provided, including clean water, carbon sequestration, wildlife habitat, and rural character.

Selling a conservation easement had the greatest impact on reducing the property tax burden of forestland. Conservation easements allow families to retain fee ownership and many of the rights (e.g., residence, forest management, and no public access) associated with the property, but they relinquish the right to develop; the easement can be applied to all or part of an ownership. The financial value of an easement is equal to the reduction in development value of the land, determined through an appraisal process. Conservation easements can represent income if the development rights have been purchased, but also can be a charitable deduction for income tax purposes if the development rights have been donated to a conservation organization. By eliminating the development potential of land, the assessed value is lowered, thus reducing the annual real estate tax burden and reducing estate tax obligations. D'Amato et al.'s (2010) results show that conservation easements can provide both a significant source of revenue from their sale and a significant reduction in assessed value and associated property taxes. Further, they point out that easements also offer permanent protection from land conversion and ensure continued flow of ecosystem services and public benefit. In summary, they recommend three forest policy directions to help landowners meet the property tax burden of their land:

- Support and promote working forest conservation easements through permanent federal and state tax incentives as well as through increased funding for working forest easements;

- Support outreach programs that build landowner awareness of multiple revenue sources and tax savings to maintain property in working forest conditions; and

- Recognize the ecosystem values and public benefits of land that is not being managed under a forest management plan and compensate landowners for providing these values through current-use tax reductions, irrespective of whether or not they have a forest management plan and manage their land for timber.

Figure 6.11 *Forests provide a multitude of ecosystem services: (a) second-growth logs headed to the sawmill, (b) mushrooms for the dinner table, (c) an environment for intense recreational activity, (d) a place for solitude and renewal, and (e) water for fishing, wildlife, and irrigation.*

highlight two ecosystem services here—one provisioning service (timber) and one regulating service (carbon sequestration). We will come back to valuing other ecosystem services in Chapter 10.

**Timber Markets**  Throughout the United States and many countries around the world, timber harvest provides much of the income from forests. Most parts of the United States have fairly active sawtimber markets for logs or stumpage, although landowners may have trouble marketing very small-diameter logs and certain species. Sometimes they sell the trees as they stand (stumpage); sometimes they sell logs at the roadside; and sometimes they sell logs at the processing facility.

With logs having a relatively high weight to value ratio, transport costs may restrict sales to a local area. In many areas, one or two timber buyers for any product operate within a range where there are many forest landowners. This market structure may result in lower prices than in competitive markets (Cubbage et al., 2003). Still, timber prices help direct or limit forest management on both private and public lands in a myriad of ways including the species planted and grown, the rotation ages chosen, and silviculture used. We will come back to the effects timber markets have on forest management many times in this book, especially in the chapters on investment and valuation (Chapters 9 and 10).

**Carbon Markets**  Until recently, timber was one of the few forest products with well-developed markets across the forests of the world. Now, though, some countries, such as those of the European Union, and individual US states, like California, are developing markets for carbon sequestration in forests. With the increasing concern about the amount of carbon dioxide ($CO_2$) being put into the atmosphere and the ability of forests to absorb $CO_2$, it seems like a natural fit.

Generally these markets are created by governments as they institute *cap-and-trade* policies that require power plants, and other $CO_2$ emitters, to limit their $CO_2$ emissions. Some of these schemes allow emitters to count *carbon offsets*, such as commitments to increase carbon sequestration in forests, toward meeting their $CO_2$ cap. California and some northeastern states have taken the lead in the United States in setting up cap-and-trade policies, but it has been a slow process because of the lack of national policies that encourage or require cap-and-trade approaches. (See the Appendix to Chapter 15 for a more detailed discussion of the California carbon market for forest offsets.)

Carbon markets can affect forest management in many ways. Since these markets generally pay landowners for storing carbon in forests beyond what would otherwise occur, they can help lengthen rotations and provide a countervailing force against the investment/income pressures for timber harvest or land conversion (Box 6.2). We will

cover climate change, forests, and carbon in more depth in Chapter 15.

## Forest Certification: Environmental Governance through Markets

Forest certification, a nongovernmental effort, uses market mechanisms to ensure sustainability. It results in a written certification issued by an independent third party, attesting to the location and management status of a forest being managed to produce timber. More specifically, forest certification involves the *green* labeling of companies and wood products that meet standards of *sustainable* or *responsible* forestry, providing market recognition for forest producers who meet a set of environmental and social standards. The premise behind certification is that people and governments value knowing their wood came from a sustainably managed forest and will therefore favor those woods in the marketplace.

The Forest Stewardship Council (FSC), started in the 1990s by the World Wildlife Fund and others, rewards landowners who adopt ecological forestry practices (as the FSC sees them) around the world with FSC sustainability certification and the ability to use the FSC logo. FSC was so successful in its early days that the forest industry started its own certification group called the Sustainable Forestry Initiative (SFI) to recognize and certify landowners who practice something closer to production forestry within environmental limits. SFI, focused on North America, is now independent from any industry group. Other certification groups that share the SFI philosophy blanket Europe and exist in other parts of the world.

The different visions of FSC and SFI parallel, to some degree, the difference between ecological forestry and production forestry, and they are in a fierce battle for supremacy. Much of that battle focuses on market access to home-construction materials, carbon offset markets, biomass markets, green building codes, and other emerging green markets in North America and Europe. We will cover certification in detail in Chapter 16.

## Implications for Ecological Forestry

Forestland markets and the markets that exist for selected ecosystem services will continue to be a major force in ecological forestry, influencing what is done and how it is accomplished. Some of these influences can have a positive effect on the potential for ecological forestry:

1. Robust timber markets help make ecological forestry possible, providing funding to undertake needed treatments and providing some financial return.

2. In turn, ecological forestry may help stall land conversion by providing an income source to family forest landowners compatible with their other objectives and also by making the forest a more highly regarded candidate for sale of a conservation easement that precludes development (see Zena Forest case in Chapter 10). Without tools that reward retaining land in forest, such as conservation easements, the financial attractiveness of selling forests for development can be a powerful force indeed, especially if the forest is taxed as developable land (Box 6.1).

3. As noted above, the spread of communities and homes into the countryside can slow and perhaps stop production forestry as communities and citizens become resistant to production forest practices in the area. There may be more tolerance of ecological forestry practices that benefit biodiversity and don't use growth-enhancing measures, such as extensive site preparation and the broadcast application of herbicides or fertilizers.

4. Markets for ecosystem services other than timber can bolster landowner interest in ecological forestry practices. With robust markets for such services as carbon sequestration, as an example, we would expect that landowners would be more willing to retain valuable trees at harvest and utilize longer rotations.

5. The focus in some certification schemes on ecological forestry, such as those of the Forest Stewardship Council, could have a significant positive effect on the breadth of adoption of ecological forestry as market access is increasingly tied to this type of certification. We will discuss this potential further in Chapter 16.

## Investment and Income Strategies

When the forest is valued primarily for the financial return it provides, without concern for retaining the trees or the land if a better investment opportunity is available elsewhere, classical investment approaches, such as rate of return and net present value analysis, can be employed to guide decisions (Davis, Johnson, Bettinger, & Howard, 2001; see Chapter 9 of this text for a detailed discussion of rate of return and net present value analysis). This is generally the case in corporate forest ownerships, which empha-

---

Box 6.2 **Yurok Tribe hopes California's cap-and-trade program can save their way of life**

The Yurok Tribe in Northern California has sold millions of dollars' worth of carbon credits, known as offsets, to some of the state's biggest polluters. The Yurok Tribe's forestry program is one of dozens of operations across the nation that has generated offsets for California's growing carbon market. The state initiative gives the Yurok Tribe a new way to make money while it improves wildlife habitat, expands its forestry staff, and acquires land in its ancestral territory near the mouth of the Klamath River in Del Norte and Humboldt counties.

Driving the new activity is California's 2006 global warming law, AB 32, which aims to cut greenhouse gas emissions to 1990 levels by 2020. The state's cap-and-trade program launched in 2012 for hundreds of the state's top carbon emitters, and has been expanded to other emitters since then, is key to meeting that target. Under the cap-and-trade program, the California Air Resources Board sets a statewide limit on greenhouse gas emissions and requires companies to buy one permit, called an allowance, for each metric tonne of $CO_2$ they emit. Allowances can be purchased in state-issued auctions or on California's carbon market. Some also are given to public utilities.

The amount of pollution permitted will decline over time, making allowances more scarce and expensive and giving businesses an economic incentive to cut emissions. Companies can also buy carbon offsets—credits obtained by essentially paying others to reduce greenhouse gases—to cover part of their emissions.

The commitment of the Yurok Tribe to manage their forest for the next 100 years in a way that pulls more carbon dioxide out of the atmosphere is an example of one type of offset. "The value of preserving trees for 100 years is something that was unheard of from an economics perspective in the past," said Timothy O'Connor, who directs the California Climate Initiative for the Environmental Defense Fund, a nonprofit advocacy group that supports the state's cap-and-trade and offset programs. "This new dimension is enabling landowners to make decisions that are both good for the planet and good for their pocketbooks."

Like any investment, a carbon project requires upkeep. That often means harvesting less timber to let trees grow older and larger. To boost forest productivity, crews thin some species of trees to maximize carbon storage by others.

Yurok Tribal Chairman Thomas O'Rourke Sr. said the tribe has embraced carbon projects because they "maximize both revenue and the ability to preserve the forest. To not only do our part with global warming, but to preserve our way of life so that our future generations can see the pristine forest that our parent's grandparents saw."

*Source:* T. Barboza, December 16, 2014. Yurok Tribe hopes California's cap-and-trade can save their way of life. *Los Angeles Times.* Retrieved from http://www.latimes.com/science/la-me-carbon-forest-20141216-story.html

size production forestry as we discussed above. However, when landowners have multiple goals that are difficult to translate into a single financial measure, as is the case with most other ownerships, classical investment analysis provides much less useful advice, and attention often turns to potential income over time as the relevant financial measure. We will discuss these different perspectives below.

## Corporate Forests

*In corporate forests, a forest is valued primarily in terms of the financial return it can generate.* Management of this forest capital is generally driven by the rate of return on investment sought by the landowners, and human-made capital is viewed as substitutable for natural capital. Outputs are valued in terms of their financial return, with timber harvest the most common source of revenue. Under aggregate measures of this return, such as net present value, maximum return in temperate forests often occurs at a stand age between 20 and 60 years, depending on the site and species. As an example, midsite Douglas-fir might have a financial rotation of 40 years, earlier than the age at which average growth is maximized or mature forest characteristics would develop (see Chapter 9 for examples of this analysis). Other outputs, such as carbon sequestration, would also be valued if they produce a revenue stream and could lengthen the financially optimal rotation.

In this type of investment analysis, value growth rate of a stand can be compared to the rate of return the landowner or manager seeks—the rate of return in some alternative investment. Once that value growth rate slips below this alternative rate of return, the stand has passed *financial maturity* and would be harvested to maximize profits. In addition, the cost of delaying future stands, beyond the one being analyzed, adds to the cost of holding the current stand and creates additional incentive to harvest.

In a similar fashion, an individual tree passes financial maturity (where the value growth rate falls below the alternative rate of return) generally much earlier than at the age which the tree would be considered ecologically mature. Not surprisingly, this approach to decision making provides little incentive to maintain legacy trees during harvest, unless income is received for keeping those trees around.

## Family, Public, and Tribal Forests

*Management of forest capital is more complicated on family, public, and tribal forests.* The diverse goals of these owners do not lend themselves to the straightforward financial calculations of the corporate world. Many of the ecosystem services of interest lack markets (or quasi-markets) that might enable valuation. In addition, some of the forest capital may be seen as critical natural capital essential to sustaining

these services, such as a distribution of forest between preforest, young, and mature, and not available for shift into some other form of capital that would provide higher financial returns. Finally, public owners generally operate under sustainability constraints that greatly limit the mobility of forest capital and restrict the choices that might be considered. For all these reasons, *the value of a forest to these owners is not well captured by a focus on net present value and rate of return.*

Family forest landowners often have a wide variety of ecological and social goals (Figure 6.3). In such cases, rate of return is not the sole determinant of harvest decisions; in fact, it may not be directly considered in those decisions at all. Rather, the financial attractiveness of forest management alternatives may be evaluated in terms of income received over time, as a component in decisions that consider many types of virtues of alternative management strategies. *This is not to say that harvest income is unimportant to these owners but rather that rate of return as an overall decision guide does not capture their interests and the values they place on their forests.*

On public and tribal ownerships, rates of harvest may be constrained by preference, agreement, regulation, or law. As an example, many public and tribal forests have sustained yield goals that do not allow the harvest to rise above the long-term sustained yield. These goals can greatly restrict and alter the investment analysis by limiting the freedom to quickly shift forest capital elsewhere. Also, under some situations, an emphasis on net present value with sustained yield goals may lead to forest degradation. (We will discuss the mischief that a focus on rate of return can cause in sustained yield management in Chapter 9.) It must be noted, though, that harvest revenue is still the grease that keeps the wheels of forest management turning on many public and tribal ownerships by paying for management and restoration, and meeting state obligations for trust payments or returning funds for tribal needs. Thus income over time is, generally, a better estimate of financial performance on these ownerships than is rate of return.

On federal forests, forest restoration also depends on harvest income, at least in part. Widespread action on federal forests to reduce the buildup in stand densities in the western USA becomes more likely if commercial timber harvest can help defray some of the cost and provide community employment. Thus timber values have an important indirect effect on forest conservation and management. This indirect effect, though, can cause tension between different conservation objectives on federal forests, leading to puzzlers such as whether we are sacrificing one important ecological value (harvesting large trees that provide wildlife habitat to generate funds) for another (reduced risk of wildfire or insect outbreaks killing the other trees and forests).

## Implications for Ecological Forestry

*In sum, we argue that focus on rate of return and maximizing net present value is limited to a fairly narrow set of forest owners.* Where financial return is the paramount value, such as with many corporate entities, rate of return is of singular importance. Similarly, family forest landowners with extensive holdings may put considerable weight on such analysis. However, we argue that, as we move beyond corporate and large family forests, the usefulness of this criterion to guide management drops sharply as an overall decision guide and net income becomes more important (Figure 6.12). Most family forest landowners have too many other goals (Figure 6.3) to use a single financial criterion to determine what to do. Yes, they are interested in periodic income, but that must be blended with their many other goals. Most state and federal forests operate under multiple resource goals, too, and also have sustained yield and habitat protection requirements, which together greatly diminishes the usefulness of rate of return analysis as a driving force in determining harvest and other management decisions. *Instead, income over time becomes a more useful criterion for financial analysis on most family forest and public ownerships.* We will come back to these ideas in Chapter 9 and demonstrate their usefulness on family forests in Chapters 18 and 19.

Figure 6.12 *Expected usefulness of rate of return as a primary criterion to guide forestry decision making.*

Ecological forestry is premised, in part, on the idea that human capital cannot entirely be substituted for natural capital in providing for human well-being from forests (See Box 1.2 in Chapter 1, and Chapter 9 for a more in-depth discussion of the substitutability of capital.) Also, landowner values cannot be entirely subsumed under the rate of return on capital, given the multiple objectives and policy guidelines under which most owners operate. Thus net income associated with achieving these multiple goals and guidelines is generally a better measure of financial performance of forest strategies and practices than is rate of return; we generally will use net income as our measure of financial performance in forest planning under ecological forestry.

## Policy Formation Processes

Policy can be defined as "a purposive course of action or inaction followed by an actor or set of actors in dealing with a problem or concern" (Anderson, 2015, p. 6). Polices focus on what is actually done instead of what is only discussed, proposed, or intended. *Policies guide and constrain decision making to achieve organizational and individual goals.*

Following Anderson (2015) and Cubbage et al. (2017), our definition of policy has three key elements: (1) A policy provides direction. It requires, allows, prohibits, limits, enables, and encourages. (2) A policy requires patterns of decisions made and implemented over time, rather than discrete, isolated decisions. It guides actions in some consistent way over time. (3) A policy reflects social choices made through institutions (government and private). *It is the product of politics (the decision-making process used to craft policies) and power—not necessarily science, research, or facts.*

All countries and organizations have many policies, as do most families. Examples of policies include:

- University regulations limiting certain parking lots to faculty use;
- Corporate policies allowing employees two weeks of vacation a year;
- Stream buffer requirements in the forest-practice regulations for private lands;
- Land use zoning that limits subdivision of forests for housing;
- Prohibiting take of an endangered species in the US Endangered Species Act;
- Federal laws that pay for part of the reforestation cost; and
- A parent's requirement that her child be home by 10:00 P.M. on school nights.

Many policy ends or goals are desirable because they are a means toward achievement of other ends (Worrell, 1970). Thus public forest policies often can be viewed as an interrelated hierarchical series of means and ends. As an example, consider the policy of maintaining a seasonal employee in a lookout tower in the summer, continually scanning the horizon in every direction for a plume of smoke (Table 6.1). The goal of this policy is to detect all new wildfires immediately, which reflects a policy of immediate detection at the next level up in the hierarchy. The goal of immediate detection is to enable suppression of all wildfires quickly while they are small and easy to extinguish, which in turn reflects a policy of rapid suppression at the next level up. The goal of the rapid suppression policy is to minimize acres burned, and so on up this hierarchy of means and ends (or policies and goals) all the way to the preeminent goal of the survival of society. This hierarchy of interrelated means and ends illustrates that the nature of a goal or policy depends on the vantage from which it is viewed in the hierarchy. An end (goal) is almost always also a means (policy) to some higher goal in the hierarchy (Cubbage et al., 1993).

Table 6.1 *A fire lookout's hierarchy of ends and means*

| |
|---|
| Ensure survival of society |
| Maintain economic stability |
| Provide adequate wood supplies |
| Conserve timber resources |
| Minimize acres burned |
| Suppress all wildfires quickly |
| Discover all wildfires immediately |
| Staff all lookout posts |

*Source:* Adapted from Cubbage et al. (1993).

In this book, we are focused on public natural resource policies, especially forest policies. To help explain how policies are developed and changed, we will start with a simple but very useful public process model. Then, we will examine assumptions behind different policy tools that might be used to achieve policy goals and also outline desirable properties of regulations, a commonly used policy tool. Finally, we will examine the dynamics of federal environmental policy formation in the United States to provide a real-life example of public policy development.

## A Policy Process Model

Anderson (2015) described a useful six-step policy process model that can help us understand how policies form and change:

*Problem formulation*: The identification of a problem with some policy means that someone or some group is not satisfied with the current policy (status quo) regarding some matter. Different individuals define problems differently. How a policy is defined constrains the set of solutions (policy changes) that will be considered by policy makers. As an example, suppose that motorists in rural areas are being injured when they hit cattle that have wandered onto the road. What is the problem? That motorists drive too fast and are not attentive to their surroundings, or that cattle ranchers are not keeping their fences in repair? How the problem is defined here will affect the solutions that are sought. *Key questions*: What is the problem that created the need for a policy? How did the condition or matter become a public problem? Are there alternative definitions of the problem?

*Recognition on the policy agenda*: Policy making first involves recognizing, acknowledging, or being made aware of a problem(s) that may require action. From among scores of requests for action a policy maker may face on a regular basis, a policy maker must decide which of these problems is important enough to place on the policy agenda. Cubbage et al. (2017), using the work of Jones (1984), argues that four factors determine whether an issue of importance to

some group reaches agenda status: (1) the events themselves in terms of the number of people affected and the intensity of feelings, (2) organization and leadership in the affected groups, (3) power and influence of the affected groups with the relevant policy maker, and (4) the policy process itself in terms of how well the group can function within it. Cubbage et al. (2017) also notes that groups often engage in issue expansion to catch the interest of other groups, with the hope of forming coalitions with enough power to force their way onto the policy agenda. *Key questions*: Which policy maker recognized the problem? Why did the problem make it onto the policy maker's agenda? Who were the key people or groups in gaining the policy maker's attention? Was the issue successfully expanded over time?

*Policy formulation and analysis*: An alternative (or alternatives) to the existing policy must be developed and a formal or informal evaluation done of whether the alternative (or alternatives) is better than the existing policy. It is one thing to bemoan the shortcomings of a policy, and quite another to find a better one. *Key questions*: What policy alternatives were considered? Who participated in the policy analysis? What goals and criteria guided the development and selection of the policy? Why did the policy maker believe that the selected policy was better than the status quo or other alternative(s)?

*Policy adoption*: Adoption occurs when the policy maker accepts a particular solution to a problem. Often the policy is mashed and morphed during the process of formulation, analysis, and adoption. In the end, though, a policy, perhaps full of vague wording and compromises, emerges. *Key questions*: What is the final policy? What are its stated goals and requirements?

*Policy implementation*: Administrative agencies interpret and implement policies, often giving the policies more definition in the process as they interpret vague wording and try to understand the intent. As we will see below and throughout this book, administrative agencies play a key interpretive role in implementing environmental law. *Key questions*: Who is responsible for implementing the policy? How did they interpret the elements of the policy? What problems have they encountered during implementation? Was the policy successfully implemented?

*Policy evaluation*: Informal or formal determination of policy effectiveness is part of the policy process, yet it often does not happen. All policies have goals; in this step, we try to understand whether the goals have been achieved. To answer this question, the policy maker, implementing agency, or other responsible group will need to gather information (formally or informally) on policy performance and then react to these findings. *Key questions*: Has the policy been effective in meeting the policy goals? What is the evidence behind these conclusions? Were adjustments made to the policy as a result of any problems that were detected?

**Box 6.3  The policy process model in action: Reducing disturbance by recreational rock climbers to the Frog Springs golden eagles**

The basalt rimrock high above the Deschutes River is ideal nesting habitat for the golden eagle (*Aquila chrysaetos*). Some of this basalt rimrock near Trout Creek, a tributary to the Deschutes River about 10 miles north of Madras, Oregon, has also become popular for recreational rock climbing. The Frog Springs golden eagle breeding territory encompasses the Trout Creek climbing area, and when the crag began attracting large numbers of climbers around 2002, fledging success of the golden eagle pair occupying the breeding territory plummeted. Much of the area is under the jurisdiction of the Prineville District of the Bureau of Land Management (BLM). The agency took action to address this problem, and the environmental analysis process undertaken by the BLM provides a demonstration of the policy process model described by Anderson (2015).

### Problem Formulation

Golden eagles prefer to nest high above the landscape (Figure 6.13), but when disturbed may leave the nest and wait nearby for the intruder to depart. While the adults are away, eggs and young are at greater risk of predation, chilling, and overheating; if disturbed early in the nesting season, golden eagles may completely abandon their nest. Fledging success of golden eagles along the Deschutes River has been monitored since 1992 by the wildlife biologists of a local utility (Portland General Electric [PGE]) that utilizes the river for hydropower. In the decade prior to 2002, breeding success for the golden eagle pair at the Frog Springs breeding territory averaged 1.3 young per year.

A climber's guidebook for the Trout Creek climbing area was published online in 2002, following which use of the area by rock climbers increased dramatically. Climbers developed access trails located above and below the eagles' nests, and some of the climbs described in the guidebook were within

25 feet of these nests. During the years 2002–2012, breeding success of the Frog Springs golden eagles declined to an average of 0.09 young per year. Biologists became alarmed, and attributed this decline to disturbance by climbers. With respect to alternative definitions of the problem, one might argue that the problem was not the fault of climbers, rather of the many nest sites available within their breeding territory, the eagles chose an inappropriate location for their active nest site. Note that these two alternative problem definitions would probably result in two entirely different policy solutions. Alternative definitions notwithstanding, the Bald and Golden Eagle Protection Act prohibits the *take* of bald or golden eagles, and the definition of take in the Act includes to molest or disturb. *Disturb* is further defined in regulations as causing a decrease in eagle productivity by interfering with normal breeding, feeding, or sheltering behavior, or by causing nest abandonment. Thus, the problem was not merely an issue of user conflict but also involved important legal considerations.

### Policy Agenda

The BLM works cooperatively with PGE and numerous other agencies to manage resources along the Deschutes River, and the declining breeding success of the Frog Springs golden eagles set off alarms in many quarters. Whereas prior to 2002 BLM recreation staff rarely encountered rock climbers at the nearby Trout Creek Campground, concurrent with declining eagle nesting success BLM staff noticed a large increase in climbers using the campground. Most of the cliffs and trails used by rock climbers are on BLM-administered lands, and by allowing disturbance of the golden eagles to continue, the BLM was itself at risk of violating the Bald and Golden Eagle Protection Act. Moreover, the protection of golden eagle nesting habitat was a requirement of BLM policy.

### Policy Formulation and Analysis

Federal law and BLM policy require the protection of golden eagle habitat, yet the agency has other management goals that include allowing recreational use of BLM lands and fostering the economic growth of local communities. Because recreational use of the Trout Creek climbing area was a growing contributor to the local economy, simply prohibiting human access to the climbing area conflicted with two important agency goals. Thus the agency needed to consider multiple, sometimes conflicting, goals in developing alternative policy solutions to the problem of diminished golden eagle nesting success at Trout Creek. After communicating with stakeholders and considering the science and policy issues at hand, the BLM developed an Environmental Assessment that considered three alternatives. Alternative 1 was *No Action*, which would allow rock climbing to continue as an authorized activity. Both Alternatives 2 and 3 closed the area to all access from January 15 to August 31, but

*Figure 6.13  A golden eagle nest. (Photo credit: © Nick Dunlop)*

provisionally opened a portion of the area for climbing to a greater (Alternative 2) or lesser (Alternative 3) degree, depending on which nest was occupied and on fledging dates. Although the BLM had multiple management goals for the area, the primary criterion for alternative selection was to prevent disturbance of nesting golden eagles. Both Alternative 2 and 3 were expected to meet this criterion, but Alternative 2 provided greater recreation access, and so was the policy alternative selected by the BLM field manager.

### Policy Adoption

The selected policy prohibits all access to 412 acres of BLM-administered lands in the Frog Springs golden eagle breeding territory from January 15 to August 31, essentially prohibiting all rock climbing at the Trout Creek climbing area during that period. Access to the entire area is allowed from September 1 to January 14, and depending on which nest is occupied and on the fledging dates for young eagles, access to a portion of the climbing area may be allowed from May 15 to August 31. The goals of the policy are to restore golden eagle nesting productivity to pre-2002 levels by reducing human disturbances during the breeding season, and to allow access to the climbing area, provided it does not present a risk to golden eagle breeding success.

### Policy Implementation

The seasonal closure has been implemented by BLM staff. Little interpretation of the policy has been required, since the policy (i.e., Proposed Action) is well-defined by the Environmental Assessment. Regular monitoring of golden eagle nest site occupancy and nesting success continues by wildlife biologists, which determines closure areas and dates. Seasonal closure dates are published online, and closure signs are placed on the road, at Trout Creek Campground,

and along the trails. BLM law enforcement officers regularly visit the area and have the authority to cite violators of the closure policy. Adherence to the closure is also monitored by the community of climbers who use the area, care about the eagles, and recognize that violations of the seasonal closure may result in a permanent, year-round closure.

Since the policy was implemented in 2013, not a single climber has been observed violating the seasonal closure, though occasionally hikers have been seen in the area. Thus, from the perspective of reducing disturbance to nest sites, the seasonal closure policy has been a success.

### Policy Evaluation

The EA required more robust monitoring by the BLM, and PGE and other cooperating agencies continue to monitor the Frog Springs golden eagle breeding territory regularly. Relative to restoring eagle nesting productivity, the primary goal of the policy, success has proven elusive. One of the eagles of the Frog Springs pair disappeared during the nonbreeding season, and the remaining eagle took up a new mate the following year. Since then the eagles have established their active nest at an alternate nest site across the Deschutes River from the climbing area, but have yet to produce any offspring. Extensive monitoring of the Frog Springs golden eagles will continue, as will the seasonal closure of the climbing area. However, reevaluation of the closure policy may be needed if nesting problems continue; thus, reinitiating the policy process model, in the hopes of improving the policy.

*Source:* USDI BLM (2012a, 2012b) and personal communication: William Dean, Associate District Manager, Prineville District, BLM, 5/13/2016.

Although Anderson (2015) presents policy making as a linear process, he and others recognize that it actually has many starts and stops, reversals, and do overs. Still, these steps provide a useful framework for thinking about the policy process. Above we provide an example of the policy process as it played out in a federal environmental assessment (Box 6.3). See Cubbage et al. (2017) for an extensive analysis of this policy process model.

## Choosing the Right Forest Policy Tool

*Public forest policies, the focus here, set the context and bounds within which forest management occurs* (Cortner & Moote, 1998). These policies set a framework within which landowners, agencies, interest groups, and others pursue their goals. As an example, private landowners pursue their goals in the context of federal, state, and local regulations.

Thus policy makers must carefully consider the effect of proposed policies, given the goals of those to whom they

will be applied. An example from the college classroom might illustrate this issue: most professors have experienced the unintended effect of allowing students to turn in a writing assignment at the end of class. While that policy may have the simple goal of minimizing class disruption caused by students who arrive late trying to hand in their papers immediately, it almost always will result in the unintended consequence of students skipping class to finish their papers. Moral: students have goals that may be different from their professors.

In a pioneering work, political scientists Schneider and Ingram (1990) investigated how to align policy tools with goals and motivations of the group toward which the policy is directed. Broadly, the purpose of a policy is to change the behavior of a group of people toward some desired end by motivating members of that population to do something they would not otherwise do, or by providing them with the means that allows them to do something they would not otherwise have been able to do (Schneider & Ingram, 1990).

As members of human societies we are immersed in policies, and at various times in our lives we may be policy makers, policy implementers, or targets of a particular policy. We may seldom give much thought as to what *motivates* us to engage with a policy, *yet policy instruments are essentially motivational devices that lead us to shift our behavior toward policy goals*.

Schneider and Ingram (1990) describe five categories of policy tools based on the underlying behavioral assumptions that motivate individuals and institutions to respond affirmatively to policy directives, and to fulfill policy goals:

- *Authority Tools*: Authority tools assume that people (that the policy seeks to influence) will follow statements or directives issued by a legitimate authority that allow, prohibit, or require action. Authority tools are frequently used in combination with (or backed up by) other policy tools, such as those described below. An example of an authority tool is the prohibition on take of any endangered fish or wildlife species under Section 9(a)(1)(B) of the Endangered Species Act. While there may be other policy tools used to attain ESA policy goals, Section 9(a)(1)(B) represents an authority tool that expressly prohibits a specific action.

- *Incentive Tools*: Incentive tools assume that people will choose the option that maximizes their utility. In other words, people make reasoned decisions that best serve their self-interests. Schneider and Ingram (1990) describe two forms of incentive tools of special interest to us: (1) *Inducements* provide a positive payoff, such as a tax incentive for homeowners purchasing energy-efficient appliances, federal or state cost sharing for reforestation of private forests, or federal grants to state agencies for water pollution control programs. (2) *Charges* are often used in connection with standards and guidelines, or with quota systems. For example, homeowners may be billed a surcharge for exceeding a certain amount of monthly water use, or a business may be charged a fee for not meeting reporting deadlines.

- *Capacity Tools*: Capacity tools assume that people are amenable to the desired policy action, but there are barriers to engagement with, or fulfillment of, the desired policy. Barriers usually take the form of a lack of knowledge or information, skills, or resources. Capacity tools remove these barriers to policy engagement or fulfillment and are intended to result in more informed decision making. University extension programs provide the archetypal capacity tool; by providing education, information, and technical advice to forest landowners about policy-relevant topics, extension programs may lead to more informed decisions that meet both landowner needs and policy goals.

- *Symbolic and Hortatory Tools*: Symbolic and hortatory policy tools attempt to shift people toward decision making that engages fundamental values and beliefs. The primary behavioral assumption behind symbolic and hortatory policy tools is that people tend to support policies—and take policy-relevant action—if they perceive the policy to be consistent with their values and beliefs. In addition to exhortations that seek to align people's beliefs and values with desired policy outcomes, symbolic and hortatory tools often associate desired policies with positive symbols, labels, images, and events. We are probably all familiar with photographs showing forests in various stages of disturbance, harvest, or recovery, all used to support a spectrum of often-conflicting forest policies, ranging from preservation to intensive management.

- *Learning Tools*: Learning tools assume that policy makers, and often the people that the policy seeks to influence, can learn about a policy issue or application through experience, experiment, or other forms of knowledge transfer. Often policy goals and preferred policy tools are unclear, unknown, or exist in an environment of scientific or social uncertainty. Learning tools represent social or institutional arrangements that help clarify policy goals, select appropriate policy tools, and reduce, manage, or adapt to uncertainty. For example, forest restoration and forest fuel treatment in the wildland–urban interface often require the coordination and cooperation of multiple agencies and public and private landholders, each with different policy goals and preferences and different motivations toward policy goals. All this takes place in an environment of physical and social uncertainty and multiple resource values. Through a collaborative learning process, policy goals can be clarified and conflicts acknowledged, appropriate action alternatives and preferred policy tools selected, and uncertainty incorporated into planning assumptions. Through time, physical conditions, assumptions, and motivations may change, leading to learning and adaptation.

Schneider and Ingram (1990) point out that research has shown that policy tools sometimes produce unexpected outcomes, which may include undesirable effects. This is not to say that the policy goals in such cases were flawed, rather, the tools used to attain those goals may have been inappropriate, given the policy goals, the physical realities associated with attaining those goals, and the characteristics of the people that must be engaged to fulfill those policy goals. *There are many public policy goals associated with conservation values on private lands; attaining these goals depends in large part on effectively engaging private landowners with the most appropriate policy tools* (Box 6.4).

## Box 6.4  Oak restoration: Fitting the policy tool to the forest landowner

In an article published in the journal *Conservation Biology*, social scientists Fischer and Bliss (2008) considered the problem of conserving Willamette Valley white oak savannah, a once-abundant habitat type that has all but disappeared due to urbanization, agricultural development, emphasis on the production of more valuable timber species, and the elimination of fire. Willamette Valley oak savannah is one of the most biodiverse ecotypes in Oregon, providing habitat for over 200 species of plants and wildlife, 45 of which are at risk. Much of the remaining white oak savannah is on family forestlands at the margins of the Willamette Valley; many of these lands have greater financial value as vineyards or as Douglas-fir plantations than they do as undeveloped oak savannah. Because private market forces tend to work against the conservation of oak savannah, conservation will likely require the creative and effective application of public policies if oak savannah is to be maintained on the landscape (Figure 6.14).

Seeking a way to effectively apply the five policy tools described by Schneider and Ingram (1990), Fischer and Bliss (2008) interviewed 36 family forest owners in the Willamette Valley, exploring their knowledge of and value orientations toward oak savannah, their views on options for the management of oak savannah, and their views on opportunities and constraints for its conservation. The authors reported that these interviews revealed three key aspects of the owners' beliefs and values that were relevant to their motivations to conserve oak savannah, and to their responses to potential policy tools: (1) owners perceived themselves to be stewards of a valuable ecological and cultural legacy; (2) owners framed their sense of duty as land stewards in utilitarian terms; and; (3) as much as they viewed themselves as stewards of a valuable legacy and desired financial support for their efforts, owners valued self-determination and autonomy in land-use decisions above all else.

Based on these findings and corresponding landowner motivations revealed in the interviews, the authors matched policy tools with landowner motivations using the logic of the underlying behavioral assumptions of these tools (Figure 6.15).

Rather than finding simple motivations that can be matched with an appropriate policy tool, Fischer and Bliss found that landowners' motivations are complex, varied, and at times contradictory. They caution that although it does not provide a "silver bullet" to conservation policy, in-depth ethnographic analysis can provide policy makers with a rich source of information with which to develop policies for an overall conservation strategy. Such analysis, they conclude, will help policy makers design strategies that appeal to landowners, rather than alienate them.

Figure 6.14  *An Oregon white oak* (Quercus garryana) *stand in the Willamette Valley with encroaching Douglas-fir.*

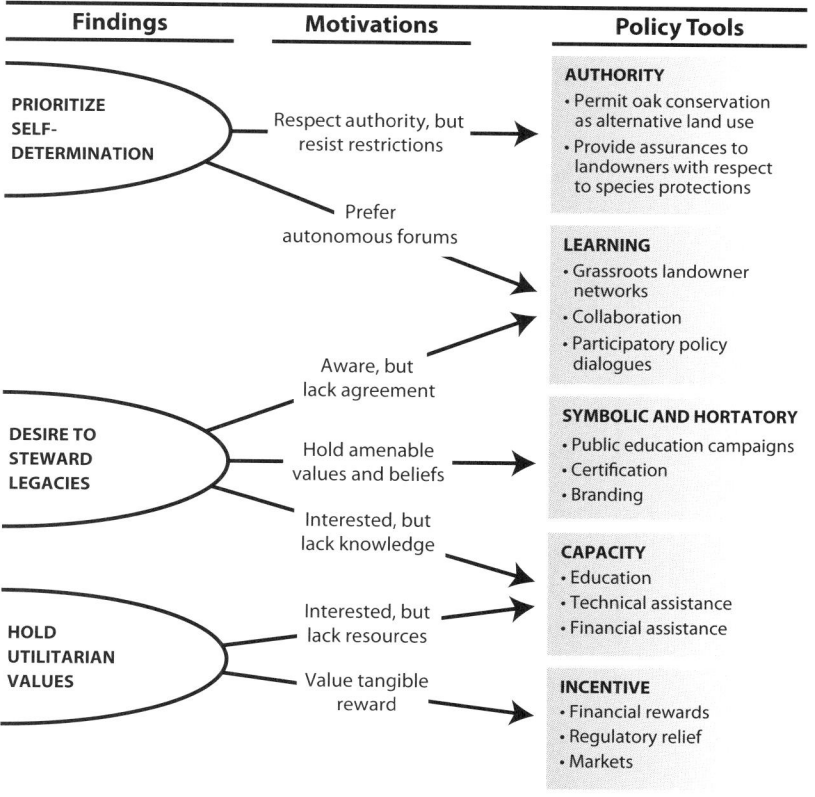

Figure 6.15  *Conceptual model of the linkage from key findings to motivations and from motivations to the policy tools in Schneider and Ingram (1990) policy analysis framework. (Source: Adapted from Fischer and Bliss, 2008)*

As another application of matching policy tools to a policy problem, let's consider the policy goal of leaving harvest buffers along small streams on private forestlands in Oregon (Figure 6.16).

Let us assume you are an advisor to the governor of Oregon. Using Schneider and Ingram's policy tool framework, describe how each tool might be applied along with potential limitations:

1. *Authority*: Develop forest practice rules requiring wider buffers on the subset of the most ecologically important small streams. Promising, but such a move would bring protest from landowners and, perhaps, cause a major political battle.

2. *Learning*: Help landowners form watershed councils that share in goal setting and policy making in a way that achieves the broader social and environmental goals of the state. Promising, but what about landowners that can't or won't participate?

3. *Symbolic and Hortatory*: Remind landowners of their moral obligation to protect these streams as a part of the responsibility of ownership that comes with the honor of stewarding Oregon's natural heritage. Promising, but would this commitment last, or would it be overwhelmed by financial realities?

4. *Capacity*: Provide training to landowners on the biophysical role of small streams, and provide technical assistance in identifying and protecting the subset of those streams that are of greatest ecological importance. Promising, but given the high commercial value of the timber along those streams, would such knowledge and advice be enough?

5. *Incentive*: Provide funds to develop conservation easements along the most important and sensitive small streams. Promising, but where would the money come from? Would incentives be used by those who would have placed buffers on their streams without them? What if the landowners holding key stream segments do not want to participate?

It is probably apparent that there may be no single policy tool that fully achieves the policy goals the governor has in mind. However, by developing knowledge about landowners and a framework for understanding how policies may affect them, much like what was done by Fischer and Bliss (2008) (Box 6.4), a suite of realistic, effective, and politically acceptable policy tools might be developed, which achieve the public policy goal while not threatening the governor's chances for reelection.

Figure 6.16  *With the increasing recognition of the ecological importance of small streams in coastal Oregon has come proposals for wider stream buffers. (Photo courtesy of Deanne Carlson)*

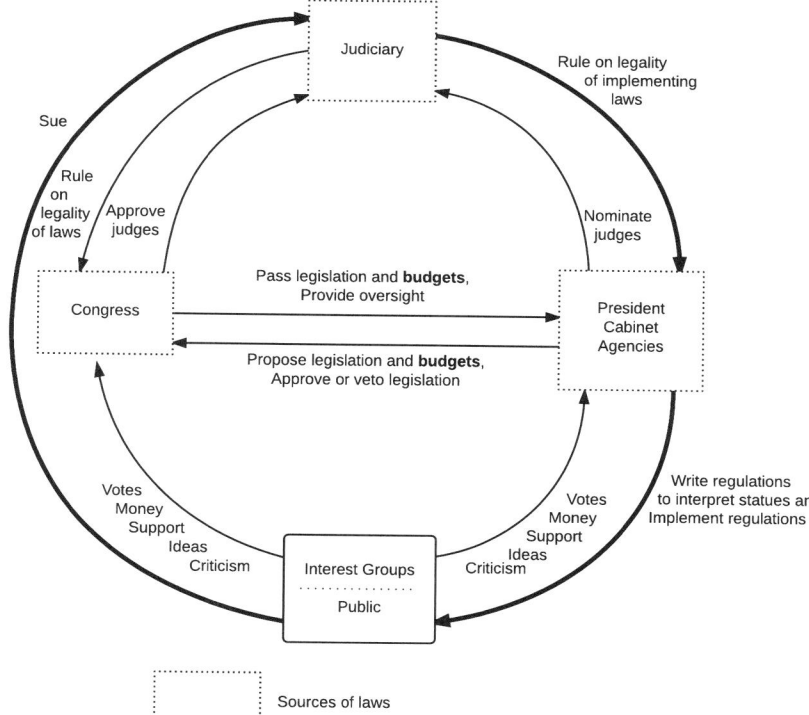

Figure 6.17  *Federal policy arena in the USA, highlighting the outer ring of policy development and the congressional budgeting process as primary sources of federal natural resources policy formation.*

## Desirable Properties of Regulations

Let us presume that policy makers have decided they will need to develop new regulations to address their policy problem. What qualities should they seek in the regulations they adopt? Ellefson (2000) summarized desirable qualities of a forest regulatory program after reviewing the regulation literature. We will briefly discuss them here for regulations that might cover private forest practices:

- *Benefits occur and are measurable.* Evidence exists that the rule will have the intended effect. If an expansion of stream shade is needed to protect salmon, scientific studies need to document that the expansion will help salmon survival.

- *Compliance with the rules is possible.* The rule is technically and economically feasible to apply, and flexibility exists to meet varying forest resource conditions. A rule that calls for additional shade to be provided by conifers may be difficult to apply if most trees near the stream are hardwoods.

- *The program is cost-effective.* The rule allows the least costly way to meet the policy goals. If shade can be provided by hardwoods, but they are not considered in the requirements, the regulation may be more costly than necessary.

- *Rule development is open and constructive.* The rule-making process is clear, predictable, and timely and has a decision endpoint. Also, and perhaps most importantly, landowners have the chance to discuss why the policy is needed and to provide their knowledge of how to achieve the policy goals at the least cost to them.

- *Statutory intent is constructively promoted.* The letter of the law is the written regulation; the spirit of the law is its intent. Merging these two aspects requires assessing whether the regulations, as written, will move forest practices toward the policy goal, given the way that landowners will adjust—how they will react to the regulations given their goals.

## Dynamics of Policy Formation: The Federal Policy Arena in the United States

In the United States, federal policies are developed in what might be envisioned as a *policy arena* with a number of players and relationships. A simplified schematic of a federal policy arena for domestic policy would show key players of the executive, judiciary, and legislative branches together with interest groups and the public (Figure 6.17). In addition, the media, other governments (such as Indian tribes), and scientists can play key roles in policy formulation and change. In the figure, the arrows connecting the players show some of the key relationships, focusing on what each player provides the other. These multiple connections help create the *checks and balances* for which the US political system is famous.

Looking at the players and the connections to each other, we can highlight some key points about creation of natural resource policy in the federal policy arena:[5]

- Through time, Congress has passed, and the president has signed, *environmental statutes* (written laws passed by a legislative body) that provide the foundation of environmental protection of the waters, air, species, and other natural resources. We will study a number of these statutes in Chapter 7. However, short of a crisis, Congress rarely passes natural resource statutes as stand-alone legislation that go through the regular process of hearings and

5 Many of the ideas in this section came from Professor Bill Lunch's booklet (Lunch, n.d.) that served as the class notes in a political science class, US Government and Institutions, at Oregon State University.

series of votes—natural resource legislation is just too controversial. Even then, the legislation may only make marginal changes in natural resource policy.

- More commonly, legislation that makes substantive changes in natural resource management comes as *policy riders* attached to other ***must pass*** legislation, such as annual budget bills. As an example, the infamous 1995 "salvage timber rider," which limited judicial review of certain federal timber sales, was added to an emergency supplemental appropriations bill for disaster assistance for the tragedy that occurred at the federal building in Oklahoma City (Nie, 2008). Each year, there are attempts to add scores of these policy riders to appropriations bills for federal agencies, such as changing the rules for granting grazing permits on national forests or building a road through a particular roadless area. These riders are seldom debated on the floor of Congress and provide a vehicle for potentially controversial legislation. While few make it through the entire legislative process, they often are more controversial than the budget bills themselves (Nie, 2008).

- The annual agency budgets passed by Congress, such as for the Forest Service or the Environmental Protection Agency, are themselves an important articulation of national priorities for natural resource management, with Congress attempting to increase the budget for programs it likes and decrease the budget for those it dislikes. These efforts can have profound effects on federal forest management, as occurred historically when western state congressmen and senators used their positions on congressional appropriation committees to fund high levels of harvest on the national forests. As stated by former US Forest Service Chief Jack Ward Thomas, "Funding is the fuel that drives most land management activities" (Nie, 2008, p. 185).

- The executive branch can influence federal policy making in many ways:

  ○ It has almost all the technical policy experts in the federal government, mostly in the many government agencies like the Forest Service or the Park Service, making it difficult for Congress to develop a totally independent view of problems and solutions. The imprint of these technical experts is felt through proposed legislation and budgets sent to Congress from the executive branch, testimony before Congress, and reports commissioned by Congress.

  ○ It can also influence legislation and budgets through the threat of a presidential veto, which often results in changes in legislation or budgets before they are passed. Overriding a presidential veto is rare, as it requires a two-thirds vote of both houses of Congress.

  ○ Finally, and perhaps most importantly, it has significant power in making natural resource policy through writing regulations that interpret legislation, and then implementing those regulations. Each new administration attempts to rewrite key regulations to better reflect its policy preferences and also puts its own twist on how the regulations will be implemented. Under most statutes, the executive branch has wide latitude in this work, as we discuss below.

- Interest groups, landowners, and the public provide votes, money, support, criticism, and ideas to both Congress and the executive branch in an attempt to influence the development of statutes and regulations (both forms of law) and their implementation. They also initiate lawsuits, mostly civil suits, to challenge either the constitutionality of the statutes or the executive branch's development and implementation of regulations that interpret the statutes.

- The judiciary has played an increasing role in natural resource policy formulation and interpretation since passage of the major environmental laws in the 1970s. In fact, it can be argued that the judiciary plays a much more assertive role in the United States than in any other Western democracy. This judicial intervention into policy formation results from environmental statutes that are complex and vague, the variety of statutes that invite citizen suits, judges that have become suspicious of agency actions, and groups that have found courts useful to advancing their cause. As pointed out by Nie (2008, p. 197): "Compared to other western democracies, the US model of policy making and dispute resolution is characterized by adversarial lawyer-dominated litigation." In general, courts are more willing to address process issues (such as whether a federal agency followed the regulations implementing the laws that apply to it) as compared to substituting their technical judgment for that of the agency in charge (such as whether a species is endangered), unless the agency's view is clearly at odds with the facts.

**How the Executive Branch and Judiciary Make Natural Resource Law**    While Congress is the source of legislation that becomes law (statutes) with a presidential signature or after Congress overrides a presidential veto, all three branches of government create law. Here, we highlight the roles of the executive branch and the judiciary in making law as key components of the outer ring of the policy arena (Figure 6.17).

*We focus on the policy arena's outer ring, because, on a day-to-day basis, most forest policy in the United States is made there.* As noted by Nie (2008, p. 44), "The ambiguity, contradiction, and overextended commitments in some . . . [public land] laws are the major reasons administrative rule making . . . , planning processes, the courts, and other venues . . . have become the dominant ways of dealing with . . . [public land] conflict."

Federal agencies write regulations to interpret statutes, such as how to interpret provisions of the Endangered Species Act, and then implement those regulations. Interest groups, such as the Sierra Club, bring lawsuits if they believe that the regulations do not derive from the statute in question or (more commonly) that federal agencies are not faithfully implementing their own regulations. The courts then judge the merits of the lawsuit and render a decision. If the decision is adverse to the executive branch, it will need either to rewrite the regulations or (more commonly) to alter the way it implements existing regulations.

Some examples of outer ring dynamics are:

- Lawsuits in the 1990s and 2000s led the Environmental Protection Agency to issue regulations under the Clean Water Act to control nonpoint sources of pollution across the United States, regulations that could affect all land uses to at least some degree for decades to come.

- The Department of Agriculture in 2012 updated regulations implementing the National Forest Management Act to help clarify the shifting emphasis of the Forest Service in managing the National Forests (see Chapter 20 for the major components of this change). These new regulations withstood the initial legal challenge.

- Litigation is generally ongoing across the United States calling for the US Fish and Wildlife Service (USFWS) to classify additional species as threatened or endangered under the Endangered Species Act; the groups that regularly bring these lawsuits claim (probably correctly) that the lawsuits have resulted in many species being listed.

The fundamental underpinning for legislative, executive and judicial action is the US Constitution—the *law of the land*; powers exercised by the branches of government flow from and are limited by the words in that document. You may wonder what part of the US Constitution enables Congress to pass laws like the Endangered Species Act. The most basic answer is that Congress can regulate natural resources because of the authority found in Article I, Section 8 of the Constitution, which provides that "Congress shall have power . . . to regulate Commerce with foreign Nations, and among the several States, and with the Indian Tribes." As you can imagine, this authority has been interpreted by the

courts, and the *commerce clause*, as it is known, has been interpreted expansively. Very few attempts by Congress to make environmental law have been ruled outside the intent of the commerce clause.

**Federal Regulations**   *Regulations that provide guidance for implementing the statutes passed by Congress and signed by the president are written by the executive branch.* Much of this regulation writing is done by the agencies within the executive branch that will implement the regulations, such as the Forest Service, since they have the expertise. Some statutes, such as the National Environmental Policy Act, are brief, leaving the details (and the teeth) needed for enforcement to the regulations, as we will see in the next chapter. Others, such as the Endangered Species Act, have detailed statutory provisions, leaving somewhat less for the agencies to interpret through regulation via their delegated authority from Congress. Even here, though, much interpretation by the agencies may be needed.

Some key points in development of regulations by the executive branch are:

- The process of developing or revising regulations is somewhat more linear, with fewer checks and balances, than the process of developing or revising legislation.

  - The executive branch publishes proposed regulations in the Federal Register, and the public has a limited time to review and comment on them.

  - The executive branch then considers the comments and publishes a final rule, which then resides in the Code of Federal Regulations and has the force of law.

- The Administrative Procedure Act (APA), 5 U. S. C. 551 et seq.,[6] passed by Congress in 1946, provides direction to agencies about rule making and opened governmental decision making to public access and participation for the first time. "The APA required federal agencies to keep the public informed of their organization, procedures, and rules, as well as provide them with opportunities for public comment and requesting judicial review of the rule-making process. Specifically, the APA granted citizens 'the right to petition for the issuance, amendment, or repeal of a federal rule'" (McGinley, 2017). Thus, the APA prescribes the process that agencies must obey, which ensures the public's access to information and public participation in the rule-making process. It also contains an important provision that prohibits *arbitrary and capricious behavior* by federal agencies in the development and implementation of regulations. While proving such egregious

---

6  We will discuss different ways of citing laws in Chapter 7.

behavior is relatively difficult, this provision has been extensively used in lawsuits to successfully challenge and invalidate proposed federal agency actions that were clearly inconsistent with law and fact.

- As natural resource policy became more complicated, Congress gradually devolved its legislative authority to technical experts who work for the executive branch. This has a lot to do with the personnel of the different branches of government, as we mentioned above—the executive branch has far more policy experts than Congress. As an example, Congress may occasionally have a member who is a professional forester, while the executive branch has thousands of foresters, many of whom have been studying forest policy issues for decades.

Federal regulations have been the source of many important policies that govern the management of natural resources in the United States, such as the process for deciding when a proposed federal project might have significant environmental impacts and the requirement to maintain habitat for viable populations of wildlife on the national forests. Also, in the first 15 years of the 21st century most federal policy that has been developed to reduce $CO_2$ emissions has come from the executive branch, such as writing new regulations for the Clean Air Act, rather than from the congressional legislative process. *The courts have allowed considerable delegation of congressional authority to executive agencies. Increasingly, agencies are essentially writing laws (regulations) under the cover of very broad direction from Congress.*

However, there are limits to this delegation such as the *ultra vires* doctrine. *Ultra vires* is Latin for "without authority," or "beyond powers." An agency has only the authority it is delegated by Congress, and that authority can be redefined through new legislation. Other important checks on executive-branch authority are oversight, confirmation of major appointments, and, notably, budgets. Congress appropriates money for the agencies via the federal budget; if an agency is doing something Congress doesn't like, that agency can find itself without funds.

*Case Law.*   Case law has developed over time as people challenged the constitutionality of the statutes written by Congress and (more importantly for us) the legality of regulations written by the executive branch and the administrative interpretations by the executive branch necessary for implementation. How did the federal courts get the right to do such a review of statutes and regulations? The source of the power of federal judicial review is contained in Article III of the Constitution. However, that power contains significant limitations (Ferrey, 2013). Federal judicial review is limited to actual cases and controversies, meaning that federal courts cannot issue advisory opinions. For there to be a *case or controversy*, there must be a real dispute, with real parties, that is capable of resolution by judicial decree.

Most alleged violations of environmental law are treated as civil (not criminal) matters. For a civil suit to be considered, someone who is dissatisfied must bring the suit to court. In such cases, courts decide disputes between litigants and about laws challenged in court. The person, group, or institution bringing the suit to court is called the *plaintiff* and the person, group, or institution against whom it is brought is called the *defendant.* In civil cases, the test for imposition of liability generally rests on the preponderance of evidence or the totality of the evidence, a lower bar than the *beyond a reasonable doubt* standard of criminal trials. The case may be heard by a judge alone or a judge and jury (Cubbage et al., 2017; Ferrey, 2013).

In terms of process, federal and most state courts have a three-tiered system, with the lowest level consisting of district courts, the intermediate level of appellate courts, and the highest level of the Supreme Court. Generally district courts are the courts of original jurisdiction and, in making their decision, they consider questions of law (the meaning of the law and its application to the case in question) and then questions of fact (the factual evidence provided by both sides). The losing litigant can appeal to the appellate court, with that court generally focusing on questions of law. Whoever loses there can appeal to the Supreme Court, but that court takes only a small percentage of cases brought to it (Cubbage et al., 2017; Ferrey, 2013).

Certain conditions must be met for courts to hear a civil case brought against a federal agency (Ferrey, 2013):

- To commence a case in federal court, a party must have *standing*. An important lawsuit—*Lujan v. Defenders of Wildlife*, 504 U.S. 555 (1992)[7]—addressed standing, that is, the conditions that must be fulfilled for the court to consider that a controversy in the application of a law exists and is ready to be adjudicated. In that case, the Supreme Court ruled that "the irreducible constitutional minimum of standing contains three elements: (1) an injury-in-fact that is (a) concrete and particularized and (b) actual and imminent, (2) causation, and (3) redressability." Thus, to have federal standing, plaintiffs must show tangible, individual harm, show that harm is imminent, and show that legal action can improve the situation (Cubbage et al., 2017). The definition of what constitutes an *injury* has broadened over time from direct economic loss

---

7 To the extent possible, we will use the following court case citation format: names of the parties, volume number, case reporter, initial page number, and date of decision, in that order. As an example, the case of 504 U.S. 555 (1992) was decided in 1992 and involved Secretary of the Interior Lujan and Defenders of Wildlife. It can be found in volume 490 of U.S. Reports starting at page 555.

to loss of valued experiences and activities among other interests, with continued judicial interpretation as to the breadth of what constitutes an injury.

- A case or controversy must be *ripe* for judicial review of an agency action. Section 704 of the APA provides that only *final* agency actions are subject to judicial review; draft plans, as an example, are generally not ripe for judicial review.

- The case or controversy must exist at all stages of litigation, or else the matter becomes *moot* and the court loses jurisdiction.

- Plaintiffs must demonstrate that they have exhausted all administrative remedies in order to commence a court case reviewing an agency action. Many agencies have administrative review processes built into their decision making, as we will see in the next chapter. Plaintiffs must avail themselves of these administrative processes before moving on to litigation.

In civil cases, plaintiffs must prove that the defendant violated a civil law. In many federal environmental cases, claims are based largely on procedural failings—that the federal agency being sued did not follow the procedures mandated for it by law. Many environmental statutes include *citizen suit* provisions that grant citizens the right to sue to compel enforcement of those laws. Also, claims may be based on the arbitrary and capricious standard of the APA (Cubbage et al., 2017; Ferrey, 2013).

In environmental law cases, if the defendant is found liable, the defendant is usually ordered to remedy the problem or injury. In this *equity remedy*, the judge may vacate (set aside) a decision by an agency, basically returning the proposed action to the agency for repair (See Box 6.5 for an example of this type of judicial decision). If the judge deems that remedy inadequate to redress the plaintiff's injury, the judge may issue a *permanent injunction*, providing that a four-factor test is satisfied (*Oregon Wild v. Bureau of Land Mgmt.*, WL 1190131 [2015]):

1. That the plaintiff has suffered an irreparable injury;

2. That remedies available at law, such as monetary damages, are inadequate to compensate for that injury;

3. That, considering the balance of hardships between the plaintiff and defendant, a remedy in equity is warranted; and

4. That the public interest would not be disserved by a permanent injunction.

As an example, Judge Dwyer famously issued a permanent injunction in 1989 (*Seattle Audubon Soc. v. Evans*, 771 F. 1989) protecting owl habitat from further timber sales pending the Forest Service's adoption of a management plan in compliance with law. The Forest Service then prepared and brought a number of management plans before the judge for his approval. Finally, Judge Dwyer ruled that one of the plans, the Northwest Forest Plan, was within the discretion of the federal government to adopt and lifted the injunction (*Seattle Audubon Soc. v. Lyons*, 871 F. Supp. 1291 [1994]).

How do federal courts evaluate the merits of a lawsuit seeking judicial review of an agency action? The approach generally taken was well captured by Judge Dwyer in his landmark 1994 decision on the legality of the Northwest Forest Plan (*Seattle Audubon Soc. v. Lyons*, 871 F. Supp. 1291 [1994]):

- The court in reviewing a challenged administrative action determines whether the action is arbitrary, capricious, an abuse of discretion, or otherwise not in accordance with law, or was taken without observance of procedures required by law.

- The standard is narrow and presumes the agency action is valid.

- While the court may not substitute its judgment for that of the agency, it should subject the action to a thorough, probing, in-depth review.

Notice that the courts assume that the agency action is valid, but put it through in-depth review to determine whether it is arbitrary and capricious, an abuse of discretion, or otherwise a violation of laws or procedure (such as guiding regulations) (See Box 6.5 for an example of such a review). The arbitrary and capricious standard has seen detailed court interpretation (*Lands Council v. McNair*, 629 F.3d 1070, 1074 [2010]):

> *A decision is arbitrary and capricious only if the agency relied on factors Congress did not intend it to consider, entirely failed to consider an important aspect of the problem, or offered an explanation that runs counter to the evidence before the agency or is so implausible that it could not be ascribed to a difference in view or the product of agency expertise. . . . Agency action is valid if the agency considered the relevant factors and articulated a rational connection between the facts found and the choices made.*

Two very important concepts underlie how the courts approach environmental law decisions—precedent and judicial deference:

- *Precedent*: The decisions made in previous lawsuits are known as precedent. Precedent is a key to understanding how the judiciary branch functions—maintaining a continuity of legal decisions through time and deviating from past decisions about similar cases only for very good reasons. In making the points above about the criteria for evaluation of agency actions, as an example, Judge Dwyer cited many previous judicial decisions.

## Box 6.5  Ecological forestry, public protest, and the courts: The case of White Castle

In fall 2010 Secretary of Interior Ken Salazar, who at the time oversaw most federal lands in the United States outside the national forests, asked us to apply our ecological forestry principles to the O&C Lands (Oregon and California Railroad Revested Lands) of western Oregon. These lands were taken back by the federal government in the early 1900s from the railroad company to which they had been granted, and now sit in a in a checkerboard landscape of O&C and private lands. Under provisions of the 1937 "O&C Act," these lands were to be managed for "permanent forest production . . . in conformity with the principle of sustained yield for the purpose of providing a permanent source of timber supply, protecting watersheds, regulating stream flow, and contributing to the economic stability of local communities and industries."

At the time (2010) the O&C Lands had been managed under the Northwest Forest Plan (NWFP) for almost 15 years. While the NWFP allowed regeneration harvest in the *Matrix* land allocation that was to provide the allowable cut under the Plan, some other provisions in that plan had been used, along with protest and litigation, to largely stop regeneration harvest on the O&C Lands. Consequently, the BLM had focused its harvests, for at least the short run, on thinning plantations and administering fuel treatments, while awaiting further policy guidance.

In response to the Secretary's request, we proposed BLM undertake pilot projects that would demonstrate the use of ecological forestry in O&C Douglas-fir–western hemlock forests under three guiding principles: (1) focus on younger, previously harvested stands (generally less than 80 years of age), (2) utilize variable-retention harvest with significant retention, mostly in aggregates, and (3) encourage the development of early successional ecosystems (a combination of shrubs, forbs, and trees) after harvest, much like would occur

following a wildfire. Such an approach appeared to provide both ecological and economic benefits, since there was an excess of younger, previously harvested stands and a shortage of preforest in western Oregon, compared with the historical range-of-variability (as described in the Oregon Coastal Province landscape assessment in Chapter 5). Importantly, such an approach would comply with the provisions of the NWFP.

We worked with the Roseburg BLM to identify a number of stands in the Myrtle Creek watershed of the Umpqua River that might be used in the pilot project effort. Most stands fit within the criteria of being less than 80 years of age and having been previously harvested. However, one identified stand was older and not previously harvested (a natural stand in the terminology of this book); this stand was about 110 years old, and contained pockets of old-growth trees. All the selected stands were in the Matrix, which had timber production as one of its goals.

We helped BLM apply the variable-retention prescription described above to a number of the younger stands, largely 50–60 year-old plantations that developed after the natural stands were cut, without any ensuing litigation (see Figure 4.14 for an example of one such harvest). Our focus here is the 110 year-old natural stand in the upper reaches of the Myrtle Creek watershed (Figures 6.18a and 6.18b), which became known as "White Castle," and the protest and litigation that ensued.

Our guiding principles for the use of ecological forestry on these lands specified that harvests should (generally) be conducted in stands less than 80 years of age. Why did we propose a harvest in an older natural stand that we knew would generate controversy? We had three main reasons:

Figure 6.18 *Public gatherings in the White Castle stand: (a) Jerry Franklin explaining the recommended prescription for the stand— a variable-retention harvest that retained all old trees, such as the one behind him. The prescription included modest planting of conifer seedlings following harvest and the nurturing of a diverse early successional (preforest) stage for a number of decades into the future. (b) BLM professionals explaining the prescription they had developed, based on our recommendations, to US Congressman Peter DeFazio, US Senator Jeff Merkley, USFWS Oregon State Supervisor Paul Henson, and others.*

1. Some participants in the public meetings we held had urged BLM to include stands of this age in the pilot projects, as there was a substantial amount of forests in this age class in the Matrix land allocation;

2. Members of the Oregon congressional delegation, which at that time were developing new legislation for the O&C Lands, requested that we not set an age limit on the stands that we would consider for pilots, specifically advising us to avoid making de facto policy calls through our selection rules; and

3. Legislation then being proposed by members of the congressional delegation included this stand (and many others like it) in the allowable cut land base. We thought that incorporating it into the pilot projects was important for informing the delegation and the general public about the implications of designating such stands as part of the harvest land base.

With some advice from us, the BLM Roseburg staff took over and developed the prescription, which included approximately 40% retention (including all trees over 150 years of age) and buffers around red tree vole (*Arborimus longicaudus*) nests—a species of special concern under the NWFP. The prescription also called for an extended preforest period after harvest.

As BLM developed the White Castle project, USFWS issued a draft and then final rule on revised Critical Habitat for the northern spotted owl that included most of the White Castle stand scheduled for harvest. Also, the USFWS issued a Biological Opinion (see Chapter 7 for explanation) that "determined the project would 'adversely affect' northern spotted owls, their critical habitat, and their prey such as the red tree voles but would not jeopardize the continued existence of the northern spotted owl as a species" (*Oregon Wild v. Bureau of Land Mgmt.*, WL 1190131 [2015]).

People opposed to the project set up platforms in trees within the stand and occupied them for months, a form of protest that had largely died out in Pacific Northwest forests (Figure 6.19). The words "White Castle" became a battle cry in the debate over federal forestry in western Oregon.

To comply with BLM decision making policy and the National Environmental Policy Act (NEPA, see Chapter 7 for details), the BLM wrote an Environmental Assessment (EA) and issued a Finding of No Significant Impact (FONSI), as it had done for other pilot projects in younger, previously harvested stands. The FONSI meant that the BLM planned to proceed with the White Castle project without writing an Environmental Impact Statement (EIS)—a more rigorous and lengthy analysis of environmental impacts required by NEPA for **major federal actions significantly affecting the quality of the human environment.**

### The Litigation

**Claims and Requested Remedy.**    In 2014, two Oregon environmental groups, Oregon Wild and Cascadia Wildlands,

Figure 6.19  *Banner and platform of tree sitters high in the trees of the White Castle stand. The hard-to-see platform is in the branches right above the banner.*

sued the BLM over the White Castle project in the federal district court in Eugene, Oregon, with Judge Ann Aiken presiding (*Oregon Wild v. Bureau of Land Mgmt.*, WL 1190131 [2015]). In their complaint, the two plaintiffs brought:

*this civil action, arising under the Administrative Procedure Act (APA) . . . challenging the United States Bureau of Land Management's (BLM) issuance of the Roseburg Secretarial Demonstration Pilot Project (Roseburg Pilot Project) Environmental Assessment (EA)/Finding of No Significant Impact (FONSI) and Decision Record for the White Castle Variable Retention Harvest Timber Sale for violations of federal laws and regulations intended to protect the public's natural resources and ensure informed, well-reasoned decision making.*

(continued)

The complaint by Cascadia Wildlands and Oregon Wild contained two key requests:

1.  *a declaration that BLM violated the National Environmental Policy Act . . . and its implementing regulations by (a) failing to prepare an Environmental Impact Statement (EIS), (b) by failing to develop and analyze an adequate range of alternatives, and (c) by otherwise failing to take the requisite "hard look" at the project's potential environmental impacts; . . .*

2.  *an injunction prohibiting the BLM and its contractors, assigns, and other agents from proceeding with the White Castle Timber Sale, unless and until this Court determines that the violations of law set forth herein have been corrected.*

## Standing

The plaintiffs argued that:

*[Their] members use the forest areas comprising the White Castle timber sale area for hiking, recreation, bird watching, nature appreciation, and other recreational pursuits. . . . members will not have the ability to use and enjoy the White Castle timber sale area if it is logged. The interests of . . . [their] members will be irreparably impaired if the White Castle sale is allowed to proceed without compliance with federal environmental laws . . .*

*These are actual, concrete, and particularized injuries caused by Defendant's failure to comply with mandatory duties under NEPA, FLPMA and the APA. The relief sought in this Complaint would redress Plaintiffs' injuries.*

Thus, the plaintiffs argued that they had met the Supreme Court standard for standing with their "potential actual, concrete, and particularized injuries caused by Defendant's failure to comply with mandatory duties," and that their requested relief would redress their injuries. Judge Aiken accepted these arguments and proceeded to try to case.

## Standard of Review

Judge Aiken then specified the standard of review, articulating many of the standards that Judge Dwyer had used in his decision on the Northwest Forest Plan described earlier in this chapter. Judge Aiken further cited a number of precedents set in previous court cases in further stating (*Oregon Wild v. Bureau of Land Mgmt.*, WL 1190131 [2015]):

*The Court need only defer to an agency's decision if it is "fully informed and well-considered" and must reject an agency decision that amounts to "a clear error of judgment." . . . Specifically, the court will reverse an agency's decision as arbitrary or capricious if the agency relied on factors Congress did not intend it to consider, entirely failed to consider an important aspect of the problem, offered an explanation that ran counter to the evidence before the agency, or offered one that is so implausible that it could not be ascribed to a difference in view or the product of agency expertise. . . . As*

*such, in order to withstand summary judgment, the "agency must articulate a rational connection between the facts found and the conclusions reached." . . . Independent of these concerns, the court will set aside an agency's action if it acted without observing procedures required by law.*

## Decision of the Court

The plaintiffs in the case argued that the BLM violated NEPA by: (1) failing to adequately analyze alternative approaches to the project in the EA; (2) not preparing an EIS; and (3) failing to take a *hard look* at the project's direct and indirect environmental impacts. In reviewing the information provided by both sides, Judge Aiken found for the plaintiffs on all counts. Perhaps ironically, in Judge Aiken's opinion setting aside the projects authorization, she frequently referenced *our* published work that recommended regeneration harvests for stands less than 80 years of age, identified uncertainties and controversies surrounding the social and legal acceptability of harvest in these older, natural stands, and called for scientific review and analysis of ecologically based timber harvest in designated Critical Habitat for the northern spotted owl.

**Range of Alternatives Considered Was Inadequate.**   As Judge Aiken noted, NEPA regulations require a federal agency to study, develop, and describe appropriate alternatives to a proposed project.

The plaintiffs argued that the EA was inadequate because it failed to analyze viable alternatives to the proposed project, in particular an alternative limiting the project's variable-retention harvest to younger trees, as was done in other pilot projects. Judge Aiken found that the BLM's failure to consider this known alternative was arbitrary and capricious, in violation of NEPA and APA.

**The Record Does Not Support a Finding of No Significant Impact.**   In determining whether potential effects of a project could be significant, and thus require an EIS, agencies and courts must evaluate a number of factors, including whether the proposed action is likely to be highly controversial (because evidence casts serious doubt upon the reasonableness of an agency's conclusions) or whether its effects are highly uncertain or involve unique or unknown risks. Judge Aiken found ample evidence in the record about the likely controversial nature of the project and the uncertainties related to project outcomes. Another test for significance is whether the action sets a precedent for future actions. As these were pilot projects to test ideas for wider application, Judge Aiken found for the plaintiffs here, too. Still another significance factor is the degree to which the action may adversely affect an endangered or threatened species or its Critical Habitat, such as the northern spotted owl. Again, Judge Aiken found for the plaintiffs. Overall, Judge Aiken ruled that the evidence supporting a finding of "significant impact" weighed in favor of an EIS.

**A Hard Look at the Environmental Impacts Was Not Done.** As Judge Aiken noted, NEPA requires that an agency must take a *hard look* at a project's environmental consequences. Crucial to determining whether an agency took a hard look is whether the agency supplied a convincing statement of reasons to explain why it concluded that the project's impacts did not meet the regulatory standard for "significant." Not only did Judge Aiken find the BLM's reasoning about significance unconvincing, she also found that the BLM had failed to take a hard look at evidence for the presence of red tree voles nest sites in the project area. Thus, Judge Aiken found that the BLM did not take a hard look at environmental impacts, making its decision arbitrary and capricious, and therefore in violation of APA and NEPA.

**Remedy.** Judge Aiken set aside the White Castle project's authorization, holding that BLM violated NEPA and APA. She did not see the need to also grant a specific injunction on action in the project area, as she reasoned that the BLM could not proceed with the project until the agency complies with NEPA by preparing an EIS.

## Some Lessons of White Castle

While the White Castle experience created more controversy than we had hoped, we did learn from it:

- Applying variable-retention harvests in ecologically degraded stands in federal forests of the United States, such as those that have been converted to plantations, is clearly more socially acceptable than applying variable-retention harvest to natural stands. It is very hard to convince people that applying such a harvest to natural stands will help restore a degraded landscape, i.e., one that lacks preforest habitats, since the stand itself is not substantially degraded. However, even applying variable-retention harvest to plantations can elicit public protest (see Box 6.7).

- Applying variable-retention harvest to stands that currently provide habitat for at-risk species, such as the northern spotted owl, is likely to be more acceptable if you can point to another at-risk species

that will significantly benefit from the preforest habitat that will follow. Making an argument that preforest is needed to maintain biodiversity in general is likely to leave many people unconvinced.

- It is crucial to start with the least controversial actions, especially when attempting to restart activities that have effectively been stopped due to protest and litigation—even if they involve different techniques and seek to achieve ecological goals (e.g., preforest habitat). A mature natural forest in northern spotted owl habitat was not a good place to begin!

- To many members of the public, it is difficult to distinguish *analysis* from *advocacy* in the creation of forest policy options, especially when deeply held contested values are at stake. During our interactions with people opposed to the White Castle harvest, most notably at a meeting in Eugene, Oregon, and during a visit with the tree sitters at White Castle, a major focus of the criticism directed toward us was to convince us to publicly renounce the timber sale. The notion that we wanted to demonstrate the implications of proposed legislation, and that the pilots were a part of this process, carried little weight with these critics.

- The courts can rely heavily on the work of scientists to determine whether a proposed project could be a major federal action significantly affecting the quality of the human environment and therefore require an EIS. Thus, scientific reports, and scientists who did them, are often at the center of this determination, whether the scientists involved want to have that role or not!

- When such a finding occurs, it sends a signal to the agency proposing the project that it must do the more detailed analysis and more extensive public involvement associated with preparation of an EIS, and that the project will almost surely draw more attention, criticism, and lawsuits as this process unfolds. Thus, the agency may choose to move on to other projects. We will discuss the NEPA process and preparation of an EIS in more detail in Chapter 7.

- *Judicial deference*: Judges seek to avoid frustrating the will of the executive branch, as carried out by federal agencies, when deciding cases. This is known as *judicial deference* and is expressed in Judge Dwyer's acknowledgement that "the court may not substitute its judgment for that of an agency."

Deference comes in many forms: deference to an agency's interpretation of a statute that it is charged with implementing; deference to an agency's interpretation of its own regulations implementing that statute; deference to an agency's interpretation of a statute or regulation that it is not charged

with implementing; and deference to an agency's interpretation or choice of science used in decision making. Generally, courts apply a two-step test in deciding whether to defer to an agency's interpretation of a statute, which is the highest level of deference afforded to an agency and is known as *Chevron deference* after the case that established the precedent (*Chevron U.S.A., Inc. v. Natural Resources Defense Council, Inc.*, 467 U.S. 837 [1984]):

*First, always, is the question whether Congress has directly spoken to the precise question at issue. If the intent of Congress is clear, that is the end of the matter;*

*for the court, as well as the agency, must give effect to the unambiguously expressed intent of Congress. If, however, the court determines Congress has not directly addressed the precise question at issue, the court does not simply impose its own construction on the statute. . . . Rather, if the statute is silent or ambiguous with respect to the specific issue, the question for the court is whether the agency's answer is based on a permissible construction of the statute.*

**In general, natural resource statutes are silent or ambiguous on many important issues relating to their interpretation and implementation. In these situations, the courts generally give the executive branch wide latitude in interpreting these statutes through the regulations agencies write** as we will see in the next chapter.

Other court cases have established somewhat lower standards of deference to an agency's interpretation of regulations implementing a statute (see Box 6.5). Relative to federal forest management, courts frequently defer to a land management agency's interpretation of its own forest plan (*Forest Guardians v. Forest Serv.*, 329 F.3d 1089 [2003]). Importantly, courts usually defer to an agency's interpretation or choice of which science to rely on in decision making (*Marsh v. Oregon Nat. Res. Council*, 490 U.S. 360 [1989]).

Plaintiffs in environmental lawsuits often seek to stop actions that they believe to be illegal under the environmental statutes and regulations they cite, whether the objectionable action is timber harvest in endangered species habitat or a road or mine near a salmon stream. The decision by the courts as to whether to grant this request can be especially pivotal in projects where time will affect the viability of the action, such as timber salvage after wildfire.

Plaintiffs, understandably, often seek a *preliminary injunction (PI)* to stop the actions while the case is heard. A PI is warranted when a plaintiff can demonstrate that (1) they are likely to succeed on the merits, (2) they are likely to suffer irreparable harm in the absence of preliminary relief, (3) the balance of equities tips in their favor, and (4) an injunction is in the public interest (*Winter v. NRDC*, 129 S. Ct. 365, 374 [2008]). Many courts recognize these traditional criteria, or, as an alternative, hold that a party is entitled to a preliminary injunction if it demonstrates: (1) the existence of serious questions on the merits and (2) a balance of hardships tipping in its favor (*Alliance for the Wild Rockies. v. Cottrell* 632 F.3d 1127 [2011]). Under this "sliding-scale" approach, the greater the risk of irreparable harm to the plaintiffs, the less probability of success they must demonstrate, and vice versa.

**Courts decide winners and losers. If either side is unsure of the merits of their case, or reluctant to wait for a decision by the court, they may seek an out-of-court settlement.** Often courts encourage such an effort. Such negotiations have elements of the collaboration process, which we will discuss in Chapter 8.

## Implications for Ecological Forestry

Public policies set the framework within which landowners, agencies, and interest groups seek their goals. Therefore these policies are mightily important to the future of ecological forestry, especially where markets do not value the contributions that ecological forestry makes toward societal goals. Until the early 1970s, public policies for public and private forests were similar, with most policies aimed at encouraging sustained timber production. With the coming of the environmental revolution in the early 1970s, the policy frameworks for public and private forests began to diverge, with the most responsibility for environmental protection being placed on federal resources followed by those of the states. In many ways, public lands, especially federal lands, have reoriented their management to conserve and enhance ecological processes and biodiversity. We would expect ecological forestry to play a significant role in achieving these goals.

Among the most interesting public policy developments for forest management in the next few decades, though, could be the shifting policy frameworks for private lands, as the United States continues to grapple with water quality, species conservation, and other problems that cannot completely be solved on public lands. Much of that policy activity may come through state policies, in terms of state forest practice rules, and state implementation of the Clean Water Act and Clean Air Act, as private owners attempt to ensure that any increased regulation comes through the states and not directly from the federal government. Including the increasing calls for evidence of sustainability in the marketplace, we see an emerging and important role for ecological forestry in helping solve many of these coming policy problems on private lands.

Although much of the legislative framework for environmental protection at the federal and state levels in the United States has been in place for decades, the policies that derive from those laws are in continual evolution. As we have discussed, much of that change occurs through actions in the outer ring of the policy arena (Figure 6.17), at both the state and the federal level, with new regulations being written and court cases being brought that challenge these regulations or their implementation. Any of these regulations and legal cases might affect forestry across ownerships. While their individual outcomes are uncertain, their direction is clear—more and more landowners are being asked to do more and more to protect species and ecosystems. Ecological forestry can play an important role in mediating the relationship of agencies and landowners to the environmental goals of the larger society.

## Social Acceptability of Forest Practices

As described by Shindler, Brunson, and Stankey (2002), the concept of social acceptability of natural resource management can be traced to the work of rural sociologist Walter Firey (1960), who was interested in understanding why certain resource practices and prescriptions in different societies persisted, whereas others did not. Firey concluded that the adoption and retention of a resource program or action depends on the extent to which that activity satisfies three key requisites:

- *Physically possible*: practices are consistent with ecological processes;

- *Economically feasible*: practices generate revenue in excess of costs; and

- *Culturally adoptable*: practices are consistent prevailing social customs and norms.

Here, we will use the term *social acceptability* to represent *culturally adoptable* in keeping with recent research and terminology, with social acceptability being the aggregate expression of shared judgments among an identifiable and relevant segment of society (Brunson, 1996). Further, Brunson and Shindler (2004, pp. 663–664) utilize the work of Brunson (1996) to describe the concept of acceptability in ecosystem management:

> as a condition resulting from comparative judgments, wherein the object being judged is "acceptable" only if rated as superior or sufficiently similar to imagined alternatives. Social acceptability is simply an aggregate of these positive and negative judgments . . . acceptability tends to be observable only insofar as it is reflected in behaviors that indicate its absence, such as testifying at a public hearing or complaining to peers about a proposed action or existing condition.

In this book, we will spend many pages grounding actions in ecological processes and evaluating their economic feasibility, which should be no surprise since we often describe ecological forestry as trying simultaneously to provide ecological and economic benefits. All these grand ideas, though, may come to naught, if we ignore social acceptability. As Shindler et al. (2002, p. 1) said:

> There is an inherent instability to resource policies that do not adequately integrate the concerns of citizens. Adverse public judgments can postpone, modify, or prevent implementation of any management strategy, irrespective of the rigor of the underlying science or its cost-benefit ratio. Rather than accept unpopular decisions, citizens can use many methods to influence policy decisions. They can,

> for example, invoke the courts, lobby federal legislators, attract media attention for their cause, or at the statewide level, develop ballot initiatives to change a state's forest practice laws. When citizens seek forums that better reflect their values, these methods often circumvent traditional agency authority.

For as long as there has been a forestry profession, the social acceptability of forestry practices has been an issue. The first forestry school at a university in the United States, 1898 at Cornell University, lost its funding in a battle over the acceptability of *scientific forestry practices* after only five years in existence (Box 6.6). Bob Marshall (1925), later chief of recreation in the Forest Service, complained about clearcutting in a 1925 *Journal of Forestry* article saying, "A young plantation may be beautiful to look at from the road, but no person who goes to the woods for recreation gets the real benefit of the forest if it consists mostly of small poles."

### Some Keys to Acceptability

What are some keys to acceptability of forest practices? In this discussion, we accept the premises of Shindler et al. (2002, Abstract):

- . . . *the political environment surrounding most forestry decisions is not about just single questions, nor is it about just ecological questions.*

- . . . *public judgments are always provisional, never absolute or final, with each situation, each context, producing a unique set of circumstances affecting the formation of public acceptance.*

- . . . *social acceptability is a process rather than an end product.*

Shindler, Peters, and Kruger (1994) studied the effects of various silvicultural treatments on visual perceptions. Among residents near the Tongass National Forest in Alaska, they found that acceptability is linked to people's need to see how specific practices will look on the land once they are implemented. They suggested four key criteria on which acceptability judgments could be based: (1) an understanding of effects on natural characteristics of the surrounding forest, (2) a belief in the information provided, (3) a sense that the practice will benefit the local community, and (4) an opportunity for a meaningful role in the planning process.

Note that we talk here about *perceptions* rather than scientific facts or concepts. In his seminal article on the social acceptability of clearcutting, Bliss (2000) argues that the continuing controversy over clearcutting is essentially a social issue, not an ecological or technical issue—that the debate is more about perceptions, values, and trust than about shade intolerance, economic efficiency, or even environmental protection. He then focuses the article on **perceptions of clearcutting**, after noting the variety of dictionary definitions of perception as a "mental image or concept; awareness of the elements of environment through physical sensation; physical sensation interpreted in the light of experience; a quick, acute, and intuitive cognition" (Bliss, 2000 p. 4).

Following these definitions, Bliss (2000, p. 4) argues: "public perceptions of clearcutting, then, result from an array of phenomena, including sensory awareness, mental imagery, personal experience, intuition, and cognition. This is important: perceptions do not arise from any particular set of 'facts' alone, but rather from many diverse sources of human sensation and experience."

With these concepts as background, Bliss challenges a common belief that the public's opposition to clearcutting (and many other practices) would dissolve if they just learned the facts. As he states (Bliss, 2000, p. 7):

*This notion assumes, incorrectly, that lack of understanding is the source of public disapproval. To the contrary, one's understanding of an issue derives from more than facts: It is born of personal experience, observation, beliefs, and values, as well as facts. Experts perceive issues in their field differently from lay people, and they are notoriously poor at understanding other's perceptions about their field. . . . It would be folly to suppose that a well-orchestrated ad campaign extolling the scientific basis for clearcutting would result in lasting changes in public acceptance of the practice.*

Finally, Bliss (2000, p. 8) summarizes the conclusions of Shindler and colleagues about what makes forest practices more or less acceptable:

*First, people judge forest settings not only by what is there but also by* why *it is there. Conditions that arise as a*

---

Box 6.6 **Scientific forestry, social acceptability, and the death of America's first forestry school**

While the Yale School of Forestry may come to mind as the first forestry school in America associated with a university, it actually was the second one. The first school of forestry at Cornell University, though, had a short and controversial life. In the late 1800s, the superintendent of New York's state-owned forests believed that the state's recent constitutional amendment setting aside the Adirondack and Catskill preserves as lands to be kept forever wild was unfortunate. He claimed that approval by the state's electorate resulted from a widespread ignorance of enlightened forest management and its implications. In his annual reports for 1896 and 1897, he advocated inauguration of a demonstration forest to educate the body politic regarding what modern forestry was all about. A promising forest near Cornell University was suggested as the site, but the issue was controversial enough that the governor of New York was reluctant to endorse the proposal.

Cornell University President Schurman suggested that a college of forestry be instituted at Cornell to carry out the demonstration. President Schurman then consulted with the nation's three leading foresters (Gifford Pinchot, Alwin Schenck, and Bernard Fernow) to develop the scheme for the new college. They settled on a four-year Bachelor's Degree in Forestry, with the possibility of a fifth year for a Master's Degree, with Fernow as the dean. The governor supported this proposal; it easily passed through the legislature in 1898; and Fernow recruited the best young forestry professors to staff his faculty.

While the College of Forestry seemed to flourish, the demonstration forest at Axton did not. From the beginning, the concept of demonstrating scientific forestry in the Adirondacks had been vigorously opposed by a group of influential landowners at nearby Saranac Lake. Working through the Forest Preserve Board and the State Senate, they mounted an attack on the demonstration, but Fernow was undeterred.

Clearcutting the existing forest, followed about a year later by replanting with conifer nursery stock, were the core activities of the demonstration. A plan of development was drawn up to spare Cornell's most influential neighbors direct views of harvesting and planting activities. Unfortunately, from the college's point of view, the first harvesting was to take place on land adjoining private summer camps. The owners of those camps, who had used the Cornell-purchased tract for hunting, took umbrage at the operations and began proceedings to stop them through a newspaper war criticizing the methods of management and getting a legislative committee to inspect the activities. Finally, they visited the governor. While the college's appropriation ($10,000) for 1903 passed through the legislature, the governor pocketed the bill thus bringing the first college of forestry in North America to an ignominious end.

*Postscript:* Within a decade, a "farm-forestry" major was started in the College of Agriculture at Cornell to provide foresters that could help manage family forests throughout the state, and it continues today. The all-star faculty of the College of Forestry had left by that time, with Bernard Fernow going to New York City to become the first consulting forester in the United States, Walter Mulford going to the University of California at Berkeley to start its forestry school, and Filibert Roth going to the University of Michigan to start the forestry school there.

Source: Lassoie, Oglesby, & Smallidge (1998).

*result of natural causes are generally accepted, whereas conditions resulting from management receive increased scrutiny. Second, acceptability judgments are based on beliefs, values, and personal observation, as well as the geographic and normative context of the practice. Finally . . . social acceptability hinges on public trust in natural resource agencies. Trust . . . results from decision making processes that involve genuine dialogue and relationship building. Public acceptance of forest practices requires not only that such practices be compatible with prevailing beliefs and values, but also that public trust in forestry and foresters be restored.*

We will return to the issue of trust and trustworthiness in Chapter 8.

## What Do People Value Most from Their Forests?

To begin to answer this question, we will examine a recent survey of Oregonians. Logging and wood products have long been important to Oregon's economic vitality and sense of cultural identity. In the last 25 years, though, Oregon's economic growth has been concentrated around its largest city (Portland), mostly in high-tech, banking, insurance, and other growth sectors, and most of the state's population lives there. On the other hand, rural areas, where timbering has historically been a mainstay of the economy, such as in southwestern Oregon, have not achieved this diversification.

A major debate has erupted over federal forests called the Oregon and California Railroad Revested Lands (commonly known as O&C Lands), federal lands managed by the BLM that are concentrated in southwestern Oregon. The BLM has a specific commitment in its enabling legislation for these lands to contribute to the economic health of local communities that goes beyond the legislative commitment of the Forest Service for the national forests.

To assist the debate, the Pew Charitable Trusts Foundation conducted a survey of Oregonians on what they value from these forests and the type of forestry they would like practiced there (see Oregonians say, 2013).

With the large urban populations, it is perhaps not surprising that Oregonians as a whole place a higher value on protecting old growth, water, and wildlife along with recreational opportunities than on the employment and county payments associated with logging the O&C Lands. However, it turns out that Oregonians in rural southwestern Oregon, where most of the lands in question are located, have very similar preferences!

Next, the survey asked whether people would prefer an approach to forest management (called ecological forestry in the survey) for the O&C lands that would protect these important values, although at significant cost in terms of lower harvest levels and payments to county government,

as compared to an approach that emphasized timber harvest and payment to counties. More Oregonians as a whole as well as those in southwestern Oregon chose ecological forestry than the alternative management scheme, with little variability in terms of age, sex, or political leaning (Democrat, Republican, and Independent).

While this is only one survey in one state, the findings are generally consistent with other studies in other places (Steel, 2009). More than anything, they suggest that forestry on public lands must protect core environmental values to achieve social acceptability and for foresters to have the social license to take action.

## Implications for Ecological Forestry

What do these and related findings mean for the social acceptability of ecological forestry? We focus on three crucial parts of ecological forestry: (1) emulating natural structures, patterns, and processes created through disturbances, (2) considering entire landscapes in evaluating forestry practices, and (3) recognizing economic and cultural values in management in addition to ecological considerations. We will consider each in turn.

**Emulating Nature**   As mentioned above, *people are more accepting of forestry practices if they retain or assist natural structures and processes, such as protecting old trees and the species diversity of the forest. However, it is crucial that these linkages be described, explained, and shown to people so they can make their own judgments.* As stated by Shindler et al. (2002, p. 38), "In short, peoples' judgments depend not only on a particular forest scene or what a specific treatment looks like, but also on their observations of the broader surrounding circumstances."

Shindler et al. (2002) cited numerous studies that found increased social acceptability of forest management treatments when people were able to see firsthand how they were implemented. The things they see in the landscape can change as they begin to look beyond the scenic to an ecological perspective. With growing public concern for keeping natural ecosystems and biodiversity intact, citizens are asking "why" with much greater frequency, and a new or different practice has a much better chance of acceptance if the public understands the rationale behind it and recognizes the potential outcomes. Because visual perceptions are such a strong influence on public judgments, it is likely that more personalized mechanisms will be needed to relate information about management practices (and options) to what people see in practice, such as involving citizen groups for monitoring treatment effects as we discuss in Chapter 11.

Relative to how much the public specifically supports disturbance-based approaches to forest management, information is more fragmentary, but encouraging. Shindler and Mallon (2009) examined public perspectives on disturbance-based management conducted in the central Cascade Range in Oregon. Their findings suggest *the public generally supports the disturbance-based concept, particularly where it emulates nature and provides ecological benefits*, but many individuals are still uncertain about details and are withholding judgment until they see the outcomes of implementation. Support was highly correlated with citizens' past interaction with, and trust in, local managers.

It should be noted, though, *the linkage of ecological forestry to destruction of forest values that citizens hold dear, such as old growth, water quality, or wildlife, or use of practices that lack broad support, like clearcutting, will jeopardize support for ecological forestry*. As an example, emulating the creation of openings associated with high-severity disturbances can be problematic in terms of its social acceptability because of the appearance immediately after harvest, which (when considered at the local site level) people may equate to clearcutting (Box 6.7).

**Considering Entire Landscapes**  Ecological forestry looks at whole landscapes in evaluating the type and placement of actions. Large-scale patterns (particularly harvest patterns) set the context for the smaller scale; without the larger view, people may unintentionally judge individual sites as acceptable or unacceptable. However, people have difficulty thinking about large landscapes (Shindler, 2000),

---

### Box 6.7  Forestry, optics, and social license

In 2014, a billboard went up along I-5, the major interstate highway running down the Willamette Valley in Oregon (Figure 6.20, top photo). It shows a forest patch from which all trees had been removed with the caption reading "Senator Wyden's Clear-Cut Solution for BLM O&C Lands." At the bottom of the billboard is a label reading, "Roseburg BLM's 'Buck Rising' Johnson & Franklin Pilot Project."

We (Johnson and Franklin) had worked with the Bureau of Land Management (BLM), a federal agency, throughout western Oregon on *pilot projects* to demonstrate ecological forestry on its forests. For the "Buck Rising" pilot project in the picture, a harvest in a 60-year-old plantation established after a previous clearcut, we suggested a variable-retention harvest.

Variable-retention harvesting, as described in Chapter 4, retains structures and organisms from the pre-harvest stand within the harvest block. Retention may include intact forest patches, individual trees, or small clusters of live and dead trees and down logs, distributed over the harvested area. So where are they in the top photo?

Actually, the billboard picture highlights the largest opening in the harvest unit. Stepping back to a landscape perspective, the harvest looks quite different with significant retention (Figure 6.20 bottom; circle indicates location of top photo).

What does this discussion have to do with United States Senator Wyden of Oregon? Well, the senator had endorsed ecological forestry and variable-retention harvesting as one cornerstone of his proposed legislation for BLM forests. The senator also had been quite outspoken that he would not endorse clearcutting these forests.

Is this harvest a clearcut? Not based on definitions in silvicultural textbooks. Not based on the very different ecological effects of variable-retention harvesting in comparison with clearcutting that has been documented in hundreds of peer-reviewed scientific articles from all around the world. Not based on the visual reality of so many trees and forest patches left on the harvest unit.

Still the *optics* here (the dramatic photo on the billboard) undoubtedly disturbs people who do not like clearcuts in a more powerful way than a handful of scientific publications may reassure them. These types of optics can greatly affect the social license for forestry.

Figure 6.20  *Top (Courtesy of Paul Carter; The Register Guard); bottom (Courtesy of Roseburg BLM)*

preferring to focus on sites they can see and feel in judging their acceptability. Thus, convincing people that the image shown in the top photo of Figure 6.20 does not represent the type of harvest being conducted, as shown in the bottom photo of Figure 6.20, can be challenging. Convincing people to consider this harvest unit in the context of an entire landscape can be more difficult still. Landscape context is essential in judging the desirability of actions, but its presentation takes thought and creativity.

**Considering Economic and Cultural Benefits** Ecological forestry moves beyond ecological restoration to consider other values, such as the revenue produced from the activity or provision of increased habitat for big game. While these management proposals and plans rest on an ecological foundation, their goals include both economic and social benefits that might not be provided if the only focus was on ecological restoration. Ecological forestry starts

with strategies to emulate natural structures and processes and then modifies them to achieve other goals. As an example, emulating a wildfire might require that all the trees be left on-site, with many of them turned into snags to represent mortality from wildfire. While significant structures were left in the harvest shown in Figure 6.20 (bottom)—some of which will be turned into snags—many trees were removed to provide wood products. Most probably there is a gradation in the acceptance of this type of harvest as a function of landowner, with highest acceptance on private lands, then on state lands, and lowest acceptance on federal lands, such as the national forests. This is an important point of discussion throughout this book.

In the end, though, as Shindler and Bliss and their colleagues emphasize, *the level of acceptability of ecological forestry and the social license to practice it will depend, in large part on the level of trust society has in forestry professionals and forestry organizations.*

*Law is nothing else but the best reason of wise men applied for ages to the transactions and business of mankind.* — ABRAHAM LINCOLN

CHAPTER 7

# Legal Frameworks for Forestry

In the first chapter we identified the role of public policies in limiting and directing forest management as one of the five major themes of this book. In this chapter, we first review some of the social history underlying policies regarding forests and compare current forest policies in a number of countries with temperate forests, highlighting similarities and differences among different countries and ownerships. Then we turn our attention to the United States to examine several federal environmental laws in detail that are important to the practice of forestry there and that illustrate one country's attempt to create a legal environmental framework within which forestry can be practiced.

## Historical Development and Partial Review of Global Forest Policies

Humankind evolved with trees and forests and has had a continuing connection with them since civilizations developed many thousands of years ago. Primal humankind depended upon the forest for shelter, protection, and food. As civilizations developed, forests were viewed as sources of raw materials, particularly wood for construction and fuel, and as habitat for game and other foods, materials, and medicines. Wood also became a strategic military resource, such as for construction of ships.

The elements of our modern relationships with forests emerged in developed countries by the end of the 19th century, including concerns for their production and protective functions, such as the provision of high quality water and habitat for game. Wood was in great demand as a primary resource for construction of infrastructure, including homes, and there were emerging concerns about the sustainability of forests and the potential for a timber famine. There was wide appreciation of the value of forests in protecting watersheds; this capacity along with timber supplies provided the impetus for establishment of the forest reserves in the United States beginning in 1894. The importance of forests in reducing dangers from snow avalanches

*A northern spotted owl nest in British Columbia, Canada. (© Jared Hobbs)*

Table 7.1 *Issue context for policy development during later part of the 20th century in several countries with significant temperate forests*

| Country | Converting Natural forest to plantations? | Indigenous people's rights at issue? | Plantation species are natives or exotics? | Significant public controversy? | Dominant policy level national or state/province |
|---|---|---|---|---|---|
| USA | Yes | Yes | Native trees | Yes | Both |
| Canada | Yes | Yes | Native trees | Yes | Province |
| Australia | Yes | Yes | Native & Exotic | Yes | State |
| Chile | Yes | Yes | Exotic trees | Yes | National |
| Argentina | Yes | No | Exotic trees | Yes | National |
| Sweden | No | Yes | Native trees | No | National |
| Central Europe | No | No | Native trees | No | National |
| Portugal/Spain | No | No | Exotic trees | No | National |

had already led to sophisticated approaches to management of landscapes in places like Switzerland. While forests had always been viewed as habitat for game, this had become a more formal sporting concern for royalty and hunting elites. In fact, many early foresters were actually game managers and many of the first *forest preserves* were actually game preserves for royalty.

These and other societal concerns resulted in rapid development of many policies for forest conservation and management that carried us through much of the 20th century. Among such policies were: aggressive efforts to protect forests, such as through the suppression of wildfires, programs to assure reforestation of logged areas, and, on public lands, harvest schedules to provide for a sustained flow of wood forever. Also, concern over destruction of streams and watersheds led to forest practice laws to control logging and road-building practices and establish stream buffers in much of the world. As we will see, the policies stimulated by these concerns are still much of the basis for existing law and regulation in many countries.

A new set of social concerns emerged in the latter part of the 20th century and continue to the present. These concerns stem from the increasing breadth of scientific knowledge, technical capabilities, sensibilities regarding social equity, and an altered global economy. Two large concerns related to forestry are: (1) the adoption of intensive plantation forestry for wood production and, particularly, its use in conversion of large areas of natural forests to plantations, and (2) the rights of indigenous peoples. The expansion of environmental science, particularly forest ecosystem science, is certainly related to concerns over plantation forestry, particularly on public lands.

We can see interesting patterns if we take a global look at where these concerns emerged (Table 7.1). Our sample of countries in this case is primarily temperate and democratic and does not include two important forest countries, Russia and China, about which it is difficult to obtain reli-

able information. Plantations are important to the forest industry in all of the countries listed in Table 7.1. In several of these countries (USA, Canada, Australia, and Chile) plantation establishment has been primarily associated with conversion of natural forests to plantations.[1] Chile is somewhat unusual in that it has subsidized establishment of plantations, although this subsidy is not supposed to support conversion of natural forests. Conversions of natural forests are still continuing in these countries, albeit at reduced rates, and such conversions remain intensely controversial on public lands.

A second interesting pattern is that countries in the southern hemisphere in Table 7.1 have plantations composed primarily of exotic species, either selected species of pine or eucalyptus or both. Of course, eucalyptus is native in Australia, but the species typically used in Australia are often different from those that were found in the natural forests on those sites. In contrast, plantations in most northern hemisphere countries are predominantly composed of native species, although there are exceptions, such as on the Iberian Peninsula. Currently there are also proposals for extensive exotic eucalyptus plantations in the southeastern USA.

Finally, every country on our list that is associated with conversion of natural forests has unresolved or only partially resolved issues with indigenous populations, which often interact with policy development in complex ways,

---

1 The United Nations Food and Agricultural Organization (FAO) divides forests into natural forests and planted forests (Kennan et al., 2015). In that context, natural forest is defined as "vegetation that evolved naturally in an area" (Kennan et al., 2015, p. 13). In application, natural forests are forests not classified as planted forest, where planted forest "includes both intensively managed forest plantations purposely established to give priority to wood production that are usually composed of a single tree species and forests established for land conservation, coastal stabilization, biodiversity conservation or other purposes" (Kennan et al., 2015, p. 13). In this book, we distinguish between natural forests and plantations. By plantations, we generally mean intensively managed forest plantations purposely established to give priority to wood production.

such as in British Columbia (see, e.g., DellaSala, 2011). Concerns with rights of indigenous peoples have intersected with forest policy issues related to conversion of natural forests in almost all countries where such conversion has been underway. These issues have both complicated and, in at least some cases, fueled the controversies over forest use, helping to force moves toward resolution, as in the case of the Clayoquot Sound controversy on coastal Vancouver Island (Scientific Panel, 1995), Haida Gwai (Takeda, 2015), and the Great Bear Rainforest (DellaSala, 2011), all in coastal British Columbia, Canada.

In general, policy responses to the issues discussed in this section have been quite idiosyncratic, even though the issues are generically similar, and there is a general pattern in policy responses that we present and discuss in the next section. The idiosyncrasies relate to the particular histories and governance structures of the countries, since most policy is generated at either the national or the subnational governmental level. For example, Canada and Australia share the characteristic of a federation in which much of the land is public, but management direction comes primarily at the level of the province or state. In the United States the central government has a strong role in setting environmental policies (also discussed below) and in managing the federal estate; however, state governments are largely responsible for creating legal policies regarding management of state and private forestlands. Another notable difference between the United States and Canada (and many other countries discussed here) is the legal standing that citizens and organizations have to engage the federal government over its activities; except for indigenous people, Canadian citizens generally do not have such standing, whereas US citizens and organizations do have standing, as discussed in Chapter 6, and have been very influential in both creating and implementing policy.

We would note that most legally enforceable policies are developed at the national or subnational level. The European Union (EU) represents the single example of a supranational organization that has some legal authority over the nations that belong to it. It can and has used that authority to create and enforce policy changes, such as in the area of conservation. Another way that multinational conservation legal policy is created is by binding agreements between nations (e.g., treaties), such as those that have been created with regard to migratory birds.

## Legal Context for Management of Temperate Forests around the World

With the historical perspective that we have just provided, we now look in more detail at some of the legal provisions in place in different countries, focusing on countries with temperate forests, and see how they relate to various policy issues and to ecological forestry. In this part of the chapter we utilize a very useful survey by McDermott, Cahore, and Kanowski (2010) for some of the information.

## Forest Ownership and Governance

We divide the ownership of forests into three general categories for analysis: (1) public, (2) private, and (3) other (Figure 7.1). Almost all of the forest in these countries fall into the first two categories, although, as mentioned above, there are partially or completely unresolved forest claims by indigenous peoples in at least Canada, United States, Australia, Chile, and Sweden (see McDermott et al., 2010 and DellaSala, 2011 as starting points for discussions of this issue). The countries we have included from the McDermott et al. (2010) survey have a wide range in the proportion of public and private ownership:

- *Canada*—over 90% of the forests are publically owned and most authority for management rests with provincial governments, which differ widely in their policies. Given their historical connection to England, public lands are often called *crown lands*. Among the Canadian provinces, only New Brunswick has considerable amounts of private forest.

- *United States*—most forests in the western United States are in public holdings while most forests in the eastern United States are in private holdings as we noted in Chapter 6. Also as noted, the individual states set most policies for private and state lands, while the federal government sets policies for federally owned forests as well as some conservation policies (such as protection of endangered species) that cover all lands.

- *Australia*—a majority of the forest is publicly held, with the individual states setting most forest management policies on both public and private forests. As in Canada's provinces, there are significant differences in forest policies among the states. Plantations provide much of the commercial harvest volume.

- *Central Europe (Germany and Poland)*—a slight majority of forest is publically held in Germany, divided between state and communal ownership, while public forests dominate in Poland. Policies set at the European, federal, and state levels are all important to forest management.

- *Scandinavia (Sweden)*—More than 80% of Sweden's forests are privately owned, with small-scale family forest ownership predominating in the southern part of the country. National forest policies are expressed through the Forestry Act and Environmental Code and other laws that guide forestry.

▪ *Chile*—a majority of Chile's forests are privately owned, divided between intensively managed plantations, which produce almost all of the commercial timber harvest, and parcels of natural forests owned by citizens, most of which are small but some of which are large (DellaSala, 2011). Significant protected areas exist as a result of both public and private efforts, but the most productive and diverse forests at midlatitudes and lower elevations are poorly represented. Authority over environmental and natural resource issues rests largely with the national government.

▪ *Japan*—most of Japan's forests are privately owned in very small parcels. Of Japan's public lands, a majority are nationally owned, with the rest owned by communities and subnational governments. The national government sets regulations for national forests and protection forests; on other forests, regional and local governments are also involved.

In general, countries with an English legal heritage (United States, Canada, and Australia) share a common perspective on land ownership. Private property is gener-ally seen as giving the owner exclusive but not absolute rights, as we discussed in Chapter 6, and responsibilities for conservation are placed more heavily on public lands, especially in the United States and Canada. In other case study countries, such as Chile and Japan, the sense of ownership giving exclusive rights to the owner is not as strong, which results in a more even distribution of conservation responsibilities between ownership groups, as we describe below.

## Environmental Policies for Temperate Forests

The discussion of environmental policies is divided into policies related to: (1) biodiversity conservation, and (2) forest practice. We are able to provide more details about forest practice policies than about biodiversity conservation policies, because the former are more specific and, therefore, amenable to analysis and classification.

**Biodiversity Conservation**   Policies related to conservation of biological diversity inevitably focus on establishment of some form of protected area or preserve (see, e.g., DellaSala, 2011); we can hypothesize that this is for two reasons: (1) conversion of natural forests to plantations appears to be a common stimulus for adopting a biodiversity conservation strategy, and the most obvious way to deal with that conversion is to reserve some significant part of those forests; and (2) alternative solutions are rarely proposed by the stakeholders involved in these debates.

***Protected Areas.***   Protected areas are recognized as essential or foundational elements of any strategy implemented for the conservation of biodiversity (Lindenmayer & Franklin, 2002). While these areas are selected for a variety of objectives, such as providing places for recreation in wild areas, providing habitat for species at risk, and protecting indigenous peoples, the limitations on activities, such as exclusion of timber harvesting, generally benefit many forms of biodiversity.

While a well-distributed and representative system of protected areas provides an important foundation for biodiversity conservation, it is almost impossible to achieve goals of representativeness, (e.g., the full range of forest types), comprehensiveness, adequacy, replication, and distribution (Lindenmayer & Franklin, 2002). In many countries, protected areas most commonly come from public lands. Thus, in countries

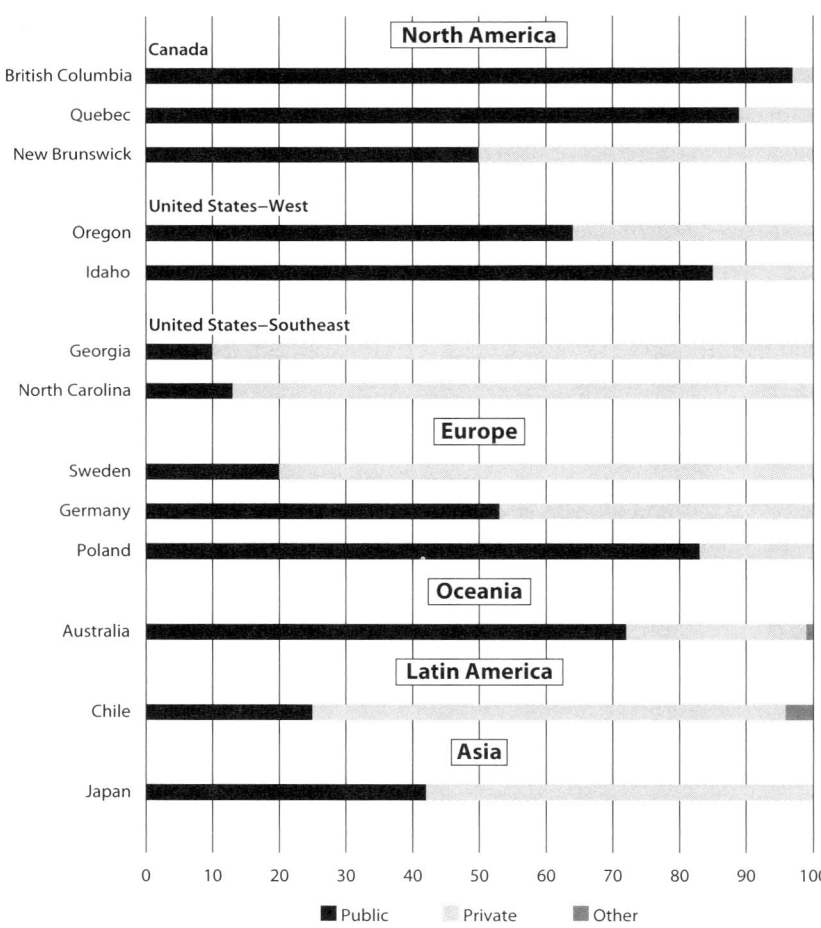

Figure 7.1 *Forest ownership in selected countries with temperate forests around the world. (Adapted from McDermott et al., 2010)*

with a public/private mixture of forest ownership, protected area distribution follows ownership distribution to a considerable degree. As an example, there is a much higher proportion of forest in reserves in the western USA than in the Southeast, on low rather than high productivity sites, and at high rather than low elevations. However, many temperate countries supplement public protected areas with formal conservation agreements with private owners. Also, most countries in our sample have groups, some public and some private, dedicated to filling in the protected areas system of their countries and seeking an adequate and representative network of protected areas.

***Biodiversity Policies.***   Protected areas are rarely judged sufficient for protection of biodiversity in a country (indeed, we would argue that it is rarely possible to conserve the majority of forest biodiversity solely with reserves), which is a consequence of many factors including the limited extent of protected areas. Thus, many countries have multiple components to their biodiversity policies, which fall logically into two groups. First, as mentioned earlier, there are international agreements, such as those that limit the trade of threatened and endangered species or products derived from them, and multinational agreements, such as the Migratory Bird Treaty Act in North America that coordinates protection across national borders. Second, countries have national, state, and provincial policies, which range from prohibitions on killing species considered to be at risk to additional requirements to protect their habitat. We will focus on habitat protection both because it is often identified as a greater threat to many species at risk (Dobson et al., 2006) and because it is most relevant to how ecological forestry might be practiced.

Of the countries that we are considering in this case study, the United States has arguably the most extensive set of federal laws and regulations for species at risk, including the Endangered Species Act (ESA). *Take* of federally listed threatened or endangered species is strictly limited for everyone, public and private, and federal agencies must consult with regulatory agencies empowered to protect these species before taking action to ensure that their actions will not jeopardize survival of the species. Finally, federal land management agencies have an affirmative responsibility to contribute to recovery of threatened or endangered species above any other goal. With many at-risk species on private land, the federal government has placed increasing emphasis on creating institutions to encourage private landowners to take proactive measures to protect species. We will explore the inner workings of the ESA later in the chapter.

We will briefly review policies that attempt to protect and recover species at risk in a sample of our other case study areas using information from McDermott (2010) and DellaSala (2011):

- In Canada, the national government has limited jurisdiction over provincial resource management. However, through the Species at Risk Act (SARA), it does have direct responsibilities for designated threatened and endangered species on federal lands and for certain other species (migratory birds and aquatic species). SARA allows the federal government more discretion in species protection than does the US ESA, encouraging the provincial governments in Canada to cooperate to protect wildlife and recover species. While most Canadian provinces compile lists of threatened and endangered species, they vary considerably in their approach to conserving the habitat of these species, and in the priority that they put on these efforts compared to other goals, such as timber production.

- The European Union has issued directives that call for protection of threatened species as a primary goal; how well they are implemented depends on the governments of the individual counties.

- In Australia, national legislation requires that species and ecosystems deemed threatened or at risk be identified, and species-specific conservation plans be developed. There is also a requirement at the national level for creation of protected areas for each major forest type (target level of 15% of the area of the type). However, the specific implementation of species and habitat protection plans varies from state to state. For example, while the majority of states have met the national objectives, others have not done as well. In one case, conservation efforts (mountain ash forests in the state of Victoria) appear to be failing catastrophically, both with regard to endangered species and the forest type itself (Lindenmayer, Blair, McBurney, & Banks, 2015).

**Forest Practice Policies**   Forest practice policies cover a wide range in topics, so to simplify the following discussion we will use the five types of forest practice policies employed by McDermott et al. (2010) in their case study:

1. ***Riparian zone management (Indicator: requirements for streamside forest buffer zones).*** Riparian zone management is often seen as the key to maintaining high-quality freshwater ecosystems, production of economically important fish species, and maintenance of biodiversity. Many countries, states, and provinces place great emphasis on policies to protect stream and riverside environments.

2. ***Roads (Indicator: requirements for culvert size at stream crossings and road decommissioning).*** Roads are one of the most important human-created factors causing major problems with the physical and

biological aspects of aquatic networks. Proper location and maintenance of roads, including stream and river crossings (e.g., culvert management) are keys to reducing erosion and preventing slope failures and debris flows that silt waterways. Roads can also be responsible for creating difficulties for the movement of aquatic organisms, including migrating fish populations. It is difficult to control the negative effects of timber harvesting without adequate road policies.

3. *Clearcutting: (Indicator: clearcut size limits).* Clearcutting is a widespread and controversial harvesting practice. Putting limits on clearcutting is often a central element of forest practice policies.

4. *Reforestation (Indicator: reforestation requirements).* Effective reforestation is a key element in sustainable forestry and a frequent focus of forest practice polices. The broader societal perception of reforestation is also important, as it is viewed as evidence that the forest is being renewed.

5. *Annual allowable cut (Indicator: harvest limits based on sustained yield).* Limiting harvest to projected sustained yield reflects the principle of sustaining timber production in perpetuity and has been a foundational concern of professional forestry around the world for hundreds of years.

Cashore (1997) classified forest management policies in two ways: (1) whether they were voluntary (discretionary) or mandatory (nondiscretionary), and (2) whether they emphasized procedures and plans (i.e., were process-based) or specified on-the-ground behavior (i.e., were performance-based). As an example, encouraging a set of management practices is different from requiring them, and calling for management plans that protect riparian areas is different from prescribing a 100-foot buffer on each side of the stream. The intersection of these two policy classifications results in four *policy styles* (Table 7.2).

Using Cashore's matrix, McDermott et al. (2010) classified forest practice policies in the countries, provinces, and states they studied into one of five categories: (1) Mandatory substantive, (2) Mandatory mixed (a combination of substantive and procedural), (3) Mandatory procedural, (4) Voluntary, and (5) No policy. We selected a subset of those cases, consistent with the countries highlighted above, to feature here.

Relative to the five types of forest practice policies described above, the selected case studies show the following results for *natural forests* (Table 7.3):

Table 7.2 *Matrix of policy styles*

|  | Voluntary | Mandatory |
|---|---|---|
| **Procedural** | Planning suggestions | Planning requirements |
| **Substantive** | Suggested performance standards | Prescribed performance standards |

*Source:* Adapted from Cashore (1997) and McDermott (2010).

- Riparian—Generally, they require mandatory riparian buffers along streams, with mandatory, substantive (fixed-width) buffers predominating. A singular exception is the Southeast USA, which utilizes voluntary policies (recommended best management practices under the US Clean Water Act).

- Roads—Generally, they have mandatory requirements for culvert size and road decommissioning, except for the Southeast USA and Chile, which lack these requirements. Where there are mandatory requirements, they are almost equally divided between substantive and mixed requirements.

- Clearcuts—Most case study areas have mandatory limits on clearcut size, except for private forests in New Brunswick (Canada), Idaho (USA), the Southeast USA, and Bavaria (Germany).

- Reforestation—Most have mandatory substantive policies covering both the amount of stocking and the speed with which that stocking has to become established, but private forests in New Brunswick and the Southeast USA operate under voluntary measures, and forests in Chile and Japan operate under mixed or procedural requirements.

- Annual allowable cut (AAC)—Here the criteria can be interpreted as follows:

  ○ Mandatory substantive—AAC calculated as part of a nondeclining yield of harvest volume over time, capped by sustained yield capacity;

  ○ Mandatory mixed—AAC capped by sustained yield capacity, but a nondeclining yield of harvest volume not required (i.e., harvest level can go up and down as long as it does not exceed sustained yield capacity);

  ○ Mandatory procedural—AAC must be calculated, but is not capped by sustained yield capacity or limited to a nondeclining yield of harvest;

  ○ Voluntary—decision of whether to calculate AAC left up to forest manager or agency; and

  ○ No policy—no rules on calculating AAC

All public case studies have a mandatory AAC requirement of some kind, as do private case studies, except for those in North America, Tasmania, New Brunswick, and Sweden.

Some summary comments about forest practices rules across the case studies (Table 7.3):

- Riparian protection is the most comprehensively regulated forest practice. This probably should not surprise us given the diverse societal values associated with streams and the fact that impacts on streams usually are not be confined to a single ownership. If private owners have one major stewardship obligation to society, protection of streams and lakes is probably it!

Table 7.3  *Approach to public regulation of five forest practices in natural forests in a variety of countries, states, and provinces. (4 = Mandatory substantive, 3 = Mandatory mixed (substantive and procedural), 2 = Mandatory procedural, 1 = Voluntary measures, 0 = no policies). Total is intended to reflect the aggregate amount of regulation.*

| Case Study | Riparian | Roads | Clearcuts | Reforestation | AAC | Total |
|---|---|---|---|---|---|---|
| **North America** | | | | | | |
| *Canada* | | | | | | |
| British Columbia (public) | 4 | 4 | 4 | 4 | 2 | 18 |
| Quebec (public) | 4 | 3 | 4 | 4 | 3 | 18 |
| New Brunswick (public) | 4 | 4 | 4 | 4 | 3 | 19 |
| New Brunswick (private) | 4 | 3 | 0 | 1 | 0 | 8 |
| *United States—West* | | | | | | |
| US Forest Service (public) | 4 | 3 | 4 | 4 | 4 | 19 |
| Oregon (private) | 4 | 3 | 4 | 4 | 0 | 15 |
| Idaho (private) | 4 | 3 | 0 | 4 | 0 | 11 |
| *United States—Southeast* | | | | | | |
| Georgia (private) | 1 | 1 | 0 | 1 | 0 | 3 |
| North Carolina (private) | 1 | 1 | 0 | 1 | 0 | 3 |
| **Europe** | | | | | | |
| Germany—Bavaria (public) | 3 | 3 | 4 | 4 | 2 | 16 |
| Germany—Bavaria (private) | 3 | 3 | 0 | 4 | 2 | 12 |
| Poland (public) | 4 | 3 | 4 | 4 | 3 | 18 |
| Sweden (private) | 3 | 2 | 3 | 4 | 0 | 12 |
| **Oceania** | | | | | | |
| Australia | | | | | | |
| Tasmania (public) | 4 | 4 | 4 | 4 | 4 | 20 |
| Tasmania (private) | 4 | 4 | 4 | 4 | 0 | 16 |
| Victoria (public) | 4 | 4 | 4 | 4 | 4 | 20 |
| **Latin America** | | | | | | |
| Chile (public) | 4 | 0 | 4 | 2 | 2 | 12 |
| Chile (private) | 4 | 0 | 4 | 2 | 2 | 12 |
| **Asia** | | | | | | |
| Japan (public) | 3 | 3 | 3 | 3 | 4 | 16 |
| Japan (private) | 3 | 3 | 3 | 3 | 3 | 15 |

*Source:* Adapted from McDermott et al. (2010).

- States in the southeast US rely mainly on voluntary and quasi-regulatory approaches or market mechanisms to meeting state-recommended environmental practices, as discussed below under the Clean Water Act and in Chapter 16.

- Overall, public lands generally have more mandatory substantive forest practice rules than do private lands, as indicated by their higher aggregate scores, except for Chile and Japan where public and private lands have similar aggregate scores.

- This five-category classification of practices gives a useful overview of similarities and differences among the sample areas. However, it is only an overview. Case studies that receive the same score for some forest practice can, in fact, still have substantial differences from one another. As an example, mandatory substantive stream buffer requirements apply both to national forests and to private lands in western Oregon. However, stream buffer requirements for national forests are extensive and go all the way to the headwaters, while those for private lands are more limited.

- These forest practice rules reflect intent; if governance and enforcement are weak, then these rules may have much less effect on forest practices than was intended.

- It should be added that some of these restrictions, particularly limits on clearcuts and reforestation requirements, do not always help emulate the disturbance processes fundamental to ecological forestry. As pointed out in the case study on the Oregon Coast Range in Chapter 5, the limitation on clearcut size there results in patch sizes much smaller than experienced naturally. Rather, the issue there is the lack of biological legacies left after harvest. Also, reforestation requirements there result in practices that hurry the site through the preforest stage after harvest, not allowing that stage to fully develop.

## Requirements for Ecological Forestry

Finally, we review the mandate for ecological forestry in some of the case study areas. By ecological forestry, we mean forestry grounded on ecological principles—a forestry based on natural processes, especially disturbance processes.

*The United States*: As will be seen later in this chapter, the collective power of several environmental laws effectively mandates an ecosystem-based approach to management of forests on federal lands (Skillen, 2015). The national forests have a particularly strong mandate to ground their management on ecological principles under the recently approved planning rule for implementation of the National

Forest Management Act (USDA Forest Service, 2012a). That rule calls for an ecosystem-based approach that retains and restores the ecological integrity of forest ecosystems as the foundation for management and planning (see Chapter 20 for a more in-depth treatment). The US Fish and Wildlife Service (USFWS), one of the agencies responsible for implementing the Endangered Species Act, increasingly requires forestry practices that emulate natural processes where harvest is proposed within critical habitat for threatened species. Also, as noted in Chapter 4, forest management practices on the wildlife refuges managed by USFWS are often at the forefront of ecological forest management because of the biodiversity goals on these properties. Elsewhere, policies for private forestlands, and some state forests, put less emphasis on ecological forestry practices, and some laws and regulations actually impede adoption of ecological forestry practices as we discussed in the last section (see Chapter 21 for further explanation). At the same time, some state and county governments and private owners have picked up elements of ecological forestry (see examples in Chapter 4) and begun incorporating them into their practices.

*Canada*: A number of provinces have laws that mandate or encourage at least some aspects of ecological forestry. British Columbia has been one of the leaders, which is not surprising because of its relatively early and extensive experience with retention harvesting. This change was largely the result of MacMillan-Bloedel Corporation's decision to shift its harvest practices from clearcutting to variable retention (see Chapter 4), after the findings of the Scientific Panel for Sustainable Forest Practices in Clayoquot Sound (1995) brought retention harvesting into the provincial consciousness. This shift required the British Columbia government to develop and formally adopt a legal definition of **variable-retention harvesting**, so that the BC Forest Service could issue MacMillan-Bloedel harvesting permits based on this approach (Lindenmayer & Franklin, 2002). As another example, the Ontario Crown Forest Sustainability Act calls for "using forest practices that, within the limits of silvicultural requirements, emulate natural disturbances and landscape patterns while minimizing adverse effects on plant life, animal life, water, soil, air and social and economic values" (Ontario Government, 2011). Reviews of the implementation of this mandate, though, have raised questions about its success (Environmental Commissioner of Ontario, 2014). As a final example, the province of Quebec has explored the incorporation of ecologically based forestry on portions of the province's forests as part of a land-zoning approach (known as TRIAD), which includes zones designated for intensive wood production, conservation, and ecosystem management (Messier et al., 2009; MacLean, Seymour, Montigny, & Messier, 2009); maintenance of resiliency, adaptability, and native biodiversity is the goal within the ecosystem management zone, where silvicultural practices are designed to mimic natural disturbances, and natural rather than artificial regeneration is often relied upon.

*Western Europe*: A number of European countries or states have passed forest acts that generally reframed the broad goals of forest management from a primary emphasis on timber production to a balance of environmental and economic goals. As an example, Bavaria (Germany) requires that most of its forestland be placed in one of its protective categories, which attempts to limit production forestry and encourage *nature-based forestry* (McDermott, 2010). Also, there is a rich array of more ecologically based approaches being developed and tried in Europe, such as *close-to-nature* and *closed-canopy forestry* (Puettmann et al., 2015). Structural retention at harvest is a well-understood and applied approach in Sweden (e.g., Gustafsson et al., 2012), despite a strong commitment to production forestry practices there. Indeed, the National Board of Forestry in Sweden made significant contributions to development and popularization of ecologically based forest management concepts (National Board of Forestry, 1992).

*Australia*: Biodiversity conservation is now a dominant theme in forest policy and practices at the national level. The National Forest Policy Statement advocates state biodiversity strategies and sets national targets (McDermott, 2010). There are wide differences among the states, however, in what has been accomplished. Some have moved away from management of natural forests and focus on plantation forestry, although many of these plantations involved conversion of natural forests. Wildfire and harvesting policies in Victoria appear to have placed mountain ash forests and associated biota in jeopardy and resulted in a call for creation of a much larger protected area (Lindenmayer et al., 2015). Significant protected areas have been created in Tasmania, and retention harvesting has been adopted as the silvicultural approach for any additional harvest (see Chapter 4).

## Key Federal Environmental Laws in the United States

Forestry in the United States operates within a complex network of federal environmental laws, many of which originated during the 1970s. As discussed in the last chapter, these laws have their most comprehensive application to federal agencies and federal forests, but many of them also affect management of private and state forests. We will examine three of those laws in this section:

- *The National Environmental Policy Act (NEPA)* was the first law to emerge in the *environmental era* of the 1970s. NEPA requires that federal agencies divulge the environmental effects of their actions. The process established to implement NEPA provides a framework for developing and analyzing federal decisions across all agencies, using interdisciplinary planning and analysis of alternatives. Also, NEPA provided an important entry point for public involvement in federal decision making.

- *The Endangered Species Act (ESA)* is often called the "bulldog of environmental laws," given its commitment to recovering threatened and endangered species as a top national priority. While the Act applies to everyone, it places special responsibilities on federal agencies to ensure recovery of *listed species*. Since many species at risk are primarily found on private lands, ensuring survival and recovery of these species can create major challenges.

- *The Clean Water Act (CWA)* is an environmental law that potentially affects all forest management in the United States, wherever it occurs. While implementation of the CWA first focused on point-source pollution, such as effluent coming out of a pipe from industrial plants, the focus has now been broadened to include diffuse pollutants from the activities of farms, forests, and people in general.

These three laws, taken together, provide a strong foundation for environmental protection, especially on federal land, and also illustrate different approaches to that protection. NEPA functions as a procedural law that specifies a process for analyzing environmental impacts; it does not mandate a particular type of resource protection or policy outcome, although the requirement to disclose environmental impacts tends to favor protective outcomes. The ESA and the CWA, on the hand, are substantive laws that mandate particular outcomes, for example, the conservation of endangered species and the reduction of water pollution. These latter laws also contain processes that must be followed, but much of their power comes from the substantive requirements within them (Skillen, 2015).

## The National Environmental Policy Act

The late 1960s was a time of ferment in the United States in many ways, including protest over the Vietnam War and the continuing struggle over civil rights in the South and elsewhere. Concerns about the environment, especially the effects of air and water pollution on human health, and the effects of pesticides on the natural world and iconic wildlife species, had also arrived at the forefront of public consciousness, culminating in the first Earth Day in April 1969. These national concerns led to creation of the National

Environmental Policy Act of 1969 (NEPA) (P.L. 91-190, 83 Stat. 852, 42 U.S.C. §§ 4321-4347),[2] which was signed by President Richard Nixon on January 1, 1970, making it the first of many environmental laws passed by the United States Congress during the environmental era of the 1970s.

*Lawmakers intended NEPA to protect the environment through a rational approach to decision making about federal actions affecting the environment.* As such, NEPA does not protect the environment through substantive environmental standards or by regulating actions, as do other laws such as the Endangered Species Act and the Clean Water Act that are covered in this chapter. Instead, NEPA is often referred to as a "procedural" or "stop-and-think" act because it requires a certain analysis and documentation process for decisions affecting the environment.

As pointed out by Reid (2010), federal courts have repeatedly said that the role of NEPA documents is to demonstrate that there has been a *hard look* taken at the potential impacts of proposed federal actions and that those impacts are understood well enough that surprises are unlikely. It is then the responsibility of agency personnel to decide how to use the resulting information: "Other statutes may impose substantive environmental obligations of federal agencies, but NEPA merely prohibits uninformed—rather than unwise—agency action" *(Robertson v. Methow Valley Citizens Council,* 490 U.S. 332 [1989]).

## The Power of NEPA

NEPA requires an analysis of environmental impacts of all proposals for *"major Federal actions significantly affecting the quality of the human environment."* While these words may sound innocuous, don't you believe it! When combined with the goals and directions for analysis contained in other provisions of the Act, NEPA has been an extremely powerful tool in the hands of conservation groups seeking to stop or revise projects they believe will degrade the environment. In fact, the importance of NEPA in shaping national natural resource policy cannot be overstated, and it has been frequently emulated. Major municipalities and many states have laws on the books that are similar to

NEPA. Scores of countries around the globe have statutes that are modeled on NEPA. Many large nongovernmental organizations, banks, and governments require NEPA-like compliance as a condition for major loans on infrastructure or energy projects.

NEPA does not address individual environmental issues, such as wildlife preservation or air quality. Rather, it addresses all aspects of the environment, as noted in the goals stated at the beginning of the Act (Sec. 2):

*The purposes of this Act are: To declare a national policy which will encourage productive and enjoyable harmony between man and his environment; to promote efforts which will prevent or eliminate damage to the environment and biosphere and stimulate the health and welfare of man; to enrich the understanding of the ecological systems and natural resources important to the Nation; and to establish a Council on Environmental Quality.*

Sometimes referred to as "the Magna Carta of environmental law," NEPA contains some of the most progressive and inclusive language in any environmental law (Sec. 101[a]): "The Congress . . . declares that it is the continuing policy of the Federal Government . . . to use all practicable means and measures . . . to create and maintain conditions under which man and nature can exist in productive harmony, . . . and fulfill the social, economic, and other requirements of present and future generations of Americans." The Act then proceeds (Sec. 101 [b]) to specify what this means with statement after statement that commits the nation to protection of the environment, both for our enjoyment and as our responsibility as a collective trustee of a valuable resource for future generations.

Benson and Garmestani (2011, p. 1422) point out that a primary author of NEPA (Lytton Caldwell) argued that "NEPA was intended to require agencies to make not just well informed but also environmentally sound decisions balancing environmental and economic concerns . . . to have the federal government's decisions reflect this new thinking and bring it to bear on agency actions." However, as they acknowledge (p. 1423, citing the work of Kalen [2010]):

*NEPA's bold intentions got lost along the way . . . [by]. . . court interpretations of the law, which held that NEPA's Section 101 was an aspirational statement lacking the necessary detail for enforcement. In the U.S. Supreme Court decision Stryker's Bay Neighborhood Council, Inc. v. Karlen (497 L. Ed. 2d 433 [1980]), the Court held that NEPA, while establishing "significant substantive goals for the Nation, imposes upon agencies duties that are essentially procedural. . . . NEPA was designed to insure a fully informed and well-considered decision." As a result of these court interpretations, NEPA essentially became*

---

2 Statute citations come three forms: (1) public law citation (*slip law*), (2) statutes at large (*session law*), or (3) code citation. The citation (*P.L. 93-205, 87 Stat. 884 16 U.S.C. §§ 1531–1544*) points to the Endangered Species Act of 1973, using all three forms: (1) *P.L. 93-205* is the public law citation, indicating that the statute being cited was public law number 205 from the 93rd session of the U.S. Congress; (2) *87 Stat. 884* is the session law citation, indicating that you can find the law, in the form it was passed, in the United States Statutes at Large in Volume 87, page 884; (3) *16 U.S.C. §§ 1531–1544* is a code citation indicating where you can find the statute in the United States Code, which organizes laws by subject, and includes expirations, revisions, amendments, and other changes. We will generally identify a law by all three types of citation when we introduce it; subsequent references will generally use one of the three forms consistently as a function of common usage.

*a series of procedural steps requiring federal agencies to take a **hard look** at the potential environmental consequences of their actions, but not requiring them to take any specific action to protect the environment or balance competing concerns*

## Key Requirements

Section 101 makes clear to the courts that Congress took environmental protection seriously, although there are no definite legal requirements there; rather (in the view of the courts) that section states a set of aspirations for the Nation relative to the environment. Section 102, though, lays out what Congress wanted federal agencies to do:

*The Congress authorizes and directs that, to the fullest extent possible: (1) the policies, regulations, and public laws of the United States shall be interpreted and administered in accordance with the policies set forth in this Act, and (2) all agencies of the Federal Government shall— (A) utilize a systematic, interdisciplinary approach which will insure the integrated use of the natural and social sciences and the environmental design arts in planning and in decision making which may have an impact on man's environment;*

The requirement to utilize a systematic, interdisciplinary approach has done more than any other provision in the federal rule book to bring consideration of the environment, in all of its aspects, into the federal decision-making process. Before NEPA, foresters, range conservationists, dam builders, and mining and road engineers had set the natural resource agenda for federal agencies, focusing primarily on the use of federal resources for economic development. With its requirement for interdisciplinary planning, NEPA mandated the inclusion of ***ologists*** in the planning process—hydrologists, wildlife and aquatic biologists, and other environmental specialists. These professionals brought not only technical knowledge but something more—a different set of perspectives and values. To reinforce the demand for increased consideration of the environment in federal decision making, Section 102 also directed federal agencies to:

*(B) identify and develop methods and procedures . . . which will insure that presently unquantified environmental amenities and values may be given appropriate consideration in decision making along with economic and technical considerations;*

With this requirement for the appropriate consideration of unquantified environmental amenities and values, Congress left no doubt that any single-minded focus on economic development in federal agency decision making had come to an end.

How did Congress propose that federal agencies achieve this new approach to decision making? NEPA called for a new kind of analysis and reporting to be done before major federal actions were taken:

*(C) include in every recommendation or report on proposals for legislation and other major Federal actions significantly affecting the quality of the human environment, a detailed statement by the responsible official.*

Section 102(C) is the heart of NEPA when it comes to federal forest and natural resource planning. Much of the legal ***gridlock*** that some say has plagued federal forest and natural resource planning can be traced to the requirement for a detailed statement about "major federal actions significantly affecting the quality of the human environment." Through the regulations implementing this law, this detailed statement became known as an ***Environmental Impact Statement (EIS).***

Notice that 102(C) focuses on the "human" environment. What does this mean? Looking back to Section 101 for guidance, we find statements like "enrich the understanding of the ecological systems," and "interrelations of all components of the natural environment." The courts refer to Section 101 to figure out what Congress meant by the phrase, "the human environment." Section 101 makes it clear that Congress meant for this term to apply to just about every part of the environment. This is not to say that all significant impacts to humans require an EIS. For example, socioeconomic impacts, such as elimination of jobs, do not directly entail an environmental impact and so do not require an EIS. Nevertheless, once an EIS is triggered by identification of potential environmental impacts, socioeconomic impacts should be considered if interrelated with these impacts (Ferrey 2013, p. 99).

What does this "detailed statement" required by Section 102(C) need to contain? Section 102(C) further specifies that this statement must contain:

*(i) the environmental impact of the proposed action,*

*(ii) any adverse environmental effects which cannot be avoided should the proposal be implemented,*

*(iii) alternatives to the proposed action,*

*(iv) the relationship between local short-term uses of man's environment and the maintenance and enhancement of long-term productivity, and*

*(v) any irreversible and irretrievable commitments of resources which would be involved in the proposed action should it be implemented.*

Section 102(C) also requires that the responsible agency consult with and obtain comments from any other federal agency that has jurisdiction by law or special expertise with respect to any environmental impact studied in the EIS, and that copies of the EIS and comments by other federal agencies be made available to the public.

Finally, in Section 103, Congress called for all federal agencies to undertake "such measures as may be necessary to bring their authority and policies into conformity with the intent, purposes, and procedures set forth in this Act." In other words, in addition to government-wide regulations implementing NEPA written by the Council on Environmental Quality (CEQ), Congress directed agencies to write regulations to implement the Act within the framework of their own existing policies and authority.

One important thing to note about NEPA is that the Act is rather short and vague. The teeth of NEPA, referenced in case law, are not found in statute; they are found written into the regulations implementing NEPA.[3] We review below two key features of these regulations: (1) the process for making federal decisions under NEPA, and (2) the commitment to involving the public in these decisions.[4]

## Federal Decision-Making Process under NEPA

*NEPA revolutionized the way that the federal government makes decisions about natural resource management.* From timber sales to grazing-allotment renewal to culvert replacement to outdoor concerts on federal lands, federal decisions affecting the environment go through the NEPA process. Congress, though, did not provide guidance as to how to decide which decisions are "major Federal actions significantly affecting the quality of the human environment" and require an EIS. Rather, Congress left that determination to the CEQ, which was established as part of NEPA. The CEQ developed the primary implementing regulations for NEPA (40 CFR §§1500-1508),[5] which are further supplemented by

the directives and policies of the individual agencies. The CEQ regulations describe an environmental analysis process with three pathways that may produce three different but related documents (Figure 7.2):

1. *Categorical Exclusion (CE)*: the decision process for types of actions that have been previously determined not to have a significant effect on the environment;

2. *Environmental Assessment (EA)*: the decision process agencies use to determine whether a proposed action may have a significant effect on the environment, and thus require an Environmental Impact Statement; and

3. *Environmental Impact Statement (EIS)*: the detailed statement that agencies must make if they conclude that proposed actions may have a significant effect on the environment.

**Categorical Exclusions (CEs)**    Federal agencies undertake hundreds of activities every day, most of which have no appreciable effect on the environment. Which ones do not need to go through the environmental analysis process to determine whether they might have significant effects on the environment? Regulations identify those activities that agencies have established do not have those effects, either individually or cumulatively. These include many policy and planning activities, such as budgeting, inventories and studies, personnel changes, and educational activities. They can also include many kinds of environmental actions with minor effects, such as small (in acreage) fuel treatments or trail renovation projects. Congress may also legislatively specify what qualifies as a CE. As you might imagine, what qualifies as a CE can be controversial.

**Environmental Assessments (EAs)**    Most projects of size and substance do not qualify for a CE. Some types of projects or planning exercises categorically require an EIS, and in some cases agencies may determine that, due to the nature, size, or scope of a project, environmental impacts are likely or inevitable, and so will proceed directly with an EIS. For projects that are not categorically excluded from NEPA analysis, but for which it is unknown or uncertain whether environmental effects of the project reach the level of significance requiring an EIS, agencies will undertake an Environmental Assessment (EA) of the project. Upon completion of the EA process, the agency may either issue a Decision Notice and Finding of No Significant Impact (FONSI) and proceed with the project or, if significant impacts have been identified, proceed with an EIS. Alternatively, an agency may drop a project altogether, or redesign the project to eliminate significant effects to the environment caused by the project. Thus environmental assessment is an important gatekeeper process used by federal agencies to formally determine whether a proposed action might have a signifi-

---

3  Regulations implementing NEPA can be found at https://ceq.doe.gov

4  For an excellent comprehensive introduction to NEPA see http://energy.gov/nepa/downloads/citizens-guide-nepa-having-your-voice-heard

5  The Code of Federal Regulations (CFR) is the repository of administrative law for the federal government. Federal agencies promulgate rules based on enabling legislation passed by Congress (and signed by the president). Proposed rules are first published in the Federal Register, where they are available for public comment. Final rules are also published in the Federal Register; rules with general applicability and legal effect become part of the Code of Federal Regulations. *40 CFR §§1500-1508* refers to the location of the implementing regulations for NEPA in the Code of Federal Regulations. *40* refers to *Title* 40 of the CFR; there are 50 titles in the CFR, each covering a general topic. Title 40 pertains to regulations for the protection of the environment. *§§1500-1508* refers to *Parts* 1500-1508, where the rules cited will be found. We will use this format to reference important elements of administrative law throughout this book. An electronic version of the CFR maintained by the US federal government can be found at: http://www.ecfr.gov/cgi-bin/ECFR?page=browse

cant effect on the environment, which would then require creation of an EIS before actions are undertaken.

At the project level, the EA is at the heart of the decision-making process for federal agencies managing natural resources, whether these decisions involve timber sales, watershed enhancement projects, or trail and road construction. Crafting EAs is a primary activity of many federal interdisciplinary teams.

When an agency writes an EA, it has made the forecast that the EA followed by a FONSI will suffice. We will use a typical Forest Service EA process as our example here. National forests are subdivided into Ranger Districts, and most EAs are written by an interdisciplinary team of specialists from the district (called the *ID Team*); some smaller districts share specialists for this effort. Environmental analysis focuses on evaluating *Proposed Actions*—the projects that the agency wishes to undertake.

Suppose that the District Ranger of a Forest Service Ranger District in the interior West wants to undertake an ecological forestry project on 25,000 acres of ponderosa pine/mixed conifer frequent-fire forests. As part of the scoping process, a field trip may be offered by the district to get a sense of public support, concerns, or criticism. On the field trip, district staff detail the activities they would like to carry out—perhaps a combination of harvest and prescribed fire, often with some detail on which portion of the project area will be treated and how that treatment will be done. They then receive scoping comments from the public and other stakeholders that help identify issues, refine the proposed action, and guide development of alternatives that address important issues, such as whether to build a road into a remote part of the project area. Unlike an EIS, a stand-alone *no action alternative* is not required in an EA; nevertheless, no action alternatives are often included because "the effects of not taking action should provide a compelling reason for taking action and, therefore, should be consistent with the purpose and need for action" (USDA Forest Service, 2010).

***Test for significance.*** The alternatives, which include the proposed action, are evaluated to see if any aspect of the proposed action (or the alternatives) might have a significant effect on the environment. If a potentially significant impact on the environment is identified, the district will often modify the project, if possible, to avoid this impact.

Recall that Section 102(C) of NEPA requires that a detailed statement must be prepared for "major Federal actions significantly affecting the quality of the human environment." This detailed statement, as we have discussed, is an EIS, which discloses the environmental effects of a federal action. Not surprisingly, the precise definition of the word "significantly" is key to determining whether an effect that has been analyzed in an EA is significant, thus requiring preparation of an EIS. The word significantly is not defined in NEPA; given the significance of the word, however, it is worth providing the official definition from the CEQ regulations implementing NEPA (40 CFR § 1508.27):

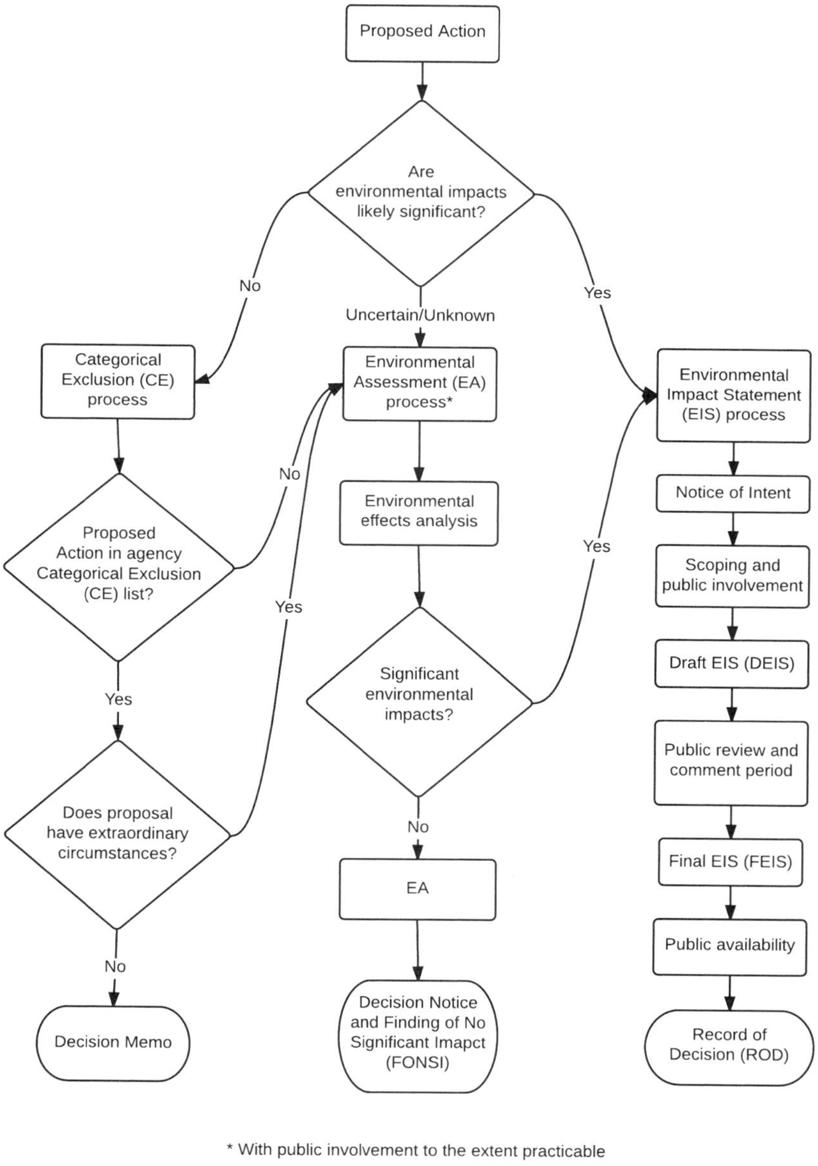

* With public involvement to the extent practicable

Figure 7.2 *The NEPA process for proposed federal actions. (Source: Adapted from Council on Environmental Quality, 2007)*

*Significantly* as used in NEPA requires considerations of both context and intensity:

*(a) Context.* This means that the significance of an action must be analyzed in several contexts such as society as a whole (human, national), the affected region, the affected interests, and the locality. Significance varies with the setting of the proposed action. For instance, in the case of a site-specific action, significance would usually depend upon the effects in the locale rather than in the world as a whole. Both short- and long-term effects are relevant.

*(b) Intensity.* This refers to the severity of impact. Responsible officials must bear in mind that more than one agency may make decisions about partial aspects of a major action. The following should be considered in evaluating intensity:

1. Impacts that may be both beneficial and adverse. A significant effect may exist even if the Federal agency believes that on balance the effect will be beneficial.

2. The degree to which the proposed action affects public health or safety.

3. Unique characteristics of the geographic area such as proximity to historic or cultural resources, park lands, prime farmlands, wetlands, wild and scenic rivers, or ecologically critical areas.

4. The degree to which the effects on the quality of the human environment are likely to be highly controversial.

5. The degree to which the possible effects on the human environment are highly uncertain or involve unique or unknown risks.

6. The degree to which the action may establish a precedent for future actions with significant effects or represents a decision in principle about a future consideration.

7. Whether the action is related to other actions with individually insignificant but cumulatively significant impacts. Significance exists if it is reasonable to anticipate a cumulatively significant impact on the environment. Significance cannot be avoided by terming an action temporary or by breaking it down into small component parts.

8. The degree to which the action may adversely affect districts, sites, highways, structures, or objects listed in or eligible for listing in the National Register of Historic Places or may cause loss or destruction of significant scientific, cultural, or historical resources.

9. The degree to which the action may adversely affect an endangered or threatened species or its habitat that has been determined to be critical under the Endangered Species Act of 1973.

10. Whether the action threatens a violation of Federal, State, or local law or requirements imposed for the protection of the environment.

A primary purpose of the EA process is to work through these factors to determine whether an EIS is needed. If, based on an analysis of these factors, an agency concludes that a proposed action will not result in a significant impact, it publishes a FONSI for the EA, along with a Decision Notice authorizing the proposed action. Some agencies have an administrative objection process before the decision is signed, as we will discuss below, and the decision can be litigated. The EA and accompanying FONSI thus become important legal documents both from the perspective of the agency and from the perspective of stakeholders, who may disagree with aspects of the EA or the FONSI and wish to challenge the agency decision.

Nothing in the CEQ definition of significantly should be brushed aside. Depending on the project, however, some factors may be more relevant than others. The **context** of a project needs to be considered because different scales of analysis usually show different levels of effects; environmental effects must be evaluated at relevant spatial and temporal scales. **Intensity** refers to the severity of impact, which is evaluated with respect to the ten criteria described above. The first criterion explains an important aspect of the FONSI: while there may be both adverse and beneficial effects, the FONSI is not a balancing test, and significant adverse effects must be disclosed, regardless of real or perceived beneficial effects that might offset any adverse effects. (See Box 6.5 for an example of how the courts evaluate whether a proposed agency action might "significantly affect the quality of the human environment.")

***Evaluating Cumulatively Significant Impacts.*** Of all the CEQ significance criteria, *cumulatively significant impacts* may be the most difficult to evaluate and may also present the greatest risk of protest or litigation (Schultz, 2010). According to CEQ regulations, a cumulative impact is

> the impact on the environment which results from the incremental impact of the action when added to other past, present, and reasonably foreseeable future actions regardless of what agency (Federal or non-Federal) or person undertakes such other actions. Cumulative impacts can result from individually minor but collectively significant actions taking place over a period of time. (40 CFR § 1508.7)

The term **cumulative impacts** did not become widely used until the CEQ produced guidelines for implementing NEPA (Reid, 2010). NEPA planning generally focuses on specific projects or programs. The CEQ realized that a broader perspective on problems could be overlooked—examination of a project in isolation would not reveal the impact levels that would actually be experienced. The CEQ thus specified that the overall, or cumulative, impact also must be evaluated. Impacts can accumulate through some actions and relationships such as (Reid, 2010):

- repetition of an activity at a site (example: repeated logging in the transitional snow zone increases rain-on-snow peak flows, increasing the cumulative cost of downstream flood damage);

- progression of the activity to new sites (example: additional logging increases the spatial scale of the increased rain-on-snow flooding, also increasing the cumulative cost of flood damage); and

- different coexisting activities, or different activities occurring sequentially (example: logging, housing developments, and fire all increase rain-on-snow flood peaks).

Much litigation has been brought over the adequacy of cumulative effects analysis in NEPA documents, and the courts have fashioned guidance on legal sufficiency. The 1985 decision for *Fritiofson v. Alexander* 772 F.2d 1225 (1985), as noted by Reid (2010, p. 291), has been especially useful to many courts:

*Given CEQ regulations, it seems to us that a meaningful cumulative-effects study must identify:*

1. *the area in which the effects of the proposed project will be felt;*

2. *the impacts that are expected in that area from the proposed project;*

3. *other actions—past, proposed, and reasonably foreseeable—that have had or are expected to have impacts in the area;*

4. *the impacts or expected impacts from these other actions; and*

5. *the overall impact that can be expected if the individual impacts are allowed to accumulate.*

Other guidance includes:

"To 'consider' cumulative effects, some quantified or detailed information is required. Without such information, neither the courts nor the public, in reviewing the Forest Service's decisions, can be assured that the Forest Service provided the hard look that it is required to provide" (*Neighbors of Cuddy Mountain v. USFS* 137 F.3d 1372 [1998]).

"The cumulative impact analysis must be more than perfunctory; it must provide a 'useful analysis of the cumulative impacts of past, present, and future projects'" (*Kern v. United States Bureau of Land Mgmt* 284 F.3d 1075 [2002]).

To balance these seemingly arduous requirements, guidance provided by the CEQ and the federal courts make clear that the preparation of NEPA documents, including cumulative impact analysis, is to be not unduly complicated or onerous: "NEPA does not require the government to do

the impractical" (*Inland Empire Public Lands Council v. USFS*, 88 F.3d 754 [1996]).

Because of their site-specific nature, EAs may be ill-suited to the evaluation of cumulative impacts. In some cases EAs are tiered to a **programmatic EIS**, such as the EIS for a land management plan for the planning area. These programmatic EISs should have already addressed many of the landscape and region-wide potential environmental impacts of the plan or program and set goals and a legal context for agency action. When tiered to these documents, EAs evaluate the site-specific implications of projects that carry out these plans or programs. The broad-scale analysis of a programmatic EIS may not provide the level of detail or the spatial and temporal scope necessary to evaluate cumulative impacts, however. Thus additional cumulative impact analysis may be required at the project level.

**Environmental Impact Statements (EISs)** While EAs are very common, EISs are, by comparison, relatively infrequent. Notably, the need to undertake an EIS only rarely comes from the findings of an EA that a proposed action has potentially significant effects on the environment, as most EAs end with a FONSI. Rather, the need for an EIS most commonly comes from one of two sources: (1) Recognition early on by the responsible agency that the proposed action will require an EIS, or (2) litigation that successfully challenges the FONSI associated with an EA. Very large projects, or projects that are inherently controversial (like fire salvage), can lead an agency to opt for an EIS from the beginning of the planning process.

NEPA regulations lay out the step-by-step process involved in creation of an EIS with great specification about components, such as the length of public comment period. Generally, EISs contain the information required by Section 102(C) of NEPA (outlined above) organized into chapters just like the five components that the law specifies, and can run several volumes and thousands of pages. In the end, however, the goal of the NEPA process is relatively straightforward: divulge the environmental impacts of a proposed action, and consider alternatives that reduce these impacts.

**Public Involvement under NEPA** *For many, significant public involvement in federal environmental decision making began with NEPA.* The Act itself calls for the agency proposing an action to seek comments from other federal agencies with jurisdiction over the actions being considered, or with special expertise concerning the environmental impacts that might occur. While this might not have meant much when NEPA was first passed, subsequent environmental legislation resulted in agencies whose legal charge and expertise focused on protection of the environment. Agencies that became involved in the formerly internal affairs of other agencies proposing actions with possible environmental effects include the Environmental Protection Agency (which administers the Clean Water Act and the Clean Air Act among other laws) and the United States Fish and Wildlife Service and the National Marine Fisheries Service (which administer the Endangered Species Act).

NEPA also required that copies of Environmental Impact Statements and agency comments be made available to the public. Regulations implementing NEPA, though, took an expansive view of the role of the public in the process of environmental impact analysis, even though NEPA itself did not discuss such a role. NEPA regulations require agencies to make diligent efforts to involve the public in preparing and implementing NEPA procedures (40 CFR §1506.6) and to respond to public comments about proposed actions (40 CFR §1503.4). These regulations opened the door to public involvement in federal decision making, creating a *public involvement process* that is now an integral part of federal decisions.

Requiring that the public be allowed to comment on the environmental analysis process and requiring that implementing agencies respond to and publish public comments about proposed actions created a source of accountability that fundamentally changed the relationship between federal agencies and the public. Being able to question how completely an agency has divulged the environmental consequences of its actions, and then seeing the agency's response, gave the environmental effects of proposed agency actions a scrutiny and visibility they had never had before. It also provided fodder for much NEPA-based litigation.

Unfortunately, as pointed out by Wondolleck (1988) in her pioneering study of Forest Service decision making, the NEPA public involvement process also encouraged extreme demands by the public. After scoping to identify issues of interest or concern to the public about a possible proposed action, an agency generally developed the proposed action on its own and asked the public to comment on it. Because members of the public were not involved in creation of the proposal, they had no stake in supporting it. Often intense criticism of the EIS by the public resulted, with some members of the public taking extreme positions in an attempt to pull the agency toward outcomes they wanted. With this decision process, the public had little incentive to grapple with the issues, budgets, and practical reality of solving the original problem that triggered the need for a NEPA analysis.

These difficulties have led federal agencies, like the US Forest Service, to involve the public sooner and more substantively in developing the proposed action than is required by NEPA. This flexibility in public involvement is probably seen most clearly in the EA process. NEPA regulations call for public involvement in development of EAs to the *extent practicable*, leaving it to agencies to determine how to accomplish this. Thus many agencies like the

US Forest Service attempt to engage the public *early and often* in development of EAs (Figure 7.3). This approach has shown promise in overcoming the problems in the public involvement process identified by Wondolleck (1988).

**NEPA Litigation**   Case law has played an important role in shaping the outcome of many federal decisions, and the NEPA process in general. We have seen that above in discussing how the courts have helped fashion a legally credible cumulative effects analysis.

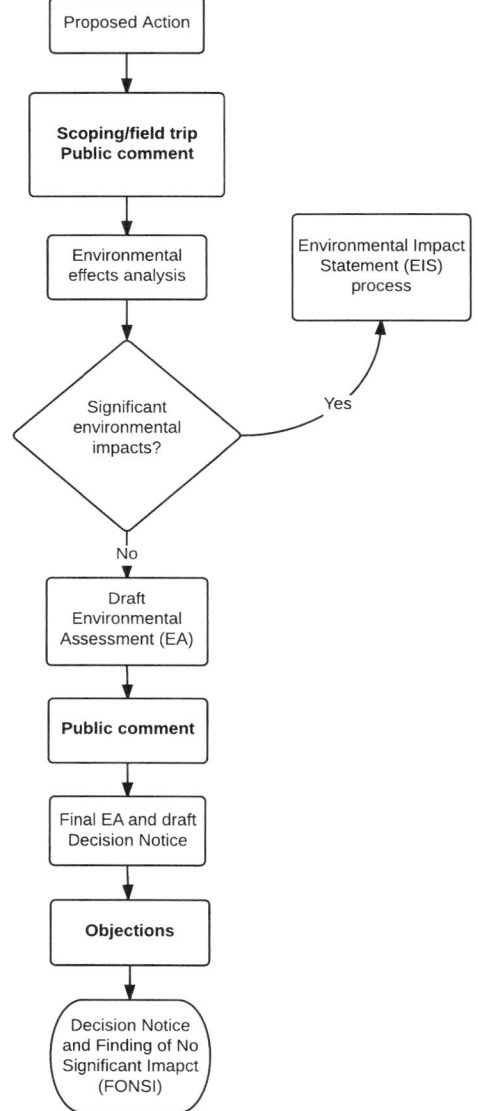

Figure 7.3 *Typical Environmental Assessment process for US Forest Service projects with opportunities for public engagement (in bold). Regulations (36 CFR §218) governing the US Forest Service NEPA process require a 30-day public comment period on draft EAs, and the opportunity for objections before the Decision Notice is signed. The US Forest Service now requires scoping for all proposed actions, including those that would appear to be categorically excluded from analysis (36 CFR §220.4[e][1]).*

Environmental litigants often attempt to use the procedural requirements of the NEPA process, combined with the provisions of the Administrative Procedure Act prohibiting arbitrary and capricious behavior, to achieve their goals. To illustrate the types of claims brought by plaintiffs in NEPA suits and examine how courts evaluate them, we summarize parts of Judge Dwyer's 1994 decision regarding the validity of the Northwest Forest Plan for federal forests in the range of the northern spotted owl, which relied on precedents set in the hundreds of similar NEPA cases that preceded his decision (*Seattle Audubon Soc. v. Lyons*, 871 F. Supp. 1291 [1994]):

*Legal claim*: Inadequate range of alternatives. *Court finding*: "NEPA requires that an agency consider a reasonably full range of alternatives. The ten alternatives analyzed in-depth span a variety of measures and strategies, and an eighteen-fold difference in harvest volume." The ten alternatives fulfilled NEPA requirement that the "agency set forth only those alternatives necessary to permit a reasoned choice."

*Legal claim*: Inadequate consideration of opposing scientific views regarding protection of the northern spotted owl. *Court finding*: Reputable scientific opinion supports the Secretaries' view.[6] "The plan must be designed by the agencies, not the courts. The question for judicial review is whether NEPA's requirements have been met. A disagreement among scientists does not itself make agency action arbitrary or capricious, nor is the government held to a degree of certainty that is ultimately illusory. The Final EIS (FEIS) does take a *hard look* at the available data and opposing opinions. The FEIS has a reasoned discussion of a myriad of factors. The FEIS adequately discloses the risks and confronts the criticisms, as required by NEPA."

*Legal claim*: Inadequate consideration of aquatic species. *Court finding*: "The FEIS adequately confronts the relevant risks and uncertainties, and arrives at a reasoned outcome, in compliance with NEPA."

*Legal claim*: Decision based on incomplete information: *Court finding*: The FEIS acknowledges that information is incomplete with regard to population viability of the northern spotted owl. The explanation given in the Record of Decision satisfies the requirements of the regulations. Agencies concluded there was sufficient information to allow a reasoned choice. The agencies' determination is not in violation of law.

*Legal claim*: Inadequate analysis of cumulative impacts relative to the northern spotted owl and other species. *Court finding*: "Agencies are required to examine in an EIS the cumulative impacts of proposed actions; that is, those that result from the incremental impact of the action when added to the past, present, and reasonably foreseeable future actions, regardless of what agency or entity (federal or nonfederal) undertakes them." The discussion is adequate for a programmatic EIS;[7] cumulative impact analysis will be made for site-specific actions.

*Legal claim*: Biased assessment of economic effects. *Court finding*: Where economic analysis forms the basis of choosing among alternatives, NEPA requires that the analysis not be misleading, biased, or incomplete. To present a full and unbiased picture of proposed alternatives, the EIS must disclose both the benefits and the costs. The FEIS discusses at length the economic and social consequences of the plan.

After rejecting these claims and many others, Judge Dwyer ruled, "All claims and arguments asserted by the plaintiffs . . . have been considered, and none would justify invalidation of the plan or a remand to the agencies." Judge Dwyer found that, in developing and authorizing the Northwest Forest Plan, the Secretaries of Agriculture and Interior had acted within the scope of their discretion.

## NEPA's Effect on Federal Decision Making

As we discussed earlier, Section 101 of NEPA attempts to establish a productive and harmonious relationship between the people of the United States and their natural environment. Its major impact on federal decisions has been to require that agencies divulge the potential impacts of federal actions that could have a significant effect on the environment, before the actions are undertaken, and to seek ways to reduce those impacts. The Act, itself, does not include specific environmental standards that an agency must meet before the action can proceed. Thus NEPA depends on other processes to set standards on what impacts are acceptable. The three major sources of those standards are: (1) agency directives, policies, and plans (like the Land and Resource Management Plans for the national forests), (2) public opinion and protest about potential impacts and; (3) other environmental laws whose substantive protection standards would be violated by impacts resulting from the proposed action.

How successful has the NEPA process been in achieving the goals of divulging environmental impacts and seeking alternatives that reduce them? We consider this question in terms of two key components called for in the NEPA

---

6 The responsible officials for the Northwest Forest Plan were the Secretary of Agriculture and the Secretary of Interior.

7 A programmatic EIS is an EIS for a plan or program, such as a forest or regional plan, rather than for a particular project.

process set up by Congress: (1) employing a balanced and impartial analysis to uncover potential environmental impacts, and (2) describing those impacts in a manner that they are understood by other agencies and by the public.

**Employing a Balanced and Impartial Analysis of Environmental Impacts**   The requirement in NEPA that agencies use an interdisciplinary approach to analyze potential impacts created a much more balanced process to decision making than existed before NEPA. Of that, there cannot be much doubt. Overall, the NEPA process revolutionized the federal government's approach to environmental decision making.

However, this powerful mechanism is somewhat diminished by the fact that the interdisciplinary team (usually) works for the agency proposing the action, creating a potential conflict of interest: interdisciplinary team members may feel pressure to conclude that there are no significant impacts (during the EA or the EIS evaluation) to a proposed action, since findings of significant impacts can greatly diminish the chances that the proposed action will be implemented.

Agencies that do not successfully implement projects may see their budgets reduced the following year, and agency leaders who do not meet management objectives will likely receive a less than glowing annual performance evaluation. In sum, asking an agency to evaluate the environmental impacts of its own actions may create a significant conflict of interest.

Without the public involvement process, this potential conflict of interest could severely limit the effectiveness of NEPA in achieving the goals intended by Congress. With give-and-take during the environmental analysis process and the potential for objection and litigation that might follow a decision, public involvement certainly helps to level the playing field. However, it must be acknowledged that it is not always easy for agencies to see the potential environmental impacts of their actions!

**Providing an Understandable Statement of Potential Environmental Impacts**   Congress envisioned the detailed statements required by NEPA as relatively short reports following the brief list of requirements they set forth in Section 102(C). What it got is multivolume EISs that can go on for thousands of pages. Even EAs can be hundreds of pages long. What is going on here? First, the increasingly recognized complexity of ecological systems and the corresponding complexity in project design can make simple, straightforward explanations difficult. Second, as agencies realized that their NEPA documentation would be challenged through protests, appeals, and lawsuits, they tried to produce documents they hoped would either respond to or prevail over these claims, i.e., bulletproof their EAs or EISs.

Thus, EAs and EISs have become inherently hard to understand in many instances, and groups that see themselves as watchdogs of the NEPA process often have NEPA specialists too! Here NEPA has been only partially successful in achieving the goals set for it.

## The Endangered Species Act [8] [9]

The Endangered Species Act of 1973[10] (ESA) (P.L. 93-205, 87 Stat. 884 16 U.S.C. §§ 1531-1544) is probably the United States' most controversial environmental law. It is difficult to overestimate the uniqueness or the impact of this law. As of 2016, there were nearly 1,600 species listed as threatened or endangered in the United States (USFWS, 2016): many other species are awaiting evaluation. The list of species protected by the ESA includes mammals, birds, fish, mollusks, conifers, flowering plants, grasses, ferns, lichen, and insects (Figure 7.4).

### Goals

*The ultimate goal of the ESA is to recover species that have been listed as threatened or endangered so that they can be delisted.* While delisting has happened only occasionally, there have been success stories. Bald eagles, peregrine falcons, and gray whales have all been delisted after tremendous increases in their populations. Also, the gray wolf has been delisted in some Rocky Mountain states; however, that delisting happened through an act of Congress and remains deeply controversial.

Section 2 of the ESA contains language with significant consequences for forest policy in the United States: "The purposes of this Act are to provide a means whereby the ecosystems upon which endangered species and threatened species depend may be conserved, [and] to provide a program for the conservation of such endangered species and threatened species." Note the use of the term *ecosystems*—one of the first references to ecosystems by any legislation. Moreover, Congress put the conservation of threatened and endangered species into the job description

---

8  This description of the Endangered Species Act and its requirements utilizes the extensive website of the US Fish and Wildlife Service on the Act and the associated regulations http://www.fws.gov/endangered/laws-policies/. For consultation, we also use http://www.fws.gov/midwest/endangered/section7/section7.html.

9  Either the US Fish and Wildlife Service or the National Marine Fisheries Service implements the Endangered Species Act, depending on the species at issue. Throughout this section, we will use the terminology, descriptions, and process of the US Fish and Wildlife Service.

10  Endangered Species Act of 1973, P.L. 93-205, 87 Stat. 884 (1973). We here use section references as found in the law passed by Congress (P.L. 93-205), since that is how the parts of the law are commonly known and discussed. The codified version of the statute, which includes revisions and amendments, is located at: 16 U.S.C. §§ 1531–1544.

of all federal agencies: "It is further declared to be the policy of Congress that all Federal departments and agencies shall seek to conserve endangered species and threatened species and shall utilize their authorities in furtherance of the purposes of this Act" (Section 2[c][1]). Finally, the definitions in Section 3 leave little doubt about the degree of effort agencies are to use in furthering the purposes of the Act: "The terms 'conserve,' 'conserving,' and 'conservation' mean to use and the use of all methods and procedures which are necessary to bring any endangered species or threatened species to the point at which the measures provided pursuant to this Act are no longer necessary."

Yes, the Endangered Species Act is a very strongly worded statute, and this wording has important implications for how the courts interpret the law. In perhaps the most famous ESA case, *Tennessee Valley Authority v. Hill* (437 U.S. 153 [1978]), the US Supreme Court ruled that a dam

on the Little Tennessee River in the southeastern United States, which was nearly complete at a cost of $100 million, could not be finished because the dam would destroy the habitat for the snail darter (*Percina tenasi*), a tiny fish the size of paperclip. In its decision, the Court ruled:

*The plain intent of Congress in enacting this statute [the ESA] was to halt and reverse the trend toward species extinction, whatever the cost.* This is reflected not only in the stated policies of the Act, but in literally every section of the statute. . . . In addition, the legislative history undergirding Section 7 reveals an *explicit congressional decision to require [federal] agencies to afford first priority to the declared national policy of saving endangered species. The pointed omission of the type of qualifying language previously included in endangered species*

Figure 7.4 *Among the species listed under the ESA as threatened or endangered in the USA are (a) Gentner's fritillary* (Fritillaria gentneri) *(photo courtesy of Tom Kaye), (b) Fender's blue butterfly* (Icaricia icarioides fenderi) *(photo courtesy of Paul Hammond), and (c) marbled murrelet (photo courtesy of Rich MacIntosh USFWS).*

*legislation reveals a conscious decision by Congress to give endangered species priority over the "primary missions" of federal agencies.* (Emphasis added.)

In response to this decision, in 1978 Congress passed legislation amending the ESA and establishing the *Endangered Species Interagency Committee*, which can exempt federal actions from the ESA if the committee deems the cost of compliance as too high.[11] The Endangered Species Committee, in the end, found that the dam on the Little Tennessee River did not qualify for such an exemption.[12] Very few exemptions have been granted, and this amendment to the Endangered Species Act has fallen into disuse.

## Types of Classifications and Responsible Agencies

In Section 3, the ESA establishes two categories of species: (1) endangered species and (2) threatened species. The term *endangered species* means "any species which is in danger of extinction throughout all or a significant portion of its range." The term *threatened species* means "any species which is likely to become an endangered species within the foreseeable future throughout all or a significant portion of its range."

In Section 3, species is defined to include any subspecies of fish, wildlife, or plants, and any distinct population segment[13] (portion of a species' or subspecies' population or range) of any vertebrate species. Even though a species may have a healthy viable population in one area, it could be threatened with extinction in another locale and listed as such under the ESA (Ferrey, 2013). Distinct populations that have been listed include the northern population of the copperbelly water snake, the interior population of the least tern, and the northern population of the bog turtle.

Two cabinet-level secretaries are responsible for implementing the ESA. The Secretary of the Interior, through oversight of the US Fish and Wildlife Service (USFWS), is responsible for threatened and endangered species that are not oceangoing, and the Secretary of Commerce, through oversight of the National Marine Fisheries Service (NMFS), is responsible for threatened and endangered species that

spend all or part of their lives in the ocean.[14] [15] These two secretaries, through their agencies, oversee the listing, protection, and delisting process. When we reference *the secretary* in our discussions below, we are referring to one of these two secretaries as the responsible decision maker, depending on the species at issue.

## Listing and Delisting Decisions

*Section 4 of the ESA directs the secretaries to* use "the best scientific and commercial data available," to *determine whether a species should be listed as threatened or endangered* because of any one of five factors:

1. *the present or threatened destruction, modification, or curtailment of its habitat or range;*

2. *overutilization for commercial, recreational, scientific, or educational purposes;*

3. *disease or predation;*

4. *the inadequacy of existing regulatory mechanisms; or*

5. *other natural or man-made factors affecting its continued existence.*

Delisting requires that the listed species has sufficiently recovered such that its population, reproduction rates, and distribution will enable its persistence, and that none of the five factors still threaten the species.

Listing involves a series of steps that can take a number of years. The process is initiated by interested parties providing evidence that a species is imperiled. During a 90-day screening process the petition is evaluated and either dismissed or deemed worthy of a status review. If deemed worthy of review, the species becomes a *candidate species* and the agency has a limited time (generally a year) to make a finding with three possible outcomes: (1) listing is not warranted (the process ends), (2) listing is warranted but precluded (higher-priority actions relegate the species to a holding status as a candidate species), or (3) listing is warranted (the agency proposes the species for threatened or endangered status). With numerous species on the "warranted but precluded list," USFWS and the NMFS have faced a multitude of lawsuits claiming that the agency

---

11 We will discuss the makeup of the committee and its criteria for exemption later in this chapter.

12 Congress then passed legislation mandating completion of the dam on the Little Tennessee River, the president signed it, and the dam was finished. Also, snail darters and their habitat were subsequently found in adjacent streams.

13 The US Fish and Wildlife Service uses the term *distinct population segment*, whereas the National Marine Fisheries Service uses the term *evolutionarily significant unit* when referring to salmonids. The terms are functionally equivalent with respect to the ESA.

14 See 50 CFR §402.01(b). The USFWS and NMFS share responsibilities for administering the Act. The lists of endangered and threatened wildlife and plants are found in 50 CFR 17.11 and 17.12, and the designated Critical Habitats are found in 50 CFR 17.95 and 17.96 and 50 CFR part 226. Endangered or threatened species under the jurisdiction of the NMFS are located in 50 CFR 222.23(a) and 227.4. If the subject species is cited in 50 CFR 222.23(a) or 227.4, the federal agency shall contact the NMFS. For all other listed species the federal agency shall contact the USFWS.

15 The two agencies sometimes split responsibilities, such as for the sea turtle where the USFWS is responsible for it on land and the NMFS at sea. Also, the USFWS has responsibility for some species that stay near the shore, such as the sea otter.

---

**Box 7.1  Listing decisions and the Administrative Procedure Act**

The decision to list a species changes the decision framework for federal agencies since it gives protection of a listed species priority over aspects of their missions. Listings can also affect state and private landowners as we shall see. Perhaps not surprisingly, lawsuits challenging listing decisions are very common.

As an example, lawsuits have successfully challenged USFWS decisions not to list wide-ranging species such as the northern spotted owl and the bull trout (*Salvelinus confluentis*)—listing decisions that would have had significant impacts on the economies and lives of many people. While the courts start by assuming the agency action is valid, as we discussed in the previous chapter, the courts also examine the agency's rationale in depth. If the weight of scientific evidence presented in court strongly suggests that the species in question is threatened or endangered, as in these two cases, the agency decision not to list can be seen as arbitrary and capricious. For the species mentioned above, reexamination of the listing decisions by USFWS, after the court's adverse judgment, led to decisions to list both species as threatened.

---

is negligent in failing to list these species, especially since some face imminent threat of extinction and some have gone extinct while on the list. In addition, decisions by some administrations to minimize listings and budgetary limitations have led to a backlog of species to consider for listing, which has led to other litigation. In the last few years, the USFWS has reached out-of-court agreements with plaintiffs to speed the listing process (Cubbage et al., 2017).

Some important considerations in the listing and delisting decisions are:

- Who can ask that a species be listed? Section 4 of the ESA affirms that any citizen of the United States can petition for a species to be listed (or delisted).

- What information does the federal government use to make the listing decision? The government must use the ***best available scientific and commercial data*** in making the determination of whether a species is threatened or endangered. Thus, data must exist that demonstrate that the species should be listed. As we previously discussed, criteria for listing may include evidence on existing or likely future habitat destruction, disease, or anything else that might threaten a species' existence. At any time, a list exists of species that various citizen groups want the agencies to consider for listing.

- What if citizens don't think the listing agency (USFWS or NMFS) used the best information available, or think authorities misinterpreted this information? They can bring a lawsuit against the government to try to force a different decision. In such a lawsuit, they often will argue that the agency engaged in arbitrary and capricious behavior in making the decision, a form of behavior prohibited by the Administrative Procedure Act. Taken together, the ability of citizens to request that a species be listed and the ability to sue when they disagree with agency decisions about listing provide citizens with a very powerful role in the Endangered Species Act listing process (Box 7.1).

- Where does the potential cost to humans come into the listing decision? Economic considerations (such as potential disruption of activities) are not part of the decision of whether to list a species as threatened or endangered—the decision must be based solely on the threat to the species.[16]

- Who oversees a species' conservation once it is delisted? Unless the species falls under other federal law, such as the federal Migratory Bird Treaty Act, states assume regulatory and management of formerly listed species, including any harvest that may occur under the state's game laws. Thus it is critical that states demonstrate that they have an ***adequate regulatory mechanism*** for delisting to occur.

- Must a species be recovered over its entire historical range for delisting to occur? No, species must be recovered over a sufficiently large area, or number of areas, to ensure persistence, but that can be well short of its historical range. We do not need grizzly bears once again roaming the University of California at Berkeley campus to declare this beast recovered!

## Declaration of Critical Habitat

Section 4 of the ESA also calls for the secretary to designate *Critical Habitat*—habitat essential to survival of the species and that requires special management—when the species is listed. Some important considerations in the declaration of Critical Habitat are:

- Does the secretary always designate Critical Habitat at the time a species is listed? No, many times this comes later, largely because the regulatory agencies lack the resources required to undertake Critical Habitat analysis.

---

16 Regulations implementing the Endangered Species Act state: "The Secretary shall make any determination . . . *solely* on the basis of the best available scientific and commercial information regarding a species' status, without reference to possible economic or other impacts of such determination" (italics in original text) (50 CFR § 424.11[b]).

- Can economic considerations enter into Critical Habitat designations? Yes, if such considerations do not jeopardize survival of the species. [17]

- Can Critical Habitat be designated on nonfederal lands, such as private forestland? Yes. Critical Habitat can affect nonfederal lands to the degree that actions there create a *federal nexus* in the sense that federal action is also needed, such as when a permit is needed from the Corps of Engineers to fill in a wetland on private lands.

- Is the secretary interested only in habitat on federal lands that have been designated Critical Habitat? No. Activities outside of Critical Habitat may be restricted to help a species survive and recover.

## Responsibilities for Listed Species

The ESA places many more responsibilities on actions taken by federal agencies than on actions taken by state and local governments and private landowners that do not require federal involvement. Major categories of responsibilities for conservation of a listed species differ between these two types of actions. We will utilize the regulations of the USFWS to illustrate these responsibilities (Table 7.4): [18]

**Avoiding Take** [19]   The listing of a species as threatened or endangered results in limitations on activities that could affect that species and in prohibitions for taking individuals of a listed species. [20] Section 3 of the ESA defines take as "to harass, harm, pursue, hunt, shoot, wound, kill, trap, capture, or collect, or to attempt to engage in any such conduct." The verb *harm* is the key word in this definition for forest management operations. Harm includes habitat modification where actual injury to wildlife can be demonstrated, [21] and includes *"significant habitat modification or degradation*

Table 7.4 *Responsibilities under the ESA for federally listed threatened or endangered species under the care of the USFWS*

| Type of responsibility | Type of Action | | |
|---|---|---|---|
| | Federal actions[#] | Non-federal actions | Primary focus |
| Avoid take[*] | Yes | Yes | Individuals |
| Consult | Yes | No | Population |
| Assist recovery | Yes | No | Population |

\# Federal actions include the granting of federal permits, federal licenses, or federal funding to state, local, and private parties.
\* Actions that may take a species listed as threatened or endangered can be allowed by the USFWS in specific instances as part of a larger agreement as we discuss in more detail below.

*where it actually kills or injures wildlife by significantly impairing essential behavioral patterns, including breeding, feeding or sheltering"* (50 CFR § 17.3).

With few exceptions, Section 9 of the ESA makes it unlawful for any person subject to the jurisdiction of the United States to take an endangered species, as defined above, within the United States or the territorial seas of the United States. However, the USFWS (and the NMFS) has broad authority under Section 4 of the ESA to issue regulations for the conservation of threatened species. Using this authority, the USFWS extended the prohibition of take to all threatened species by regulation in 1978 (often referred to as the blanket 4[d] rule). Therefore take (harass, harm, pursue, hunt, shoot, wound, kill, trap, capture, or collect or attempt to engage in any such conduct) of threatened species managed by the USFWS is prohibited by regulation. However, this blanket 4(d) rule for threatened species can be modified by a species-specific 4(d) rule. [22]

The USFWS primarily uses species-specific 4(d) rules to streamline ESA compliance for actions that have long-term species conservation benefits, but that might result in take actions in the short term or that result in low levels of take but do not contribute to the threats facing a species' continued existence. As an example, the 4(d) rule for the threatened Preble's meadow jumping mouse (*Zapus hudsonius preblei*) provides flexibility to private landowners for ongoing activities that would not impede the conservation of this species, such as limited rodent control, continuation of ongoing agricultural practices, and maintenance of existing landscaping. As another example, Minnesota wolves that have preyed on domestic animals can be trapped and killed by designated government agents. This 4(d) rule was developed to avoid even larger numbers of wolves being killed by private citizens who might otherwise take wolf control into their own hands. As still another example of this

---

17 50 CFR § 424.19. Note that decisions about listing a species are different from decisions about designated Critical Habitat.

18 The NMFS has a slightly different regulatory approach to some of these responsibilities, especially avoiding take.

19 Much of the material from this section comes from https://www.fws.gov/pacific/news/grizzly/esafacts.htm.

20 There is no penalty for the take of listed plant species on nonfederal lands.

21 In *Babbitt v. Sweet Home Chapter of Communities for a Greater Oregon*, 515 U. S. 687 (1995), the US Supreme Court found that harm includes habitat modification that could foreseeably result in actual injury or death of individuals of a listed species.

22 Take of plants listed as threatened or endangered is not prohibited on private land.

## Box 7.2.  Reestablishing species in their former ranges: the concept of experimental populations

Reestablishing a threatened or endangered species in areas of its former range is often necessary for recovery. However, residents and businesses could oppose such reintroductions because they fear the presence of the species will also bring severe restrictions on the use of private and public land in the area. To help overcome this obstacle to species reintroductions, Congress added the concept of *experimental populations* to the ESA. An experimental population is a geographically described group of reintroduced plants or animals that is isolated from other existing populations of the species. Members of the experimental population are considered to be threatened under the ESA and thus can have special regulations written for them under Section 4(d). If the experimental population is determined to be *nonessential* to the survival of the species, the experimental population can be treated like a species proposed for listing as threatened or endangered. In other words, the nonessential experimental population is not given the full ESA protections. The gray wolf introduced to Yellowstone, as an example (Figure 7.5), was deemed a *nonessential experimental population*, which allowed

more control of the population than would have otherwise been possible. Among numerous examples of experimental populations are the Colorado pikeminnow (*Ptychocheilus lucius*), the southern sea otter (*Enhydra lutris nereis*), and the black-footed ferret (*Mustela nigripes*).

Figure 7.5  *First gray wolf release in Yellowstone National Park. (Photo credit: Jim Peaco/National Park Service)*

flexibility, coho salmon (*Oncorhynchus kisutch*) are listed as threatened along the Oregon coast, but the 4(d) rule for anadromous fish allows a limited number of these salmon to be caught by sport fisherman in abundant coho years. In addition, the USFWS occasionally deems a species that it is reintroducing into its former range as an *experimental population*, which gives it more flexibility in its management (Box 7.2).

Beyond the flexibility provided by 4(d) rules and experimental populations, the USFWS can also issue *incidental take permits* for federal actions after consultation and for nonfederal actions after development of a Habitat Conservation Plan. We discuss both of these possibilities below.

**Consultation**    Each federal agency must ensure that any action it authorizes, funds, or carries out is not likely to jeopardize the continued existence of any endangered or threatened species,[23] or result in the destruction or adverse modification of Critical Habitat of such species. Toward that end, Section 7 of the ESA requires federal agencies

proposing actions that may affect listed species to consult with the USFWS or the NMFS, depending on the agency responsible for the species at issue (Figure 7.6).

Before initiating an action, the *action agency* works with the relevant regulatory agency—USFWS or NMFS—to assess whether a listed species in or around the project area may be affected by the proposed action. If so, consultation may be required. If the action agency determines (and the USFWS or the NMFS agrees) that the project is *not likely to adversely affect* a listed species or designated Critical Habitat, the relevant regulatory agency concurs in writing (a *concurrence letter*) and the consultation process (informal to this point) is concluded.

If an agency proposing an action determines that a project *may adversely affect* a listed species or designated Critical Habitat, the action agency initiates *formal consultation* by producing a *Biological Assessment* of the proposed action and the nature of anticipated effects. The appropriate regulatory agency—NMFS or USFWS—then prepares a *Biological Opinion* (*BiOp*), which analyzes whether the proposed action is likely to jeopardize the continued existence of the species or adversely modify designated Critical Habitat. If the regulatory agency concludes that the action is not likely to jeopardize the species or adversely modify Critical

---

23 *Jeopardize* has been formally defined by the USFWS as "to engage in an action that reasonably may be expected, directly or indirectly, to reduce the reproduction, numbers, or distribution of the species" (50 CFR 402.02).

Habitat, the project can proceed as designed, consistent with the ***Terms and Conditions*** as specified in the BiOp.

If the NMFS or the USFWS concludes that a project is likely to jeopardize the continued existence of a listed species and/or adversely modify the species' Critical Habitat, it provides ***reasonable and prudent alternatives*** to the project in the BiOp (if any are identifiable) that would avoid these problems while meeting the goals of the original action. Reasonable and prudent alternatives vary from slight project adjustments to extensive redesign or relocation of the project. The USFWS and the NMFS pride themselves on usually being able to suggest reasonable and prudent alternatives that will meet both their conservation goals for the listed species and those of the action agency.

The USFWS or the NMFS may include an ***incidental take statement (ITS)*** with an incidental take permit as part of the BiOp. The ITS allows take of a set number of individuals of a species, provided the take occurs incidental to implementing the action and under the Terms and Conditions expressed in the BiOp. An ITS may be issued as long as the actions in question do not jeopardize survival or recovery of the species, or adversely modify Critical Habitat.

The BiOp is only a recommendation to the agency proposing the action. Given a set of reasonable and prudent alternatives in the BiOp, the action agency then has five choices: (1) implement one of them; (2) modify the proposed project and consult again with the USFWS; (3) decide not to undertake, fund, or authorize the project; (4) disagree with the opinion and proceed (an extremely rare occurrence); or (5) apply for an exemption from the ESA (also extremely rare).

The last two choices bear additional explanation. The agency undertaking the action may, by law, proceed, even if the USFWS (or the NMFS) finds that the action will jeopardize survival of the species or adversely modify Critical Habitat. In such cases the action agency assumes full responsibility for compliance with the ESA; such a course of action will undoubtedly lead to litigation by US citizens.

As mentioned earlier in this chapter, federal agencies may request exemption from the requirements of the ESA for particular actions from the ***Endangered Species Committee*** (the ***God Squad***), a committee composed mostly of cabinet-level officials of the federal government. The committee will grant an exemption to the ESA if it finds that: (1) there are no reasonable alternatives to the proposed action; (2) the action is in the public interest, and the benefits of such action clearly outweigh the benefits of alternative courses of action that are consistent with conserving the species or its Critical Habitat; and (3) the action is of regional or national significance. For an exemption to be granted, five out of seven members of the Endangered Species Committee must approve of the exemption. The God Squad was developed by Congress as a safety valve for cases where protecting a

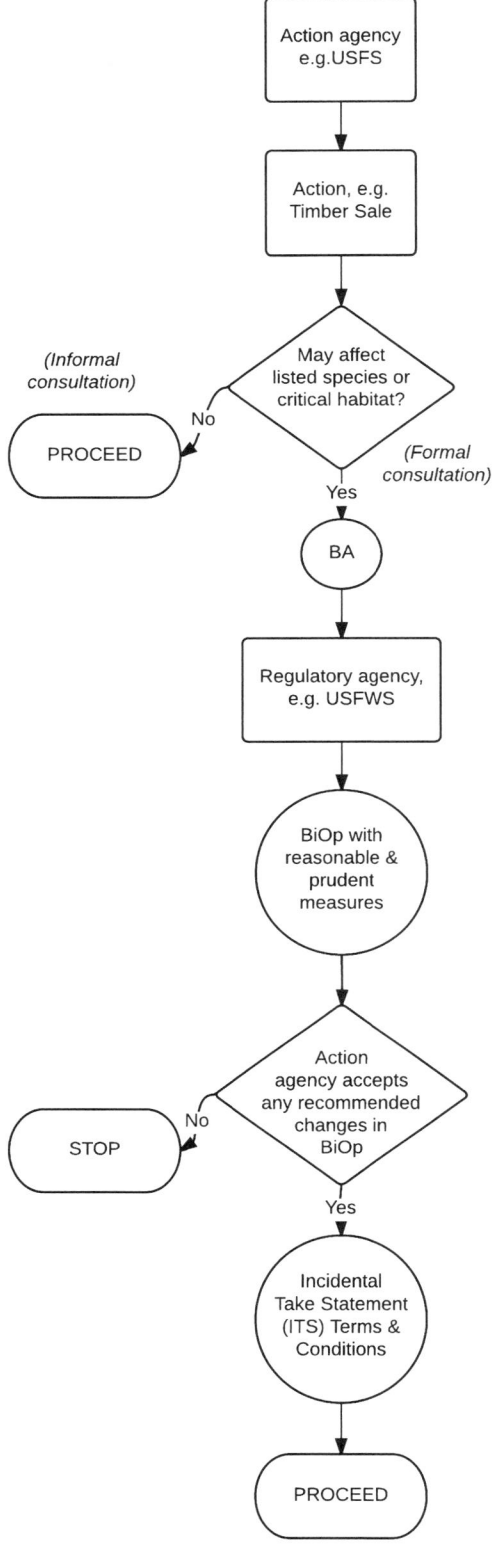

Figure 7.6 *Typical consultation process for a federal agency wishing to undertake an action that may affect a listed species. BA = Biological Assessment (written by action agency). BiOp = Biological Opinion (written by regulatory agency responsible for the species). ITS = Incidental Take Statement (Incidental take permit granted by regulatory agency).*

listed species is deemed too costly; few exemptions have been requested, however, and even fewer have been granted. Some notes about consultation:

- As discussed above, the Supreme Court has ruled that Congress intended that federal agencies give "the highest of priorities" to the recovery of listed species. Therefore, this goal comes before the pursuit of other agency goals, unless an exemption is obtained from the Endangered Species Committee.

- Neither the law nor the regulations specify quantitative thresholds of protection that must be met. Therefore, the BiOp relies heavily on the professional judgment of the USFWS (or the NMFS), utilizing both what is known of the species and their understanding of its current status.

- Consultation generally occurs after the proposed action has been fully developed but before a final decision is issued under the NEPA process (Environmental Assessment or Environmental Impact Statement). Where it is required, consultation is a significant part of the analysis and decision process of federal agencies.

- Consultation proceeds more smoothly, and with fewer surprises, if the two regulatory agencies (the NMFS and the USFWS) are involved in project development from the beginning, rather than only during formal consultation on the proposed action.

**Recovery Planning**   Section 4(f) of the ESA calls for the secretary to develop recovery plans for listed species. Recovery plans are intended to be the central documents for federal agency planning to conform to the ESA. In general, they are comprehensive landscape plans that provide both the spatial and temporal design for recovery of the listed species. They generally include:

- *Management recommendations for both federal and nonfederal actions.* While only federal actions have a statutory obligation to contribute to recovery, recommendations on other actions can help direct public investments in habitat restoration. This may include identifying where funds might best be spent on conservation easements on private lands (see Chapter 10 for discussion of conservation easements).

- *Quantitative measures of recovery.* Recovery plans often describe recovery goals in terms of number of individuals needed in local populations and the distribution of these local populations across the recovery area necessary to recover the species.

Recovery plans provide a framework for planning by federal agencies; as such, they supply the basis for future

consultation, development of reasonable and prudent measures, and granting of incidental take permits. For species with a large geographic distribution, such as the northern spotted owl, recovery plans provide region-wide goals and provide a foundation for federal forest planning.

Section 4 of the ESA also requires public review and comment on recovery plans before they are adopted. Usually, a draft recovery plan is published, which is followed by a public comment period. A final recovery plan is then published that considers new information received in response to the draft plan.

## Voluntary Conservation Planning on Nonfederal Lands

Few endangered species occur exclusively on federal lands: a number of listed species have a majority of their habitat on nonfederal land, and some listed species occur exclusively on nonfederal land. In spite of the importance of nonfederal lands to threatened and endangered species, *private landowners have neither consultation nor recovery responsibilities.* Private landowners must follow take rules for individual members of a listed species, but they do not have responsibilities for conserving the species itself, as does the federal government. No wonder Bean and Wilcove (1997, p. 1) said "conserving rare species on privately-owned land is the most challenging and politically volatile aspect of the US Endangered Species Act."

*Recognizing these difficulties, Congress adopted amendments to the ESA, starting in the mid-1980s, as a way to promote creative partnerships between public and private sectors in the interest of species and habitat conservation.* Since the 1980s, the USFWS has worked through regulations implementing the ESA to craft agreements with nonfederal landowners that preserve private property rights and state interests while enabling interested landowners to contribute to survival and recovery of threatened and endangered species. We discuss three of these agreements below: (1) Habitat Conservation Plans, (2) Safe Harbor Agreements, and (3) Candidate Conservation Agreements with Assurances.

**Habitat Conservation Plans**   Habitat Conservation Plans (HCPs) are negotiated agreements in which private landowners or state and local governments develop and commit to implementing a long-term habitat conservation program in return for federal permits allowing the *incidental take* of protected species. These are long-term agreements—at least 20 to 50 years in most cases—allowing landowners to proceed with actions on their lands without fear of prosecution for violation of the ESA take prohibitions, as long as they stay within the parameters of the HCP.

In developing their HCPs, landowners applying for incidental take permits describe measures designed to minimize and mitigate the effects of their actions on listed species. HCPs must meet four criteria: (1) take will be incidental; (2) impacts of take will be minimized and mitigated to the maximum extent practicable; (3) adequate funding must be available to implement the plan; and (4) take will not appreciably reduce the likelihood of recovery of the subject species.

Some notes about HCPs:

- Landowners can be wary about committing to long-term federal limits on their actions. On the other hand, such agreements can reduce the risk to long-term investments that may result from concern about violations of the ESA take prohibitions.

- The need to go through the NEPA process (since they are requesting a federal permit) can further complicate this decision, as it may require landowners to divulge more about their management plans to the public than they would like.

- A landowner's interest in developing an HCP can be influenced by how many individuals of the listed species exist on their property. If their property contains numerous individuals, take avoidance requirements can be very troublesome, as compared to an HCP agreement. If, on the other hand, species occurrence is rare on their property, take avoidance may be less costly to landowners than an HCP.

- Through the HCP process, the USFWS and the NMFS can provide *No Surprises* assurances to nonfederal landowners. Essentially, state and private landowners can be assured that if unforeseen circumstances arise, the USFWS or the NMFS will not require commitment of additional resources or add additional restrictions beyond the level otherwise agreed to in the HCP.

**Safe Harbor Agreements**   Safe Harbor Agreements address the conundrum in which many well-meaning forest owners may find themselves: Their forests have potential habitat for a listed species, but very few (if any) individuals of the species are currently present. The owners might like to let their forest grow until it is mature, but they do not want to fall under take restrictions if individuals of a listed species are attracted to the mature forest. Without safeguards, landowners may feel compelled to prematurely harvest their trees to avoid facing federal restrictions; Safe Harbor Agreements may help resolve this dilemma. When landowners enter into a Safe Harbor Agreement, they agree to maintain or improve the habitat of a threatened or endangered species, thereby producing a *net conservation benefit* for the species. In exchange, landowners are permitted to take individuals of the listed species attracted to the land in the future above the number of those initially present—they will not be stopped from taking actions due to the appearance of additional members of the species to their forest. In addition, a Safe Harbor Agreement may enable landowners to obtain habitat improvement funds (Box 7.3).

**Candidate Conservation Agreements with Assurances**   Candidate Conservation Agreements with Assurances (CCAAs) provide nonfederal landowners with incentives and assurances for engaging in voluntary conservation measures for *candidate species*: species meeting criteria for threatened or endangered status, but that have not yet been

---

Box 7.3  **Safe Harbor successes**

The plight of the red-cockaded woodpecker (*Picoides borealis*) in the southeastern USA provided much of the original impetus for creation of Safe Harbor Agreements. That bird was on the edge of extinction across much of the longleaf pine belt in the 1970s, and much of the potential habitat was in family forest ownership—a famously independent group of people. Safe Harbor Agreements have played an important role in convincing landowners to retain mature longleaf pine stands without fear of federal restrictions should the stands attract red-cockaded woodpeckers (Zhang & Mehmood, 2002).

The Oregon chub (*Oregonichthys crameri*) was another species in trouble where Safe Harbor Agreements made a difference. This small fish came close to disappearing from Oregon's Willamette Valley after its historic haunts of beaver ponds, oxbows, and backwaters of the Willamette River were drained and ditched to make way for farms, homes, dams, and cities. The USFWS worked with landowners to restore the complexity of the Willamette River and its back chan-

nels, creating shallow ponds and backwaters into which the USFWS reintroduced chub taken from remnant populations located elsewhere along the river. With Safe Harbor Agreements, the USFWS was able to guarantee landowners that they would not face restrictions on their actions relative to the restored chub habitats. In addition, many landowners placed these restored habitats into conservation easements, in which the private landowners were paid for the loss in value they incurred from not being able to use these lands for economic gain. Because the USFWS regards these conservation easements as a form of permanent protection, population increases on these lands were counted toward recovery goals for the chub. With these efforts, along with those of other federal agencies like the US Army Corp of Engineers, and with the help of state and local governments, the Oregon chub is back! The Oregon chub was listed as endangered in 1993, downlisted to threatened status in 2010, and in 2015 became the first fish to be delisted (USFWS, 2015)!

Box 7.4  **Candidate Conservation Agreements with Assurances (CCAAs) and the greater sage-grouse**

Many ranchers in eastern Oregon, southern Idaho, and other parts of the interior West signed CCAAs for the conservation of habitat of the greater sage-grouse (*Centrocercus urophasianus*), a species proposed for an ESA listing by the USFWS (i.e., a candidate species) (Figure 7.7). Ranchers agreed to voluntarily manage their rangelands to reduce or remove threats to the sage-grouse, such as by providing protections to core grouse habitat and removing western juniper encroaching on this habitat. In return, the ranchers received assurances that, should the species become listed under the Endangered Species Act, the landowners would not face additional regulatory requirements. Scores of landowners with ranches in the Steens Mountain of Oregon and other sage-grouse strongholds enrolled their lands in the program. By 2015, 5.5 million acres of federal and private lands were covered by CCAA commitments. In September 2015 the USFWS decided that the greater sage-grouse did not warrant listing as a threatened species, in part due to the CCAAs covering millions of acres of sage-grouse habitat (USDI, 2015).

Figure 7.7  *Greater sage-grouse.*
*(Photo credit: Pacific Southwest Region, USFWS)*

formally listed as threatened or endangered. Importantly, CCAAs provide landowners the assurance that, if they implement various conservation activities, they will not be subject to additional restrictions should the species become listed under the ESA (Box 7.4).

## The Clean Water Act

### Goals

Like the Endangered Species Act, the 1972 Clean Water Act (CWA)[24] is a substantive law that requires specific actions that are intended to result in specific outcomes, including the elimination of the discharge of pollutants into the nation's waters and the control of other sources of pollution. The Congressional Declaration of Goals and Policy of Section 101(a) of the CWA unambiguously declares, *"The objective of this Act is to restore and maintain the chemical, physical, and biological integrity of the Nation's waters."* As we shall see, eliminating the discharge of pollutants and

restoring the nation's waters has proven a daunting task and has led to the development of a complex legal framework.

### Reach of the Clean Water Act: "Waters of the United States"

The jurisdictional basis for federal regulation of the waters of the United States under the CWA arises from the Commerce Clause of the US Constitution. The Commerce Clause reserves for the federal government the power to "regulate Commerce with foreign Nations, and among the several States, and with the Indian Tribes" (US Const. art. I, § 8, cl. 3). The CWA makes numerous references to navigable waters; such waters have a clear connection to commerce and are thus subject to federal jurisdiction. The CWA further defines navigable waters as "the waters of the United States, including the territorial seas." Congress clearly intended that the CWA apply to more than just waters that are navigable in fact, but precisely defining which waters fall under federal jurisdiction has been a contentious issue.[25] Federal agencies have interpreted what constitutes "waters of the United States" quite broadly to include "waters such as intrastate lakes, rivers, streams (including intermittent streams),

24 The original 1948 federal statute controlling water pollution (P.L. 80-845, 62 Stat. 1155), the Federal Water Pollution Control Act, authorized the Surgeon General of the Public Health Service, in cooperation with other federal, state and local entities, to prepare comprehensive programs for eliminating or reducing the pollution of interstate waters and tributaries and improving the sanitary condition of surface and underground waters. The 1972 amendments to the Federal Water Pollution Control Act are what we know today as the Clean Water Act (P.L. 92-500, 86 Stat. 816 33 U.S.C. §§ 1251-1388).

25 The five conflicting opinions written by Supreme Court justices in *Rapanos v. United States*, 547 U.S. 715 (2006) attest to the contentious nature of this issue and provide an in-depth account of the many different perspectives regarding federal jurisdiction over waters of the United States. The definition cited in the next sentence comes from https://www.epa.gov/wotus-rule/about-waters-united-states, which, in turn, references 40 CFR 230.3(s).

mudflats, sandflats, 'wetlands,' sloughs, prairie potholes, wet meadows, playa lakes, or natural ponds, the use, degradation, or destruction of which would affect or could affect interstate or foreign commerce."

The definition of waters of the United States (WOTUS) is especially contested with respect to wetlands. Three major cases involving federal jurisdiction over wetlands have been decided by the US Supreme Court since 1985;[26] one was especially important for the definition of WOTUS. In the 2006 *Rapanos v. United States* (547 US 715 [2006]) decision by a divided Supreme Court, Justice Kennedy wrote an influential opinion asserting that a *significant nexus* to navigable waters must exist to demonstrate federal jurisdiction and for provisions of the CWA to apply. Since the time of the *Rapanos* decision, courts have largely applied Justice Kennedy's significant nexus standard to determine jurisdiction under the CWA (Adler, 2015). For the purposes of our discussion of the CWA, the waters of the United States includes nearly all rivers, lakes, and streams, and most wetlands, but exactly which waters fall under federal jurisdiction continues to evolve through revision of regulations, litigation, and judicial review.

## Implementing the Clean Water Act: A Joint Federal–State Responsibility

The Clean Water Act has a shared implementation and enforcement structure reflective of the federalist structure of the United States. Although the federal government reserves the right to regulate commerce, and by extension regulates the chemical, physical, and biological integrity of waters of the United States, the CWA devolves some of this responsibility to the individual states. The EPA is the lead federal agency in charge of implementing the CWA. However, state agencies, such as the Oregon Department of Environmental Quality, issue permits, set water quality standards, and enforce water quality standards, subject to EPA oversight. As a result, most states administer their own CWA programs, and we will examine this shared federal–state responsibility in the discussion here.

## Types of Water Pollution: Point vs. Nonpoint Sources

The CWA distinguishes between two types of water pollution—*point source* and *nonpoint source*—and addresses them in very different ways. In the simplest sense, point sources of pollution come from discrete sources and nonpoint sources come from diffuse sources. A typical example of point-source pollution is a pipe from a pulp factory that delivers chlorine, a byproduct of the paper bleaching process, to a river. A typical example of nonpoint-source pollution is fertilizer from farms, typically consisting of phosphorous and nitrogen, that makes its way into rivers by diffuse above- and belowground flow.

**Controlling Point-Source Pollution**    In Section 402 the Clean Water Act defines a point source as "any discernible, confined and discrete conveyance, including but not limited to any pipe, ditch, channel, tunnel, conduit, well, discrete fissure, container, rolling stock, concentrated animal feeding operation, or vessel or other floating craft, from which pollutants are or may be discharged." How does the CWA regulate point sources? It's very simple: Section 301(a) says that point sources of pollution are illegal without a National Pollution Discharge Elimination System (NPDES) permit. Thus, an NPDES permit is required when a pollutant is discharged to waters of the United States from a point source. If you plan to discharge something out of a pipe into a stream, you need an NPDES permit. There are two kinds of NPDES permits: (1) general permits, and (2) industrial permits. General permits cover activities such as stormwater permits for municipalities. Industrial permits cover activities of factories and other businesses and can be difficult to obtain, since the CWA is aimed at stopping this type of pollution.

*The Clean Water Act's NPDES permitting system has been very successful in controlling traditional point sources of pollution* (Andreen, 2013). As an example, we no longer see many pulp mills discharging chlorine into rivers of the United States. However, residual effects of that pollution, such as PCBs, dioxins, heavy metals, and pesticides at the bottoms of major rivers, continue to bedevil attempts to meet CWA objectives. For example, the Willamette River Harbor in Portland, Oregon, is listed as a Superfund Site due to residual contaminates following over a century of industrial use (EPA, 2016b).

**Identifying Point-Source Pollution: Legal Interpretations** It should be easy to determine whether a source of pollution is a point source and, hence, whether such pollution requires an NPDES permit. But this is not necessarily the case, especially in natural resources, as court decisions demonstrate.

In *Oregon Natural Desert Association v. Dombeck* 151 F.3d 945 (1998), environmental plaintiffs argued that cows pollute streams by introducing sediment into streams and therefore USFS grazing permits require an NPDES permit. The Ninth Circuit Court of Appeals ruled that the Forest Service can issue a grazing permit without requiring a permit for sedimentation that results from cattle trampling stream banks; animals are not included in the definition of a point source.

---

26 *Solid Waste Agency of Northern Cook City. v. Army Corps of Engineers*, 531 U.S. 159 (2001); *United States v. Riverside Bayview Homes, Inc.*, 474 U.S. 121 (1985); *Rapanos v. United States*, 547 U.S. 715 (2006).

In *League of Wilderness Defenders/Blue Mountains Biodiversity Project v. Forsgren* 309 F.3d 1181 (2002), the Forest Service's plan to aerially spray 700,000 acres of forest with pesticide to combat tussock moths was at issue. Plaintiffs argued that spraying from a plane was a point source and required an NPDES permit. The Ninth Circuit agreed; the pollutants (pesticides) are stored in a tank on an aircraft and expelled out of a pipe. A pipe, the court ruled, is a *discrete conveyance* and thus a point source of pollution.

An issue in the *League of Wilderness Defenders/Blue Mountains* case was a CWA regulation known as the *silviculture rule* (40 CFR 122.27), which provides an exemption to the NPDES permit requirement for silvicultural point sources that it defines as

*any discernible, confined and discrete conveyance related to rock crushing, gravel washing, log sorting, or log storage facilities, which are operated in connection with silvicultural activities and from which pollutants are discharged into waters of the United States.*

The rule also confirms that the term *silvicultural point sources* does not include

*non-point source silvicultural activities such as nursery operations, site preparation, reforestation and subsequent cultural treatment, thinning, prescribed burning, pest and fire control, harvesting operations, surface drainage, or road construction and maintenance from which there is natural runoff.*

The Forest Service argued that their aerial pesticide spraying operations were covered by the silviculture rule. The court held that aerial pesticide spraying of forests was a point source, and an NPDES permit was therefore required.

The silviculture rule resurfaced in another potentially far-reaching case concerning logging in Oregon's forests. During precipitation events, water and sediments run off of logging roads, into ditches, and (often) into a culvert, which may then carry these sediments into streams. A culvert is arguably a discrete conveyance. Is this a point source of pollution requiring a permit? Historically, logging road runoff had been regulated by the EPA as a nonpoint source and addressed through state-adopted *best management practices (BMPs)*. A lawsuit challenging this interpretation went all the way to the US Supreme Court, which reversed a lower-court ruling (*Northwest Environmental Defense Center v. Brown*, 640 F. 3d. 1063 [2011]) that runoff from logging roads is a point source of pollution, thus requiring an NPDES permit.

In the Supreme Court ruling overturning the lower court (*Decker v. Northwest Environmental Defense Center*, 133 U.S. 1326 [2013]), the court found that the EPA's interpretation that runoff is not a point source of pollution was reasonable, and deferred to the agency. However, concerns continued in the forest industry that the EPA might someday interpret logging road runoff as point-source pollution. In response, Congress inserted a brief provision into the Agricultural Act of 2014 (better known as the Farm Bill) that prohibits the EPA from requiring NPDES permits, or directly or indirectly mandating states to require permits for storm water runoff from forest roads. The Farm Bill provision thus preserves the EPA's existing policy of treating forest roads as nonpoint sources of pollution under the Clean Water Act, including the policy of addressing logging road runoff through BMPs.

To summarize our discussion about point sources: the Clean Water Act prohibits point-source pollution without a permit. Although there have been some gray areas about the definition of point sources (sediment produced by cows, pesticides sprayed from planes, and runoff from logging roads), two key points to remember are: (1) the CWA requires NPDES permits for point sources, and (2) the NPDES permit system has been effective in cleaning up pollution entering waterways from traditional point sources (Andreen, 2013).

## Controlling Nonpoint Pollution: A Watershed Approach

*Nonpoint sources of pollution have proven to be much more difficult to regulate under the Clean Water Act than point sources.* Thus nonpoint sources are a major reason why many rivers, lakes, and estuaries in the country are still not clean enough to meet basic uses such as fishing or swimming (Andreen, 2013).

What does the CWA consider a nonpoint source of pollution? Notably, the 1972 Clean Water Act does not specifically define nonpoint-source pollution, although it is discussed throughout the Act. In regulations, the EPA defines nonpoint pollution as "any source of pollution that does not meet the legal definition of 'point source' in Section 502(14) of the Clean Water Act" (EPA, 2016a). Common nonpoint-source pollutants from forestlands are sediment, temperature, and nutrients. Other nonpoint-source pollutants include pesticides, pathogens (bacteria and viruses), salts, oil, grease, toxic chemicals, and heavy metals. Beach closures, destroyed habitat, unsafe drinking water, fish kills, and many other severe environmental and human health problems result from nonpoint-source pollutants. The highly publicized water quality and habitat difficulties in Chesapeake Bay and at the mouth of the Mississippi River are caused primarily by nonpoint sources of pollution.

In addition to prohibiting the discharge of point-source pollution without an NPDES permit, the CWA in Section 303 requires individual states to control nonpoint-source pollution through a three-step approach: (1) adopt water quality standards; (2) identify waters with insufficient controls (i.e., identify waters that exceed the standards), and; (3) limit pollutant discharge into those waters so as not to exceed the water quality standards adopted for them. [27] The EPA must approve each state's findings at all three steps.

Section 303 water quality standards are based on the designated use of a waterbody, and anything that impedes the designated use of the waterbody is pollution. For example, if a designated use is salmon habitat—a common designated use in streams along the US Pacific Coast—toxic substances, water temperature, and sedimentation may constitute pollution. If a designated use is drinking water—a common designated use throughout the United States—toxic substances and sedimentation (among many other things) may constitute pollution, whereas water temperature may not. In these contexts, establishing water quality standards has two parts: (1) determining the designated use of the waterbody, and (2) setting the water quality standards, such as the maximum temperature or sediment levels that a waterbody may have and still be fit for the designated use.

Waterbodies that exceed water quality standards are commonly known as *water quality limited* or simply *303(d)* streams, after the section of the CWA that requires states to list and prioritize all waters that are determined to be water quality limited. When a stream is designated as water quality limited, the state must develop a Total Maximum Daily Load (TMDL) plan. To develop a TMDL, the state determines the maximum amount of a pollutant (e.g., thermal or sediment pollution) that a waterbody can receive and still meet state water quality standards.

The source of the pollution that is degrading the water quality can be nonpoint pollution, residual pollution from NPDES-permitted point sources or, most commonly, a combination of both point and nonpoint sources. Thus, in developing TMDLs, regulators allocate the Total Maximum Daily Load for a waterbody between point sources and nonpoint sources. The TMDL for the Willamette River in Oregon illustrates how this process works and the land uses where major improvements in stream protection are needed (Box 7.5).

While these nonpoint-source requirements under the CWA have been in effect for decades, little progress was made in developing TMDLs until environmental groups began litigating the implementation of water quality standards. All told, tens of thousands of streams in the United States will need improvement to achieve compliance with TMDL standards.

How does the EPA enforce water quality standards on nonpoint sources in water quality limited streams (streams on the 303d list)? Congress recognized that federal regulations controlling nonpoint sources of pollution would require exercising unprecedented and unwelcome federal authority over local land and water uses within individual states. Therefore, federal clean water legislation devolves responsibility for control of nonpoint-source pollution to the individual states. Through nonpoint-source management programs, individual states establish BMPs for different categories and subcategories of nonpoint-source pollution (Box 7.5). To aid in the development of BMPs, the EPA publishes guidelines for several sources of nonpoint-source pollution, one of which is forestry (USEPA, 2005). These guidelines are not themselves regulatory, but are intended to help states establish their own nonpoint-source pollution programs that best fit the different conditions and concerns unique to each state, while meeting federal clean water goals and standards. Thus, BMPs vary from state to state.

Not only are there differences in BMPs between states, the policy instruments employed to implement BMPs are different, as well. These policy instruments may be broadly classified as either voluntary, regulatory, or quasi-regulatory (Aust & Blinn, 2004). Voluntary approaches rely largely on education and incentives-based programs to engage landowners in policy-preferred actions. For example, university extension programs may provide training for landowners on BMPs for crossing streams during logging operations and cost-share agreements may subsidize replacement of inadequate road culverts. Regulatory measures for implementing BMPs make their use mandatory, such as where BMPs for logging and road building are incorporated into state forest practice rules. Quasi-regulatory approaches to BMP implementation do not directly mandate implementation of BMPs, but may lead to BMP implementation through some other regulatory means. For example, although a BMP recommending that operators avoid log-hauling during periods of heavy rain may be voluntary, activities that result in stream sedimentation may be regulated through other means.

## Fill Permits

Section 402 of the CWA carves out two exceptions to the EPA's permitting authority: "except as provided in Sections 318 and 404 of this Act." Section 318 of the CWA concerns aquaculture, which we don't discuss here; Section 404 of the CWA authorizes an entirely different permitting scheme that has garnered a great deal of attention by the courts—a scheme implemented not by the EPA or by the states but instead by the US Army Corps of Engineers, a branch of the US Army and the Department of Defense.

[27] Almost all states of the United States take the roles discussed here. Where they don't, the EPA takes a more primary role in enforcing nonpoint-source pollution.

---

Box 7.5  **Water quality restoration needs in the Willamette Valley, Oregon**

Oregon Department of Environmental Quality (DEQ) maintains a water quality assessment database of all 303(d) listed waterbodies throughout the state.* The Willamette River is one such waterbody. The DEQ determined that the Willamette River does not meet water quality standards for the following three pollutants: temperature, mercury, and bacteria. TMDL allocations for the Willamette River Basin were established by the DEQ for each of these pollutants in 2006. For temperature, the load allocation to nonpoint sources is 91%; that is, the DEQ determined that 91% of the thermal pollution in the Willamette River comes from nonpoint sources and that 9% of the thermal pollution is attributable to point sources. For mercury, the load allocation to nonpoint sources is 27% and for bacteria the load allocation to nonpoint sources is from 80% to 94%, depending on sub-basin (Oregon DEQ, 2014).

The NPDES permitting process effectively deals with the point-source component of the Total Maximum Daily Load, but in the Willamette River most thermal pollution is attributed to nonpoint sources. How, then, does the state achieve the temperature standard it set for the Willamette River? With respect to Oregon forestry operations, compliance is accomplished through incorporation of state recommended BMPs into the regulatory requirements of the Oregon Forest Practices Rules and through voluntary and incentive-based measures of the Oregon Plan for Salmon and Watersheds.

Control of nonpoint-source pollution from agricultural lands is, by comparison, much less stringent. Other than Oregon's Forest Practices Rules, implementation of TMDL standards in Oregon are often limited

to the regulation of land use (rather than practices) and to educational, voluntary, and incentive programs. For many reasons, including the lack of enforcement mechanisms and the nature of agricultural crops (e.g., unlike trees, agricultural crops seldom provide shade to streams), agricultural areas within the Willamette Valley have the greatest restoration needs: restoration of functioning riparian areas in agricultural areas would provide the most benefit for improving (lowering) stream temperatures (Figure 7.8).

---

* The database is accessible to the public on the DEQ website: http://www.deq.state.or.us/wq/assessment/rpt2012/search.asp

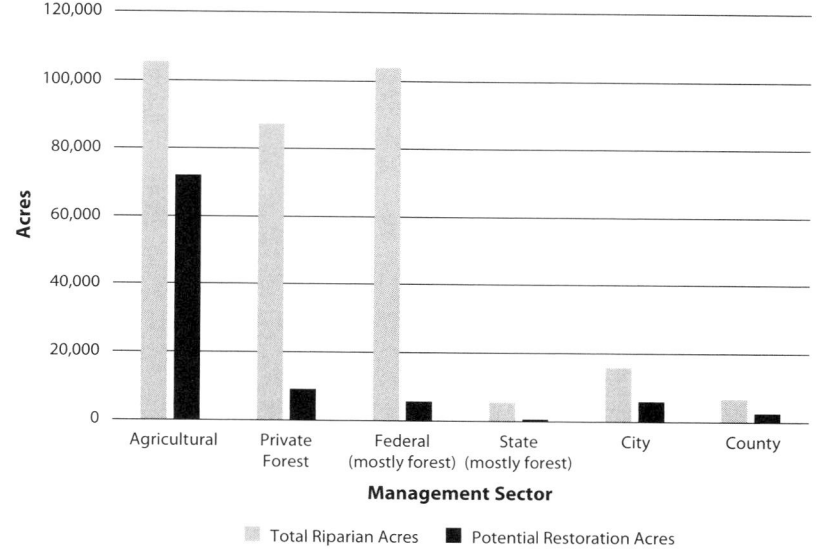

Figure 7.8  *Riparian restoration needs in the Willamette Valley by land use category. Planting trees, in part to restore shade, would be the most widespread restoration activity. (Source: Based on data from DEQ, 2010)*

---

Section 404(a) of the CWA provides that: "The Secretary of the Army, acting through the Chief of Engineers, may issue permits, after notice and opportunity for public hearings for the discharge of dredged or fill material into the navigable waters at specified disposal sites." Thus discharges of pollutants (which include dredged spoil, sand, and rock) are regulated by the EPA, but a subset of pollutant discharges—discharges of "dredged or fill material into the navigable waters at specified disposal sites"—are regulated, instead, by the Army Corps of Engineers, giving the Corps a major role in controlling the placement of fill material into wetlands as people and companies develop low-lying land. Cases involving Section 404 of the CWA have played a major role in defining federal jurisdiction over waters of the United States.

## Implications of US Federal Environmental Laws for Ecological Forestry

We have examined three federal environment laws in the chapter: (1) National Environmental Policy Act (NEPA), (2) Endangered Species Act (ESA), and (3) Clean Water Act (CWA). These federal environmental laws, and others, like the Clear Air Act, create a legal framework for the application of ecological forestry.[28] As such, these laws may both encourage and limit its application.

---

28 We will discuss one other federal environmental law, the National Forest Management Act, in Chapter 20 when we cover planning the future of the national forests.

Although NEPA, as implemented, is largely a procedural act, on-the-ground practices that emulate ecological processes, such as those of ecological forestry, are consistent with the declaration of national environmental policy described in Section 101 of NEPA, which Congress directs federal agencies to follow "to the fullest extent possible." In addition, NEPA requirements to divulge the environmental consequences of actions to the public may result in a call for actions more consistent with ecological processes.

Among the federal laws discussed here, the ESA potentially has the greatest influence on the use of ecological forestry. While NEPA applies to federal actions and has been interpreted by the courts as largely a procedural law, the ESA applies to everyone and has substantive requirements that can affect forestry practices across all ownerships. In addition to the protections for individuals of federally listed threatened and endangered species, the ESA applies to the ecosystems on which these species depend—the habitats that forestry affects through harvest and other management actions.

Federal agencies, such as the US Forest Service, have a special responsibility to recover listed species and to consult with the appropriate regulatory agency about potential impacts on listed species before taking action. Thus, attempts to maintain and restore ecosystem processes and structures—a logical outcome of the statutory requirement to recover listed species—can lead directly to the call for the use of ecological forestry on federal lands where trees are to be cut. As an example, the *Revised Recovery Plan for the Northern Spotted Owl* calls for the use of ecological forestry on federal lands throughout its range (USFWS, 2011).

The listing of a forest species as threatened or endangered may lead to curtailing forestry activities on federal lands, through including ecological forestry, because of the threat that any short-term loss of habitat may pose to a species' survival. Actions may thus be limited even if long-term ecosystem benefits would occur from the action. With a species on the brink, extreme caution must be exercised.

The application of the ESA to nonfederal actions is more complicated, for a number of reasons. First, unlike federal actions[29] that require consultation and assistance of recovery, nonfederal actions are only legally required to comply with take guidelines. Second, such actions are undertaken by thousands of nonfederal forest landowners and managers, including family forest owners and managers. Third, the United States has a long history and tradition of valuing private property rights. Given these considerations, the USFWS has developed, and continues to develop, different types of voluntary agreements with private landowners—such as the Safe Harbor Agreements that have proven crucial to the survival of species like the red-cockaded woodpecker—policies that encourage landowners to voluntarily undertake practices favorable to the recovery of species and the ecosystems on which they depend. By and large, only a modest amount modification of private forest practices to help recover listed species has thus far taken place across the United States; perhaps the use of ecological forestry in species recovery instruments, such as Safe Harbor Agreements, Habitat Conservation Plans, and Candidate Conservation Agreements, will become an important component in modifying private forest practices to benefit

29 Federal actions include the granting of federal permits, federal licenses, or federal funding to state, local, and private parties.

listed species in the future. Achieving these modifications represents the greatest challenge of the ESA, especially with so many at-risk species found primarily on private lands.

Although state-owned forests have the same requirements as private forests with respect to the ESA, managers of state forests may recognize recovery responsibilities more readily than their private counterparts. First, state-owned forests often must comply with state laws and policies that recognize a commitment to biodiversity in general, and to species at risk in particular—this may include a state endangered species act. Second, public forestlands are generally much more in the public eye than are private forests. Thus, a number of states, such as Washington, have either developed HCPs for their lands or otherwise modified their management to conserve and restore the ecosystems on which listed species depend. These agreements and modifications often commit state forest managers to ecological forestry practices.

The CWA is a substantive act that applies to everyone. It calls for restoration of the chemical, physical, and biological integrity of the nation's waters that is similar in some respects to the commitment of the ESA to conserve the ecosystems on which listed species depend. The effects of the CWA on forestry practices are more diffuse than the effects of the ESA, however. Whereas the ESA focuses on specific requirements for individual species (and on individuals of those species), the CWA broadly addresses water quality across entire watersheds, typically through nonpoint pollution standards.

On state and private lands, these standards are administered by the states, and, unless standards are rolled into other laws or regulations, the implementation of nonpoint-source pollution standards is often in the form of suggested BMPs or other voluntary measures. Incorporating elements of ecological forestry into BMPs may lead to greater fulfillment of CWA goals than conventional forestry practices.

On federal lands, the EPA can comment on proposed actions through the NEPA process, which become part of the public record. That process can put a spotlight on a proposed federal action the EPA believes violates the CWA before the action is taken, offering the possibility of litigation by citizens and groups and creating a powerful force for adherence to the CWA. It also creates a strong force for adoption of ecological forestry practices that can help address EPA concerns.

*You can't stay in your corner of the Forest waiting for others to come to you. You have to go to them sometimes.* — A. A. MILNE, *WINNIE-THE-POOH*

# CHAPTER 8

# Resolving Forestry Conflicts through Collaboration

## Negotiation: An Essential Element of Modern Forest Management

Life involves lots of bargaining and negotiation. You negotiate the terms of your employment and the price of a house or car. If you have children, you probably negotiate what time the little ones go to bed and what seems like a thousand other things. Forestry is no exception—negotiation is an important part of a forester's professional life.

For foresters, at least, it was not always that way. In the middle of the 20th century, when the senior authors of this book started their careers, foresters in the United States were at the top of their game—they were in charge of forests and the destiny of forestlands. With a decline in public confidence of foresters to act in society's interests, though, many other groups and individuals began to demand a place at the decision-making table (Box 8.1). *More broadly, decentralized and collaborative decision making has become increasingly prominent in a number of environmental policy contexts,* for many reasons, including (Koontz et al., 2004; Weber, 2003):

- A public that is fed-up with top-down *command-and-control* management;

- The resurgence of an ethic of civic engagement and responsibility nationally;

- A recognized need for greater accountability to a broader array of stakeholder interests;

- The need for alternatives to adversarial approaches to decision making and a way to move past gridlock, conflict, and polarization among stakeholder interests; and

- Declining federal budgets that have reduced the ability of federal agencies to accomplish their objectives.

In general, the notion of shared decision making is more the norm than the exception in forestry. While the participants in the negotiation may vary between federal, state, and

*Stakeholders on a field tour, Flathead National Forest. (Courtesy of Sustainable Northwest)*

private forestry, the central idea that foresters are no longer an omnipotent force free to do what they think is best seems here to stay. This is certainly the case in federal forestry, and is often the case in state and private forestry, too.

## Federal Forestry

As discussed in Chapter 6, the National Environmental Policy Act of 1969 (NEPA)—the first major federal environmental law in the United States—signaled the end of unlimited discretion by federal foresters to make decisions about public lands and resources without first consulting others. NEPA requires that environmental values be considered by an interdisciplinary team when designing federal actions that may significantly affect the quality of the environment and that the public have an opportunity to comment on these proposals. In addition, the appeal and objection process that has grown up around federal forestry invites negotiated settlements with individuals or groups that are unhappy with decisions, as does the litigation that may follow an unresolved complaint.

The Endangered Species Act (ESA), passed in 1973, requires that land management agencies consult with regulatory agencies responsible for the Act's administration (the US Fish and Wildlife Service and the National Marine Fisheries Service) to make sure proposed actions do not jeopardize species listed as threatened or endangered. In addition, the potential for citizen suits against regulatory agencies

---

**Box 8.1  Federal forestry in 1968: Omnipotent foresters in a democratic society**

Norm Johnson arrived in Corvallis, Oregon, in the fall of 1968 to begin graduate studies at Oregon State University. With his interest in forest management planning, he thought it would be useful to obtain the forest management plan for the Siuslaw National Forest—the national forest in the Coast Range immediately west of Corvallis that (at the time) had one of the highest harvest levels of any national forest in the Pacific Northwest. To obtain the management plan, he went over to the forest headquarters, also in Corvallis. The person at the main desk sent him to see the timber management officer, who responded abruptly to Norm's request, "Why do you need that?" They normally did not give it to just anyone. Upon realizing he was dealing with another forester, though, the officer quickly provided a copy and made himself available to explain it.

This brief document, about 50 pages, carefully followed the requirements set up by the Forest Service for such plans: (1) Describe the timber inventory and harvest history; (2) Explain how the forest would be moved to a regulated condition; and (3) Estimate the resulting allowable cut for the next decade and beyond. The document was efficient and sparse, without many complications or concerns except that the high level of red alder in some stands would lower conifer yield. No NEPA process. No endangered species considerations. No review by other agencies. No public comment. No collaboration groups. Foresters did what they knew to be right using time-tested formulas they had learned on the job or in school.

Professional education traditionally provided young foresters with an enormous amount of technical information and problem-solving skills, along with tenets of faith that focused on sustained wood production, as described in Chapter 1, and the planning frameworks described in Chapter 17. Foresters are a proud and independent lot, and it should not be surprising that they believed they had the answers—the knowledge, technical skill, strategies, and tactics necessary to solve any problems that came their way, without the guidance (or interference) of nonforesters, including the public.

The problem this approach presents in a democratic society such as the United States, especially on the national forests, was captured eloquently in the *The Myth of the Omnipotent Forester* (Behan, 1966), and revisited by Luckert (2006). One of the main messages of Behan's article was many foresters misunderstood the role society wished them to play in managing these forests. Although foresters may have seen themselves as being in control of publicly owned forests, the public had other ideas and viewed foresters as public representatives managing a public resource. Behan (1966, p. 399) describes how the European roots of forestry established foresters as an esteemed profession with "an almost holy resource to be managed by an almost holy man, the forester." This view of forestry did not fit well in the United States, where, according to Behan (1966, p. 399), "we imported a professional ethic inconsistent with our sociology and an attitude inconsistent with our politics, which denied professional arbitration." Behan continues:

*The public surged into the forest with camping trailers, fishing rods, rifles and skis, and there encountered a little-known and long-ignored dweller in the woods, the professional forester. Never again would forestry and foresters go unnoticed, but the attention carried with it a warning: the respect and confidence of the public from forestry's days of obscure custodianship would not fare well in this new age of conspicuous management.* (Behan, 1966, p. 400)

A fundamental point of Behan's article, and of Luckert's subsequent analysis is that the role of professional foresters in the United States is not to tell the public how best to manage public forests, but rather to manage them according to society's wishes, as best as they can be determined. Within the legal framework we described in Chapters 6 and 7, the determination of society's wishes increasingly occurs through collaborative processes.

when stakeholders are dissatisfied with the actions that agencies approve creates a fertile environment for negotiation to achieve out-of-court settlements.

*Collaboration*, a particular form of negotiation, has emerged as a mechanism for people and groups to develop projects, plans, or policies jointly. Much of this effort started as bottom-up or *grassroots* collaboration: Parties to a dispute organize themselves to work through the conflict without being required to do so. We have seen an explosion of this form of negotiation on federal forests in the United States, and we will use examples of grassroots collaboration throughout this chapter. Recognizing the value of this approach, the US Forest Service emphasized the importance of public engagement and collaboration in the 2012 regulations implementing the National Forest Management Act (USDA, 2012).[1]

Efforts to collaborate, as a way to make decisions about natural resources, cover a much broader spectrum than the national forests, however. An example is the National Cohesive Fire Strategy (USDA-USDI, 2014), which attempts to bring all landowners and stakeholders together to develop a comprehensive strategy that addresses wildland fire management across all lands in the United States.

## Private, State, and Tribal Forestry

Negotiation is also often the watchword for private, state, and tribal forestry, although it may occur more under different circumstances and in different contexts than on federal forests. Private- and state-lands foresters frequently must negotiate with neighbors, conservation groups, enforcers of state forest practice laws, and certifiers of *green* forestry. In addition, the actions of foresters in forest industry have increasingly come under internal scrutiny by corporate financial analysts as firms strive to become more efficient and competitive.

Family forest management can be a continuous negotiation process among siblings and between generations as family members sort out their different interests and perspectives on forest ownership. This negotiation can become especially emotional and contentious when siblings inherit forests from their parents; such negotiations can determine whether the family continues to hold the property or sells out and moves on.

Historically, forest management on Indian Reservations in the United States was governed by the commercial forest focus of federal foresters working for the Bureau of Indian Affairs. With the ascent of tribal autonomy and vision as the guide to forest management on reservations, negotiation among tribal members and tribal governments has become commonplace.

In sum, negotiation principles and skills are as integral to successful forest management as the forest measurement and planning tools learned on the job and taught in school. Thus, foresters need to master negotiation skills as well.

*In this chapter, we first review principles of mutual gains negotiation as the foundation of what we call collaboration— a process whereby people who might otherwise be adversaries develop solutions that simultaneously advance their differing interests.* We then provide some advice on thinking through the best alternative to a negotiated settlement and how that bounds the negotiation space. Next, we provide insights on effective collaboration from two decades of experience by both practitioners and researchers, emphasizing social learning. Finally, we provide suggestions for forest managers who work with collaboration groups, and discuss the concepts of trust and trust building as foundational elements in successful collaboration.

## The Many Forms of Collaboration

Throughout the world, groups of people are addressing complex environmental management problems through collaborative planning and management processes. Collaboration involves stakeholders and the public in a process of consensus building to address some of the most difficult environmental management problems facing society today (Margerum, 2008). As described by Margerum (2008), the literature on collaboration highlights several common characteristics of these collaborative efforts:

- Collaboration involves a wide range of stakeholders representing a cross-section of organizations, interest groups, and people with a stake in the outcome (Healey, 1997; Innes & Booher, 1999).

- Collaboration engages the participants in an intensive and creative process of consensus building (Fisher, Ury, & Patton, 2011; Wondolleck & Yaffee, 2000), which can lead to more creative solutions and increased likelihood of acceptance (Innes & Booher, 1999; Weber, 2003).

- Collaboration works to achieve consensus on problems, goals, and proposed actions (Innes & Booher, 1999; Weber, 2003; Wondolleck & Yaffee, 2000).

- Collaboration often requires a sustained commitment to problem solving (Selin & Chavez, 1995; Weber, 2003).

It is becoming increasingly clear that collaborative approaches to decision making can address ecological, social, and economic issues in ways that traditional public and private processes cannot (Moote, Jakes, & Cheng, 2005; Charnley, Long, & Lake, 2014) including:

- Sustaining broad-based participation and support;

---

1 See Chapter 20 for a detailed discussion of the 2012 planning rule.

- Integrating multiple forms of knowledge and information to define problems and potential solutions; and

- Combining human, financial, and technical resources in new ways.

Collaboration can take many forms:

- Collaboration can involve large or small numbers of people; however, collaboration usually involves at least one and often more face-to-face meetings. Sociologists have long recognized that large groups can be unwieldy and do not always function very well. Many successful collaborative groups involve meetings of less than 24 people; as few as two or three people can collaborate. The size of the collaboration is often determined by how many stakeholders care about the conflict, but sometimes membership is limited.

- Collaboration can be informal, with people meeting around a table at a bar, or it can be very formal, with complex rules and procedures for meetings, communication, and decision making.

- Collaboration can involve individuals who represent only themselves, or it may involve groups represented by one or more people. Often collaborative efforts involve a mix of individuals and groups.

- Collaboration can have a fixed life span, or it may be ongoing.

- Collaboration can tackle big problems or small problems, be narrowly focused or have a broad mandate. Often a collaborative effort will start small and tackle relatively easy problems, and then expand over time as collaborative members gain confidence and trust in each other, as we discuss later in this chapter.

- Collaborations may use a neutral third party to facilitate the collaboration process, or they may "go it alone."

*Margerum (2008) developed a useful topology of collaboratives* from his study of 36 collaboratives in the United States and in Australia. He recognized three kinds of collaboratives—action (operational), organizational, and policy—based on work by Ostrom (1986), and Gregg, Born, Lord, and Waterstone (1991)—and gave an example of each:

- *Action (operational) collaboratives, which focus on direct action or "on the ground" activities, such as monitoring, education, and restoration.* An example of this form of collaborative is the Long Tom Watershed Council in Oregon, a locally initiated community-based collaborative, established to improve water quality and fish habitat that works directly with landowners to restore wetlands

and riparian corridors. Members include local stakeholders, such as farmers, rural and urban residents, timber companies, local environmentalists, and field staff of natural resource agencies.

- *Organizational collaboratives, which focus on the policies and programs of organizations.* One example is the collaborative effort to manage the Trinity Inlet in North Queensland, Australia, a small estuary along a vast coastline. The ecological importance of the fishery combined with the economic importance of the Great Barrier Reef tourist traffic resulted in a process with high-level agency involvement to develop a management plan. Members of the Trinity Inlet Management Plan Committee include the local mayor, chair of the Port Authority, local parliamentary members, and chair of the Citizens Advisory Committee.

- *Policy collaboratives, which focus on governmental legislation, policies, and rules, such as the San Francisco Estuary Partnership in California.* This collaborative engaged a wide range of interest groups, local governmental entities, and federal and state agencies to develop new policies for management of the estuary, which could require new institutions or new legislation. Members include the US Environmental Protection Agency, Citizens for a Better Environment, Association of California Water Users, and the California Department of Water Resources.

Margerum (2008) summarizes some contextual characteristics of different types of collaboratives:

- *Participants*: Action collaborative participants are more likely to be individuals or represent local groups while management and policy collaborative participants are more likely to represent regional or national organizations.

- *Scale*: Action collaboratives tend to concentrate on local, small-scale issues while collaboratives at the policy end of the spectrum are more likely to address large-scale issues.

- *Institutional complexity*: The number of jurisdictions, organizations, and interest groups involved tends to increase as you move across the spectrum from action to policy collaboratives.

*In this chapter, we emphasize local action collaboratives, as they are the form of collaborative with which stakeholders and professional resource managers are most likely to be involved* (Figure 8.1). The principles covered here may also be useful in the other organizational and policy collaboratives, but these other collaborative types tend to

1. *People:* Negotiate as if relationships matter; separate the people from the problem.

2. *Interests:* Focus on underlying interests, not positions.

3. *Options:* Invent multiple options for mutual gain.

4. *Criteria:* Use objective criteria to evaluate outcomes.

We review each of these principles in some detail below. They are often used in successful negotiations whether those involved know it or not (Box 8.2).

## People

**Negotiate as if Relationships Matter**    Most forestry negotiations take place in the context of an ongoing relationship. Generally, the participants want to be sure that they do not damage that relationship. In addition, it is important to remember that negotiators (including you) are people first, with fears, emotions, and deeply held values. We bring all this to the table, and need to figure out how to work through all of these issues to get to the underlying resource problems. This human aspect of negotiation can be either helpful or disastrous.

Every negotiator in a collaboration has two kinds of interests: the substance and the relationship. As for relationships, you need to maintain a working relationship good enough to produce an acceptable agreement, if one is possible. Usually more than this is at stake, however; most negotiations take place in the context of an ongoing relationship you do not wish to damage. Ongoing relationships are often far more important than the outcome of any particular negotiation.

Natural resource conflicts are so contentious because people are so deeply invested in their outcomes. People who are invested do not go away. Most likely, you will have to deal with them again.

In addition, the parties in these natural resource negotiations tend to have a degree of dependence on one another. What do we mean by dependence? In the simplest form, dependence means that a party needs something from the other party to achieve its objectives. Parties can be dependent on one another by virtue of their ability to deny something to another party, or by virtue of their ability to give another party something. Dependence by virtue of one party being able to prevent or forestall action by another party is very common in environmental conflict. The very nature of the structure of natural resource laws and policies—indeed, the system of governance in the United States—creates a large degree of dependence among parties to environmental conflict, typically the ability to deny something to another party.

We teach integrative negotiating strategies because they best account for dependency relationships that typify

Figure 8.1 *Tim Lillebo, a crucial member of many collaboratives in eastern Oregon representing Oregon Wild, speaking at the Glaze Forest Restoration Project.*

have a more formal process and structure. For a detailed discussion on how they function, see Heikkila and Gerlak (2005).

## Collaboration: A Mutual Gains Approach

Many books on collaboration and negotiation use the mutual gains framework presented in the book *Getting to Yes*, written by Roger Fisher, William Ury, and Bruce Patton (Fisher et al., 2011). This brief, influential book has become required reading in business schools, military academies, and universities. We incorporate the principles from *Getting to Yes* into our approach to collaboration and highly recommend these principles as an effective approach to help resolve conflict through people working together on difficult problems to find mutual gains.

The authors of *Getting to Yes* offer four types of principles for mutual gains negotiation that they call Negotiation on the Merits:

natural resource conflicts. As an example, consider the Klamath Basin water management conflict in southern Oregon and northern California. The dispute is fundamentally about the distribution of water between farms, pastures, endangered fish species, and tribal needs. It came to a head in 2001, when irrigation water for crops was shut off to provide adequate instream water flows for endangered species. Advocates for each side in the conflict have powerful legal and political tools at their disposal. Because different interests could block the goals and aspirations of other interests, these parties share a high degree of dependence, and because of this dependence, parties who have been adversaries in the past—conservationists, farmers, ranchers, and Native American tribes—have negotiated, and may continue to negotiate, agreements to share the water and other resources in the Klamath Basin.

**Separate the People from the Problem**   Fisher et al. (2011) stress that destructive human interactions can overwhelm negotiations, especially at the beginning, making getting to the substance of the problem nearly impossible. Further, understanding how people think about the problem is a key to solving it. To help address these issues, they recommend focusing on perception, communication, and emotion:

---

**Box 8.2  Farmers and wildlife officials work out their differences in the Yachats River Valley**

In the mid-1980s, the Oregon governor's office asked Norm Johnson to negotiate a disagreement between farmers in the valleys along the Yachats River in coastal Oregon and the Oregon Department of Fish and Wildlife. The management of elk was at the heart of the disagreement. Rather than feed in an area set up as an elk refuge, elk tended to congregate on the farmers' pastures and eat grasses that would otherwise go to the farmers' cattle. Moreover, sightseers would park in driveways along the road to view the elk, creating a nuisance to local residents. To make matters worse, some hunters had begun shooting at the elk in the farmers' fields from the road, a practice that is illegal in Oregon and a nuisance and hazard to local residents. The dispute had deteriorated into insults and name-calling between the farmers and the ODFW professionals.

Norm showed up a local ODFW office at 9:00 A.M. where the meeting was held and walked into a room with about 10 people (half farmers and half ODFW) and almost total silence—the anger on both sides was palpable. He had been chosen by the governor's office to negotiate an agreement largely because he knew nothing about the issue, and knew none of the people involved in the dispute—thus he could be considered a neutral source, as long as he did not appear to take sides.

Since Norm really did not know anything about the issue, he innocently asked what the problem was that brought us all together. Out poured complaints from the farmers along with occasional rejoinders from the ODFW personnel. Near as Norm could tell, the position of the farmers was that the ODFW people were incompetent and should be fired. The position of the ODFW people was that the farmers were irrational. Not a promising beginning.

After about an hour of claims and rejoinders by the two sides, Norm began to assert himself by asking a number of questions that turned the discussion away from personal attacks to something the two sides could deal with. He asked the farmers whether they wanted the elk totally off their pastures. No, they said. They love the elk and want to see them, but they wished the elk would also use the refuge, that hunt-ers would not shoot at them when they were in the farmers' pastures, and that the people who wanted to view them would park elsewhere.

Norm asked why the elk did not feed on the refuge. The farmers immediately said that the grasses on the refuge were rank and unpalatable due to lack of use or maintenance; the elk liked the young grasses of the farmers' pastures associated with cattle grazing. One of the ODFW people spoke up at that point and admitted that they had an agreement with a person in the area to mow the refuge but that he had not done it for the last few years. One of the farmers said that he knew him and that the fellow was too old and infirm to do the mowing anymore. Someone from ODFW then said that ODFW was paying him to do the mowing and could pay someone else, too. One of the farmers said he would mow the field, and all agreed that mowing would lure the elk back to the refuge for at least part of their feeding. Now they were getting somewhere!

Next, they turned to compensating the farmers somehow for the elk that still would graze on their property. One of the ODFW people asked whether the farmers knew of the **green forage** program whereby ODFW would provide fertilizer to farmers as compensation for elk eating their grasses. The farmers said they did not know about it and they would be interested in obtaining that fertilizer. The two sides were on a roll!

On to the parking problem. ODFW acknowledged that sightseers could use public areas along the main road, but ODFW had not maintained or signed them, so people did not realize they could park there. ODFW said they would fix that. This problem-solving mood was working!

Finally, they turned to the problem of hunters shooting elk illegally in the farmers' pastures. ODFW said they would send a patrol up there more regularly. By 3:00 P.M. they were done. The very next day, ODFW began fixing the parking lots. More importantly, the farmers and ODFW had the beginning of a collaborative relationship.

Without knowing it, they had used many of the principles from *Getting to Yes* (Fisher et al., 2011), and they had worked!

*Perception (understanding their thinking)*

- Put yourself in their shoes.

- Do not deduce their intentions from your fears.

- Discuss each other's perceptions and look for chances to act differently from their perceptions of you.

*Communication*

- Listen actively and acknowledge what is being said.

- Ask questions to confirm you understand.

- Speak to be understood, and speak about yourself, not about them.

*Emotion*

- Recognize and understand emotions—theirs and yours.

- Make emotions explicit and acknowledge them as legitimate.

- Create vehicles for allowing everyone to let off steam.

- Don't react in kind to emotional outbursts.

In the formative days of a collaborative, the group's future might have hung by a thread, requiring creative efforts to get everyone over emotional rough spots. Consider these simple suggestions:

- Use meeting rooms with windows (to avoid a feeling of being trapped) and comfortable chairs.

- Serve healthy food. Sugary and salty foods (e.g., cookies, candy, pretzels) create temporary euphoria and a burst of energy, followed by a physiological and psychological crash— mood swings. Foods that are low in fat and sugar and that contain complex carbohydrates are fuel for successful collaborations. Think wheat bread, cheese, nuts, and fruit.

- Invite a friendly dog to meetings. It is hard to stay mad when petting a friendly Labrador.

- Be sure there is a nearby venue where informal conversations can continue after the formal meetings end (e.g., the local bar).

Out of such small things, great actions may grow!

## Interests

*Positions are points of view we decide are important. Interests are the reasons behind our decisions.* Often, parties to a negotiation state positions, while interests remain unstated. Positions tend to reflect interests, but interests and positions are generally not synonymous.

Parties to a negotiation may become fixated on their positions and forget their underlying interests, or they may confuse their positions (what they say they want) with their interests (what they really need). We see this all the time when discussions turn into arguments: Something someone says strikes us as very unreasonable and the person refuses to retract his or her statement or back down from his or her stated position. We then forget all about the original topic of conversation and fixate on what the other person has said. Positions have a way of taking over a dialog.

**Approaches to Discovering Interests**    How do you get beyond positions and discover someone's interests? Here are four suggestions:

- Focus on what the other party is saying, and ask questions to test your understanding of their position.

- Gently investigate why they have that position as you attempt to surface their interests.

- Think through what interests might lead to their position as if the position was yours.

- Research past speeches or writings of the parties you will be working with for clues about interests that underlie their position.

Usually people are forthcoming about their positions. Figuring out someone's interest often takes some effort.

**Interests Are Often Easier to Reconcile**    *In many cases, interests are easier to reconcile than are positions.* For example, the two positions in Pair 1 of Table 8.1 appear to be mutually exclusive. You are either for or against building nuclear power plants—you cannot adopt both positions. However, once you understand the interests that underlie these positions, you realize you could potentially come to an agreement about energy development. The positions are mutually exclusive, but the interests are not. Look at Pair 2 and Pair 3 and think about how the people involved might be able to reach agreement once they move from positions to interests. It is more common than you might think for people who apparently have contradictory positions to come to an agreement, once they get past their positions and understand the interests that lie behind them.

Pair 4 of Table 8.1 is somewhat different from the previous examples. In this last set, the interests may be largely incompatible, and collaboration may not resolve the conflicting interests.

It is critically important to move beyond positions and learn about the other party's interests, as well as your own. This tells you whether the mutual gains bargaining approach stands a good chance of success and gives you an idea of what sorts of agreements might be reached to satisfy each party's interests. Learning about interests is a prerequisite to inventing options for mutual gains.

**Positions Have Value Too**   Understanding positions can be useful too. Provis (1996, pp. 312–313) notes:

> *Because of their open, explicit nature, positions perform functions that interests cannot. Explicit, concrete positions allow parties to make explicit and recognizable concessions. Since interests are more general and abstract, interest-based concessions may be difficult to recognize. In situations of limited trust or knowledge, parties may be reluctant to reveal their basic interests. Furthermore, positions serve to communicate interests. It is frequently not possible to discern what [the parties'] interests are except through attending to parties' positions.*

Provis suggests that negotiation is a journey—you start with positions and work toward interests.

Table 8.1 *Pairs of positions and interests*

|  | Position | Interest |
|---|---|---|
| **Pair 1** | We want the US to build more nuclear power plants. | We want to develop sources of energy that do not contribute to global warming. |
|  | We do not want the US to build more nuclear power plants. | We want to make sure nuclear waste is stored safely. |
| **Pair 2** | I will not support any timber sale that logs trees greater than 16″ in diameter. | I care for old-growth trees and the wildlife species they support. |
|  | I will not accept any diameter limit on logging. | I need to have access to a diverse supply of timber for my mill. |
| **Pair 3** | I oppose all proposed timber sales on the Coos Bay BLM district. | The sales in question are in my favorite mushroom hunting areas. |
|  | I demand the northern spotted owl be taken off the Endangered Species Act list. | I am worried about losing my job at the mill in Coos Bay. |
| **Pair 4** | I am against the White Castle timber sale. | I believe that it is wrong to have commercial harvest of trees on federal forests. |
|  | I demand that the White Castle timber sale go forward. | Federal harvests are an essential source of wood supply for my mill. |

## Options

*The identification of options that provide mutual gains is the heart of collaboration.* The process of identifying mutual gain options is part science and part art. We will suggest some concepts and approaches that might help make the quest for these win-win solutions a little easier, but you should recognize that they will take you only part of the way—the rest is up to you!

**Five Tactics for Achieving Mutual Gains**   Let us start with five time-honored tactics for achieving mutual gains:

*Expanding the pie:* Redefine the issues in the conflict so that more material is negotiable. The parties move from an *either-or* (zero-sum) to a *both-and* (variable-sum) perspective. Expanding the pie generally means adding more resources to the negotiation. As an example, many restoration agreements on federal forests include requests for increased budgets to underwrite the restoration activities that were a key to settlement.

*Log rolling:* Simultaneously discuss more than one conflict and, assuming priorities differ, the parties trade-off these issues so that parties each get their top priority accounted for. Example: On a national forest in Oregon,

two fires occurred within a single year—one in a roaded area and one in a roadless area. In exchange for leaving the roadless area alone, local environmental groups agreed not to protest salvage logging in parts of the roaded area (see Blue Mountains Forest Partners example, Box 8.3).

*Bridging:* Invent new means to meet each other's interests. This typically involves fundamentally reorienting the parties' positions. Example: In the early 1990s, a number of new federal forest plans in the dry forests of California and Oregon called for clearcutting degraded forest stands across large areas, and local environmental groups successfully stopped plan implementation in many places. Some of these groups came to realize that a buildup of stand densities in those stands would threaten forest sustainability over time; moreover, many group members had relatives or friends that worked in the timber industry. The forest industry, while viewing clearcutting as the most efficient wood production strategy, realized that with continued protest their chances were slim of obtaining a stable timber supply from a clearcutting management strategy. In a number of places, and after much discussion, the warring groups settled on a partial cutting strategy focused on reducing fuel loads and stand densities in ways that would provide some commercial timber.

*Fractionating the conflict:* Breaking up complex issues into smaller manageable chunks. Example: Reaching agreement on how to manage a national forest covering millions of acres is understandably difficult. However, you may be able to reach agreement on how to proceed on a particular restoration project and expand your efforts from there.

*Starting with the low-hanging fruit:* Begin with fairly noncontroversial projects where agreement looks promising. As Ansell and Gash (2008) and Shindler et al. (2014) point out, these *small wins* deepen trust, commitment, and shared understanding. We will come back to this approach when we discuss approaches to *deepening trust* at the end of this chapter.

It is difficult to expand the pie; logroll, bridge, or fractionate the conflict; or pick the low hanging fruit unless you move beyond positions and understand interests. Using the example of salvage logging from above, a logging company's position may be that they want to salvage log both areas that burned, but their interest as a company is much broader and encompasses their profitability and legal profile. The environmental group's position may be to protect all areas from salvage, but their interest is also much broader, encompassing long-term sustainability, biodiversity, and the protection of existing forest resources.

**Improving Your Chances for Inventing Options** People often believe they have the right answer and that their view should prevail. As valuable as new options can be to settling disputes, Fisher et al. (2011) point out that people involved in a negotiation may not sense a need for them. Why don't people back down from their positions and suggest mutual gains options for settling the dispute? Assumptions of a fixed pie (a zero-sum game) and concerns over immediate rejection can limit willingness to brainstorm novel options. Perhaps most importantly, they may think being open to new options undermines their bargaining position, and that suggesting a different course of action will cause them to be perceived as soft and uncommitted to their stated position.

How can you help groups be amenable to the important task of inventing creative options? Fundamentally, you should strive to provide an environment in which people feel comfortable thinking creatively. Here are few ideas from the experts (Fisher et al., 2011; Ury, 1993; Wondolleck, 1988):

- Separate the act of inventing options (brainstorming) from the act of judging them.

- Broaden the options on the table rather than looking for a single

solution—surface particular problems that are bothering people and identify specific and plausible courses of action to address them.

- Look at the problem through the eyes of scientific and technical experts.

- Invent agreements of different strengths (completeness).

- Consciously search for shared interests and values.

- Find ways to make the agreement easier (begin to draft an agreement/think about the easiest path to an acceptable option).

## Criteria

*Objective criteria can be a critical component of collaborative negotiation because they enable all sides to fairly and collectively evaluate the merits of a proposal.* Thus, with a comprehensive set of objective criteria, each proposal can be scored; those proposals with relatively high scores for most criteria should rise to the top. In addition, these criteria can guide the search for a proposal that groups can rally around.

What are some desirable characteristics of *objective criteria*?

- They should reflect the interests of different parties, as judged by the parties themselves: different people with different interests will be inclined to use different sorts of criteria to evaluate options.

- They should be practical. For instance, they should be easily measurable under each proposal that is considered.

Criteria come in all shapes and sizes, with as much variety as the interests of the people involved (Table 8.2). Considerable effort may be required to go from an interest (e.g., *keeping areas wild*) to an objective measure (e.g., *portion of the area accessible by roads*).

Table 8.2 *Examples of interests and objective criteria*

| Interests | Objective criteria |
|---|---|
| Wildness | Portion of area accessible by roads |
| Timber harvest | Board feet produced by project |
| Risk of high-severity fire | Portion of the area that will receive fuel treatments |
| Protection of old-growth trees | Proportion of trees over 150 years retained |
| Protect water quality | Size of riparian buffers |
| Maintenance of native plant diversity | Commitment made in marking and reforestation guidelines |
| Maintenance of native wildlife diversity | Retention of important habitats for particular species |

Box 8.3  **Forest collaboratives finding solutions of mutual gain: The Blue Mountains Forest Partners and the Malheur National Forest**

John Day, Oregon, is a small, relatively isolated community in eastern Oregon surrounded by the Malheur National Forest. Historically, its economy was heavily dependent on timbering and ranching. Five sawmills provided hundreds of jobs cutting large old-growth ponderosa pine from the vast federal forest—the economic lifeblood for much of the community. In the mid-1990s that relationship was shaken by new federal policies limiting harvest to the smaller trees. Timber sale volume from the Malheur National Forest collapsed over the next few years.

Mills ran through their log inventories, existing federal contracts, and any private timber they could find. By the early 2000s, mills started closing while the Malheur National Forest continued to have great difficulty putting together timber sales that could survive litigation. It became increasingly clear at the same time that the forests were also in trouble, based on both scientific reports and local knowledge. There had been a massive increase in the number of small trees in the forests as a result of fire suppression and past grazing and timbering practices. These denser forests were more vulnerable to wildfire, drought, and insect attack. The local community could see these problems in the forest and thought that some forms of harvest might help; however, the Forest Service seemed unable to move forward with harvest proposals.

Emotions in John Day ran high in those days as many in the local community realized that their way of life might be ending. Once honorable livelihoods were now being vilified and were disappearing, and known environmentalists were not welcome in many stores and restaurants.

This is the story of how a number of people from diverse backgrounds came together to do everything they could to achieve a different outcome for the community. The process began when a politically conservative county commissioner saw what was happening and decided the community needed a new approach. To understand how and why the environmentalists, who were (in his eyes) successfully shutting down federal timber sales, thought so differently from him, he met with one of the main environmental litigators in Portland in 2003 and invited her to come to John Day. Soon the commissioner and the environmental litigator were out on the Malheur National Forest comparing perspectives on forest management. The visit stirred their mutual interest in finding common ground that would benefit both the forest and the community. They were soon joined by a number of community leaders and interested citizens, including a local, well-respected environmentalist who had grown up in these woods and a young timber buyer for the local mill.

Discussions were difficult in these early days of the Blue Mountains Forest Partners, as might be imagined given the recent history. Still, they realized they might be the last hope for avoiding the shutdown of the remaining mills in town, which would result in the loss of both the local economic base and a mechanism (timber harvest) that could help restore the forest. After many meetings and discussion, the Blue Mountains Forest Partners found agreement on some restoration projects, but the sawtimber volume produced by those projects was very modest.

By late 2007, it appeared that the most modern sawmill in John Day, and the best hope for a mill that could survive on restoration thinning, would soon need to close due to lack of wood supply. At the same time, a number of wildfires blackened parts of the Malheur National Forest and many in the community urged immediate salvage of the dead trees, arguing that the mill should not close when all this dead timber was going to waste. Some of the burned timber was near roads and some was in a roadless area. While environmental litigants had successfully stopped many salvage sales, they had some concern that stopping the proposed sales in these new burns might elicit a political response similar to the establishment of the salvage rider in 1995, which effectively banned challenge to salvage sales for approximately a year and a half.

With such a contentious issue and such a short time frame for agreement, two key members of the Blue Mountains Forest Partners (the local environmentalist and timber buyer) broke off from the main group and began to negotiate in earnest away from the crowd. They worked out an exchange—the environmentalist would back salvage near roads if the timber buyer would back leaving the burned roadless area alone. They then both worked hard to get their constituents and the Forest Service to go along. They succeeded, and the mill stayed open to process the salvage timber.

Salvage timber was a stopgap: it would keep the mill running for a short time but would do little for the forest. However, it gave the Partners breathing space and also established the precedent that the disparate local interests could find solutions of mutual gain. With the impetus from the salvage agreement, the Partners and many other local people began to conceive of forest health projects that would, in fact, achieve both ecological and economic goals. These projects increased people's trust and respect for each other as they tackled more controversial projects—those that increased the survivability of the forest while producing substantial commercial volume from medium-sized younger trees and leaving the old growth alone (Figure 8.2).

Along the way, the group brought in two scientists (Jerry Franklin and Norm Johnson) to explain their ecological forestry restoration strategy for Dry Forests, such as the pine and mixed-conifer forests in the Blue Mountains. They also suggested identifying the old trees that were to be left behind by utilizing a key developed by another scientist (Bob Van Pelt). This approach provided a scientific footing for the collaborative to proceed with bolder projects.

Throughout this effort, the Forest Service maintained an informal advisory role. Recently, with the collaborative's assistance, the Forest Service has signed a stewardship agreement

Figure 8.2  *The Blue Mountains Forest Partners working with the Forest Service on the Jane Project on the Emigrant Creek Ranger District, Malheur National Forest. (Photo credit: Blue Mountains Forest Partners, bluemountainsforestpartners.org)*

both forest sustainability and community well-being where traditional management approaches no longer worked. Leadership came from within and outside the community. The Partners had a natural resource problem amenable to new ideas. They managed to separate the people from the problem, find common ground, and invent options for mutual gain. Finally, they started with projects of low controversy and moved to more controversial projects as they built trust, employing science to help guide their path (Figure 8.3).

with a local logging company that could provide sufficient volume for the mill for up to a decade. What a change!

In real life, though, new challenges are always on the horizon: a large fire in 2015 burned much of the forest, including some collaborative projects developed using the principles of Franklin, Johnson, and Van Pelt, and the question of salvage and its role in forest restoration again came to the forefront. In addition, a militant takeover of a federal wildlife refuge just south of John Day reignited the issue of local versus national control of federal lands.

On the bright side, the Malheur National Forest was named one of the Collaborative Forest Landscape Restoration Program (CFLRP) project areas in 2012, which brought funds and recognition to this collaborative effort. In 2016, the funding was increased to $4 million per year, part of which will be spent on a multiparty monitoring effort to assess the effects of their restoration actions. As Forest Supervisor Steve Beverlin said at the announcement of the new funding:

*We're the only forest in the nation that's tripled our timber target in the last four years. We're the only forest in the nation I know of that has not had a vegetation management project litigated in the past four years. We're the only forest in the nation that nearly doubled the size of their CFLR project. With the collaborative's assistance, we've brought in more funding in the community to do more work in the community to provide more stability of forest products in the community to the mill. . . . (The collaborative process is) really the proven method to work through those sticky issues and continue to get work done and not come to a stalemate and have things stop. (Reported by Hart, 2016)*

The story of the Blue Mountains Forest Partners has many characteristics of **place-based** local forestry collaboratives that have grown and prospered. It was born in a crisis for

Figure 8.3  *The Blue Mountains Forest Partners are a diverse group of stakeholders who work with the USFS on the Malheur National Forest in eastern Oregon. (Photo credit: Blue Mountains Forest Partners, bluemountainsforestpartners.org)*

Increasingly, objective criteria are strongly interwoven with scientific information and the expert opinions of scientists. For example, how do you describe the maintenance of native wildlife diversity? You might turn to the scientific literature or seek the advice of scientists. In fact, you might invite scientists to participate in your collaboration meetings to help you brainstorm options and criteria. You might even ask scientists to evaluate some options that the group thinks are promising.

## BATNA: The Real Power in Negotiation

With such well-tested principles, why don't all negotiations lead to mutually satisfying decisions? Too often, it may seem that other parties have all the leverage. They know you need a deal, and maybe they do not need a deal. These are very tough situations. That may be especially true in federal forestry, where citizen suits, under the environmental laws to stop actions, have a long history of success (see Chapter 7). In contrast, litigation to force action on federal forests has been much less successful. Thus some would argue that this one-sided leverage creates an unfair power dynamic between those who would be willing to litigate versus those who would or could not. Others would argue that access to the courts helps make sure that actions do not cause environmental damage.

Professionals who study negotiation often refer to a *resistance point*, which may be expressed as the lowest (or highest) price that a negotiating party will take (or offer), or some other threshold at which point that party will decide to walk away from the negotiation. A good negotiator thinks very carefully about what his or her resistance point is, and never goes past it. Knowing your resistance point will accomplish two objectives: (1) it will protect you against making an agreement you should reject, and (2) it will help you make the most of the assets you do have so that any agreement you reach will satisfy your interests as well as possible.

In *Getting to Yes*, Fisher et al. (2011) offer a somewhat more sophisticated take on the resistance point called the *Best Alternative To a Negotiated Agreement*, or *BATNA*. In the simplest terms, your BATNA answers the question: If this negotiation does not succeed, what are you going to do instead?

*Remember, you negotiate to produce something better than the results you can obtain without negotiating.* What is your alternative to negotiating that produces the best possible outcome? The alternative is your BATNA. The BATNA is the standard against which any proposed agreements are measured. If a proposed agreement produces a worse outcome for you than your BATNA, then you reject the agreement. A BATNA protects you from accepting terms that you are better off without, and from rejecting terms that would be in your best interest to accept.

The difference between a resistance point and a BATNA is that a resistance point establishes a position, and thereby limits your options. Thus, you may have a preconceived notion of what offer(s) you will reject before you have an opportunity to evaluate offers and possible solutions. A BATNA should be flexible enough to permit exploration of imaginative solutions. Instead of ruling out any offer that does not meet your bottom line (i.e., your resistance point), you should compare a proposal with your BATNA to see whether it better satisfies your interests.

The insecurity of an unknown BATNA contributes to the danger of being too committed to reaching an agreement. If you do not have a BATNA, you are essentially conceding that you are at the mercy of a negotiated agreement. This can easily lead to outcomes that seem to meet your negotiating position, but that you may later regret. If you do not have a BATNA, you are asking for trouble.

People may think that negotiating power is determined by wealth, political connections, friends, and the like; this is not necessarily the case. *The relative negotiating power of two parties depends primarily upon how attractive the option of not reaching agreement is to either party.*

BATNAs should be carefully developed. They must be realistic. They need to take into account all of the important variables. Some BATNAs can be quite complex. Generating possible BATNAs requires at least three distinct steps:

1. Develop a list of actions you might conceivably take if no agreement is reached.

2. Improve some of the more promising actions and convert them into practical alternatives.

3. Select, tentatively, the one alternative that seems best.

Some example BATNAs are:

- Seek a resolution in another venue (courts, legislature, the market).

- Seek a resolution at another time (delay, wait them out).

- Withdraw—you don't get what you want, but they don't get what they want either.

Should you disclose your BATNA to the other party(ies)? This may depend on whether you have a powerful BATNA or a weak one (and how the other parties will perceive it). You should think about the other side of this question: What is the other party's BATNA? What alternatives to a negotiated agreement are available to the other side? The more you learn of the other party's alternatives, the better prepared you are for negotiation. If both sides to a negotiation have attractive BATNAs, the best outcome for both parties may be to forego an agreement.

BATNAs need to be flexible. Developing your BATNA can help you determine the minimally acceptable agreement, and identify tangible alternatives (and options!) that may be illusive during the negotiation process. Also, you should be open to reconsidering your BATNA as you learn more about the problem, potential solutions, and the BATNAs of others.

## Comparison of *Mutual Gains* Collaboration to Other Approaches

With the discussion of the BATNA, we have completed our introduction to *mutual gains* negotiation. Not only has this approach been advocated in many books on collaboration, it has proven useful in many of the disputes and controversies about forest management (Box 8.3) and elsewhere. We will focus on the mutual gains approach to collaboration throughout the rest of this chapter and this book.

It should be noted, though, that other, related approaches exist to encouraging collective action to solve environmental problems. One well-known approach comes from the work of political economist Elinor Ostrom (Ostrom, 1998) and is designed to deal with problems associated with the allocation and use of *common pool resources*. Common pool resources are those resources that can easily be overused or destroyed if property rights to these resources are poorly defined and each resource user maximizes his or her own gain from the resource. Oceans, lakes, forests, river systems, grazing lands, and Earth's atmosphere often fall into the category of common pool resources.

Ostrom found through theoretical investigation and empirical trials that, in some cases, such as with small groups, using face-to-face communications and long time horizons, people will choose collective action to manage common pool resources that improves the gain to the whole, even at some cost to themselves. See Ostrom (1998) for a brilliant treatment of this topic. Key attributes of the social relationships that enable successful collective action are the development of long-term relationships, trust, and reciprocity. These attributes have similarities to the concepts utilized in mutual gains approaches discussed above, including establishing long-term relationships, recognizing interdependency, and building trust.

## Effective Collaboration: Lessons from Two Decades of Experience

Collaboration is now one of the social processes that permeates forestry, especially public forestry. In many places (Figure 8.4), it has become as much a part of the public discourse and decision-making process as are NEPA documents, forest management planning, and grassroots campaigns against controversial proposals for land management. Many people and organizations have placed a lot of faith in collaboration as a way to navigate through the contentious issues over the conservation and use of forests.

While the general enthusiasm for collaboration is certainly admirable, and potentially provides one avenue for an improvement in civil discourse over forestry, the question remains: Does collaboration lead to improved outputs and outcomes? Following Koontz and Thomas (2006), we distinguish between outputs (plans, projects, and other tangible items generated as part of the collaborative effort) and outcomes (effects of outputs on environmental and social conditions). As Koontz and Thomas (2006) note, relatively little research has linked outputs with outcomes, with the notable exception being that scholars have demonstrated that successful collaborative efforts lead to increased trust and social capital (Leach & Sabatier, 2005; Lubell, 2005). In other words, the clearest evidence we have so far about positive effects of collaboratives is that they improve civil society.

What about positive environmental outcomes and improvements in community economic well-being, two commonly expressed goals of public forest collaboratives? Regarding these issues, strong evidence is sparse, however. Taking our Blue Mountains Forest Partners case as an example, it is true that harvest levels on the Malheur National Forest have significantly increased since the birth of the collaborative, which has helped maintain an important source of employment there. It is also true that the number of acres treated to reduce forest fuel loads and stand densities have greatly increased. However, while we see a strong correlation between outputs of the collaborative (projects that treated stands and produced timber volume useful to the local mill) and these results, that relationship does not constitute proof, in a scientific sense, that the collaborative caused or enabled these projects. Perhaps, given the dire economic and ecological situation, the gridlock on the Malheur National Forest would have broken up anyway, allowing projects to go forward. These causal links are inherently hard to establish in the absence of an experiment where we might test the effect of a collaborative. It is true that the Umatilla National Forest, north of John Day, did not have a forest collaborative during this time and has not seen economic benefits like the Malheur National Forest, but other factors may have been at play. Certainly, there seems to be a connection between the collaborative in John Day and a steady stream of projects, but this does not establish cause and effect in a scientific sense.

The impact of collaboratives on environmental outcomes is especially difficult to untangle, partly because agencies often don't gather the data needed for such analysis, partly because environmental effects often take a long time to express themselves, and, as above, partly because we need some sort of experiment to help assess the impact of the collaborative. Thus we generally lack scientific proof of the effect of collaboratives on environmental outcomes, even though projects have been implemented with the intent of achieving those outcomes. As Koontz and Thomas (2006) concluded, more analysis is needed.

Although the scientific evidence on the effectiveness of collaboratives in achieving environmental and economic outcomes may be fragmentary, agencies, communities, and individuals have invested in them. Thus, for the short-run, a key question is: How can we improve the ability of collaboratives to reach agreements that address important issues surrounding forest conservation and management?

So what are the secrets to collaborative success? Is it enough to employ the principles of mutual gains negotiation that we described above? While these can be enormously helpful, and we strongly recommend them, they don't guarantee victory. Collaboration groups come in many shapes and sizes, each with its own dynamic as a function of this political and social setting as well as the personalities of the participants. As a result, we lack a collaboration cookbook that will guarantee success every time.

Still, there have been enough successful collaboration efforts over the years and in a wide variety of settings to enable us to summarize useful advice. We have organized these ideas into five parts: (1) learn from the successes and failures of others; (2) promote social learning; (3) understand the *collaboration universe*; (4) evaluate whether you have the elements of success; and (5) recognize the limits of collaboration.

## Learn from Others' Successes and Failures

We will look at these lessons from two perspectives: (1) those of a local group, and (2) those of collaboration experts. Each provides very valuable insights and advice.

A number of groups that have been successful in coming together to address forestry and natural resource problems have summarized the keys to their success. Eight members of White Mountains Natural Resource Working Group, which focuses on restoration of the forests of the southwestern United States, shared their advice with other groups wishing to form an effective working group. Their many recommendations, summarized by Lenart (2006), are worth remembering:

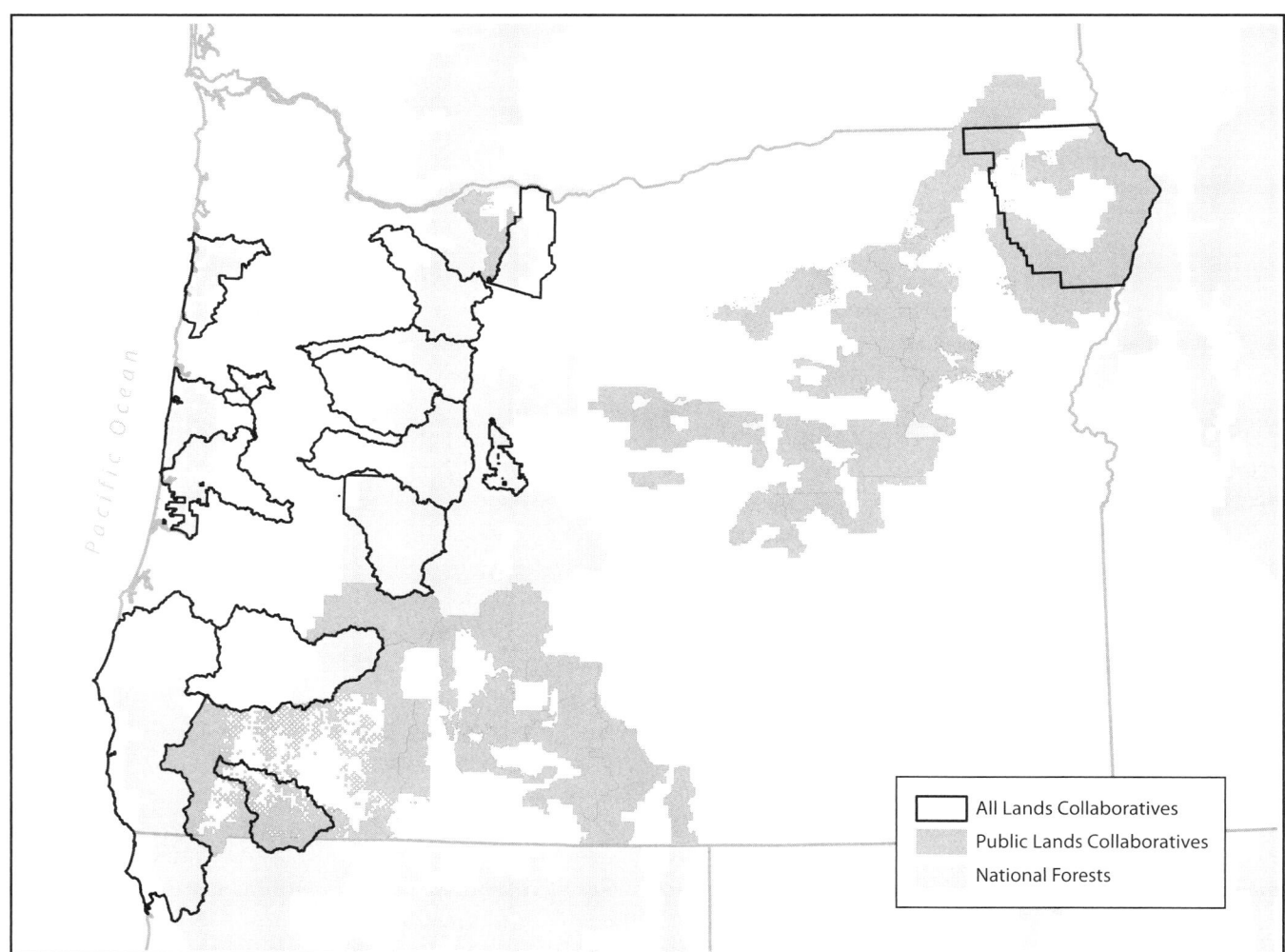

Figure 8.4  *Location of Oregon forest collaboratives in 2014. (Source: Ecosystem Workforce Program, University of Oregon)*

- *Build trust before tackling contentious issues.* Be sure to leave plenty of time to develop relationships and share philosophies before potentially controversial issues arise.

- *Respect the viewpoints of others, even if you disagree with them.* Encourage everyone to listen respectfully to others, regardless of their philosophies; anybody who attends a meeting should be welcome to join the debate as long as they don't filibuster.

- *Do not criticize other members, inside or outside of meetings.* This is crucial to forming trust among group members. The group as a whole should reprimand members who stray from this directive.

- *Search for common ground on a significant issue.* Pick a defining issue that encompasses the interests shared by members. Develop a working group that covers the interests of all members. Be willing to solve problems as a team. Be persistent—stick with it even through the difficult times.

- *Incorporate scientific findings.* Making scientific results a regular part of the discussion can help develop a shared understanding of the issues at hand, and provide an incentive to attend meetings when new science is discussed.

- *Look for leaders.* Pick a group leader who will track issues and cross boundaries. Find out who the informal and formal leaders in the community are, and encourage them to attend meetings.

- *Understand the group's role.* Understand the real extent of the group's power without artificially inflating it. Collaborative groups generally depend upon agencies or government bodies to implement their ideas, so they tend to be advisory in nature.

- *Recognize when the time is right for action.* The White Mountains Natural Resources Working Group spent years meeting and planning before having a concrete project to consider as a basis for further action. Once a large fire struck the region, members knew they had a window of opportunity to gain support from area residents for their ideas on improving forest health.

Julia Wondolleck and Steven Yafee are recognized experts in collaboration, and studied roughly 200 collaborative initiatives (Wondolleck & Yafee, 2000). They found eight factors that explain the successes of these collaborative efforts:

1. *Build on common ground established by sense of place or community, mutual goals or fears, or a shared vision.* Something needs to exist to draw people together. Powerful forces to help bring people together might include concerns about the future of forests in the local area, loss of the economic base in an isolated community, or the potential for legislation or federal regulation to make decisions without local involvement.

2. *Create new opportunities for interaction among diverse groups.* Establish new forms and means of communication that cut across the way people and agencies traditionally organize and interact.

3. *Employ meaningful, effective, and enduring collaborative processes.* Make sure that forums or meetings are well managed and productive, and are respectful of the time and energy people contribute to such efforts.

4. *Focus on the problem in a new and different way by fostering a more open, flexible, and holistic mindset.* Focus on fresh ideas, as opposed to rehashing old arguments. Field trips, joint problem solving, and joint fact-finding (see Box 8.4) can all create a fresh environment for new ideas.

5. *Foster a shared sense of responsibility, ownership, and commitment.* Take responsibility for the place or resources of concern, and think about them in their entirety. Shift from talking about what they will do to what we will do. Identify and highlight the area or resources of concern so people can relate to them. Focus on problems and solutions that have real meaning to people.

6. *Recognize that people, not institutions make up partnerships.* Developing, nurturing, and sustaining human relationships are at the heart of collaboration.

7. *Move forward through proactive and entrepreneurial behavior.* Think outside the usual bureaucratic processes and solutions. Support leaders who are willing to suggest and try new ideas. Build on early successes to think even more broadly. Make use of social networks to spread the word and create enthusiasm.

8. *Mobilize support and resources from numerous sources.* Aggressively recruit and utilize technical and scientific advice. Link with other groups working on the same problems. Connect to local officials and the media.

See Wondolleck and Yaffee (2000) for an extremely thoughtful elaboration on these ideas.

## Promote Social Learning

*Many students of collaborative processes highlight social learning as integral to collaborative success* (Wondolleck & Yaffee, 2000; Pahl-Wostl & Hare, 2004). Wondolleck and Yaffee (2000, p. 132), as an example, state that a key step in collaborative initiatives is "committing to a process of mutual learning in which participants agree that they individually do not have all the answers." Schusler, Decker, and Pfeffer (2003, p. 311) more generally define social learning as "learning that occurs when people engage one another, sharing diverse perspectives and experiences to develop a common framework of understanding and basis for joint action."

One of the first proponents of the importance of social learning to collaboration was Julia Wondolleck (1988) who studied why the Forest Service's NEPA process on forest planning seemed gridlocked, and what changes could help move the process forward. She coined the term *joint fact-finding* in which members of a study group would highlight points of disagreement or controversy and then figure out how to investigate them further. Wondolleck viewed joint fact-finding as essential to the development of shared understanding and group cohesion (see Box 8.4).

One important vehicle for social learning is *deliberation*, which includes any process to communicate, raise, and collectively consider issues, increase understanding, and arrive at substantive decisions. As summarized by Reich (1985, p. 1636), public deliberation at its best "allows people to discover latent public values that they have in common with others, and in the process create other public values.

Together, citizens begin to define targets of voluntary action, to identify what they value most about the community, and to uncover goals and commitments that transcend their narrower self-interests."

Further, social learning is "intended to help improve the quality and wisdom of decisions we take when faced with complexity, uncertainty, conflict, and paradox" (Roling & Wagmakers, 1998, p. 54 as quoted in Schusler et al., 2003, p. 312). Complexity, uncertainty, conflict, and paradox—what a great expression of the condition of most natural resource problems!

Schusler et al. (2003) used a conference that engaged diverse stakeholders from local communities in planning for the Lake Ontario Islands Wildlife Management Area in New York's Eastern Lake Ontario Basin as a vehicle to assess whether and how social learning occurred among the participants, and the contribution it made to identifying a common purpose and developing collaborative relationships. The organizers developed a sequential set of modules they asked the participants to work through, such as shared history, ideal future, probable future, objectives, and action planning. They then engaged the participants in discussions of each module, letting that discussion develop as the participants wished.

---

### Box 8.4  The power of joint fact-finding

**Learning in the Field:**
**Applegate Partnership & Watershed Council**

The Applegate Partnership of Southwest Oregon is one of the most successful collaborative efforts in the West. It focuses on the Applegate watershed—a mostly forested watershed with a mix of private, BLM, and Forest Service lands. The Partnership has a membership that spans the different interests people in southwestern Oregon have in federal lands. In the beginning, federal agencies were officially members of the collaborative, but issues about the relationship of the collaborative to the agencies caused the agencies to move to informal status. However, federal agencies still regularly present their proposed projects to the Partnership to get their comments and suggestions. Norm Johnson happened to be at a meeting of the Partnership one day when the BLM proposed cutting hazard trees in a campground. Questions to the BLM by Partnership members were quick and intense, focused on whether the hazard claim was just a pretense to help meet the allowable cut. After about an hour of discussion, a BLM employee suggested they go look at the campground. About 10 people piled into vans, and off they went. Within two hours, they were back. Norm asked some of the most skeptical questioners from the morning session about what they had found. Their response: "Yep, those trees need to go. We all use that campground and those trees are

dangerous." Case closed. The moral: Joint fact-finding can be a powerful tool in successful collaborations, and field trips are often a key component of that effort.

**Partitioning Winter Use Zones in Vail, Colorado.**[*]
The Forest Service recreation manager near Vail was near her wits' end: cross-country skiers and the snowmobilers were at each other's throats. The cross-country skiers complained that the snowmobilers were loud, smelly, and ran them off the trails. The snowmobilers complained that the cross-country skiers were always in the way, and were unfriendly. Both groups wanted the trails exclusively for themselves. A volunteer mediator suggested an exercise in which members of each group were given a stack of chips worth 100 points, and a map on which to place the chips to indicate the trails of greatest importance to them. After a few hours of work, the two groups got back together and looked at the results. Lo and behold, the snowmobilers and cross-country skiers had valued the trails very differently—there was much less conflict than people had imagined. That exercise could now be used as a foundation of forest zoning for winter use. Joint fact-finding in action.

---

[*] Adapted from a talk by Todd Bryan, School of Natural Resources and Environment, University of Michigan.

In a postconference survey, Schusler et al. (2003) found that a significant majority of respondents reported learning about the concerns of other participants, where they agreed and disagreed with others, problems and opportunities of which they were unaware, and actions to address problems or capitalize on opportunities. Most participants reported that the conference contributed to identification of a common purpose and that the conference created new relationships. Perhaps most important, over 80% of participants reported that they had gained trust in others through the conference.

Based on the participants' reflections and their own observations, the authors identified eight process attributes that fostered social learning (Schusler et al. 2003).

1. *Democratic structure*: Although the organizers developed the structured sequence of activities, participants themselves determined the content of the discussion and decided on the priorities for action.

2. *Open communication*: Working together in small groups provided an opportunity for dialogue among participants, with guidelines for interaction establishing norms for small group work.

3. *Diverse participation*: A purposeful selection of participants using the peer reference system achieved a diversity of interests, which enhanced learning by exposing participants to a breadth of viewpoints.

4. *Multiple sources of knowledge*: Fish and wildlife professionals provided valuable information about their understanding of the natural resources of the area, while other participants shared equally relevant knowledge of their own experiences about the region's natural resources, history, culture, and economy.

5. *Extended engagement*: The two and a half day conference was enough time for the participants to attend numerous work sessions, which helped build collaborative relationships and provided enough time to engage at a more personal level.

6. *Unrestrained thinking*: Participants considered the system of islands (the planning focus) in the context of the much larger landscape that helped broaden the thinking. Creating a shared history also contributed to creative, unrestrained thinking, revealing the intricate links between the region's natural and cultural resources and the tourism-based economy.

7. *Constructive conflict*: Rather than striving for consensus on all issues, the conference focused on identifying common ground, which serves to differentiate the points of agreement from those of disagreement. This enabled participants to identify areas where they could constructively focus on shared values and areas where they needed further deliberation and negotiation.

8. *Facilitation*: Involvement of a neutral entity in the role of a facilitator lent credibility to the process.

The authors concluded that these eight process attributes "created an atmosphere in which participants could share diverse views and opinions, respectfully question one another, and explore complex and challenging issues with sensitivity and humor" (Schusler et al., 2003, p. 322).

A weakness of the conference design became evident in a follow-up meeting: there was no continuing group commitment made, leaving the local state agency to carry on largely alone in the absence of conference participants. This realization emphasized that social learning is essential, but not sufficient, for successful collaboration and comanagement. Appropriate structures and processes are needed to sustain learning and enable joint action (Schusler et al., 2003).

Collaboratives also provide opportunities for social learning through participation in multiparty monitoring. As Cheng (2006) and Butler, Monroe, and McCaffrey (2015) point out, public land collaboratives provide some of our best working examples of adaptive ecosystem management on US public lands, with these collaboratives utilizing *learning-based* approaches to public lands planning and management. We will discuss this relationship between collaboration and monitoring in more detail in Chapter 11 on adaptive management. A recent example from the Pinelands Region of southern New Jersey illustrates the power of social learning in helping people see problems in a new light and move toward solutions to resource problems (Box 8.5). It also illustrates that successful efforts take persistence and patience.

## Recognize the Collaboration Universe

To say that collaboration can try your patience is probably an understatement. Often you are sitting down to work with people with whom you have disagreed for years. Changing from fighting to working together is rarely easy. Moreover, some people may seem beyond reason, no matter how long negotiations proceed—in fact, they may seem determined to stop any agreement from occurring. You may believe that you have found a mutual gains solution with key members one month only to see it blow up the following month due to forces outside the collaborative. We attempt to capture below the social dynamics of what we call the *Collaboration Universe*.

**Rings of Engagement**  To understand the personal dynamics of collaboration groups, it may be helpful to think of four concentric rings of engagement, representing the people that are involved, in one way or another, in a collaboration (Figure 8.8):

## Box 8.5  Forest collaboration in the Pinelands Region of southern New Jersey

*Author: Bob Williams, Pine Creek Forestry LLC*

As with many forest regions, the issue of active forest management within the Pinelands National Reserve, a 1.1 million acre area of federal, state, and private lands in southern New Jersey, has been difficult and controversial. Since the reserve's creation in 1979, the issue of cutting trees has been the focus of a major public discussion. By the early 2000s, active forest management had declined to such a degree that many stakeholders began to seek solutions that would allow forest management to return in a fashion that would support and perpetuate the unique ecology of the Pinelands Region.

As an active forester who manages many tens of thousands of acres of private pine forests in the Pinelands National Reserve, I became very active in these forest policy discussions. Many people believed the forest just needed to be left alone and nature would take its course. But this approach neglects the overall intent of the Pinelands Protection Act that requires forestry be a permitted use and that "severe disturbances continue to perpetuate the unique ecological character of this forest region." The issue came to a peak in 2004 when former governor James Florio and then chairman of the Pinelands Commission, announced a series of new appointments to the Pinelands Forestry Advisory Committee and established a new charge to review, clarify, and refine the forestry provisions of the Pinelands Comprehensive Management Plan. In particular, he directed the committee to recommend practices designed to protect and maintain the Pinelands environment while ensuring that forestry remains a viable economic and cultural resource in the Pinelands.

This committee was made up of a wide range of stakeholders with many experts that included a wildlife biologist from the New Jersey Audubon society. Although it was not formally called a collaboration, it ended up being one. Views and opinions varied in the beginning. New Jersey Audubon had a long history of being skeptical of forest management that was supported by landowners or timber interests. I was appointed as one of the foresters with significant experience with the regulatory process that had largely eliminated forestry as a viable land use.

I entered the process with great skepticism, too, but very soon recognized the New Jersey Audubon biologist as a well-trained wildlife expert and appreciated his approach to forestry. He, too, was concerned about the loss of forest management that had resulted in the decline of many plant and animal species, which included most threatened and endangered species.

The lack of disturbance has resulted in the severe decline of American chaffseed (*Schwalbea americana*)—a federally endangered plant. Additionally, plants such as Pine Barren reed grass (*Calamovilfa brevipilis*) and Pine Barren smoke-grass (*Muhlenbergia torreyana*) have declined and benefit from an ecological approach to forest management. Also, at-risk animal species such as northern pine

Figure 8.5  *Red-headed woodpecker—a species that benefits from ecological forest management.*
*(Photo credit: Dave Menke/USFWS)*

snake (*Pituophis melanoleucus*) (see Figure 4.18), corn snake (*Elaphe guttata*), and red-headed woodpecker (*Melanerpes erythrocephalus*) (Figure 8.5) have all done well in many of the managed forest stands after an ecological treatment.

The review process was long and hard and lasted more than a year and a half. However, that process enabled common ground to be found and placed the ecological health of the forest as the standard to be met. That difficult collaboration process allowed professional relationships to develop. Both sides grew in the understanding of the need for the management of the forest on a landscape level (Figures 8.6a and b). The review process also has allowed the economic aspect of forestry to be a major linchpin in any future long-term success.

By late 2005, the committee chair released this statement: "Forestry activities undertaken by farmers and other private landowners, public agencies, and non-profit conservation organizations, can provide wood and forestry products while promoting better stewardship while enhancing the ecological integrity of the Pinelands Reserve." A diverse group of interests came together for the good of the forest and New Jersey Audubon has become one of the strongest supporters of an ecological approach to forest management; so much so that in June of 2013, I was given the New Jersey Audubon's Annual Conservation Award—The Richard Kane Conservation Award.

A prestigious conservation award given to a forester clearly demonstrated Audubon's commitment to ecological forestry. New Jersey Audubon and other interests are committed to seeing an ecological approach to forest management being used across the landscape of the Pinelands National Reserve.

Figures 8.6a and b  *Photo (a) is a typical pitch pine/shrub oak forest where fire was excluded for more than 50 years. The closed, dense canopy has resulted in the loss of early seral habitat needed for many rare plants and animals. Photo (b) shows this forest type one growing season after a treatment that removed 60% of the basal area. A more diverse ground cover has regenerated and planning for prescribed fire can begin. (Photos courtesy of Bob Williams)*

In addition to restoring habitat, the use of an ecological approach to forest management within the Pinelands Reserve has provided opportunities to address concerns for both uncontrolled wildfire and for finding methods to reintroduce fire safely into this fire-dependent forest ecosystem.

These pine forests need fire; however, it has been a struggle to allow fire in the forest while simultaneously providing the needed protection of homes, lives, and infrastructure within and near the forest. This ecological forestry approach in the Pinelands Region allows for the reduction of fire fuel loads, as well as manipulation of forest structure, which also allows for improved and safe fire management in terms of both ecological fire needs and fuel hazard management.

By 2015, after many years of using an approach of ecological forest management, New Jersey Audubon Society began the reintroduction of wild, northern bobwhite quail (*Colinus virginianus*) from the state of Georgia. Biologists and ecologists from the Tall Timbers Research Station and Land Conservancy helped determine that the best hope for successful reintroduction of bobwhite quail, which had been extirpated from the Pinelands Reserve, would be the managed forest at Pine Island Cranberry Company. Ecological forestry treatments, along with the return of fire, had been successfully completed for more than ten years. Quail were released in 2015 (Figure 8.7) and have begun to build their populations! For the first time in more than

35 years, quail now can be heard calling in a portion of the Pinelands National Reserve.

We live in a world that will only place more pressures on our forests, and it is a critical time for diverse interests to seek the common ground that may lead to important solutions. An ecological approach to how we sustain our natural lands will provide many answers and solutions to these most difficult questions and problems as we seek to sustain our forests and the species within them.

Figure 8.7  *Bob Williams (third from the left) and John Parke, Stewardship Project Director from New Jersey Audubon (far right), working with the public to release northern bobwhite quail in the Pine Island Cranberry forest. (Photo credit: ©Sugar Shock Media, LLC)*

1. *Shared Vision*—members who have a similar definition of the problem, and similar values and interests. Collaboration nirvana! This shared vision often develops as the result of participating in the collaboration process and broadening values and interests to include those of other members in the collaboration.

2. *Overlapping Interests*—members who differ in the interests they consider most important to pursue. Perhaps some members are focused on habitat and others on employment. Still, they are able to find options that accommodate many of these different interests. Finding options that satisfy differing interests is a necessary condition for successful collaboration.

3. *Intrigued Skepticism*—members who have reservations about the collaboration's potential, but still participate. They may participate in the hope that success can be found, or because they do not want to be left behind if something positive happens. Most collaboration groups have at least a few of these folks.

4. *Active Disruption*—members who participate with the goal of preventing the collaboration from succeeding. These folks do not want new options to be found that satisfy other participants. They might like the status quo, or feel that stopping the collaborative effort will enable better options to surface through other avenues. Active disruption is fairly common, especially in collaborations concerning the management of federal forest resources.

Some observations about the rings of engagement:

- While a shared vision is ideal, collaborations do not always need it to succeed (Box 8.6). Finding a quorum of participants willing to seek and find options for mutual gains may often be enough. Nevertheless, developing a shared vision, at least among core members, is helpful to the stability and longevity of the collaborative.

- The composition of the rings will change over time, with some interested people (or groups) occupying the outer rings at the beginning of the collaborative process. As people get to know each other and let down their guard, they begin to recognize their shared interests and gradually migrate toward the center.

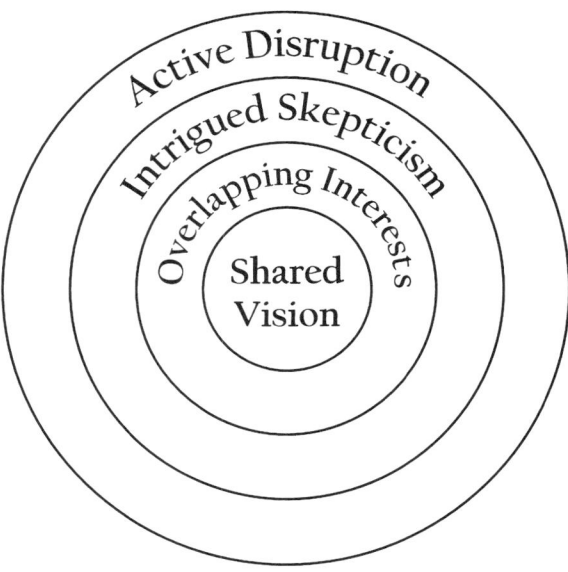

Figure 8.8 *Potential rings of engagement in a collaborative group.*

- Individuals may shift back and forth between rings, depending on the issue and the larger political milieu in which the negotiation occurs.

- Active disrupters will try to set up rules that make it easy to destroy the collaboration. Setting up a pure consensus model, where everyone must agree before a group will accept a proposal is an open invitation to active disrupters who might like to destroy the collaborative effort. Previously, we noted that allowing admission to all who seek to be involved could be an important element in building community support.

---

### Box 8.6  Don't fight the final battle: Finding overlapping interests within divergent visions

Ever since creation of the national forests, at least two dominant visions for those forests have been paramount in battles over their management (Nie, 2008). One emphasizes the use of those forests for goods and services, like timber and range that contribute to economic development and local community sustenance. The other emphasizes the preservation of wildness and nature in those forests. These alternative visions, in one way or another, still drive many of the political battles over the national forests, and advocates of both views will often be represented in collaboration groups for the national forests of the West, whether it be for the Malheur National Forest (John Day, Oregon) or the Lolo National Forest (Missoula, Montana).

   With such divergent visions, how can people come together on proposals? If the focus of discussions is on which long-term vision will prevail (preservation or development), the collaborative group may soon disintegrate. *Rather, the search needs to be for actions in the near term that advances*

*both visions*. Over the last decade, this approach has become increasingly common in forests where past management has resulted in conditions that can be described as unnatural or degraded. In the dry forests of the interior West, we find this condition in the buildup in fuels due to fire suppression and past logging and grazing practices. In the moist forests of the Pacific Coast, we find this condition in tree farms created after natural forests were clearcut. Often actions may be proposed to put these stands on a trajectory to develop into more natural forests that also produce wood products. In such actions, *collaboration members may be able to find overlapping interests within divergent visions*! It must be noted that such successes leave the long-term future of these forests unresolved. This should not be surprising, since the citizenry of the United States also appears conflicted about which direction to take. We hope the ecological forestry approach offered in this book may be a part of a long-term solution. We shall see.

It is necessary to strike a balance between having policies that allow admission to all who would like to be involved in the process and establishing decision rules that prevent a few active disrupters from derailing the process. A tricky business! (See Box 8.7.)

**Linkage to the Outside World**    It often is easiest to negotiate with a few individuals who have the authority to make firm commitments. However, most modern conflict over forests is a group sport, with individuals in the collaboration representing timber companies, conservation groups, philanthropic organizations, or government agencies. These groups work through their representatives on the collaborative to make sure their interests are protected and their representatives do not give away too much (Figure 8.9). Negotiations between individuals representing groups can be far more complicated than negotiations between individuals who are on their own.

*The real difficulty in having a successful collaboration often is not the relationship between opposing groups, or the representatives of these groups; rather, it is a lack of cohesion or agreement within the membership of groups that belong to*

---

### Box 8.7  Degrees of agreement: What is consensus anyway?

Using a pure *consensus model* in which everyone must agree before a group will accept a proposal, is certainly wonderful if a group can get there. Unfortunately, it also gives a single individual enormous power to stop things. Thus many collaboration groups sooner or later need to refine consensus to allow the group to support projects/programs/policies, even if some dissent occurs.

One approach is simply to utilize a decision rule that almost everyone must agree; that is, one or two people can be against the project yet the group may still approve it. Making such a process work does require that a sufficiently broad coalition agrees, meaning that some from each of the major interests (ranchers, loggers, local environmental groups) support the project. It must be recognized, though, that people who are consistently overruled will most probably deploy their BATNA at some point!

Another approach is to develop a formal set of rules describing the level of support that exists for a proposal within the collaboration group. Such a protocol was developed by the Northeast Washington Forest Coalition, a collaboration group that works with the Colville National Forest (CNF) in Washington near the Canadian border. It is shown below:

| Board Vote | Support Level | Member commitment |
|---|---|---|
| Consensus w/o Reservation (All members vote for approval without recorded reservations) | High | No members (or organizations represented by members) will appeal/litigate or support outside challenges. All members will express support for the project* and work to resolve any issues raised later by noncoalition entities if the opportunity arises. |
| Consensus w/ Reservation (All members vote for approval but some have their reservations recorded in meeting minutes) | Medium | No members (or organizations represented by members) will appeal/litigate or support outside challenges. Members who had reservations recorded may express those reservations* if the opportunity arises; however, all members agree that any statements expressing reservations about the decision will not be directed at the collaborative process itself. |
| No Consensus, but Majority Vote Approval (Some members have such strong reservations that they vote against approval; reasons are recorded in minutes) | Low | Members (or organizations represented by members) reserve the right to appeal/litigate or support outside challenges. Members who voted against approval reserve the right to express their reasons for voting against approval* and may actively pursue opportunities to do so; however, all members agree that any statements expressing reservations about the decision will not be directed at the collaborative process itself. |
| Majority Vote Disapproval | None | Coalition will inform CNF that the coalition does not support the project and recommend the CNF drop the proposal. All members reserve the right to express their reasons for voting recommendation to drop the proposal* and may actively pursue opportunities to do so; however, all members agree that any statements expressing reservations about the decision will not be directed at the collaborative process itself. |

\* in media or elsewhere

*Source:* Northeast Washington Forestry Coalition. http://www.newforestrycoalition.org/opguide.htm

*the collaborative.* Representatives may come to an agreement relatively easily with other members of the collaborative, only to see the deal fall apart when they take it back to their parent group from which they must seek approval. Woodrow Wilson famously negotiated the League of Nations with the European powers following the First World War and brought it back home to the US Senate, which refused to ratify the treaty. This kind of outcome is common in natural resource conflict, and managing this dynamic without letting it damage or destroy the collaborative effort can be a major struggle. Moreover, the local and national perspectives of organizations are sometimes in apparent conflict. National organizations may opt out of local agreements, or may attempt to squash community-based planning (sometimes when the local chapter favors involvement) because these agreements are viewed as inconsistent with the group's overall mission (McClosky, 1999).

Why can individuals cut a deal, but not groups? Individual parties to a dispute may be bitter foes, but they often get to know and understand each other very well. They also understand that they will face one another again, so there is an incentive to treat each other respectfully, or at least carefully. While these conditions often hold for individuals directly involved in negotiations, they do not necessarily hold for the groups or individuals the negotiators represent. Opposing groups and individuals represented by members of a collaboration group during a negotiation may have never met and may never have to deal with each other; they may feel free to hold very strident, destructive views of one another. Thus it helps enormously if collaboration members are highly respected by the groups or individuals they represent.

Beyond the problem of the relation of people within the collaboration group and those they represent, it is a rare collaboration group that does not leave someone or some group behind as the members attempt to find common ground and actions they can support. As we mentioned above (Box 8.7), those left behind may retreat to the edge of the rings of engagement and then withdraw entirely, unfurling their BATNA and going off to war as best they can. Alternatively, perhaps those people or groups never engaged, either because they did not want to engage or were not asked; seeing directions they do not support, they may try their best to derail the collaborative effort. While such an outside threat may help bring the collaboration group together, it can also create great stresses, and bring things to a halt.

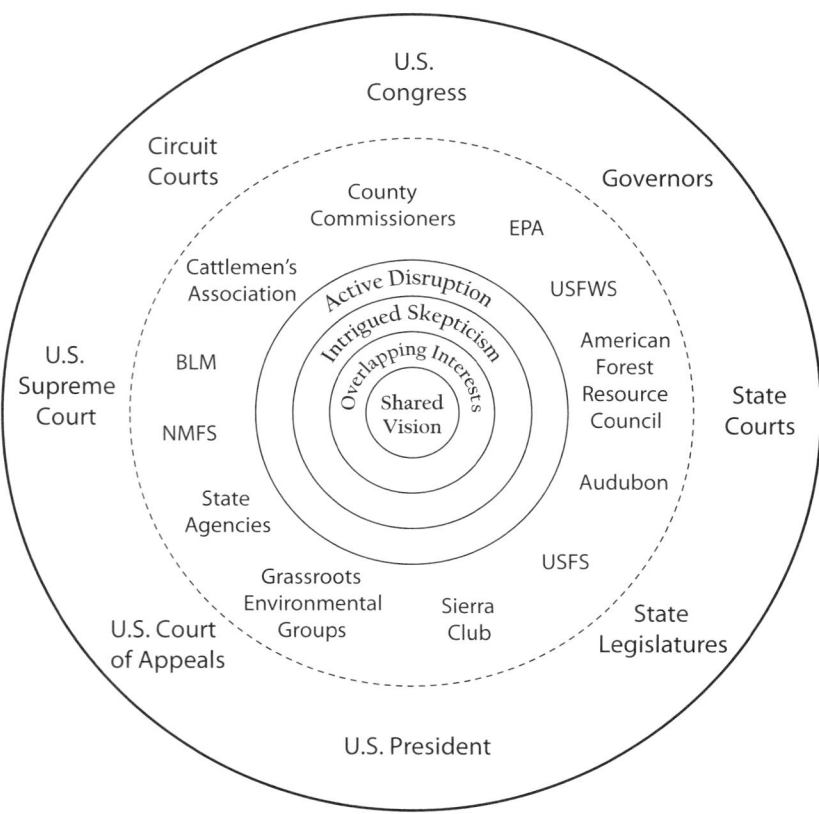

Figure 8.9 *A Collaboration Universe: Rings of engagement of a collaboration group, nested within a variety of interested groups and agencies, and those groups and agencies nested, in turn, within the broader political environment.*

**The Broader Political Context**    The interest that people or groups have in collaborative solutions depends on what they can achieve in other ways, or in other venues, such as the courts, Congress, state legislatures, and the federal or state executive branch (Figure 8.9). Thus, *the dynamics of the policy arena, which we discussed in Chapter 6, can increase or decrease the effectiveness of the collaboration group*, due to the effects of policy and political changes on the BATNAs of collaborative participants. For example, if congressional legislation or court decisions change the legal framework for natural resource decisions, the USFWS decides to list (or not list) a species as threatened or endangered, or elections change the political party that occupies the White House (the presidency), the interest of participants in further collaborative effort may change accordingly.

## Evaluate Whether You Have the Elements for Success

Suppose you and others feel that a collaborative effort could help you solve a natural resource problem. What characteristics or conditions are needed for you to be successful? We have mentioned many of them earlier in this chapter, but here we pull them together in one place. We first present a brief, general summary of key elements, largely drawn from earlier parts of the chapter or our experience. Then we present a comprehensive, research-based assessment of collaboratives, specifically involved in community-based public forest management.

**A Short Checklist**   We suggest five fundamental elements are needed for a successful collaboration on a contentious problem:

1. Many of those involved or affected by the issue at hand, and representing more than just one side of the issue, are unhappy with the existing situation.

2. They feel stuck in this existing situation.

3. An option can be found that simultaneously advances their differing interests.

4. The proposed agreements are better than their BATNAs.

5. Those in the collaboration are able to convince others (on their side) as needed of the merits of the agreement. Often, participants must take the proposed agreement to headquarters for approval. As we said above, things can easily fall apart at this stage.

It is also very helpful to meet three additional conditions:

1. It is legally feasible to implement the agreement under current law and regulation.

2. It is financially feasible to implement the agreement under current budgets.

3. The decision maker (responsible official) supports the agreement.

We characterize these three conditions as helpful, but not essential, because laws and budgets change as do decision makers, especially if such changes will solve an important policy problem. However, the need for such changes reduces the likelihood of implementation of any agreement.

Some collaborative efforts may come into being as a means of solving a single problem, then dissolve when the problem no longer exists. Others may attain a more permanent status and become an important component of decision-making frameworks for a community. We suggest three more conditions for collaboratives to function successfully over time:

1. The broader community, of which the collaborative is a part, has the capacity and desire to support the collaborative and help it grow. If the people the collaborative participants see in their everyday life are not supportive, or their efforts are not recognized, it will be hard to keep the collaborative process going.

2. The agency or organization that administers the resource that is the subject of concern of the collaborative (e.g., forest, watershed, park, fishery) supports the collaborative's efforts. It is one thing for an individual decision maker to be unsupportive (a decision maker can always be replaced), but agency resistance to collaborative efforts can undermine the collaborative, rendering its efforts largely a waste of time.

3. The collaborative itself evolves into more than a collection of a few key individuals. People move, die, and wear out. Among the greatest challenges to collaborative groups on our public lands is finding the next cohort of leaders ready to give time and energy to the effort.

**A Comprehensive Assessment**   Collaboratives have operated long enough and have been transparent enough for researchers to undertake a comprehensive analysis of what makes them function well over time and for researchers to develop a framework for organizing desirable features and traits. Toward that end, Cheng and Sturtevant (2012) developed a comprehensive framework for assessing *collaborative capacity* in *community-based public forest management*—the type of collaborative to which we give much attention in this chapter. They derived their framework from case study research and observations of 30 federal forest-related collaborative efforts. Largely, these groups were self-organizing and self-governing.

Cheng and Sturtevant (2012) first focus on the underlying capability of a community to solve problems, or "the interaction of human capital, organizational resources, and social capital existing within a given community that can be leveraged to solve collective problems and improve or maintain the well-being of a given community" (Chaskin, 2001, p. 295). *Social capital*, the norms and networks that facilitate collective action (Beckley et al., 2008), is seen as particularly important, since it provides the fabric of relationships that enable and promote collaboration. Social capital itself can grow through collaborative efforts. They emphasize that the greater the underlying community capability for problem solving, the greater the chances that a collaborative effort within the community will succeed over time. It is also true, as we see with the Blue Mountains Forest Partners, that collaborative efforts can help build this community capability (Box 8.3).

Based on the scientific literature and their case studies, Cheng and Sturtevant (2012), then build a framework for assessing collaborative capacity around six arenas of collaborative action, and provide advice on how to build capacity in each arena. Some of their key points for each arena are:

### Organizing

- Leadership is essential in determining the fate of a collaborative; community, organizational, and agency leaders can build support and allocate resources for the collaborative's benefit.

- Collaboratives must find a way to organize and sustain themselves by obtaining and utilizing skills, knowledge, and assets to activate and sustain participation by a broad spectrum of respected people in the community.

- Collaboratives with formalized structures and work groups tend to be more adept than informal groups in attracting resources and managing projects.

### Learning

- A fundamental attribute of public forest collaboration is an emphasis on learning so that all have shared understandings of the situation and potential improvements, as documented in the case study on social learning by Schusler et al. (2003) discussed earlier in the chapter and also noted by Daniels and Walker (2001). Fostering conscious collective self-reflection and learning through interactions in a group setting can be the key to collaborative success.

- Some individuals need to assume leadership roles in thinking systematically and effectively communicating to foster group learning.

- Participants need to *actively listen* and to shift their points of view to better align with new information and shared learning—the essence of social learning as we discussed previously.

### Deciding

- Individuals within the collaborative need good negotiation skills (see the section above on mutual gains solutions) and the authority to make decisions on behalf of their home organizations.

- Collaboratives need a shared knowledge of the set of decisions they can influence and the ability to conduct strategic planning to guide their efforts to influence those decisions.

### Acting

- Collaboratives need to be able to translate goals and priorities into operationally feasible actions, and to acquire and coordinate human, technical, and financial resources to take part in project implementation.

- Collaboratives also must able to affect institutional and policy changes needed to facilitate implementation.

### Evaluating

- Collaboratives should possess the skills, knowledge, and resources to help monitor outcomes, evaluate effectiveness, and adapt changes to future activities.

### Legitimizing

- At least in the beginning, collaboratives need to convince a diverse set of institutions that a new set of relationships, which collaboratives can help provide, are needed between communities and public forests.

- Over time, collaboratives need to demonstrate that they can function in a way that obeys laws and regulations, includes a broad diversity of perspectives and interests, does not allow any one entity to dominate the process, employs consensus-based decision making, and uses currently available science.

## Recognize the Limits of Collaboration

When collaborative processes work, they can transform warring parties into cooperative participants in wonderfully creative solutions to difficult resource problems. That cooperative spirit can uplift whole communities (see Box 8.3, Blue Mountains Forest Partners). Still, collaboration is not the silver bullet for all natural resource problems or issues. We describe here some of the limitations of collaboration:

- Collaboration can be time-consuming and inefficient. It may take months or years for a collaboration group to produce many useful ideas. If you need an answer tomorrow, starting a collaboration group is probably not the approach to take. On the other hand, working with such a group over time can enable quick action by the collaboration group when a crisis comes.

- The collaborative effort may not get there—they might not be able to agree on anything. In the end, the BATNAs of the respective participants may get the better of the effort. Unfortunately (or in some instances, fortunately) the political dynamics in the outside world may shift, making yesterday's agreements obsolete.

- People may not function well in a collaborative setting. Collaborative efforts, as emphasized in this chapter, rely on the give-and-take of face-to-face meetings, often in a local community near the forest (or other resource) of concern. This process is not ideal for everyone who might want to have a say in decisions involving a collaborative—some people might not function well in a group setting, some live a long way from the where meetings take place, and some people just want to state their positions and go home.

- The collaborative process may unfairly favor those who have the time, energy, and location to participate. Some argue that community-based collaboratives, that we emphasize here, tend to favor local interests over national interests (McClosky, 1999). While the linkage of local participants to national groups may mitigate this effect, it does not entirely go away. In addition, processes that take extended time commitments, as collaboratives often do, tend to favor people paid to be there as compared to those who volunteer. Thus collaborative groups are one important mechanism for improving decisions, especially on federal lands, but cannot be the only social mechanism connecting the public to the forest.

- Not all questions or problems are inherently amenable to the collaborative approach outlined here. As an example, questions about the way the world works, whether coming from the perspective of science or local traditional knowledge, do not necessarily lend themselves to a group of interested citizens reaching a consensus decision. While a social learning process with joint fact-finding can make important contributions to common understanding, the underlying knowledge at issue is not entirely amenable to negotiation.

- Most fundamentally, collaborative groups composed of affected stakeholders may not be able to take on some important problems. Collaborative solutions, as we describe them here, rely on finding mutual gains, i.e., on solutions that advance the interests of the participants in the collaborative. Not all natural resource problems have the potential for such solutions. In fact, many of the major forest resource shifts in this country, whether they be creation of the national forests or the development of the Northwest Forest Plan, did not arise from collaborative processes. In these instances, decisions were going to result in winners and losers, and there was really no way to paper that over; political leaders made those decisions with different groups influencing them as best they could.

Collaboratives often try to avoid dealing with those types of problems as they can threaten the groups' existence. As an example, a number of collaboratives in Oregon involve private landowners and conservation groups working on how to improve salmon habitat in coastal streams. They have made significant progress identifying where culverts should be replaced on private lands to allow fish passage and obtaining funds to do that. In general, though, they have not tackled whether state forest-practice regulations provide sufficient buffers on streams, an issue that could tear the collaborative apart.

## Successful Conflict Management and Dispute Resolution as a Forest Manager [2]

Suppose you are forest manager of public lands, say a USFS District Ranger, or a state or county forester. Your ecological forestry ideas are being challenged on all sides; industry says there will not be enough timber volume produced and environmentalists say your proposed work will destroy the forest. You realize you have little chance of getting anything done without some coming together of the disparate interests. We will assume that you have read the earlier sections of this chapter on working with people to find mutual-gain solutions, but you wish to have some additional guidance specifically for professional resource managers.

Before we begin, we might review some basic assumptions about natural resource decisions that we will make here:

- Natural resource decisions nearly always involve disputes over deeply held values.

- People/groups generally work from a model of self-interest, although many also desire a sense of community.

- People/groups will participate in a conflict resolution/collaboration process if there is no better alternative to achieve their goals.

- Effective conflict resolution/collaboration inevitably involves the sharing of power by professionals with stakeholders, but NOT the abdication of decision-making responsibility (a delicate balance).

This is not going to be easy!

In this section, we present some ideas on how a forest manager can successfully work in a collaborative way on public forest management issues. We differentiate between traditional and collaborative approaches to working with stakeholders and the public, provide an example of a national forest that has made the big shift in public engagement, stress the importance of creating a shared learning and problem-solving environment, and address the issue of trust—the cornerstone of successful collaborations.

Many of us who got our professional education in the last century were imbued with the mantra, "professionals know best," as we discussed at the beginning of this chapter. The collaborative approach we have discussed in this chapter provides an alternative view. Rather than "we have the answers," collaboration for professional managers begins

---

2  Many of the ideas in this section started with *Public Lands Conflict and Resolution: Managing National Forest Disputes* by Julia Wondolleck (1988), a wonderful book that greatly influenced the thinking of Norm Johnson. Julia has been a leader in collaboration theory and practice ever since, and continues to this day (see also Wondolleck and & Yaffee [2000]).

with a heartfelt indication that "we need your help" (Table 8.3). If managers do not sincerely believe this, they should not bother to engage in or encourage a collaborative effort, as everyone involved will be sadly disappointed. People can smell a traditional approach a mile away, and it soon will become obvious to everyone that the so-called collaboration is nothing more than window dressing.

**Making the Big Shift** Collaborations rely on creativity that emerges through the interaction of people with different perspectives and abilities. Successful collaborations are an emergent, improvisational, and nonlinear learning and problem-solving process. Generally, managers do not control collaborations or run them. Often, managers are not even officially part of them. Managers can greatly influence their chances of success, though, as described by Jerry Ingersoll, supervisor of the Siuslaw National Forest, whose forest has won many awards for collaboration (Box 8.8).

## Creating a Shared Learning and Problem-Solving Environment

Collaboration is more than the just art of the deal; technical knowledge is still important. Scientific and technical knowledge is necessary to provide a foundation for discussion, to help delineate realistic options and their implications, and to help translate scientific findings into a framework for management. The more that a shared learning environment can be developed, the more the collaboration group can become a cohesive unit for addressing problems and developing solutions. Professional resource managers have a key role in creating a productive collaborative environment. This includes:

- *Be open and candid.* Provide information in ways that people can make up their own mind, fairly address the scientific basis of plans and policies, and recognize uncertainties in policy and plan success.

- *Acknowledge the need for joint learning (we learn from you; you learn from us).* Be willing to listen to different points of view about the way the world works, be willing to seek outside expertise, and build a common language.

- *Create an environment for joint investigation of controversial claims and issues.* Encourage independent review of your efforts and ideas. For instance, if someone claims that you are not keeping your word to leave trees over 150 years of age, or to maintain marten habitat, don't be defensive. Ask where this happened.

Table 8.3 *Highlights of traditional and collaborative approaches*

| Traditional approach | Collaborative approach |
|---|---|
| We have the answers. | We need your help. |
| Professionals have knowledge and solutions; the public has issues and values. | We all have knowledge, solutions, issues, and values. |
| Give us your input. | Let's jointly develop ideas. |
| People should get out of the way and let professionals do their job. | We need to work collectively to create options and solutions. |

Arrange for a credible review by a recognized expert. If possible, schedule a field trip for members of the collaborative to see the offending action as we described in Box 8.4. Decide together what claims and issues need investigation and work together on a method for that investigation. Find ways for the collaboration group to take part in the investigative effort.

## Trust: The Cornerstone of Successful Collaborative Efforts [3]

Trust has been identified as a crucial element of multiple forms of natural resource management processes and outcomes in numerous studies, whether they be compliance with park regulations, social acceptability of management decisions and planning efforts, or collaboration, conflict resolution, or enhanced group performance (Sharp, Thwaites, Curtis, & Millar, 2012; Shindler et al., 2014). In fact, if you read much collaboration literature, you will see that trust is the currency of collaboration—*the higher the level of trust in a collaboration group, the more the group is able to accomplish*. What is *trust* anyway? A useful definition is *belief that someone or something is reliable, good, honest, and effective.* [4]

Much of the advice in this chapter on working with people relates to increasing the level of trust in a collaborative effort. This requires creating an environment in which people feel comfortable putting down their ideological armor and working with others—people with whom they may have been in conflict with for years—because they begin to view others as trustworthy.

---

3 This section depends heavily on the synthesis work on trust building by Dr. Bruce Shindler and his colleagues at Oregon State University, especially Shindler, Brunson, and Stankey (2002) and Shindler et al. (2014).

4 http://www.merriam-webster.com/dictionary/trust. A more formal definition is "a psychological state in which one actor (the trustor) accepts some form of vulnerability based on positive expectations of the intentions or behavior of another (the trustee) despite inherent uncertainties in the expectation" (Stern and Coleman, 2015).

Four conditions make trust an important ingredient in relations among people (adapted from Sharp et al., 2012 and Shindler et al., 2014):

1. *Interdependence*: Situations in which the interests of one party cannot be fulfilled without depending on the actions of another.

2. *Uncertainty*: Situations in which the physical and social conditions are complex and continue to change.

3. *Personal risk*: Situations where people are vulnerable to the actions of others. These situations often require a leap of faith that others

---

**Box 8.8  Leadership the Siuslaw Way** *

**The Siuslaw National Forest Brand**

The Siuslaw is known for *Restoration, Recreation, and Partnerships*. We're pioneers in ecosystem restoration and provide outstanding coastal recreational experiences. We're trusted. We get things done. Our partners tell our story.

But our brand is as much about *how* we operate as what we do. We work naturally in a multiparty environment, sharing responsibility, authority, and resources with a wide range of partners. We encourage leadership wherever we find it. We take care of each other. We care more about results—caring for the land and serving people—than about the process, or even who gets credit.

**Leadership Principles**

The following leadership principles express the essence of the Siuslaw culture. They're expressed as ideals and, of course, we sometimes fall short of them. But articulating our ideals helps us to know who we are and what we aspire to be:

1. We Don't Need to Drive the Bus

The Siuslaw takes leadership wherever it is found. A GS-5 employee can lead a major regional initiative. A watershed council can contract restoration projects on National Forest System land. A third-party can facilitate a working group. Actually, that's the way we prefer it. Our role can be convener, facilitator, advisor, participant, or leader, as needed. In our work, leadership roles are taken by whoever is best able to accomplish each individual mission. We have a keen stake in where the bus is going. *We make sure we're on the bus.* We can drive when that's what's necessary. *But we don't need to drive the bus*.

2. We're All Ambassadors

All employees can speak for the Siuslaw National Forest, and all partners can speak for the work we do. We err on the side of open dialogue rather than message control, and accept uncertainty as a natural part of the process. We trust each other's motives while respecting different points of view—we can disagree without being disagreeable. We encourage partners and employees to utilize all forms of communication, with only those internal controls required at the regional and national level. Our goal is not only to tell our own story of success but to have our partners tell successful stories of working with us to care for the land and serve people, in their own words.

3. Process? We Don't Need Much Process!

The Siuslaw takes pride in operating with a minimum of formal organizational structure. We're a *flat* organization with few standing committees or formal processes for decision making. When an issue arises, the critical players come together and resolve it themselves. Ad hoc approaches and teams apply to everything from work planning to project management to external collaboration. The Forest Leadership Team provides strategic guidance and information sharing rather than management controls.

4. Trust and Responsibility are Keys to Our Success

The Siuslaw culture requires a high degree of trust and open communications among partners, employees, and managers. We don't need to drive the bus because we share a commitment to the bus's destination. We can all speak for the Siuslaw because we share a consistent message and vision. We don't need formal committees because we include all parties in decisions affecting them.

If we fail to include key players, we abuse that trust, and ultimately lose it. So it is incumbent on each participant and every employee to ensure they've established trust, participation, and common purpose—with their supervisors, their colleagues, and their partners.

5. Leaders Still Play an Important Role

Supervisors and line officers play a key integrating role. It's our responsibility to articulate strategic priorities across program areas. It's our responsibility to balance workloads, choose among competing agendas, establish a trusting atmosphere, and resolve differences that can't be solved collaboratively. Supervisors on the Siuslaw generally set expectations in terms of desired outcomes and allow maximum latitude in terms of means. The more that supervisors, employees, and partners are able to express a common purpose and vision, the more each are free to take action to support that vision.

---

* Adapted from the annual "State of the Forest" letter sent by Jerry Ingersoll, supervisor of the Siuslaw National Forest, to all employees in 2014.

will act responsibly. In this sense, the presence of risk creates the opportunity for trust.

4. *Expectations*: Situations in which others must fulfill their obligations in a relationship for success. Essentially, this is faith in both the ability and follow-through of others, whether it be agencies or other citizens.

When we think about it, we can understand how a forestry collaborative will often have these elements. Interdependence is there—the power of a collaborative comes from the members jointly proposing actions. Uncertainty usually exists, whether it is about forest processes and conditions, evolving scientific knowledge, or changing political context. A willingness of collaborative members to take personal risks—to move off past conditions and embrace new ideas—is a function, in part, of their belief that others will reciprocate and not regress once they leave the room. Expectations abound that the members will go out into the broader community, including to their own peers, and fairly tell the story of what has been accomplished, why it is a good idea, and why decision makers will seriously consider recommendations from the collaborative.

**The Art of Trust Building**    It is also true that skepticism—rather than trust—will usually be the starting point in most interactions, both among members of collaboratives and between those members and any agency they are trying to advise and influence. In these situations, a lack of trust may be beneficial when it promotes healthy skepticism and associated critical thinking. For example, potential participants might evaluate the level of expertise among managers, whether local concerns will get adequate attention, or whether a person or agency will act responsibly. The parties will need to trust each other enough to allow them to begin to work together, develop and examine options, and eventually agree on decisions. From a practical standpoint, people need time and experience before they come to trust others. In this way, healthy skepticism can help foster respectful discussion and deliberation (Parkins, 2010; Shindler et al., 2014).

*It is useful to think about trust building as a spiral-like process in which the positive feedback from successful agreements enables the collaborative group to take on ever more challenging tasks* (Figure 8.10). When participants first interact, they form expectations about intended outcomes and how others will contribute to achieving them, often based on reputations and past behaviors. However, sufficient trust must

exist for the parties to risk entering into a cooperative effort. Thus, the need (often) is to start with simpler, less controversial projects (Shindler et al., 2014). To put it another way, building trustworthy relations may be most realistic at the forest or ranger district level, essentially **places where the war won't be won or lost** (Shindler & Neburka, 1997).

Each time an outcome meets expectations, trust is reinforced. That outcome becomes part of the relationship, increasing the likelihood of further positive interaction. Increased trust reduces the sense of risk among parties and provides the basis for more ambitious efforts, enabling work on more complex projects as needed (Figure 8.10).

**Central Factors in Trust Building**    Research from forest and range communities confirms the importance of a genuine participation process in building trustworthy relations (Shindler et al., 2002). As an example, Shindler and Aldred-Cheek (1999) conducted an examination of citizen–agency interactions and concluded that effective, trustworthy relations could be organized around six common factors: (1) inclusiveness, (2) sincere leadership, (3) innovative and flexible methods, (4) early commitment and continuity, (5) sound organizational and planning skills, and (6) efforts that result in action. Shindler and Aldred-Cheek further note that having good scientific data is certainly useful, but that outcomes were more credible and relations were strengthened when managers invited citizens to help analyze information to form new alternatives, new knowledge, and new solutions. Across all cases they studied, interactions between even the most strongly opposed groups tended to soften as people, over time, got to know others around the table and realized their personal concerns were common concerns. The authors found that genuine dialogue and real listening that occurs when people

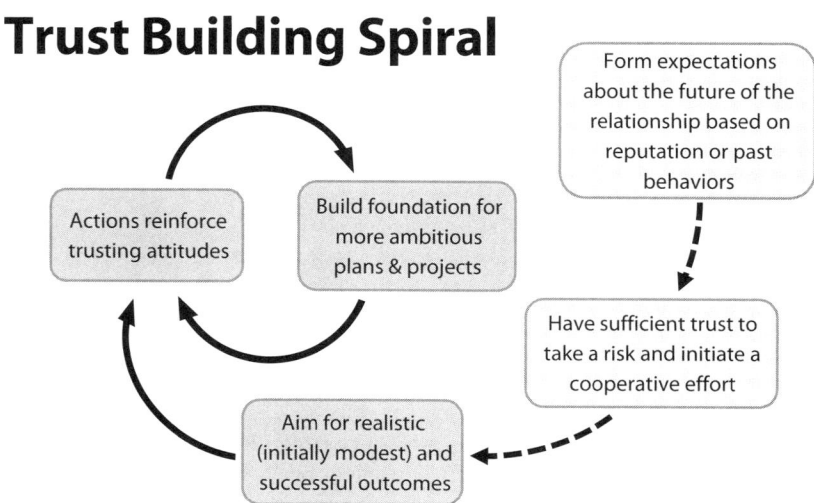

# Trust Building Spiral

Form expectations about the future of the relationship based on reputation or past behaviors

Build foundation for more ambitious plans & projects

Actions reinforce trusting attitudes

Have sufficient trust to take a risk and initiate a cooperative effort

Aim for realistic (initially modest) and successful outcomes

Figure 8.10  *A trust-building spiral that enables consideration of ever more complex and controversial projects. (Source: Adapted from Shindler et al., 2014)*

begin to discuss problems, lay out the range of options, and eventually see patterns in their interactions is a key to finding acceptable solutions.

It also must be noted that stakeholders don't place the same level of trust in all parties in a controversy. This is reflected in differences between personal trust and institutional trust. Shindler (2000), for example, found that many citizens have a personal relationship with local resource managers but are skeptical of the larger organization's motives. In addition, individuals who view nature as fragile, and therefore focus their attention on environmental risks, tend to trust traditional institutions less than they trust citizen groups (Steel, Shindler, & Brunson, 1998). Stakeholders, though, repeatedly said that developing trust is more likely when resource professionals articulate their reasons for involving the public and then make good on their commitments (Shindler & Aldred-Cheek, 1999).

As emphasized by Shindler et al. (2014, p. 4):

*Central factors in building trust—and sustaining the trust-building loop—most always involve skillful communication and attention to group dynamics that help foster meaningful give-and-take. These more informal interactions are perhaps the most productive form of relationship building. Thus, coming to trust one another is about building relationships. Certainly, this means attention to open, interactive approaches as a way to include multiple parties who have a stake in the outcomes. This will involve giving people a chance to air their concerns or ideas, understand one another's views, and creating an atmosphere in which individuals can find common values among many positions . . . Stakeholders will see a more collaborative approach as recognition that their opinions are valued and utilized. This working style builds both community and agency capacity for reaching good decisions.*

*Another feature of the trust-building loop is the importance of procedural elements. These are the formal mechanisms that help assure equity and achieve balance in deliberations. These include identifying each participant's role, how decisions will be made, and who will make them. Essentially, these are guidelines for how people will work together.*

Although we believe that increasing levels of trust among participants facilitates effective collaboration, we must acknowledge that high levels of trust may engender less skepticism, less critical analysis, and less interest in asking questions or challenging dominant discourses on the part of participants. Parkins (2010) found such a result in his study of public advisory committees for large timber companies in Alberta, Canada, which hold long-term management agreements on public lands under sustainable

forestry objectives. As the relationship between the companies and the advisory committees developed, "committee members were much more willing to take a passive role in group settings, relying primarily on a cultivated sense of trust in the company and government officials to do the right thing" (Parkins, 2010, p. 833). To counter these tendencies, he argues for maintaining a more critically engaged membership through:

1.  Seeking a broad range of public values in members (with the caveat that these advocates adhere to the norms of procedures of democratic processes—a willingness to learn and to find common ground);

2.  Ensuring that committee members take leadership positions, organizing and leading meetings, with less dominance by company or government officials; and

3.  Tapping into the constellation of public discourses on forest management, through rotating membership or hearing occasionally from people who are not regular members to aid group learning about contentious topics.

In combining elements of general trust with skepticism, Parkins (2010) calls this approach "critical trust."

**Characteristics of Trustworthiness**    Researchers have identified three general qualities that foster trust in natural resource management settings (Sharp et al., 2012; Shindler et al., 2014).

1.  *Ability*: Perceptions of knowledge, skill and competence in others. Characteristics that demonstrate this component include professional expertise, leadership and decision-making skills, and open communication about risks and benefits.

2.  *Goodwill*: The extent to which an individual believes others will act in their best interests. Characteristics demonstrating this component include sincerity, inclusiveness (giving others a say), responsiveness, and empathy for negative impacts that a decision may have on values that individuals hold dear.

3.  *Integrity*: Belief that others are acting in accord with a set of values and norms shared by the community. This component includes fairness, transparent decisions, reliability, and promise keeping.

These characteristics may apply to trust placed in individuals or trust placed in agencies (Shindler et al., 2014).

We will illustrate trust building, relative to these three characteristics, for a federal forest manager in the USA, such as a district ranger or forest supervisor. Usually, a forest collaborative is a group of citizens who come together to pool their ideas on projects and planning with the belief that, should the group reach agreement, the decision maker will give them a fair hearing and seriously consider their ideas. The members generally are volunteers (that is, not in the employment of the professional resource manager), so they may abandon their efforts at collaboration if they come to believe they will not get that fair hearing. Especially at the beginning, relationships within the collaborative may be fragile, so it behooves the manager to think deeply about how best to build trust with the group. We list below *contributory actions* to trust building that a forest manager might make utilizing both Schindler et al. (2014) and our own ideas.

*Ability—Perceptions within the collaborative of the knowledge, skills, and competencies of the forest manager.*

- Utilize on-the-ground projects as vehicles for all to teach and learn; encourage questions of your proposed actions.

- Describe the trade-offs of management alternatives as you see them, but acknowledge uncertainties where they exist.

- Demonstrate the ability to listen and understand new or different points of view.

- Encourage scientific review of plans and projects, including inviting scientists to give their latest findings on relevant issues.

*Goodwill—The extent to which stakeholders believe the forest manager will act in their best interest.*

- Let the collaborative know the problem on which you would like their help, and be open to addressing problems that they identify.

- Encourage locally derived solutions and value local experience.

- Use neutral, respectful language—don't tag people with labels like, "Well, I see the environmentalists are here today."

- Treat everyone the same—don't just greet your friends or hang out with them when you come to collaborative meetings, or give them information you do not share with others.

- Acknowledge the legitimacy of the major interests and values represented in the collaborative. Be careful that you do not send signals that, in reality, you really favor one of them.

- Don't assume that you know someone's point of view, or prevent them from giving it. It is hard to hear views with which we disagree. Still, that is often the price to be paid to get from positions to interests—being willing to hear everyone out.

- Through your words and your actions, make sure the collaborative knows that you take their suggestions very seriously (e.g., willingness to talk to them, the tone you set with your employees and with folks around town).

*Integrity—the extent to which the forest manager is acting in accord with acceptable values and norms.*

- Be open and honest about your goals and the limitations on your actions; let the collaborative know your decision space. If you have budget constraints, let them know. If you must reach a certain allowable cut, let them know. Don't surprise them later with news that you really can't implement the project on which they worked so hard to develop.

- Provide consistent leadership—don't at one time tell the group that budgets are not an issue, and the next time say your hands are tied because of budgets (unless you can explain how things have changed).

- Give the same message to all groups. It is natural to want people to like you; this can lead you to tilt your message toward the views of whomever you are speaking with. Such an approach, though, almost always will have negative consequences for you once people with different views compare notes about what you have said.

- Do what you say you will do (keep your word). If you say you plan to implement a suggestion from the group, you better do it or have a darn good reason why you did not. If you say you will leave trees over 150 years in the stand when you thin it, you sure better try, to the best of your ability, to leave them.

## Some Concluding Thoughts

The rise of collaborative efforts to navigate disputes over natural resources is one of the defining changes in natural resource management in the last 30 years. In some ways, it reflects deep conflicts over conservation and natural resource use, and the loss of trust in professionals and governments to decide, on their own, what is best for the land, the landowners, and society in general.

This change has been especially apparent in the management of public resources. As noted by Kathleen McGinley (2017, p. 474) in writing on natural resource participation, collaboration, and partnerships, "as public participation evolved to provide substance to policies in addition to accountability from policy makers . . . , government shifted toward 'governance' in many cases and places. Public, private, and civil society roles reorganized and restructured, interacting and engaging in altered and new ways, leading to more involved and enduring collaborative arrangements and partnerships."

We argue throughout this book that ecological forestry is inherently compatible with collaboration in that it seeks to retain forest ecosystem structures and processes, which, in turn, eases the recognition and integration of a wide variety of ecological, economic, and social values. As collaboration groups work toward management practices that have broad support, we hope and believe that ecological forestry can provide a helpful framework for such efforts.

*We have theorized that the economics man would not use land for growing timber unless the returns represented an acceptable rate of compound interest on all investments. . . . This thoroughly logical theory about what a pure economics man would not do is often automatically transmuted into a doctrine about what no man should do.*— DAVID SMITH

# CHAPTER 9
# Capital, Income, and Sustainability

Since at least the middle of the 19th century, a debate has raged in forestry about whether or not a forest should be viewed as financial capital and managed according to the concepts and tools of investment analysis. As an example, the first forest regulation book in the United States (Roth, 1925) acknowledged this debate and the dilemma it caused in setting rotation ages, with *financial rotations* often much shorter than foresters wished.

Forestry has three features that make the discussion about whether to view forests as financial capital central to forest management decisions (Davis et al., 2001): (1) forestry is a very *capital intensive* enterprise due to the value of the standing trees, which usually make up most of the financial value of a forest business; (2) the capital in these trees is relatively *liquid* for much of the life of a stand—trees can be turned into revenue through harvest; and (3) forestry has relatively long production periods compared to other endeavors—anywhere from tens to hundreds of years. As we shall see, combining financial capital and time through something called *compound interest* can work strongly against keeping the forest intact.

Perhaps not surprisingly, consideration of whether to view the forest as financial capital, to be treated as any other investment, helps to separate production forestry from ecological forestry, as we discussed in Chapter 1. In production forestry, the forest is seen as a financial instrument much like a mutual fund. In this view, capital is capital, whatever its source, and nonproductive capital is transferred to other investments, with financial performance measured by rate of return on capital. Ecological forestry, in contrast, recognizes the importance and potential uniqueness of natural capital, where natural capital can be defined as "a stock that yields a flow of natural services and tangible natural resources. This includes solar energy, land, minerals, . . . water, living organisms, and the services provided by the interactions of all of these elements in ecological systems" (Daly & Farley, 2011, p. 17). In some cases, this natural capital is considered *critical natural capital*, which cannot be

*The Deumling family in their forest in the Willamette Valley of western Oregon. (© Andrea Lonas)*

substituted with other forms of natural or man-made capital without the possibility of causing irreversible or immoderate losses in ecosystem function, in turn diminishing or destroying ecosystem services that landowners and society seek from forests (Ekins et al., 2003). As an example, the multitude of ecosystem services provided by standing dead and down trees may cause these trees to be viewed as critical natural capital for which substitutes generally do not exist. Recognition of critical natural capital constrains the use of classical investment analysis in decisions or makes it largely irrelevant. We discuss these differing views of natural capital in the three sections of this chapter.

In the first and longest section of the chapter, we lay out the principles, concepts, and analytical approaches used in classical investment analysis and illustrate their application on a hypothetical family forest property. Such an approach is widely used in business, taught in forestry schools, and appears extensively throughout the forest economics literature. Our goal here is to help you understand the assumptions, terms, and concepts of investment analysis so you can discuss them with confidence and judge their potential usefulness to your management objectives in different situations.

In the second section, we consider the financial concerns for the large array of landowners, including families, communities, tribes, conservation organizations, and large public properties, whose primary goal is not return on capital. While these landowners have significant economic interests, they need measures of financial performance other than rate of return. We argue that a focus on the production of income over time, in the context of their other goals, better serves the interests of many of these landowners.

In the third section, we discuss the relationship of capital management to sustainability and intergenerational equity. We revisit weak and strong sustainability in the context of two important concepts: (1) providing for nondeclining per capita human well-being through time as a measure of equity across generations, and (2) recognizing and conserving natural capital that is critical to sustaining ecosystems and humankind. In this way, we hope to relate the somewhat isolated and peculiar topic of financial analysis to larger social and philosophical themes.

## Classical Investment Analysis: A Primer

Suppose you decide to form a consulting firm called "Ecological Forestry Services" to assist landowners who wish to pursue the ideas in this book. To get started, you place a small ad with that title in the local paper. Over the first few weeks business is slow, but soon local forest landowners begin to hear about you. Still, you learn they are suspicious about your firm because most of their experience with ecologists has been with people who, in their view, want to shut down forestry.

To gain a hearing, you ask to speak at the family forest association. One pleasant fall evening, about 30 people gather. You look out at your audience, most of whom are many years your senior, and begin with a short discussion of the meaning of ecological forestry and the joys that it can bring. When you finish, a hand shoots up and an elderly gentleman says, "I appreciate all that you're saying. We all love our forests and the creatures living in them, and you make a powerful argument for ecological forestry. However, you haven't covered how we are going to pay for all this and make a little money each year for our kids and our own health care." Then his son says, "You have not told us whether ecological forestry would be a good investment." You gulp and realize you are not ready to have that discussion.

In another instance, perhaps your firm has been hired by The Nature Conservancy (TNC) to investigate the purchase of a forest tract containing habitat for a wildlife species of concern. More specifically, the TNC would like you to estimate the *fair market value* of the property. To do that you may look at other similar properties that have sold in the area. You also might need to estimate *value in use*, which generally requires that you estimate the net discounted value of the forest based on the stream of income it could produce.[1]

Beyond the need for understanding discounted value analysis for discussions about investment performance and appraisal, mastering the rudiments of investment analysis will enable you to better understand the conceptual models that underlie production forestry. This thinking is most clearly seen in the rise of Timber Investment Management Organizations (TIMOs) and Real Estate Investment Trusts (REITs) in private forest management. TIMOs and REITs have elevated *rate of return* to the paramount decision criterion in production forestry for buying and selling forests, determining when to harvest, and deciding how much to invest in wood production. Knowledge of investment analysis will prepare you for policy discussions about the TIMO/REIT approach to forest management—an approach that has become a national and worldwide phenomenon in production forestry (Box 9.1).

## Interest: Paying for the Use of Capital

When people *invest*, they acquire a capital asset, such as a stock or bond or rental house that produces goods or services for which they anticipate receiving rent, revenue, or other utilities. Over the period of an investment, the investor expects to receive some increment above what he or she originally paid; this increment is called interest. In the world of finance, investors expect this payment as compensation for foregoing alternative uses of their financial capital; after all, by investing financial resources in

---

1 We will study different types of appraisals in depth in the next chapter.

## Box 9.1  The TIMO/REIT investment mentality and forest conservation in the United States

Corporate forestland covers less than 20% of the forestland in the United States (Oswalt, Smith, Miles, & Pugh, 2014) but provides much of the softwood timber harvested there. Prior to the 1990s, industrial forestlands were largely owned by lumber and pulp and paper companies to supply their mills, both as a primary supply and as an emergency supply when other sources of wood were not available. Since the 1990s, though, most industrial forestlands have been financially isolated from mill operations and turned into separate profit centers, with the objective of maximizing financial returns. Forestlands once owned by lumber and pulp and paper companies have been reorganized as subsidiaries of the companies, or (more commonly) sold to Timber Investment Management Organizations (TIMOs) or to Real Estate Investment Trusts (REITs), who in turn hire TIMOs to manage the properties (Bliss, Kelly, Abrams, Bailey, & Dyer, 2010; Gunnoe & Gellert, 2011).

A number of factors led to this massive shift of land from vertically integrated industrial firms to TIMOs and REITs. One of the most proximate causes was a change in United States federal tax law in the 1990s, which taxed the profits from timber harvest at higher rates for vertically integrated firms than for forest and land companies without processing facilities, and the desire of shareholders to separate mill operations from forest management to make sure that inefficient mills were not being supported (Bliss et al., 2010; Gunnoe & Gellert, 2011). The globalization of capital markets and the woods products industry were other factors in the change.

Whereas the integrated companies were interested in continuity of supply for their mills and the use of woodlands as an insurance policy against raw material shortages, TIMOs and REITs generally want to maximize their profits from use of forestland. This has a number of implications for forest and conservation:

1. More forestland might be sold for development. TIMOs generally are interested in making the most money they can from their properties, including selling the land for development, unlike past industrial owners who were often more interested in a secure wood supply.

2. Less support may be provided for land-use laws that control development. While past industrial owners often wanted to limit development in the wildland forest to reduce conflicts with timber production, TIMOs and REITs may want to promote development to enable land sales.

3. The focus on financial returns at relatively high interest rates will generally result in shorter rotations as a way to reduce the cost of holding the forest capital (Figures 9.1 and 9.2). The former objectives of supplying wood to a mill over time or keeping trees as an insurance policy for use during log shortages, which may have resulted in longer rotations, no longer applies.

4. Keying harvest time to meeting a specified rate of return, without harvest flow restrictions, will often result in irregular wood flows, unlike the practices of some past owners who also had processing facilities and often wanted a stable supply of wood.

5. Unlike the integrated firms that previously owned the lands, these companies are largely anonymous and do not have a retail brand to protect. Thus, they worry less about incurring public pushback as a result of their management practices. As such, they can be expected to do what the law requires and no more; leaving forest structures (e.g., live trees, snags, and logs) on site beyond legal requirements will occur only if the removal costs are greater than the monetary value from turning those structures into wood products.

6. Highly productive forestland can most easily provide the rate of return demanded by TIMOs and REITs; as a consequence, less productive forestlands (such as

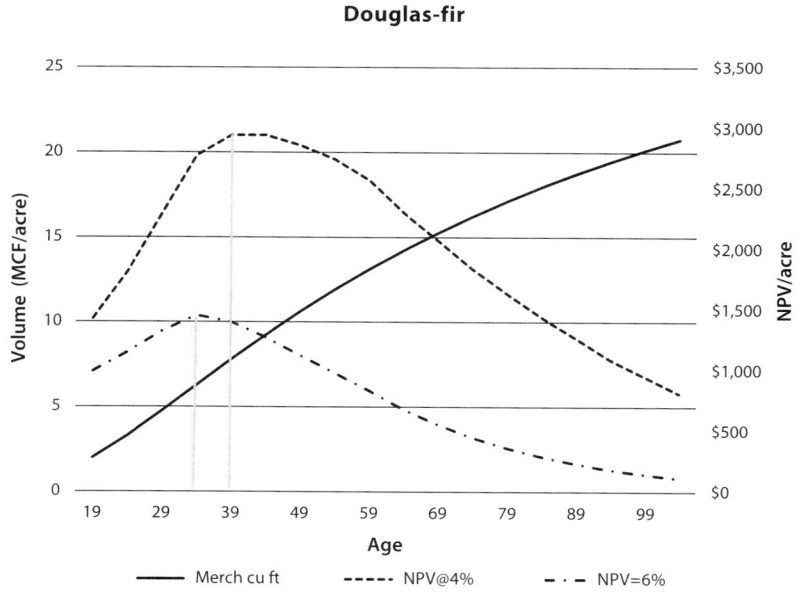

Figure 9.1  *Volume and net present value (NPV) at two interest rates for a Douglas-fir stand in western Oregon at different stand ages. Highest NPV occurs at 39 years (4%) and 33 years (6%). (Volume data source: Oregon State University College Forests; value data source: Department of Revenue, Washington State, 2015).*

*(continued)*

those in the Intermountain West and parts of the Northeast) will likely be sold or converted to some other use, such as real estate development.

7. The focus on financial returns at relatively high interest rates limit investments in the forest, which, in turn, can limit how much effort is put into such practices as herbicide spraying to eliminate shrubs and hardwoods that compete with conifers. This focus on rate of return can have some positive ecological outcomes, such as providing greater potential for diverse early seral habitats in those areas, albeit without much residual woody structure.

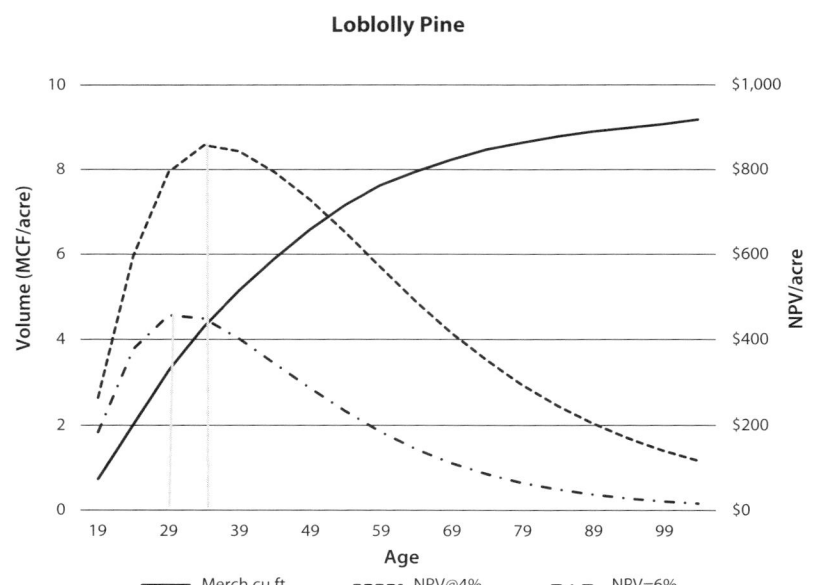

Figure 9.2 *Volume and net present value (NPV) at two interest rates for a loblolly pine stand in the southern US for different stand ages. Highest NPV occurs at 33 years (4%) and 29 years (6%). (Volume data source: USFS Forest Inventory and Analysis [FIA] National Program; value data source: Dickens et al., 2014)*

one thing, they are not available for something else. For example, when we make an investment in forests growing trees, we forego a promising investment in the stock market, or a vacation to the South Pacific. The rate of return associated with an alternative investment is often called the *alternative rate of return*.

A loan is a form of investment; if a bank makes a loan to someone, it generally expects to be paid back a percentage of the original loan amount in addition to the original loan amount. For example, the bank may expect to be paid 10% of the original amount as *interest* on the loan. Of course, there is more to it than that, since we haven't accounted for the *period* of the loan: One day? One year? A decade? Interest is not an especially useful concept unless it is expressed as an amount per unit of time, and as you probably are already aware, interest is often expressed as percent per year, which is the convention we use in our discussions here.

## Compounding and Future Value

Interest has a peculiar property that pleases lenders and investors, and infuriates borrowers—it grows on itself through a process known as *compounding*. If you were to invest one dollar at 10% interest per year for four years, how much would you expect in return? You might calculate the yield of the investment as 10% of the invested amount, multiplied times four years: That amount would be 0.1 × $1.00 × 4 years = $0.40 for the four-year investment, giving you a total of $1.40 at the end of four years. However,

this calculation procedure does not account for the income your investment has accumulated each year—the interest from each year's investment becomes part of the capital of the following year. Had we done so, we would have ended up with an extra six cents at the end of the four-year investment period. Take a look at Table 9.1 to see the year-by-year effects of compounding on our one-dollar investment.

The increment earned in a year rises from year to year because interest is earned not only on the original capital, as occurs in year 1, but also on the accumulated interest, as is shown in years 2, 3, and 4 (Table 9.1). More generally, the relationship between investment amount (present value), interest rate, length of investment, and the cumulative value of the investment (future value) can be expressed as:

$$V_n = V_0 \times (1 + i)^n \qquad \text{(Equation 9.1)}$$

where:

$i$ = periodic interest rate expressed as a decimal

$n$ = number of investment periods—number of periods over which interest will be compounded

$V_0$ = present value—value of the investment at period 0

$V_n$ = future value—value of the investment $n$ periods into the future

Table 9.1 *Compounding the investment of one dollar for four years at an annual interest rate of 10%*

| Year | Cumulative value of investment | | | Annual increment |
|---|---|---|---|---|
| 0 | $1.00 | = $1.00 | = $1.00 | — |
| 1 | $1.00 × (1 + 0.1) | = $1.00 × (1 + 0.1) | = $1.10 | $0.10 |
| 2 | $1.00 × (1 + 0.1)(1 + 0.1) | = $1.00 × (1 + 0.1)$^2$ | = $1.21 | $0.11 |
| 3 | $1.00 × (1 + 0.1)(1 + 0.1)(1 + 0.1) | = $1.00 × (1 + 0.1)$^3$ | = $1.33 | $0.12 |
| 4 | $1.00 × (1 + 0.1)(1 + 0.1)(1 + 0.1)(1 + 0.1) | = $1.00 × (1 + 0.1)$^4$ | = $1.46 | $0.13 |

Compounding at interest rate $i$ for $n$ periods increases the initial value $V_0$ to the future value $V_n$. Note that we haven't expressly said in equation 9.1 how long one investment period is—it could be a month or a year or some

---

**Box 9.2  Doubling your money and the Rule of 72**

Have you always wanted to be able to do compound interest problems in your head? Probably not, but it's a very useful skill to have because it gives you a lightning fast benchmark to determine how good (or not so good) the financial return from a potential investment is likely to be.

The *Rule of 72* states that you can divide the number 72 by the interest rate to estimate the number of years required to double your money, assuming the interest is annually compounded. For example, if you want to know how long it will take to double your money at an annual interest rate of 8%, divide 72 by 8 = 9 years. As you can see (Table 9.2), the rule is remarkably accurate, as long as the interest rate is less than about 20%; at higher rates this approximation begins to deteriorate.

You can also calculate the rate of return you will need to double your money in any specified time. If you want to double your money in six years, just divide 72 by 6: this tells you that it will require an interest rate of about 12% to double your money in six years.

---

other length of time. ***For our analyses we generally will measure time in years: our periodic interest rates are therefore annual interest rates.***

We can illustrate the effects of compound interest on future value over time under different annual interest rates (Figure 9.3). Note how the amount curves upward exponentially over time; this is the essence of compounding (accumulation) and compound interest as interest accrues over time.

As you might imagine, people have created many shortcuts to estimate the growth rate of compound interest. As an example, it is relatively easy to estimate how long it would take you to double your money at a given interest rate (Box 9.2).

The effects of compound interest are also apparent when viewed in table format, where the influence of high interest rates over long time periods, such as in forestry, can be dramatic (Table 9.2). Note that $1.00 invested at 4% interest would be worth $50.50 in year 100, but invested at 8% would be worth $2,199.76. What a difference a few percentage points of interest can make!

Let's apply the future value concept to a forest investment problem. Suppose you own a stand of trees, currently 30 years old, that you expect to harvest at some time in the future (Table 9.3). At harvest, you plan to retain about 10% of the stand as a legacy for wildlife. Beyond that reserve, you wish to subject your harvest decisions to classical investment analysis: you wish to keep the stand as long as it grows at or above a compound annual rate of 4% or, a factor of 1.48 in a decade. You can find this factor by going to Table 9.2, finding the 4% column and going down to the coefficient opposite year 10.

In the first ten years (0–10 years), as shown in Table 9.3, column 5, the portion you will harvest (i.e., 90%) doubles in value; in the next 10 years (10–20 years), it increases by a factor of 1.60. Between the 20 and 30 years, though, the stand value increases only by a factor 1.50 and then by 1.17 in the 10 years after that. If your criterion for harvest is that

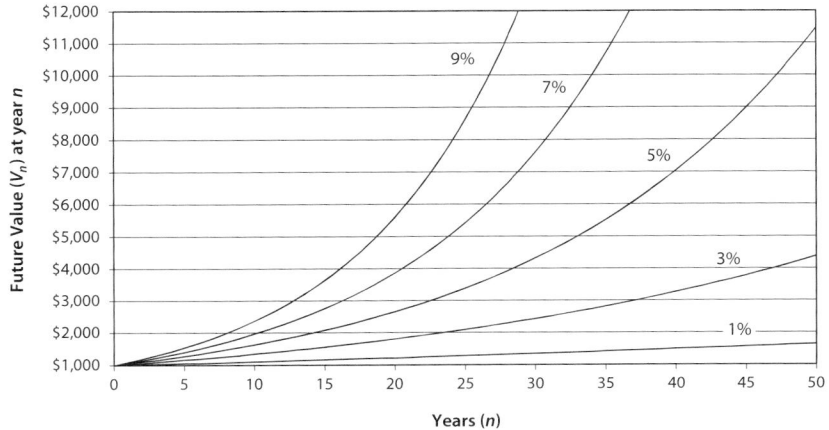

Figure 9.3 *Future value ($V_n$) at different years into the future of an initial investment ($V_0$) of $1,000 at 1%, 3%, 5%, 7%, and 9% annual interest rates.*

Table 9.2 *Compounded value over time of one dollar invested at different interest rates*

| Number of periods (years) | Interest rate (annual) | | | | | | | |
|---|---|---|---|---|---|---|---|---|
| *n* | 1% | 2% | 3% | 4% | 5% | 6% | 7% | 8% |
| 1 | 1.01 | 1.02 | 1.03 | 1.04 | 1.05 | 1.06 | 1.07 | 1.08 |
| 2 | 1.02 | 1.04 | 1.06 | 1.08 | 1.10 | 1.12 | 1.14 | 1.17 |
| 3 | 1.03 | 1.06 | 1.09 | 1.12 | 1.16 | 1.19 | 1.23 | 1.26 |
| 4 | 1.04 | 1.08 | 1.13 | 1.17 | 1.22 | 1.26 | 1.31 | 1.36 |
| 5 | 1.05 | 1.10 | 1.16 | 1.22 | 1.28 | 1.34 | 1.40 | 1.47 |
| 6 | 1.06 | 1.13 | 1.19 | 1.27 | 1.34 | 1.42 | 1.50 | 1.59 |
| 7 | 1.07 | 1.15 | 1.23 | 1.32 | 1.41 | 1.50 | 1.61 | 1.71 |
| 8 | 1.08 | 1.17 | 1.27 | 1.37 | 1.48 | 1.59 | 1.72 | 1.85 |
| 9 | 1.09 | 1.20 | 1.30 | 1.42 | 1.55 | 1.69 | 1.84 | 2.00 |
| 10 | 1.10 | 1.22 | 1.34 | 1.48 | 1.63 | 1.79 | 1.97 | 2.16 |
| 11 | 1.12 | 1.24 | 1.38 | 1.54 | 1.71 | 1.90 | 2.10 | 2.33 |
| 12 | 1.13 | 1.27 | 1.43 | 1.60 | 1.80 | 2.01 | 2.25 | 2.52 |
| 13 | 1.14 | 1.29 | 1.47 | 1.67 | 1.89 | 2.13 | 2.41 | 2.72 |
| 14 | 1.15 | 1.32 | 1.51 | 1.73 | 1.98 | 2.26 | 2.58 | 2.94 |
| 15 | 1.16 | 1.35 | 1.56 | 1.80 | 2.08 | 2.40 | 2.76 | 3.17 |
| 16 | 1.17 | 1.37 | 1.60 | 1.87 | 2.18 | 2.54 | 2.95 | 3.43 |
| 17 | 1.18 | 1.40 | 1.65 | 1.95 | 2.29 | 2.69 | 3.16 | 3.70 |
| 18 | 1.20 | 1.43 | 1.70 | 2.03 | 2.41 | 2.85 | 3.38 | 4.00 |
| 19 | 1.21 | 1.46 | 1.75 | 2.11 | 2.53 | 3.03 | 3.62 | 4.32 |
| 20 | 1.22 | 1.49 | 1.81 | 2.19 | 2.65 | 3.21 | 3.87 | 4.66 |
| 21 | 1.23 | 1.52 | 1.86 | 2.28 | 2.79 | 3.40 | 4.14 | 5.03 |
| 22 | 1.24 | 1.55 | 1.92 | 2.37 | 2.93 | 3.60 | 4.43 | 5.44 |
| 23 | 1.26 | 1.58 | 1.97 | 2.46 | 3.07 | 3.82 | 4.74 | 5.87 |
| 24 | 1.27 | 1.61 | 2.03 | 2.56 | 3.23 | 4.05 | 5.07 | 6.34 |
| 25 | 1.28 | 1.64 | 2.09 | 2.67 | 3.39 | 4.29 | 5.43 | 6.85 |
| 26 | 1.30 | 1.67 | 2.16 | 2.77 | 3.56 | 4.55 | 5.81 | 7.40 |
| 27 | 1.31 | 1.71 | 2.22 | 2.88 | 3.73 | 4.82 | 6.21 | 7.99 |
| 28 | 1.32 | 1.74 | 2.29 | 3.00 | 3.92 | 5.11 | 6.65 | 8.63 |
| 29 | 1.33 | 1.78 | 2.36 | 3.12 | 4.12 | 5.42 | 7.11 | 9.32 |
| 30 | 1.35 | 1.81 | 2.43 | 3.24 | 4.32 | 5.74 | 7.61 | 10.06 |
| 31 | 1.36 | 1.85 | 2.50 | 3.37 | 4.54 | 6.09 | 8.15 | 10.87 |
| 32 | 1.37 | 1.88 | 2.58 | 3.51 | 4.76 | 6.45 | 8.72 | 11.74 |
| 33 | 1.39 | 1.92 | 2.65 | 3.65 | 5.00 | 6.84 | 9.33 | 12.68 |
| 34 | 1.40 | 1.96 | 2.73 | 3.79 | 5.25 | 7.25 | 9.98 | 13.69 |
| 35 | 1.42 | 2.00 | 2.81 | 3.95 | 5.52 | 7.69 | 10.68 | 14.79 |
| 36 | 1.43 | 2.04 | 2.90 | 4.10 | 5.79 | 8.15 | 11.42 | 15.97 |
| 37 | 1.45 | 2.08 | 2.99 | 4.27 | 6.08 | 8.64 | 12.22 | 17.25 |
| 38 | 1.46 | 2.12 | 3.07 | 4.44 | 6.39 | 9.15 | 13.08 | 18.63 |
| 39 | 1.47 | 2.16 | 3.17 | 4.62 | 6.70 | 9.70 | 13.99 | 20.12 |
| 40 | 1.49 | 2.21 | 3.26 | 4.80 | 7.04 | 10.29 | 14.97 | 21.72 |
| 50 | 1.64 | 2.69 | 4.38 | 7.11 | 11.47 | 18.42 | 29.46 | 46.90 |
| 60 | 1.82 | 3.28 | 5.89 | 10.52 | 18.68 | 32.99 | 57.95 | 101.26 |
| 70 | 2.01 | 4.00 | 7.92 | 15.57 | 30.43 | 59.08 | 113.99 | 218.61 |
| 80 | 2.22 | 4.88 | 10.64 | 23.05 | 49.56 | 105.80 | 224.23 | 471.95 |
| 90 | 2.45 | 5.94 | 14.30 | 34.12 | 80.73 | 189.46 | 441.10 | 1,018.92 |
| 100 | 2.70 | 7.24 | 19.22 | 50.50 | 131.50 | 339.30 | 867.72 | 2,199.76 |

Table 9.3 *Determining when to harvest a stand, currently 30 years old, based on the value growth rate, the present value of the stand, and the internal rate of return*

| Year *t* from present | Age | Inventory volume/ac (M bd ft/acre) | Harvest volume/ac (M bd ft/acre) | Harvest value/ac ($/acre) | Value growth rate from holding stand from year *t* to year *t* + 10 | Present value/ac at 4% discount rate ($/acre) | Internal rate of return from holding a stand from year *t* to year *t* + 10 (%) |
|---|---|---|---|---|---|---|---|
| (1) | | (2) | (3) | (4) | (5) | (6) | (7) |
| 0 | 30 | 5 | 4.5 | 900 | | 900 | |
| 10 | 40 | 10 | 9 | 1800 | 2.00 | 1800/1.48 = 1216 | 7.2 |
| 20 | 50 | 16 | 14.4 | 2880 | 1.6 | 2880/2.19 = 1315 | 4.8 |
| 30 | 60 | 24 | 21.6 | 4320 | 1.50* | 4320/3.24 = 1333* | 4.1* |
| 40 | 70 | 28 | 25.2 | 5040 | 1.17 | 5040/4.80 = 1050 | 1.6 |

* Time to harvest, from a financial standpoint, as determined through comparing the value growth of the stand to an alternative rate of return of 4%

the stand must grow at or above an annual rate of 4% (value increases by a factor of at least 1.48 per decade), time to harvest will be close to year 30 (stand age of 60 years). From the standpoint of when to harvest the stand, though, the key decision is that you should hold the stand for at least a few decades.

How might the choice of interest rate affect the harvest decision? Looking at Table 9.2 again, we see the compound value of 6% at year 10 is 1.79 and that of 8% at year 10 is 2.16. Comparing those compound factors to our value growth rates, we see that the value growth rate sinks below the 6% rate between years 10 and 20 and sinks below the 8% rate between years 0 and 10. Using the criteria of achieving these higher rates, we would cut the stand before it reached year 20 if we sought a 6% rate and before year 10 if we sought an 8% rate. Proof again that selection of the rate of return matters in investment analysis!

## Discounting and Present Value

In performing a financial analysis for an investment we often have a need to determine what some future value is worth today; this is referred to as *discounting*. We already know that money invested today will be worth more in the future (assuming our rate of return is positive!). If we interpret Table 9.2 backwards, we can see that $50.50 in year 100 (the future value) is worth $1.00 in year 0 (the present value) when discounted at a 4% interest rate, and that when discounted at an 8% interest rate for 100 years, $2,199.76 is worth $1.00 in year 0. Rather than rely on a table of values, we can rearrange our basic compounding formula (Equation 9.1) to calculate the *present value* of some *future amount*. Recall that Equation 9.1 is:

$$V_n = V_0 \times (1+i)^n$$

Solving this equation for present value ($V_0$), the expression becomes:

$$V_0 = \frac{V_n}{(1+i)^n}$$    (Equation 9.2)

where, as before:

$i$ = periodic interest rate expressed as a decimal
$n$ = number of investment periods
$V_n$ = future value in period $n$

When we are discounting some future amount, the interest rate we use is called the *discount rate*. Like compounding, discounting is also an exponential process, but with the reverse effect of compounding. The effect of discounting at different rates on the value now of receiving $1,000 at year 50 is illustrated in Figure 9.4.

Let's return to our example problem in Table 9.3 in which we assess when to harvest a portion of a stand. Using the factors of Table 9.2, we can calculate the present value of the revenue associated with different times to cut the stand (Table 9.3, column 6). As with the value growth analysis (Table 9.3, column 5), the present value calculation indicates that, from a financial standpoint, the stand should be harvested in about 30 years from present (stand age of 60 years) to maximize present value.

Equation 9.2 can be manipulated to estimate the value of a *perpetual annual annuity*—the sum of payments that will be made every year in perpetuity. While the derivation of the formula is somewhat complicated,[2] the result is simple:

2 See Davis et al. (2001) for the derivation of the formula for an annual annuity.

$$V_0 = \frac{a}{i}$$    (Equation 9.3)

where:

$a$ = annuity received at the end of each year

$V_0$ = present value

$i$ = annual interest rate expressed as a decimal

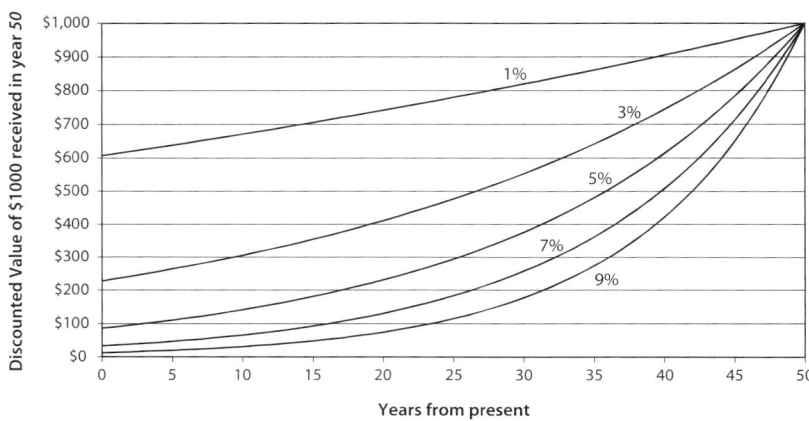

Figure 9.4  *Value now ($V_0$) of $1,000 ($V_n$) received at 50 years into the future that has been discounted to the present at 1%, 3%, 5%, 7%, and 9% annual interest rates.*

Suppose that you will receive $10 at the end of every year forever, and you have a discount rate of 4%. The present value of your annuity is:

$$V_0 = \frac{\$10.00}{0.04} = \$250.00$$

If you receive the annuity at the beginning of each year, you would just add $10 to your total, making the value $260.

Equation 9.3 for the value of a perpetual annuity is quite valuable for quick estimates of the present value of annual costs or revenues, even those for a finite period. Let's suppose you want to estimate the present value of an annual tax that you must pay for the next 50 years. You can approximate that value by using Equation 9.3, since the payments after year 50 would not add much to the total, anyway.

## Internal Rate of Return

We have seen that we can calculate the future value of an investment given the present value and an interest rate (Equation 9.1). We can also use this relationship to calculate the interest rate that relates the present and future values of an investment. To do this, we solve the compounding equation (Equation 9.1) for $i$ (interest rate), which produces the average annual rate of return, given known (or estimated) present and future values. We begin with our basic compounding equation:

$$V_n = V_0 \times (1+i)^n$$    (Equation 9.1)

This can become

$$\frac{V_n}{V_0} = (1+i)^n$$

which is the same as

$$\sqrt[n]{\frac{V_n}{V_0}} = 1+i$$

With a little rearranging this becomes

$$i = \sqrt[n]{\frac{V_n}{V_0}} - 1$$    (Equation 9.4)

The solution for $i$ (interest rate expressed as a decimal), when based on known (or estimated) present and future values, is called the ***internal rate of return***, or IRR of the investment. We can use values from Table 9.2 to test our formula. In Table 9.2 we see that $1.00 invested at 6% for 25 years grows to $4.29. If all we knew was the present value, future value, and the number of years of investment, we could calculate the internal rate of return using the equation for IRR derived above. If a present value of $1.00 yields a future value of $4.29 in 25 years, our calculated internal rate of return for this investment would be:

$$IRR = \left( \sqrt[25]{\frac{4.29}{1}} \right) - 1 = .06$$

or 6%, as we would expect.

Let's use a hypothetical case for another example. If your brother-in-law were to ask you to invest $10,000 in his business venture, which he claims will increase your money tenfold in just 20 years, you could quickly determine that your annual internal rate of return for his proposed investment would be:

$$IRR = \left( \sqrt[20]{\frac{100,000}{10,000}} \right) - 1 = .122$$

or 12.2%.

Should you invest in your brother-in-law's business venture, or are there better alternatives? Considering alternative investments is a vital aspect of classical investment analysis, as we discuss below.

We can also calculate the IRR associated with keeping the stand in our analysis (Table 9.3) for each additional 10-year period to help us decide when to harvest the stand. To calculate the internal rate of return from holding the stand from year 0 to year 10, we utilize the harvest value for year 10 ($1,800) and year 0 ($900):

$$IRR = \left( \sqrt[10]{\frac{1800}{900}} \right) - 1 = 7.2\%$$

Based on our alternative rate of return of 4%, we should hold the stand through year 10.

Similarly, we can calculate the internal rate of return from holding the stand from year 20 to year 30:

$$IRR = \left( \sqrt[10]{\frac{4320}{2880}} \right) - 1 = 4.1\%$$

Based on an alternative rate of return of 4%, under classical investment analysis we could not justify (from a financial standpoint) holding the stand much beyond year 30.

## Selecting the Interest Rate

We have covered the three basic calculation procedures commonly used in investment analysis: (1) compounding, (2) discounting, and (3) estimating internal rates of return. These procedures are fundamental to investment analysis and underscore the importance of interest rates. As we have seen from the graphs and tables used in the preceding discussion, the interest rate used in our calculations of present and future values can make a tremendous difference in outcomes, especially at the timescales common in forestry investments. For example, $1,000 invested for 50 years yields just under $4,400 at 3% annual interest (Figure 9.3) but yields nearly $75,000 at 9% interest![3] Conversely, a future value of $1,000 in year 50 has a present value of about $230 when calculated using a 3% discount rate, but a paltry $13.45 at a 9% discount rate (Figure 9.4).

The choice of interest rate clearly has a major impact on the results from classical investment analysis, and forest economists, silviculturists, and managers have argued about the appropriate interest rates to use in forestry investments ever since technical financial analysis of forestry

investments became well recognized in forestry literature. As an example, Filibert Roth pointed out in 1925 in his book *Forest Regulation* that financial rotations often were shorter than foresters wished. One compromise he suggested was to lower the discount rate, which lengthens financial rotations; another was to choose a rotation length that balanced the demands of the national market for wood over time with securing a fair return (Roth, 1925).

What discount rate should we use in our analyses of present and future values? What rate of return would be acceptable to a person considering an investment? Neither of these questions can be answered without considering the alternatives available to the investor. As we discussed earlier in this chapter, an *alternative rate of return* is the rate of return from an alternative investment (or investments), which we can compare to one we are considering, and provides a foundation for determining the interest rate to use in our analysis and what would be an acceptable rate of return. In addition, we might consider forgoing investment altogether and instead use the capital for immediate expenses such as doctors' bills or a college education, especially if none of our potential investments has a sufficiently high return. In the discussion below, we subsume this additional alternative under the general heading of *alternative investments*, but the reader should remember that this additional option exists if the investment choices don't rise above the investor's consumption threshold.

The upshot of this discussion is that the interest rate used in rate of return analyses of forest investment alternatives is closely coupled to the alternative rate of return available to the forest owner or manager. For a private investor, the appropriate discount rate for investment analysis is often the result of an internal negotiation that weighs the risks, benefits, and constraints of all realistic and relevant investment alternatives in the context of an overall business strategy.

In this type of financial analysis, it is important that both the forest investment and the alternatives being considered make consistent assumptions about inflation. Often we project future timber revenues from an investment in *real* terms (one that is net of inflation). Then, to be consistent, we should use a real alternative rate of return in our investment analysis to enable us to compare the productivity of the forest resource investment to the real rate of return on alternative investments. As an example, suppose that your best alternative investment is US Treasury certificates (Table 9.4). Generally you would key on inflation-indexed yields, which are approximately 2 to 2½% less than *nominal* yields that include inflation (Table 9.4). However, we must remember that US Treasury certificates are considered almost *risk-free*. Most forest investments cannot make that claim. Thus, as we discuss below, we also need to adjust for the relative riskiness of the different investments.

3  $1,000 invested at 9% interest for 50 years yields $74,357.50; note that this value is well off the chart in Figure 9.3.

Real discount rates of 3–10% have been suggested at one time or another for forest investments in the United States, with even lower rates used in other countries. Generally, large timber companies and TIMOs have used real rates of return on the order of 6–8%, and perhaps even higher. As an example, Aronow, Washburn, and Binkley (2004) found that timberland in the southeastern and western USA was expected to earn a real rate of return of 7–8% for corporate landowners. States tend to use real discount rates in the 4–6% range to assess their growth investments in forestry. At times, and in some places, real discount rates for future returns can be much higher, as we discuss below in our coverage of risk. In forestry, the issue of the correct rate to use is the subject of continuing debate!

What leads to the use of higher discount rates for forestry investments? Assume that you have the chance to invest in a plantation of genetically modified trees, using a new genetic process, where increased growth rates are promised. You might be worried whether the plantation will be a success: What if the genetically improved stock is susceptible to disease or drought, for example, and the investment in management practices is wasted on trees that do not produce much wood?

Risk is an important element of interest rates, with lower-risk investments typically carrying a lower *risk premium* than higher-risk investments (Klemperer, Cathcart, Haring, & Alig, 1994). We are probably all familiar with the concept that high-risk investment strategies must provide investors with higher returns in order to compensate them for a greater probability of loss compared to lower-risk alternatives. Low-risk investments, by comparison, have relatively low probability of loss and serve as a baseline for determining the risk premium associated with riskier investments. Examples of low-risk investments are stable financial instruments, such as AAA corporate bonds and US Treasury securities (Table 9.4). Although they are very low risk, they also tend to yield lower returns than their higher-risk counterparts.

As readers are no doubt aware, there are many forms of risk related to forestry investments. These risks are not limited to natural calamities, such as disease or wildfire, but also can include market risks, the risk of future changes in regulatory policy, and even extend to civil liabilities associated with management operations, such as prescribed fire or herbicide application. As we discuss throughout this book, ecological forestry may provide a way to mitigate some of these risks, thus making it a lower-risk investment than production forestry.

Table 9.4 *Yield of financial instruments (percent/year)*

| Year | Moody's AAA Corporate Bonds | 10-year US Treasury Securities | |
|---|---|---|---|
| | | Nominal Rate | Inflation-Indexed Rate |
| 2003 | 5.66 | 4.01 | 2.06 |
| 2004 | 5.63 | 4.27 | 1.83 |
| 2005 | 5.23 | 4.29 | 1.81 |
| 2006 | 5.59 | 4.8 | 2.31 |
| 2007 | 5.56 | 4.63 | 2.29 |
| 2008 | 5.63 | 3.66 | 1.77 |
| 2009 | 5.31 | 3.26 | 1.66 |
| 2010 | 4.94 | 3.22 | 1.15 |
| 2011 | 4.64 | 2.78 | 0.55 |
| 2012 | 3.67 | 1.8 | −0.48 |
| 2013 | 4.23 | 2.35 | 0.07 |
| 2014 | 4.16 | 2.54 | 0.44 |

*Source:* US Federal Reserve (2015).

State and federal agencies commonly use lower real rates, such as 4–6%, and apply rate of return criteria only to a limited portion of their management decisions, such as added investments in timber productivity. A study of investment factors used in determining discount rates for the economic analysis of US Forest Service projects (Row, Kaiser, & Sessions, 1981) concluded that AAA corporate bonds provide a straightforward means of determining return on capital investment. Based on an analysis that made adjustments for inflation and the effect of corporate tax on after-tax AAA corporate bond returns, the authors recommended that the Forest Service adopt a 4% real discount rate for evaluating long-term investments in resource management.

Actually, the issue of the relevance of rate of return analysis to decision making in forestry may be a more important consideration than the rate itself, and that gets us back to considerations of owner goals and how sustainability is measured. As we described in Chapter 6 and cover in more detail in the section on capital, goals, and intergenerational equity, nonfinancial goals and requirements (such as a need to provide a sustained yield of timber) greatly reduce the importance of rate of return analysis in the forestry decisions of many forest landowners.

## Investment Analysis with Multiple Costs and Returns

Suppose a landowner has the stand that we analyzed in Table 9.3. After harvest, she and her family plan to replant with the intention of quickly establishing a conifer forest. You propose, instead, that the landowner do only a modest amount of planting so that the site will provide important early seral habitat for a decade or two, at which time natural and planted conifers and hardwoods will occupy the site. You have emphasized the importance of early seral habitat and suggested that she and her family would enjoy the lush abundance of early seral plants, game animals, birds, and butterflies that would be abundant for a decade or two following harvest. As the forest matures, the trees will begin to develop characteristics that will attract a different set of species. The landowner seems interested, and after a visit to her forest, you provide an estimate of the following costs and returns from this ecological forestry approach:

1. Planting costs of $200/acre;

2. Thinning to open up the stand at year 50 that you calculate will return $2,000/acre; and

3. Final harvest at year 80 that will return $5,000/acre, while leaving 10% of the stand as a legacy.

Will this strategy pay? A quick look at the numbers suggests that it will (Table 9.5).

Total revenue of $7,000 per acre is certainly greater than the total cost of $200 per acre—case closed. But wait! All the costs are incurred immediately, but the revenues don't occur until many years later. How does investment analysis play into this? Specifically, how do the planting costs in year 0 stack up against the revenue from commercial thinning in year 50 and the final harvest in year 80? To answer that question, we will introduce a common measure of investment performance called *net present value (NPV)*, where we modify our discounting formula (Equation 9.2) to account for costs and revenues that come at different times during the investment cycle. [4]

NPV is the present value of the income stream considering all revenues and costs:

$$NPV = \sum_{t=0}^{n} \left[ \frac{R_t}{(1+i)^t} - \frac{C_t}{(1+i)^t} \right]$$    (**Equation 9.5**)

where

$R_t$ = revenue in period $t$
$C_t$ = cost in period $t$
$i$ = periodic discount rate expressed as decimal
$t$ = the period in which a cost or revenue occurs
$n$ = number of planning periods

Table 9.5 *Cash flow associated with an ecological forestry prescription*

| Year | Treatment | Revenue per acre | Cost per acre |
|------|-----------|------------------|---------------|
| 0 | Tree Planting | | $200 |
| 50 | Commercial Thin | $2,000 | |
| 80 | Final Harvest | $5,000 | |
| | Total Revenue or Cost | $7,000 | $200 |

If investors utilize a discount rate equal to their alternative rate of return, after any adjustments for relative risk, in calculating the NPV of an investment, an NPV greater than 0 indicates that they can earn more from the investment than their alternative. The NPV also represents the maximum amount they can spend on that particular investment and earn the alternative rate of return.

Now we are almost ready to answer the question put to us about the ecological forestry prescription: Will it pay more than our investor's alternative investment? We are about to find out! For our example, we will again use a discount rate of 4%.

## A Four-Step Approach to Investment Analysis

Projects, plans, or policies generally have a schedule of events or actions occurring over some period of time, which can be represented as a series of costs and returns. Investment analysis requires four procedural steps (Davis, Johnson, Bettinger, & Howard, 2001):

1. Deciding on the length of the planning period over which costs and revenues will be evaluated;

2. Identifying the schedule of events associated with a project, plan, or policy;

3. Converting the events to their equivalent schedule of dollar-measured costs and revenues; and

4. Adjusting the costs and revenues for time, using compound interest formulas.

On a time line, the first two steps of investment analysis produce an event schedule for our ecological forestry project (Figure 9.5).

Note that since only activities or events occurring up to year 80 in the future have been included, we have implicitly decided on the length of the planning period. More events will surely occur on the land after this, but by selecting 80 years as the planning period, they are effectively assigned a value of zero in our calculations of NPV.

We then convert the activity time line into a stream of costs and revenues (Figure 9.6).

To calculate the present value at time $n = 0$ for the fourth step of the investment analysis, our guiding rate of interest is used to discount each cost or revenue item using the

4 For related criteria for evaluating investments with multiple costs and revenues, see the Appendix I to this chapter.

present value equation (Equation 9.5). The example below (Figure 9.7) uses a discount rate of 4%.

Subtracting the discounted values of the costs from the discounted values of the revenues gives an NPV of one rotation of $298.35 (Table 9.6). Thus, the analysis reveals that an investor could pay $298.35 per acre for the land and still earn a 4% rate of return on the investment.

The family who owns the forest is very interested in using ecological forestry, but wonders how much they might be giving up in NPV under this new approach. They ask you to rerun the analysis with an intensive management prescription suggested by a neighbor. This prescription involves site preparation with herbicides, planting twice as many seedlings of a fast-growing conifer, precommercial thinning at age 10, and harvest at age 50 with 10% legacy retention. Site prep and planting costs total $400 per acre and precommercial thinning runs $100 per acre. The final harvest in year 50 will yield $8,000 per acre. Using the same interest rate as your previous analysis (4%) you come up with the following numbers (Table 9.7), which yield a NPV of $658.15 per acre.

Note that we now need to compare a rotation that takes 50 years—the intensive management prescription (Table 9.7) with one that takes 80 years—the ecological forestry prescription (Table 9.6). How do we fairly evaluate the two alternatives when they have rotations of different lengths? And what about the rotations after the first one? Shouldn't they be counted, too?

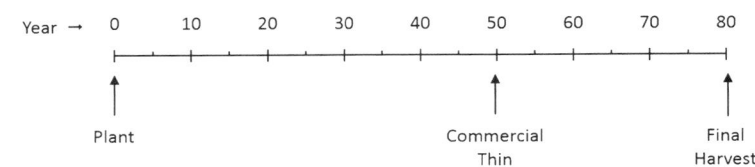

Figure 9.5 *Project time line for a simple ecological forestry project: Plant in year 0, commercial thin in year 50, and final harvest (with retention!) in year 80.*

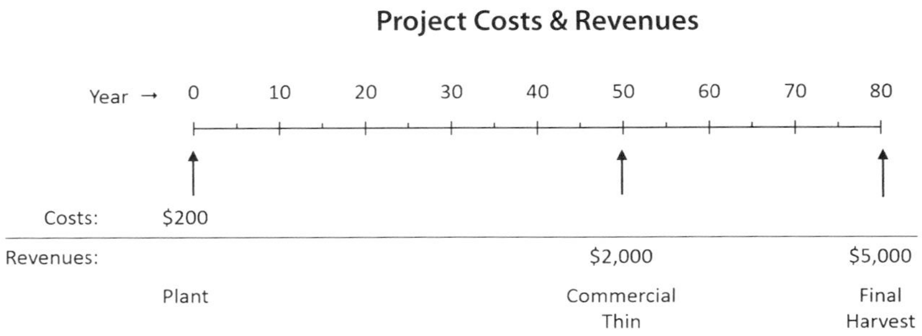

**Project Costs & Revenues**

| Year → | 0 | 10 | 20 | 30 | 40 | 50 | 60 | 70 | 80 |

Costs: $200

Revenues: $2,000  $5,000

Plant  Commercial Thin  Final Harvest

Figure 9.6 *Project time line for a simple ecological forestry project, with costs and revenues included.*

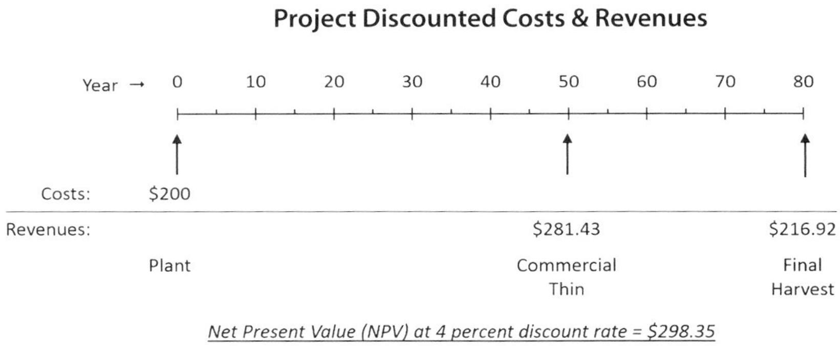

**Project Discounted Costs & Revenues**

| Year → | 0 | 10 | 20 | 30 | 40 | 50 | 60 | 70 | 80 |

Costs: $200

Revenues: $281.43  $216.92

Plant  Commercial Thin  Final Harvest

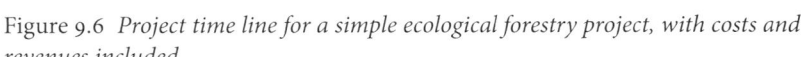

Figure 9.7 *Project time line for a simple ecological forestry project, with discounted costs and revenues.*

## Estimating the Discounted Value of Future Rotations

To deal with these issues, foresters often use the formula for the present value of a perpetual series of rotations that produce a net income of *p* every *r* years, forever, with payments that occur at the end of each rotation. This formula is:

$$V_0 = \frac{p}{\left(1+i\right)^r - 1}$$

(Equation 9.6)

When used to financially value alternative rotations for an acre of land, this formula is often called the **soil expectation** *value or SEV*. It is also called the **Faustmann formula** after Martin Faustmann, the German forester from long ago with whom it is identified. It is the foundation of investment analysis of land value for timber production and occupies a hallowed place in the investment analysis of TIMOs and REITs.

Notice that we now need to calculate the value *p* of each alternative rotation at the year in which the stand is cut, *r*; that is, we need to calculate the future value of the ecological forestry alternative at year 80, and the future value of the intensive forestry alternative at year 50. To calculate future value, we use Equation 9.1 from earlier in this chapter; the results are displayed in Table 9.8, with ecological forestry producing a higher future value at year 80 than intensive management at year 50.[5]

Given these future values, we can use the SEV formula (Faustmann formula) to calculate the NPV of an infinite series of rotations. The calculations result in SEVs of $311.88 for ecological forestry, and of $765.92 for intensive management (Table 9.8).

**Site Productivity Assumptions in an Infinite Series of Identical Rotations**   SEV calculations generally assume an infinite series of rotations that are identical in every way. Thus they assume undiminished site productivity from rotation to rotation into the indefinite future. Some scientists question whether we can remove substantial biomass from the forest without diminishing productivity, especially as rotations become much shorter than experienced under natural disturbance regimes. Assuming that diminished ecosystem productivity is a real possibility, pointing out that reduced productivity so far in the future has almost no impact on SEV is probably disconcerting to some readers; it emphasizes the reality that long-term consequences of management and intergenerational concerns simply don't carry much weight in capital markets, especially at high discount rates.

If you wish to recognize a change in productivity from rotation to rotation, or other changes, consider breaking the calculation of payoff from a series of identical rotations into separate rotations. Calculating the contribution to NPV for each rotation individually, for perhaps the first few rotations, will enable you to recognize particular features of each rotation into the distant future.

Such an approach recognizes, but does not fix, the problem that productivity declines may occur without much financial penalty under the NPV approach. A commitment to long-term sustainability is needed to combat this potential problem. We will discuss this issue again toward the end of the chapter when we cover the effect of sustainability requirements on management decisions.

---

5 Does that mean the ecological forestry prescription produces more revenue over time than does the intensive management prescription? Not quite, as we need to equalize the time periods of the investments. To do that, we also need to account for the value of the intensive management investments for 30 more years to equalize the investment length of the two alternatives (from year 50 when the regeneration harvest occurs under intensive management) to year 80 (when regeneration harvest occurs under ecological forestry). Thus, we would need to add two more components to the future value of the harvest at age 50 of the intensive management regime: (1) the income received from investing the revenue received at age 50 at 4% for 30 more years, and (2) the net value of a plantation at age 30 created when we harvested at age 50. With these adjustments, the intensive management regime would have a higher future value 80 years into the future than the ecological forestry regime.

Table 9.6 *Calculation of NPV per acre of an ecological forestry prescription for one rotation (with a 4% discount rate)*

| Year | Treatment | Revenue (Cost) | Present Value (year 0) |
|------|-----------|----------------|------------------------|
| 0 | Tree Planting | $ (200.00) | $ (200.00) |
| 50 | Commercial Thin | $ 2,000.00 | $ 281.43 |
| 80 | Final Harvest | $ 5,000.00 | $ 216.92 |
| | *NPV* | | $ 298.35 |

Table 9.7 *Calculation of NPV per acre of an intensive management prescription for one rotation (with a 4% discount rate)*

| Year | Treatment | Revenue (Cost) | Present Value (year 0) |
|------|-----------|----------------|------------------------|
| 0 | Site Prep/ Tree Planting | $ (400.00) | $ (400.00) |
| 10 | Precommercial Thin | $ (100.00) | $ (67.55) |
| 50 | Final Harvest | $ 8,000.00 | $ 1,125.70 |
| | *NPV* | | $ 658.15 |

Table 9.8 *Calculation of the NPV of an infinite series of rotations (SEV) for an ecological forestry prescription and an intensive management prescription (with a 4% discount rate; values are per acre)*

| Year | Treatment | Ecological forestry | | Intensive Management | |
|------|-----------|---------------------|--------------------|----------------------|----------------------|
| | | Revenue or (Cost) | Future Value (year 80) | Revenue or (Cost) | Future Value (year 50) |
| 0 | Tree Planting | $ (200.00) | $ (4,609.95) | $ (400.00) | $ (2,842.67) |
| 10 | Precommercial Thin | — | — | $ (100) | $ (480.10) |
| 50 | Commercial Thin | $ 2,000.00 | $ 6,486.80 | — | — |
| 50 | Final Harvest | — | — | $ 8,000 | $ 8,000 |
| 80 | Final Harvest | $ 5,000.00 | $ 5,000 | — | — |
| *Net Future Value =* | | — | $ 6,876.85 | — | $ 4,677.23 |
| *SEV =* | | $ 311.88 | | $ 765.92 | |

**Interpreting SEV: The NPV of All Future Rotations**   In the case demonstrated in Table 9.8, switching from ecological forestry to intensive management for the next rotation increases SEV by $454.04 per acre ($765.92 minus $311.88).

What do these numbers mean? For starters, they tell you the most that a person focused on rate of return would pay for the land immediately after the existing stand had been harvested, given he or she were planning to implement one of these prescriptions and used the same estimates of yield and income and the same discount rate. If that person had a higher alternative rate of return (i.e., discount rate), the person would pay less, and if he or she had a lower alternative rate of return, the person would pay more. In terms of the appraisal methodologies of the valuation (discussed in Chapter 10), these numbers provide *value in use* estimates per acre right after harvest. [6]

Binkley, Beebe, New, and von Hagen (2006), though, described some of the financial advantages of ecosystem-based forest management (EFM), a management strategy much like the ecological forestry strategy that we describe throughout this book. EFM works from a different premise (than production forestry) that can be characterized in several different ways (Binkley et al., 2006, pp. 7–8):

*We focus on what is left in the forest rather than what is removed; we are more concerned about building the balance sheet of the firm than squeezing the income statement. The general approach focuses on growing large logs of a variety of natural species with continuous forest cover and regular harvests. There is more (but not exclusive) reliance on natural regeneration. This means that capital expenditures are lower in EFM than in the industrial model, a fact that is especially important in building good time- and dollar-weighted returns. EFM builds higher levels of standing inventory so total returns are weighted more heavily towards capital appreciation—consistent with our "build the balance sheet" approach. EFM naturally operates at a standard of environmental protection that is well above the minimum prescriptions of local forest practice regulations. This means that there is less regulatory risk. This approach also opens avenues for the sale of ecosystem services, sales that generally require "additionality" above statutory minima. EFM forests harbor a greater diversity of timber species (as well as other flora and fauna), age classes and ecological structure. This diversity may reduce both financial risk as well as the risk of insect and disease epidemics. As a result of the focus on maintaining continuous forest cover, certification under the Forest Stewardship (FSC) standard, the international "gold standard" in forest certification, should be readily achievable. FSC certification* opens certain markets that might otherwise be unavailable, and further reduces environmental and operating risks. [7]

*Given the potential risk of intensive management prescriptions (as pointed out above by Binkley et al., 2006), we might argue for using a higher discount rate under an intensive management prescription than under an ecological forestry prescription.* If we were to accept this reasoning and raise the discount rate for the intensive management prescription by 1% over that of the ecological forestry prescription (4% for ecological forestry; 5% for intensive management), the SEV of the intensive management prescription drops to $258.81, which is $53.07 less than the SEV of the ecological forestry prescription! Of course, these results are sensitive to the yields, revenues, and costs associated with the different prescriptions for the future forest. Still, to the degree that ecological forestry prescriptions for the future forest help reduce risk (as we have argued throughout this book), these results suggest that they may provide a more competitive investment alternative to intensive forestry prescriptions for the future forest than might first seem.

In addition to considerations for risk, let's suppose that the family in this example plans to keep the forest and pass it down generation to generation. Although the intensive management prescription for the future forest has a higher SEV at a 4% discount rate, this income is at least 50 years into the future. If the family in our example switches to intensive management, they will miss out on many years of the benefits from ecological forestry that are hard to put into a financial calculation, such as enjoyment of the plants and wildlife that would otherwise have been attracted to their wonderfully diverse pre-forest habitats.

Finally, they will avoid the much larger immediate costs of establishing the next stand, saving $300/acre (see Table 9.8). Lower cost, less risk, more biodiversity, and more potential for sale of other types of ecosystem services in the future—something to consider!

## How Consideration of Future Rotations Might Influence the Harvest of Existing Stands

We will now incorporate the value of the future rotations managed under the ecological forestry prescription into our financial determination of when to harvest the existing stand. To do this, we first must recognize that by delaying the harvest of an existing stand we are also delaying the harvest of all future rotations. Thus, when we allow our existing stand to grow $n$ years into the future we must discount SEV (the value of all future rotations) $n$ years to the present. Adding together the present value of harvest-

---

6 Of course, the 10% retention on each acre would also have financial value to the buyer, but that does not differ between the two strategies.

7 FSC certification is discussed in Chapter 16.

ing the existing stand (Table 9.9, column 4) and the present value of SEV (Table 9.9, column 5) gives us the aggregate NPV considering both the existing stand and all future rotations (Table 9.9, column 6). Note that the highest aggregate NPV occurs when we harvest the existing stand at about year 20 (Table 9.9, column 6) instead of year 30, which we found when we did not consider future rotations (Table 9.9, column 4). We should also note, though, that the aggregate NPV in year 30 is only slightly less than that of year 20, so we have flexibility there. For our planning under ecological forestry, the key finding from this analysis is that, from an NPV standpoint, the family should keep the stand until year 20 (for another 20 years).

How would the use of the intensive management prescription for future rotations influence this conclusion? When we estimate the intensive management SEV using the same discount rate that we applied to our ecological forestry analysis (4%), we find that intensive management has a higher aggregate NPV than does ecological forestry, for all times to harvest (compare columns 6 and 9 in Table 9.9). We also see that the highest aggregate NPV now occurs when we harvest the existing stand at year 10. Under intensive management, the higher discounted value of future rotations causes the cost of delaying them to rise, which pushes the harvest time for the current stand that results in the highest aggregate NPV toward the present. On the other hand, when we use a higher discount rate to calculate SEV for intensive management to reflect the potentially greater risk of intensive management (5%), the two strategies result in about the same aggregate NPV for all times to harvest (compare columns 6 and 10 in Table 9.9). They also show the same time to harvest the existing stand (year 20) to achieve the maximum aggregate NPV.

Perhaps the most important conclusion from the analysis is that the family should keep the existing stand for at least another decade. They can revisit their choices at that time.

In the investment analysis described above we retained 10% of the stand at harvest under both the ecological forestry and the intensive management prescriptions. Given the financial objectives of production forestry, however, we should expect that the intensive forestry prescription for existing stands would generally not retain this biological legacy if it contained commercial value. Thus, the NPV and SEV reported for intensive management in Table 9.9 would be somewhat higher under a production forestry management strategy. While some ecologically important biological legacies may have lower commercial value, such as trees with large branches and broken tops, retaining biological legacies generally reduces the commercial value removed at harvest. In fact, the difference between ecological forestry and production forestry with respect to biological legacies retained at harvest can be a major source of the difference in financial return between the two strategies, as we discuss further in Chapter 16.

## Summary

We have now come to the conclusion of our primer on classical investment analysis. As you might imagine, though, we have only scratched the surface of all the configurations of present and future value calculations you might need to undertake sometime in your career. To assist your efforts, we have provided a decision tree to help select the appropriate formula for such calculations (Appendix II). That decision tree covers the present and future value formulas covered above and others that we think may be useful.

Table 9.9 *Determining when to harvest a stand considering both its discounted value and the discounted value of the rotations that will come after it (using a calculator, as is done here, obtains slightly different answers than using Table 9.2)*

| Year | Harvest volume/ac (M bd ft/ac) | Net revenue | NPV of existing stand | SEV of future stands discounted to present (Ecol-for) | Aggregate NPV (Ecol-for) | SEV of future stands discounted to present (Inten mgt) | | Aggregate NPV (Inten mgt) | |
|---|---|---|---|---|---|---|---|---|---|
| $/acre | $/acre | $/acre | $/acre | $/acre | $/acre | $/acre | $/acre | $/acre | $/acre |
| (1) | (2) | (3) | (4) | (5)[#] | (6)[#] | (7)[#] | (8)[##] | (9)[#] | (10)[##] |
| 0 | 4.5 | 900 | 900 | 312 | 1212 | 766 | 259 | 1666 | 1159 |
| 10 | 9.0 | 1800 | 1216 | 211 | 1427 | 517 | 175 | 1733[**] | 1391 |
| 20 | 14.4 | 2880 | 1314 | 142 | 1456[**] | 350 | 118 | 1664 | 1432[**] |
| 30 | 21.6 | 4320 | 1332[*] | 96 | 1428 | 236 | 80 | 1568 | 1412 |
| 40 | 25.2 | 5040 | 1050 | 65 | 1115 | 160 | 54 | 1210 | 1104 |

\# SEV calculated with a 4% discount rate
\## SEV calculated with a 5% discount rate
 \* Time to harvest to obtain the maximum NPV when considering only the existing stand
\** Time to harvest to obtain the maximum NPV when considering both existing stands and future stands

We now turn to the uses and limitations of such analyses in forest planning and management. Then we address the issue of how investment analysis and discounting fit into the broader considerations of sustainability and intergenerational equity.

## Fitting Financial Considerations into the Multiple Goals of Many Landowners

Rate of return/NPV analysis is a well-recognized approach to evaluating financial alternatives in forestry. It has been taught as the lynchpin of economic analysis in forestry schools and textbooks for generations. Until recently it had only occasional application in the lumber and pulp and paper firms that controlled most of the industrial timberland around the world, because of their focus on sustaining wood supplies for their processing facilities rather than on maximizing return on investment. Since much of the historical industrial forestlands have been sold to TIMOs and REITs, rate of return/NPV analysis has become the cornerstone of decision making for these forests. In this section of the chapter we argue that such financial decision criteria are poorly suited to guide the financial decisions faced by many who might practice ecological forestry, such as family forest landowners and public forest managers.

### Family Forests

As we described in Chapter 6, timber production is not the primary goal of many who own family forests in the United States, and this is probably the case for small forestland owners in other temperate regions of the world. Rather, enjoying scenery, protecting nature, protecting and improving wildlife habitat, privacy, the opportunity to pass land on to heirs, hunting and fishing, and pursuing other forms of recreation are more important goals to these landowners than timber production (see Figure 6.3) (Butler, 2016). With this wide variety of ecological and social goals, rate of return is not the sole determinant of harvest decisions and, in fact, it may not even be directly considered in those decisions. As Smith (1969, pp. 374–375) pointed out about family forest landowners in the New England region of the United States:

> A large and increasing proportion of private landowners . . . are eager to own land and to keep it in forest provided the costs are not unduly large. They may do so for hunting, bird-watching, privacy, growing trees as a hobby, or merely because they like the woods. . . . Many owners are, of course, happy indeed if the tangible forest revenue will pay part of the real and theoretical costs of ownership. Further, the silvicultural treatments necessary to beautify the forest or make it more productive of water or wildlife

> become ruinously expensive unless timber is consciously grown and sold as a by-product.

This is not to say that harvest income is unimportant to family forest landowners, but only that harvest decisions are difficult to represent through rate of return analysis. Their interests and objectives are too broad to capture in a single financial calculation. Thus it is doubtful that many see their forest solely as a capital plant to be optimized. Yes, they often are interested in income from their forest, whether this income be used to deal with a health emergency, provide funds for college for the kids, or pay for restoration activities, such as the removal of invasive plants from their meadows. *In general, family forest owners want their forests to be able to produce income when they need it, while at the same time providing many other benefits. Thus the goal of obtaining an income over time from a forest will generally be a more useful representation of a forest landowner's financial goals than achieving a certain rate of return.* (See Chapter 19 for a case study that illustrates these concepts in detail.)

### State, Provincial, and Federal Forests

We have seen in Chapter 6 that state, provincial, and federal forests all over the world have commitments to manage their forests for a sustained yield of timber harvest. How does that affect the usefulness of rate of return analysis? Actually, a sustained yield timber harvest goal greatly reduces the value of this kind of analysis. In fact, utilizing an NPV goal to guide management under sustained yield can lead to liquidation of the higher value portions of the forest. (See Box 9.3 on p. 274 for a detailed example.) When you consider the many other goals that most public forest management agencies have, the usefulness of rate of return analysis diminishes still further.

In Chapter 6, we pointed out that income production is vitally important to public forest agencies, whether to cover the costs of harvest, produce income for other good works, or provide income to the beneficiaries who own the forests. As with family forest landowners, they want to produce a cash flow over time from their forest, and much of that income often comes from timber harvest. While they may have a limited use for rate of return analysis to help analyze investments to increase growth rates or reduce mortality, they rarely subject their entire forest capital to achieving some rate of return. Their multiple goals do not lend themselves to such a perspective. *Thus, providing a sustained cash flow over time from a forest will generally provide a more useful representation of the financial goals of public forestry agencies than achieving a specified rate of return.*

# Capital, Sustainability, and Intergenerational Equity

We illustrated the impact of financial discounting on future values earlier in this chapter. That discussion should make it clear that high interest rates result in heavily discounted future values—the most distant values are, in fact, inconsequential in the investment calculus. At interest rates above 4%, future values rapidly diminish when discounted to the present, even on relatively short timescales (Figure 9.4). On the longer timescales common in forestry, even moderate interest rates make future values appear trivial; for example, discounting a future value of $1,000 for one hundred years at an annual rate of 4% produces a present value of $19.80.

Is this really how our society regards future generations and the long-term viability of the planet? Such results have led to debate and anger in many forums as people have questioned the appropriateness of this approach to evaluating investments in our common future. How can we discount the future so much? Won't this approach lead to a bias toward investments that can make a quick buck no matter their long-term implications? Won't this approach cause us to ignore investments that pay off in the long-run in favor of immediate consumption or short-term gain? It's one thing to talk glowingly about sustainability, but what purpose does such talk serve if we apparently have so little regard for the future?

A counterargument is that we owe it to future generations to put our resources into those investments that will increase wealth the most, and that this is best accomplished by putting our resources into investments that have higher rates of return. In theory, at least, by putting our capital in investments that provide high rates of return, we will leave more wealth to future generations.

## Weak and Strong Sustainability

Following Neumayer (2013), our assessment of capital, sustainability, and intergenerational equity will employ two important concepts: (1) the provision of *nondeclining per capita human well-being* through time, and (2) the recognition of *critical natural capital* as a vital component in sustaining ecosystems and the benefits they provide humans.

Further, we recognize two different sustainability frameworks for our discussion: (1) *weak sustainability* and (2) *strong sustainability.* We first introduced these frameworks in Chapter 1; we focus here on how weak and strong sustainability address our responsibilities to current and future generations.

*Both sustainability frameworks start with an ethical premise—provision of nondeclining human well-being through time is our goal*—and both fit within the domain of *sustainable development*, defined by the Brundtland Commission (Brundtland et al., 1987): "development that meets the needs of the present without compromising the ability of future generations to meet their own needs." Weak sustainability and strong sustainability, though, have fundamentally different economic assumptions about the substitutability of natural capital with human-made capital (Neumayer, 2013), leading to fundamentally different views on the use and allocation of natural resources (Ang & Van Passel, 2012).

*The weak sustainability paradigm assumes that all forms of capital are substitutable and that a constant or increasing level of human well-being can be supplied by well-functioning market mechanisms, provided total capital is maintained* (Ang & Van Passel, 2012; Neumayer, 2013). Special considerations for critical forms of natural capital are therefore unnecessary, because human well-being will be optimized through market mechanisms that substitute forms of capital based on human preferences and their relative scarcity and abundances, irrespective of the form of capital. This approach is at the heart of weak sustainability. Its underlying economic assumption is that human-made capital can be fully substituted for natural capital in the provision of human well-being; in other words, natural capital does not have unique properties that cannot be substituted for by human-made capital. Capital is capital, and the key to sustainable development is to keep the capital plant in good shape.

Strong sustainability also recognizes the importance of market mechanisms in promoting social welfare but, in contrast, asserts that the *substitutability assumption* of neoclassical economics, which is embraced by the weak sustainability paradigm, does not necessarily apply to natural capital; that is, natural capital does not always have a human-made substitute. *Thus, strong sustainability requires both provision for nondeclining human well-being through maintenance of total capital and conservation of critical natural capital, for which there are no human or natural substitutes* (Neumayer, 2013).

We will discuss these ideas in more depth below, starting with a focus on provision of a constant or increasing level of human well-being over time. Then we will recognize an important role for critical natural capital. Through our discussion we will highlight the uses and limitations of classical rate of return analysis.

## Weak Sustainability: Maintaining the Capacity to Provide for Human Well-being through Time with Completely Substitutable Capital

Let's start with the premise that we can measure the value of resources to humans—their contribution to human well-being, or *utility*, as economists call it. Given this assumption, we are able to evaluate our potential investments—whether they are in forests and streams or highways and high-rises, in terms of the well-being they provide through time. Under weak sustainability, as we discussed above, capital is capital and natural and man-made capital are interchangeable in achieving the goal of maintaining human well-being through time.

Following Neumayer (2013), we will define this well-being goal in terms of maintaining the capacity to provide nondeclining per capita utility for infinity. Capital would still be directed toward more productive investments, but these investments would be constrained by the requirement that the capacity to provide this utility would not diminish over time. In this way, we would make sure that our investment/consumption choices now did not compromise those of future generations (Neumayer, 2013). Two key aspects of this approach to sustainability are (Neumayer, 2013):

1.  *Sustainability is defined in terms of maintaining the capacity to provide nondeclining per capita utility forever.* It is not defined as per capita utility for infinity itself, as the current generation has no control over how future generations will use the capacity they inherit. There are likely to be many development paths that maintain the capacity to provide for nondeclining utility for infinity. Those choices are still to be made.

2.  Population growth is exogenous to the analysis. Whatever the size of the population, sustainability (sustainable development) calls for maintaining the capacity to provide nondeclining per capita utility. That requirement seems reasonable since the present generation is responsible for the population growth curve. Thus, an increasing population would call for an increasing aggregate utility over time.

The requirement of nondeclining utility can be seen as overly restrictive, ruling out utility paths that have ups and downs on an increasing trajectory. As an example, given a choice of $U_1$ or $U_3$ and a constraint requiring nondeclining utility, depicted in Figure 9.8, the lower trajectory ($U_1$) must be chosen. However, such difficulty can potentially be overcome by redirecting capital toward creation of the modified trajectory, $U_3'$.

**Effect on Financial Evaluation of Investments**    It is also true that the addition of this nondeclining yield constraint to the flow of utilities potentially changes the effect that an individual investment has on that flow, with a resulting modification in the results of rate of return analysis. Rather than relating future returns from an investment to its costs to calculate the rate of return, we relate the increase in aggregate benefits over time, resulting from this investment, to these costs. This increase in aggregate benefits from the investment can occur in two ways: (1) by enabling a perma-

nent increase in utility over time through adding a recurring investment to the capital plant, or (2) by addressing a bottleneck in the production of utilities at some point in the future, which holds down the nondeclining level of utilities.

Such a change in financial calculation procedures can substantially negate the effect of discounting on those future returns and greatly affect the calculated rate of return itself, since the positive impact on aggregate benefits will often be realized sooner than would occur if the investment were considered in isolation. Thus, in general, more investment can be financially justified. We will illustrate these ideas with sustained yield forestry.

**Sustained-yield Forestry as an Early Attempt to Maintain Human Well-being through Time**    Forestry in its early days took what we now describe as a weak sustainability approach, with its focus on sustained yield of timber harvest through time as the overarching goal of forest management. The key to sustainability was to keep the timber plant in good order, capable of producing the maximum volume of timber through time. As stated in Duerr and Duerr (1975, p. 37) in discussing how a government bureau selects a harvest-flow policy: "You can do what virtually every public forest administrator in the Western world has done for the past few centuries: take shelter in a policy of sustained yield. Under this policy, you will manage the forest to the goal of producing the same, hopefully large, physical quantity of wood period by period into the indefinite future."

Initially, sustained yield projections covered only the period of time over which the existing stands (generally old-growth forest) were harvested, usually the length of time equal to one rotation of the forest that would be

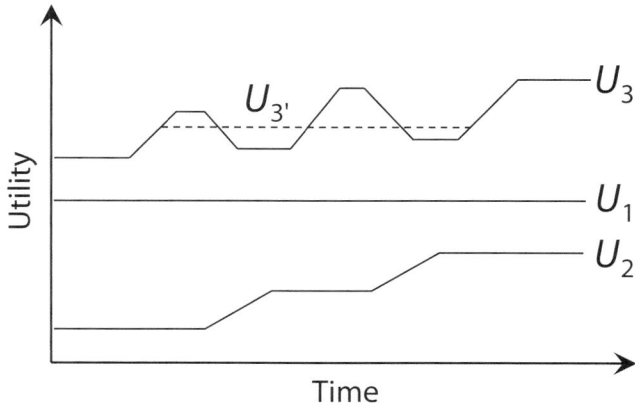

Figure 9.8 *Sustainability (i.e., sustainable development) does not require that utility remain constant ($U_1$). It can also gradually increase ($U_2$). With foresight, a development path with periods of declining utility ($U_3$) might be modified so that declines do not occur ($U_3'$) and meet the requirement of nondeclining utility. (Adapted from Neumayer, 2013)*

grown after harvest of existing stands. Often, yield from these future stands was less than that of the existing stands, potentially resulting in a drop in harvest as conversion from old growth to young growth was completed.

With the advent of computers, however, agencies such as the US Forest Service were able to project many rotations into the future. To prohibit a drop-off over time, and to allow an increase, the Forest Service in the early 1970s redefined sustained yield as the nondeclining yield of timber over multiple rotations into the future (Davis et al., 2001)—much like a sustainable development requirement that per capita utility be nondeclining.

It must be noted that defining sustainability through the ability to provide a nondeclining yield of timber harvest over time requires that we do not place a special value on old-growth forests or wildlife habitats beyond their timber volume and growth rates—old-growth and plantation forests are substitutable with respect to timber volume. This approach has great similarity to the weak sustainability assumption of the substitutability of different forms of capital for each other and the ability to define social welfare (utilities) in a single numeric, which in this case was board feet of timber harvest.

**How Nondeclining Yield Requirements Can Reduce Financial Pressures for Capital Liquidation and Short Rotations**   As described above, the change in the aggregate flow of benefits from a forestry investment can reduce the effect of discounting on those future returns, since the positive impact on aggregate benefits can often be realized immediately. Probably forestry's most famous example of this phenomenon is called the *allowable cut effect*, in which investments in future growth can enable an increase in harvest immediately, thus making those investments display higher returns than if they were evaluated on their own.

As mentioned above, the imposition of a multi-rotation nondeclining yield left foresters with the choice of either lowering the harvest rate of existing stands or raising the volume that would be produced in future stands. They often chose to invest in raising the growth rate of future stands to the point that the harvest rate of existing stands could continue. Such an investment has an immediate payoff in allowing an increase in near-term harvest over what would otherwise be permitted, making the investment look much better (have a higher rate of return) than it otherwise would. See Davis et al., 2001 for a more detailed discussion of the allowable cut effect.

However, the phenomenon has more impact on forestry than simply elevating the financial attractiveness of investments in stand growth rates. Some of these changes have a positive impact on lowering the cost of ecological forestry. As an example, a nondeclining yield requirement tends to lengthen rotation age beyond the age that

maximizes unconstrained NPV. Maximizing NPV can result in rotation lengths far shorter than those that would maximize growth and provide mature forests. Imposing a nondeclining requirement on harvest volume generally reduces pressure for this early harvest:

- Rotations over time tend toward those that maximize growth since they will enable the highest sustained yield level.

- Rotation ages and practices that lead to site degradation over time would be penalized through negatively impacting the long-term sustained yield level.

**The Dangers of a NPV Goal with a Nondeclining Yield Requirement**   In the case of forestry though, applying a nondeclining yield constraint on harvest with an NPV goal for a finite period, such as a rotation or two, has other problems: It does not ensure a sustainable level of net revenue, even when net revenue approximates the utility that people seek from the forest in question. In the context of the computation techniques like linear programming used to make these estimates, such a formulation will attempt to pull the value from the forest forward, with the result that a constant or increasing volume produces less and less revenue through time, leaving an increasingly impoverished future forest (Box 9.3).

Where one goal of forest managers or forest owners is to ensure they do not use the forest in ways that impair its value for future generations, a different formulation is needed that guards against the forest being depleted over time. This revised formulation might limit fluctuations in both harvest volume and revenue over time, while also requiring that a substantial inventory value be left at the end of the simulation. Within these constraints, a financial objective, like NPV, becomes much less controlling, and there is much less chance of economic depletion. Our key point here is that *focusing on maximizing NPV subject to a nondeclining yield of timber harvest can largely defeat the goal of using the resources now in ways that do not impoverish future generations*.

## Strong Sustainability: Recognizing the Role of Critical Natural Capital in Maintaining Human Well-being through Time

Proposals to identify the limits of the substitutability of human-made capital for natural capital have a long history that predates the development of the concepts of weak and strong sustainability. In 1952, Siegfried Von Ciriacy-Wantrup introduced the idea of *Safe Minimum Standards* (SMS), which were originally applied to species and biodiversity protection, such as granting a species some minimally viable standard of protection (Neumayer, 2013). The concept

---

Box 9.3  **Hollowing out forests over time: Combining NPV maximization with a nondeclining yield requirement**

As described by Duerr and Duerr (1975), forest managers and policy makers have clung to the mantle of sustained yield for hundreds of years as a way to ensure sustainability. While providing a nondeclining yield of timber harvest over time may be its most recent incarnation, the general idea has been with us for a very long time. With the addition of a financial objective to guide harvest under this requirement, especially one that discounts the future, the potential exists to impoverish the forest rather than sustain it.

A goal of maximizing NPV subject to a nondeclining yield of timber will tend to shift the harvest of the most valuable portions of the forest toward the present, while maintaining the volume of timber that can be harvested over time, considering both the inventory and its growth. This problem can show up in at least four different ways:

1.  Where a mix of valuable old stands is mixed with younger, less valuable stands, the NPV analysis with nondeclining timber harvest will tend to single out those older stands for harvest first. This approach is reinforced by that fact that the older stands are growing more slowly (in percentage terms) than the younger stands and are thus strategic targets for replacement with younger, faster-growing stands.

2.  Where there are species of different values, either in separate stands or as individuals, NPV optimization analysis will try—to the degree permitted by the prescriptions and different growth rates—to harvest the most valuable species first, leaving the less valuable species for the future.

3.  Where a unit of measure like cubic feet or cubic meters is utilized to measure compliance with the sustained yield constraint, rather than a measure like board feet that is better correlated to value in many instances, the potential of devaluing the forest over time is magnified if the average diameter of the harvest will decline over time.

4.  When nondeclining yield is simulated for a finite time horizon, an approach often used in timber harvest scheduling, the NPV analysis will attempt to minimize the value left after harvest in the last simulation period.

---

of SMS has been officially embraced by the United Nations' Global Biodiversity Programme (Crowards, 1998) and, with its stringent standards for protection of threatened and endangered species, the Endangered Species Act in the United States has many characteristics of Safe Minimum Standards (Castle & Berrens, 1993). In a similar fashion, the 1982 regulations implementing the National Forest Management Act call for protection of habitats to ensure the viability of native vertebrates on the national forests of the United States (USDA, 1982a).[8] More generally, SMS also can help bridge the two sustainability concepts: Safe minimum standards for elements of natural capital judged most at risk can be embedded within the weak sustainability paradigm.

*Over time, the idea of SMS has been broadened and redefined as the conservation of critical natural capital—that natural capital for which human-made capital cannot substitute in the functioning of Earth's natural systems.* Broad application of these requirements moves us from a paradigm of weak sustainability to one of strong sustainability. We see this approach expressed in the 2012 planning regulations for the National Forest Management Act, which call for maintaining the *ecological integrity* of the ecosystems on the national forests as a foundational responsibility of forest managers (USDA, 2012).[9]

By itself, the identification of a portion of a forest as critical natural capital does not necessarily negate the potential usefulness of rate of return analysis in forestry decision making. Remember the example that started this chapter in which the landowner identified 10% of the stand to be retained (as critical natural capital) and then applied rate of return analysis to determine when to harvest the rest of the stand? In such a simple case, forest capital could possibly be partitioned between nonsubstitutable and substitutable natural capital, and the analysis could, in theory, proceed, much as ours did.

However, most ecological forestry problems are not that simple. *Multiple goals, sustained yield mandates, and other requirements greatly complicate the analysis and can largely negate the ability to partition the forest into substitutable (available for conversion into other investments) and nonsubstitutable natural capital.* Also, conservation of individual species may necessitate both a mix of forest types and ages and a particular spatial arrangement. In such cases, at different times, any of the stands might be considered critical natural capital until structural changes occur in adjacent stands. As these concepts broaden into conservation of entire ecosystems, the ability to divide natural capital clearly between substitutable and nonsubstitutable components diminishes further, largely negating the ability to conduct classical rate of return analysis.

---

8  See Chapter 7 for a discussion of the Endangered Species Act and Chapter 20 for discussion of the National Forest Management Act.

9  See Chapter 20 for a discussion of national forest planning under the 2012 planning rule.

## Implications for Ecological Forestry

*Recognition of multiple objectives, maintenance of future options, and the conservation of critical natural capital are hallmarks of ecological forestry.*[10] *As such, little free-floating capital may exist at any time for application of classical investment analysis. Rather, financial analysis that focuses on the potential to produce income over time, associated with different options for managing the forest, will generally be more useful.* We take that approach in addressing forest planning problems in Chapter 19.

It should be noted, though, that discounting, compounding, and calculating NPVs are skills that all people interested in natural resources should have. NPV is a widely used measure for estimating the value-in-use of a forest for buying and selling a forest or estimating the market value of a conservation easement, as we will discuss in Chapter 10. In addition, discounting is a valued technique for developing different cash-flow possibilities of a forest; maximizing NPV under different interest rates in forest planning analysis, in the context of achieving other goals, can help delineate different potential income streams over time. However, a requirement to maintain long-term economic productivity is essential in this type of analysis to ensure that the forest is not depleted over time. We will provide a demonstration of cash-flow analysis that maintains long-term economic productivity in Chapter 19.

---

10  See Chapters 1 through 5 for a description of ecological forestry.

# Appendix I: Additional Approaches to Financial Analysis

## Benefit-Cost Ratio

The benefit-cost ratio (BCR) of a project is the present value of all project revenues divided by the present value of all project costs. Using the components of Equation 9.5 for calculation of NPV, we can create the equation for the benefit-cost ratio:

$$BCR = \frac{\text{Sum of discounted revenues}}{\text{Sum of discounted costs}}$$

$$BCR = \frac{\sum_{t=0}^{n}\left[\dfrac{R_t}{(1+i)^t}\right]}{\sum_{t=0}^{n}\left[\dfrac{C_t}{(1+i)^t}\right]}$$

We can see from this equation that when the present value of project revenues is equal to the present value of project costs, the BCR of the project will be equal to one (BCR = 1). Note that when the present value of project revenues is equal to the present value of project costs, the net present value of the project will be equal to zero (NPV = 0). Given this relationship, if the BCR is greater than 1, then NPV will be greater than 0.

## Internal Rate of Return with Multiple Costs and Revenues

You will recall that internal rate of return (IRR) is the rate of return for a project, given known (or estimated) present and future values. Here is a slightly different twist on IRR: The internal rate of return of a project is the interest rate at which the present value of the revenues equals the present value of the costs (i.e., NPV = 0). Using the components of Equation 9.5 for calculation of NPV, we seek the interest rate ($i$) that solves the equation.

$$\sum_{t=0}^{n}\left[\frac{R_t}{(1+i)^t}\right] - \sum_{t=0}^{n}\left[\frac{C_t}{(1+i)^t}\right] = 0$$

Solving the equation directly for this discount rate is not possible, but a solution can be found iteratively.

NPV, IRR, and BCR are very closely related. Our example ecological forestry project summarized above in Table 9.6 can also be evaluated by NPV and BCR at interest rates of from 3% to 8% (Table 9.10). Note that at the lower discount

Table 9.10  *NPVs and BCRs for our ecological forestry project at different discount rates, including the calculated project IRR (5.56%)*

| Discount Rate | NPV | BCR |
|---|---|---|
| 3% | $ 726.10 | 4.63 |
| 4% | $ 298.35 | 2.49 |
| 5% | $ 75.29 | 1.38 |
| 5.56% | $ 0.00 | 1.00 |
| 6% | $ (44.16) | 0.78 |
| 7% | $ (109.81) | 0.45 |
| 8% | $ (146.76) | 0.27 |

rates, NPVs are positive, with corresponding BCRs greater than 1, and at higher discount rates, NPVs are negative, with corresponding BCRs of less than 1. The calculated IRR for the project, based on the estimated costs and revenues, is 5.56%, at which point the NPV for the project equals zero, and the BCR equals 1.

However, we must add a caution here about using these criteria to rank projects in terms of their financial performance: NPV and BCR may give a different ranking than IRR. Generally, NPV or BCR proves a more reliable measure than IRR in ranking projects, except where investment funds are strictly limited while land for these investments is abundant. This topic, though, can get complicated quickly and has been the fodder for debates among economists for decades. See Davis et al. (2001) for an extensive treatment of ranking projects with these criteria. We use NPV as our financial measure rather than IRR in rate of return analysis in this book.

# Appendix II: A Decision Tree for Choosing Present or Future Value Equations

A decision tree covering the most common situations fits this need well. By working through the tree, the appropriate interest formula can be found. To use the tree in Figure 9.9, the user makes four sequential choices to characterize the problem to be solved.

1. Is it a single sum or series of equal payments?

2. Is the present or future value desired?

3. Is the payment cycle annual or periodic?

4. Is it a perpetual or terminating series?

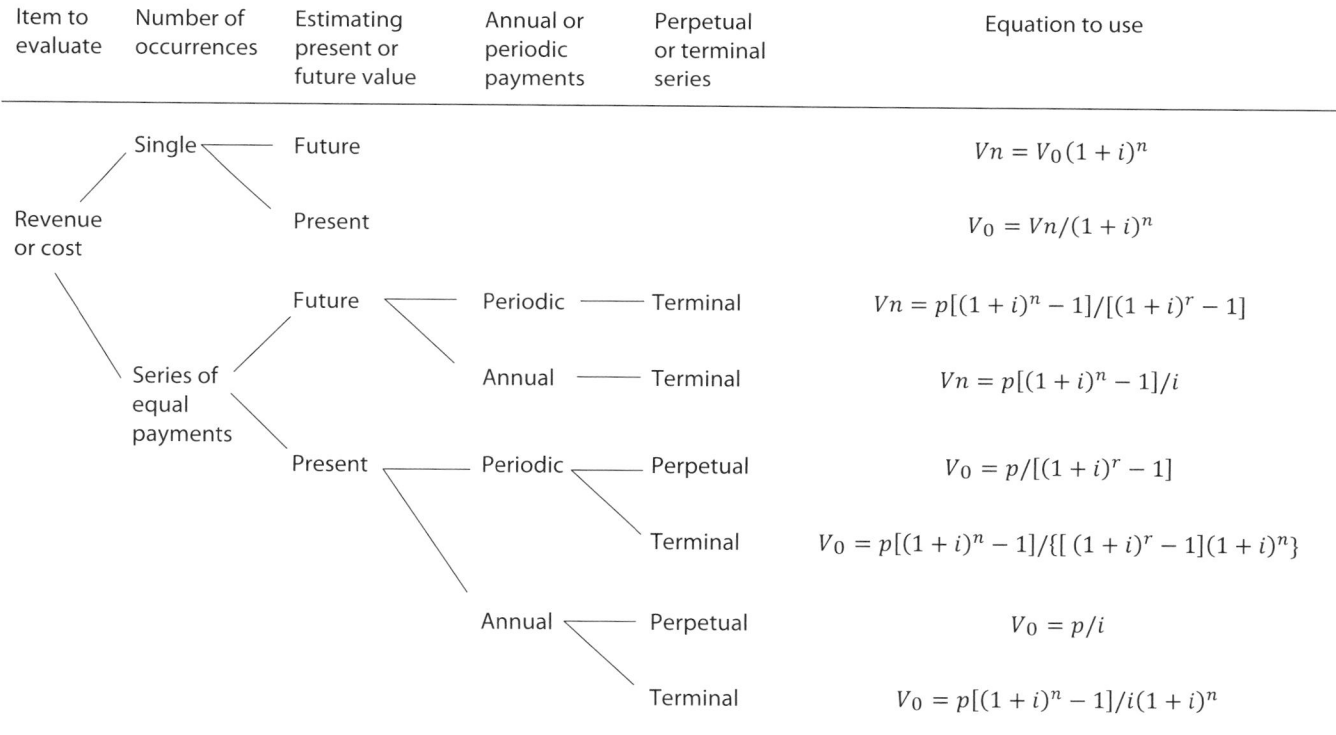

| Item to evaluate | Number of occurrences | Estimating present or future value | Annual or periodic payments | Perpetual or terminal series | Equation to use |
|---|---|---|---|---|---|
| Revenue or cost | Single | Future | | | $Vn = V_0(1+i)^n$ |
| | | Present | | | $V_0 = Vn/(1+i)^n$ |
| | Series of equal payments | Future | Periodic | Terminal | $Vn = p[(1+i)^n - 1]/[(1+i)^r - 1]$ |
| | | | Annual | Terminal | $Vn = p[(1+i)^n - 1]/i$ |
| | | Present | Periodic | Perpetual | $V_0 = p/[(1+i)^r - 1]$ |
| | | | | Terminal | $V_0 = p[(1+i)^n - 1]/\{[(1+i)^r - 1](1+i)^n\}$ |
| | | | Annual | Perpetual | $V_0 = p/i$ |
| | | | | Terminal | $V_0 = p[(1+i)^n - 1]/i(1+i)^n$ |

$Vn$ = future value—value of the investment $n$ periods into the future (value of the investment at the end of period $n$)
$V_0$ = present value—value of the investment at period 0
$i$   = interest rate per period expressed as a decimal
$p$  = amount of payment occurring every $r$ period
$r$  = number of periods in one multiperiod group
$n$  = total number of periods considered for compounding or discounting

Figure 9.9  *Decision tree for choosing among present and future value equations.** 

* See Davis et al. (2001) for application of these formulas to many different investment problems.

*Value is not made of money, but a tender balance of expectation and longing* — BARBARA KINGSOLVER

# CHAPTER 10

# The Economic Value of Forests

Suppose you and your siblings have inherited from your aunt a 5,000-acre forest of mixed conifers and hardwoods with a beautiful stream running down through the middle. She loved those woods and used a system of partial cutting to maintain their diversity and to protect the stream banks while making a modest, regular income. You promised your aunt that you would ensure that the forest will stay wild and not go the way of other nearby forests that have been turned into housing developments.

As much as you all love this forest, you may encounter situations in which you need to estimate its economic value:

- The Nature Conservancy or the US Fish and Wildlife Service has expressed interest in buying it, promising to manage it according to your aunt's wishes. What would be a fair price?

- The stream running through your property contributes to the water supply of the nearby town. What is the value of that water supply to the community?

- Your neighbor partially burned the forest and you sue him to recover damages. What should the damages be?

- Local residents in your county start a movement to buy your land as a park. How much should the county be willing to pay, i.e., how much do the residents value that land as a park? Or perhaps, the land contains some old-growth forest. How much should the county be willing to offer to keep the forest in old growth, i.e., how much do local residents value that old-growth forest?

How might you determine these values? And doesn't the forest have value beyond any benefits it might give humans? Difficult questions indeed!

In this chapter we will consider the complex issues associated with valuing forests and the diversity of approaches that are utilized, illustrating these approaches with many examples. We will begin by considering two fundamentally different ways of thinking about forest values, which we refer to as the utilitarian and intrinsic perspectives, and the

*Moosehead Lake and surrounding forests in Maine. (© Jeff Moose)*

contrasting perspectives of consumers and citizens. Then we cover some of the ways in which people use information from markets or social surveys to estimate the value of forests to humans. Following the literature of ecological economics (Farber et al., 2006), we divide valuation methods into *revealed preference*, such as *appraisal*, which relies on market information; *stated preference*, which relies heavily on surveys; and *cost* which primarily utilizes market information to estimate damage or replacement costs.

These methodologies, while valuable, capture only a portion of the multitude of values that forests contain. Many decisions lie beyond our analytical abilities and ultimately require social engagement at the levels of political processes and policy development for resolution. Still, understanding forest valuation will be helpful to you as a forest stakeholder and as a citizen. Perhaps someday you may even want to sell or buy a forest, making it important for you to understand how to estimate a fair price for that landscape!

## The Many Values of Forests

*Valuation of forest ecosystems and their services can be particularly challenging because different disciplines, philosophical views, and schools of thought assess the value of ecosystems in different ways*, as Aldo Leopold eloquently expressed in *A Sand County Almanac* (see Box 1.1). Thus people have very different perceptions regarding the value of forest ecosystems, and these perceptions are not necessarily in harmony with each other. Some people and institutions express these values in monetary units and evaluate investments based on rate of return to the investor, as we discussed in the previous chapter (Aronow, Washburn, & Binkley, 2004; Binkley, Beebe, New, & von Hagen, 2006). In contrast, others feel that many values associated with forests cannot be expressed monetarily and that there are more appropriate ways than financial return to value the well-being of ecosystems, their inhabitants, and benefits to society (Daily, 1997; Farley, Schmitt, Burke, & Farr, 2014; Leopold, 1949; Rolston, 1994; Sagoff, 2008).

As Leopold observed, the schools of thought that regard ecosystems as something broader than commodity production—which include ecological forestry—at times appear to be in a state of doubt and confusion as to the breadth of values that should be considered when contemplating activities that affect the land. Whereas people who focus on commodity production might arrive at decisions based on an economic analysis grounded in accounting principles and market reports, those who recognize the suite of ecosystem services must consider a multitude of often-contested values, not all of which can be so easily translated into money. Moreover, there is sometimes little agreement about which values to include in such an analysis, which units of analysis to use, and the framework by which to undertake the analysis.

## Utilitarian and Intrinsic Values

To help make sense out of these perspectives and disputes, we turn again to the Millennium Ecosystem Assessment (MEA) and the conceptual framework used there for the valuation of ecosystem services (MEA, 2005). In that work, as we introduced in Chapter 1, the authors defined ecosystem services as benefits that ecosystems provide humans and recognized four categories of these services: (1) *provisioning services*, such as providing food, wood, fuel, and water, (2) *regulating services*, such as climatic conditions, floods, diseases, and water purification, (3) *supporting services*, such as maintaining nutrient cycling, soil formation, and primary production, and (4) *cultural services*, including aesthetic, spiritual, educational, and recreational values.

As a foundation for understanding the value of these ecosystem services, the MEA describes *two general categories of value—utilitarian and intrinsic. The utilitarian (anthropocentric) value paradigm is based on the principle of humans' preference satisfaction (welfare). In this case, ecosystems and the services they provide have value to human societies because people derive utility from their use, either directly or indirectly.* Within this utilitarian concept of value, people also may give value to ecosystem services that they are not currently using, such as the value of maintaining the option for use in the future (option or bequest value) or the value of knowing a resource exists (existence value). Option and existence values may involve deeply held historical, national, ethical, religious, and spiritual values that people ascribe to ecosystems—the values that the MEA recognizes as cultural services of ecosystems. Although option and existence values may be difficult to quantify, they nevertheless are based on the utility they provide to humans and human society.

Apart from their value to humans, the MEA authors recognized that *some things—humans, animals, plants, ecosystems, the planet—can possess intrinsic value; that is, something can be of value in and for itself, irrespective of its utility to humans.* Many ethical, religious, and cultural systems recognize the intrinsic value of the natural world as a foundational moral principle, independent of its contribution to human well-being. As Aldo Leopold observed long ago about the evolving view of songbirds in the USA: "We have no land ethic yet, but we have at least drawn nearer the point of admitting that birds should continue as a matter of biotic right, regardless of the presence or absence of economic advantage to us" (Leopold, 1949, p. 211).

It must be acknowledged that existence value, discussed above with ecosystem services, may overlap with intrinsic value. Still, it is useful to specifically recognize values of the natural world beyond what that world can do for humans.

Intrinsic values may complement or counterbalance considerations of utilitarian values (MEA, 2003, 2005).

For example, if the aggregate utility of the services provided by an ecosystem outweighs the value of converting it to another use, its intrinsic value may provide additional support for conserving the ecosystem. If, however, economic analysis indicates that the value of converting the ecosystem outweighs the aggregate value of its services, its ascribed intrinsic value may be deemed great enough to warrant a social decision to conserve it anyway. Such decisions essentially involve political or moral considerations, rather than strictly utilitarian considerations, in the sense that they move beyond conventional consumer theory.

## Consumer and Citizen Values

*Confounding these analyses and decisions is the possibility that people will behave differently when acting as individual consumers than when acting as public citizens.* Such a dichotomy has been suggested by Sagoff (2008) among others. Sagoff (2008) uses the example of the court challenge of the decision by the US Forest Service to grant a permit for Walt Disney Enterprises to build a resort in a quasi-wilderness area in the middle of Sequoia National Park. In a class he taught, Professor Sagoff would ask his students how many would plan to visit the remote area in its present state. Very few would raise their hands. Next, he asked the students how many would plan to visit the proposed Disney resort, if built. Many would raise their hands. Finally, he asked whether Disney Enterprises should be allowed to build the resort (Sagoff, 2008, pp. 46–47):

> *The response was near unanimous. The students believed that the Disney plan was loathsome and despicable, that the Forest Service violated a public trust by approving it, and that the values for which we as a nation stand compel us to preserve the limited wilderness we have for its own sake and as a heritage for future generations. On these ethical and cultural grounds and in spite of their consumer preferences, the students opposed the Disney plan to develop Mineral King.*

While it may be possible to contort economic theory to explain this dichotomy, this example does raise the fundamental question of whether people act differently when they think of themselves as consumers as opposed to thinking of themselves as citizens.

Going back to Aldo Leopold's musings over the difference in the way that people value forests (see Box 1.1), we can see many valuation perspectives considered in this chapter: commodity versus noncommodity values, utilitarian versus intrinsic values, and people acting as consumers versus as citizens. It is no wonder that ecosystem valuation can seem a confusing and hopeless tangle at times!

*In sum, as noted in the MEA (2003, 2005), utilitarian values, based on consumer preferences, are only one of the bases on which decisions are and should be made in ecosystem management. Many other factors, including notions of intrinsic value and other objectives that society might have, such as equity among different groups or generations, can affect decisions* (Farley et al., 2014; Rolston, 1994).

Even when decisions are made on other bases and in other venues, though, estimates of utilitarian value can provide useful information for planning and policy. *We focus on utilitarian values of ecosystem services, expressed in monetary terms, in the remainder of this chapter.*

## Challenges in Valuing Ecosystem Services

Many countries, such as the United States, rely on markets to determine the monetary value of some ecosystem goods and services and as a mechanism for deciding what will be produced. Thus we rely on timber markets to help determine what types of trees will be grown and harvested and to help determine the comparable value of a forest for timber production or, perhaps, as a site for vacation homes. For many ecosystem services, though, markets can be imperfect mechanisms for this purpose, as the services may not have established markets or may have properties that make their value difficult to measure through markets. As discussed in Chapter 6, examples of these properties include cases where property rights cannot be enforced, which makes it difficult to exclude people who don't pay for an ecosystem service, or where everyone obtains the ecosystem service if anyone does (such as protection of endangered species).

Compounding these difficulties, many ecosystem services are simultaneously produced in a forest—that is, they are the result of *joint production*—yet just a few can be marketed. Thus a forest provides not only timber but also water, wildlife, and carbon sequestration benefits for which the forest owner is rarely compensated. On the other hand, timber harvests release $CO_2$ into the atmosphere, an environmental cost for which the forest owner is rarely charged.

These problems frequently afflict the marketing of many ecosystem services, with the result that monetary values are unobservable or misleading (Cubbage et al., 2017; Pearce & Turner, 1990). Where markets are deeply imperfect or nonexistent, we may turn to other methods to elicit the value people place on selected ecosystem services, such as a survey of people's stated willingness to pay for them or accept compensation for giving them up (see Box 10.1). We can then use this information to help guide public policy. As we will see, though, identifying valid and credible estimates of a group's willingness to pay without a market to test these claims can be challenging!

Beyond the issues of how well markets work and the degree to which they represent economic values, we also recognize that some utilitarian values cannot be monetized:

- Many forms of natural capital are *nonsubstitutable* in the sense that manufactured, human, or social/ organizational capital cannot substitute for them, as we have discussed in Chapters 1 and 9. In such cases, sustaining ecosystem goods and services requires that physical stocks of critical natural capital be maintained at levels that retain both their ecological functions and their regenerative capacity (Neumayer, 2013). While critical natural capital has utilitarian value, assigning a monetary value to critical natural capital could be misleading because it implies that substitutes exist when they do not (Farley, 2012) ( Box 10.2). In such cases we generally turn to public policy to ensure that adequate levels of critical natural capital are maintained.

- Cultural and spiritual values are extremely difficult to classify and value. The values of ecosystem goods and services often include cultural values of historical, religious, spiritual, or national significance (Rolston, 1994). The Millennium Ecosystem Assessment (MEA, 2003, p. 140), for example, recognizes that some aspects of sociocultural values fall between utilitarian and intrinsic value paradigms and, therefore, may not be fully captured by traditional economic valuation techniques. Moreover, attempts to monetize cultural or spiritual values or to suggest that they are somehow substitutable or compensable, may be morally or ethically objectionable to some cultures and religions.

As the Millennium Ecosystem Assessment authors advise, "Human preferences for all values can, to some extent, be measured with economic valuation methods, but ecological, sociocultural, and intrinsic value concepts have separate metrics and should be used in the decision making process in their own right" (MEA, 2003, p. 129). Recognizing these thorny issues, governments generally rely on a combination of markets and public policies to direct forest conservation and use, as we discussed in Chapter 6.

*In this chapter, we focus on market- and survey-derived processes to assess the monetary value people place on ecosystem services from a forest.* We will refer to the process of obtaining this information as *economic valuation* and the results as *economic values*. We have pointed out above some limitations of these approaches, and how they must be seen in the context of the broader set of public policies and values that guide forest conservation. Still, people, organizations, and governments often use estimates of the economic value of forests and their ecosystem services to evaluate forest conservation alternatives and to guide development of forest policy. Thus, understanding how these estimates are made can make you more effective in these analyses.

## Valuation Methods

We cover some of the commonly used methods for estimating the economic value of forest ecosystem services in this chapter from these different perspectives. Valuation methods for ecosystem goods and services often are categorized as belonging to one of three methodological groups: (1) revealed preference, (2) cost-based, and (3) stated preference (Table 10.1).

---

### Box 10.1 **The economic value of an owl**

In the 1980s and 1990s, the northern spotted owl was the center of significant controversy about the future of federal land management in the Pacific Northwest. Once it was listed as a threatened species, public land managers were required to take steps to protect the species, including protecting habitat comprised of financially valuable old-growth forests.

Contingent valuation methods were used to estimate the value that society placed on protection of the northern spotted owl (Rubin, Helfand, & Loomis, 1991). In their random survey of Washington State residents, the researchers described the owl's perilous situation and the commercial value of its habitat, and then asked respondents to mark a box corresponding to the annual amount they would be willing to pay to protect the northern spotted owl from extinction. The maximum value available to check was $500 per year. Respondents were also queried about their demographic and economic characteristics; the response rate was 23%.

Survey results showed that the average annual willingness to pay was $49.72. Based on the responses to the demo-

graphic questions, it was clear that the respondents' average income and education levels were higher than Washington State averages.

Using statistical regression analysis, the researchers established willingness to pay as a function of education and income and then used Washington State data to expand the sample to the population of the entire state. Next, using a distance decay function (10% per 1,000 miles), they generated a total value to the US population of $1.5 billion for protecting the northern spotted owl.

Not surprisingly, these conclusions were controversial. McKillop (1991), who focused mostly on a related study by Hagen, Vincent, and Welle (1992), critiqued the study methods and argued that biased procedures led to overestimates of the value of protection and underestimates of the related costs, such as impact on wood product prices to consumers. Despite these criticisms the findings of Rubin et al. (1991) and Hagen et al. (1992) were used by the US Fish and Wildlife Service (USFWS) in its proposals to protect the northern spotted owl.

*With revealed preference methods*, we derive information from markets or related economic data to infer monetary value for goods or services of interest. We will start with *appraisal* in which we estimate the monetary value of an ecosystem service by analyzing information from markets and following well-establish appraisal procedures.

We will look at appraisal methods in depth along with a number of example applications. Then we will briefly cover *hedonic pricing* in which we estimate amenity values, such as the value of a mountain view, through the differential value expressed through marketed goods like home sales.

---

**Box 10.2  When money is not enough: Tribal preferences for traditional foods**[*]

A group of Indian Tribes in the United States was placed on a reservation over a century ago, and their forest and rangelands were managed by the federal government primarily for commercial production of timber and livestock with little regard for traditional foods (like deer [*Odocoileus* spp.], camas [*Camassia* spp.], and huckleberries [*Vaccinium* spp.]) that are important to these Tribes (Figure 10.1).

To pursue a damage claim, the Tribal Council for these Tribes was informed that their attorneys would need a monetary estimate of the damages to traditional foods in order to be compensated for the damage through the courts. Many on the Council were apprehensive about this strategy, afraid that if they put a monetary value on traditional foods, these foods would be sold like the timber. Nevertheless, they deferred to their lawyers and allowed the analysis to proceed.

A nonmarket economist devised a valuation estimation program that utilized a method of paired comparisons, a method that we will cover later in the chapter. He designed a computer program for these paired comparisons that presented, randomly, all possible binary combinations of items in the choice set and asked the respondent to select the most preferred item in each pairing. The application for estimating the Tribes' values of damaged resources had choice sets that included four natural resources, two community resources, and five sums of money. Respondents were asked to choose the item that he or she felt would mitigate any loss to the Tribes associated with not having the other, or the one that he or she believed the Tribes would prefer to have. Each respondent was additionally asked to rate the importance of each of these items on a scale from "Not important at all" (= 1) to "Very important" (= 7).

The choice sets included four natural resources—water, deer, huckleberries, and camas—described in terms of their value from having the resources undamaged over the past decades compared to having a new community center, scores of scholarships for young people, or sums of money up to many millions of dollars. As an example, a comparison would be along the lines of: would you rather have the huckleberries as they used to be (i.e., would you rather have avoided the damage to huckleberries caused by timber harvest and cattle) or have the Tribes receive $25 million?

An initial survey was undertaken of a dozen Tribal members who worked in or around the Tribal headquarters. That survey revealed that, in general, the money or other alternatives being offered could not compensate the Tribal members for the loss of their traditional foods. The community

center did score as more important than camas, but it turned out that the camas beds had been destroyed so long ago that Tribal members had little memory of them, so that was not seen as a fair test. With these initial results, the lawyers, with some disappointment, abandoned their effort to put a dollar value on the loss of traditional foods.

In the end, the members of Tribal Council who had been most apprehensive about the survey were overjoyed: the survey proved to them that, in eyes of Tribal members, money or community resources, could not substitute for traditional foods.

---

[*] A few of the details of this story have been modified to maintain the anonymity of the Tribes and Tribal members involved. Related applications of this method may be found in Chuenpagdee et al. (2001) and Rosenberger, Peterson, Clarke, and Brown (2003).

Figure 10.1  *Deer (a), camas (b), and huckleberries (c) are important traditional foods. (Deer photo © Ryan Hagerty, USFWS; camas photo courtesy of the Institute for Applied Ecology)*

With *cost-based methods*, we estimate the cost of losing or replacing some ecosystem service. We often use variations on appraisal methods to make these estimates and will discuss them as part of the appraisal section of this chapter.

With *stated preference methods*, we generally estimate the monetary value of a good or service from survey instruments. These methods pose questions about hypothetical markets to determine a consumer's *willingness to pay* (WTP) for a good or service, such as the value people place on turning a forest into a public park or maintaining a pristine meadow/aspen complex. The methods also examine a consumer's *willingness to accept* compensation (WTA) to forgo a good or service. Here we will cover two important stated preference valuation methods: *contingent valuation*, in which informants are asked directly about their WTP for ecosystem goods or services (or their WTA for giving up these services) and *discrete choice experiments (DCE)*, in which information from choices or trade-offs presented to

informants, typically in a survey instrument, is used to infer the monetary value they attach to certain ecosystem goods or services. We will illustrate both of these WTA/WTP approaches with examples.

In many instances, individuals and organizations seeking to estimate WTA/WTP will not have the time or resources to make their own estimates. As a result, a field of research called *benefit transfer* has developed that can help improve the use of existing studies to estimate WTA/WTP and to address related valuation problems. We will briefly discuss benefit transfer after covering the two stated preference valuation methods.

Finally, we will come back to the issue of people acting as consumers versus citizens in stating preferences for ecosystem management. Toward that end, we will describe ways in which these valuation methods may be integrated with a *deliberative democratic process in group valuation*, where participants are asked to shift their perspective

Table 10.1 *Methods for estimating the economic value of ecosystem services (note: those identified in italics are discussed below)*

| Revealed Preference Methods | |
| --- | --- |
| *Market pricing* | Valuations are directly obtained from what people pay for an ecosystem service in a market. Example: Timber sold in a local stumpage market. |
| *Hedonic pricing* | The value of an ecosystem service is implied by purchases in related markets. Example: Housing prices along a coastline tend to exceed those of homes farther inland. |
| **Production approaches** | Ecosystem service values are estimated from the impacts of those services on economic outputs. Example: Improvement in watershed health leads to an increase in commercial salmon catch. |
| **Travel cost** | Cost of travel required to consume or enjoy ecosystem services is utilized as a proxy for their value. Example: The cost to travel to Yosemite National Park is used as the (minimum) value of visiting the park. |
| **Cost-based Methods** | |
| *Replacement cost* | Cost of replacing ecosystem services with man-made systems is utilized as an estimate of their minimum value. Example: The cost of replacing a watershed's natural filtration services with a water filtration plant. |
| *Avoidance cost* | Costs avoided or mitigated by ecosystem services are utilized as an estimate of their value. Examples: Wetlands buffer storm surges and reduce damage along a coast; climate regulation prevents temperature increases that would cause seas to rise and damage coastal cities. |
| **Stated Preference Methods** | |
| *Contingent valuation* | People are asked about their willingness to pay for or accept compensation for some change in an ecosystem service. Example: Willingness to pay for preservation of wilderness or maintaining the quality of an estuary. |
| *Discrete choice experiments* | People are asked to choose among or rank different ecosystem service scenarios or choose between ecosystem services and other benefits. Example: Choosing among wetlands scenarios with differing levels of flood protection and fishery yields; choosing between wild foods and monetary compensation. |
| *Deliberative monetary valuation* | Discourse-based contingent valuation or discrete choice experiments in which a group of stakeholders discuss values to depict society's willingness to pay. Example: Government, citizens' groups, and businesses come together to determine the value of restoring a wetland. |

Sources: Farber et al. (2006); Batker et al. (2014); National Research Council (2005).

from themselves as individuals to that of members of a broader community.

We should note that the results from revealed preference and stated preference approaches to estimating economic value are not strictly comparable, and there is a continuing debate among economists about how real and significant the differences between revealed and stated preference value estimates actually are:[1]

- Revealed preference methods focus on how much people *did* pay in markets. Stated preference methods focus on how much they *would be willing* to pay. Since people may be willing to pay more than they actually need to pay in the marketplace, willingness to pay estimates recognize more completely the economic value of a good or service to potential consumers. This additional value going to the consumer is often called *consumer surplus* (Pearce & Turner, 1990).

- With revealed preference, valuation results are directed and constrained by the preferences and income distribution of those able to participate in the market. With stated preference, the valuation results are directed and constrained by the income distribution of the participants only to the degree that the participants wish to take into account that consideration. Both approaches have been criticized for how reasonably and equitably they handle issues related to the distribution of income.

## Appraisal[2]

*Appraisal, as the term is ordinarily used, is the act or process of estimating monetary value.* The process entails a set of established concepts. Generally, appraisal seeks the **highest and best use** value that can be obtained, given the context of the analysis.

Appraisals must follow customary and accepted procedures, must be performed by a recognized and qualified appraiser, and must be as accurate as possible. To understand appraisals, we first need to master seven key concepts (Appraisal Institute 2000; Appraisal Foundation 2016–2017):

1. *Market value.* Appraisals in the United States generally utilize market value in their assessment—the most probable price in cash, terms equivalent to cash, or in other precisely revealed terms, for which the property will sell in a competitive market under all conditions requisite to fair sale, with the buyer and seller each acting prudently, knowledgeably, and for self-interest, and assuming that neither party is under undue duress.

2. *Highest and best use.* Appraisals generally utilize the highest and best use for the property being assessed— the reasonable and probable use that supports the highest net present value (see Chapter 9), as of the effective date of the appraisal or, alternatively, the use that results in the highest demonstrated value in a market, from among reasonably probable and legal alternative uses, found to be physically possible, appropriately supported, and financially feasible. When there is a claim that the highest and best use of a property is something other than the property's existing use, the burden of proving a different highest and best use is on the party making the claim.

3. *Before and after appraisal.* When only a portion of the property rights of forestland is being considered for sale or acquisition, such as with a conservation easement, the appraisal estimates the market value of the property rights at issue by comparing the value of the property before the sale of these rights to the value after the sale. The difference is the market value of that portion of the property rights.

4. *Ownership assumptions.* All parcels are valued as if they were privately owned. Thus, in a land exchange between the federal government and a private party, both federal and private parcels will be valued as if privately owned. This often increases the value of the federal parcel for purposes of exchange or sale. It also ensures that the private party always pays or receives market value for parcels that are bought or sold.

5. *Consideration of other values.* Under established law, the criterion for just compensation is the market value of the property or portion of the property being considered. No consideration should be given in the appraisal to any special value of the property not directly reflected in the market value, such as the sentimental value of the property.

6. *Unitary value principle.* The property being appraised must be valued as a whole. The market value of the entire property is the standard of valuation, rather than the total of the money values of its separate parts. This is often called the unit rule—properties must be valued as a whole and not a sum of components. Contributory value is the value of a particular component in terms of its contribution to the value of the property as a whole. The separate value of a component may be different than its contributory value.

7. *Administration, cost of capital, profit, and risk.* A wide variety of costs and risks accompany owning

---

1 In this discussion we will focus on willingness to pay to represent revealed preference methods. Similar conclusions can be drawn about willingness to accept.

2 This section on appraisal was provided by Jim Spitz, consulting forester, as are the appraisal vignettes in Appendix I.

and managing forests. These costs are usually already included in appraisals based on transaction evidence prices, but they must be incorporated into income and cost approach appraisals. There are usually some labor and overhead costs associated with owning and managing real property, and owners will want to be reimbursed for these expenses whether they do this work themselves or pay someone else to do it. Also, many risks are associated with ownership of real estate, including pricing mistakes, obsolescence, market price changes, and natural disasters. While insurance can protect from some of these risks, others must be borne by the owner. In addition, real estate buyers hope for at least a small financial gain as a reward for assuming the work, expenses, and risk associated with real estate ownership.

A number of useful references exist that provide much more detail on these concepts and many other aspects of appraisal (Box 10.3).

## Basic Appraisal Requirements

With the above concepts as a foundation, we can outline the basic requirements for an appraisal:

- The first step in appraisal is determining the *highest and best use*—all subsequent analysis must be responsive to the highest and best use of the property.

- The appraisal must be reasonable and supportable—the trail of logic in the appraisal must be obvious and traceable.

- The analysis must be based on local analysis procedures, revenues, and costs (including the cost of capital).

- The analysis must assume reasonably knowledgeable and economically motivated buyers and sellers, and an *arms-length* transaction.

- Only market values can be considered.

## Why Do We Need Appraisals?

In forestry, virtually all professional appraisals are concerned with buying or selling assets, establishing a basis for taxation, evaluating investment performance, or finding a value for settling a variety of legal actions. The following paragraphs review common forestry situations requiring appraisals. See Table 10.2 for some real-life examples.

**Buying and Selling Forestland and Forest Use Rights**
Whether selling, buying, or trading forestland, or leasing the rights to use a forest property, appraisals play a significant role. Major timber and land sales are usually inventoried and appraised by both buyer and seller. The recent surge in sales of industrial land to Timber Investment Management Organizations (TIMOs), as an example, created a brisk business for forestland appraisers. The family forest landowner with small acreage and infrequent transactions is often the least knowledgeable about timber appraisal procedures and may be more susceptible to exploitation by knowledgeable buyers. Assisting such landowners in appraisals and sales is consequently a dominant activity of consultants and service foresters, as acceptable appraisals are based upon the assumption of a knowledgeable buyer and seller.

---

### Box 10.3  Useful references on appraisal

- Appraisal Foundation. 2016–2017. *Uniform Standards of Professional Appraisal Practice (USPAP)*. Washington DC. Available for purchase online at http://www.uspap.org/#1. Broadly accepted quality control (ethical standards) for real property, personal property, intangible, and business valuation appraisal in the United States. Also sets minimum qualifications for licensing appraisers.

- Appraisal Institute. 2000. *Uniform Appraisal Standards for Federal Land Acquisition* (known as the "Yellow Book"). Chicago, IL. Available online at www.justice.gov/enrd/land-ack/Uniform-Appraisal-Standards.pdf. Federal requirements for acceptable appraisal practices and contents. Widely adopted by public agencies, private businesses, and appraisal associations.

- Colorado Coalition of Land Trusts. 2004/2010. *A Conservation Easement Appraisal Guide: A Brief Overview of Easement Valuation*. Denver, CO. Available online at

https://www.uwyo.edu/law/centers/rural-law-center/conservation-easement-conference/weston%20cclt%20appraisal%20guide%206-01-04%20updated%2020201.pdf. Guidance for obtaining conservation easement appraisals, including hiring an appraiser, appraisal contents, and common errors to avoid.

- Steigerwaldt, E. F., and L. A. Steigerwaldt. *A Practical Guide to Tree Appraisal*. Can be ordered from http://www.steigerwaldt.com/a-practical-guide-to-tree-appraisal/. An overview of tree appraisal requirements with practical examples of common challenges and ways to address them.

- National Timber Tax Website, Frequently updated. http://www.timbertax.org/publications/. Overview of current Federal income tax, Federal estate tax, and state timber and timberland tax laws with links to more detailed sources of information.

Table 10.2 *Examples of forest appraisals*

| Name | Purpose | What was appraised? | Description/ environmental and other issues |
|---|---|---|---|
| Knapp | Land purchased by US Forest Service to protect endangered pond turtles and scenic quality in the Columbia Gorge National Scenic Area. | Fee ownership of entire parcel | Private landowner wanted fair payment for high-value post, pole, and export logs on the property. Forest Service wanted control over scenic quality and use of selective logging to bring water in ponds up to optimal temperatures for pond turtle habitat. |
| Bandon Dunes | US Fish and Wildlife Service acquisition for addition to an existing refuge and to prevent conversion of an important estuary into a private campground and golf course. | Fee ownership of entire parcel | Intermingled aquatic ecosystems complicated logging, with numerous streams and ponds important for spawning and rearing of anadromous fish and the estuary food web. |
| Wind River | US Army Corps of Engineers wanted to purchase replacement fishing sites to local Indian fishermen in lieu of traditional fishing sites flooded by reservoir construction. | Partial taking from a large forest ownership | This was a mostly steep, rock point jutting into a side channel of the Columbia River. Logging was feasible as part of a larger cable setting. Access was available by steep trail or boat. |
| Malone Springs | US Forest Service purchase to provide public access to a canoe trail through a marsh in Upper Klamath Lake. | Fee ownership of entire parcel | Trophy home site with occasional, commercial timber harvests was the highest and best private use of this property. Charging for boat launching or other commercial services was not economically feasible, due to isolation. |
| Smith Rock Fire | An insurance company contracted for this appraisal of damages from a fire, which started in a state park and burned juniper woodlands surrounding private homes. Settlement was adjudicated by a judge. | Determine work and costs required for clean-up, soil stabilization, and revegetation | A market analysis showed little difference in value between cleared lots and juniper covered lots in this area, therefore, juniper restoration was limited to landscaping patches and screening of critical views. Dealing with angry landowners was difficult in this appraisal and is often a problem in trespass, damage, divorce, and condemnation appraisals. |
| Zena Forest (Box 10.4) | Bonneville Power wanted to use fish and wildlife mitigation funds to purchase a conservation easement that will prevent forest from being converted to vineyards or houses. | Cost of requiring the forest not converted to other uses and require use of FSC certification standards in forestry | Estimating market value of parcels suitable for vineyards, and estimating higher management costs and lower returns associated with FSC certification. |

Leases of forestland to other parties for special commercial uses, such as siting telecommunications equipment or a downhill ski area, need appraisals of the value of the land's contribution to the intended use. The US Department of Agriculture (USDA) Forest Service, for example, maintains a fee schedule, based in part on appraisals, for a wide variety of communications facility uses of national forestland.

**Conservation Easements**    There are also many public and private initiatives to protect specific conservation values by acquiring certain rights to forestlands. One of the most common approaches is to acquire a conservation easement—an agreement establishing a set of restrictions on the use of a subject property requiring that stated conservation values be protected (see Boxes 10.4 and 10.5 about conservation easements on Zena Forest in Oregon and Moosehead Lake in Maine). In agreeing to sell an easement, the landowner grants the easement purchaser the right to enforce those restrictions. The land stays in private ownership and the landowner typically reserves certain rights to the property, such as the ability to maintain a residence, continue to harvest trees according to some conservation standards, or use the property for recreational purposes. Federal or state tax incentives for easement purchase programs generally require that the easement be perpetual; that is, the easement is in place on the property forever, and the easement restrictions transfer with the property title to subsequent owners. Appraisals are needed to determine the value of conservation easements for acquisition purposes, gift tax treatment, valuing residual property rights retained by the owner for subsequent sale, or property and estate tax purposes (Colorado Coalition of Land Trusts, 2004/2010).

**Taxation**    Appraisals of forest resources are important in all major tax systems. The *ad valorem* property tax, often applied by cities and counties to their residents, requires an assessment of the fair market value of land, building(s), and other marketable assets to determine the taxes to be levied. This is more concerned with an equitable appraisal of similar and adjacent properties than with absolute market values.

Market values are used to determine forest yield or severance taxes in several states, which come due at time of harvest. The tax paid at harvest is often combined with a small *ad valorem* tax on the land.

*Value-in-use* appraisals (also called *income capitalization*) are important for setting values of forestland in those jurisdictions that have current use or productivity tax systems for forestlands. The value-in-use assessment for forestry purposes is usually lower than market value, especially in rapidly urbanizing areas. The lower taxes resulting from the lower assessment reduces the economic pressure to convert the forest to another use with higher financial

returns. In Oregon, for example, forestland and farmland is zoned Forest Conservation or Exclusive Farm Use, respectively. Tax rates are much lower, but nonforest or nonfarm uses are strictly limited. In many places, these tax reduction programs have penalty provisions that recover avoided taxes if and when the land use changes. These penalties are sometimes linked to the market value of the land at the time of conversion to a higher-valued use.

The death of a forest landowner can lead to an appraisal of forest resources owned by the decedent to set the basis for estate and inheritance taxes, and a basis for the distribution of property to heirs. Market value is the usual standard, although there are provisions for value-in-use and for treating the value of donated conservation easements.

Appraisals are also vital to landowners claiming a tax deduction for donating lands or easements for conservation purposes. In fact, the federal government and most state governments require an appraisal using standard methods to determine the tax deduction amount (Colorado Coalition of Land Trusts, 2004/2010).

**Loans and Investments**    Banks and other financial institutions often provide the acquisition and working capital needed to operate a forest business. Land and timber are common collateral for such loans. Lenders will often require an independent market value appraisal as a condition of the loan and will usually loan only a percentage of that appraised value.

In recent years, TIMOs and other investment institutions have purchased and managed forests on behalf of pension funds, foundations, and other investors. Because pension funds must track the performance of all investments on an annual basis, annual appraisals of their forest holdings are needed. Due to cost considerations, complete appraisals are done only periodically; annual updates are estimated using data on growth, harvests, and market conditions.

**Damage and Legal Activities**    Many forestry-related civil lawsuits involve a claim by one party against another to obtain financial compensation for damages. Often, each side has an appraisal done and the court may also have a third party do an independent appraisal or review the appraisals of the litigants to get a more objective, unbiased opinion. Market value at the time of the damage, death, divorce, or taking is the dominant concept of value used by the courts.

Timber damage appraisal is particularly complex when the damaged trees are only partly destroyed, or if the appraisal is made several years after the damage occurred. Critical issues include estimating stand condition and structure before and after the damage and determining how an undamaged stand would have grown compared to the observed growth, in volume and value, of the partly damaged stand.

## Special Difficulties of Forest Appraisals

Appraising forestland, even without damage claims, can be very complicated (Table 10.2). Certainly, some outputs such as timber and forage have fairly well-established markets, but active markets for determining prices may not be available. Also each forest property is unique in terms of productivity, composition, distance from markets, and management restrictions. In addition, it takes a long time to bring a tree or forest stand to merchantable size, and the available markets may only be able to absorb a large supply of timber over an extended time period. Investment periods of 20 to 100 years are not uncommon, depending on the products to be produced, growth rates, and other factors. Projections of values into the distant future are inherently difficult, and interest expenses for the use of capital will often be the dominant cost, as we learned in Chapter 9. Furthermore, many wildlife, visual, or environmental services of forests are not traded in markets, making the estimation of their contribution to the value of forestland problematic.

Thus forestland appraisal is complicated by difficulties of locating comparable properties, projecting forest conditions into the future, determining the appropriate interest costs for using resources over time, and putting a value on environmental services that often come with forests. Even after all the analysis is done, judgment will still be needed!

In addition, we should not expect classical appraisal methods to be useful for all of our economic valuation problems. Later in this chapter, we will turn to approaches that rely on social science methods, such as assessing the willingness of a selected group to pay for ecosystem services. These latter approaches round out and greatly expand our ability to determine the value of nature to humans.

## Three Approaches to Determine Monetary Value through Appraisal

*Value is a human perception—it is the worth of something to a particular individual, at a given place and moment in time—and appraisals help establish monetary values of goods and services traded in markets.* There are three interconnected perspectives for determining monetary value that we will discuss here and use throughout the chapter: (1) sales comparison (transactions evidence), (2) income capitalization (value-in-use), and (3) cost.

**Sales Comparison** Markets have the virtue of establishing prices empirically. Because prices recorded from completed transactions show how much people actually paid, comparable sales from competitive markets for the good or service in question are the preferred source of information for appraisal, if available. In forest appraisals, though, finding comparable market prices can be difficult.

To illustrate these difficulties, suppose the subject property is the 30-acre "Blackwood" woodlot, and that the appraiser has data on three similar properties that sold recently (Table 10.3). None of the properties is a perfect match to the Blackwood property; property *A* is located in a more rural area, property *B* is larger, and property *C* is closer to town than the Blackwood property and has some development value. The weighted average per-acre value of the three recently sold properties is $533.58, which the appraiser might conclude is too high, due to the influence of property *C*. Given these factors, the appraiser may reach the conclusion that "the market value of the Blackwood woodlot was $480/acre on the date of the appraisal."

**Income Capitalization** An investor who purchases income-producing forestland is essentially trading present dollars for the expectation of receiving future dollars. The income capitalization approach uses procedures (such as discounted cash flow analysis, discussed in Chapter 9) to analyze a property's capacity to generate revenue and convert these revenues into an indication of net present value (NPV). The anticipation of receiving future benefits creates value, but the risk of losing future benefits and the need to wait for a payoff subtracts from value. Investors expect to earn a higher rate of return on investments that are riskier and occur farther in the future;

Table 10.3 *Blackwood woodlot appraisal (June 18, 2000)*

| Item | Blackwood woodlot | Property A | Property B | Property C |
|---|---|---|---|---|
| Size of property (acres) | 30 | 21 | 60 | 36 |
| Sawtimber volume (MBF/acre) | 6 | 12 | 8 | 4 |
| Distance from subject property (miles) | — | 30 | 3 | 10 |
| Distance to town (miles) | 10 | 16 | 7 | 3 |
| Date of sale | — | 5/1/00 | 2/15/00 | 1/7/00 |
| Selling price per acre | | $430 | $500 | $650 |

*Source:* Davis et al. (2001)

these considerations should be reflected in the discount rates applied by the appraiser.

Income capitalization can be used to value forests where timber production is the economic output in question. The merchantable timber, nonmerchantable timber, and land can all be valued through the discounted cash flow analysis we described in Chapter 9:

- *Merchantable Timber.* The merchantable timber is valued by calculating the NPV based on a harvest schedule for the subject property. That often utilizes a stumpage value from the cost approach called *conversion return* (see below). Real stumpage appreciation and biological growth are factored in for each potential harvest period, and the projected value of each potential harvest is discounted to present time.

- *Submerchantable Timber, Land, and Other Uses.* The submerchantable timber, land, and other uses are valued by calculating the NPV of projected future net cash flows by class (stand) type.

Income capitalization can also be used to value forests where recreational activity is the economic output in question. As an example, an annual lease for quail hunting in the longleaf pine forests of the southern USA might be valued this way.

When transaction evidence is not available, or highly questionable, then income capitalization is often used. To determine what land, timber, or other assets are worth in use to an individual, the appraiser must forecast a schedule of costs and revenues for the planned activities, with the results often reported in terms of the NPV of a specific plan of use or as a rate of return on investment. The NPV of the plan is often referred to as the (capitalized) income value. It gives an estimate of what the buyer can pay for the asset and still make the guiding rate of return on the invested capital, as we discussed in Chapter 9.

The estimated income value from one individual's perspective does not necessarily give a totally accurate estimate of the market value. Market value is the result of buyers and sellers interacting, each with their own calculated income values. When several buyers are bidding for a single asset, such as forestland, the buyer with highest capitalized income estimate will likely be the successful bidder, all other things being equal.

**Cost** This approach considers the cost to either replace property that has been destroyed or repair damages to it (*cost to cure*). In cases of damage, theft, or loss of an asset, good, or service, the current cost of replacement with a comparable item may be the basis for appraisal. In the case of forests, the cost approach often divides the subject property into components (such as buildings, crops, and timber), and

then appraises the value of each component separately. This separation is made for analytical purposes only; the goal is still the value of the property as a whole and often requires adjustments to arrive at a final appraised value.

Suppose your neighbor starts a fire that burns up your house and car and sweeps through your forest, which consists of both merchantable and submerchantable timber. With the cost approach, an appraiser would attempt to estimate the cost of replacing your house, furnishings, and car. (Sorry—the sentimental value of your family photos would not be included, except for the cost of replacing their frames.) While estimating the value of your house, furnishings, and car may be difficult, estimating the damage to your forest can be far more complicated. Even if the merchantable timber was all killed, it probably has some salvage value. Thus you would need to estimate the difference between what you could sell the timber for before and after the fire. To do the latter you might use market transaction evidence (described above), but it might be hard to find recent sales of burned timber. So you might turn to a cost approach called *conversion return*. Conversion return starts with the point of sale, say the local mill, and works backward, deducting all the costs of conversion, such as logging and hauling, to estimate stumpage value. The submerchantable timber is probably a total loss, so you might use transaction evidence from previous sales or income capitalization of the potential future output if there had not been a fire. In some cases, the loss of submerchantable timber can also be valued in terms of how much it cost to grow to that point, including compound interest!

**Summary** Three generally recognized methods used in forest appraisal are: (1) sales comparison, (2) income capitalization, and (3) cost. The most useful appraisals employ multiple methods and compare the results. Evaluating differing estimates of value and supporting the resulting conclusions of value is often the most difficult task in completing an appraisal. To help the reader get a feel for the complexities of appraisal, we provide 10 vignettes in Appendix I that demonstrate the thorny problems that confront appraisers.

## Using Appraisal Principles for Evaluation of Different Types of Ecosystem Services

Appraisal principles and techniques are often used to estimate the economic value of ecosystem services that are difficult to directly value in markets. In this section we give examples of how all three appraisal methods are employed in this way.

**Sales Comparison** The sales comparison approach is applicable to all types of real property interests when there are sufficient recent, reliable transactions to indicate value patterns or trends in the market. Beyond its more traditional use in property valuation, *sales comparison is a primary method in appraisal for valuing wildlands, such as properties with extensive wetlands, alpine forests, or a mountain-top inholding in a national forest that cannot be connected to production of economic outputs.* Since we do not have a potential stream of economic benefits, the value-in-use approach does not apply. Also, the cost approach is often difficult to use. Rather, the question becomes: what do comparable properties sell for? *That may seem heartless, but setting a price based on what people pay for such types of properties is the contribution appraisal makes to the value question here.* It also provides the estimate the federal government would most probably use in bidding for the property.

Interestingly, private entities, such as the Nature Conservancy, are less restricted in how much they might offer for such a property than a federal government agency like the US Fish and Wildlife Service. Government agencies will need to follow accepted appraisal procedures in setting the property's value; the Nature Conservancy could go higher in consideration of these other amenities and the ecosystem services they provide.

### Income Capitalization

Income capitalization can be an especially useful appraisal approach for income producing properties, especially those that can yield significant revenue in the near future. Local market information on potential revenue, costs and discount rates should be used in this approach to the extent possible. However, the need to look into the future in the discounted cash flow analysis at the heart of income capitalization requires many assumptions and variables that cannot be clearly demonstrated by direct market data.

Income capitalization is often used to value a conservation easement on a forested property, especially where the easement will restrict the flow of income that will occur over time, with the appraisal estimating the NPV of the property with and without the easement (see Box 10.4). Also, income capitalization can be used to estimate the monetary value of development rights or land use zoning changes, with the resulting information becoming part of complex negotiations over partitioning a landscape between development and conservation easements (see Box 10.5).

*As we noted above, income capitalization is often used in a with-and-without analysis of the restriction on income (value-in-use) over time from a property due to the imposition of a conservation easement,* as was done in the Zena Forest case (Box 10.4). However, it must be remembered that this analysis computes the cost of the conservation easement in terms of lost income, rather than the value of the easement in terms of the variety of ecosystem services that it helps conserve. If the conservation easement is pur-

chased, we can assume that the services protected are worth the price paid; however, they may be worth much more to the people who purchase the easement.

Income capitalization can also be used to estimate the increased value from expanded development rights, again estimating the effect on the flow of income over time, as was done in the Moosehead Lake case (Box 10.5). However, that estimate does not necessarily represent the value of the ecosystem services attained through any expanded conservation measures that become part of the development package.

### Cost

The cost approach is very useful for damage estimates, often including aspects of income capitalization described above as needed. Also, concepts developed for the cost approach, such as conversion return, have use in income capitalization. Thus, these two approaches can seem somewhat intermingled, although they are distinguished in the appraisal literature.

*The cost approach is becoming increasingly important in estimating the value of ecosystem services.* We will examine two applications of the cost approach to valuing ecosystem services (see Box 10.6): (1) replacement cost: assessing the economic cost of replacing a well-functioning watershed to supply water to New York City with a filtration plant, and (2) avoidance cost: assessing the economic cost of allowing continued degradation of the natural climate regulation processes of Earth. In both cases, the economic loss of those processes is valued through a with-and-without analysis. While these cases may not fully employ "appraisal" in the classical sense described above, they did capture the appraisal principles of estimating the monetary value of the loss of the ecosystem service. As we continue to improve our linkages between natural processes and the outputs we seek, this appraisal approach can work on the side of maintaining natural systems and processes.

## Hedonic Pricing

A fundamental principle of microeconomic theory is that consumers seek to maximize utility under budget constraints. A look at a real estate website that offers search functions to prospective home buyers provides a demonstration of this and is especially relevant to the hedonic pricing method. At the website of the National Association of Realtors (www.realtor.com), prospective buyers are prompted to enter a price range for homes they may be interested in; this is the budget constraint. Next, the buyers enter preferences they may have about a home that serves to maximize their utility, such as number of bedrooms, number of bathrooms, size of home, lot size, and so on. Buyers are also given the opportunity to select from lists of amenity characteristics they may value in a property, which might include ocean view, city view, waterfront, or

Box 10.4  **Estimating the cost of a conservation easement: The Zena Forest in Oregon**[*]

The 1,400 acre Zena Forest of the central Willamette Valley of Oregon stands out as a forest-meadow complex in a sea of croplands and vineyards (see Figure 10.2). It contains some of the largest remaining parcels of several types of grasslands, oak savannas, oak woodlands, wet prairies, and emergent marshland in the area, along with a number of threatened and endangered plant species. Streams with threatened steelhead have their headwaters there, and wildlife utilize it as they migrate through the area. Without special restrictions, this forest would likely be clearcut, land suitable for vineyards would be converted to that use, and much of the rest would become Douglas-fir plantations. The owner at the time of the valuation wanted any buyer to commit to managing the forest to Forest Stewardship Council (FSC) certification standards—widely recognized by environmental groups as the most credible forest certification system to

Figure 10.3  *Sarah Deumling and her son Ben outside of the Zena Forest Products sawmill.*

ensure forest sustainability, and to strictly limit conversion of the forest-meadow complex to nonforest uses. (See Chapter 16 for a discussion of FSC certification.)

To understand the reduction in the flow of income that would likely occur under the commitments that the owner sought, a before and after appraisal was done comparing the NPV of forest management on much of the property without the restrictions (before) and with them (after). By comparing the two appraisals, the effect of the conservation easement on the estimated market value of the property for forestry could be ascertained. In addition, the relatively small portion suitable for vineyards was appraised using the comparative sales approach. Integrating these analyses, the appraisers estimated that the easement reduced the total market value of the property by more than one-third. With this appraisal in hand, the Deumling family bought the Zena Forest, with a public utility paying for the conservation easement and the family paying the rest (Figure 10.2); see the opening photo in Chapter 9 for a photo of the Deumling family and Figure 10.3 for their sawmill. See Appendix II for a more detailed report of the appraisal.

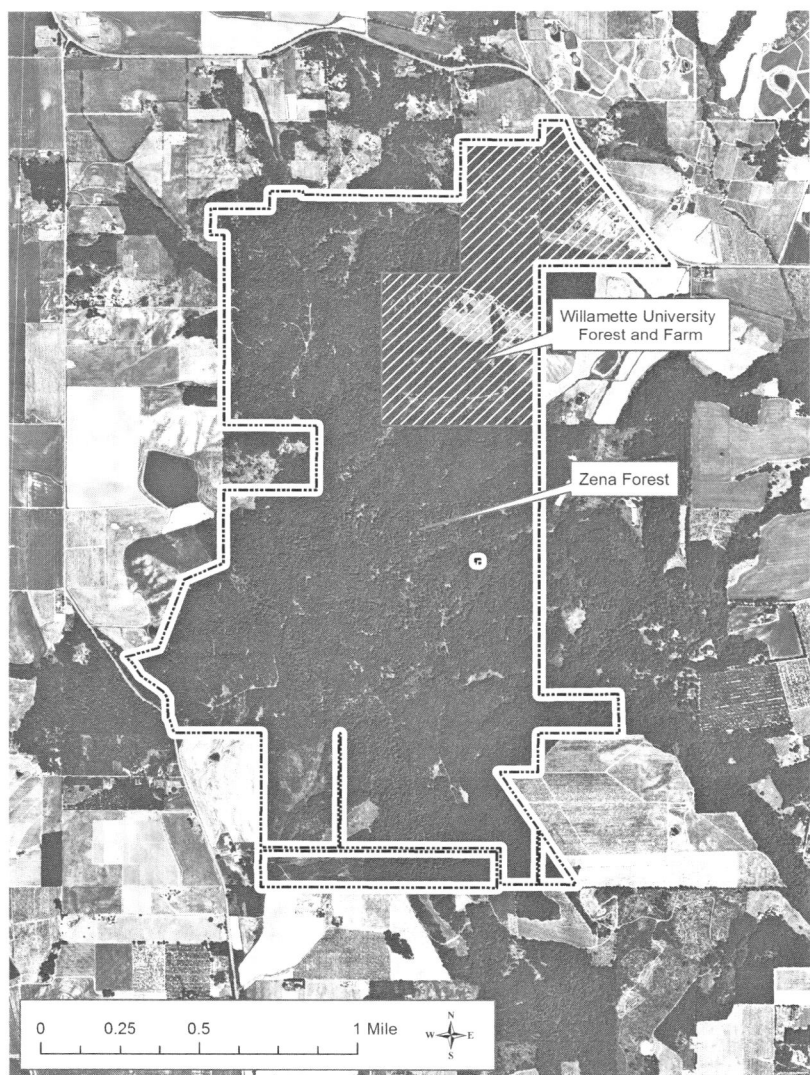

Figure 10.2  *The Zena Forest is one of the largest contiguous blocks of forest-meadow complex remaining in the Willamette Valley.*

[*] For more about the history of the Zena Forest and its people, see both Appendix II and Reinhardt, 2013.

## Box 10.5  Estimating the value of development rights: Moosehead Lake in Maine

Plum Creek Timber owns much of the shoreline and surrounding forest at Moosehead Lake, one of the most well-known recreational lakes in Maine (see opening photo of this chapter). In April, 2007, Plum Creek

*submitted a revised application to Maine's Land Use Regulation Commission (LURC) for a comprehensive development project on 408,000 acres in the Moosehead Lake region. The proposed development includes as many as 975 house lots and the potential for two resorts allowing for an additional 1,050 accommodations. According to the company's LURC application, conservation measures proposed as balance for development will result in 90,000 acres of permanent conservation including 156 miles of lake and pond frontage, 10 miles of Moose River frontage and 153 miles of permanent trail easements within the Plan Area. Plan approval will provide the opportunity, through the Conservation Framework, to secure another 266,000-acre conservation easement, a 29,500-acre conservation sale, both within the Plan Area, and a 45,000-acre fee sale outside the Plan Area for permanent conservation (Industrial Economics, 2007, p. 1).*

Without approval of this proposal by the LURC, Plum Creek timber would have to substantially scale back its development proposal. Not surprisingly, its proposal triggered a major statewide controversy. To aid in the public discussion and policy review, Industrial Economics (2007), a consulting group, performed a with and without development analysis (with and without the LURC approval), that simulated alternative build-out scenarios over time. Industrial Economics also calculated the NPV to the company under each scenario. It concluded that LURC approval had considerable value to the company.

To help increase support for its requested zoning change, Plum Creek worked with The Nature Conservancy and the Forest Society of Maine to increase the conservation easement to 363,000 acres (see Figure 10.4), sell other areas for permanent conservation, and make other conservation enhancements to its proposal (Nature Conservancy of Maine, 2012). The agreement greatly limited development on the conservation easement, but forestry could continue there under Sustainable Forestry Initiative certification (see Chapter 16 for discussion of this certification scheme).

The LURC approved the revised development and conservation plan. After a legal battle that went all the way to the state supreme court, the LURC decision was affirmed. Development must still meet a variety of standards as it proceeds.

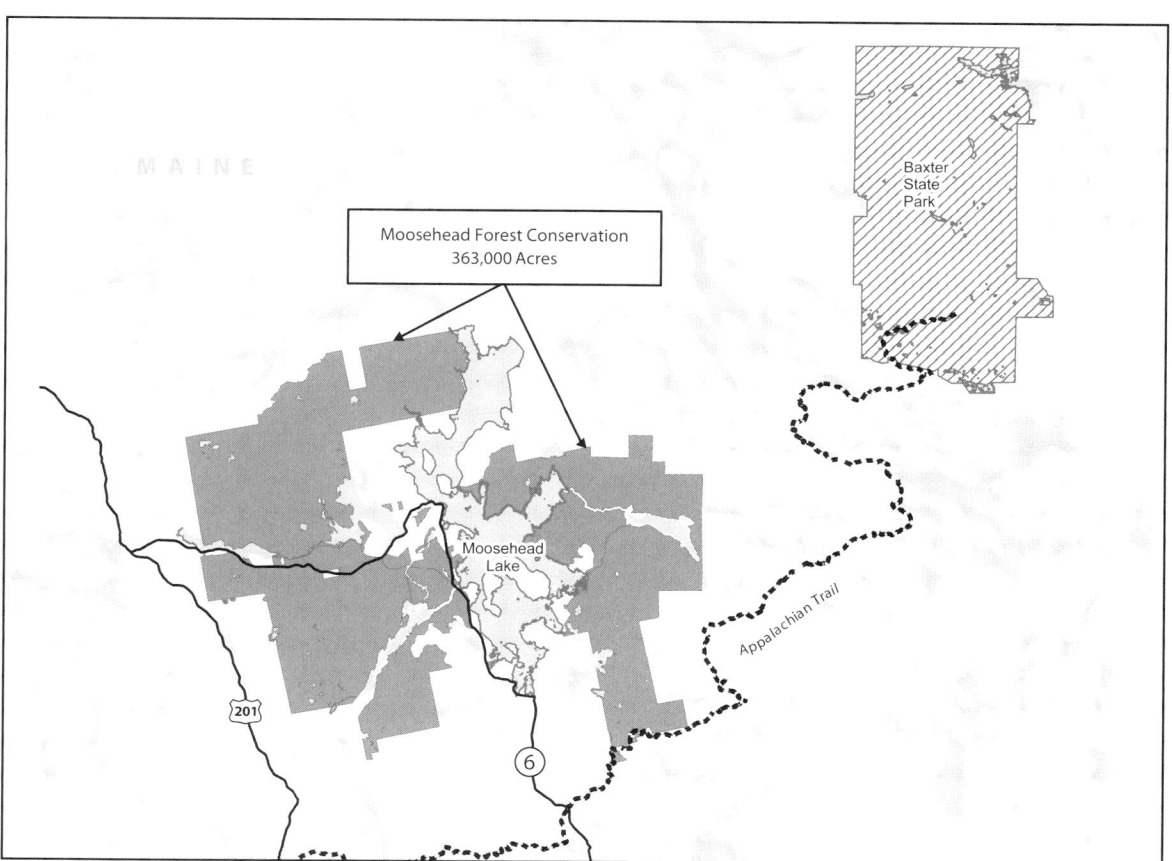

Figure 10.4  *Location of Moosehead Lake and the conservation easement.*

## Box 10.6  Valuing ecosystem services through estimating the cost of losing them

### Case #1: The Cost of Losing the Ability of a Watershed to Supply Domestic Water[*]

The clean, plentiful water that New York City residents drink comes mostly from the natural ecosystems of upstate New York's Catskill/Delaware watershed. While other cities spend billions of dollars on filtration systems, New York City depends predominantly on the natural landscape to filter the 1.4 billion gallons of water it uses each day.

The Surface Water Treatment Rule of the (federal) 1989 Safe Drinking Water Act mandates filtration of any surface water used in public water supply systems. However, suppliers can receive a waiver from that rule if they demonstrate the ability to minimize waterborne disease contamination, phosphorus loads, and turbidity in their waters. To fend off the $6 billion price tag for construction of a new filtration facility and the associated $300 million per year for operating costs, New York City invested up-front in nature's filtering services by:

- Establishing a program to purchase land and encourage conservation easements in watersheds that provide water to the city;

- Sharing the cost of implementing agricultural, forest, and stream best management practices (BMPs), such as buffers and setbacks, soil-conserving tilling and grazing practices, streambank fencing to keep animals out of waterways, and erosion-preventing forestry strategies; and

- Systematic and careful monitoring for disease-causing organisms and pollutants, which will help determine the success of New York City's protection strategies.

In sum, analysts for New York City did a classic with-and-without analysis, calculating what a water treatment and purification plant would cost without the upstate watershed to maintain water quality. They found that the cost of the water treatment and purification plant was much greater than the cost of maintaining water quality on their watershed, which led to a new appreciation of the value of that ecosystem service and a program to maintain watershed condition in the city's watershed.

### Case #2: The Cost of Losing Climate Regulation

An interagency group, working with the Environmental Protection Agency, has used a set of sophisticated models to estimate the future damage to the world economy from increased levels of $CO_2$ in the atmosphere, which the group calls the Social Cost of Carbon (SCC). The SCC is an estimate of the monetized damages associated with an incremental increase in carbon emissions in a given year. It is intended to include (but is not limited to) changes in net agricultural productivity, human health, property damages from increased flood risk, and changes in the value of ecosystem services due to climate change. The EPA reports the SCC estimates to federal agencies that then incorporate the social benefits of reducing carbon dioxide ($CO_2$) emissions, in terms of damage avoidance, into cost-benefit analyses of regulatory actions that impact cumulative global emissions.

To calculate the benefit of reducing $CO_2$ emissions, the future monetized value of emission reductions in each year (the value of emission reductions/metric ton of $CO_2$ in year $t$ multiplied by the change in emissions in year $t$) were discounted to the present to determine its total NPV for use in regulatory analysis (Table 10.4). Values are based on the average SCC from three integrated assessment models, at discount rates of 2.5%, 3%, and 5%. The last column of values, which represents the 95th percentile SCC estimate across all three models at a 3% discount rate, is included to represent higher-than-expected impacts from temperature change further out in the tails of the SCC distribution. The SCC increases over time because future emissions are expected to produce larger incremental damages as physical and economic systems become more stressed in response to greater climatic change. Recently, the costs at 2020 have been a policy focus, with the $42/metric tonne cost at a 3% discount rate often quoted. This might be seen as a measure of the social benefit of reducing $CO_2$ emissions or, conversely, the social cost of the damage from not reducing them.

[*] *Source:*    http://smapp.rand.org/ise/ourfuture/NaturesServices/sec1_watershed.html. Accessed: April 26, 2015.

Table 10.4  *Revised social cost of $CO_2$ emissions, 2010—2050 (in 2007 dollars per metric tonne of $CO_2$) at different discount rates*

| Year | 5.0% Avg | 3.0% Avg | 2.5% Avg | 3.0% 95th |
|------|----------|----------|----------|-----------|
| 2010 | 10 | 31 | 50 | 86 |
| 2015 | 11 | 36 | 56 | 105 |
| 2020 | 12 | 42 | 62 | 123 |
| 2025 | 14 | 46 | 68 | 138 |
| 2030 | 16 | 50 | 73 | 152 |
| 2035 | 18 | 55 | 78 | 168 |
| 2040 | 21 | 60 | 84 | 183 |
| 2045 | 23 | 64 | 89 | 197 |
| 2050 | 26 | 69 | 95 | 212 |

*Source:* EPA (2015).

recreation facilities. In making an offer on a home, buyers are assumed to weigh their perceived utility of the home, including its amenities, against their budget constraints.

The primary assumption behind the hedonic pricing method is that the price consumers are willing to pay for a good reflects the characteristics of the good the consumer finds desirable; *consumers will spend more for a good that includes a desirable amenity than they will for an otherwise identical good without that amenity.* The hedonic pricing method is most often used to evaluate amenity values associated with the price of residential housing. By comparing market data for sales transactions in a study area that include an amenity of interest and those that don't, researchers can estimate the contribution the amenity makes to the sales price. In addition to evaluating value contributions of amenities to sales prices, hedonic models can be used to measure reductions in value due to *disamenities,* such as air or noise pollution, proximity to hazardous sites, or proximity to *nuisance* operations, like landfills. We give examples below of these phenomena.

## Example #1: The Value of Forest Amenities

For many people, forests are attractive places to live. Buyers are attracted to homes and communities in the wildland–urban interface (WUI) for their amenities, such as forested surroundings, peacefulness, and proximity to recreation available on public lands. These areas are also susceptible to wildfire. When wildfires do occur, the lives of humans, and their pets and livestock, are at risk, and residences may be damaged or destroyed. Even if property is not lost during a wildfire, some of the amenity value that attracted residents to the forest in the first place may be lost. Loss of amenity value may not be restricted to areas inside of the burn perimeter; fire can affect the visual character of areas miles from the fire and may affect the perception of risk by residents, and by prospective residents.

A study by Stetler, Venn, and Calkin (2010) used hedonic pricing to evaluate the effects of amenities and wildfires on home values in northwestern Montana between 1996 and 2007. The investigators used data from 17,693 residential sale transactions and spatially located these in a database using a geographic information system (GIS). Fire perimeter data from 256 fires that burned at least ten acres were also located in the GIS database. Using spatial analysis, the researchers were able to determine distances from homes to amenities, such as golf courses, ski areas, wilderness, and Glacier National Park. Additionally, the investigators used topographic information within the GIS to determine the visibility of burned areas from each residence used in the study.

As might be expected, the researchers found that environmental amenities strongly influenced home values. For example, after accounting for other variables that might

affect home value, being situated on a navigable waterfront increased residential values an average of $214,034. Proximity to golf courses and the Whitefish Mountain Ski Resort also significantly increased residential values.

The researchers also found that proximity to wildfire had a negative effect on home values. They found that sales prices for homes within five kilometers of the perimeter of a fire were 13% less than for comparable homes more than 20 kilometers from the perimeter of a fire. Moreover, homes with a view of the area burned by wildfire sold for $6,610 less than comparable homes without a view of the burned area, suggesting that loss of visual amenity or risk perceived by prospective home buyers affected sales prices. Interestingly, properties located in areas that were assessed a WUI fire protection fee were valued $7,076 less than comparable homes that were not assessed the WUI fire protection fee. Because the WUI fire protection fee is only $50 per year, the authors hypothesized that, like homes with a view of a recent wildfire, the fee increases the perception of risk by home buyers.

## Example #2: The Cost of Living near a Pig Farm

In 2007, a concentrated animal breeding operation for hogs was constructed in a rural area near the town of Benton, Kentucky. Some neighbors were not pleased. Using sales data from 271 real estate transactions for the years 2002 to 2012, Simons, Seo, and Robinson (2014) conducted a hedonic regression analysis of the effect of wind direction and distance from the hog operation on residential home values. For the period 2009 to 2012 the authors found a statistically significant reduction in home values of 23% for homes within 1.25 miles of the facility and, based on an analysis that considered prevailing wind direction, they found an even more substantial reduction in the value of homes located downwind of the facility.

## Contingent Valuation

While revealed preference methods rely on some form of market data to infer monetary value of ecosystem services, stated preference methods are typically used where no such data exist. Contingent valuation (CV) uses a survey approach to describe a hypothetical marketplace in which survey respondents are asked to participate. *A CV survey elicits monetary values from survey participants for willingness to pay for an environmental amenity, or willingness to accept compensation for the loss of an environmental amenity.* Participant responses are contingent upon the scenario described in the survey, hence the name contingent valuation (Carson, 2012).

The first use of contingent valuation by an economist is attributed to R. K. Davis, who conceived of the idea while taking a graduate-level class in survey methods (Carson, 2012). Davis felt he could simulate a market by introducing a bidding-game approach to valuing hunting in the deep woods of Maine. In the late 1960s and early 1970s, CV studies were performed on such subjects as recreation, wilderness, air quality, water quality, and even medical services. By the mid-1970s, use of the method had become more widespread, and in the 1980s and 1990s the method acquired legitimacy through theoretical development in scientific journals and by approval for use by US government agencies. In the 1990s the methodology gained both notoriety and acceptability as a result of a contingent valuation study performed in response to the 1989 *Exxon Valdez* oil spill (see Box 10.7).

CV has been widely used to elicit the value people place on ecosystem goods and services, whether they directly use a resource, such as during a recreation visit, or by valuing them indirectly in terms of existence or option value (Box 10.1). The popularity and usefulness of CV stems from its adaptability in measuring the value people place on a range of ecosystem services, such as water quality (Carson & Mitchell, 1986), the benefits of preserving Mono Lake in California (Loomis, 1987), a private trout-stocking program in West Virginia (Rosenberger, Collins, & Svetlik, 2004), or the existence or option value of protecting pristine coastal waters from oil spills (Box 10.7). Contingent valuation methods have also been used widely in forestry, such as to determine the willingness to pay for preservation of spotted owl habitat in the Pacific Northwest (Rubin et al., 1991; see Box 10.1), gypsy moth control (Miller & Lindsay, 1993), and fire hazard reduction in Pacific Northwest old-growth forests (Loomis, González-Cabán, & Gregory, 1996).

Most contingent valuation methods employ some form of survey. In-person surveys provide opportunities for follow-up questions but are expensive and subject to interviewer bias and respondent yea-saying (a respondent's desire to please the interviewer or to appear generous). While telephone surveys are less expensive, some potential interviewees may resent the invasion of privacy. Mail surveys are generally even less expensive but lack opportunities for clarification, as is afforded by personal interviews and telephone surveys. Internet surveys using panels are becoming increasingly common and may be an attractive alternative where budgets are tight (De Valck et al., 2014).

A frequent criticism of contingent valuation is that the difference between monetary values elicited depends on whether a question has been framed as willingness to pay (WTP) for a good, or as willingness to accept (WTA) compensation for the loss of a good. The difference between WTP and WTA is based on a respondent's interest in the hypothetical item of commerce. WTP assumes that a respondent intends to acquire an interest in a good, whereas WTA assumes the respondent intends to relinquish an interest in a good. Another important distinction is that WTP is limited by a person's sense of how much they can pay (i.e., budget constrained), whereas WTA is not. Empirically WTA has usually been found to be greater than WTP (Brown & Gregory, 1999). For example, Hammack and Brown (1974) found that the average WTP for a season of waterfowl hunting was $247, whereas the average WTA (forego the season) was $1,044. Needless to say, this kind of disparity may call into question the reliability of an analysis. While these findings suggest attention should be given as to whether the valuation problem is about WTP or WTA, researchers typically use WTP, unless there are compelling reasons to use WTA, to obtain consistent and conservative estimates of economic values.

*Because CV is based on a hypothetical market and not a real market, it can be argued that the value estimates obtained by CV are not as powerful as real transactional evidence.* Respondents have not actually paid money for the good or service—the analyst has only the word of the consumer that the value is as the consumer states. Even with this shortcoming, economists and others have forged ahead in improving the method and in applying it to a broad range of goods and services that are not represented in markets (Carson, Flores, & Meade, 2001). We provide two examples below.

## Example 1: The Value of Outdoor Recreation in Finland

Finland is a sparsely populated country, and the common right of access to undeveloped areas, public and private, is deeply rooted in Finnish culture. Access to state-owned park services is provided without fee, and the costs of providing these services are financed from the government budget. Given the tradition of nonfee access to outdoor recreation in Finland (and in other Nordic countries) a market price for outdoor recreation amenities does not exist, yet many Finnish people clearly value opportunities for outdoor recreation.

A study by Huhtala (2004) used CV to estimate the value of outdoor recreation in state-owned parks in Finland. The study was part of the larger Finnish Outdoor Recreation Survey, which included 12,649 participants. The subsurvey conducted by Huhtala on the valuation of outdoor recreation was sent to 2,912 participants from the larger study, of which 1,871 responded. In addition to monetary valuation of outdoor recreation in state-owned parks, the survey was designed to elicit attitudes about recreation fees in general, and about how recreational services should be paid for. Many respondents showed reluctance to pay for nonconsumptive outdoor activities, such as berry picking, hiking, or cross-country skiing, and expressed satisfaction with the existing system of public funding. Nevertheless,

## Box 10.7  The Exxon Valdez, contingent valuation, and passive use value

Shortly after midnight on March 24, 1989, the oil tanker *Exxon Valdez* ran aground on Bligh Reef in Prince William Sound, Alaska, spilling an estimated 11 million gallons of Prudhoe Bay crude oil (Carson et al., 2003). The oil spread southwest more than 460 miles along the Kenai Peninsula, Alaska Peninsula, and Kodiak Island archipelago, contaminating at least 1,300 miles of shoreline. An estimated 250,000 seabirds, 2,800 sea otters, 300 harbor seals, 250 bald eagles, as many as 22 killer whales, and possibly billions of salmon and herring eggs were killed as a result of the disaster (see http://www.evostc.state.ak.us/index.cfm?FA=facts.QA).

The economic and environmental effects of the oil spill were vast. Exxon Corporation spent over $2 billion on cleanup and settled civil and criminal claims in 1991 with the State of Alaska and the US government for approximately $1 billion in US district court. Prior to the settlement, and in anticipation of litigation, the State of Alaska commissioned a state-of-the-art contingent valuation study to estimate the loss of passive-use values (existence values) resulting from the damage to natural resources caused by the *Exxon Valdez* oil spill (Carson et al., 1992). The study team was composed of six core members: three economists, two survey researchers, and an econometrician. Other survey researchers, psychologists, and economists served as advisors to the project, including Nobel-prize-winning economist Robert Solow. This was a first-class effort!

The study was concerned only with passive-use values— direct economic damages were evaluated in separate studies. Unlike a study population directly affected by economic damages, which would be expected to be found near the site of the disaster, the Carson et al. study was based on survey respondents selected at random from across the United States. Few survey respondents would have suffered direct financial damages, and the responses measured by researchers would therefore be damages resulting only from lost passive-use value, rather that active-use value. From an initial random sample of 1,599 households, 1,043 interviews were completed for the survey.

The research team wanted to determine the maximum monetary amount survey respondents would be willing to pay to prevent the *Exxon Valdez* oil spill from ever occurring. This was not possible, of course, because they could not go back in time, prior to the disaster, to conduct their survey. Instead, the researchers developed an alternative scenario: Respondents were told that if no action is taken over the next ten years, an accident comparable in scope to the *Exxon Valdez* oil spill would be almost certain to occur; they were then asked their willingness to pay for a program that would prevent the damage caused by such a spill from occurring. The lower-bound estimate for willingness to pay for such a prevention program was $31 per household. Multiplying this value by the total number of households in the US produced a lower-bound estimate of $2.8 billion for lost passive-use value as a result of the *Exxon Valdez* oil spill (Carson et al., 1992).

As noted above, this valuation study was produced in anticipation of litigation with Exxon over damages arising from the *Exxon Valdez* oil spill. Would the $2.8 billion estimate of lost passive-use value hold up in court? A 1989 ruling by the District of Columbia Circuit Court of Appeals suggested that it had a sound legal basis. In *Ohio v. U.S. Department of Interior* 897 F.2d 1151 (D.C. Cir. 1989), the court remanded to the Department of Interior regulations about giving preference to market values over nonmarket values in determining environmental damages. In its opinion, the court wrote:

*While it is not irrational to look to market price as one factor in determining the use value of a resource, it is unreasonable to view market price as the exclusive factor, or even the predominant one. From the bald eagle to the blue whale and snail darter, natural resources have values that are not fully captured by the market system.... We find that DOI erred by establishing a strong presumption in favor of market price and appraisal methodologies.*

Referring to the failure of DOI to recognize nonmarket values in damage assessment regulations, the court opinion continued: "Option and existence values may represent 'passive' use, but they nonetheless reflect utility derived by humans from a resource and thus, prima facie, ought to be included in a damage assessment." Although the legal action against Exxon was settled before the Carson et al. contingent valuation study was completed, the emergence of contingent valuation as a court-sanctioned means of assessing environmental damages led to considerable debate among economists about whether contingent valuation studies produced results that were sufficiently reliable to use in the assessment of environmental damage claims.

In response to the *Exxon Valdez* oil spill, Congress passed the Oil Pollution Act in 1990. Charged with creating the administrative regulations that would implement the Act, and quite aware of the contentious debate about the use of contingent valuation studies for estimating damages for lost passive-use values, the National Oceanic and Atmospheric Administration (NOAA) needed to decide whether contingent valuation studies were sufficiently reliable to use as a passive-use value assessment tool in the new regulations. NOAA therefore appointed a **blue-ribbon** expert panel to study the reliability of contingent valuation, and to make recommendations to the agency about its use. This six-member panel was led by two Nobel prize-winning economists—Kenneth Arrow and Robert Solow—and included three additional highly regarded economists—Paul Portney, Edward Leamer, and Roy Radner. Howard Schuman, former director of University of Michigan Survey Research Center, rounded out the panel. The task of the Contingent Valuation Panel was to assess whether contingent valuation "is capable of providing reliable information about lost existence or other passive-use values." In their report, the panel made

*(continued)*

clear their collective misgivings about contingent valuation but nevertheless concluded that contingent valuation studies can be the "starting point of a judicial process of damage assessment, including lost passive-use values" (Arrow et al., 1993). NOAA included contingent valuation in regulations implementing the Oil Pollution Act, and the use of contingent valuation by the agency in the regulations withstood a subsequent legal challenge.

Contingent valuation played a large role in the discourse concerning damages resulting from the *Exxon Valdez* oil spill, and stronger theoretical and methodological foundations have been developed as a result of the ensuing debate

over its merits (Kling, Phaneuf, & Zhao, 2012). Despite surviving legal and theoretical challenges, though, assessment of passive-use value through contingent valuation or other survey instruments played only a small role in assessment of damage to ocean ecosystems caused by the 2010 Deepwater Horizon disaster (Petrolia, 2014), which released many times the oil into the Gulf of Mexico that the *Exxon Valdez* released into Prince William Sound. Rather, the focus of the economic damage assessment shifted to negotiations over the damage done to ecosystem services, such as fisheries and recreation (tourism), without much survey research.

the study found that, on average, Finns were willing to pay €19 per person per year for outdoor recreation in state-owned parks; multiplied by the number of Finns aged 15 to 74 years, the total value of outdoor recreation provided by state-owned parks in Finland was estimated to be €75 million annually. The author concluded that the majority of Finns are satisfied with the current system of public financing of outdoor recreation services through taxes and that the annual maintenance expense of €13 million seems justified.

When asked why they might be willing to pay for services, approximately 60% of respondents indicated they would pay as a way to protect nature and wildlife and to promote the conservation of natural and cultural values for future generations. Only 7% of respondents indicated their willingness to pay was to ensure recreational opportunities for themselves. As this study suggests, a well-designed CV study is able to not only elicit information on willingness to pay but also provide information about *why* respondents are willing to pay.

## Example 2: A Conservation Easement in New Hampshire[3]

As we discussed toward the end of Chapter 5 in one of our case studies of landscape assessment and planning, the people of New England, USA, are interested in protecting forestland from development. As a result, conservation easements have been used throughout New England to protect forestland values there. A conservation easement, as we introduced earlier in the chapter, is a legally recorded agreement in which a landowner conveys, in perpetuity to a government unit or other organization, certain rights to be enforced by the holder for public benefit. The land itself remains privately owned and taxable, albeit at a lower rate.

To determine how much people of Coos County, New Hampshire, were willing to pay to protect forest benefits through the use of conservation easements, a contingent valuation survey was mailed to 1,600 randomly selected

resident households in the county (Cooksey & Howard, 1995). Over a four-week period in the spring of 1994, survey participants were sent a nine-page questionnaire with cover letter, a reminder post card, and if necessary, a follow-up letter and second copy of the survey.

Provided in the survey's center pages were a photo, a contingent valuation scenario, and a dichotomous choice (yes/no) questionnaire with a stated market value. Two situations were described: (1) continued access to the benefits of forests, fields, lakes, streams, and wetlands through conservation easements, and (2) loss of access to those benefits as a result of residential/industrial development without such easements. The key question was: "Would you be willing to pay $_____ each year, when you register your vehicle, for a special license plate tag that indicates you have made a contribution to a Land Conservation Easement Fund? These contributions would support public or private organizations in the purchase of conservation easements to ensure the conservation of forestland benefits in Coos County, New Hampshire" (Cooksey, 1994, p. 157).

Twenty-one percent of the people surveyed returned the questionnaire. Mean WTP was $31.23. Multiplying the mean WTP value of $31.23 by 7,314 (21% of the total population in the county) equals $228,416, the estimated lower bound of the range of aggregate annual amount that all Coos County residents would pay to protect forestland benefits in their county. This value assumes the remaining 79% would not pay. Multiplying the mean value by the total number of people in the county (34,828, according to 1990 Census) equals $1,087,678, assuming all residents would pay the mean WTP. This represents the estimated upper bound of the range that residents would be willing to pay each year into a protection fund.

Decisions based on this analysis must be tempered by the reality that, as in all CV studies, the respondents do not actually pay the money they say they would pay. This particular example has an additional flaw in that it is impossible to separate the demand for forestland protection from the demand for a distinctive motor vehicle license plate.

3 Adapted from Davis et al., 2001.

## Discrete Choice Experiments

Over time, detractors have posed serious theoretical and practical objections to CV (Hausman, 2012). That has led to an increased use of *discrete choice experiments (DCEs)* to elicit nonmarket values of ecosystem services. DCE may also be referred to as *choice experiments, conjoint analysis,* or *contingent choice.* Like CV, DCE can be used when sufficient market data does not exist to make inferences about the value of ecosystem goods or services. As with CV, DCE uses a survey to elicit responses from a target population; thus, there are many similarities between DCE and CV. Recall, however, that *CV elicits monetary values from respondents directly as their willingness to pay for a good or service (or willingness to accept a loss or reduction in a good or service). DCE, in contrast, do not ask those kinds of questions; rather, they present respondents with choice sets and elicit comparative judgments from respondents,* such as we discussed in Box 10.2 on the value of traditional foods to Indian tribes. Each choice set contains two or more alternatives, options, or scenarios composed of a mix of mutually exclusive attributes that define differences among them, from which respondents choose a preferred alternative, option, or scenario. In many applications, each choice set includes a status quo or current condition alternative (i.e., "I prefer the current conditions over the alternative conditions presented"). Respondents' choices reveal trade-offs that, when combined with attributes that include price, can be used to infer a value for willingness to pay for an ecosystem service or willingness to forgo an ecosystem service (Hoyos, 2010).

Hanley, Mourato, and Wright (2001) list several advantages DCE has over CV including:

- DCE specifically models trade-offs that involve many attributes. Thus, it is especially well suited to multidimensional problems where many values may be at stake.

- DCE is better able to measure changes in monetary values resulting from changed conditions than is CV.

- DCE respondents have multiple opportunities to express their preferences over many scenarios, providing more information about respondent preferences than CV studies, enabling tests for consistency.

- DCE does not explicitly ask for respondents' willingness to pay, but instead asks for choices among sets of alternatives, from which willingness to pay is inferred. DCE may thus avoid problems of protest bids, strategic bidding, and related problems.

Disadvantages of DCE listed by Hanley et al. (2001) include:

- Multiple complex choices may be cognitively too demanding, leading to increased random errors in DCE results.

- If large numbers of choice sets are used, learning and fatigue effects may occur, leading to apparently irrational choices by respondents.

- With large or complex choice sets, respondents may resort to heuristics or rules of thumb to make selections, leading to results that do not reflect their actual preferences.

Compared to CV, DCE is a relatively new valuation technique, and exploration and refinement of the methodology by researchers continues. The valuation of ecosystem goods and services using DCE is playing an increasing role in environmental decision making (Hoyos, 2010); expect to see more DCE studies, such as the examples below, in the future.

### Example 1: Forest Restoration in Belgium

Drongengoed is an 860-hectare natural area in the province of East-Flanders, Belgium. Prior to the 18th century, the area was covered by moor and heath. It was converted to farmland in 1746 but proved unsuitable for cultivation and much of the farmland was planted to conifers. The area currently is covered by conifer (29%), broadleaf (35%), and other (pasture, arable land, peat) (33%). Heathlands are rich in biodiversity, and European Union initiatives designed to protect biodiversity have led to restoration efforts that convert agricultural lands and forest plantations such as Drongengoed back to heathland or native broad-leaf forest. Clearing forests for restoration may be perceived as clearcutting by some members of the public, however, and people who object to clearcutting may thus oppose restoration efforts.

A study by De Valck et al. (2014) used DCE to elicit public preferences for restoration initiatives involving the conversion of conifer plantation forests to more natural ecosystems and to help inform policy makers on how to design restoration policies that will have community support. The survey designed for the study contained three parts: (1) questions about respondents' opinions concerning environmental issues; (2) the DCE, which asked respondents to choose between three nature restoration scenarios, one of which was always the *status quo* (Color Plate 10.1); and (3) questions about demographics. Results of the study suggest that respondents were willing to pay an average of €65.2[4] to convert 100 hectares of conifer forest to heathland, and pay

---

[4] 1 Euro = 1.14 US Dollars in July 2017.

€58.8 to convert 200 hectares of conifer forest to heathland. Respondents were also willing to pay €80.2 to convert 100 hectares of conifer forest to hardwood forest, and pay €41.4 to convert 200 hectares of conifer forest to hardwoods. Results of the study varied widely by demographic factors; respondents categorized as retired or ecofriendly showed much greater willingness to pay than other respondents, for instance. The authors conclude: "Though people generally prefer the forest habitat type, our results suggest that public support exists for converting forest plantations if this contributes to increasing landscape diversity and species richness" (De Valck et al., 2014, p. 65).

## Example 2: Shifting to Nature-Based Forest Management in Denmark

There is a growing trend in Europe to transform even-aged, plantation-style conifer forests to more natural forests using *nature-based forest management*. These more natural stands will have greater species, age, size, and structural diversity, and a larger compliment of snags and down wood than conifer plantations. A study in Denmark (Nielsen, Olsen, & Lundhede, 2007) sought to understand public perceptions of this change in management by measuring public preferences for tree species composition, stand structure, and the amount of dead wood left in the forest. The researchers sent a survey containing the DCE to a random sample of Danish residents between the ages of 18 and 75. Of these, 548 valid surveys were returned. The survey included questions about respondents' recreation activities in forests, attitudes and knowledge about forests, and the DCE itself, which contained six choice sets (Color Plate 10.2).

With respect to species composition, the study authors reported that respondents expressed a strong preference for converting the baseline, even-aged conifer stand to other tree species. This was expressed as WTP (in the form of a tax increase) of 969DKK ($145US) for conversion to a mixed conifer and hardwoods stand, and 770DKK ($115US) for conversion to a pure hardwood stand. Estimated monetary values showed a strong preference for variable tree heights in stands, with a change from single tree heights (even-age management) to a variable height structure valued at 856DKK ($128US) by survey respondents. Support for dead wood was not as robust as support for mixed species and tree heights, and showed a WTP of 114DKK ($17US) for a few (five per hectare) standing snags or down logs. Overall, the scenario with the greatest WTP was the mixture of conifers and hardwoods, of variable tree heights, with a few standing snags and down logs. The authors caution that the context of the study was understood by respondents to be at the stand level and that findings should not be interpreted to apply to all the forests of Denmark. They point out that their findings demonstrate the value respondents placed on variation within a forest stand, but that the same treatment applied at the landscape level would have a uniform appearance.

## Benefit Transfer

In most cases, you will not have the resources or time to do your own willingness to pay studies, whether they be focused on the value of a park to local residents or the value of nature-based management. Thus you will have to utilize studies that have already been completed. Which study or studies should you choose? And how might you use them?

This question brings us into the field of *benefit transfer*—the use of existing primary studies at one or more sites or contexts (often called the study site or context) to predict estimates of willingness to pay or related information for the site or context of interest (often called the policy site or context) (Rosenberger & Johnston, 2013, 2014). The many types of benefit transfer are often grouped into two broad categories: (1) unit transfers that use the actual values from previous studies, and (2) function transfers that utilize the functions (relationships) developed in a previous study or that constructs a function that synthesizes results from multiple studies. The benefit transfer literature generally favors function transfers over unit transfers, due to their greater adaptability, but unit transfers can perform well if the study and policy contexts are very similar (Rosenberger & Johnston, 2014) (Box 10.8).

Most benefit transfers begin with the information needs and characteristics of the policy site, including the type of value needed, the affected resource and population, and the ways in which resource changes affect the relevant population. Then literature and other sources are searched for studies with similar characteristics and contexts that can provide the needed information. Once the studies are located, models are developed to transfer the information from the existing studies to the policy site (Rosenberger & Johnston, 2014).

Ultimately, of course, the quality of benefit transfers depends on both the availability of accurate and valid transfer information and the quality of the underlying valuation research from which these transfers are done. Fortunately, the quality of benefit transfers is improving as analysts become increasingly aware of the challenges of conducting valid and accurate transfers, the scientific literature suggests improved methods, and valuation databases increase their treasury of valuation studies (Box 10.9).

## Deliberative Monetary Valuation

This valuation method combines stated preference methods discussed above (either contingent valuation or contingent choice) with deliberative processes involving a *citizens' jury* or other stakeholders as a means of valuing environmental change (Spash, 2008). A review of deliberative monetary valuation (DMV) methodology by Álvarez-Farizo and Hanley (2006) lists four shortcomings of stated preference methods that DMV responds to:

1. Stated preference methods may not provide survey respondents enough time or information to make informed choices about the goods or services they are being asked to value.

2. Because survey respondents may be unfamiliar with the goods they are being asked to value, they could find valuations difficult.

3. When making purchasing or voting decisions, people have time and opportunity to discuss relevant issues with family and friends, something that may not be possible in a stated preference survey.

4. Decisions about social values, such as moral, environmental, health, and safety issues, may produce different results when based on community preferences, rather than on aggregated individual preferences.

The effect on valuation from embedding a stated preference approach (here contingent choice) in a DMV is illustrated by a case study by Álvarez-Farizo and Hanley (2006). The study concerned implementation of the European Union's Water Framework Directive (WFD), which was to bring significant changes to regulation and management to watershed resources throughout the European Union. The specific case discussed here is based on the consultation process used for development of a watershed management plan for the Cidacos River in Navarra, Spain.

Environmental problems identified during WFD planning for the Cidacos River included high levels of water extraction, agricultural pollution, and pollution from domestic sewage. Many groups and individuals participated in the consultation process, and the study drew on information gathered from these participants to develop a contingent choice survey.

The contingent choice survey (hence: survey) assessed attitudes and values toward condition of the river ecology,

---

**Box 10.9 Additional information on nonmarket valuation of ecosystem services**

- The Ecosystem Valuation website, located at www.ecosystemvaluation.org, contains easy-to-read background information on the economic theory that supports valuation, description of valuation methodologies, and examples of the application of these methods.

- The Champ, Boyle, and Brown (2014) book entitled *A Primer on Non-Market Valuation*, 2nd Edition, is a very good reference on these valuation methods

- Additional information on benefit transfer can be found in Rosenberger and Loomis (2016) and Johnston, Rolfe, Rosenberger, and Brouwe (2015)

- The Environmental Valuation Reference Inventory (EVRI), located at www.evri.ca, is a searchable database of over 4,000 valuation studies for potential use in benefit transfer.

---

**Box 10.8 Using benefit transfer methods to estimate the damage to recreation from an oil spill**

What is the value of lost recreation due to the *American Trader* oil spill in the Southern California area in 1990? The primary needs are an estimate of lost recreation days and a value per recreation day.

- *Lost recreation days*: The study used historical data to derive a function predicting number of recreation days lost due to beach closures and impeded access due to oil spill and mitigation efforts.

- *Value per recreation day*: Existing literature was reviewed, with a study of beach recreation in Florida being selected as the best available match for benefit transfer of beach-related recreation in Southern California.

Combining these estimates for general beach recreation led to an estimated damage to that activity of almost $10,000,000 (Table 10.5).

During the litigation over the appropriate damages, the plaintiffs' and defendants' expert economists testified about methodology, assumptions, and the results of different analyses to address areas of disagreement about data, countervailing factors, and modeling assumptions. In 1997 the jurors awarded the Natural Resource Trustee Council $12.7 million in recreation damages, including estimates for beach, surfing, boating, fishing, and whale watching recreation (adapted from Rosenberger & Loomis, 2016).

Table 10.5 *Results*

| | Lost Days | Value per Day | Total Lost Value |
|---|---|---|---|
| Loss During Beach Closure Period | | | |
| General beach recreation | 454,280 | $13.19 | $5,991,953 |
| Loss Outside Beach Closure Period | | | |
| General beach recreation | 278,986 | $13.19 | $3,679,825 |
| TOTAL BEACH RECREATION LOSS | | | $9,671,778 |

the surrounding area, development of facilities, and reliability of water supply. Of the survey respondents that had agreed to participate further, 24 were chosen to serve on two citizen juries of 12 participants each. The juries met for three jury sessions, between three and four days apart.

*First jury session.* During the first session, participants were given detailed information about the problems facing the watershed and about the solutions proposed under WFD. Next, participants were again given the survey, which participants completed individually and confidentially. They were given instructions to consider their choices from a perspective of self-interest and to consider such factors as their income and family. After the survey was administered, a debate was facilitated between participants, and questions and problems were discussed. Finally, members were asked to discuss the issues raised with friends and family before the next session and explore the issues as they wished with their own resources.

*Second jury session.* Facilitators provided a summary of the problems in the watershed and details of the watershed management plan were reviewed. Participants then discussed among themselves and with facilitators issues and questions that had been raised since the first meeting. Participants were asked to express and discuss issues they felt were important for themselves and for the entire community as well as economic implications of different levels of ecological health of the watershed. Next, each individual responded to a confidential survey with the same structure and content as the first. Participants were reminded that their role in the jury was to take part in a process to select a plan of action on behalf of the community, which was defined as present and future generations sharing the same local environment. Following administration of the survey, jury members were shown aggregate results of the survey from the first session. Finally, they were reminded to have conversations with friends and family about the issues being addressed by the group in the time before the final session.

*Third jury session.* As before, facilitators summarized the watershed planning process, and presented survey results from the previous two sessions. Collective responsibility for the watershed management plan was discussed, along with the implications that decisions about management of the watershed could have for the community. Participants were told that this would be their last opportunity to influence the management plan and were given a survey instrument identical in design to the choice experiments used in the previous two sessions. As in the second session, participants were asked to make their choices on behalf of the community, expressing their values as a citizen. Rather than take the survey individually and confidentially, however, jury members were asked to make their choices collectively. They were instructed to choose the option that garnered the highest number of votes from all members of the jury, so long as the result did not make any jury member unhappy.

In discussing their findings, the authors reported that there was little change in attitudes and perceptions expressed by jury members between the initial survey and the survey administered during the first jury session. By the third jury session, however, there were significant changes in attitudes and perceptions, and the ranking of monetary values also changed between the first and last workshop. During the first workshop, the value of the security of water supply ranked highest, whereas in the third workshop the value of the river ecology ranked highest. The authors noted that the level of development preferred was significantly different between the initial conventional contingent choice survey and the results from the third jury session. In sum, the authors found that: (1) compared to conventional contingent choice studies, preferences change significantly when people are given more information, time to reflect, and the opportunity to converse with others about an issue; (2) values, as measured by implicit prices, were significantly different when measured in the valuation workshop setting, as compared to conventional survey settings; and (3) the shift from individual to community perspectives produced changes in both preferences and values.

DMV raises questions about the nature of valuation studies: The study summarized here by Álvarez-Farizo and Hanley (2006) found a significant difference between the aggregated individual results of the contingent choice study and the results of collective deliberation by a citizen jury. Or as we described in the example of student attitudes toward a winter Disneyland in the Sierra Nevada of California, it makes a difference whether we approach a valuation as an individual consumer or as a citizen concerned about the greater good.

## Summary

We started this chapter with a problem of valuing a small forest that a group of siblings had just inherited from their aunt. While that may have seemed relatively easy and straightforward at the outset, we soon saw that valuation can take many different paths depending on the kind of values that we emphasize (utilitarian or intrinsic), the method we use to estimate them (revealed preference, cost, or stated preference), whether we are considering the values as a consumer or a citizen, and the particularities of the ecosystem services of interest.

*With all of the complexities of forests and the many values they provide, no one method of valuation applies universally. Furthermore we must acknowledge that many decisions about forest values lie beyond our analytical abilities and require the back and forth of policy and political processes to resolve. Economics can provide us with useful information, but the wonder of forests will always lie somewhat beyond its grasp.*

# Appendix I: Vignettes to Illustrate the Application of Appraisal Principles[5]

1. Marion Ratchet is appraising the market value of a 20-acre highway right-of-way through a landowner's 1,000-acre forest. Marion identifies the highest and best use of this 20-acre property and completes an appraisal that meets all normal criteria for a market value appraisal. Is this appraisal an acceptable estimate of damages from the condemnation? Not necessarily. This is a *partial taking* (20 acres out of the entire parcel). Partial takings include outright acquisitions of land, as well as taking of an access easement, a conservation easement, mineral rights, timber cutting rights, or other partial interests. Appraisal of partial takings normally requires a before and after appraisal. In a before and after appraisal the value of the entire parcel and the value of the residual parcel are appraised separately. Damages from the taking are measured by comparing the value of the entire parcel before the taking with the value of the residual parcel after the taking. This more complicated approach to appraisal is usually required, because access, economies of scale for management, highest and best use, and many other characteristics of the residual property can be significantly affected by a partial taking of land or rights.

2. Willard Wingnut appraises federal and private forest parcels for inclusion in a land exchange. Timber on the federal parcels is not legally exportable, so only domestic markets for timber are considered in this appraisal. Timber from the private parcels can legally be exported, so higher net value export markets are also considered in this appraisal. Willard argues that this compensates both federal and private owners with the maximum value legally obtainable from their properties. Is this procedure acceptable? No. Legal precedence requires that government agencies provide just compensation to private landowners on both sides of a land exchange. When a private parcel is taken, the private owner must receive compensation, based upon the highest market value legally available. When the private owner receives a public parcel, public land use rules are normally replaced by private land use rules. Thus, the fair market value of public land converted to private use must be based upon private land use rules. Therefore, both sides of public–private land exchanges are normally appraised as if both sides of the exchange are privately owned.

3. Harry Cockroach is given what appears to be a very simple appraisal job. The property consists of a buildable lot, a small house, and a small quantity of merchantable timber. Based upon market information, Harry assigns a market value to the lot, a depreciated value to the house, and commercial stumpage value to the timber. He then adds them together and determines that this is the market value of the property as a whole. Is this an acceptable appraisal? Definitely not. This violates the unitary value principle, which says that the property must be valued as a whole. The unity principle recognizes that it is difficult to build an accurate list of the components of a property and that the value of individual components may interact and overlap in complex ways. In this situation, some or all of the trees may also provide scenic or other amenity values to the property that increase the sale value of the lot and that greatly exceed their commercial stumpage value. In this situation, analysis of comparable sales can be helpful in assessing missing, overlapping, and interacting values.

4. Sally Savvy is appraising an isolated, heavily timbered private parcel that is located deep within a national forest. Removal of the timber via road construction, helicopter logging, or other methods is not economically viable. Sally is not able to identify other viable economic uses for this property now or in the foreseeable future. What is the market value of this property? Appraisals of parcels, like this, are usually based heavily on transaction evidence. Comparable sales are often few, in distant markets, and of different character. Adjusting for these differences can be a significant challenge for the appraiser.

5. In another instance Sally is hired by the US Forest Service to appraise an inholding, which the Forest Service wants to purchase. Harvesting timber on this property by the owner would yield the greatest return via construction of a low-standard road and conventional logging. Helicopter logging is also possible, but would yield a lower financial return. Sally contacts a forest engineer, who is responsible for road construction in this area for the Forest Service. He provides a conceptual road construction and removal plan, which meets very high environmental and safety standards. He also states that he would fight any lesser access plan to the highest levels in the Forest Service. What access should Sally assume is possible in her appraisal? Complex legal issues are involved here, so Sally should obtain competent legal advice before completing this

---

5 These vignettes were developed by Jim Spitz, consulting forester, and come from real appraisal cases but the names have sometimes been changed to protect the innocent.

appraisal. In general, however, the most economically beneficial access must be used and the road standards and costs must be those that are common on private property in the local area.

6. Bill Bigdeal is appraising a very large forest property consisting of hundreds of parcels with a total value of over $100 million. To reduce this project to a manageable size, he combines these parcels into general groups based upon tree species, economic maturity of timber, logging costs, and other common factors that affect market value. These appraisals are based upon local costs and revenues and follow valuation practices used by local timber and forestland buyers and sellers. Bill considers values based upon cost, income, and comparable-sale approaches. He relies most heavily upon transaction evidence, when available, but also gives greater consideration to the income capitalization approach for older, immature timber and the cost approach for younger immature timber in his value reconciliation, as appears to be common local practice. Has Bill missed any major elements in this appraisal? Yes. High-value transactions also need to assess whether there should be a discount (or rarely premium) for size. Discounts for size at times have exceeded 50%. Discounts for size tend to be largest when there are more sellers than buyers, when local markets need multiple years to absorb timber from the subject property, when the value growth rate for the timber is low, and when the cost of money is high. Characteristics of the property and information about recent, large timber and forestland transactions in similar markets are needed to assess the need for a size adjustment to the appraised value.

7. A small rural town in Northern California is swept up by political turmoil. The owner of beautiful, mature stand of timber that adjoins the town and a major highway has applied for a permit to clearcut his property. This landowner says that he will proceed unless the property is bought at his asking price. Current zoning for the property allows clearcutting, but no developed uses. A local environmental group has offered to save the property by purchasing it for the asking price, if they can raise sufficient money. This situation is major statewide news and both state and federal congressional representatives become involved. A federal matching grant for a significant portion of the purchase price has been made available. Joe Forester is hired to develop an appraisal, which meets the requirements of the federal grant. Interested parties quickly tell Joe that this property has extremely high environmental and social values, which must be recognized in his

appraisal to get the value high enough to match the asking price. What should Joe Forester do? In fact he has little choice. He must appraise this property for its private market value to meet ethical (USPAP) and acceptable appraisal practice requirements (Appraisal Foundation, 2016–2017 also known as *Yellow Book* appraisal requirements). All federally funded appraisals and land purchases are subjected to a review process to ensure that these requirements are met. Market value is the highest price available to the landowner for this timber and land in the private market.

8. A conservation organization wants to acquire a property containing important fish and wildlife habitats on Willapa Bay in Washington State for eventual transfer to a federal wildlife refuge. Intergalactic Appraisal is hired to appraise the property. Intergalactic lacks timber and natural resource expertise, so it subcontracts a timber cruise and timber appraisal to Bob Boyscout. Bob encounters an incredibly complex environment and regulatory situation. This is an extremely productive forest with young, but economically valuable timber. The property borders Willapa Bay and contains an estuary with harvest constrained by Shorelines of the State and riparian protection regulations. Due to heavy annual precipitation, the property contains many wetlands and streams, and forest practice regulations require wide buffers and equipment entry restrictions. Anadromous cutthroat trout and two species of salmon use the streams. Two marbled murrelet nests are known to exist on upper slopes and receive forest practices protection. Road access is only available on upper slopes and unstable areas limit this access. Development possibilities for home sites are very limited. Further complicating this situation is a difference in harvest regulations and support programs between small and large forest landowners. Small landowners have lesser buffer requirements and can receive compensation for selling a 50-year stream buffer easement to the state. Thus, large landowners have business relationship and economies of scale advantages and small landowners have regulatory and financial support advantages. Bob determines that, if offered on the open market, small woodland owners would be in an advantaged position and would be the most likely buyers. A combination of shovel and cable logging provides the highest market value for harvesting available timber. Bob tells Intergalactic Appraisal that the remaining timber has no commercial harvest value and should be included in the land appraisal as an amenity that would slightly increase its value. Did Bob's timber appraisal and inclusion of the remaining timber as amenity to the land pass the federal review process? It did.

9. The Malone Springs property consists of a beautiful 12.5-acre parcel with a slope overlooking Klamath Lake and a flat area providing easy lake access. The US Forest Service wanted to acquire this property to provide access to a large area of marsh with canoe trail, bird watching, and trophy fishing opportunities. Amalgamated Appraisal decided that the highest and best use for this property in the private market was a trophy home site with minor income from commercial timber harvesting and appraised it accordingly. Was Amalgamated correct in ignoring the much larger value of public benefits available from this property? The review appraiser agreed with Amalgamated's appraisal. Under these circumstances, it was unlikely that a private landowner could earn net income from providing services or allowing public access to the lake.

10. The US Forest Service wanted to purchase the Knapp property to protect scenic views and endangered pond turtles under the Columbia River Gorge Scenic Area Act. Pond turtles occupied ponds within the unstable slopes on the property and were suffering from increasing tree shading, which was reducing water temperatures to well below optimum for turtle reproduction. This property contained productive forest and dense patches of trees with premium values in telephone pole, piling, and Japanese export markets. The property was appraised, based upon the highest value markets available to a private landowner. No economic consideration was given to protecting the pond turtles. Was this the correct procedure? Yes, the Endangered Species Act prohibits taking, but does not require active measures to enhance habitat for species of concern.

11. A wildfire started within Smith Rock State Park in Oregon, burned through, and seriously damaged vegetation on adjoining private parcels. In this situation the landowners were angry, because they believed their property was unnecessarily damaged by the state's failure to provide prudent fuel reduction and firefighting services. The landowners, insurance companies, and state agreed to settle damage claims, in this case via arbitration. Prior to the fire these properties were heavily stocked with 100-year-old western juniper, a noncommercial species. Petunia Pepper, a consulting forester, was hired by the insurance companies to provide an appraisal and expert witness services for use in the arbitration proceedings. Pepper developed and presented two analyses for consideration. One analysis compared the selling prices for similar, undeveloped parcels with parcels having heavy, light, and no juniper stocking. Prices were little different to slightly higher for

parcels with little or no juniper stocking. Perhaps many landowners preferred open views, grass, and wildflowers to a dense, juniper forest. In the second analysis Pepper provided a cost to cure damages for each parcel—removal of dead trees, dust abatement, erosion control, and screening from undesirable views. Screening from undesirable views was the biggest challenge, since 100-year-old juniper trees could not be replaced, except over an extended period of time. In this case Pepper provided for replanting and maintenance of clumps of the largest practical juniper trees, and argued that these clumps were of equal utility to the original forest because they were attractive and were expected to provide good screening for longer than the original forest. She also argued that additional, attractive views were present. Was this appraisal procedure acceptable? The landowners and judge accepted this cost to cure; however, the private landowners remained unhappy because they were not compensated for emotional distress.

12. The City of Seattle pursued a land exchange with the US Forest Service for many years, which would give the city management control over critical areas within their watershed. Seattle purchased over 10,000 acres of land scattered throughout the state of Washington, which they thought would be of interest to the Forest Service for use in the exchange. Little interest was expressed, so Seattle turned to Congress and obtained enabling legislation, which mandated an exchange deadline and a requirement that lands within spotted owl Habitat Conservation Areas (HCAs) be managed and appraised to optimize spotted owl habitat. An appraisal firm with a consulting forester subcontractor was awarded the appraisal contract. The consulting forester determined that only light salvage near roads and thinning intermediate-aged stands were possible if HCAs were to be managed to optimize spotted owl habitat. This resulted in a reduction in total appraised values on both ownerships of over $200 million. Special appraisal instructions, like optimizing spotted owl habitat, are unusual. Was this appraisal acceptable? The appraisal and underlying silvicultural assumptions were approved by both parties and their review appraisers and the exchange closed within the requirements of the enabling legislation.

# Appendix II: Zena Forest Appraisal and Conservation Easement [6]

## Background

Located in the Eola Hills about eight miles northwest of Salem, Oregon, the Zena Forest of approximately 1,500 acres provides refuge for sensitive native plant and animal species. In a landscape dominated by farm fields and by residential and vineyard expansion, the Zena Forest features one of the largest contiguous blocks of mixed conifer and oak forest in the central Willamette Valley (Figure 10.2). Conservation of this property would protect some of the last and largest remaining parcels of several types of grasslands, oak savannas, oak woodlands, wet prairies, and emergent marshland in the area. A number of rare, threatened, and endangered plant species are found here, including Kincaid's lupine (*Lupinus sulphureus* ssp. *kincaidii*), Nelson's checkermallow (*Sidalcea nelsoniana*), and the Willamette daisy (*Erigeron decumbens*). The headwaters of streams that contain the upper Willamette steelhead, a federally listed threatened species, originate on the property. In addition, the Zena Forest provides corridors for wildlife that venture from the Coast Range into the Willamette Valley.

Since 1998 the Zena Forest has been managed under Forest Stewardship Council (FSC) certification standards—widely recognized by environmental groups as the most credible forest certification system to ensure forest sustainability. Partial cutting of timber that maintains the forested character of the property has been the major forest management activity. Forest management practices include maintaining a diverse forest and valuing all native tree species, conserving native shrub species, delaying the harvest of trees to an older age than is practiced on most industrial forestland, and retaining biological legacies such as snags, large live trees, and downed wood on the forest floor. Logging occurs on designated skid trails to limit soil compaction, and careful attention is paid to matching species composition to site suitability, allowing the oaks to recapture sites where Douglas-fir does not do well.

## The Issue

The Zena Forest was purchased in the early 1980s by the Hatzfeldt family forestry business in Germany, and managed for them by the Deumling family who cared for it in an environmentally sensitive manner under FSC certification. In the mid-1990s the owners began focusing their

investments closer to home in large tracks of forestland that were formerly in East Germany (Henken, 2013) and eventually decided to sell the Zena Forest, but only under terms that would ensure long-term, sustainable forest management and protection of the natural environment. The land is zoned "Farm Forest" under Oregon's land use rules. This zoning class allows forestry and agriculture (including vineyards), and very limited home building (perhaps one house per 80 acres). Therefore, the highest and best use was either forestry or agriculture for most of the property, and full exploitation of these uses would threaten the owner's vision for environmentally sensitive management. Existing stands of mature timber provided the basis for a large fraction of the monetary value of the property, much of which could be immediately liquidated by a purchaser; it therefore appeared likely that a private purchaser would clearcut much of the property, in part to help pay for the purchase price. Additionally, the Eola Hills, where the property is located, is now coveted for growing Pinot Noir grapes, for which Oregon has become well-known around the world. Conversion to vineyards would be the most valuable use of the property in those locations where the land is suitable for growing grapes, but could compromise the environmental values the owners wished to preserve.

## The Conservation Easement

The owners engaged The Trust for Public Land to help structure sale terms that would ensure that they would achieve their goals of long-term forest management and protection of the natural environment. To make sure that key wildlife habitat and watershed features are protected and enhanced over time, a conservation easement was created to restrict development and conversion of the property into nonforestry uses. FSC certification was required for future operations. In addition, the long-term plan required restoration of oak-meadow complexes, which contain a number of rare plants but are being invaded by conifers. With this easement, the Zena Forest would provide a working forest model of ecological forestry for demonstration and study.

## The Appraisal

Before and after appraisals were completed by an independent rural land appraiser, with assistance from a consulting forester. The *before appraisal* estimated the market value of the property under existing land use regulations. The *after appraisal* estimated market value of the property with the encumbrances and requirements contained in the proposed conservation easement. The difference between these appraisals was the cost of the conservation easement. The land appraiser was responsible for determining the value of the property as a whole in both appraisals, and also

6  Jim Spitz, Consulting Forester appraised the timber and Ted Foster and Associates (Salem, OR) appraised the land.

provided value estimates for vineyards and the residential parcels that would be allowed under existing zoning. The forester provided the NPV of the timber (considering the harvest value of financially mature timber and the future value of immature timber) both before and after application of the easement.

The land appraiser relied most heavily on the sales comparison approach in assessing the monetary value of suitable parcels for vineyards, using other land sales that converted forest into vineyards in the local area. Due to the lack of comparable, private-land timber harvests for use in a comparable sales approach, the forester relied most heavily on the conversion return approach to estimating timber value. The before appraisal assumed the harvest of all timber as soon as it became financially mature and discounted future net harvest revenues to present values using the local industry discount rate. Under the conservation easement, the appraisal assumed that harvest would be limited to current growth, forest management would meet FSC certification standards, and conifers encroaching into hardwood stands would be removed to help maintain and restore oak savannah and woodland ecosystems. Finally, forest management costs under the conservation agreement were assumed to be higher. Using these assumptions for the after appraisal, periodic harvests were forecast and appraised,

and net income was discounted to present values. On balance, requirements in the conservation easement reduced the estimated market value of Zena Forest by more than one-third. Most of this reduction came from restrictions on timber harvest.

## The Outcome

Bonneville Power Administration purchased the conservation easement on the property to mitigate fish and wildlife habitat impacts caused by federal hydroelectric facilities on the Willamette River. Willamette University purchased 305 acres of the property for use in sustainable farming and forestry education. The remaining 1,232 acres was purchased by the Deumling family, who live on and manage the property, practice sustainable forestry, and run a sawmill that processes hardwood logs on-site into finished flooring, furniture, and cabinet stock.

For further information, see:

http://www.zenaforest.com/

http://dfw.state.or.us/conservationstrategy/news/2008/
2008_november.asp

Reinhardt (2013)

*Why did the policy-makers close their minds to the evidence and its implications? This is a classic case of folly: refusal to draw conclusions from evidence.* — BARBARA TUCHMAN

# Adaptive Management: Achieving Resilience in the Face of Change and Uncertainty

If there is a single unifying issue confronting all people interested in forests, it is uncertainty about the future. These uncertainties come from many sources—how changing climatic conditions will affect forest growth and associated biodiversity, how our social system will evolve over time with regard to what people want from forests, and how new scientific findings will emerge that change the way we understand forest function, to name but a few. Given the long time horizons of forest management, these uncertainties can dominate decisions.

In Chapter 1 we suggested four tenets of ecological forestry that help us address these uncertainties:

- *Restore and sustain the integrity of forest and associated ecosystems.*

- *Develop policies and management practices that consider and sustain a broad array of ecosystem services.*

- *Be attentive and adaptive to new scientific and technical developments and to changes in societal goals, priorities, and concerns.*

- *Choose management approaches that will reduce risks to forest assets and increase future options.*

In this chapter, we explore approaches to accelerating learning—expecting and looking for change and actively adapting to what is found. We begin with a theory of how complex systems behave—periods of stability intermixed with occasional bursts of instability that, in human systems, can be associated with catastrophic policy failure. We then suggest a role for adaptive management in increasing the resilience of the system in the face of these cycles and describe the process of monitoring to provide the information base for adaptation. We next turn to why adaptive management has proven so difficult to apply in natural resource management, *emphasizing that the greatest challenges to*

*Teachers learning how to begin stream monitoring projects with their students in North Carolina.*
*(Courtesy of Gary Peeples/US Fish and Wildlife Service)*

*adaptive management are social rather than technical, as suggested by the quote that opens this chapter.* Finally, we offer practical advice on how to make adaptive management an effective early warning system on the need for policy change.

## Understanding Transformations in Natural and Human Systems

The temporal dynamics of natural and human systems have been captured in the famous conceptual, heuristic model of the *adaptive cycle* by Holling (1986, 1992) and Gunderson (1999), which they first applied to biological systems. This model recognizes four stages (Gunderson and Holling, 2002): (1) exploitation (rapid colonization of recently disturbed areas), (2) conservation (slowing accumulation and storage of energy), (3) release (creative destruction), and (4) reorganization (processes reorder the system for the next phase of exploitation). As Gunderson (1995) and Janssen (2002) point out, the dynamics of natural resource policies in the United States can exhibit similar phases and transitions (Figure 11.1): (1) Initial robust policy implementation followed by increasing rigidity over time as the policy matures and bureaucracies become committed to it; (2) Challenge to the policy by activists based on differences between expectation and observation, which can create a crisis and lead to policy collapse (creative destruction); (3) Catalysts for change taking action, helping create a bridge to a new policy; (4) Development of new policy alternatives followed by policy selection and implementation, and the cycle beginning again. Also, in more extreme cases, policy collapse can lead to entirely new institutions.

It can be argued that federal forest policy development has sometimes exhibited the Holling/Gunderson characteristics of the adaptive cycle through policy selection, implementation, collapse, and rebirth through time. Initially robust policies become rigid, often with a single-minded emphasis on maximizing one aspect of resource management. The responsible agency becomes so invested in the policies, and the social forces that benefit from them are so powerful, that the agency cannot adjust as problems and circumstances change. Political and legal activists eventually take actions that result in policy disintegration, followed by individuals and groups whose ideas serve as catalysts for change. Decision makers utilize these ideas for change in settling on a new set of policies (and potentially a new set of institutions)

and the process begins again. This four-stage adaptive cycle is illustrated by the major change in federal forest policies in the Pacific Northwest in the 1990s (Box 11.1).

Are catastrophic policy failures, such as those described in Box 11.1, inevitable with all of their attendant costs? Gunderson (1999) and Gunderson and Holling (2002) argue *there is growing evidence that acknowledging and confronting uncertainty can add resilience to managed ecosystems. As part of that process, people have often turned to adaptive management—a process of accelerated learning in which uncertainty is winnowed, followed by actions to shift course as needed.* Through such a process, the adaptive cycle described above might be moderated and the rollercoaster ride of Figure 11.1 might have gentler slopes. The rest of this chapter is devoted to suggesting how this process of accelerated learning and remedial action might be crafted.

## Adaptive Management

As discussed by Gunderson (1999), ecosystems and the people whose fates are intertwined with them, form inherently complex systems that display cycles of alternately stable and unstable periods, as well as unexpected behaviors. In these coevolving systems of humans and nature, Gunderson further points out that surprises are the rule rather than the exception, with surprise defined as a qualitative disagreement between outcomes and expectations.

*Given that surprise is the rule and not the exception, resilience in natural and human systems—the ability to recover readily from disturbance or change—is a key property*

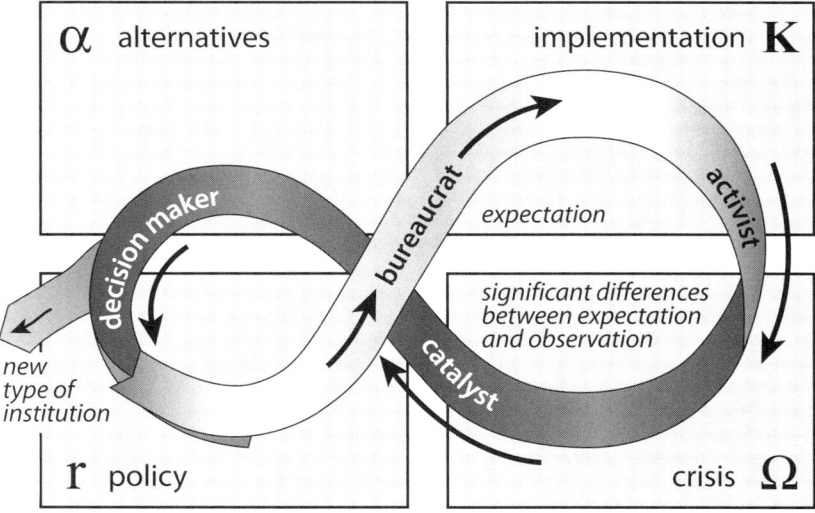

Figure 11.1 *Four-phase heuristic of the adaptive cycle applied to policy development and change, indicating the domination of different groups at different stages of policy development (From Panarchy, edited by Lance H. Gunderson and C. S. Holling. Copyright © 2002 Island Press. Reproduced by permission of Island Press, Washington, DC.) See Gunderson and Holling, 2002, for more on the theory and practice of the adaptive cycle.*

## Box 11.1  Federal forest policy in the Pacific Northwest: An illustration of policy development, rigidity, collapse, and renewal

The pent-up demand for wood for housing after World War II, combined with the inability of private forests to meet this demand, led to a major expansion of harvests in the magnificent old-growth Douglas-fir forests on the national forests of western Oregon and Washington. The Forest Service encouraged construction of new lumber and plywood mills to process the timber, and many communities expanded to accommodate the arrival of more mill workers and loggers. For the first time, these federal forests harvested their entire *allowable cuts*, which were based on the principle of sustained yield. Federal timber harvest became a central element in the regional economy. Tens of thousands of people found employment logging and milling the harvest. Through the 1950s and 1960s, timber management was the dominant use of these federal forests, and this emphasis was strongly supported by the congressional delegations of the two states.

By the early 1970s, the Northwest's federal timber economy functioned as a highly efficient machine, clearcutting thousands of acres of old forests each year to provide logs for hundreds of mills and replacing the cut forests with fast-growing plantations. Allowable cuts were based on the promise of intensive management and high yields from the plantations. Other uses of the forest were given only modest consideration, under the presumption that a sustained yield of timber harvest, carefully done, would benefit the other resources, whether they were fish, wildlife, or watersheds.

Passage of the National Forest Management Act (1976), in large part a reaction to the increased emphasis on timber production in the national forests, required development of integrated forest plans following procedures specified in the National Environmental Policy Act of 1970. The necessity for interdisciplinary planning and development of integrated forest plans resulted in a major challenge to the mantra that sustained yield provided for all uses. Through the 1980s, the Forest Service worked on developing forest plans, but meeting nontimber resource goals frequently required reductions in allowable cuts, which resulted in major opposition from both internal and external sources. Largely ignored were repeated pleas from district rangers that existing allowable cuts could not be sustained without damaging other resources and scientific studies that documented the threat of these harvest levels to wildlife and to forest ecosystems. Each year the Chief of the Forest Service sat before congressional appropriation committees and assured them the Forest Service could maintain the harvest level, and the allowable-cut juggernaut rolled on.

After more than a decade of work, the national forests released forest plans that called for slight reductions in allowable cuts; old-growth forests would still provide much of the harvest. The plans were litigated over protection for the northern spotted owl, and the courts granted an injunction prohibiting harvest in northern spotted owl habitat until the agency developed a scientifically credible plan for conservation of the owl. With that injunction, timber harvesting on national forests in the region essentially ceased, with wrenching disruptions in the lives of thousands of people.

After the Forest Service failed repeatedly to satisfy the courts with new plans that protected the owl while maintaining relatively high harvest levels, the agency created a team of scientists with expertise in the ecology of the northern spotted owl and charged them with developing a forest management strategy that would satisfy the courts. The science team developed a strategy based on the principles of conservation biology, greatly increasing the area that would be placed in reserves and also modifying management practices in intervening areas to facilitate dispersal of owls between the reserves. However, the White House would not allow the Forest Service to adopt the strategy because of protest from Congress.

Congressional committees concerned with national forest management recognized that the owl was just one of many issues that needed to be addressed. They chartered another scientific committee and charged it with synthesizing relevant information in developing and evaluating management alternatives for conserving old-growth forest ecosystems and their constituent species, aquatic habitat for at-risk fish stocks, and species listed as threatened or endangered such as the northern spotted owl and marbled murrelet. While accepting the alternatives that the scientists developed as a fair representation of the choices, Congress did not pass legislation that addressed the issues involved—the reduction in timber harvest needed to conserve species and ecosystems was just too great.

Building on the preceding reports, newly elected President Bill Clinton created yet another scientific committee, which included social scientists for the first time, to develop alternatives that could provide the basis for a comprehensive plan for these forests (FEMAT, 1993). These efforts culminated in his decision to adopt what became the Northwest Forest Plan in 1994. This plan placed conservation of biodiversity and watersheds first and timber harvest second, reversing historical post-WWII priorities on the national forests, and substantially reducing the timber harvest level.

All elements of the adaptive cycle appear in this story: (1) initial robust growth of a vibrant policy for advancing social well-being, with rigidity and inflexibility developing as maintaining allowable cuts became too economically and politically important to modify; (2) abrupt collapse of the policy after being challenged in court; (3) development of new policy ideas and alternatives by ad hoc groups of scientists outside of agency control; and (4) adoption of a policy by a decision maker (President Clinton) that put the federal forests of the region on a new path.

*needed to cope with the unexpected nature of these systems.* Gunderson's (1999) assertion regarding the importance of resilience in dealing with uncertainty has been strongly echoed in many recent scientific papers, often with reference to climate change (e.g., Pace, Carpenter, & Cole, 2016; Seidl, 2014).

With systems that are only partly knowable, the relationship between uncertainty and resilience is key: How people choose to deal with uncertainty either increases or decreases resilience of a system (Gunderson, 1999). As an example, foresters historically often attempted to reduce uncertainty by preventing or controlling disturbances, such as wildfire and insect outbreaks, rather than incorporating the reality of such events into their plans. In many situations, these policies resulted in increased vulnerability and loss of resilience, such as creation of highly vulnerable forest conditions in frequent-fire forest sites with fire suppression. *In sum, attempts to replace the uncertainty of nature with the certainty of control tend to create unsustainable systems in the face of the inevitable occurrence of disturbances* (Holling and Meffe, 1996; Gunderson, 1999).

More broadly, the uncertainties surrounding natural resource management have many sources (Gunderson, 1999):

- We have an imperfect understanding of the relationship between actions we might undertake and conditions and outcomes of interest.

- We will be managing in the context of considerable uncertainty for the foreseeable future.

- We have multiple hypotheses about the effects of actions on conditions and outcomes of interest.

- We will always be subject to surprises— the qualitative disagreement of outcomes with expectations is inevitable.

- Most of our policies are more questions (hypotheses) than answers.

Given these concerns, we can seek to:

- Have early warnings about policy failure;

- Address impending crises and necessities for change prior to collapse;

- Accelerate the rate at which we learn; and

- Manage for resilience.

An approach called **adaptive management** has been suggested to address these concerns and desires. Of course, successful managers have always adjusted their management policies as unforeseen events occurred and they learned about the success of their endeavors. Adaptive

management, however, attempts to systematize and accelerate this learning and adaptation. As described by Bormann, Haynes, and Martin (2007) in their assessment of the role of adaptive management in implementation of the Pacific Northwest Forest Plan (p. 187): "Adaptive management is not simply changing management direction in the face of failed policies; rather, it is a planned approach to reliably learning how to improve policies or management practices over time in the face of uncertainty."

This approach derives from the work of Holling (1973), Walters (1986, 1997), and Walters and Holling (1990) who proposed a highly integrated adaptive management strategy involving research, monitoring, and management designed to assess (test) and improve the effectiveness of resource management prescriptions. As described by Holling (1973), an effective adaptive management system can absorb and accommodate future events in whatever form they may take, with experimentation viewed as the core element in improving understanding of the system. With this approach, the goal is to learn as much as possible from both successes and failures while utilizing natural disturbances and human activities as experimental opportunities.

This formalized adaptive management approach, which we will later call **active adaptive management**, can be described in a number of linked steps (Lindenmayer & Franklin, 2002):

- Create alternative models regarding management of the system.

- Derive a set of hypotheses from those management alternatives.

- Develop an experimental design to test the hypotheses (measure the success of different management options).

- Implement management changes based on the results of experiments.

- Continue monitoring, documenting, and assessing the management results.

- Modify management in light of the findings and begin the process again.

While a very powerful approach to learning, as we will demonstrate later in this chapter, these steps may seem formidable and beyond the reach of many people interested in accelerating learning about the effectiveness of their policies and management actions. Much can also be learned from less formal approaches, as we describe below.

However, the fundamental point of Holling and Walters still prevails: *we need to view policies and management strategies as hypotheses, to see them more as questions than as answers. If policies are questions, then it makes sense to view management actions as treatments in an experimental sense (Gunderson, 1999), recognizing that they are working hypotheses* whether at the level of a large regional plan or the specific management prescription for a local project.

As described above, the process of adaptive management includes highlighting uncertainties, developing and evaluating hypotheses around a set of desired system outcomes, and structuring actions to evaluate or test these ideas. Although learning occurs regardless of the management approach, adaptive management attempts to make that learning more efficient. Just as the scientific method promotes efficient learning through articulating hypotheses and then testing them, a similar approach can be taken in adaptive management (Gunderson, 1999).

Adaptive management can be done passively or actively. In *passive adaptive management*, data about ongoing operations are reviewed and used to inform and improve decisions. In *active adaptive management*, different management approaches are tested in similar circumstances, the results are evaluated, and the information is used to select approaches and make decisions (Committee of Scientists, 1999).

Figure 11.2 *Monitoring the release of juvenile California condors (Gymnogyps californianus) with radio telemetry. (Photo courtesy of Scott Frier/USFWS)*

Thus, adaptive management is a process involving the fundamental features of learning (the accretion of understanding through time) and adaptation (the adjustment of management through time). The iterative application of learning and adaptation leads naturally to two salutary consequences: (1) improved understanding of the resource system, and (2) improved management based on that understanding. The feedback between learning and decision making is a defining feature of adaptive management, with learning contributing to management by helping to inform decision making, and management contributing to learning with actions that elucidate responses from the resources of interest (Figure 11.2).

## Monitoring: Developing the Information Base for Adaptive Management

Five types of monitoring have been identified by Aplet et al. (2014) (Table 11.1), based on information gathered from a variety of sources (Deluca, Aplet, Wilmer, & Burchfield, 2010; Hutto & Belote, 2013; Lindenmayer & Likens, 2009). We focus here on implementation and effectiveness monitoring, which are the most recognizable types.

Surveillance monitoring and unintended-effects monitoring are also important, and an adaptive approach to monitoring is essential. In fact, detecting changing baseline conditions that give concern or detecting the unintended consequences of actions often lead to the formation of new questions and issues to tackle with monitoring (adaptive monitoring) and changes in policies. One of us has argued elsewhere that, in fact, continual adaptive changes in monitoring programs will often be one of the most pressing and challenging needs (Franklin, Harmon, & Swanson, 1999).

Table 11.1  *Types of monitoring*

| Monitoring Type | Description |
| --- | --- |
| Implementation monitoring | Assesses whether a management action has been performed as designed (Deluca et al., 2010) |
| Effectiveness monitoring | Assesses whether an action has achieved the objective set for it (Deluca et al., 2010) |
| Surveillance monitoring | Assesses the background stability and change in biological systems by surveying response variables across well-distributed locations, which can provide fundamental information on what is happening in the world. (Hutto & Belote, 2013). |
| Unintended consequences monitoring | Searches for unintended ecological, economic, and social consequences of management action or inaction (Hutto & Belote, 2013). |
| Adaptive monitoring | Assesses whether the monitoring program needs adjustment, especially relative to new questions, new information, or new methods (Lindenmayer & Likens, 2009) |

*Source:* Aplet et al. (2014).

## Elements of Implementation and Effectiveness Monitoring

Implementation and effectiveness monitoring can be seen as having four key elements (Davis, Johnson, Bettinger, & Howard, 2001):

1. *Identify key uncertainties.* Adaptive management starts with an acknowledgement of the uncertainties surrounding proposed management actions. As Gunderson (1999) has said: you must *keep a ruthless hold on uncertainty*. Ideally, actions are a means to one or more goals, and a set of beliefs/claims/suppositions link the actions to attainment of the goals. You may be sure of some of the linkages but unsure about others. Both social uncertainty (e.g., members of the public do not believe you will leave all old trees at harvest) and scientific uncertainty (e.g., you are not sure how the actions will affect goshawk habitat, as scientific studies are inconclusive in your area) may exist. Identifying key uncertainties—those suppositions crucial to goal achievement about which you are unsure—is a critical step in successful application of adaptive management. It allows forest managers and collaborative groups to focus their energies on them when developing a monitoring plan.

   Further, we suggest grouping key uncertainties into a few major categories, such as (1) implementation (Was the action performed as designed?), and (2) effectiveness (Did the action achieve its goals?). We illustrate this with a project to restore the resistance and resilience of ponderosa pine forests on the Fremont-Winema National Forest, by addressing the increased stand density that has significantly increased the risk that scattered old pines will be killed by wildfire and insects and has also caused a decline in bitterbrush (*Purshia tridentata*). This project will remove trees established as a result of fire suppression and timber harvest, using both mechanical and prescribed fire treatment. We wish to identify and evaluate key uncertainties about the implementation and effectiveness of these actions at both the stand and landscape level (Table 11.2). At the project level, a key uncertainty about implementation might be whether the harvest will retain old trees, while a question about effectiveness might be whether the treatment will revitalize bitterbrush needed for big game forage. At the landscape level, one key uncertainty about implementation might be whether the projected treatments will cover a substantial portion of the forest in five years, while a key uncertainty about effectiveness might be whether these actions over five years will substantially reduce

the chances of wildfire impacting resources we wish to sustain, such as old trees and dense habitat patches.

2. *Develop testable hypotheses about treatment success.* We need to turn the key uncertainties into testable hypotheses by reframing them as testable statements (as needed) and by adding two attributes to each statement: (1) determining what will be measured to assess the validity of the hypothesis, and (2) determining what standard (expectation) will be used to judge whether the hypothesis should be accepted or rejected (Table 11.2). As an example, the uncertainty over whether timber harvest will retain old trees can be turned into a testable hypothesis that old trees will not be cut with a measure (number of fresh stumps of trees over 200 years of age) and standard (expectation) by which the hypothesis will be judged (an average of less than one tree over 200 years of age per acre will be cut). The uncertainty whether treatments will improve deer forage can be turned into a testable hypothesis that actions will revitalize bitterbrush (an important deer forage) with a measure (change in the extent and palatability of bitterbrush in five years) and standard by which it will be judged (productivity doubles within five years).

3. *Search for information to test the hypothesis or hypotheses.* Relevant information can range from informal observations by professional resource specialists, results of the latest formal research projects, or formal replicated experimental design; however, all approaches require a commitment to assess the validity of the proposed hypotheses. For example, a post-project survey could be done to determine the number of live trees over 200 years of age that were cut and pre- and post-project surveys could be done on bitterbrush productivity.

   As noted above, the search for information to test our hypotheses can be either: (1) "passive" in which information is gathered from regular management activities conducted in pursuit of plan goals, or (2) "active" in which alternative approaches to achieving plan goals are systematically compared (i.e., an "experiment"). In our example one of the key uncertainties about management effectiveness is whether timber harvest and prescribed fire will revitalize bitterbrush, an important food source for deer. We might measure the effect on bitterbrush abundance and vigor associated with our projects (passive adaptive management) or systematically test different approaches to timber harvest and prescribed burning and compare their impacts on bitterbrush (active adaptive management).

4. *Develop mechanisms that ensure monitoring results and methodologies will undergo periodic, fair-minded review, with the goal of revising policies that are not achieving the goals set for them.* Bella (1992) has noted the difficulty that people and organizations have in admitting that policies in which they are invested have failed to achieve their intended goals. This makes it is important to create mechanisms that will increase the probability that management success and failure will be fairly considered and policies can be altered as a result. One approach used by organizations is the establishment of independent review of monitoring results. The need for these mechanisms is discussed further below, because they are often the missing link in successful adaptive management.

A real-life example of a forest-oriented monitoring program that attempts to address all of these elements is provided in Box 11.2. It demonstrates both the thoughtfulness of a well-designed monitoring program and the challenges of translating monitoring results into management action in a dynamic economic environment.

## The Difficulties of Adaptive Management

Since these four steps are logical and straightforward, why do we have so few successful applications of adaptive management in natural resource management (Gunderson, 1999)? What makes it so difficult for organizations to incorporate adaptive management into their activities? Why do they so often need crisis and collapse in the adaptive cycle? We would argue that, in many ways, adaptive management, as defined here, is an unnatural act for organizations. It requires that organizations acknowledge the limitations of their knowledge and the potential for policy or management failure (fallibility), recognize the likelihood of error in fundamental assumptions (e.g., surprises), maintain a willingness to search for evidence of failures, and ultimately, possess the courage to let the evidence surface and be acted upon.

We identify below common barriers to successfully implementing adaptive management that should be anticipated:

- *The mantra of "adaptive management" as a way to avoid challenge and change.* As pointed out by students of adaptive management (Lee, 1999; Stankey et al., 2003), adaptive management has

Table 11.2 *Sample monitoring outline for a forest restoration project in a ponderosa pine forest*

| Key uncertainty | Hypothesis | Measure | Standard (Expectation) | Monitoring method |
|---|---|---|---|---|
| **IMPLEMENTATION** | | | | |
| *Project level* | | | | |
| Whether harvests will cut old trees | Treatments will not cut old trees | Number of trees cut over 200 years of age | An average less than one tree cut per acre | Post-project survey |
| *Landscape level* | | | | |
| Whether actions will move rapidly over the forest | A substantial proportion of the forest will be covered in five years | Number of landscape units finished in five years | At least 20% of landscape units finished in five years | Review annual accomplishment reports |
| **EFFECTIVENESS** | | | | |
| *Project level* | | | | |
| Whether project will improve deer forage | Timber harvest and prescribed fire will revitalize bitterbrush within five years | Change in extent and palatability of bitterbrush by year five | Bitterbrush in the project doubles in aggregate productivity | Pre- and post-project surveys |
| *Landscape level* | | | | |
| Whether threat of "destructive" wildfire will be reduced | Wildfire threats across large landscapes will be substantially diminished over five years | Risk of crown fire | Risk of crown fire decreases over 50% | Analyze pre- and post-project inventory information |

Box 11.2  **Adaptive management in the Coast Forest Strategy in British Columbia**

An exemplary approach to monitoring and other aspects of adaptive management was developed as a part of the Coast Forest Strategy in British Columbia. This strategy was initiated in 1998 when MacMillan-Bloedel, then the largest forest products company in Canada, announced that it would no longer clearcut coastal forests and would transition to variable retention harvesting over a five-year period. This was called the Coast Forest Strategy and affected approximately 2.75 million acres of lands managed under a governmental tree farm license. Two years later MacMillan-Bloedel was acquired by Weyerhaeuser Corporation, who agreed to continue and complete the transition from clearcutting to variable retention. This was successfully accomplished with an emphasis on safety and on education of both employees and the public on the rationale for the change.

A comprehensive adaptive management program, including a carefully-reasoned set of monitoring activities, was developed as a part of the strategy. This was not surprising given the seriousness of the company's commitment to conserving native biodiversity while continuing to maintain its economic viability. The monitoring was needed to provide credible evidence that the company was implementing the strategy in the field as promised and that it was achieving the ecological goals that were laid out. Since the strategy involved implementing new management techniques as well as addressing previously unexplored scientific issues, the adaptive management program also was expected to provide feedback for making both management and monitoring more efficient and effective.

The design, implementation, and lessons from the adaptive management program conducted under the Coast Forest Strategy are comprehensively presented in the book, *Forestry and Biodiversity: Learning How to Sustain Biodiversity in Managed Forests* (Bunnell and & Dunsworth, 2010). Four broad management questions were addressed in developing the program: (1) Where do we want to go? (2) How do we get there? (3) Are we going in the right direction? and (4) How do we change if the direction is wrong? The adaptive management program primarily was directed toward addressing questions (3) and (4).

The major ecological goal of the Coast Forest Strategy was to sustain biological diversity, defined as native species richness and associated ecological values, within the company's land base. Three "indicators of success" were identified and elaborated, which guided the monitoring program:

- *Indicator 1:* Ecologically distinct ecosystem types are represented in the non-harvestable land base to maintain lesser-known species and ecological functions;

- *Indicator 2:* The amount, distribution, and heterogeneity of stand and forest structures important to maintain native species richness are maintained over time; and

- *Indicator 3:* The abundance, distribution, and reproductive success of native species are not reduced by forest practices.

The third criterion proved to be the most difficult in terms of developing an effective monitoring program, since it is impossible to monitor all species, and, therefore, a subset of focal species had to be identified.

Implementation monitoring was conducted to determine whether the company did what it said it would do. One important element was assessing whether variable-retention harvesting was being done at the planned levels of retention and in ways that fulfilled the intent of retention, such as the presence of a biological legacy of old-forest attributes well distributed in each harvest unit. Definitions of retention harvesting provided in new laws and regulations assisted in such assessments. Both the quantity and quality of the retention was found to increase over the five-year transition period and significantly exceeded initial target minimums.

Effectiveness monitoring involved both monitoring of operational practices and experimental approaches, the latter providing opportunities to identify causal mechanisms. Three indicators were identified: (1) representation of distinct ecosystem types on the non-harvestable (reserved) land base; (2) maintenance of the amount, distribution, and heterogeneity of forest structures important to sustain native species richness over time; and (3) stability (abundance, distribution, and reproductive success) of populations of native species over time. Setting targets or decision thresholds for ecological indicators was an essential but difficult part of the process. As Bunnell, Huggard, and Dunsworth (2010, p. 80) put it:

> Some idea of targets or decision thresholds is needed for the indicators or attributes of the resources being monitored. Targets allow us to judge how good a particular management option is, relative to the target. . . . Targets can be derived externally, as with regulatory requirements, or they may require field measurements under some concepts of benchmarks. Thresholds . . . are most clearly derived from discontinuities in ecological responses. . . . Where targets have been specified or thresholds derived, it is easy to discern the better approach among comparisons. Most relations in nature, however, are curvilinear, without evident thresholds . . . Assigning a decision threshold value is thus somewhat arbitrary.

The initial goal in the third element of effectiveness monitoring was a pilot program to help identify a relatively small set of native species that would ultimately be used in the long-term monitoring program. A very large number of species was initially screened using criteria to assess their utility for monitoring. These requirements included the species be (1) forest dwelling, (2) sensitive to the forest practices being used, (3) practical to monitor, and (4) able to provide useful information for guiding forest practices. Species were selected from a broad range of organismal groups: vascular plants, mosses, lichens, liverworts, invertebrates, and vertebrates. Ultimately the selected candidate focal species were stratified by specific habitat elements or phenomena that they were intended to index: canopy closure, late seral/large trees, snags, down wood, humus, shrubs, deciduous trees, edge, interior/patch size, and riparian areas. Significant information for selecting species for long-term monitoring was acquired during the pilot phase.

The adaptive management program developed as a part of the Coast Forest Strategy was a well-structured and initially well-supported effort by scientists and managers highly versed in the importance and philosophy of adaptive management. A great deal of useful information relevant to better integration of ecological and economic goals in management of forest properties was produced in less than ten years, including the feasibility and benefits of variable retention.

There were significant failures in the program, however. These included difficulty in closing the adaptive loop by influencing changes in management actions as a result of monitoring and other learning activities. This traditional pattern of failure had been a concern from its outset, which had led MacMillan-Bloedel to create three new structures to avoid such failure—the Adaptive Management Working Group, the Variable Retention Working Group, and the International Scientific Advisory Panel. Yet, *"Despite these new structures there was less response to the monitoring program than was originally expected . . . [for] . . . two broad reasons—naiveté with regards to the world of management decisions . . . and failure to implement a shared vision within the world of researchers"* (Bunnell, Huggard & Kremsater, 2010, p. 279, emphasis added). Underlying problems included: poor communication of goals of the monitoring program among scientists designing, running, and conducting the research; diverse funding resources and reward systems; and instability of ownership (four owners in six years).

Despite these difficulties, important elements of the adaptive management program, including aspects of the monitoring system, continue to be implemented by Western Forest Products (WFP) on tree-farm license lands that were once managed by MacMillan-Bloedel. WFP is also continuing to do much of its harvesting utilizing variable retention.

become a fashionable label or buzzword that often delivers less than it seems to promise. When agencies or organizations are challenged about their policies, they may claim they are using "adaptive management" as a shield between themselves and their critics.

- *The difficulty in reaching agreement on the questions to be asked and hypotheses to test.* Selecting the questions to ask can be a difficult and contentious problem (Lee, 1999). Only a limited number of "uncertainties" can be addressed. Yet an almost endless list of questions quickly can be compiled (which is very similar to the challenge in selecting variables for monitoring programs). Where a shareholder-driven collaborative process will be utilized to identify questions to study, finding agreement can test the mettle of the most patient person. On the other hand, the support of a collaborative group for a monitoring plan can be priceless when attempts are made to eliminate monitoring because of its expense or potential to produce news of policy failure.

- *The long time period that may be needed before monitoring results are conclusive.* We are impatient people—even a few years may seem too long to wait for monitoring results. Yet, some biological responses will take many years or decades to express themselves, let alone do so in a definitive fashion.

- *The tendency of organizations to view learning as a luxury rather than a necessity.* Monitoring is often the first item cut during budget shortfalls. The choice between keeping the people who lay out and administer timber sales versus those that sustain long-term monitoring is usually easily and swiftly made!

- *The inability to accept the risk of failure during experimentation.* As Gunderson (1999) points out, if risk of failure during experimentation is not acceptable, then active adaptive management is not possible. In cases where threatened or endangered species are involved, experimentation is often strictly limited. Also as Stankey (2001, p. 3) said: "It is a Catch-22 phenomenon: experimentation is not permitted until sufficient evidence is available to predict confidently that the treatment will not have an adverse impact, but until such experiments can be undertaken, it is not possible to generate such knowledge."

- *The unwillingness to acknowledge uncertainty and the need for assessments of policy success.* The concepts of continuous change and uncontrollable disruptions are difficult for almost everyone with interests in forest management, including resource managers, conservationists, government agencies, and politicians. Many advocacy groups seek certainty in policy and management outcomes (Stankey et al., 2003; Lindenmayer & Franklin, 2002)—of course, with their view prevailing. Much professional education has been aimed at equipping graduates with the answers to resource problems, and professions have traditionally presented themselves as omniscient; who would want professionals who are uncertain about their proposals! Governments are also eager to embrace certainty as a way to resolve difficult and often socially divisive issues. Interest groups may view adaptive management approaches as mechanisms that will allow consideration and "test" of management strategies they view as unacceptable.

- **Institutional difficulties in recognizing, implementing, and monitoring alternative pathways to achieve goals.** Adaptive management assumes that there is no best practice (Bormann, 1999). By accepting that more than one pathway can achieve a given goal and then comparing the alternative pathways, managers are seeking to learn and thereby expand their decision options over time. Yet much management is based on the use of **best management practices** as we discussed in Chapters 6 and 7. In addition alternative pathways may reflect conflicting worldviews about the effects of actions on goals, making it doubly difficult to endorse their use.

- **The inability of organizations to allow information to survive that contradicts management assumptions.** As convincingly described by Bella (1992), people and organizations tend to selectively produce and retain information favorable to their preferred management system. Positive assessments of management, which do not disrupt organizational systems, thrive in such organizations while contrary assessments tend to be systematically filtered out. The cumulative outcome is systematic distortion of information. Bella (1992) asserts that organizations tend to distort information through the normal practices of its members—practices that, from the local view of each participant, appear reasonable and proper. Such organizations may place their executives in **information bubbles**, where they hear only highly filtered information. **Organizational processes, thus, tend to distort information, not through the malicious intent of its members (although that might occur), but rather as an unplanned but systematic outcome** (Figure 11.3).

In describing Figure 11.3, Bella (1992, p. 22) writes:

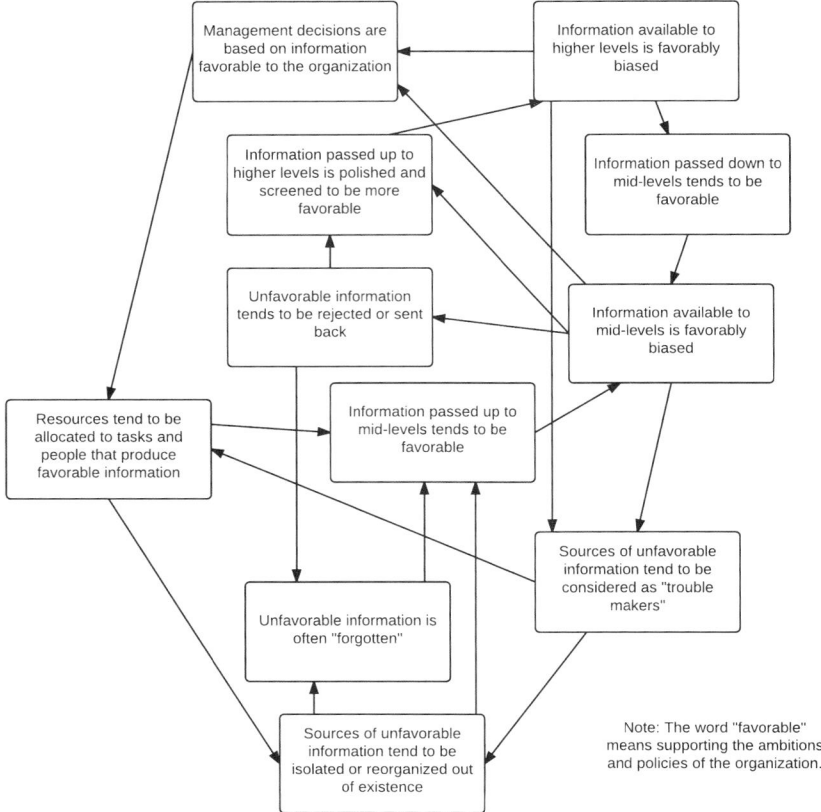

How to read the figure:
1.   Start by reading any statement.
2.   Move from that statement along an arrow to a connecting statement.
3.   If you move forward along an arrow, insert the word "therefore."
4.   If you move backward along an arrow, insert the word "cause."
5.   After following an arrow (forward or backward) to a statement, read this statement.
6.   Repeat steps 2 to 5 as shown above.
7.   Read your way through the entire figure, moving forward or backward on arrows as you wish until you have gone through as many loops and cycles as you can find.

Figure 11.3 *Typical distortion of information within an organization. (Source: Bella, 1992, Figure 1, p. 21)*

*The model was presented and discussed in workshops and seminars with colleagues who do environmental impact assessments. I was surprised by how many examples the participants cited. In effect, the model was saying something that almost everybody already knew.*

*The commission that investigated the Challenger shuttle explosion in 1986 found similar organizational behavior in the National Aeronautics and Space Administration (NASA) before the accident (US Presidential Commission, 1986). Unfavorable information concerning risks was filtered out right up to the time of launch. These systematic distortions resulted in misperceptions that, in turn, resulted in poor decisions. I sent Figure [11.3] and Table [11.3] to Nobel physicist and commission member Richard Feynman, who wrote back: "I read [Table 11.3] and am amazed at the perfect prediction of the answers given [by NASA personnel] at the public hearings. I didn't know that anybody under-*

*stood these things so well and I hadn't realized that NASA was an example of a widespread phenomenon."*

*Feynman's own study had found systemic distortions of perceptions. Before the accident, managers perceived the risk of catastrophic loss to be about a thousand times less than perceived by the engineers that worked for them (Feynman, 1986).*

Bella (1992, p. 22) goes on to discuss problems at nuclear weapon complexes, including a memo written by a supervisor attempting to warn upper management of the risks. That memo read: "I am convinced that you do not and cannot (with the present administrative system) know the residual risks that remain after we do what we do. This is not a criticism of you or any individual personally. The problem lies with the system . . . it is not realistic to expect any chain of command to report unfavorably upon itself."

It may be human (or organizational) nature to invest in particular management strategies, promote them, and be reluctant to believe they do not work. In most cases, mechanisms outside the control of these organizational forces, such as external review, will be needed to counter the tendency to bury "bad news" about favored management strategies. Otherwise it may be necessary to await a catastrophic failure for change to occur. The circumstances leading to the development of the Northwest Forest Plan provide an example of this phenomenon in natural resource policy (see Box 11.1, Yaffee, 1994, and Skillen, 2015).

## So What to Do? Practical Advice on Adaptive Management

The difficulties of adaptive management that we have described above could discourage even an optimistic person. How then might you approach monitoring and adaptive management with at least a modest hope of success? Here are 13 suggestions that might prove useful:

1. *Get started quickly.* Much of the literature on adaptive management calls for the use of simulation models to set up hypotheses and elaborate and expensive monitoring designs. While that approach is helpful in some situations, it is not the necessary first step in learning about the effects of management actions. The first three steps listed above—identifying key uncertainties, turning them into testable hypotheses, and finding relevant information for evaluating them—can result from the emergence of some important topics generated by a few meetings of a collaborative group or interdisciplinary team. As an example, our forest restoration case (Table 11.2) highlighted key concerns that actions do not remove old trees and that they do enhance understory bitterbrush communities. Arguments may occur over what to measure, but that doesn't prevent the process from getting started and, in fact, reveal what participants feel is important in gauging success—a critical element in effective adaptive management.

2. *Focus mostly on information that can be gathered at little additional cost.* Costly monitoring programs generally cannot be sustained unless they have

Table 11.3 *Organizational system (Figure 11.3) as seen from within (assuming that a biased report had been produced by the organization)*

| Person | Question | Answer |
|---|---|---|
| *High-level manager* | Why didn't you consider the unfavorable information your own staff produced? | I'm not familiar with the information that you're talking about. I can assure you that my decisions were based on the best information available to me. |
| *Mid-level manager* | Why didn't you pass the unfavorable information up to your superiors? | I can't pass everything up to them. Based on the information available to me, it seemed appropriate to have this information re-evaluated and checked over. |
| *Professional technologist* | Why wasn't the unfavorable information checked out and sent back up to your superiors? | That wasn't my job. I had other tasks to do and deadlines to meet. |
| *"Trouble-maker" who developed the unfavorable information* | Why didn't you follow up on the information you presented? | I only worked on part of the project. I don't know how my particular information was used after I turned it in. I did my job. Even if I had all the information, which I didn't, there was no way I could stop the project. |

*Source:* Adapted from Bella (1992, Table 1, pp. 23–24).

a guaranteed funding source, which is very rare. Often key information, such as cost data, is already being gathered by the organization for other purposes but has not been organized to be useful for monitoring. At other times, a lot can be learned by simply having field staff systematically record observations, such as sightings of large predators. In still other cases, volunteers can be engaged to record measurements, such as bird counts.

3. *Get as many people involved as possible.* Separate monitoring departments, isolated from the rest of the organization, generally last only until the next round of budget cuts. A monitoring program that engages people both inside and outside the organization in gathering information is much more likely to have continued support. This larger group of participants also can contribute mightily to determining what information needs to be gathered. Also, integrating monitoring into local collaborative efforts is a promising way to ensure long-term organizational commitments—a collaborative group that views monitoring as important to their deliberations and direction will defend it.

   Working with resource managers and scientists, stakeholders can also play an important role in interpreting the results of the monitoring program and whether changes are needed in management or the monitoring program itself (see items 10 and 12 and also the section below on multiparty monitoring). Of course, there is always the possibility such an approach to a monitoring program will take things in unexpected or unintended directions!

4. *Measure some effects that have an immediate payoff.* Monitoring programs that take years or decades to produce results only rarely will be supported until conclusion. As least some of the hypotheses should provide testable information in a year or two at most. For example, the hypothesis that "old trees will not be cut in timber sales" can be tested immediately after the first harvest. Some quick-test hypotheses are needed to encourage people that their efforts will produce meaningful results. In fact, monitoring data need to undergo regular evaluation or "exercising" rather than simply compiled for some future review.

5. *Utilize monitoring methods that are useful to the organization in other ways.* To the degree that information gathered is directly useful in forest management and conservation, the greater the likelihood the measurements will be continued. As an example, think about how the information can help with future forest planning.

6. *Be flexible on the standards of proof.* Even though adaptive management and associated monitoring borrows from the scientific method, it should not be seen solely as a scientific experiment in which a confidence interval of 95% is needed. A standard based on *preponderance of evidence* will be more helpful. In addition, useful information may come from different sources and be of many different types. In the case of whether old trees were cut, sampling may miss those few stumps off in a corner that a hiker finds and reports to the paper. That information should become part of the monitoring results, too. As noted below (items 10 and 12), evaluation of monitoring results ultimately should be a collective process.

7. *Be alert for information beyond your forest that may bear on your hypotheses.* Many other people may be studying the same things and new scientific results come out all the time. You should utilize this information. As an example, Sharon Hood's approach to monitoring old tree loss during prescribed fire is very instructive (Hood, 2010) for forest restoration efforts in the frequent-fire forests of the western United States.

8. *Focus on issues that match your scale of investigation.* As noted by Gunderson and Holling (2002, p. 27) "management has to be flexible, adaptive, and experimental at scales compatible with the scales of critical ecosystem functions." Spending considerable resources monitoring the effect of management on a single pair of a wide-ranging species will rarely have large benefits; rather, such a monitoring effort will need to be more regional in scope. On the other hand, monitoring whether the variable retention harvests in your local area result in the early-seral response you seek can provide much useful information.

9. *Find an advocate for your adaptive management program that is respected by those who might be affected by the results.* Leadership is important, and this person will often be the messenger of the monitoring results—describing either policy success or policy failure. Leaders who are widely trusted to follow the truth wherever it leads should be highly valued.

10. *Work on creating a regular independent review of policy success.* As noted earlier it is very difficult for organizations to acknowledge policy failure. Even if information is collected on an issue, there may be attempts to bury "bad news," and mechanisms are needed to prevent this. Regular, open review of monitoring results is important and will help, but independent review is very useful in bringing a fresh and objective eye to the problem. Knowledge of a coming review can also make monitoring seem more

real and important. Involvement of a collaborative group in this task can also be extremely helpful.

11. *Save active adaptive management for problems of significant scientific and social uncertainty.* Much can be learned by gathering information about implementation and effectiveness of management actions (passive adaptive management) that can help you understand what is happening on your forest as a result of management actions. It does not, however, reveal why it is happening—whether the effects measured are the results of the management actions or something else. To determine whether selected treatments are actually producing the desired outcome, active adaptive management will generally be required. It is more expensive but also more informative (Box 11.3).

12. *Understand and acknowledge the challenge of interpreting the ecological significance of changes observed in a well-designed, operational monitoring program* (Franklin, Harmon, & Swanson, 1999). If a statistically significant change is observed, is it ecologically important? Existing scientific knowledge will rarely provide a definitive (or even any) answer to that question and will most likely involve uncertainty. Outcomes from monitoring programs will often include uncertainties and varying levels of concern. Consequently, the interpretation activity needs to be an open process engaging a broad array of stakeholders—it is a social and not strictly a scientific or technical activity. Obviously, this also means that the results of the monitoring program have to be widely available to all interested parties.

13. *Recognize that some questions about consequences of management activities can be definitively resolved only by activities that are equivalent to regular scientific studies.* There may be some important aspects of management, such as assessing the effectiveness of a silvicultural system in conserving cryptic biota or the long-term effects of management on productivity, that can be credibly resolved only by experiments that meet the standards of regular scientific research. These standards would require the important criteria of replication, random assignment of treatments, and inclusion of controls (see Box 11.3). For example, definitively assessing the long-term sustainability of a proposed management program on thousands of hectares of lenga (*Nothofagus pumilio*) forests in Tierra del Fuego required determining the long-term balance between inputs and outputs of nutrients in this high-latitude forest ecosystem (Franklin, Harmon, & Swanson, 1999). Researchers concluded that this question could be definitively answered

## Box 11.3  Active adaptive management for problems with high levels of scientific and social uncertainty[*]

Active adaptive management (AAM) explicitly recognizes uncertainty and then confronts it by monitoring the outcomes of alternative policies or actions. It is especially useful where high levels of scientific and social uncertainty exist (Figure 11.4). By using the principles of experimental design, AAM enables "confident" learning about treatment effects. Different stakeholder perspectives can be represented as alternative treatments. In addition, the approach can serve as a platform for joint fact finding—a key to successful collaboration (McCreary, Gamman, & Brooks, 2001). Further, the application of different treatments creates a hedge against uncertainty by producing a variety of conditions across the landscape (Millar, Stephenson, & Stephens, 2007).

Three aspects of experimental design are key to AAM: (1) inclusion of untreated controls, (2) replication of treatments, including controls, and (3) unbiased (random) assignment of treatments, including the controls. Untreated control sites must be chosen from the same universe of potential treatment sites as the sites receiving the treatments to ensure an unbiased ("fair") comparison. Treated and untreated control sites are systematically replicated in time and space to allow managers to generalize their findings and avoid drawing conclusions caused by unique site characteristics.

With an experimentally valid design, AAM monitoring results provide much more definitive information than does passive adaptive management. It allows participants to begin to move beyond "what happened" to drawing inferences about "why it happened."

### A Case Study of AAM on the Lincoln National Forest

The Lincoln Restoration Committee (LRC), located in Lincoln, Montana, collaboratively designs and monitors projects on the Lincoln District of the Helena National Forest, guided by restoration principles developed by a statewide forest restoration committee. Those principles emphasize treating low-elevation ponderosa pine and other stands that historically burned under a low-severity fire regime. Much of the Lincoln District is composed of mid-elevation lodgepole pine and mixed conifer types thought to have historically burned under mixed-severity and high-severity fire regimes. Since the mid-2000s, the district has experienced widespread tree mortality caused by mountain pine beetle and spruce budworm.

In response to this mortality and fire managers' assessment of crown fire risk and spread, the Lincoln Resource Collaborative (LRC) evaluated conditions in a 40,000-acre landscape southwest of the town of Lincoln. With an interest in restoration of this mixed conifer and lodgepole pine landscape, and recognizing the contentious nature of restoration in mixed- and high-severity fire regimes, the LRC approached this collaborative project using an experimental design framework.

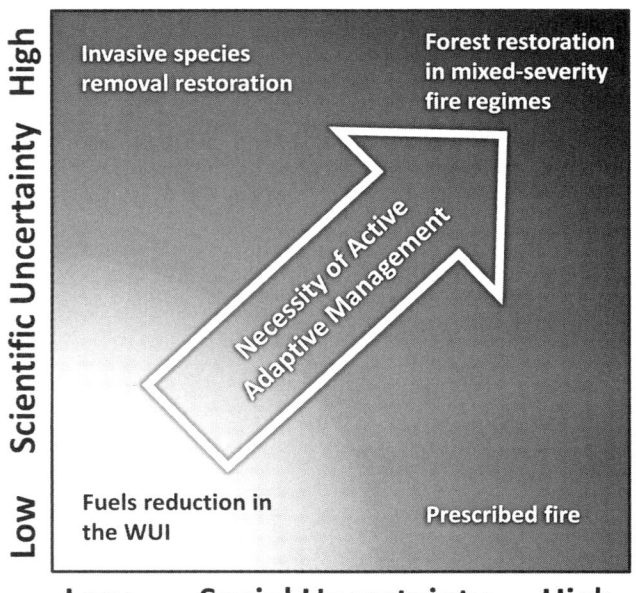

Figure 11.4 *Active adaptive management is of the greatest potential value in situations where both scientific and social uncertainty are high. (Reprinted from Larson et al., 2013, with permission of the Society of American Foresters)*

Given the scientific uncertainty about treatment outcomes and associated social controversy, the LRC embarked on a series of weekly meetings to discuss options for forest management. As a first step, stands adjacent to nearby homes and cabins and representing high-risk wildland–urban interface (WUI) were removed from the pool of candidate stands to be included in the experimental design. These stands were considered separately outside the AAM framework, but still within the overall project planning process. Thirty stands remained after this initial screening.

The diverse perspectives represented on the LRC were grouped into three alternative treatment types: (1) regenerate stands of high mountain pine beetle mortality through seed-tree harvests; (2) create within-stand spatial heterogeneity and structural complexity while also regenerating a new cohort using aggregated retention harvest; and (3) retain untreated controls to provide a means to isolate treatment effects from background variability (and because some stakeholders did not consider lodgepole pine/mixed conifer forests a priority for restoration). The three treatment types were randomly assigned to the 30 carefully screened stands, allowing for ten replicates of each treatment. After LRC consensus, an update of lynx habitat maps eliminated some of the replicates but did not substantially compromise the management objective of learning (Figure 11.5).

As stated by Larson et al. (2013, p. 355):

[*] This discussion is drawn largely from Larson, Belote, Williamson, & Aplet (2013).

*In sum, this project design screened out areas of high risk (those near homes), eliminated bias by randomly assigning treatments within a carefully selected pool of candidate treatment units, considered variability by replicating treatments, and provided an opportunity to compare alternative mixed-severity restoration approaches and stakeholder perspectives by comparing different treatments including an untreated control. This robust statistical design enables confident learning and thus represents an application of best available science.*

## Implications

Larson et al. (2013) state three important implications for this AAM approach: (1) It elevates learning to the level of other management objectives; (2) it makes monitoring integral to the entire forest management process, including the earliest project planning stages; and (3) it recasts the forest manager as a practitioner of the scientific method. Such a method cultivates an approach to forestry that values humility, acknowledges uncertainty, and recognizes learning as a key element in forest conservation and management.

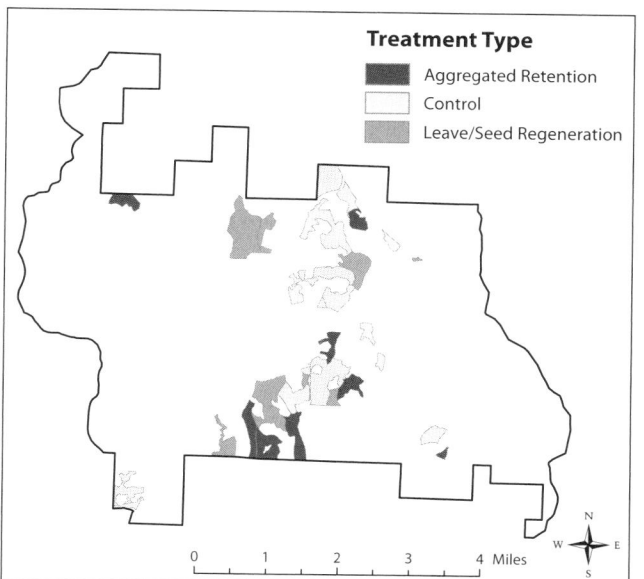

Figure 11.5 *Map of the Dalton Mountain project area where elements of experimental design (e.g., use of untreated controls, replication, and unbiased assignment of treatments) were collaboratively incorporated into treatment plans for lodgepole pine-mixed conifer forests. Lynx habitat stands were dropped from the study. (Source: adapted from Larson et al., 2013)*

only by a replicated experiment comparing nutrient balances on multiple replicates of paired harvested and unharvested (control) watersheds. Similarly, sustaining ground beetles, mosses, lichens, and liverworts was an objective in the harvested lenga forests. The working hypothesis was that variable-retention harvesting with 20% of the harvest unit retained in small aggregates would sustain these organisms. However, validating this hypothesis required comparative study of paired plots (harvested and unharvested controls) replicated across the environmental gradient of the project.

## Collaborative Learning, Multiparty Monitoring, and Adaptive Management

The contribution of collaborative groups to monitoring and adaptive management may be one of the happy surprises of the rise of collaborative processes. As Cheng (2006) pointed out, public lands collaborations provide some of the best working examples of adaptive ecosystem management we see on US federal lands. In such cases, public lands collaborations are "learning-based" approaches to public lands planning and management, based on the assumption that there is no one "right" way to manage a piece of land— for "right" is necessarily a social construction. Moreover, as Cheng (2006, p. 846) summarized:

*Any desired condition is fraught with uncertainty. Hence, the piece of land has many possible futures, each of which can be achieved by many possible management strategies and tactics. For many public lands collaborations, any land management objective must be treated as provisional, for its attainment is never assured. To see if management strategies actually achieve desired goals and objectives, monitoring strategies are developed and implemented by participants in the collaboration—commonly called "multiparty monitoring." Results are interpreted and debated and management goals, objectives, and strategies are adjusted accordingly. While these lofty ideals often fall short in practice, they are a new set of pathways for how public lands planning and management are taking place.*

Cheng (2006) gives two compelling examples of the primacy of learning and linkage to monitoring in public lands collaboration:

- Wallowa Resources, a conservation group in northeast Oregon, spearheaded a collaborative assessment of the Upper Joseph Creek watershed as a first step in learning about historical and current ecosystem conditions, defining desired conditions, prioritizing management actions, and building trust and credibility among traditional adversaries, such as loggers, environmentalists, the US Forest Service, landowners, and local officials. As a result of the Upper Joseph Creek Watershed Assessment, numerous projects were identified that would restore historical ecosystem conditions and functions, especially in the ponderosa pine forests on the Wallowa-Whitman National Forest, as well as generate raw material to sustain a few local, small-scale wood products firms. Wallowa Resources also catalyzed a multiparty monitoring process.

- The Public Lands Partnership in western Colorado developed a collaborative process to design, implement, and monitor a salvage timber sale on the Grand Mesa, Uncompahgre, and Gunnison National Forests. The US Forest Service subsequently offered three salvage timber sales to remove merchantable timber as a way to offset rehabilitation costs. Several national and local environmental groups immediately filed appeals of these sales. The environmental participants on the Public Lands Partnership, many with histories of appealing and litigating timber sales, sought to learn more about why the appellants opposed the salvage sales. After field trips and discussions led by forest ecology and management experts, the appellants agreed to two of the sales because they had little chance of causing irreversible damage, provided that the projects were monitored more extensively than the agency had planned.

As Cheng (2006) suggests, collaborative groups can contribute significantly to successful adaptive management programs. Not only do they have the potential to turn traditional adversaries into problem-solving allies, but they also have a vested interest in understanding how successfully their ideas are being applied on the ground. These contributions can take many forms, including helping agencies design monitoring plans, participating in the actual monitoring activities, participating in the interpretation of the monitoring results, and serving as a review board to ensure that issues are appropriately addressed should problems be found. While still in the formative stage, multiparty monitoring shows promise.

The effectiveness and political attractiveness of collaboration led to the passage of legislation by the US Congress that would facilitate such activities. The Omnibus Public Lands Management Act of 2009 created the Collaborative Forest Landscape Restoration Program (CFLRP) to encourage landscape-scale ecosystem restoration on the national forests with the goals of reducing wildland fire management costs, enhancing ecological health, and promoting the use of small-diameter trees as biomass. The CFLRP requires a collaborative process with multiple stakeholders throughout planning, implementation, and monitoring Collaborative groups work with the local Forest Service managers to create a landscape-scale restoration strategy,

which they then submit to the regional and national office of the Forest Service for consideration. Selected projects then receive extra funding. By requiring collaboration in implementation and monitoring, CFLRP has the potential to embed collaboration deeper within national forest management (Schultz, Coelho, & Beam, 2014; Schultz, Jedd, & Beam, 2012).

Butler, Monroe, and McCaffrey (2015) recently examined how these CFLRP requirements affect the contribution of collaborative groups to ecosystem restoration on ten CFLRP projects across the western US. They found that CFLRP requirements provide a set of mechanisms for strengthening accountability, as stakeholder values and perspectives are integrated into the design and implementation of monitoring plans.

Butler et al. (2015) identify three interconnected feedback loops (Figure 11.6) by which collaboratives contribute to adaptive management:

1. Providing guidance to national forest managers in setting priorities for treatment in both landscapes and stands, steering the agency away from locations that will trigger major controversies;

2. Participating in training the staff that will implement projects (such as marking crews) or the actual tree marking in the field. This involvement provides managers with valuable information about the values and expectations of the stakeholders in the collaboratives;

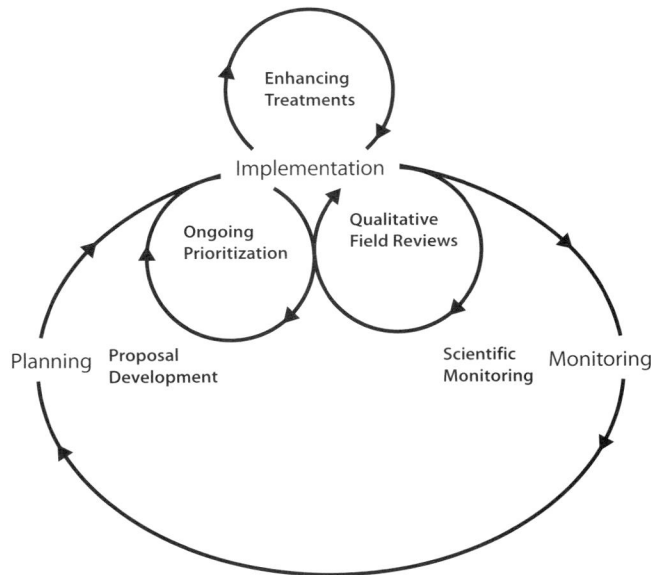

Figure 11.6 *Collaborative implementation (as three interconnected feedback loops) and the adaptive management cycle. (Republished with permission of Springer New York LLC, from Butler et al., 2015; permission conveyed through Copyright Clearance Center, Inc.)*

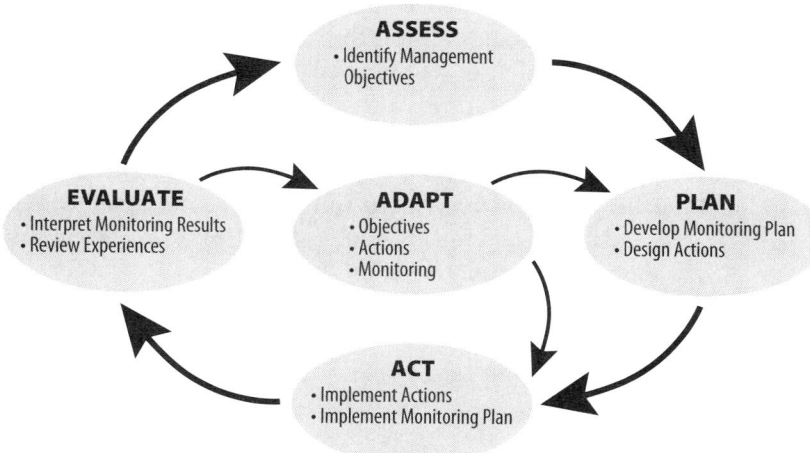

Figure 11.7 *Adaptive management as the center of planning and management. (Source: Moote, 2013)*

3. Qualitative field reviews, which can provide immediate feedback to managers who can then adjust their strategies and tactics. They noted that these field reviews have been particularly valuable for stakeholders to clarify their own values, assumptions and expectations of forest management while evaluating landscape conditions following treatments. This feedback enables local managers to incorporate these reactions into the next projects they design, providing quick, informal but important feedback on treatments.

While such engagements do not substitute for scientific monitoring, they can provide local feedback on how well field implementation matches the understanding and expectations of the collaborative. They also can strengthen relationships in ways that can increase the speed and scope of restoration activities.

## Adaptation as the Hub of Planning and Management

Many discussions of adaptive management portray the monitoring and adaptive management cycle as a closed stepwise loop. We see that illustrated in the cycle of planning, implementation, and monitoring (Figure 11.6), although it is augmented by three other concentric circles that describe ways in which collaboration groups, often informally, provide feedback and cause organizational response. A number of authors (Aplet et al., 2014; Bliss et al., 2001; Larson et al., 2013) have recoiled against viewing monitoring (and adaptive management) as just steps in this closed system. Instead, they suggest that the philosophy of adaptive management be integrated into all steps in the cycle.

One key element in this altered visualization is the shifting of monitoring and adaptation from elements in the cycle to the central hub (Figure 11.7). In this approach, the adaptive management cycle has adaptation at its core in a dynamic interaction with other elements in the cycle. While it can be argued that one more graphical representation of the adaptive management cycle may not add much value, the principles suggested by this diagram capture the broadening conceptual frame in which adaptive management is being considered.

## Continuing Development of the Scientific Base

Last but by no means of least importance to successful adaptation is the need for strong scientific programs that continue to expand our fundamental knowledge of forest ecosystems and how they work. The revolution in our understanding of forests and streams in the last 50 years, which provides much of the basis for ecological forestry, has come from basic but highly problem-relevant scientific study, much of it sponsored by the National Science Foundation. Research directed to solution of practical questions is and will remain important, but strong programs addressing fundamental questions about forest ecosystems have never been more critical than they are in this century.

It is important that some of this research address fundamental assumptions or premises of management programs—something that few managers are likely to be enthusiastic about! Think of how important research challenging fundamentals has been to changing our views about old-growth forests and old trees, early successional ecosystems, and ecosystem development! Consider how our recognition of biological legacies and the importance of early successional (preforest) ecosystems arose from fundamental scientific research following the eruption of Mount St. Helens. One of us has described this as "wild" science that challenges underpinnings of management programs as opposed to "domesticated" science that works to simply make managers more efficient at doing what they already propose to do. While few managers or management organizations may be enthusiastic about "wild" science that examines and has the potential to result in challenges to management assumptions, such investigation can be fundamental to successful adaptive management. It can also be a rich source of epiphanies that alter our fundamental perspectives on the structure and function of forest ecosystems!

Long-term observational studies, such as permanent sample plot networks, and large-scale experiments, such as experimental watershed studies, are absolutely critical because so much of ecological science is about long-term trends. Studies at places like the Hubbard Brook,

H. J. Andrews, Coweeta and Teakettle Experimental Forests of the US Forest Service's research branch, at outstanding academic stations like Harvard Forest (MA), and at privately funded stations like the Jones Ecological Research Center (GA), have been vitally important in the past, and others like them will continue to be absolutely critical to advancing our understanding of forest ecosystems and adaptive forest management in the 21st century.

It is important that much of this science be long term and field based, since many of the fundamental scientific questions about forests can only be answered through field-based studies. How is the forest really going to change with succession or as the result of altered environmental regimes? What are the rates and pathways of tree death, are they undergoing change, and, if so, how? *The definitive answers to many important questions in ecology and natural resource management will not be found in computer simulations—they will only be found by observing what really happens "out there," in the forests.*

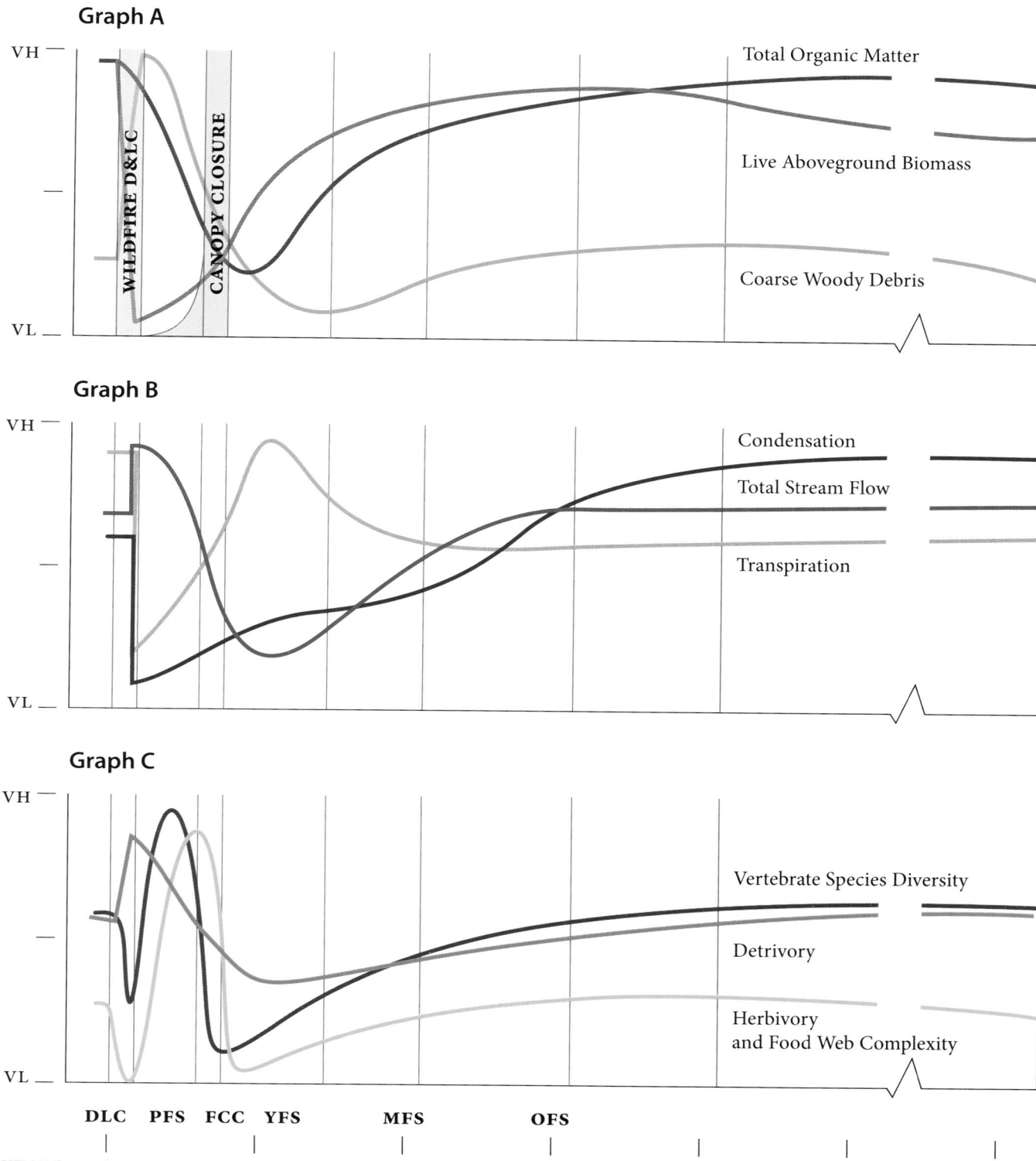

**Color Plate 2.1** *Generalized examples of relationships between some structural, functional, and biodiversity attributes and the developmental stages of a Douglas-fir–western hemlock* (Pseudotsuga menziesii–Tsuga heterophylla) *forest ecosystem following a stand-replacement wildfire. Note that the Y-axis is a relative scale that goes from very low (VL) values to very high (VH) values and the X-axis is age with abbreviations of episodes and stages as follows: DLC = Disturbance and Legacy Creation; PFS = Preforest Stage; FCC = Forest Canopy Closure; YFS = Young Forest Stage; MFS = Mature Forest Stage; and OFS = Old Forest Stage. Note also that the trace of each attribute (e.g., Total Organic Matter) is independent and not related quantitatively to other traces on the same graph. Production state variables are shown on Graph A; Hydrologic functions are shown on Graph B; and Biodiversity attributes are shown on Graph C.*

**Color Plate 3.1** *Photographs illustrating the effects of some intense forest disturbance events in coniferous forests and the characteristic biological legacies they leave behind. (a) Stand-replacement wildfire (Warner Creek Fire, Willamette National Forest, Oregon). (b) Wind blowdown event (Bull Run Watershed, Mount Hood National Forest, Oregon). (c) Volcanic eruption where trees were killed by the heat of an eruptive blast but remained standing (Mount St. Helens National Volcanic Monument, Washington). (d) Snow avalanche (Mount Rainier National Park, Washington).*

**Color Plate 3.2** *Stands illustrating the four developmental stages in the Douglas-fir–western hemlock sere. (a) Preforest Stage showing the diversity of plant life forms and species, which are the basis of numerous food webs, along with regeneration of conifers after a variable retention harvest (Willamette National Forest, Oregon). (b) Young Forest Stage showing the dominance of an even-aged cohort of Douglas-fir and absence of a significant mid-story tree canopy (Gifford Pinchot National Forest, Washington). (c) Mature Forest Stage dominated by 175-year-old Douglas-fir but with a well-developed intermediate canopy of western hemlock (Willamette National Forest, Oregon). (d) Old Forest Stage dominated by mixture of Douglas-fir and western hemlock and showing significant decadent features, including recently generated down logs (Mount Rainier National Park, Washington).*

**Color Plate 3.4** *Illustrations of attributes of deciduous hardwood forests. (a) Preforest Stage conditions developed following an intense windstorm, which blew down the overstory of hardwoods and red pine* (Pinus resinosa). *Vegetation includes early successional opportunists (e.g., raspberry* [Rubus spp.], *willow* [Salix spp.], *and bracken fern* [Pteridium aquilinum]), *sprouting hardwoods (quaking aspen* [Populus tremuloides], *northern red oak* [Quercus rubra], *and red maple* [Acer rubrum]). *White bud-protectors have been placed on planted seedlings of red jack* (Pinus banksiana), *and eastern white pine* (Pinus strobus) *to discourage browsing (Chippewa National Forest, Minnesota). (b) Mature Forest Stage, which is dominated by a mixture of hardwoods (red and sugar maple* [Acer sacharum]), *northern red oak, and quaking aspen, and red pine (Chippewa National Forest, Minnesota). (c) Forests dominated by deciduous hardwoods are notable for outstanding fall color displays as in this stand, which includes a mixture of hardwood species and eastern white pine (Chequamegon National Forest, Wisconsin). (d) Cross-section of a mixed stand of hardwoods (sugar maple, northern red oak, American elm* [Ulmus americana], *and American basswood* [Tilia americana]) *with associated conifers (eastern hemlock* [Tsuga canadensis], *eastern white pine, and northern white-cedar* [Thuja occidentalis]), *such as occurs near Lake Superior in upper Michigan. (Illustration by Robert Van Pelt)*

Eastern
white pine

Northern
red oak

Sugar
maple

b

c

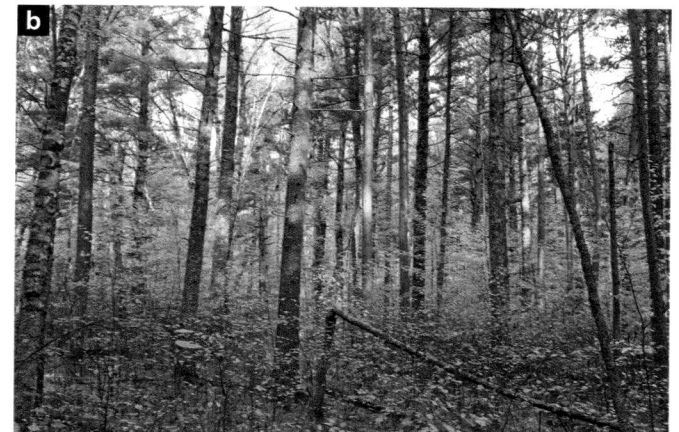

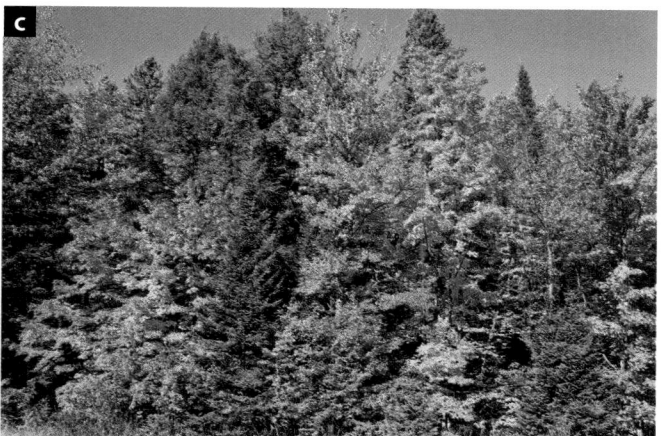

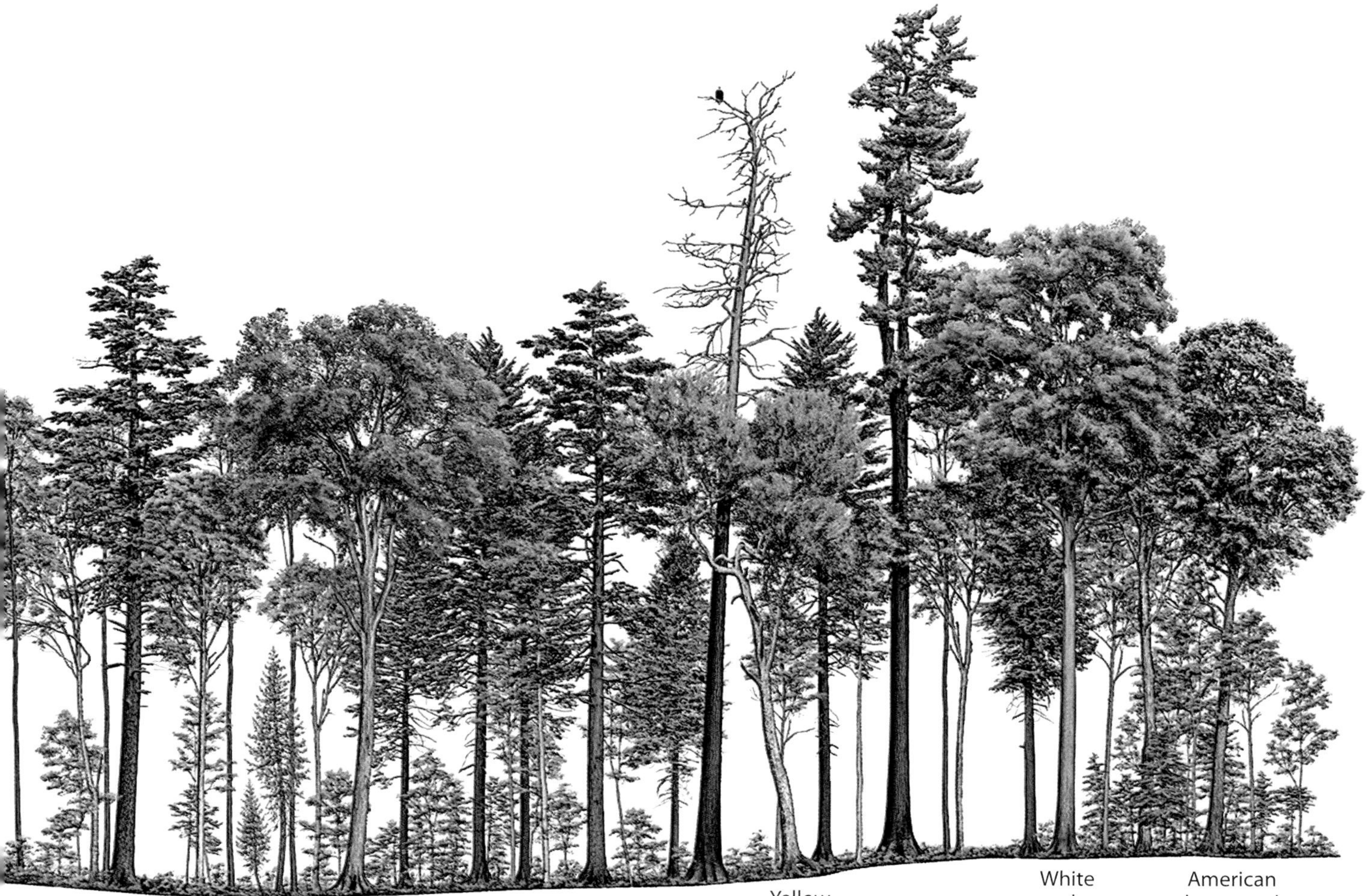
Eastern hemlock
White cedar
American elm
Yellow birch
White ash
American basswood

**Color Plate 3.3** *Examples of preforest. (a) Legacies of wood debris may dominate early periods of the Preforest Stage, as in the case of this blowdown lenga (Nothofagus pumilio) forest in Tierra del Fuego; such legacies can be significant in facilitating tree regeneration where populations of tree-grazing animals are present, as in this area. (b) Preforest conditions (early successional ecosystems) can be very persistent due to repeated disturbances and/or difficult environmental conditions, such as at high elevations and on very dry sites; Native American's maintained such ecosystems using repeated fire to maintain huckleberry (Vaccinium spp.) fields, such as in this area on the Gifford Pinchot National Forest in Washington. (c) Typical area of naturally created early successional habitat near the eastern boundary of the blast zone at Mount St. Helens. Area is predominantly open (i.e., free of dominance by tree canopies) although the tree life form is well represented in this photograph taken approximately 20 years after the May 1980 eruption. Legacies include logs of trees blown over by the volcanic blast and seedling and sapling Pacific silver fir and western hemlock that survived the blast by being buried in snowbanks. (d) Preforest conditions in the western Cascades after a variable-retention harvest and the planting of conifers. Development of preforest is generally compatible with moderate levels of tree planting, and not difficult to achieve in many cases, where attempts to suppress native shrubs and forbs do not occur.*

**Color Plate 3.5** *Photographs illustrating aspects of frequent-fire forest types, including their savanna-like architectures and dominance by a population of larger, older trees. (a) Ponderosa pine* (Pinus ponderosa) *forest east of the Cascade Range (Fremont-Winema National Forest, Oregon). (b) Longleaf pine* (Pinus palustris) *forest on the Joseph E. Jones Ecological Research Center in southern Georgia, emphasizing its bunchgrass understory.*

Time zero

+ 60 years

**Without fire suppression**

+ 20 years

+ 80 years

+ 40 years

**With fire suppression**

+ 80 years

**Color Plate 3.6**  *Interaction of fire and the patchwork or structural mosaic in ponderosa pine forests subject to frequent fire. (Illustration by Robert Van Pelt)*

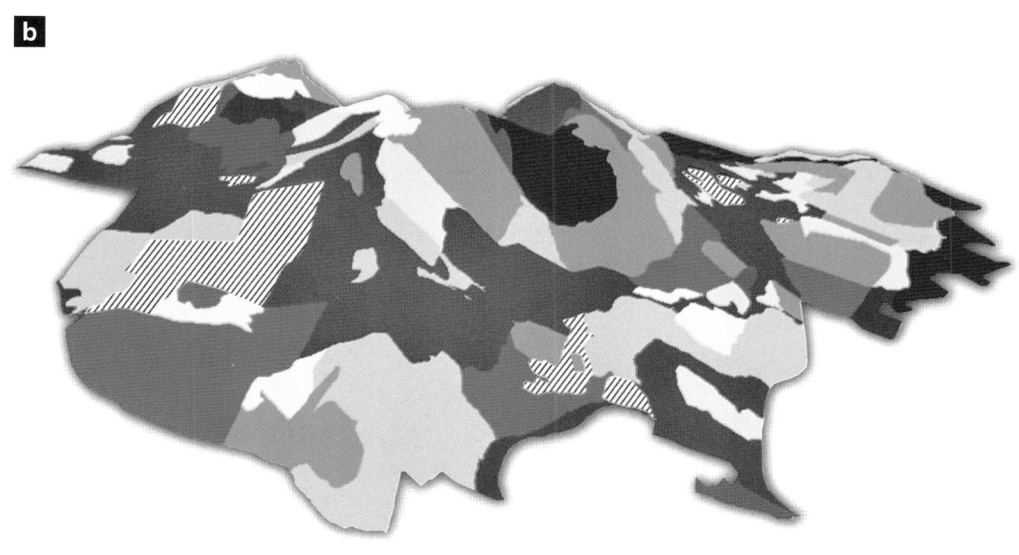

**Color Plate 5.1** *Two contrasting visions of managed forest landscapes. (a) A traditional view of a forest landscape in which reserved areas (shown here as black) are embedded in a matrix, which is managed without significant consideration of ecological values (shown here as white). The reserved areas are intended to provide any habitat needed to sustain forest biodiversity. This landscape vision encourages management decisions that will tend to create a black-and-white reality, since there is neither a plan nor an expectation for harvested areas to help sustain biodiversity and diverse ecological functions. (b) A landscape managed according to ecological forestry principles in which all landscape patches are managed to sustain at least some elements of habitat and ecological functionality. This landscape can be viewed as a patchwork that is "shades-of-green." Essentially all patches in this landscape retain significant ecological content (e.g., organisms, structures, and moderated microclimates) and thereby contribute to goals of maintaining ecological functions and biodiversity, even immediately following a timber harvest. The ecological contribution of the light green patches may come primarily from retention of live trees, logs, and snags during harvest. Dark green patches could include mesoscale areas of ecological emphasis, ecological reserves, and natural and near-natural structurally rich young, mature and old forest, and preforest conditions. Nonforest is shown as patches with diagonal lines.*

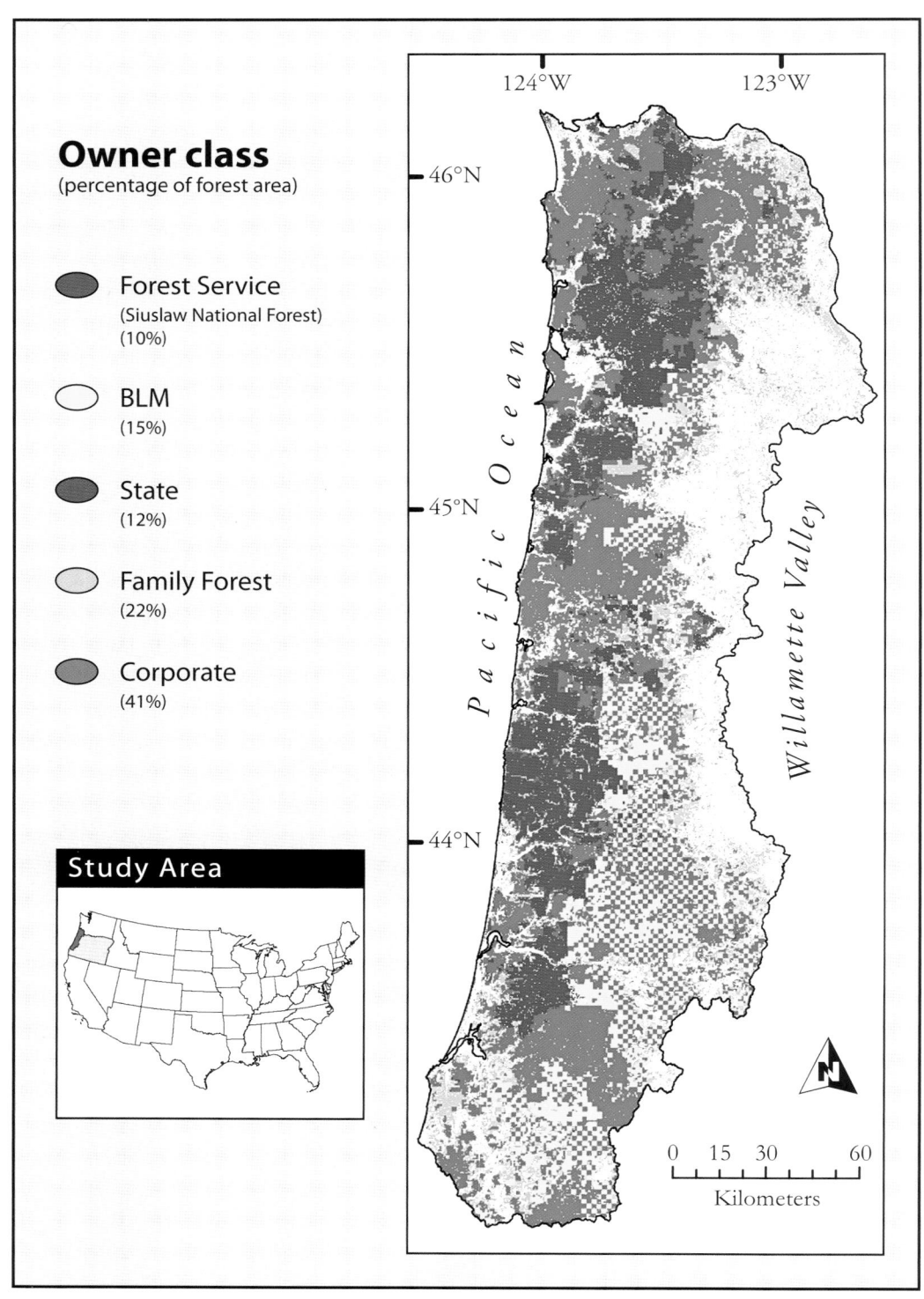

**Owner class**
(percentage of forest area)

- Forest Service
  (Siuslaw National Forest)
  (10%)

- BLM
  (15%)

- State
  (12%)

- Family Forest
  (22%)

- Corporate
  (41%)

**Study Area**

Color Plate 5.2 *Map of ownership classes for forestland in the Coast Range Physiographic Province in Oregon (abbreviations in legend are: BLM, Bureau of Land Management; State, State of Oregon).*

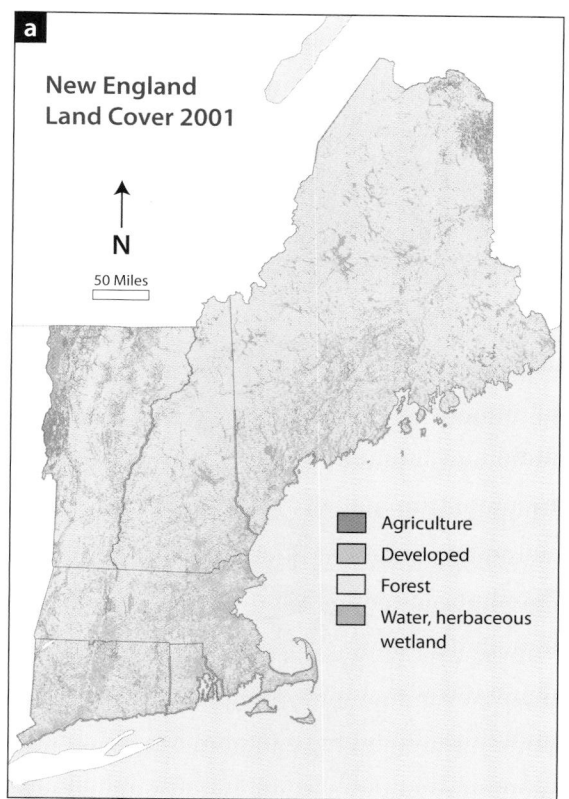

**a**

New England
Land Cover 2001

N

50 Miles

Agriculture
Developed
Forest
Water, herbaceous
wetland

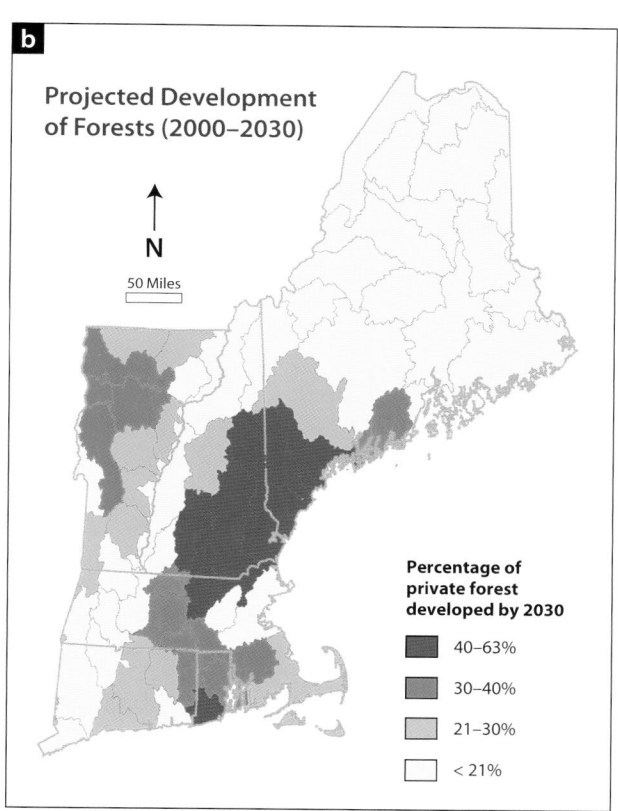

**b**

Projected Development
of Forests (2000–2030)

N

50 Miles

**Percentage of
private forest
developed by 2030**

40–63%
30–40%
21–30%
< 21%

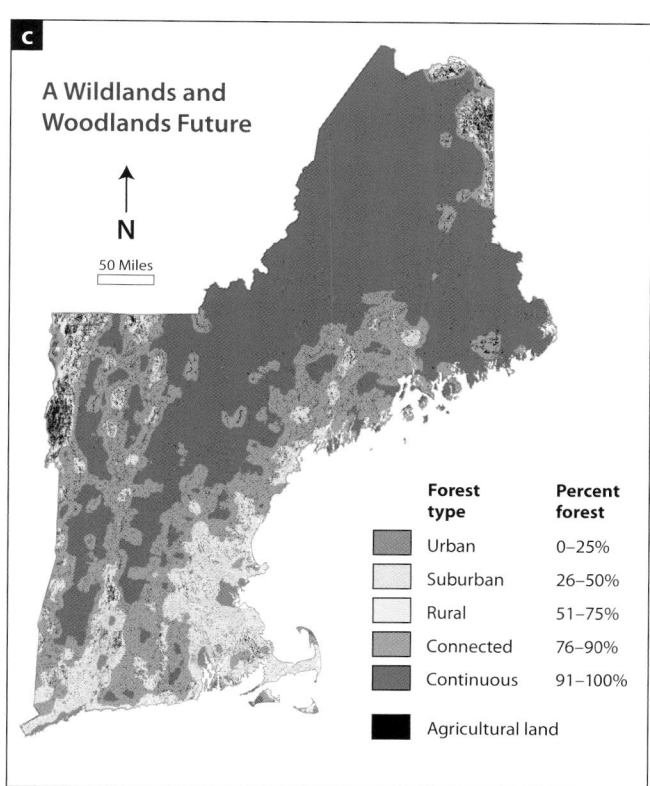

**c**

A Wildlands and
Woodlands Future

N

50 Miles

| Forest type | Percent forest |
|---|---|
| Urban | 0–25% |
| Suburban | 26–50% |
| Rural | 51–75% |
| Connected | 76–90% |
| Continuous | 91–100% |
| Agricultural land | |

Color Plate 5.3 *An analysis of the future of forests in six
northeastern states of US ("New England"). (a) Land cover,
(b) Projected development, (c) A vision for the future
(as shades-of-green), and (d) Areas protected from development
(both shades-of-green). (From the work of David Foster and his
colleagues at Harvard Forest [Courtesy of David Foster])*

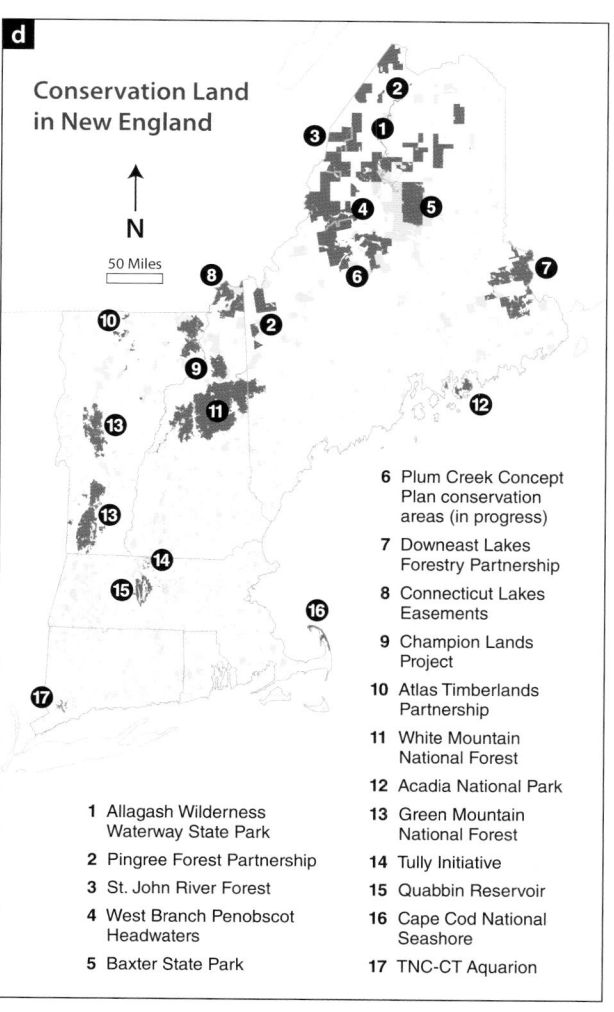

**d**

Conservation Land
in New England

N

50 Miles

1 Allagash Wilderness
   Waterway State Park
2 Pingree Forest Partnership
3 St. John River Forest
4 West Branch Penobscot
   Headwaters
5 Baxter State Park

6 Plum Creek Concept
   Plan conservation
   areas (in progress)
7 Downeast Lakes
   Forestry Partnership
8 Connecticut Lakes
   Easements
9 Champion Lands
   Project
10 Atlas Timberlands
   Partnership
11 White Mountain
   National Forest
12 Acadia National Park
13 Green Mountain
   National Forest
14 Tully Initiative
15 Quabbin Reservoir
16 Cape Cod National
   Seashore
17 TNC-CT Aquarion

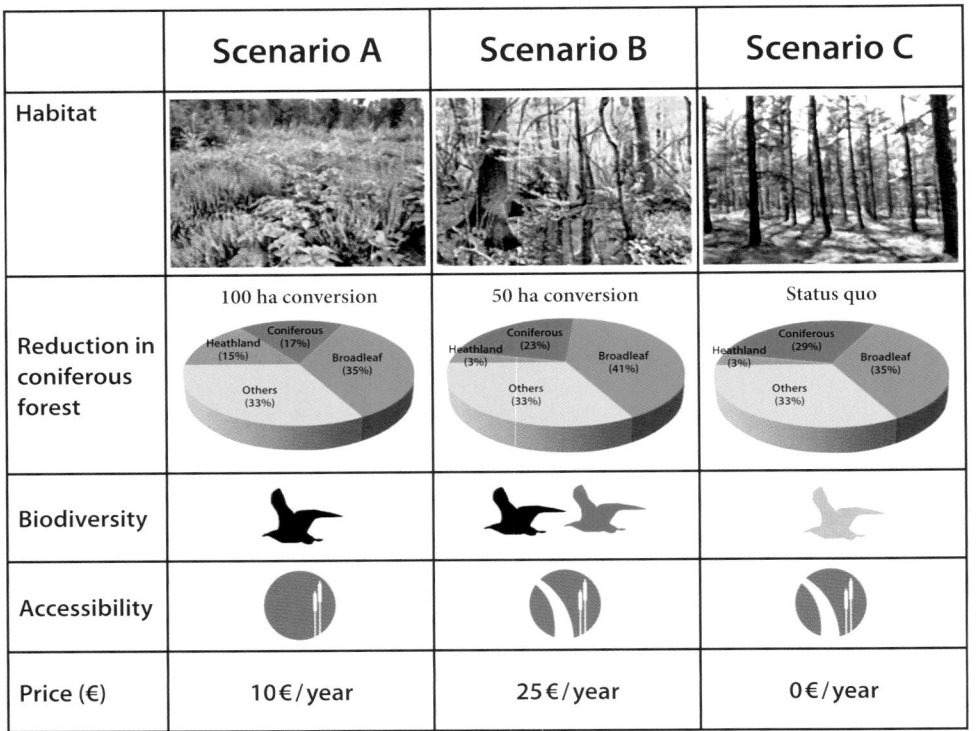

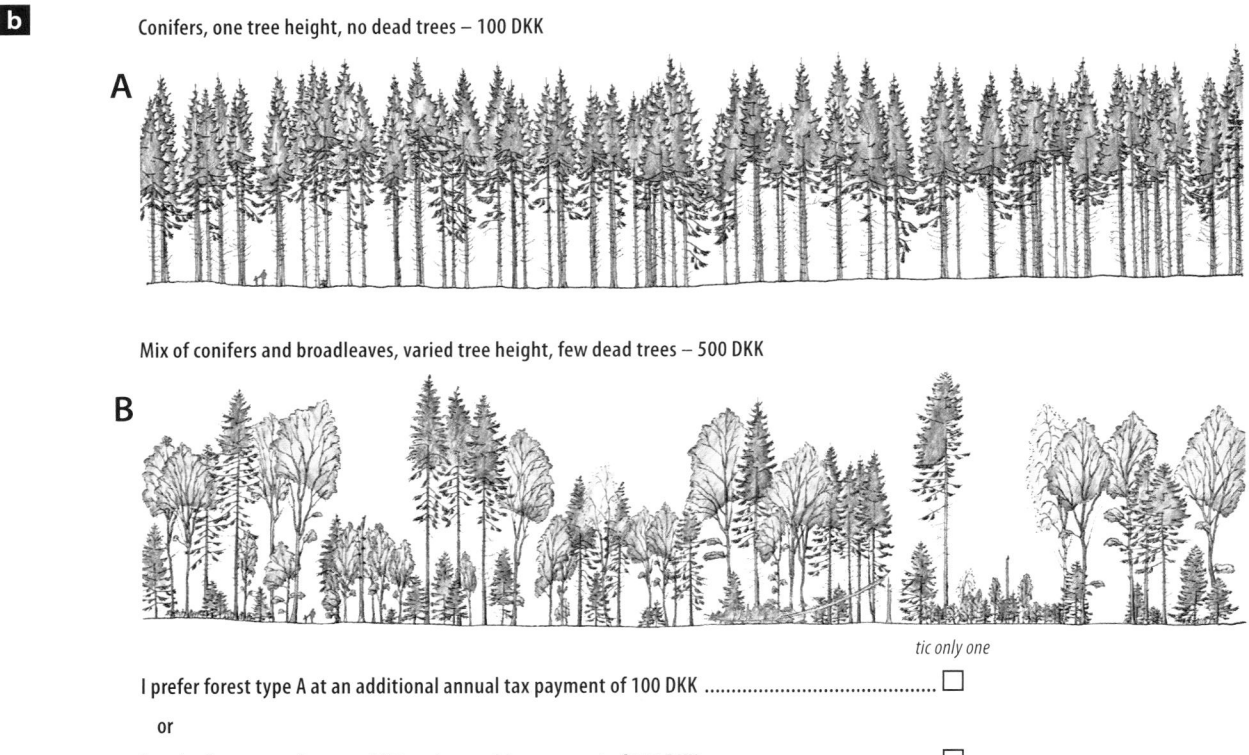

Color Plate 10.1 *Examples of choice sets in discrete choice experiments in (a) Belgium and (b) Denmark to elicit public preferences for transformation of even-aged, plantation-style conifer forests to more natural forests. Respondents were asked to choose among nature restoration scenarios, each with a different price. ([a] Republished with permission of Elsevier BV, from De Valck et al., 2014; permission conveyed through Copyright Clearance Center, Inc. [b] Republished with permission of Elsevier BV, from Nielsen et al., 2007; permission conveyed through Copyright Clearance Center, Inc.)*

**Color Plate 12.1** *The four primary types of wildland fires.*
*(a) Ground or smoldering fires typically occur behind the flaming front and may last for days or weeks. (b) The most common are surface fires, which have been the basis of most fire behavior modeling. (c) As intensity increases, individual or group tree torching may occur in passive crown fires. (d) The most intense fire type in wildlands is active crown fires, which may have flame lengths exceeding 200 feet with fires moving from crown to crown. (Source: [c] and [d]: Kari Greer/US Forest Service)*

**Color Plate 12.2** *Examples of fires of different severity (tree mortality). (a) Fires that burn with low intensity often result in low severity and can help maintain fire resistant vegetation like ponderosa pine trees. (The Miller Fire [2011] in New Mexico, photo taken by Tessa Nicolet) (b) Mixed-severity fires create complex spatial mosaics of low, moderate, and high severity (two years after the Clark Fire [2004] in the foothills of the western Cascades of Oregon). (c) High-severity fires in subalpine fir in the Washington Cascades burn with great intensity at broad scales. (d) High-severity fires in Douglas-fir–western hemlock forests in the western Cascades of Oregon will generally contain patches that burn at lower severity and numerous individual trees that survive.*

Color Plate 13.1 *Stands in the frequent-fire forests of the Fremont-Winema National Forest (Oregon), where mechanical treatment will be needed to reduce stand density and remove ladder fuels before introduction of prescribed fire.*

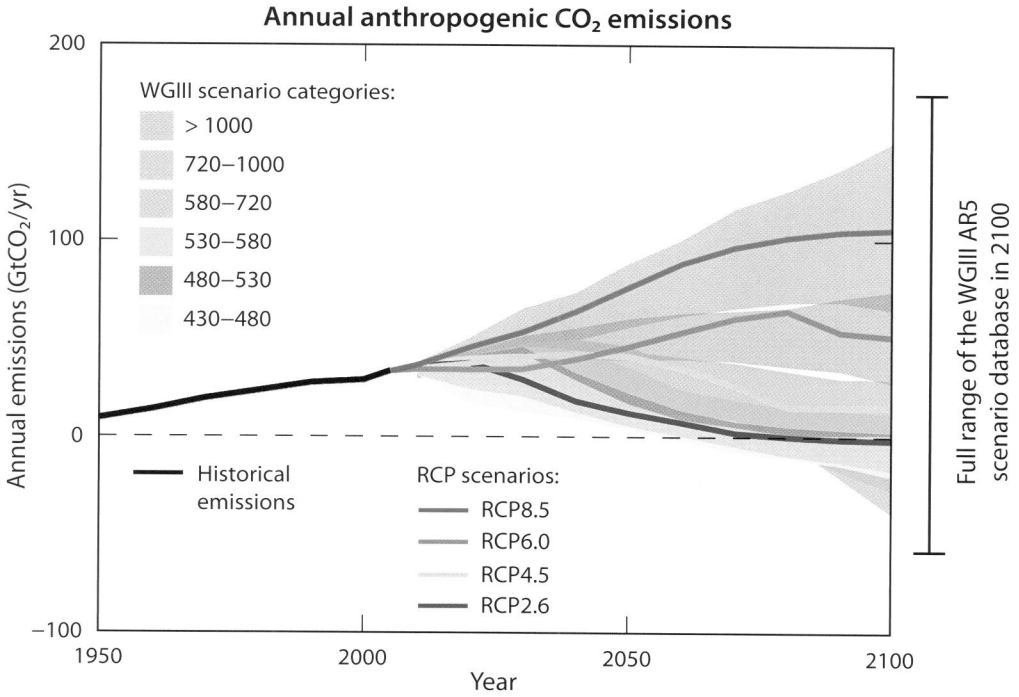

Color Plate 15.1 *Annual anthropogenic $CO_2$ emissions in the four Representative Concentration Pathways (RCPs) (lines) and the associated scenario categories used in WGIII (colored areas). The WGIII scenario categories summarize the wide range of emission scenarios published in the scientific literature and are defined on the basis of $CO_2$-eq concentration levels (in ppm) in 2100. Scenarios without efforts to constrain emissions lead to pathways ranging between RCP6.0 and RCP8.5. (Reproduced with permission of IPCC, 2014).*

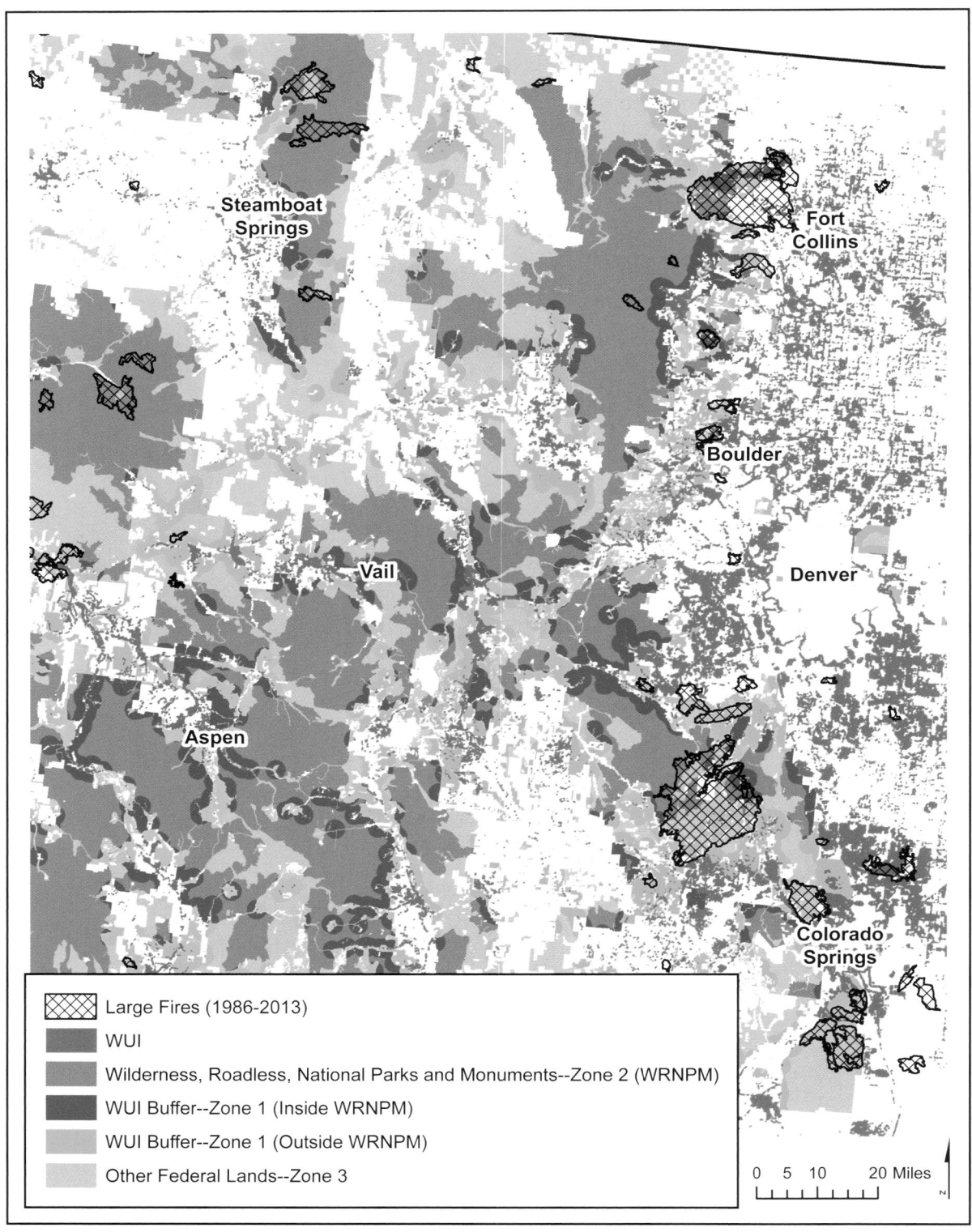

**Color Plate 13.2** *Illustrating the complexity of managing federal lands in Colorado near the wildland-urban interface. Federal lands are broken into three zones based on their goals and proximity to people and property, after recognizing wilderness, roadless areas, national parks and monuments (WRNPM): Zone 1—protection of life and property as a primary goal in a buffer zone in and around the WUI, which is further broken into two parts: (1) WUI buffer inside WRNPM where treatments might employ prescribed fire in some areas, and (2) WUI buffer outside WRNPM where both mechanical treatments and prescribed fire might be employed. Zone 2—WRNPM outside the WUI buffer where treatments to restore and maintain ecological integrity might use managed wildfire or prescribed fire in some areas. Zone 3—remainder of the national forests where treatments to restore and maintain ecological integrity, along with other goals, might use mechanical methods, prescribed fire, and managed wildfire. Note: WUI buffer on federal lands here is 1.5 miles wide; in actual application the WUI buffer would be refined based on local conditions. (Source WUI GIS layer: Colorado State Forest Service)*

Legend:
- Large Fires (1986-2013)
- WUI
- Wilderness, Roadless, National Parks and Monuments--Zone 2 (WRNPM)
- WUI Buffer--Zone 1 (Inside WRNPM)
- WUI Buffer--Zone 1 (Outside WRNPM)
- Other Federal Lands--Zone 3

0  5  10        20 Miles

# Part III

## Current Issues
## in Forest Management

*We are uniquely fire creatures on a uniquely fire planet.* — STEPHEN PYNE

CHAPTER 12

# Forests on Fire:
# Nature's Thermal Creativity

Christopher J. Dunn

*Las Conchas Fire, New Mexico 2011.*
*(Courtesy of Kari Greer/US Forest Service)*

## Introduction

Fire was born of oxygen and hydrocarbons and given life by a spark of lightning or perhaps the touch of lava. Fire has been part of Earth's terrestrial ecosystems since photosynthetic plants provided our atmosphere with oxygen and fire with fuel, dating back to at least 440 million years ago (Pausas & Keeley, 2009). Throughout this long history, Earth's terrestrial biota adapted to fire's presence. Some species resisted fire's wrath by developing fire-resistant traits, such as the thick bark of giant sequoias or heat-dispersing needles that protect the buds on regenerating longleaf pine. Others became resilient by cheating death, as some eucalyptus species and pitch pine do, by sprouting new photosynthetic structures from buds protected beneath bark on stems and branches. Still others accepted death by fire, like knobcone and lodgepole pines, only to be reborn in a newly shaped landscape by increasing seed dispersal in direct response to fire (fire-mediated serotiny). Terrestrial biota coevolved with fire and now assemble into communities at different points in time-since-fire, resulting in vegetation composition and structure being variously distributed through space and time while supporting faunal diversity across landscapes.

The arrival of *Homo sapiens* approximately 200,000 years ago brought forth a unique relationship between Earth's biota and fire: the intentional use of fire to modify landscapes for resource acquisition (Figure 12.1). Whether Prometheus (Greek god of fire) bestowed fire upon humans, or coyote stole fire and brought it to us (Native American oral history), fire has become as much a part of global human culture as any tool used to advance the human condition. Native Americans tended fire to promote food sources (e.g., camas root, huckleberries), to improve grazing for ungulates as a method to increase hunting prospects, and to defeat their enemy in warfare (Boyd, 1999). Today, we still gather ourselves around fire to be soothed by its warmth and light, but our most audacious move has been to capture fire via internal combustion, taking it from wildlands into our lives for light, heat, and other uses.

North America's terrestrial ecosystems are increasingly recognized as coupled human–natural systems, and fire was the dominant method by which humans historically altered these landscapes. Human-ignited fires likely contributed to the evolution of historical forest conditions well before Euro-American colonization, dominating ignitions in some ecosystems while augmenting natural ignitions in others (Taylor et al., 2016). Euro-Americans changed the human–fire interaction in North America by transitioning from fire tender to firefighter, greatly reducing the frequency and extent of wildfire compared to historical experience (Figure 12.2a).

This reduction in wildfire, along with other management practices, has resulted in structural and compositional changes across many forests (Sugihara, van Wagtendonk, Shaffer, Fites-Kaufman, & Thode, 2006). These broadscale alterations of forest structure and fuel loadings have occurred at a time when the Earth is becoming hotter. Combined, these factors have contributed to wildfires that are increasingly difficult to suppress, triggering an increase in the frequency and extent of area burned over the last few decades (Figure 12.2b). Also, the changes in structure and fuel loadings have decreased the resilience of many forests. Only recently have we begun to understand the profound influence and benefit wildland fires had on developing and sustaining North American forests, as well as the important role played by indigenous cultures.

Throughout this chapter we describe the role of disturbance processes in creating and maintaining resilient and resistant forests—important goals in ecological forest management. As we have discussed elsewhere in this book, *a resilient forest has the capacity to absorb a disturbance and reorganize so as to still retain its pre-disturbance ecosystem function and feedbacks. A resistant forest has the capacity to be impacted by a disturbance without undergoing significant reorganization*. Resistance is often the restoration goal in frequent-fire forests, based on historical rather than current forest conditions, as most of these forests have undergone significant change (see Part 4 below). In contrast, resilience is often the restoration goal in episodically or infrequently disturbed forests (e.g., the "conifer-dominated forest initiated by infrequent, high severity wildfire"), which typically have not been significantly altered by fire suppression programs.

Figure 12.1 *Fire use varied by preindustrial humans and ranged from agricultural use to aiding wartime efforts. Indigenous use of fire continued late into the 19th century, and was adopted by early settlers of the western USA until policy changes precluded its use in the early 20th century. ("Blackfeet burning Crow buffalo range," Charles Russell, 1912)*

A basic understanding of fire behavior and effects as well as fire's functional role in forest development is necessary to fully appreciate fire as an ecosystem process and its varying effects on different forest types. This chapter will provide an introduction to these concepts as well as a framework for integrating historical fire regime characteristics into ecological forestry programs. We have organized our discussion into five parts: (1) fundamentals of fire behavior, (2) fire's effect on forest communities, (3) fire regimes: characteristics and use, (4) origins and effects of wildfire policies based on suppression, and (5) fire history as a guide for ecological forest management.

## Part 1: Fundamentals of Fire Behavior

Fire behavior is derived from interactions among factors operating at multiple scales. These factors are best depicted as a series of embedded triangles where triangle size is relative to spatial or temporal scales and the interacting factors are identified along the triangle sides (Figure 12.3). The smallest scale is commonly referred to as the "fire triangle," although *fire combustion triangle* is more descriptive and appropriate because it depicts the basic fundamental components of the chemical and physical processes necessary for the initiation and perpetuation of fire. The intermediate scale is the *fire behavior triangle*[1] and contains envi-

---

1 Sometimes the fire behavior triangle is referred to as the fire environment triangle, but this name is not as descriptive and is better suited for describing broader controls on the environment fire is burning within.

ronmental moderators that control the magnitude of fire behavior. The broadest scale is best referred to as the *fire environment triangle* and contains circumscribing factors that control and bound the environmental moderators and ecological conditions where a wildland fire burns. Fire behavior is the expression of conditions occurring at and among these scales and can be reasonably predicted if all are considered.

**(a)**

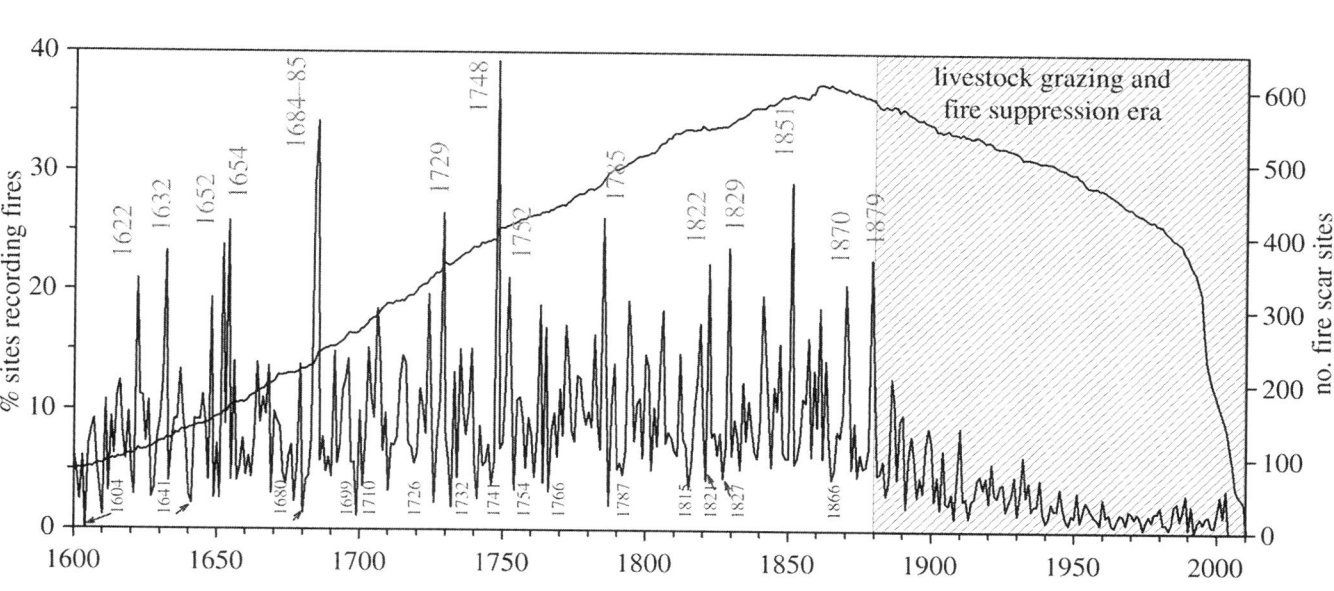

**(b)**

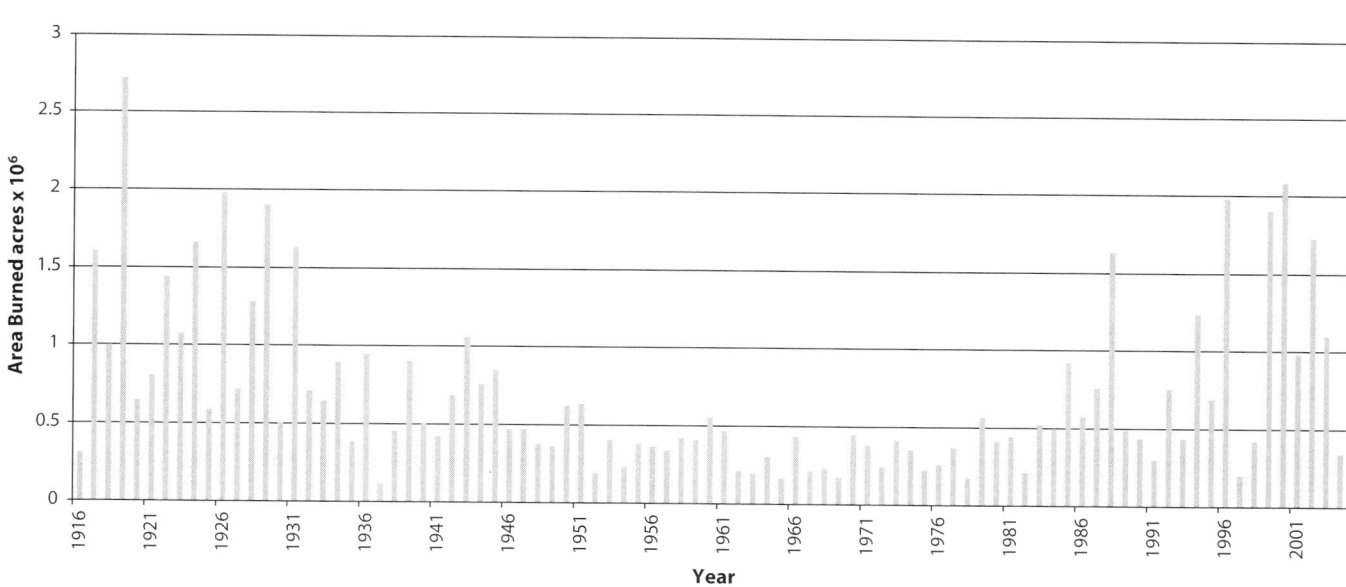

Figure 12.2 *Historical information on wildfire frequency and extent helps provide perspective on current amounts of wildfire. Two studies provide this documentation: 12.2a is the combined record of fire occurrence from more than 800 sites in western North America and shows relatively high fire frequency prior to ca 1900, and a high degree of synchrony in both large and small fire years. The 15 largest and smallest fire years before 1900 are labeled. A pronounced decrease in fire frequency occurred at the time of Euro-American colonization, coinciding approximately with the arrival of railroads, intensive livestock grazing, removal of many Native American populations, and subsequently organized and mechanized firefighting by government agencies (Source: Swetnam et al., 2016) 12.2b is a detailed look at fire extent in the most recent century across eleven western states of the USA, using reports on amount of fire, and shows a reduction in annual area burned followed by a recent increase. Even as we observe this increase, we must recognize that wildfire remains well below pre-Euro-American colonization extent and frequency, as shown by Figure 12.2a. (Source: Adapted from Littell et al., 2009, and updated from data available through the National Interagency Fire Center)*

## The Fire Combustion Triangle: Chemical and Physical Processes

At the smallest scale, three variables are necessary for combustion: (1) *fuel*, which in wildlands typically consists of cellulose-based vegetative structures and released volatile gases, (2) *oxygen*, which is required to release energy by oxidizing cellulose, and (3) a *heat* source that initiates the chemical combustion reaction. There is an optimal mixture of fuel and oxygen for various fuel types and arrangements. Combustion may be inhibited if fuel particles are spaced too far apart to effectively transfer enough heat to perpetuate the combustion process. Alternatively, highly compacted fuels limit oxygen mixing and may halt the chain reaction of combustion.

Wildfires spread and burn in three distinct phases (Figure 12.4). Prior to combustion, fuel particles are a *heat sink* or an object that absorbs heat from the surrounding environment. The *preheating phase* raises these fuel particles to the temperature of combustion. When a fuel particle reaches temperature of combustion (~400°F), it becomes a *heat source* and begins the chemical process of combustion in the *flaming phase*. Subsequently, heat is transferred to the next fuel particle to perpetuate this process. After the flaming phase passes, the *smoldering/glowing phase* commences and may continue for a long time.

## The Fire Behavior Triangle: Moderators of Fire Behavior

There are four primary wildland fire types (Color Plate 12.1): (1) ground, (2) surface, (3) passive crown, and (4) active crown fire. *Ground fires* typically burn the forest floor or upper soil horizons after the flaming front has passed and

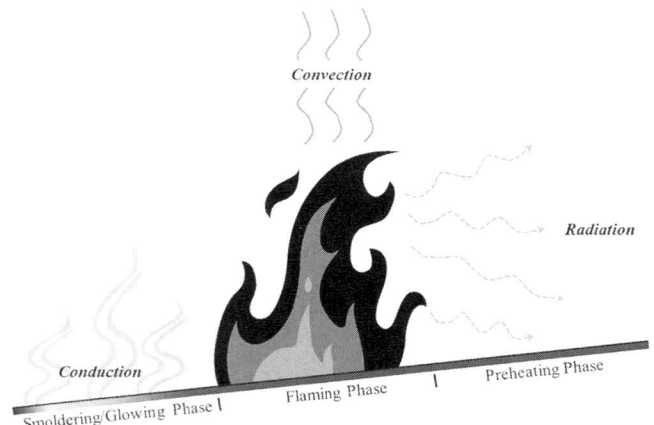

Figure 12.4 *The three dominant phases of combustion in wildland fires: (1) preheating of fuels to raise their temperature to the point of combustion, (2) the flaming phase created by the release of volatile gases from fuels that ignite when mixed with oxygen and heat (flaming front), and (3) smoldering combustion following the passage of the flaming phase as more compacted fuels slowly combust. This smoldering phase can lead to long-duration fires and residual heating, especially when logs, upper soil horizons, or peat burn. The dominant heat transfer mechanism changes with each phase as identified in bold italics. Convective heat transfer occurs when fluid particles (e.g., air) are heated by the energy released in the combustion process. Radiant heat transfer occurs through emitted energy rays from the flaming front. Conduction occurs by heating solid fuel molecules directly in contact with each other and is the slowest form of heat transfer.*

may burn for weeks or months depending on the combustible substrate. In some cases, ground fires dominate fire spread, like the Alaskan taiga or peatlands mixed within boreal forests of Canada. *Surface fires* burn within the surface fuel layers (e.g., fine woody fuels, grasses, shrubs) and typically dominate wildland fire spread. Fire may transition to canopy fuels of individual trees via ladder fuels or fire moving vertically along a tree stem. While surface fires drive the horizontal spread of the flaming front, *passive crown fires* are the combustion of individual or small groups of tree crowns. When fires move among tree canopies they are known as *active crown fires* and can be sustained over large areas depending on fuel, weather, and topographic conditions. The potential for passive or active crown fire is primarily a function of flame height, fire intensity, and canopy fuel structure. Crown fires typically require the simultaneous combustion of surface and canopy fuels, potentially resulting in flame lengths in excess of 200 feet.

Beyond general fire type, fire behavior can be characterized by several metrics (Table 12.1), many of which we will use in this chapter. All are influenced by fuel, weather, and topography that interact to increase or decrease their magnitude.

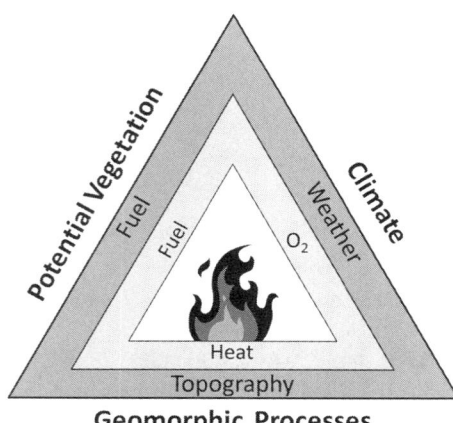

Figure 12.3 *Multiscale determinants of fire behavior can be viewed as a set of embedded triangles where the spatial and temporal scale of influence increases with increasing triangle size. The factors depicted on the sides of the triangles interact within and across scales.*

**Fueling the Fire** "Wildland fuels" is a catchall phrase referring to all live and dead combustible material regardless of size or shape. The most dominant fuel characteristics influencing fire behavior are surface-area-to-volume ratio, fuel loading, and moisture content. *Surface-area-to-volume ratio* is important because the higher the ratio (i.e., smaller diameter fuel particles), the more quickly heating occurs and the more rapidly moisture can be exchanged with the atmosphere. Surface fuels are categorized into time-lag fuel moisture size classes to capture this effect. They are 1-, 10-, 100-, and 1000-hour fuels (<¼″, ¼–1″, 1–3″, >3″ diameter, respectively) and represent the amount of time it takes that fuel particle to reach 63% of equilibrium moisture content with atmospheric conditions (i.e., relative humidity). *Fuel loading* is the total amount of fuel mass present in a given area and is important because it determines the amount of fuel available for generating heat. When combined with fuel bed depth, one can derive the bulk density of the fuel layer. *Fuel moisture content* is the amount of water in fuel, expressed as a percentage relative to the oven dry weight of the fuel particle. This characteristic is important since more energy is required to combust fuels with higher moisture contents because water must be evaporated before combustion begins. Fuel continuity, arrangement, and bulk density are also important characteristics that influence the propagation of the flaming front.

Fuels are typically separated into four categories based on their contribution to fire type and behavior (Figure 12.5), forming a vertical continuum of fuel layers that include: (1) ground (duff, belowground organic matter), (2) surface fuels (litter, fine and coarse woody detritus, live herbaceous and understory woody vegetation), (3) ladder fuels (understory and midstory woody vegetation creating continuity between surface and canopy fuels), and (4) overstory canopy fuels. It is important to understand how fuels con-tribute to fire behavior and effects so they can be modified appropriately if preventing excessive tree mortality is your management objective.

*Ground fuels* contribute little to flaming combustion or fire spread because of their high bulk density, which limits oxygen mixing needed for combustion. Although these fuels have limited influence on common fire behavior metrics like rate of spread, flame length, or fireline intensity, they can have profound effects on ecosystems because of their long-duration burning and total heat release. Also, combustion of ground fuels may be the primary facilitator of fire spread and effects in environments where soils have very high organic matter content, such as the coal seams of Pennsylvania or the peatlands of the Alaska taiga.

*Surface fuels* include live and dead vegetative material within the flame profile as fires spread across the surface of wildlands generally, driving rate of spread, flame length, and fireline intensity (Rothermel, 1983). Surface fuels include fine and coarse woody fuels, herbaceous vegetation, lichen, moss, shrubs, and tree seedlings. Fine woody fuels include all dead woody material <3 inches in diameter, although they are typically separated into the three previously defined size-classes (Figure 12.6). The type of fuel carrying the flaming front is considered the dominant fuel layer when estimating fire spread. Live surface fuels are a heat sink if their moisture contents are high enough to prevent sustained combustion, but as a fire season develops over time these fuels begin to dry and become readily available for combustion.

*Ladder fuels* facilitate the spread of fire from surface fuels to tree crowns, leading to passive (combustion of single or small groups of tree crowns) or active (transfer among overstory crowns) crown fires. Although snags can carry fire vertically, they tend to combust too slowly to facilitate the horizontal transfer of flames to tree crowns.

Table 12.1 *Commonly utilized fire behavior metrics*

| Metric | Definition | Units |
|---|---|---|
| Fireline intensity | The rate of energy release per unit length of an active flaming front | Btu ft$^{-1}$ s$^{-1}$ |
| Rate of spread | The speed of forward progression of the active flaming front | Ft min$^{-1}$ |
| Flame length | Total distance from the back of the flaming zone to the tip of the active flaming front | Ft |
| Flame height | Vertical distance of the active flaming front (typically smaller than flame length, especially in rapidly advancing fires) | Ft |
| Flame depth | The horizontal distance between the back and front of the flaming zone | Ft |
| Residence time | Length of time an active flaming front persists at a given location | Min |
| Reaction Intensity | The rate of heat release per unit area of the flaming fire front | Btu ft$^{-2}$ min$^{-1}$ |
| Heat per unit area | The amount of energy released by combustion in a defined area | Btu ft$^{-2}$ |
| Torching Index | The open wind speed at which some kind of crown fire is expected to initiate | mph |
| Crowning Index | The open wind speed above which an active crown fire is possible for the specified fire environment | mph |

Therefore, ladder fuels are dominated by live vegetation with foliage that readily transfers heat vertically when combusted. Ladder fuels are typically associated with shade-tolerant understory trees that have increased in abundance because of fire exclusion (Figure 12.7), although overstory trees may contribute to this category if they have retained lower branches and foliage.

Three variables characterize *canopy fuels*: (1) canopy cover, (2) canopy bulk density, and (3) canopy base height. Canopy cover is the proportion of the forest floor covered by tree crowns, which can influence fire activity directly through crown fire behavior and indirectly through the amount of sunlight reaching and, therefore, drying understory fuels. Canopy bulk density is the mass per unit volume of available canopy fuels and is a determinant of the potential for crown fire behavior because bulk density must be high enough to facilitate heat transfer and fire spread. Canopy base height is the average height from the ground to the base of continuous canopy; all else being equal, the higher the canopy base height the lower the likelihood of surface fires transitioning to passive or active crown fires. Ladder fuels effectively lower the canopy base height and increase the potential for crown fire. The distribution of canopy fuels can be highly variable across stands and landscapes.

**Weather and Fire**  Weather directly and indirectly moderates fire behavior through several dynamic variables. Two key weather variables are wind speed and relative humidity. Atmospheric stability (potential for vertical lifting of heated air masses), air temperature (influences relative humidity), drought (reduces live and dead fuel moistures), and synoptic weather patterns (e.g., frontal passages that increase wind speed and change its direction) are other dominant weather factors impacting fire behavior (Schroeder & Buck, 1970).

*Wind speed* is typically reported as "20′ wind speed" which is the wind velocity 20 feet above the dominant vegetative cover (i.e., trees, shrubs, grasses). Wind speed may be reduced by as much as 90% in dense canopies before influencing the flaming front. *Midflame wind speed* is the velocity of wind at half the flame height and has the greatest direct impact on fire rate of spread and intensity of any weather variable. Wind mixes oxygen into the flaming

Figure 12.5 *The vertical continuum of wildland fuels and potential fire types. Ground fuels include duff and belowground organic matter, facilitating smoldering and residual combustion. Surface fuels include litter, surface woody material, and live understory vegetation and are the primary carrier of the flaming front. Ladder fuels provide vertical continuity between surface and canopy fuels, the latter of which can sustain crown fire causing high mortality and extremely difficult fire control.*

front, where it may otherwise be rapidly depleted by the chemical combustion process, thereby increasing the rate of combustion. In many cases, fire draws air into the flaming zone to replenish oxygen and heated air that is vertically lifted into the atmosphere, giving the perception that fire is actively breathing. Wind also bends flames toward fuels in advance of the flaming front, increasing the rate of preheating of fuels. As wind speed increases, so too does fire rate of spread and intensity, although thresholds may be reached if combustion becomes limited by fuels.

*Relative humidity* and time since last precipitation indirectly impact fire behavior by influencing fuel moisture content. Relative humidity is dependent on the dew point of an existing air mass and the diurnal fluctuations of air temperature. *Dew point* is the temperature at which water vapor condenses into liquid water, forming dew on solid surfaces or fog suspended in air. When temperature equals the dew point, relative humidity is 100%. Relative humidity changes throughout a day (Figure 12.8). These diurnal fluctuations cause fuel moisture content to vary at rates consistent with their time-lag fuel moisture class discussed previously.

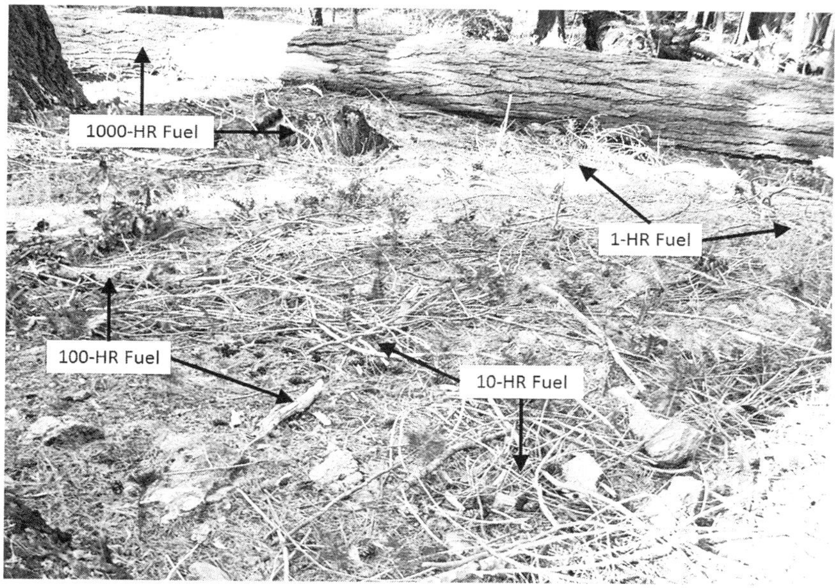

Quantifying potential fire behavior for a given forest is important for many applications, including the development of stand-level treatments that reduce fire hazard or landscape-level fuels-reduction plans to reduce fire risk (Ager, Vaillant, & McMahan, 2013). The potential fire behavior for a given landscape is often modeled using various "fire weather conditions" estimated from historical weather data. Fire weather conditions can be summarized from records collected at remote automated weather stations (RAWS) and broken down into percentages depicting *percentile weather or fuel conditions*. For example, one can derive estimates of weather and fuel conditions historically observed in 3% of all days during a defined fire season. In other words, 97% of all days during a fire season will likely have values that result in a lower fire intensity or rate of spread. These estimates are commonly referred to as the 97th percentile weather and fuel conditions that can be estimated for multiple variables (Table 12.2). These 97th percentile weather conditions are often used as a benchmark for predicting the effectiveness of fuels treatments under conditions when most fires escape control. Many fire weather and fuel parameters are correlated and will occur simultaneously, but not all weather parameters necessarily align on any single day.

Figure 12.6 *Surface fuels are separated into the time-lag fuel moisture size classes of 1-, 10-, 100-, and 1000-hour fuels (<¼″, ¼–1″, 1–3″, >3″ diameter, respectively). These classes represent the amount of time it takes that fuel particle to reach 63% of equilibrium moisture content with atmospheric conditions (i.e., relative humidity). 1-hour fuels are considered the most important surface fuel influencing fire rate of spread, intensity, and flame length because of their propensity for rapid heating and combustion and relatively rapid moisture fluctuations with atmospheric conditions.*

**Terrain and Fire**    *Topography*, or the distribution of physical features and landforms across a landscape, is the third moderator with direct and indirect influences on fire behavior. Landforms can be highly variable across a geographic area with important consequences for fire behavior. For example, slope increases preheating of fuels in advance of an upslope-moving head fire, accelerating its rate of spread. In contrast, slope may reduce heat transfer in the direction of spread when the fire is moving

Figure 12.7 *Ladder fuels are dominated by understory and midstory vegetation readily combusted by surface fires. As lower crowns combust they can propagate fire vertically into the overstory crowns leading to passive and, potentially, active crown fires. For example, fire exclusion has increased the abundance of understory white fir, which provides ladder fuels in giant sequoia groves threatening the persistence of heritage trees that exceed 2,000 years of age (Sierra Nevada Mts., California).*

downhill as a backing fire because convection transfers the majority of heat back into the burned area. Therefore, complex topography results in highly dynamic fire behavior as fires spread across landscapes.

Indirect effects of topography on fire behavior are often more influential than direct effects. For example, fuel loading and type can change abruptly along an aspect and elevation gradient in mountainous terrain, also altering fire behavior as fire spreads across the landscape. Topographic features affect air temperature, precipitation, snowpack retention, and solar radiation, each of which influences live and dead fuel moistures, the timing of fire season, and the potential boundaries of fire spread (especially in early and late season fires).

Wind direction and speed are partially controlled by topography in mountainous terrain. This interaction is particularly important because wind speed and direction control the direction and rate of maximum fire spread. Topographic features funnel winds up canyons and toward draws, often in different directions than the general wind. Additionally, as air masses are compressed over ridges wind speed increases significantly and becomes turbulent on the leeward side, affecting both fire spread and the potential for firebrands to ignite spot fires ahead of the flaming front. When slope and wind align, fire behavior can increase dramatically, especially when fine fuels such as grass are exposed to wind and solar radiation.

### The Fire Environment Triangle: The Bigger Picture

Wildfires continue to burn across much of the North American landscape (Figure 12.9) despite increasing suppression efforts and expense (Calkin, Gebert, Jones, & Neilson, 2005). Fire occurrence should be assumed in fire-prone landscapes and therefore incorporated into how we manage resilient forests for an uncertain future. This requires one to consider broader-scale influences on the fire behav-

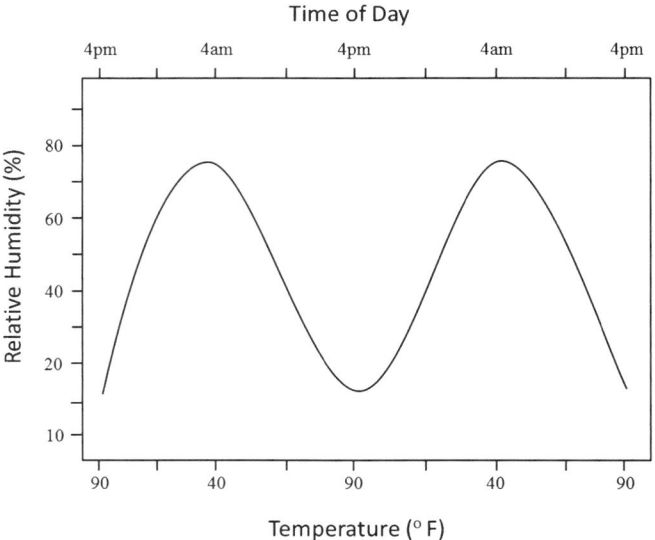

Figure 12.8 *Daily patterns in air temperature result in fluctuations in relative humidity. As relative humidity increases, fine fuel moistures also increase, leading to slower rates of spread and fireline intensity. Typically, rates of spread and fireline intensities increase significantly during the warmer part of the day (burn period), but subsequently decrease during the night as humidity rises (humidity recovery) on wildland fires. This is especially evident in steep, mountainous terrain.*

ior as identified by the fire environment triangle: potential vegetation, geomorphic processes, and climate. These circumscribing factors provide a linkage between fire behavior and effects and vary at broad spatial and temporal scales (Chapin, Matson, & Mooney, 2011). One should always consider fire behavior within the context of the biological and physical environment to better evaluate the potential or observed positive and negative fire effects.

**Potential Vegetation** To better understand fire dynamics in a particular region, one should always consider the poten-

Table 12.2 *Percentile weather and fuel conditions for ponderosa pine forests of eastern Washington*

| | 50th Percentile | 90th Percentile | 97th Percentile |
|---|---|---|---|
| Max. Temperature (° Fahrenheit) | 82.5 | 86.3 | 95.3 |
| Relative Humidity (%) | 36.3 | 22.0 | 9.3 |
| 1-hr Fuel Moisture (%) | 5.8 | 3.2 | 2.3 |
| 10-hr Fuel Moisture (%) | 7.2 | 4.6 | 3.5 |
| 100-hr Fuel Moisture (%) | 13.3 | 10.6 | 9.8 |
| 1000-hr Fuel Moisture (%) | 13.5 | 10.6 | 9.8 |
| Herbaceous Fuel Moisture (%) | 60.5 | 37.3 | 33.3 |
| Live Woody Fuel Moisture (%) | 102.0 | 75.5 | 67.0 |
| 20' Wind Speed (mph) | 6.9 | 8.3 | 13.5 |
| Midflame Wind Speed (mph) | 2.1 | 2.5 | 4.0 |

Figure 12.9 *The extent of fires >1,000 acres that burned between 1984 and 2013. It is evident that even in today's fire suppression paradigm wildfires remain inevitable across much of the United States landscape. (Source: MTBS, 2014)*

tial vegetation (available pool of species) from which fuels are generated, fire effects are evaluated, and responses are derived. For example, longleaf pine forests of the southeastern USA are arguably the most fire-adapted and fire-dependent forest systems in North America (the "bookend" frequent-fire forest type described in Chapter 3). Grasses, such as wiregrass, dominate fire-maintained understories of longleaf pine forests and, along with longleaf pine litter, are the primary carrier of the flaming front. These well-aerated fuels dry to combustible states rapidly despite the generally humid climate and high fuel-moisture content in these forests. Prescribed burning in these forests is optimal around 50% humidity, as compared to fuels in the American West that are not readily combustible until humidity drops below 30% (humidity this low would be considered too low for prescribed burning in the southeastern USA). This difference is attributed to the relative abundance of volatile organic compounds that facilitate combustion of fuels at a higher humidity. The increased combustibility of wiregrass and pine litter at higher humidity than other regions could be considered an adaptation to fire because return intervals <3 years are needed to prevent fundamental changes in the understory and eventual conversion to another forest type. Additionally, potential vegetation also controls postfire regeneration and may be important for facilitating the establishment of future

vegetative communities. Therefore, understanding the potential vegetation within a region and its interaction with fire will help develop appropriate fire management plans that maintain resilient forest conditions over long time periods.

**Geomorphic Processes**    Long-term geomorphic processes created the steep mountainous terrain in many regions of North America. We have previously described how topography influences weather and fuels, but broader-scale geomorphic processes (e.g., mountain development) also influence fire behavior because mountain ranges interact with the climate of a given region. For example, the Cascade Range of northwestern North America is oriented north–south at a right angle to the prevailing winds and air mass movements. As air masses from the Pacific Ocean move across these mountains they compress and cool, leading to heavy precipitation on the western slopes and a rainshadow to the east. This variation in precipitation influences fire behavior by altering fuel type, fuel loadings, and live and dead fuel moistures. Mountains in other regions may interact with climate differently, so local or regional knowledge is needed to understand the influence of this factor on fire behavior and effects.

More subtle variations in landform also arise from long-term geomorphic processes and can have a significant influence on fire behavior and effects. For example, within the southeastern USA Coast Plain, upland forests dominated by longleaf pine are often found in proximity to wetlands dominated by cypress and other hardwood species. The upland forests tend to burn at 2–10-year intervals, while the lowland swamps are estimated to burn at intervals of 100 years or greater, depending on their hydrologic cycle (Watts, Kobziar, & Snyder, 2012). A wetland's hydrologic cycle is influenced by proximal climatic variation and water drainage from across the region. In some cases, such as along rivers like the Mississippi, the area influencing these processes can be broad. In addition to differences between the uplands and lowland swamps, cypress domes, or islands of seasonally dry land, are distributed throughout the swamps and may burn every decade depending on their ignition by lightning. Hydrologic cycles similarly affect the prairie pothole region of central North America. These land features were created by the recession of the Laurentide ice sheet following the last glacial period 10,000–20,000 years ago and still has a legacy observable today.

**Climate**    We have already discussed several climatic influences on potential fire behavior, but additional climate effects should be considered. In particular, climate can influence the timing and length of fire seasons. Much of western North America is dominated by a Mediterranean climate, characterized by cool, wet winters and warm, dry summers. Fire season in this region is generally limited to summer months after fuels have dried to the point that fire can ignite and spread. Alternatively, in the Appalachian Mountains of Tennessee and Kentucky, summer months often experience significant precipitation so fire season typically occurs in autumn. The monsoon season in June and July often results in precipitation in the US Southwest, splitting fire season into a late spring and a late summer–fall season. When precipitation is absent during the monsoon season, dry lightning can coincide with drought conditions and produce an extreme fire season. Understanding regional variation is paramount to successful ecosystem management since forest and fire managers' careers typically include spending time in various regions.

The most extreme fire behavior occurs because of high winds that develop as a result of interactions between climate and mountains. *Foehn winds* are extreme wind events that occur when high-pressure systems reside over the inland dry regions of the western USA, and a low pressure system is present on the leeside of the mountains. This pressure gradient causes warmer, drier winds to travel from the high to low pressure systems. As winds travel over the mountains they compress and subsequently increase in velocity as they travel down the leeward side of the mountains. The Santa Ana winds of southern California are the most notable Foehn wind, but east winds in the Pacific Northwest and the Chinook winds of Colorado are common Foehn winds too. Most of the large historical wildfires in the dense conifer forests west of the crest of the Cascade Range in the Pacific

---

### Box 12.1  Climate change and wildfire*

Climate change is likely to dramatically alter fire regimes as argued earlier (Chapter 3) with consequent effects on forest ecosystem structure and function. Effects are likely to be both direct and indirect, although specific changes in temperature and moisture depend on geographic location and may arise during different time periods. Global temperatures have increased and are projected to continue on this trend as climate change effects are realized (IPCC, 2014). Higher temperatures increase potential evapotranspiration, which decreases live and dead fuel moistures and therefore can exacerbate fire behavior and effects. These climatic conditions also increase vegetative stress and susceptibility to mortality (van Mantgem et al., 2009), altering ecosystem structure and function and potentially leading to a positive feedback on fire extent and severity as tree mortality adds to fuel loadings.

Climate change has already decreased winter snow pack and caused earlier snow melt in some regions of North America. Concurrently, fire season length has expanded by several weeks in parts of the western USA (Westerling, Hidalgo, Cayan, & Swetnam, 2006). As winter precipitation declines or transitions from snow to rain, fire season length may continue to increase in the coming decades with the added effect of reducing prescribed burning opportunities needed to restore fire to these systems.

Increasing global temperatures are altering atmospheric cycles and their effects on weather patterns. Jet streams have been correlated with historical fire occurrence (Morgan, Hardy, Swetnam, Rollins, & Long, 2001) because they influence precipitation patterns across the continental US (Ellis & Barton, 2012). The North Pacific jet stream appears to be more variable and moving northward as a result of climate change (Coumou, Petoukhov, Rahmstorf, Petri, & Schellnguber, 2014). This change in the jet stream led to an extraordinary drought in California from 2013 to 2015 (Swain et al., 2014) and, if persistent, could lead to more large fires like the 2013 Rim Fire (Lyderson, North, & Collins, 2014). Ultimately, wildfires may increase in areas where fires were infrequent historically or decrease in areas where they were abundant historically, resulting in dramatically altered fire regimes at broad scales.

---

* See Chapters 3 and 15 for more discussion of climate change and forests.

Northwest have been associated with a synoptic weather pattern in which air pressure differences bring hot and very dry east winds over the Cascade Range, which cause rapid declines in fuel moisture; consequences are dramatic when these conditions coincide with ignitions (lightning, human-caused) or encounter preexisting fires.

Coming climate change will add significantly to the challenges of understanding fire behavior and managing and controlling wildfires (Box 12.1). Much remains to be learned.

## Predicting Fire Behavior

Many decades of research have gone into developing computer models that capture the interactions among the multiscale factors influencing fire behavior. Recently, significant advances in our understanding of wildland fire behavior (Finney et al., 2015) coupled with the development of increasingly sophisticated computer models (Hoffman et al., 2012) are rapidly advancing the field of fire science to meet contemporary and future challenges.

*Fire models* are computer programs developed to predict fire behavior for use in conducting prescribed fire and suppressing or managing wildfires. Fire models focus primarily on surface fire behavior to predict the metrics described in Table 12.1. These models integrate factors from the fire combustion and fire behavior triangles to predict average surface fire behavior across a stand (see the Appendix for more information on these models). Most fire behav-

ior models also predict the potential for passive or active crown fire but generally do not estimate crown fire behavior (e.g., rate of spread, fireline intensity, and flame length) because parameterizing these models requires observations of these fire types, which are difficult to obtain. Stand-level models have been incorporated into landscape models to capture diverse topographic, fuel, and weather conditions across landscapes. These models are important for managing landscape-fuels programs and fire suppression efforts, but they should be viewed as supplementary to the judgment and experience of managers and fireline personnel (Box 12.2).

## Part 2: Fire's Effect on Forest Communities

Natural disturbance is an important ecosystem process with a functional role that depends on the disturbance type, its spatial and temporal characteristics, and the magnitude of its effects. In their seminal book on the ecology of natural disturbances, Pickett and White (1985, p. 7) defined a disturbance as "any relatively discrete event in time that disrupts ecosystem, community, or population structure and changes resources, substrate availability, or the physical environment." Fires certainly qualify as events that disrupt and alter availability of resources, and, as noted in Chapter 3, fire is quite unique among most natural disturbance agents in that humans have significant capacities to both introduce fire and prevent it, for at least a period of time.

---

### Box 12.2  Leverage technology, but trust your instincts

Fire behavior analysts are responsible for determining the appropriate fuel model that best represents observed fire behavior. Often this requires the use of multiple fuel models to account for observed fire behavior, with the appropriate models changing as a function of fire weather and topographic conditions. As depicted in the image below, an analyst might assume the flaming front burns through timber litter and focus on its contribution to fire behavior. As fire weather conditions become more severe, fire behavior may be driven by the combustion of shrubs as the shrub layer becomes the primary fuel layer carrying the flaming front.

Wildfires are landscape-scale events, so planning suppression operations or prioritizing fuel treatments requires fire behavior estimates across landscapes. Models such as FlamMap (Finney, 2006) can predict landscape fire behavior and provide context, but managers or fireline personnel should also base their decision on information they directly observe. These observations are often limited to visual and auditory cues from the crew members and fire lookouts, including smoke color, dispersion, smoke plume size, and the sound of the fire burning. Models do not always predict accurately, so managers and fireline personnel must be

mindful and develop a sense for fire weather and fuel interactions to be effective and safe in their work environment (Figure 12.10).

Figure 12.10  *The author at work.*

Fire effects span all scales of biological organization and are both a limiting and a regulating force in terrestrial ecosystems. We discuss some of these effects below.

## Fire Kills Trees

*Wildland fires directly impact vegetation by disrupting the physiological processes of water, nutrient, and energy acquisition and transfer necessary for tree growth, maintenance, and defense.* The three primary causes of tree death from fire are: (1) root necrosis (death), (2) cambial necrosis, and (3) crown scorch or combustion (Figure 12.11). Long-duration combustion of ground and coarse woody fuels may result in tree death by killing fine or coarse roots, thereby inhibiting the acquisition of water and nutrients. Similarly, long-duration fuel combustion at the base of trees, or fire intensities high enough to penetrate a tree's protective bark, may kill trees via cambium necrosis that, in turn, inhibits water, nutrient, and energy transfer within the tree. Crown combustion or scorch reduces energy and carbon acquisition, leading to tree mortality unless the species is specifically adapted to sprout new leaves (e.g., pitch pine in New Jersey). This effect does not require a crown fire because combustion of heavy fuel loadings releases a high amount of heat over a longer time period that may significantly scorch tree crowns to the point of death. In most cases, increased fuel loading and continuity cause higher mortality, but this can be a result of one or more of these mortality pathways. Keep in mind, however, that tree death is a natural process and provides habitat resources for many invertebrate and vertebrate species.

## Fire Protects Trees

Many tree species have characteristics such as thick bark, deep roots, and elevated crowns that aid in their resistance to low- and moderate-intensity fires. These characteristics allow fire to be an agent of protection primarily by maintaining fuel loadings below a threshold such that a tree can resist death. For example, frequent fires consume bark and other detritus that sloughs off trees and gathers around their base (duff mounds), reducing the potential for a long duration and intense fire that damage fine roots or girdle the tree at its base. These low-intensity fires also scorch lower branches, thereby raising crown heights and reducing the chance of fire scorching or consuming tree crowns. Small-diameter trees typically have not developed fire-resistant characteristics so they remain susceptible to low-intensity fires. Therefore, frequent low-intensity fires prevent the development of ladder fuels that increase the risk of death to larger-diameter trees (see Figure 12.12a and b). Overall, frequent fires can modify all fuel layers and provide long-term benefits to individual tree survival of fire adapted species.

Reducing fuel loadings is not the only mechanism of tree protection provided by frequent fires. The maintenance of an open forest structure with widely spaced individual or small groups of trees prevents active crown fires and allows for greater heat dissipation to the atmosphere when surface fuels are combusted, reducing the potential for excessive crown scorch or combustion. Additionally, fire improves tree vigor by increasing resource availability for surviving trees, and improved tree vigor has been shown to reduce fire-induced mortality (van Mantgem et al., 2003). Tree productivity and vigor may also be enhanced by the release

Figure 12.11 *Heating vegetative structures to ~200°F (93°C) for one minute causes cellular necrosis (death). Death occurs when the physiological function of a tree is disrupted and nutrient, water, and energy resource acquisition and transfer are inhibited. This may be caused by root necrosis (a), vascular cambium necrosis (b) or crown necrosis (c). (Photo credit: Ari Cowan and Rebecca Miller)*

Figure 12.12  *Short-interval fires (<3 years) maintain wiregrass-dominated understory communities in longleaf pines of Florida (a). On some sites, such as (b), understory communities may shift from a dominance of graminoids to one of southern palmetto, which burn with greater intensities and may result in morality of the overstory pines. More commonly, fire-return intervals of longer than 3 years in longleaf pine result in establishment and growth of hardwoods, which gradually shades out the graminoid-dominated understory—a critical fuel for sustaining low-severity fire—and reproduction of longleaf pine, potentially converting the site to dominance by a mixed-hardwood forest. Images (c) and (d) depict high-severity fire effects on an old-growth Douglas-fir–western hemlock forest. These fires promote natural regeneration of early seral conditions and communities important to many species reliant on snags, logs, or shrubs for nesting, roosting, or foraging.*

of nitrogen from combusted fuels to the surviving and new vegetation. These derived benefits can be part of the long-term objectives for broadscale fuels reduction and restoration plans that include maintenance burning at intervals similar to historical fire regimes.

## Fire Shapes Plant and Animal Communities

Fire directly impacts vegetative communities by altering successional trajectories, often favoring one floral and faunal community at the expense of another. This underlies the importance of maintaining natural disturbance processes since the lack of fire, or conversely uncharacteristic fires, may be detrimental to the resilience of these ecosystems. Two dominant fire–vegetation interactions (frequent low-

severity fire and infrequent high-severity fire) that influence community composition and structure are consistent with the two-class system for categorizing disturbances: chronic-disturbance and episodic-disturbance.[2]

In frequent-fire forests, wildland fires can regulate understory and overstory structure and composition by inhibiting the establishment of species not adapted to persistent fire disturbance. Although an individual fire is discrete in space and time, the cumulative effect of frequent fires maintains the biological community in a pseudo steady-state or successional stage by mediating forest density and promoting dominance by fire-tolerant

2  See Chapter 3 for more discussion of the two dominant fire–vegetation interactions.

species. These effects are more aligned with chronic- than episodic-disturbance, and therefore the historically resilient forest condition is the mediated state. Without recurring fire, understories and midstories gradually transition to dominance by fire-intolerant species and to forests different from historical conditions and not considered resistant or resilient to contemporary fires. This fire–vegetation interaction is evident in longleaf pine–wiregrass forests of the southeastern USA that quickly transition to dominance by other species in the absence of fire (Figure 12.12a and b). Many ponderosa pine and mixed-conifer forests of the Intermountain West and Sierra Nevada Range in California were also of this type historically. Woodlands of southern British Columbia, as well as some western larch forests of Montana, were also maintained by short-interval fires that excluded the establishment of denser forests or encroachment by other species.

Fire's functional role is different in forests with longer fire-return intervals that are subject to high-severity fire; however, fire is no less important to their resilience. Episodic-disturbances control the distribution of biological legacies (live and dead structures present following a disturbance) across space and time. Live biological legacies provide refuge for species reliant on crowns for nesting and roosting; they maintain a seed source for propagating the next generation of forest; and they also support belowground mycorrhizal symbionts that increase water and nutrient acquisition. Dead biological legacies provide structural habitat (as both snags and logs) valuable to multiple vertebrate and invertebrate species such as cavity nesting birds, denning mammals, and wood-boring insects. These biological legacies provide ecological functions for several hundred years depending on the dynamic nature of their postfire existence.[3] An example of the importance of the changes wrought by intense but infrequent wildfires is evident when high-severity fire creates early seral conditions that support distinct biological communities otherwise excluded by dominance of long-lived species like Douglas-fir–western hemlock trees in western Washington (Figure 12.12c and d).

## Fire Creates Landscape Patterns

Wildfires are, by nature, landscape-scale events. Fires control the distribution of forest structure and composition across landscapes where they are the dominant disturbance agent. The cumulative effects of individual tree or stand-level mortality create landscape-scale structural and compositional diversity. These patterns are dependent on a fire's mortality patch-size distribution, the distance between patches, and their clustered or even distribution within a

fire boundary. As fire frequency decreases, mortality patch size typically increases, as we depict below. Wildfire's influence on forest development is often dominated by one of the severity classes (Perry et al., 2011), but, as with all large disturbances, wildfires are characterized by substantial heterogeneity in their intensity and effects.

The distribution and size of high-mortality patches directly controls the connectivity of forest habitats. A species' persistence is partially dependent on its ability to migrate from various patches to share genetic resources or colonize areas with abundant habitat resources. For example, seed dispersal from live biological legacies and the successful establishment of the next generation forest is partially controlled by the distance from seed source (Donato et al., 2009). Therefore, high-mortality patch sizes exceeding seed dispersal distance of pioneering trees may lead to protracted regeneration and a longer transition to old-growth conditions. Maintaining the abundance, size, and distribution of mortality patch sizes (often referred to as spatial complexity, as we describe below) across landscapes may improve species resilience by maintaining widely distributed and diverse conditions that prevent loss from a single wildland fire.

## Fire Affects Ecosystem Processes

There are a multitude of ecosystem processes influenced by wildland fires. Three of the four important ecosystem processes (as described in Chapter 2 of this book) are those associated with production (carbon or energy), water, and material (including nutrient) flows or cycles. Wildfires impact these processes primarily by altering the distribution of live and dead biological legacies that directly contribute to the magnitude of the resource pools and their turnover rates. Legacy abundance also supports above- and belowground micro- and macro-communities reliant on various live and dead structures for energy and nutrient acquisition (Odum, 1969). Frequent fires often maintain a forest in a state of reduced primary productivity relative to the maximum site potential by maintaining lower density forests. Similarly, these forests only support a modest abundance of saprophytes (species whose primary energy source is dead vegetative material such as logs) because of low mortality rates of large trees and persistent combustion of woody material.

Forests with longer fire-return intervals exhibit larger fluctuations in ecosystem processes because of relatively long periods between disturbances and their greater magnitude of change. This is evident when considering the energy or carbon cycle of forests (Meigs, Donato, Campbell, Martin, & Law, 2009), which is directly related to the abundance of live and dead biological legacies (Figure 12.13). Nutrient cycles are also affected by fire disturbance in similar ways,

---

3 See Chapter 3 for a more extensive discussion of biological legacies.

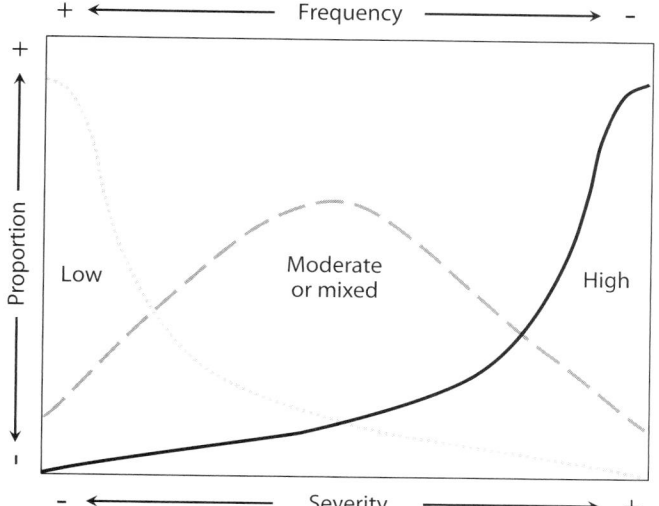

**Figure 12.14** *Fire regimes are typically identified by their frequency and severity (i.e., mortality) and can be broadly fit into three idealized classes: (1) high frequency, low severity, (2) moderate frequency, moderate or mixed severity, and (3) low frequency, high severity. These regime types differ by the proportion of each fire-severity level typically observed and describe the dominant long-term fire regime of an ecosystem. However, a fire regime will exhibit variation in the mixture of fire severities at broad spatiotemporal scales often associated with synoptic weather events or changes in climatic conditions. (See Color Plate 12.2 for landscape pictures of low-, mixed-, and high-severity fires.) (Source: Adapted from Agee, 1993)*

although fire can promote increased nitrogen abundance by creating conditions favorable to nitrogen-fixing species like red alder in Oregon and Washington's coastal mountains (Perakis, Sinkhorn, & Compton, 2011).

## Part 3: Fire Regimes: Characteristics and Use

Understanding fire's historical role in developing North America's forested communities is critical for creating management practices that improve forest resilience for an uncertain future (Box 12.3). Fire ecologists typically refer to conditions that existed prior to Euro-American colonization to quantify historical characteristics of wildfires and summarize them into site-specific fire regimes. *Fire regimes are a suite of characteristics that describe the spatial and temporal attributes and magnitude of wildfires over relatively long time periods. Fire regimes are commonly described by their relative frequency and severity for a particular forest type* (Figure 12.14). Estimates of fire frequency are linked to a forest's age structure to understand fire severity and fire's ecological role in developing the forests supportive of the floral and faunal communities present upon Euro-American arrival. Severity is most often described as overstory tree mortality, as we do in this section, but can be a measure of fire effects on other resources of interest. Although we cannot re-create all the factors influencing

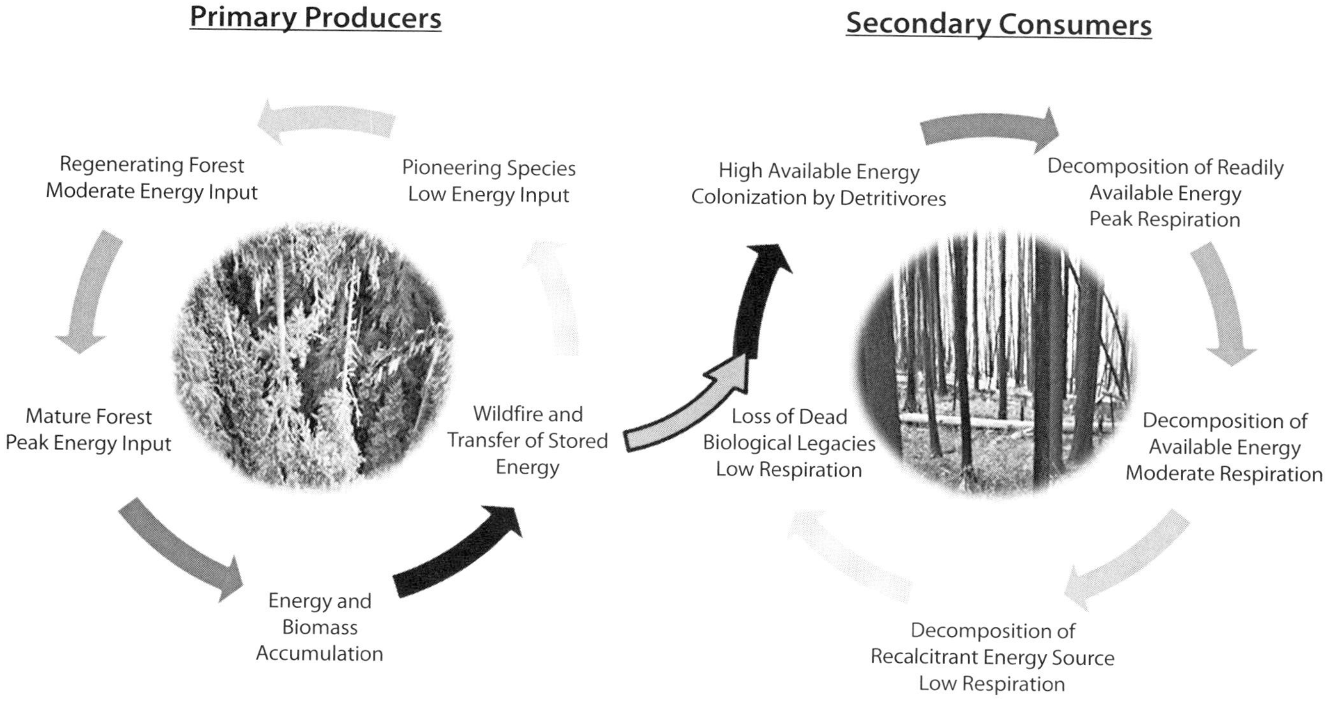

## Primary Producers            ## Secondary Consumers

Regenerating Forest
Moderate Energy Input

Pioneering Species
Low Energy Input

High Available Energy
Colonization by Detritivores

Decomposition of Readily
Available Energy
Peak Respiration

Mature Forest
Peak Energy Input

Wildfire and
Transfer of Stored
Energy

Loss of Dead
Biological Legacies
Low Respiration

Decomposition of
Available Energy
Moderate Respiration

Energy and
Biomass
Accumulation

Decomposition of
Recalcitrant Energy Source
Low Respiration

**Figure 12.13** *Fires alter the distribution of live and dead biological legacies, thereby altering the energy distribution within the system. The magnitude of this effect is dependent on the severity of the fire, time since last fire, and potential productivity of the site. In this example, there is an increase in energy for consumers of energy stored in dead wood (heterotrophs) and a spike in ecosystem respiration. Commensurate with this increase is a decrease in photosynthesis and net primary productivity until regenerating vegetation recovers over time.*

## Box 12.3 **Dendrochronology and fire history**

Frederick Clements' published work on lodgepole pine regeneration strategies following fire in 1910 brought the importance of fire in forested ecosystems to western science. Over the past 100+ years, fire ecology has grown as a subdiscipline of forest ecology and brought forth an understanding of the crucial role disturbance plays in terrestrial ecosystem development.

Dendrochronology and fire scar analysis (Figure 12.15) have been the most dominant scientific method for quantifying temporal and spatial characteristics of historical fire regimes (paleoecology offers a longer but coarser picture of disturbance history). Dendrochronology takes advantage of fire damage to the lower tree boles that routinely experience fire, such as ponderosa pine trees. As future annual growth occurs, the tree begins to heal the injured area, which retains a fire scar under the new growth. The mean fire-return interval is determined as the average number of years between fires across the recorded fires.

Dendrochronology uses trends in tree ring widths to accurately date fire years. This technique is possible since trees respond to environmental conditions (i.e., moisture regimes) in similar ways, allowing for patterns to develop across years. A master chronology is developed for a site from tree cores or partial cross-sections. Inspection of tree rings at the fire scar can also indicate the season during which the fire burned.

Temporal fire regime characteristics can be coupled with spatially explicit age structure and tree composition to quantify mortality patch size and regeneration response. When conducted across landscapes, one can reconstruct the spatial extent of historical fires and within-fire spatial complexity. Together, the long-term legacy effects of fires can be expressed as fire regimes to inform management.

Figure 12.15 *Dendrochronology and fire scar analysis have been the most dominant scientific method for quantifying temporal and spatial characteristics of historical fire regimes.*

the development of these forests, we can use this information to inform us of how ecosystems respond to long-term disturbance processes, which will aid in restoring resilient forests for an uncertain future.

To this point we have focused exclusively on frequency and severity, but other characteristics are necessary to fully describe a fire regime. Not surprising, one important characteristic is mortality patch size, with patch size decreasing with increasing fire frequency (Figure 12.16). Other important characteristics that further define fire's ecological function and provide a framework for developing management regimes that emulate fire's historical role are provided in Table 12.3.

Forests with *low-severity fire regimes* burned at high frequencies (<20-year mean fire-return intervals) during dry periods when fine fuels have dried and annual grasses have completed their growth cycles. These fires could burn across broad areas because of relatively contiguous dry fuel conditions, although many would be impeded by recent fires that consumed fuels. The spatial complexity, or distribution, size,

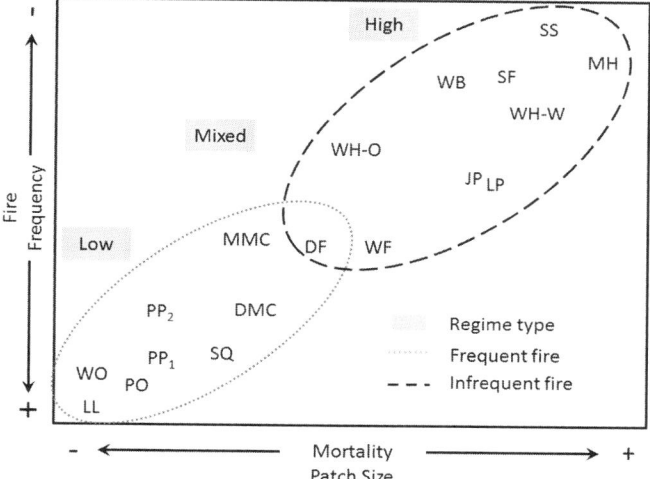

Figure 12.16 *Dominant mortality patch size is another way of thinking about fire regimes in addition to the dimensions of frequency and severity. For example, longleaf pine (LL) forests of southern Georgia experience very frequent fires, but mortality is typically limited to single or small groups of trees. In contrast, jack pine forests in Michigan have much larger patches of high mortality indicative of their high-severity fire regime. The gray boxes represent typical fire regime severity nomenclature (i.e., low = low severity, etc.) and the dashed circles provide a grouping of forest types into either frequent-fire or infrequent-fire regimes. LL (longleaf pine), WO (Oregon white oak), PO (Ozarks pine-oak), PP1 (ponderosa pine), PP2 (pitch pine), SQ (giant sequoia), DMC (dry-mixed conifer), MMC (moist-mixed conifer), DF (Douglas-fir), WF (white fir), WH-O (western hemlock-Oregon), WH-W (western hemlock-Washington) JP (jack pine), LP (lodgepole pine), SF (subalpine fir), WB (whitebark pine), SS (Sitka spruce), MH (mountain hemlock). (Source: Adapted from Perry et al., 2011)*

and severity of mortality patch sizes, was driven by individual or small-group mortality (Figure 12.17). This resulted in relatively low recruitment of single or small groups of overstory trees across time, creating forests with high spatial complexity at small scales. Most frequent-fire forests across the North American landscape, such as ponderosa pine forests of the western USA, historically had a low-severity fire regime. Longleaf pine forests of the southeastern USA had the highest frequency, low-severity fire regime in the United States and typically burned at intervals <3 years.

*Mixed-severity fire regimes* are the most variable and least understood of all fire regime types. Forests with a mixed-severity fire regime burn at highly variable intervals that average as low as 30 years to more than 150 years depending on the forest system. At millennial time scales even more variability can be observed in association with climatic fluctuations that increase or decrease fire occurrence. Fire extent also ranges significantly in forests with a mixed-severity fire regimes and includes relatively small (<100 acres) to very large (>100,000 acres) fires depending on the timing of ignition and interval between fires. Spatial complexity will typically be higher than that found in forests with other fire regimes; often >70% of a fire extent burns at low or moderate severity creating highly variable conditions at multiple scales (Figure 12.18). High spatial complexity increases landscape-scale structural and compositional diversity and is a prominent characteristic of forests with this type of fire regime. Both chronic- and episodic-disturbance responses likely occur, although our scientific understanding of these responses remains limited. The coming decades will bring new knowledge and understanding as mixed-severity fires burn across much of the American West allowing researchers and managers to observe short- and long-term responses. Forests historically having a mixed-severity fire regime include mixed evergreen–conifer forests of the Klamath Mountains of southwestern Oregon, mixed conifer forests of the northern Rockies and the Sierra Nevada, and some of the Douglas-fir forests of southwestern Oregon (Figure 12.18).

Forests with a *high-severity fire regime* had mean fire-return intervals ranging from 100 to >300 years. Fires can be very large in forests with this fire regime, often exceeding 100,000 acres when ignited during extreme fire weather conditions (e.g., 2006 Tripod Fire, 1988 Yellowstone Fires). The longer fire-return intervals result in greater fire severity, and less spatial complexity, because a larger proportion of the fire burns at high severity (Figure 12.19). Mortality patch sizes are relatively large and develop with relatively homogenous structural conditions as forest succession is reinitiated. Forest structure diversifies over time as succession proceeds toward old-growth conditions and individual or small-group mortality occurs from other disturbance agents, especially in productive forests like the Pacific silver fir or Douglas-fir–western hemlock forests of Washington's western Cascades (See Chapter 3). It is important to recognize that these fires do include other severity types and therefore the high-severity patches are embedded within a larger complex of fire severities and unburned forests. Lodgepole pine forests of the greater Rocky Mountain Region historically had a high-severity fire regime and, over time, have developed regeneration strategies (fire-mediated serotiny) to cope with this

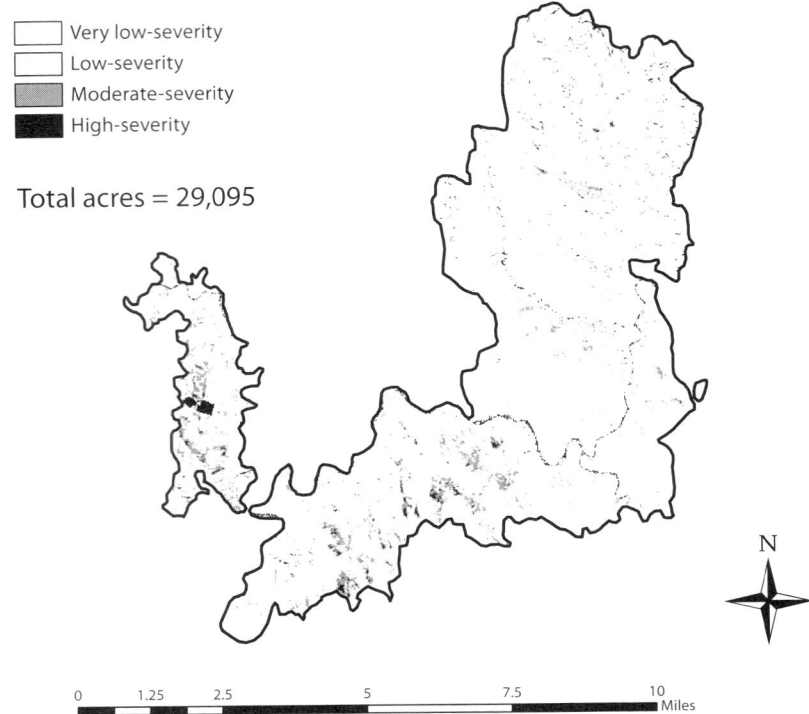

☐ Very low-severity
☐ Low-severity
▨ Moderate-severity
■ High-severity

Total acres = 29,095

0   1.25   2.5   5   7.5   10 Miles

N

Figure 12.17 *Low-severity fires are dominated by surface fire with occasional single or small groups of overstory tree mortality. Concurrently, frequent surface fires typical of low-severity fire regimes result in significant mortality of small-diameter trees, maintaining low-density forests dominated by species adapted to these processes and conditions. The Mallory Fire (2001) burned through a pine-grass system in northeastern Oregon and provides an example of what the mortality patch-size distribution would be in low-severity fire regimes.*
*Very low = 22,560 acres (ac) (79%), low = 5,094 ac (18%), moderate = 889 ac (3%), and high = 99 ac (<1%).*

Table 12.3 *Fire regime characteristics describing fire's functional role as an ecosystem process*

| Fire Regime Characteristics | | |
|---|---|---|
| *Magnitude* | Intensity | A measure of the amount of heat released from combustion of wildland fuels. Typically this is quantified as fireline intensity, heat-per-unit-area, or flame length. |
| | Severity | The impact fire has on a resource of interest which may include tree mortality, soil heating, habitat loss, etc. Often fire has both positive and negative consequences depending on the resource of concern. |
| | Fire Type | Categorized as ground, surface, or crown fire depending on the fuel layer facilitating fire spread. |
| *Temporal* | Return Interval | The average interval between fires within a particular geographic area. Estimates are determined by collecting and cross-dating fire scars from live and dead trees, augmented by age structure of trees. |
| | Seasonality | The season in which fires typically occur. Seasonality is important because of phenological responses of vegetation to seasonal cycles, and the reproductive strategies of flora and fauna. |
| *Spatial* | Extent | Contemporary fire extents (i.e., fire sizes and annual area burned) are often the only characteristic discussed, but distributions of fire-size frequencies may be more important when characterizing fire regimes. Historically, frequent-fire forests tended to exhibit a high abundance of moderate-sized fires with few stochastic, large-fire events. |
| | Complexity | Fire complexity is a measure of the abundance, size, and distribution of mortality patches within a fire boundary. These include unburned, low-severity, mixed-severity and high-severity patches. Most forests experience mixed-severity fire at some spatial scale, but the size and proportion of mortality patches may be dominated by one severity class depending on regime type. Their distribution and spatial relation to each other can vary significantly, influencing available resources for different wildlife species. |

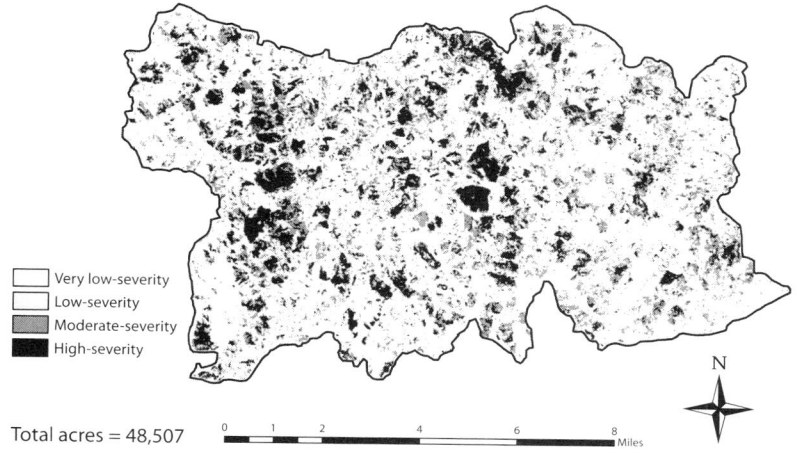

Total acres = 48,507

Figure 12.18  *Mixed-severity fires result in patches of mortality extending from individual tree to broader patches of high-severity fire, usually of moderate size and distributed across a fire boundary. These fire regimes created highly diverse structural conditions across multiple scales, which often resulted in high floral and faunal diversity. Boulder Fire (2002) burned in Douglas-fir dominated forests of the south-central Cascades of western Oregon with mixed severity, exhibiting relatively high spatial complexity. Very low = 17,140 ac (35%), low = 16,289 ac (34%), moderate = 9,036 ac (19%), and high = 6,039 ac (12%).*

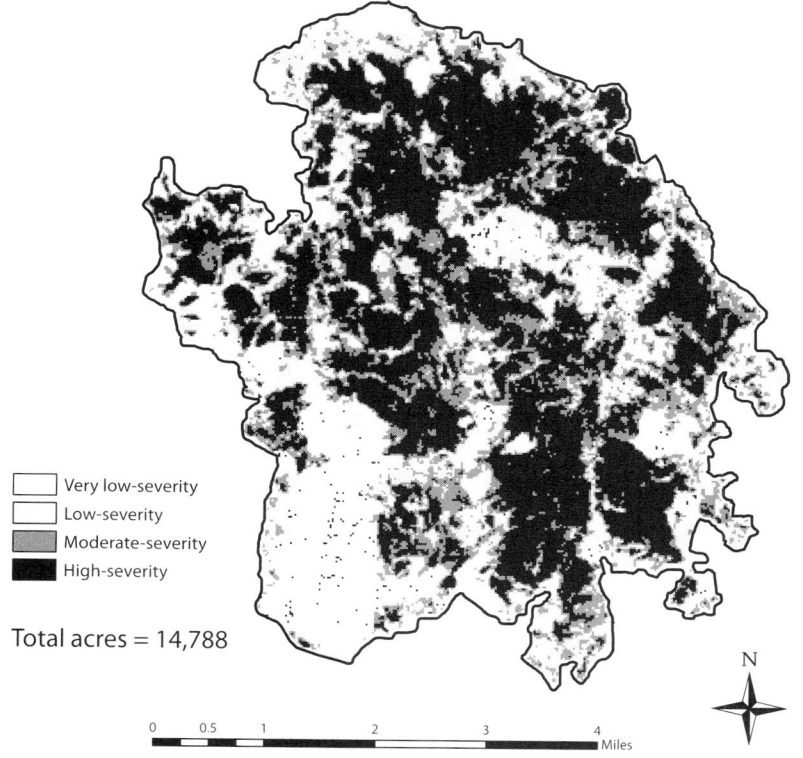

Total acres = 14,788

Figure 12.19  *High-severity fires have large patches of high mortality, but also generally have patches of moderate and low severity scattered across the landscape. Although significant change is evident following these fires, species have adapted to these natural conditions and benefit from these disturbances. This is particularly evident in the creation of early seral habitat that result from fires like the Tumblebug Fire (2009) in Douglas-fir and true fir forests (large patches of mortality are dominated by true fir) of the central Cascade Range in Oregon. Very low = 2,731 ac (18%), low = 3,153 ac (21%), moderate = 3,038 ac (21%), and high = 5,866 ac (40%).*

type of disturbance. Most of these forests have not missed a *fire cycle* and therefore often burn with similar characteristics as historical fires (Steel, Safford, & Viers, 2015).

Increasingly, managers evaluate whether a stand or forest has missed one or more fire cycles in setting priorities for fuel treatments or restoration actions. However, focusing exclusively on missed fire cycles can be counter-productive (Box 12.4).

## Forest Types and Fire Regimes in a Landscape Context

Forest types (e.g., ponderosa pine, lodgepole pine, pine-oak forests of the Ozarks) are generally classified based on their potential vegetation type. Potential vegetation types are the dominant overstory species that would arise in the absence of disturbance. These forest types are often attributed to a particular fire regime as we implied in Figure 12.16. In some cases, a forest type may exhibit an unexpected fire regime because of its location within a broader landscape. For example, in areas with steep topographic relief, forest types can change within a relatively short spatial distance in response to changes in elevation or aspect. Different forest types remain spatially connected at relatively short distances and therefore can have similar fire regimes, especially in landscapes experiencing frequent fire.

When planning a landscape-scale ecological forestry program one could consider the landscape as a series of *firesheds*, or spatially contiguous landforms with similar ignition probabilities and potential to support continuous fire spread. Within a fireshed, fire-return intervals are likely similar across several spatially intermixed forest types. Fire interacts with productivity to develop diverse forest types and structural conditions by mediating densities and composition. For example, in the Siskiyou Mountains of southwestern Oregon, topographic gradients transition across short distances and fire ignitions are common. Historically, fire-return intervals were less than 20 years from valley bottoms to ridgetops, yet historical forest types transitioned from Oregon white oak savanna and woodlands at low elevations to low-density forests dominated by larger, fire-tolerant Douglas-fir. That is, fire mediated the composition of these forests despite potential natural vegetation transitioning from Douglas-fir to white fir along the elevation gradient from valley bottoms to ridgetops. Managers should understand local fire regimes when designing an ecologically focused forest management plan.

## Part 4: A Wildfire Policy Based on Suppression: Origins and Effects

### The 10A.M. Policy

Forest fire policies in North America have changed significantly as a result of Euro-American colonization. Profound consequences resulted from these changes, many of which are linked directly to human–fire interactions. Prior to Euro-American colonization, fire was common across much of the North American landscape and was partially driven by Native American and First Nation communities using fire to modify the landscape for their benefit (Boyd, 1999) (Figure 12.2a). These indigenous communities have been present across North America for more than 14,000 years, during which wildland fires were common and often part of indigenous peoples' cultural identity. Indigenous fire management practices persisted in wildlands through the mid-1800s in the American West.

Settlers routinely encountered burned landscapes across broad regions and often attributed these fires to indigenous people. Many settlers adopted the practice of light burning to maintain grazing and farming opportunities by perpetuating the landscape conditions they encountered. Fire was also used by Euro-American settlers to clear land of logging debris and trees to expand pasture or farmlands to support domesticated plants and animals. Light burning and large natural or human-caused fires occurred late

---

### Box 12.4 Missing the mark: Missed fire cycles are an unsure guide to prioritizing fuel treatments

"Missed fire cycles" quantify the number of fires missed based on a site's natural fire frequency and the time since the last wildfire. It is one attribute used to set fuel treatment priorities in many forests, but isn't the only metric that should be considered (Haugo et al., 2015). For example, suppose we map forest types and fire regimes across a landscape and find three dominant forest conditions with the following mean fire-return intervals (MFRI): (1) 10–25 years, (2) 35–100 years, and (3) greater than 100 years.

Let's assume the entire landscape burned in the Great Fires of 1910. Based on how long it has been since these forest types have experienced fire, one would assume the first fire regime (10–25 MFRI) has missed 4–10 cycles, the 35–100 years missed up to 2 cycles, and the last one hasn't missed any cycles. To describe the current conditions, we often attribute these forests to a fire regime condition class (FRCC), which is a classification of the amount of departure from the natural regime (Hann & Bunnell, 2001). These generally include:

- Condition Class 1: Within the natural range of variability of (1) vegetation characteristics, (2) fuel composition, (3) fire frequency, severity, and pattern, and (4) other disturbances
- Condition Class 2: Moderately departed from the natural range of variability of (1) vegetation characteristics, (2) fuel composition, (3) fire frequency, severity, and pattern, and (4) other disturbances
- Condition Class 3: Highly departed from the natural range of variability of (1) vegetation characteristics, (2) fuel composition, (3) fire frequency, severity, and pattern, and (4) other disturbances

This classification system is used to identify forests or stands that are at most peril from an *uncharacteristic fire*.

Thus the forest type with the lowest MFRI rises to the top of the treatment priority list using missed fire cycles only. However, site productivity is also an important variable in determining both the priority for restoration in frequent-fire forests and the return interval for subsequent treatments. In historical landscapes, fire often occurred frequently enough that it generated forests with comparable structures across gradients of moisture, which were also gradients of potential productivity (see, e.g., Hagmann, Franklin, & Johnson, 2013, 2014; Merschel, Spies, & Heyerdahl, 2014). Once frequent fires were removed, forests on the moister and more productive sites grew much more rapidly than forests on lower-productivity sites. In addition, shade-tolerant species (e.g., white or grand fir), which occurred on these sites but had previously been held in check by fire, grew rapidly to create superb fuel ladders. Consequently, the fire-suppressed, mixed-conifer forests that developed are where forest values, including remnant old trees, are most at risk. Although forests on low-productivity sites may have missed more natural fire cycles than those on high-productivity sites, both fuel loads and structures may be at much lower and less critical levels.

Another important aspect to consider is other disturbances (e.g., budworm, mountain pine beetle) that altered the structure and composition of these forests. Higher-productivity sites often have longer MFRIs and are the target of timber harvesting activities. If these productive sites were harvested from 1970 to 1990, much of this forest would be less than 40 years old. These broad conditions could be considered highly departed from natural conditions and vegetation characteristics, potentially characterized as Condition Class 3.

into the 1800s in the midwestern and western USA, without garnering significant political support for policy change. The 1871 Peshtigo Fire in Wisconsin, caused by several slash fires escaping because of unexpected high winds, burned approximately 1.5 million acres and cost the lives of 1,500 or more people. Further west, large fires burned into the early 1900s, including the Yacolt Burn (1902) and associated homesteading fires of western Washington and Oregon that burned well over 500,000 acres. Many of these fires were the result of careless human activity or burning for railroad, logging, or agricultural purposes, but still failed to generate political support for change.

Forest conservation became a social-political issue in the late 1800s in the United States, leading to the creation of Forest Reserves by presidential proclamation (later becoming the National Forests) as early as 1894. In 1905, the newly formed Forest Service was given responsibility for managing the Forest Reserves, but neither the reserves nor the Forest Service were popular across all political parties at that time. This changed following the 1910 Great Fire complex of Idaho and Montana that burned approximately three million acres, fundamentally altering the social-political landscape regarding wildfires and legitimizing the Forest Service's utility (Egan, 2009). The trauma of the "Big Blowup" led the Forest Service to adopt a "zero tolerance" policy for wildland fire and the goal of complete suppression, which had broad public support except in the southern states (Pyne, 2010). This goal eventually became known as the "10A.M. policy" because all fires were intended to be suppressed prior to 10A.M. the day following discovery.

Fire suppression significantly reduced fire extent across much of the western USA for several decades during the 20th century, creating a "fire deficit" compared to historical fire frequency and extent (Figure 12.2a and 12.2b). Two dominant factors contributed to successful fire suppression. First, relatively cool and moist climatic conditions were observed from the late 1940s through the mid-1980s. Second, fire suppression effectiveness increased as surplus military equipment was conscripted into suppression operations in the 1940s and 1950s following World War II and the Korean War (Figure 12.20). This highly mechanized suppression force leveraged the expanded network of roads, communication systems, lookout towers, and ranger stations developed during this period. Which of these dominant factors had the greatest influence on fire suppression is difficult to discern and that effect was likely the result of interactions among multiple factors.

Not all land managers supported the Forest Service's fire management policy, and many argued for continued light burning into the 1920s. Foresters in the southeastern USA resisted the suppression policy because of the need for frequent fire in longleaf pine forests to maintain their composition and structure. They also recognized fire's role in creating and maintaining bobwhite quail habitat, which was a popular game species in the South. By the middle of the 20th century, foresters in the West began to raise concerns about the consequences of suppression and benefits of prescribed burning (e.g., Biswell, 1958; Weaver, 1943). During the 1960s and 1970s research increasingly demonstrated the positive benefits of fire in ecosystems, but suppression still remains the dominant fire management policy today.

Attitudes about wildland fires continue to evolve, but in general there is a greater recognition of the essential role fire has played in forest development, especially in frequent-fire forests. Use of prescribed fire and acceptance of wildfires in many remote wilderness areas and national parks continue to expand. The National Park Service was an early adopter of modified fire policies and expanded prescribed fire and wildland fire use on a significant scale around 1968 with the intention to restore this important ecosystem process. This wildland fire use program has been a positive step forward, although the 1988 Yellowstone Fires did set this concept back; these fires (called prescribed natural fires at the time) burned 793,880 acres within the park boundary at greater intensities than expected because of high winds and drought conditions. These fires continue to influence fire management policies today, although public perception of the Yellowstone Fires has gradually become more positive (Romme et al., 2011). Today, there are regionally distinct fire cultures influencing national-scale fire management in the USA that include: (1) the wildland–urban interface in California, (2) the extensive prescribed fire programs of the southeastern USA, and (3) large wilderness fires of Idaho and Montana (Pyne, 2015). Nationally, these challenges create a complex and regionally diverse set of human-fire interactions in North America that influence current and future policies.

Despite changing attitudes and the extensive use of prescribed burning in parts of North America, fire suppression remains the dominant fire management strategy today. Agencies remain successful at suppressing approximately 98% of fire ignitions, leaving 2–3% of fires to account for 95% of fire effects (Calkin et al., 2005). Unfortunately, the fires typically escaping initial attack do so under weather and fuel conditions conducive to increased fire intensity. These fires tend to impact ecosystems to a greater extent than would occur under more benign fire weather conditions. Changing our fire management decisions and policies might be our greatest opportunity to catalyze positive change across broad landscapes that improve and maintain forest resilience (North et al., 2012; North et al., 2015a).

## Unexpected Consequences

Gifford Pinchot, the first chief of the US Forest Service, wrote in 1905, "Where conflicting interests must be reconciled, the question shall always be answered from the

Figure 12.20  *A photo was taken in 1955 to generate support for waging war against fire. Not only does it represent the significance of the propaganda supporting fire suppression during that period, but it also provides a depiction of the transition to mechanized suppression resources following World War II and the Korean War. (Photo courtesy of the Forest History Society, Durham, NC)*

standpoint of the greatest good of the greatest number in the long run." This statement is certainly idealistic and founded in utilitarian principles, both of which describe the sentiments of the era when forestlands were first being acquired and managed as a public asset. Today we can look back with a critical eye and see the limitations of this statement and subsequent actions, but arguably the fire suppression and forest management policies of the 20th century attempted to meet this idealistic and utilitarian approach to forest conservation. Unfortunately, forest structure has been altered significantly by management and fire suppression such that many forests are not resilient in the face of wildfire. Scientists and managers have observed a shift in species composition toward dominance by shade-tolerant species, altered forest structure, and increased hazardous fuels in these types of forests (Agee & Skinner, 2005). In turn, they are therefore more susceptible to higher levels of mortality (Hessburg, Salter, & James, 2007). These changes have been most profound in frequent-fire forests. Today's

managers must reconcile the legacy of historical policies and subsequent management actions with the needs of "the greatest number in the long run," which now encompass a broad array of ecosystem services.

The proportion of fires burning with high severity has increased over the past several decades (Miller, Safford, Crimmins, & Thode, 2009), although this effect varies by forest type. The mortality patch size, spatial configuration, and overall complexity of wildfires have changed as a result of fire exclusion in forests with historically low- and mixed-severity fire regimes (Steel et al., 2015). This effect reduces the amount of single or small-group mortality and increases the abundance of large patches of mortality, fundamentally reshaping the spatial and temporal dynamics of these forests (Figure 12.21). Changing mortality patch-size distributions alter the abundance of various biological legacies, habitat availability and connectivity, and the trajectory of forest succession. This effect has been observed in California (e.g., Miller et al., 2009; Steel et al., 2015) and in

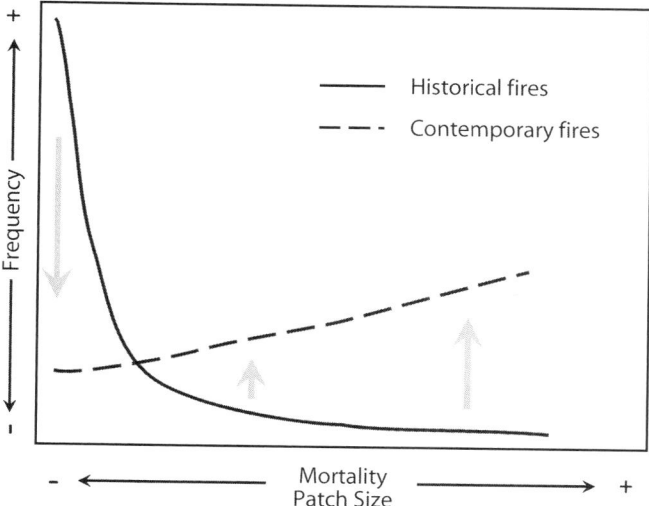

Figure 12.21 *A theoretical depiction of fire exclusion effects on mortality patch size for a frequent-fire forest. Fire exclusion and land-use changes have altered the mortality patch-size distribution such that fires exhibit less single or group-mortality patches and an increased abundance of larger morality patches (Hessburg et al., 2007). This change can have profound effects on landscape structure, forest regeneration, wildlife habitat, and long-term forest resilience.*

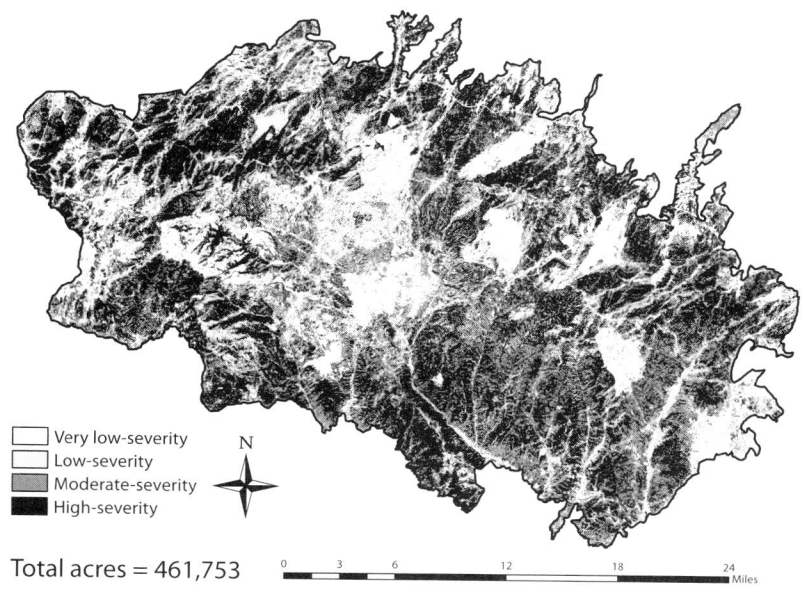

Total acres = 461,753

Figure 12.22 *Mortality patch sizes in contemporary fires have increased significantly across many frequent-fire forests, such as ponderosa pine forests in Arizona (Schoennagel, Veblen, & Romme, 2004). The Rodeo-Chedeski Fire (2002) burned 500,000 acres in east-central Arizona and included several large contiguous high-mortality patches exceeding 3,000 acres. The largest patch size was 18,649 acres. Forest recovery, especially in an age of climate change, may be inhibited for several decades or not occur at all as the fire regime shifts from low to high severity. Compare to Figure 12.17 for a visual image of how fire effects have changed. Very low = 69,660 ac (15%), low = 76,754 ac (17%), moderate = 146,296 ac (32%), and high = 169,043 ac (37%).*

recent large fires of the American Southwest, such as the 2002 Rodeo/Chedeski Fire (Figure 12.22) and 2012 Wallow Fire in Arizona, USA.

The legacy of historical management and fire suppression may result in an ecosystem state change, which is a transition to a self-perpetuating system significantly different than historically observed at a given site. For example, fire exclusion facilitated and perpetuated the expansions of juniper throughout the Great Basin and oaks in grasslands of the Great Plains. In many frequent-fire forests, the potential for this transition to occur began with fire exclusion and an increase in forest density, especially of species with varying adaptations to fire (Figure 12.23). Because of the shift in the abundance of seed source by species, a high-severity fire might facilitate the dominance of the encroached species, especially if fire exclusion persists. A state change may also occur with increasing fire occurrence as individual species' life-history strategies interact to deal with frequent fire (Enright et al., 2015). Anticipating undesired fire effects remains a challenge today, especially since the compounding effects of climate change are likely to develop novel forest conditions in the future.

Fire management policies in much of western North America remain inconsistent with creating and maintaining resilient forest conditions. If the suppression paradigm continues to perpetuate the existing fire deficit, there could be a regime shift whereby larger patch-size distributions become self-reinforced and repeat through time (Turner, 2010). This effectively transitions fire from being a chronic-disturbance that mediates forest density and composition to an episodic-disturbance that promotes a different forest structure or cover type than historically occurred in these landscapes. Reversing this trend requires restoring resilient forest structures on a landscape-scale followed by reintroduction of fire or mechanical treatments at intervals that will maintain resilient forests under future climate and land use regimes. To minimize the potential for unexpected consequences in the future, managers should utilize ecological principles and projections of future climate to develop plans that will remain effective several generations into the future. We will discuss opportunities to meet these challenges in Chapter 13.

It should be added, though, that a policy of fire suppression may be an appropriate strategy in managing forests subject to an infrequent, high-severity wildfire regime, like the forests described as the first archetype in Chapter 3. For example, we may not want large stand-replacement events in the remaining mature and old-growth forest in this archetype because we want to maintain as much of it for as long as we can for a variety of reasons, including critical wildlife habitat. Given the ecological and wildlife goals for these forests, wildfire suppression remains an important strategy for sustaining them. Particularly as the climate changes, and with it the potential for fires, aggressive detection and suppression in these forests may be a very important response, especially given that it is not credible ecologically to significantly alter the fuel loadings in these forests to make them less vulnerable to high-severity fires.

## Part 5: Fire History as a Guide to Ecological Forest Management

Fire history, organized into fire regimes, provides useful insights into fire's functional role in forest development over relatively long time periods, as we discussed in Part 3 above. Fire regimes also can help guide the development of an ecological forestry program with the goal of conserving and restoring resilient forests. They provide especially important information where wildfire has been a dominant disturbance process in shaping forests, as it is for two of the archetypes highlighted earlier in this book (conifer-dominated forests initiated by infrequent, high-severity

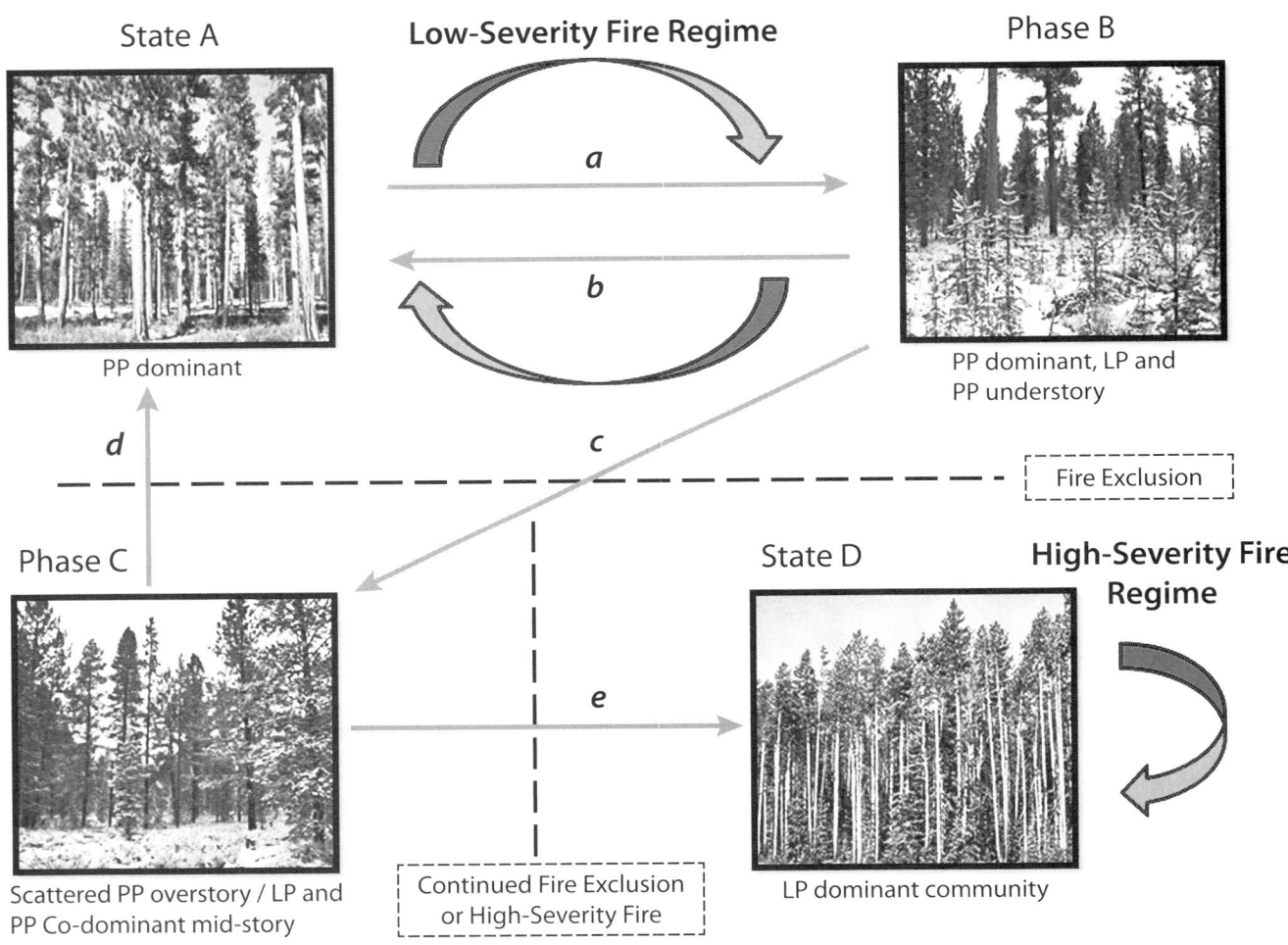

Figure 12.23 *State-and-transition models are useful ways to depict ecological change and consequences of exceeding ecological thresholds. This example represents regime change within central Oregon's pumice zone where forests predominantly of ponderosa pine but with associated lodgepole pine historically occurred. These forests (State A) were maintained by frequent fires that killed the lodgepole pine and its abundant regeneration (Phase B) while leaving the thick-barked ponderosa pine (pathways a and b). Fire exclusion and forest management reduced recruitment and maintenance of large ponderosa pines and increased the abundance of lodgepole pines (Phase C). At this point the system has exceeded an ecological threshold where the forest will not return to ponderosa pine dominance without management intervention (pathway d). Rather, it will become a lodgepole pine dominated forest (pathway e). High-severity fire is now likely to occur in this altered state. Subsequent regeneration following the fire will be dominated by lodgepole pine, and a new state (State D) will be maintained as a high-severity fire regime. (See Heyerdahl, Loehman, & Falk, 2014, for more details.)*

Table 12.4 *Characteristics of the historical fire regime of southwestern ponderosa pine*

| Fire Regime Characteristics | | |
|---|---|---|
| *Magnitude* | Intensity | Low (typically sparse grass and pine litter fuels) |
| | Severity | Low (mortality of overstory trees was low) |
| | Fire type | Mostly surface fires burning grass and pine litter, but individual passive crown fires could occur |
| *Temporal* | Return interval | Short (high-frequency) |
| | Seasonality | Spring and early summer, followed by a second season in late summer. Typically split by monsoon season. |
| *Spatial* | Extent | Generally small fires because of fuel limitations by other fires, although large fires occurred occasionally. |
| | Complexity | Low (individual or small group tree mortality) |

wildfire and conifer-dominated forests characterized by frequent, low-severity wildfire). In such situations, fire regimes can help in the design of silvicultural treatments to restore and maintain resilient forests by providing historical information on continuity in forest structure, function, and biota between pre- and post-disturbance conditions; structural complexity and biological richness; spatial heterogeneity at multiple spatial scales; and the time interval between disturbances. This historical information can be especially valuable in describing forests that have proven resilient in the past, but where fire suppression and management (as discussed in Part 4) has fundamentally altered forest processes and structures.

For consideration in management, fire regimes, as we discussed in Part 3, are typically organized and described by their magnitude (intensity, severity, and fire type), as well as the temporal (return interval, seasonality) and spatial (extent, complexity) characteristics (Table 12.3). These characteristics help frame a "reference condition" for comparison to current conditions, which can help determine the need and type of management action necessary to improve forest resilience. As an example, we have described the fire regime of ponderosa pine forests in the American Southwest on relatively gentle slopes in Table 12.4. Fire exclusion policies and historical forest practices, as described in Part 4 of this chapter, have fundamentally changed the disturbance regime in these frequent-fire forests. Fire effects have increased from low severity (Figure 12.17) to high severity (Figure 12.22) in many instances and can no longer be considered resilient to current or future disturbances. Most likely, this effect will be exacerbated by climate change.

In such situations, ecological forest management can be implemented to increase forest resilience by developing management guidelines to restore many of the effects and attributes of the reference conditions.

## Magnitude

The severity of a disturbance is often the most visible fire effect and an important control over the distribution of live and dead biological legacies. Thus, forests that have undergone regime shifts are often a high priority for ecological forest management:

- The buildup of understories and generation of ladder fuels in frequent-fire forests of state and federal lands, such as in the ponderosa pine forests of the southwest, have changed the fire regime in many places from one of low severity to one of mixed or high severity. In such cases, shifting the forest back toward the forest composition and structure associated with a low-severity regime is often a major focus of ecological forest management. Using a combination of thinning and prescribed fire, foresters will attempt to (Franklin et al., 2013):

  ○ Retain and release old trees by removing competing trees from around them This is particularly important where these highly valued ecological resources, which take a very long time to replace, are at increased risk of loss and therefore require more immediate attention than other sites. Over time an ecological forestry program can also recruit and retain more of these ecologically valuable structures.

  ○ Reduce stand density while increasing mean stand diameter. Greatly reducing the numbers of small trees, often of noncommercial sizes, offers one of the greatest challenges in this work.

  ○ Shift composition toward more fire- and drought-tolerant species, especially in mixed-conifer forests.

- By comparison, forests that historically had infrequent, high-severity wildfire regimes, like the forests described under the first archetype in Chapter 3, have generally seen much less regime shift. Mixed-severity regimes fall between these other two historical regimes in terms of regime shift and resulting concern.

## Temporal

The historical disturbance interval should be considered when determining how often treatments occur in ecological forest management. The mean interval is a valuable characteristic to target, but accounting for its variability could be equally important since longer fire-free periods may correlate with successful regeneration.

- Forests with frequent, low-severity regimes present some of the greatest challenges for matching silvicultural treatments with the historical disturbance intervals, since some of these forests have an average return interval of less than 10 (or even 5) years. Matching that temporal pattern may call for resources, such as funds for prescribed fire, that stretch agency budgets, resulting in somewhat longer intervals between treatments.

- On the other hand, the disturbance interval of infrequent, high-severity forests may be much longer than the landowner's desired return interval considering social and financial goals, resulting in somewhat shorter intervals. As discussed in the Chapters 3 and 4, biological legacy strategies can help moderate the interval between treatments.

- Mixed-severity fire regimes, as might be expected, often fall between these two regimes. Especially here, one might also consider return intervals of various fire severities, although these are often challenging to quantify.

## Spatial

Spatial extent and complexity are important regime characteristics to capture when building resilience into a forested landscape. Capturing spatial heterogeneity in fire severity patterns is important for maintaining habitat connectivity and resources that support a diverse array of faunal species. This spatial complexity ranges from the spatial distribution of individuals and groups of trees to the spatial distribution of fire-severity patterns across a landscape.

- In the case of low-severity fire regimes, like those of southwest ponderosa pine, restoring a fine-scale mosaic across the landscape, with individual trees, tree clumps, and gaps can provide that spatial heterogeneity as discussed in Chapters 3 and 4.

- When forests have a mixed- or high-severity fire regime, landscape-scale plans are necessary so that the cumulative magnitude of each stand-level treatment is considered in the larger landscape context. For example, Figure 12.18 depicts the distribution of severity patterns across a mixed-severity fire and Figure 12.19 illustrates the distribution across a high-severity fire. When matching management actions with these spatial patterns, the distance between treatment units of various severities must be carefully planned to prevent the creation of unduly uniform forest conditions across an area. Such an error could miss an important developmental stage, such as early seral vegetative conditions, or the distribution of biological legacies across landscapes.

Climate change influences both fire and forest dynamics, so history can help guide us, but it is not the complete story for achieving resilient forest objectives (Millar et al., 2007). Rather, we must combine what worked in the past with what is possible in the future. In some places, what we need to do is reinforced by expected climate change, such as the need to reduce stand densities in frequent-fire forests that are projected to have a hotter, drier climate. More generally, though, we need to keep asking how projected climate change will influence what we would otherwise do to increase resilience (maintain and restore ecosystem function) in forests and adapt our management strategies accordingly.

## Conclusions

This chapter covered several fundamental aspects of fire beginning with basic concepts of fire behavior and effects and then combining them into fire regimes. We concluded our discussion with ways to incorporate the characteristics of historical fire regimes into ecological forest management. Though often thought of in terms of damages and costs, wildfires play critical roles in forested ecosystems.

In fact, part of the reason wildfires are thought of in such destructive terms has been society's failure to recognize the benefits of wildfires. Subsequently, fire exclusion and forest management have resulted in excessive accumulation of hazardous fuels, alteration of forest structure, and the potential for undesirable fire effects, especially in historically frequent-fire forests. Improving forest resilience with ecologically focused forest and fire management practices, while minimizing undesirable losses associated with wildfire, is more important than ever. The principles described within this chapter can help guide an ecological forest management program to improve and maintain resilient forests in the face of an uncertain future.

## Appendix: Fuel Models

*Fire behavior models* incorporate variables from the fire combustion triangle and moderators from the fire behavior triangle. Analysts often begin with series of abstracted *fuel models* to summarize important fuel characteristics necessary to predict surface fire behavior (Table 12.5). For example, sufficient mixing of oxygen molecules with volatile gases is necessary to sustain combustion, but fuel particles must also be within close enough proximity for effective heat transfer. Therefore, fuel layer bulk density is an important characteristic derived from total fuel loading and fuel layer depth. This estimate is then contrasted with the bulk density that maximizes fire spread to estimate reaction intensity and the propagation of the flaming front. Fine woody fuels are often the focus of hazardous fuels reduction treatments because their relatively high surface-area-to-volume ratios result in more rapid heating to temperature of combustion than larger fuels. Wind and slope effects are added to these predictions, which can be modeled across landscapes to predict landscape fire spread (Figure 12.24).

Table 12.5 *General characteristics of fuel models used to predict fire behavior in the example fire behavior output provided below*[*]

| Fuel Model (Primary Fuel Carrier) | Description | 1-Hr Fuels (tons ac$^{-1}$) | 10-Hr Fuels (tons ac$^{-1}$) | 100-Hr Fuels (tons ac$^{-1}$) | Live Herb Fuels (tons ac$^{-1}$) | Live Woody Fuels (tons ac$^{-1}$) | Fuel Bed Depth (ft) |
|---|---|---|---|---|---|---|---|
| Grass (GR1) | Arid to semiarid climate. Grass is short, patchy, and possibly heavily grazed. | 0.10 | 0.00 | 0.00 | 0.30 | 0.00 | 0.40 |
| Grass (GR9) | Subhumid to humid climate. Very heavy, coarse, continuous grass 5 to 8 feet tall. | 1.00 | 1.00 | 0.00 | 9.00 | 0.00 | 5.00 |
| Shrub (SH1) | Arid to semiarid climate. Low shrub fuel load, fuelbed depth about 1 foot; some grass may be present. | 0.25 | 0.25 | 0.00 | 0.15 | 1.30 | 1.00 |
| Shrub (SH9) | Subhumid to humid climate. Dense, finely branched shrubs with significant fine dead fuel, about 4 to 6 feet tall; some herbaceous fuel may be present. | 4.50 | 2.45 | 0.00 | 1.55 | 7.00 | 4.40 |
| Timber litter (TL1) | Fuel bed is recently burned but able to carry wildland fire. Light to moderate load, fuels 1 to 2 inches deep. | 1.00 | 2.20 | 3.60 | 0.00 | 0.00 | 0.20 |
| Timber litter (TL9) | Very high load broadleaf litter; heavy needle-drape in otherwise sparse shrub layer. | 6.65 | 3.30 | 4.15 | 0.00 | 0.00 | 0.30 |
| Slash (S11) | Light logging slash | 1.50 | 4.51 | 5.51 | 0.00 | 0.00 | 1.00 |
| Slash (S13) | Heavy logging slash | 7.01 | 23.04 | 28.05 | 0.00 | 0.00 | 3.00 |

*Note: This table does not include all of the important fuel attributes incorporated into fuel models. For a more in-depth understanding of fuel models see Scott & Burgan (2005).

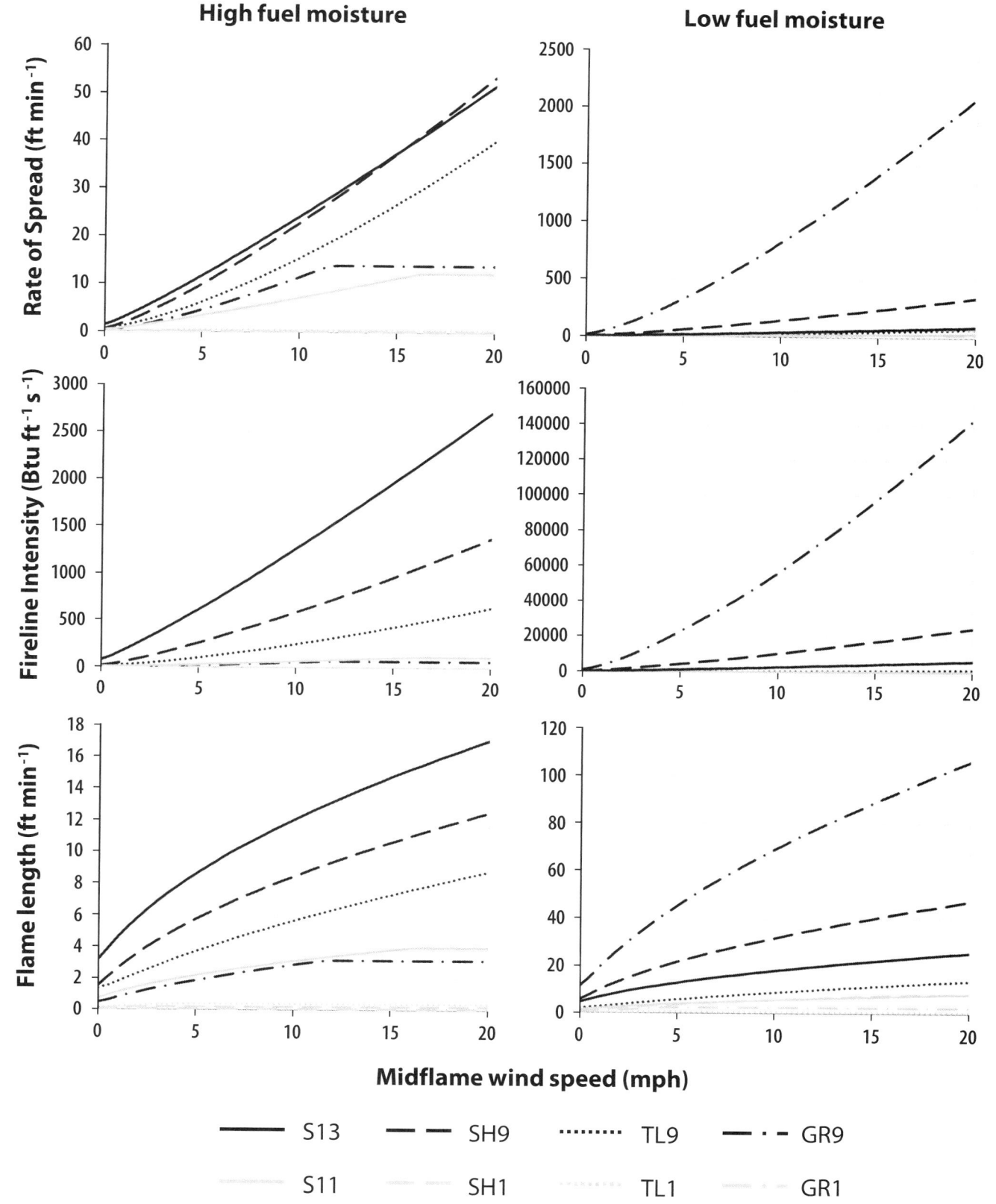

**Figure 12.24** *These graphs depict rate of spread, fireline intensity, and flame length for various fuel models across a distribution of midflame wind speeds. High fuel moisture conditions were 12%, 13%, and 14% for 1-hr, 10-hr, and 100-hr fuels and 120% and 150% for live herbaceous and woody fuels. Low fuel moisture conditions were 2%, 4%, and 5% for 1-hr, 10-hr, and 100-hr fuels and 30% and 60% for live herbaceous and woody fuels.*

*By suppressing fires in all the conditions we can, we're saving the landscape for the worst conditions. We won't say that's our policy, but by our actions, we are selecting for only the most extreme fires. We need to choose good fire over bad fire.* — MARK FINNEY

# The Fire Next Time:
# Strategies for Fire and Fuels Management

Christopher J. Dunn and Matthew P. Thompson

Wildfire is an important process in many terrestrial eco-systems where it influences their structure and function at all levels of biological organization. For example, fire influences nutrient cycling by combusting and mineralizing nutrients stored in dead vegetative material, while simultaneously creating a new pool of dead vegetative material that stores nutrients for future assimilation as the material decays. Fire also exerts significant influence over the horizontal and vertical distribution of forest vegetation (Pickett & White, 1985), often promoting the existence of one vegetation community at the expense of another. Of course wildfires are, by nature, landscape-scale events. The cumulative effects of individual tree- and/or stand-level mortality create landscape patterns that promote structural and compositional diversity at broad scales. Over long time periods, interactions among top-down climate and topography and bottom-up fuels controls result in fire regimes that flora and fauna adapt to across space and time (Agee, 1993; Bond & Keeley, 2005; Perry et al., 2011; Sugihara et al., 2006). More detailed discussions of fire as a disturbance agent and a process are provided in Chapters 3 and 12.

However, wildfires can harm wildlife habitat, watershed integrity, human life and property, and other highly valued resources. These negative impacts are especially evident where past actions, such as fire suppression and timber management, have homogenized forest conditions and led to a buildup in wildland fuels. These historical management practices tend to reduce the resiliency of these forests by making them more susceptible to uncharacteristic levels of mortality. In addition, climate change may intensify these risks in many ways, such as by increasing the frequency and magnitude of droughts or lengthening fire seasons by decreasing winter snow pack or increasing spring and fall temperatures (see Chapters 3 and 12).

Even where forests are currently in relatively resilient conditions, human developments (e.g., homes and infra-

*Aftermath of the Waldo Canyon Fire in Colorado, which burned into the Colorado Springs wildland–urban interface, destroying some homes while leaving others intact.*
*(Courtesy of Kari Greer/US Forest Service)*

structure related to telecommunication, energy, and water supply) elevate concerns over fire-related losses even though the fire would have little impact on the ecosystem itself. Landscapes with complex mosaics of forest and human infrastructure are commonly labeled as the *wildland-urban interface (WUI)* and require special attention. Fire and fuels management issues have become increasingly important in the WUI in recent years as residential development expands into fire-prone areas (Figure 13.1). Wildfire-related losses to homes and communities occur yearly, highlighting the need to mitigate the potential risks from future fires.

In addition to socioeconomic and ecological losses, expenditures for suppression of large wildfires place great financial strain on land management agencies responsible for responding to wildfires. This

Figure 13.1  *Wildfire burns near a home during the 2003 Wedge Canyon Fire, Montana. (Photo courtesy of Rick Trembath)*

is a particularly prominent issue for federal land management in the United States—our main focus here. Federal agencies, especially the US Forest Service, control much of the remaining wildland forest, have major ecological goals and responsibilities, and have a long history of fire suppression. This situation is well exemplified by the US Forest Service, which is responsible for the majority of federal wildfire management expenditures. Between 1995 and 2014 total costs of wildland fire management (including firefighting expenditures, hazardous fuels management, research, and assistance programs) ballooned from 17% to 51% of the US Forest Service budget (Figure 13.2). The escalating costs of managing wildfires have resulted in reduced budgets for other programs focused on vegetation and watersheds,

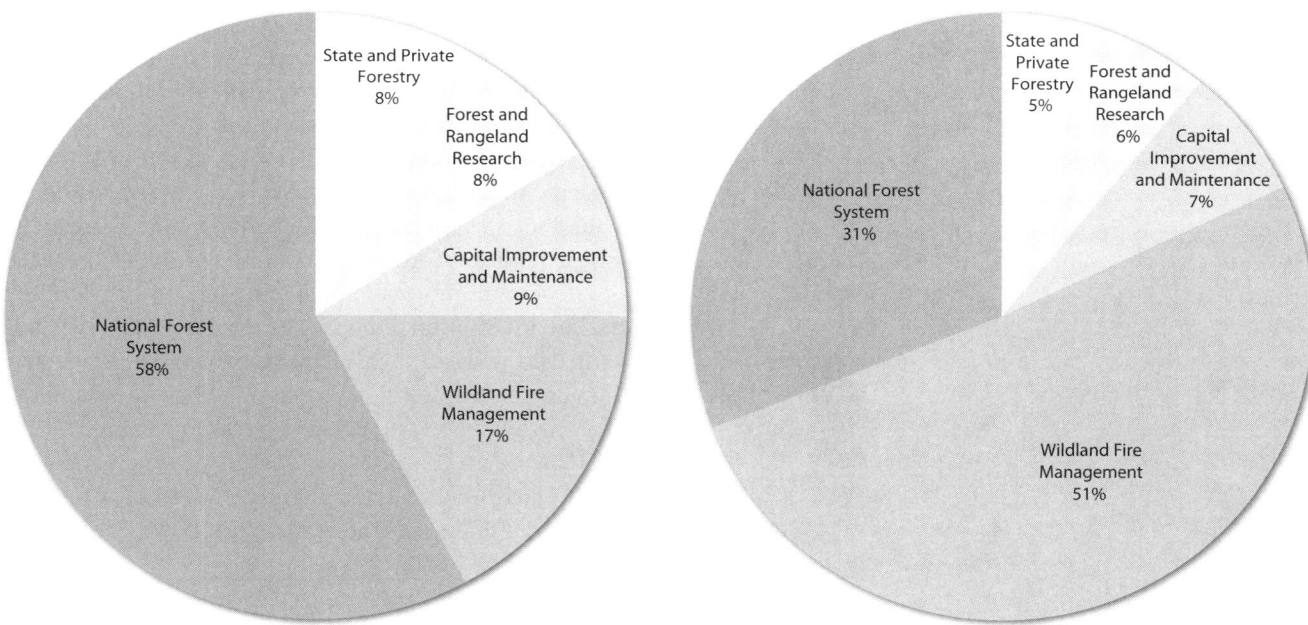

Figure 13.2  *The growing share of Forest Service appropriations devoted to wildland fire management from fiscal year (FY) 1995 to FY 2014. (Source: US Forest Service)*

facilities, road networks, trail systems, fisheries and wildlife habitat, planning, and research.

As we will see in this chapter, *reducing hazardous fuels is one prominent option for proactively managing wildfire risk.* Managing fuels can be particularly important in frequent-fire forests where suppression practices focused on fire exclusion have led to the accumulation of excessive fuels. Not surprising, federal agencies have focused much of their forest management energies on utilizing silviculture, especially mechanical treatment and prescribed fire, to reduce fuel loadings. While agencies have invested in hazardous fuels reduction programs, broadscale implementation has been constrained by access, limited budgets, and other resource objectives, such as protection of threatened wildlife that need dense forest (North, Collins, & Stephens, 2012). Combined with continued fire suppression, these difficulties have led to an ever-growing backlog of landscape treat-

ment needs. Although estimates vary depending on metrics used to identify sites in need of treatment, tens of millions of acres clearly need hazardous fuel and/or restoration treatments to reduce fuels and restore ecosystem resilience. For example, estimates for treatment backlogs on Forest Service land in California's Sierra Nevada alone are nearly three million acres (North et al., 2012). An additional important challenge is to design these treatments in ways so that other ecological values are sustained and even enhanced while dealing with fire-related goals (i.e., treatments are designed to restore ecosystems while reducing fuels).

To summarize, it is increasingly clear that a broader strategy for addressing fuel and fire issues is needed, which goes beyond a focus on wildfire suppression and fuel treatments. We attempt to address that broader strategy in this chapter, while still providing a framework and advice on the important role of silviculture in fuel treatments and forest restoration. We first give an overview of fire management options. Then we describe silvicultural approaches to fuel treatments in some detail, both at the stand and landscape level. Next, we address the potential role for managing wildfires as an alternative to immediately suppressing them; managed wildfire could be an important component of a fire and fuels strategy. While attempts to use wildfire to accomplish ecological and social goals have occurred in the past, we expect managed wildfire to receive renewed emphasis in the future; thus, we cover it here as part of a fire and fuels strategy. Finally, the important role of these fuel treatments in protecting lives and property in the WUI is considered as part of a coordinated strategy of homeowners, communities, and public agencies.

With all the recent interest in fire and fuels, especially in the western United States, has come extensive analysis and the development of a fire terminology. We will use many of these terms in this chapter (Box 13.1).

## Fire Management Options: An Overview

The conceptual model provided in Figure 13.3 illustrates fire management options and the environmental moderators influencing the success of those options. At the scale of a single wildfire incident, three factors jointly influence fire outcomes—a sustained ignition, fuel condition, and responses to the wildfire by fire managers (interior dark gray boxes in Figure 13.3). Incident management teams utilize strategies, tactics, and firefighting resources to manage the extent and intensity of the wildfire consistent with resource and fire management objectives; typically their objectives focus on reducing damages, but they can also include the enhancement of ecosystem values. However, environmental factors such as temperature, relative humidity, and wind moderate the degree of control that fire management efforts have on fire dynamics. In some cases, fire weather can be

---

### Box 13.1  Words on Fire

*Wildland fire vs. prescribed fire vs. wildfire.* Wildland fire is an umbrella term used to describe all fires, whether intentional or unplanned, that occur outside urban and suburban areas. Prescribed fires are intentionally ignited fires during predefined fire weather conditions, often used for resource benefit and/or to reduce hazardous fuel conditions. By contrast, wildfires are unplanned ignitions, which, depending upon context, may require aggressive suppression or may be allowed to burn under moderate conditions to achieve resource benefits and/or to reduce hazardous fuel conditions.

*Intensity vs. severity.* It is important to distinguish fire intensity from fire severity. Intensity refers to fire behavior itself, and can be quantified in a number of ways, including fireline intensity, flame length, and heat-per-unit-area. Severity refers to the effects of fire on a particular resource of interest, including fuel consumption, tree mortality, wildlife habitat, or impacts to soil. For more information, see Keeley (2009).

*Wildland fire use vs. let-burn vs. prescribed natural fire vs. ??* Fire scientists, ecologists, and managers have a knack for developing new words to describe the myriad of relationships fire has with the human and natural worlds. In some cases this may include new terminology to describe the same concept, such as has occurred for wildfires managed to meet resource objectives. Since the establishment of this management strategy in the late 1960s, managing fires has been variously described as prescribed natural fires, let-burn, wildland fire use, beneficial fire, or wildfires managed for resource benefit. While none are perfect, the terms are intended to describe intentionally managing fire as a natural process following natural ignition.

the dominant factor in fire outcomes, and suppression is only successful when extreme fire weather conditions abate (Finney, Grenfell, & McHugh, 2009).

Management goals of teams also may include the production of desired ecosystem effects in addition to or in place of suppression. For example, management response may be focused on suppressing the side of the fire near a community but letting the other flank burn through a more remote area if weather conditions are moderate enough to enable fuel consumption without continuous crown fire. Thus, the wildfire may accomplish, perhaps in a somewhat crude way, the goals of fuel reduction and increased resilience of that portion of the forest.

There are a number of treatment options that land and fire managers can implement before a fire event. Three primary prefire management options are illustrated at the far left of Figure 13.3 (left side, light gray boxes): prevention programs (e.g., education, campfire bans) can reduce the frequency of human-caused ignitions; fuel treatments can reduce hazardous fuel loads and moderate fire behavior; and investments in fire suppression and management capacity (e.g., training, additional firefighting resources like engines and aircraft) can lead to more effective and efficient responses to wildfire incidents. Ultimately these options are intended to change the likelihood, extent, and intensity of wildfires in a manner consistent with land and fire management objectives. However, there are other environmental factors outside of human control that can moderate the

effectiveness of any of these options (right side, light gray boxes): fire weather patterns lead to variability in lightning-caused ignitions and conditions sufficient to sustain fire growth after an ignition; ecosystem productivity/dynamics can influence the rate of fuel accumulation and type of fuels; and factors such as topography can limit firefighter accessibility, compromise firefighter safety, or increase fire intensity and spread.

## Understanding Fuel Treatments

Fuel treatments are one of the primary tools in wildfire management that can influence wildfires when implemented across broad landscapes. It is important to recognize that all types of vegetation manipulation, regardless of objective, alter fuels and fire behavior. Fuel treatments are simply a subset of vegetative treatments where the specific purpose is to alter fire behavior and/or effects. Fuel treatments can achieve a broad range of objectives, including facilitating suppression efforts (Figure 13.4), protecting fire-susceptible resources/assets (Figure 13.5), or directing a future fire toward areas where it can provide ecosystem benefits. While treatments can significantly change fire behavior, it should be emphasized that treatments rarely if ever stop fire, absent concurrent changes in fire weather and/or suppression efforts. That is, if and when fuel treatments experience wildfire, they will not prevent fire occurrence but rather change the type (e.g., from crown to surface fire)

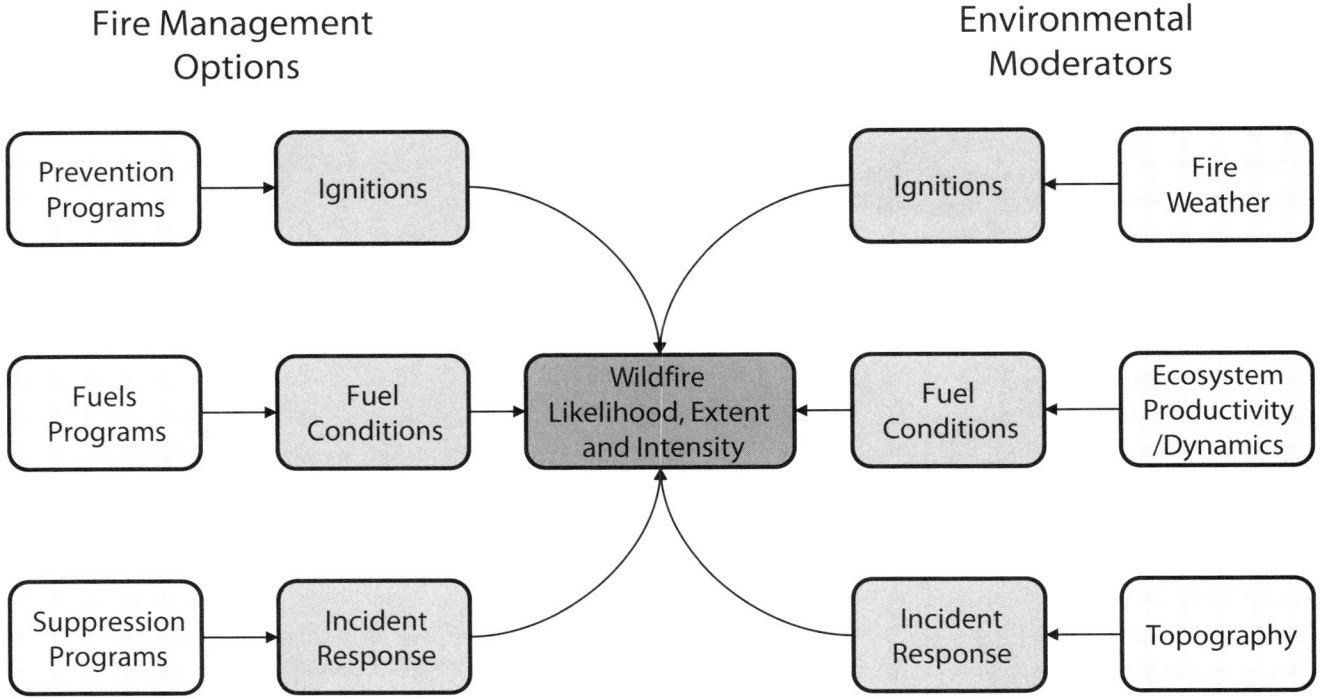

Figure 13.3 *Conceptual model of wildfire management options and environmental moderators influencing those options.*

Figure 13.4 *Stand that had been treated to reduce hazardous fuels, before (top) and immediately after (bottom) it was used as a control point on the 2013 Pole Creek Fire in Oregon. This forest was thinned to a set spacing and masticated (fuels were mechanically shredded) prior to the fire. In the future, we would expect these types of treatments to be integrated into restoration strategies, beyond the immediate fire control point, which retain old trees and emulate the clumpy structure of historical ponderosa pine forests (See Chapter 3 for more discussion). (Photo courtesy of Bill Aney)*

Figure 13.5 *Fuel treatments near homes (located in the area with green and scorched trees) facilitated burnout operations, provided safe firefighter access, and ultimately helped protect homes from the 2012 Fontenelle Fire in Wyoming. Treatments reflecting the principles of ecological forestry can prove effective near homes, as we discuss later in this chapter. (Photo courtesy of Jim Menakis)*

and potential consequences (e.g., reduced tree mortality) of the wildfire.

Fuel treatments can also achieve a host of other land and resource objectives, including reducing competitive stress and density-dependent mortality, improving wildlife habitat (ungulate forage), increasing resilience of retained trees to insects and disease, and protecting watershed integrity. In many instances, trade-offs in the attainment of different resource objectives will be needed. For instance, the desired stand density from a fuel hazard perspective may be much lower than desirable for northern spotted owl habitat. As another example, uniformly reducing fuels to achieve a desired residual stand density (Figure 13.4) and increase crown spacing poorly emulates the historical spatial architecture such as the signature "clumpy" nature of ponderosa pine forests (Larson & Churchill, 2012). Integrating fuel hazard reduction into the multiple objectives of landowners can be challenging, especially on federal forests!

However, with careful planning, it may be possible to create treatment strategies with a broad suite of benefits. For example, application of prescribed fire may reduce hazardous fuel loads while simultaneously increasing herbaceous diversity, lifting crown base heights to protect tree crowns from future wildfire, and preparing seed beds for the establishment of trees that may ultimately replace existing large structures.

Fundamentally, the design of fuel treatment strategies is based on fuel conditions and their relationship to wildfire in the context of landowner objectives. Modeling is often a useful tool to help consider the benefits of alternative treatment strategies (see the section below on Using Fire Models to Support Treatment Planning). In one example, Ager, Vaillant, and Finney (2010) used fire simulation modeling to illustrate how changing the scale and location of treatments could influence treatment performance in protecting areas within the WUI and preserving old forest structures. Treatments placed near residential structures reduced the likelihood and intensity of fire near structures but had little influence on expected loss of large trees. By contrast, treat-

ments placed in the wildlands (as far as 5–10 km from residential structures) reduced expected large tree mortality and the likelihood and intensity of fires in the WUI. These findings illustrate two important points, both of which we return to later:

1. The effects of landscape-scale treatment can include not only on-site (i.e., within-treatment) changes in fire behavior but also potentially off-site changes in fire likelihood and intensity as well, highlighting the importance of strategically locating treatments.

2. The results are unique to the spatial pattern of at-risk resources and assets as well as local landscape and fire weather conditions for the specific study area; fuel treatment strategies must be designed for the specific planning context.

Treatment objectives may vary within and across landscapes, owing to a number of factors such as land ownership, current forest condition relative to desired future condition, historical fire regime, potential wildfire occurrence and behavior, and the potential consequences of wildfire. Thus, place and management contexts are essential

---

Box 13.2  **Prescribed fire as an effective fuel treatment in the southern United States**

Some areas of the USA still have active prescribed fire programs, most notably in the Southeast (Figures 13.6 and 13.7). Fuel management in this region is largely characterized by frequent (typically 3–5 years) application of prescribed burning to maintain and/or restore fire regimes across ecosystems, in particular fire-dependent longleaf pine systems (see Chapters 3 and 12). Protection objectives also drive fuel management such as in areas with a history of larger fires or fires that threaten a WUI area. Fire and fuel issues in the Southeast can be quite different from the western USA, including

different patterns of land ownership, higher population densities, different topography, and a greater number of roads and other fire barriers to facilitate containment. Importantly, many communities in the Southeast are accustomed to smoke from a history of burning. Thus, while air quality regulations can still exert a major influence on the timing and extent of prescribed burning, land and fire managers are able to implement prescribed fire on a much broader scale to reduce risk and promote resiliency.

Figure 13.6  *Prescribed underburn in a longleaf pine forest of Florida.*

Figure 13.7  *Terra torches provide a safe and efficient means of ignition in longleaf pine stands, facilitating broad application of prescribed fire in the Southeast.*

variables to consider when evaluating potential objectives and how treatment objectives align with options for managing wildfire.

For example, in many areas such as private- and state-owned lands, existing management policies call for aggressive suppression tactics to keep all fires as small as possible. Treatments designed to promote more ecologically beneficial wildfire may have limited success in these areas, because as a matter of policy the fires are mandated to be aggressively suppressed without consideration of ecological concerns. Instead, periodic application of prescribed fire in such areas are likely to be more acceptable in achieving land and fire objectives, such as in restoration and management of longleaf pine in the southeastern USA (see Box 13.2 and discussion of longleaf pine in Chapters 3, 4, and 12). In areas with more flexibility for managing wildfire for resource benefits (e.g. wilderness areas, national parks, public lands desiring future resilient forests), fuel treatments based on the principles of ecological forestry can help restore resilient forest conditions and set the stage for allowing wildfire to work its beneficial effects with much lower risk.

Like any other natural resource decision process, it is critical to begin with a clear articulation of short- and long-term treatment objectives along with metrics to measure their success (Marcot et al., 2012; Thompson et al., 2013a). At the most basic level, treatment objectives relate to linkages between fuel conditions and fire hazard. Broadly speaking *fire hazard can be most effectively reduced by following these "fire-safe" principles: (1) treat surface fuels to reduce fire intensity, (2) treat ladder fuels to raise canopy base height and reduce crown damage, and (3) break up the continuity of crowns to reduce active crown fire spread.* A fourth principle calls for retaining larger fire-resistant trees, which has less to do with hazardous fuel conditions per se but rather emphasizes tree survivability and is consistent with ecological objectives (Agee & Skinner, 2005).

For fire-specific objectives, there are two fundamental conditions for assessing treatment success: first, the type of treatment must be tested (i.e., burned) by an actual wildfire, and second, the treatment must mitigate fire behavior according to defined objectives. However, since the likelihood of wildfires burning in any given location in any given year is typically low, planning will also need to consider treatment impacts in the absence of fire.

Because of the diversity of objectives and forest conditions, there is no "one size fits all" approach to treating fuels. Often, treatments have multiple objectives, so congruence among these objectives should be pursued and evaluated. The need to consider other objectives and ecosystem functions is true even when treating areas within WUIs.

There are two primary forms of silvicultural fuel treatments: (1) mechanical treatment and (2) prescribed burning. The two most common types of mechanical fuel treatment are thinning and mastication (cutting and grinding up small trees and shrubs). Selection of the particular prescription and associated equipment depends on objectives, forest conditions, accessibility, intended forest product removals, and other site-specific factors. Pretreatment and posttreatment conditions, respectively, are shown in Figures 13.8 and 13.9 for a thinning operation performed in 2004; the objective was to reduce fire hazard, improve fire management opportunities, and mitigate wildfire risk to homes by raising the canopy base height and reducing canopy bulk density. This type of treatment helped protect the homes from the Fontenelle Fire in 2012 (see Figure 13.5).

Thinning can reduce ladder fuels (and thus increase canopy base height) and canopy bulk density, which in turn reduces the potential for passive or active crown fire and

Figure 13.8 *Pretreatment forest conditions exhibit a fairly dense understory with hazardous ladder fuels. (Photo courtesy of Jim Menakis)*

Figure 13.9 *Posttreatment forest conditions are less dense and the canopy is more open. The activity fuel piles are burned after curing, typically during winter months when the potential for fire escape is minimal. (Photo courtesy of Jim Menakis)*

therefore increase the safety and effectiveness of fire management activities. Generally these treatments do little to affect surface fuel loadings and may actually increase them, requiring subsequent treatment of activity fuels (e.g., tops and branches left on the ground during harvest) to achieve treatment objectives. This typically entails pile-burning to remove activity fuels, followed by underburning to reduce pretreatment surface fuel loadings (see Figures 13.10, 13.11, and 13.12). Mechanical treatments can also influence fire behavior because reduced canopy closure may result in increased midflame wind speeds and solar radiation. The latter may decrease surface fuel moisture and stimulate understory growth that contributes to surface fuel loadings. Both factors can increase fire rate of spread and fire intensity, so long-term fuel management is necessary.

Prescribed burning is typically needed for fuel treatments to be effective and meet management objectives. This is because, in contrast to most mechanical treatments, prescribed fire removes (burns) surface fuels, the primary carrier of fire spread. Prescribed fire can also increase canopy base height, and has thermal effects that thinning cannot replicate (see Box 13.3). Mechanical and prescribed fire treatments are often implemented together, which in many circumstances is the ideal treatment strategy (Stephens et al., 2012). In fact, a number of studies (simulations and actual events) suggest that thinning without a subsequent fire can create such a fuel hazard that it may be worse than doing nothing—at least until the natural decay of the residue dissipates the hazard (Raymond & Peterson, 2005). In such cases, the role for mechanical treatment would be to manage ladder and crown fuel conditions prior to burning so that the prescribed fire does not burn so hot that too many trees are killed.

## Fuel Treatment Planning

Translating treatment objectives into on-the-ground implementation can be guided by the following generalized process to identify fuel treatment needs and prescriptions (Finney & Cohen, 2003):

1. Identify the specific problems and how they relate to fuels or fire behavior;

2. Describe the desired outcomes from the treatment;

3. Describe the relationships between treatments and desired conditions and how much change in fuel or fire behavior is necessary; and

4. Identify the appropriate scale and type of treatment needed to effectuate the desired outcome(s).

Figure 13.10 *Forest conditions with reduced stand density after a mechanical treatment on the Dixie National Forest in Utah; thinning creates activity fuels, and creating slash piles and burning them is one way to deal with the problem.* (Photo courtesy of Eric Eastep)

Figure 13.11 *Pile-burning of fuels created from mechanical treatment to reduce hazardous surface fuel loads; burning often occurs outside of the fire season under cooler and wetter conditions to reduce the chance of the fire escaping control.* (Photo courtesy of CUSP)

Figure 13.12 *Underburning or broadcast burning is an important tool for reducing surface fuel loadings after thinning. Prescribed fire also can sometimes be used as an initial entry into stands or landscapes that have missed fire cycles or can be used to maintain fuels in a relatively low-hazard state following mechanical treatments.*

lyzed, with managers tasked with balancing trade-offs and contemplating uncertainties. A host of fuel management and environmental factors may be incorporated into fuel treatment planning to help ensure high-quality treatment decisions are made and evaluated from both stand-level and landscape-level perspectives (Table 13.1).

Treatment decisions at the stand level are in many respects similar to other forest management decisions, driven by differences between current forest conditions and desired forest conditions (see examples in Chapter 4). Decisions about thinning priorities are often keyed to how existing stand density relates to desired stand density or to the number of highly valued ecological resources, such as large, old trees, that are at risk. Prioritizing stands for treatment can also be based on fuel loading or modeled fire behavior thresholds, the probability of active or passive crown fire, and expected mortality.

Additional factors that should be considered in designing treatment prescriptions include species composition and age and the spatial pattern of retained trees within the stand. Prescriptions range from simple and homogenous to complex with variable spatial patterns of tree clumps and gaps in uneven age distributions

As described earlier, identification of fuel treatment needs will necessarily tie back to broader land and fire management objectives, and fuel management concerns will in many instances be integrated with other resource concerns. Typically alternative fuel treatment scenarios will be ana-

---

**Box 13.3  Is thinning a surrogate for fire in forest restoration? An ecologist's perspective**

Well-designed thinning operations can, in certain respects, look very similar to conditions created by wildfire. For instance, stand density is reduced, crown spacing is increased, and the residual structure of the forest may broadly resemble historical, heterogeneous forest conditions as described in Chapters 3 and 4. Selectively logging fire-intolerant trees promotes dominance by fire-tolerant species that are more resistant to mortality, thereby improving forest resilience. In addition, mechanical treatment of stands can reduce fuels in forests where introduction of fire without such treatment would be risky (Color Plate 13.1). Finally, mechanical treatments that produce commercial timber volumes may fund much of the treatment costs, allowing more area to be treated.

However, thinning can have significantly different effects on the forest than natural fire processes. First, thinning treatments often poorly emulate the random spatial patterns of gaps and clumps of trees that resulted from historical disturbance and succession; achieving this heterogeneity can be quite difficult operationally, although recent work by Churchill et al. (2013) should help overcome these difficulties. Second, fire can produce specific biological and chemical effects that thinning cannot mimic. For example, certain tree

species with serotinous cones depend on fire to melt the resin surrounding the cone to release seeds, such as in jack pine (found in the north-central USA) and the Table Mountain pine (*Pinus pungens*) found in dry sites in the Appalachian Mountains). Fires also heat-scarify seeds of many understory species stimulating them to germinate (e.g., *Ceanothus* spp.) and provide favorable seedbeds for their establishment. Smoke itself has been found to stimulate germination in many species. Third, fire mineralizes nutrients so they are available for uptake by trees and other vegetation. Lastly, fire can create snags and logs that are often not part of the thinning objectives despite their important ecological function and high abundance following fires (Sugihara et al., 2006).

Some of these potential differences between the effects of fire and thinning on the forest, such as emulating clustered spatial patterns or creating snags and down logs, can be reduced through careful planning. In the end, though, it is important to remember that mechanical treatment alone does not fully duplicate the effects of fire. Thus, combining mechanical treatment with prescribed fire is often recommended to move silvicultural treatments more closely to the physical and ecological effects produced by natural fires in forests.

(Larson & Churchill, 2012, Churchill et al., 2013). Reducing ladder fuels around existing old trees is often a high priority because of their ecological value and the treatment's effect on increasing the likelihood of surviving fire. Treatments with restoration-oriented objectives, such as generally are a part of ecological forestry, will often follow more complex prescriptions (Franklin et al., 2013; Reynolds et al., 2013). Given its inherent variability, wildland fire may often be a promising option to promote spatial heterogeneity if the fuel loadings are not so high as to threaten achievement of stand structure or landscape goals and the harvest of commercial products is not an issue.

Variability across stands is also an important factor in treatment design. Because wildfire is a spatial process, and because large wildfires account for the vast majority of area burned, it is necessary to consider the broader landscape conditions. Thus, while a given treatment may have localized impacts on stand-level fire behavior and fire effects, the overall efficacy of treatments may be overwhelmed when considering wildfire impacts across a landscape (Finney, McHugh, & Grenfell, 2005). Effective implementation of hazardous fuels reduction and forest restoration treatments therefore depends on understanding the linkages between stand and landscape variables.

Some differences between stand- and landscape-level treatment planning are summarized in Table 13.2. Primary variables in landscape-scale fuel treatment planning include the size, extent, and spatial pattern of treatments. In principle, multiple treatments can be spatially aggregated in such a way as to disrupt large fire spread and impact fire potential outside of treated areas. As an example, Parisien, Junor, and Kafka (2007) found through modeling that clustering treatments and strategically connecting treatments to natural fuel barriers (e.g., road and stream networks) were effective at reducing landscape-level burn probabilities.

Table 13.1 *Illustrative set of fuel management options and environmental moderators influencing those options*

| Fuel Management Options | Environmental Moderators |
|---|---|
| Silvicultural prescription (e.g., tree species and sizes to remove, residual density, and spatial complexity) | Forest/vegetation type |
| | Fuel loading conditions (stand) |
| | Fuel continuity (landscape) |
| | Ecosystem productivity |
| Treatment type (e.g., mechanical) | Historical fire regime |
| Treatment size, shape, and location (stand level) | Topography |
| | Climate & weather |
| Treatment timing/seasonality (if burning) | At-risk resources (e.g., watersheds, habitat, human communities) |
| Treatment extent and pattern (landscape level) | Land ownership and land designation (e.g., wilderness area) |
| Treatment maintenance rates | |

## Risk and Resiliency Concepts for Fuel Treatment Planning

Risk analysis principles are increasingly being applied in wildfire planning, creating significant opportunities to inform and improve fuel management decisions. It is useful to begin this discussion by briefly reviewing some basic principles of wildfire hazard and risk, which are related but distinct concepts:

- *Hazard* is typically defined as a physical situation with the potential to cause damage or harm. In the wildfire context, hazard can be measured in terms of potential fire behavior, using metrics such as fire intensity. Fuel and vegetation characteristics are often used as proxies for wildfire hazard, with the identification of hazardous fuel conditions as those that can lead to undesired fire behavior. Much of the fuel treatment planning to date has been based on assessments of hazard.

- *Risk* is a broader concept that incorporates information on hazards and their consequences as well as

Table 13.2 *Stand- and landscape-level characteristics influencing relationships between fuel treatment strategies and impacts on wildfires*

| | Stand-level | Landscape-level |
|---|---|---|
| *Primary Fuel Characteristics* | Fuel type, density, surface-ladder-crown loads | Spatial continuity and distribution of stand conditions |
| *Fuel Treatment Variables* | Prescription, residual density, spatial architecture of residual trees, activity fuels treatment | Location, extent, and pattern of treatments |
| *Direct Impacts on Fire* | Fire intensity | Fire spread |
| *Indirect Impacts on Fire* | Fire effects and burn severity | Fire likelihood; fire size distributions |
| *Impacts on Suppression* | Firefighter safety and effectiveness | Firefighter safety and effectiveness; Strategic choices for where to engage the fire |

information on the probabilities of hazards occurring. Together three main components—(1) the likelihood of wildfire, (2) the intensity of wildfire, and (3) the susceptibility of resources to wildfire—make up the legs of the "wildfire risk triangle" depicted in Figure 13.13. That is, assessing wildfire risk entails asking where fire is likely to occur, how intensely it might burn, and what the ecological, social, and economic consequences are.

Understanding how the three main components contribute to risk can be very important for determining fuel treatment needs and developing spatial fuel treatment strategies. For example, the type of treatment may lead to significant changes in localized fire intensity, whereas the total area treated and the spatial pattern of treatments may lead to significant changes in how fire can spread across the landscape and subsequently change fire likelihood. In particular, an emphasis on likelihood of wildfire can lead to different strategies than those developed with a focus on stand-level hazard alone. Across large enough time periods the occurrence of wildfire is all but certain; however, in time frames relevant to fire and fuels planning, the location and timing of wildfires are highly uncertain. Spatial variation in ignition and weather patterns, topography, and forest conditions can all influence spatial variation in the likelihood of wildfire. All else being equal, treating stands that are more likely to burn is more likely to yield treatment benefits. Furthermore, *strategic location of multiple treatments implemented simultaneously can alter spatial patterns of wildfire likelihood at the landscape-scale, thereby reducing the likelihood of undesirable fire effects to resources* (Ager et al., 2013).

Local knowledge of landscape conditions and fire history can help to identify variation in wildfire likelihood and intensity. For instance managers may be able to identify fuel treatment locations with the greatest chance for success based upon knowledge of ignition potential, predominant wind directions, and the type and continuity of fuels. Computer models can also help, as we discuss below, with the models ranging in complexity from nonspatial spreadsheet tools to estimate fire behavior to spatial modeling systems that simulate the spread of thousands of fires under different ignition and weather conditions.

If we knew exactly when and where the next wildfire would start, and under what conditions, fire and fuels management would be much easier. Managers would know

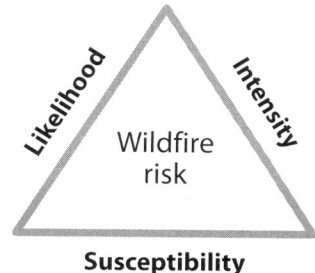

Figure 13.13 *The "wildfire risk triangle." (Source: Adapted from Scott, Thompson, & Calkin, 2013)*

where to treat fuels, where to locate firefighting crews, even where lightning strikes would land. Of course, this is not the case. Instead, the best we can do is estimate which areas are *more likely* to experience wildfire given information regarding fire occurrence patterns, fire weather patterns, and landscape conditions. Thinking in terms of **likelihoods**, or **probabilities**, is simply a reflection of this reality (Box 13.4).

Wildfire risk, though, is not just about fire likelihood and intensity. It is also important to evaluate the potential consequences of wildfire by considering the susceptibility of various resources and assets to fire (Figure 13.13). Typically when we think of **risk** we think only of negative consequences. However, wildfires can lead to substantial ecological benefits, and these benefits should be integrated into assessments of the potential consequences of wildfire. As an example, fires can promote regeneration of decadent aspen stands, can mineralize nutrients in the soil, and can create desirable habitat conditions for fire-dependent wildlife. Fuel treatment planning, especially in restoration-oriented contexts, can therefore directly target attainment of these benefits, whether through intentional application of prescribed fire or treatments designed to enable future use of wildfire for beneficial objectives.

Even for fire-susceptible resources and assets like critical infrastructure, for which fire is never beneficial, it can be important to differentiate levels of susceptibility; for instance, a wooden utility pole may be more susceptible to damage than one made from steel. Though difficult, systematically thinking through the possible consequences of fire with relevant experts (e.g., wildlife biologists, soil scientists) can help better characterize the risks and benefits that wildfire poses (Scott et al., 2013). Such thinking can, in turn, help refine the treatment strategy and spatial design.

## Fire Modeling to Support Treatment Planning

Fire models can be helpful to managers as they develop treatment strategies. It is rare, though, that fire modeling results alone provide clear or definitive answers regarding the best course of action. Instead, models are useful as tools for learning and evaluation, and their results can help confirm intuition, generate new insights, or even cause managers to question assumptions and dig more deeply into the problem. That is, fire models are decision-support tools, not decision-making tools in themselves.

A simplified model of treatment strategy development, which is informed by landscape conditions, expert judgment, and fire modeling, is provided in Figure 13.14. Incorporating fire modeling into treatment planning can be an iterative process, and fire modeling results can help with the *design* of treatment strategies as well as their *evaluation*.

Fire modeling used for treatment design often seeks to identify areas that could burn with undesirable intensity, or to see patterns of fire spread across the landscape, such that spread can be impeded. For instance, Ager, Vaillant, and McMahan (2013) developed a treatment location algorithm premised on simulation to first identify the main travel pathways of fire across a landscape, and then to locate treatments to interrupt these pathways based on various resources of concern or to support fire suppression. With such an algorithm, analysts can project an *optimal* treatment design given treatment goals (Figure 13.15).

Fire modeling used as an evaluative tool, on the other hand, seeks to identify how the proposed treatment strategy could change fire behavior within and possibly outside of treated areas (Box 13.5). Where fire modeling is used for evaluation, managers typically have to specify the type and possibly the location(s) of treatment, enabling generation of a *hypothetical* treated landscape. Thus, treatment strategies are developed according to other information and/or user-defined logic. For instance, Kim, Bettinger,

---

### Box 13.4  Thinking in terms of probabilities

***Is wildfire really a rare phenomenon: defining the frame of reference?*** Imagine you are asked the following question: What is the chance of rain? Your initial reaction might be to request more specificity, for instance regarding where, when, and how much (does a single rain drop count?). An answer "at least 1 inch, across the entire US over the next year" is radically different than the answer "at least 1 inch, in Portland, Oregon, over the next hour." The latter answer might also be very different if the location was Tucson, Arizona. We need to think about wildfire occurrence in the same way and very clearly define the frame of reference we are considering. While over large enough spatial and temporal scales wildfire is an inevitable phenomenon, as the spatiotemporal window narrows, fire occurrence probabilities inevitably decline. Across an entire national forest, it may not be uncommon to see one or several wildfires each year. And yet at the stand scale, modeled burn probabilities can be lower than 1 in 1,000 for a given year. Probabilities of that same stand burning at a given intensity level can be even lower.

***Why does it matter?*** Identifying areas that have a higher probability of burning by wildfire in turn can help managers identify areas of high concern where fuel treatments may be most beneficial. All else being equal, a treatment is more likely to be effective if the treatment is located in an area that is more likely to burn. Using probabilistic information on potential fire occurrence and behavior moves us one step closer to risk management.

***Why can't the probabilities be reduced to zero?*** Wildfire is a reality that cannot be stopped, only partially controlled, and thus the probability of experiencing wildfire at a given location can never be completely eliminated. Consider that even if all fuels were treated according to the guiding *fire-safe* principles, the landscape could still support fire, and under extreme conditions could still produce high-intensity behavior and be resistant to control. On top of that, consider our inability to prevent lightning strikes or to change wind patterns. And lastly, consider that treatments do not outright stop fire but rather reduce its intensity, slow its spread, and enhance containment opportunities.

***Are there different types of probabilities?*** In casinos and other gambling contexts the probabilities of winning are often well defined and easily calculated. For instance with a pair of dice there are a total of $6 \times 6 = 36$ possible combinations, and there is only a chance of 1 in 36 that a given roll will yield a sum of 12 (both die need to land on 6, which has a chance of 1 in 6 for each die). In wildfire, however, probabilities aren't as easily calculated or interpreted and it can be difficult to determine what the realm of possible fire outcomes could be. Qualitative probabilistic information can help identify in a relative sense which areas are more or less likely to burn. Quantitative information from fire models can augment this qualitative information. As an example, burn probabilities from modern Monte Carlo simulation systems count the number of times a given location burns and compare that to the total number of simulation runs performed—if the given location burned 10 times out of 100 runs, the probability of burning is 0.10.

Quantitative probabilities are often presented in *conditional* terms, i.e., the probabilities are calculated conditional on wildfire occurrence in the first place. But the probability of wildfire occurrence in a given landscape of interest in a given year may be quite low, so calculating the probability that a treatment will be tested by fire using conditional burn probabilities may overstate treatment benefits. *Annual* burn probabilities additionally consider the likelihood of experiencing ignition(s) over the course of a year. Since most fuel treatments last more than a year, calculating the probability that a treatment will be tested by fire using only annual burn probabilities may understate treatment benefits. Confused yet? Don't worry, you are not alone. The fire management and research community are still trying to wrap their collective heads around how best to generate realistic probabilities and how to use that information in fuel and fire management planning. For now, keep this main point in mind: if you estimate the potential benefits of a treatment assuming that the treated area will have a 100% chance of burning, you are certainly overestimating the treatment's benefits.

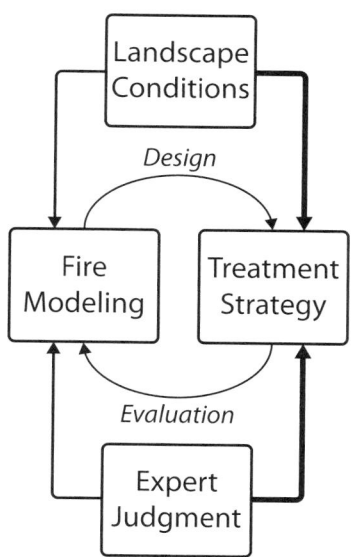

Figure 13.14 *Landscape conditions and expert judgment are typically the primary sources of information in developing treatment strategies (thicker arrows). Fire modeling can also be quite useful, for designing as well as evaluating alternative fuel treatment strategies.*

and Finney (2009) relied on spatial forest management optimization techniques to generate four different patterns of treatment to be evaluated.

Again, there is no one size fits all approach, and it is important to reiterate that fire models in and of themselves don't provide an answer. Rather, landscape conditions and expert judgment are particularly important inputs into any fuel treatment planning process (importance indicated by the width of the arrows in Figure 13.14). A number of fire and fuel modeling systems are available with differing levels of sophistication and capability, ranging from describing fire behavior and effects, to computing wildfire growth and behavior, to doing stand-level risk assessments, to doing full spatial simulation of large fires (see Appendix for more details).

## Developing Landscape-level Fuel Treatment Strategies

Treating all hazardous fuels at the scale of a landscape generally is not ecologically, operationally, or financially feasible. Managers must therefore design efficient and effective treatment strategies subject to real-world constraints. Although guiding principles for stand-level treatments are well established (as we outline above using the fire-safe principles of Agee and Skinner), development of a similar set of principles for landscape-level treatment has not fully materialized. Nevertheless, we can begin to outline a number of principles that can help guide the process of developing landscape fuel treatment strategies:

As with any stand-level prescriptions, one should begin with establishing management goals followed by the development of meaningful performance measures to evaluate alternative treatment strategies against. Subsequently, consider the following:

- Across the landscape, broadly identify zones where the different types of fuel treatments (mechanical, prescribed fire, managed wildfire) might be considered to achieve management goals.

- Within each zone, spatially identify areas where fuel treatments cannot occur or must be modified to address other objectives.

- Adhere to stand-level fire-safe principles for the design and implementation of individual treatments.

- Spatially identify areas of high fire likelihood and intensity; this analysis can range from a map-based exercise considering forest conditions and predominant wind directions all the way to sophisticated fire modeling considering thousands of possible fire scenarios.

- Spatially identify highly valued resources and assets (e.g., critical habitat) and their relation to areas of high fire likelihood and intensity.

- Consider realistic scenarios of how firefighters would manage the wildfire and how treatments may enhance firefighter safety or effectiveness.

- Integrate fuel treatment patterns and prescriptions with other land and resource management objectives.

- Evaluate and iteratively update treatment strategies; compare strategies against a no-treatment scenario, with and without wildfire during the effective lifespan of the treatment effects.

Thus, the development of spatial fuel treatment strategies is dependent on many factors including current forest conditions, the historical fire regime, land and fire management objectives, and the spatial patterns of valued resources and assets (see Figure 13.15) (Ager et al., 2013). Where treatment objectives are oriented around fire exclusion and localized protection of the WUI, a treatment strategy could be to create a series of defensible fuel breaks to reduce the intensity of wildfire as it moves from the wildland into the community, thereby facilitating suppression efforts. A strategy similarly focused on localized protection of resources dispersed across the landscape (e.g., legacy trees, habitat patches) could instead result in a dispersed rather than a concentrated placement of treatments, but with a similar aim of reducing localized intensity and potentially enhancing suppression. Treatment planning can integrate suppression response even more directly, for instance by leveraging existing barriers such as road networks to create additional opportunities for safe and effective containment by firefighters (see Figure 13.4).

Developing spatial treatment strategies becomes more complicated when considering potential treatment effects across the larger landscape outside of treated areas. This type of strategy is premised on arranging fuel treatments in such a way as to interrupt patterns and pathways of fire spread, thereby reducing fire likelihood and intensity across the overall landscape (Figure 13.16). While informative, optimal strategies have drawbacks. First, there is no guarantee that the wildfire that ultimately tests the treatments will be oriented in the same direction as the presumed *problem fire* (if the treatments are ever tested by wildfire). Second, and more importantly, a litany of real-world constraints (e.g., restricted access areas and operational feasibility) may limit implementation of optimal treatment patterns. However, generation of efficient spatial treatment patterns can provide a useful starting point for incorporating constraints and opportunities into designing effective treatment strategies.

Strategic treatment locations are typically based on fuel conditions, fire weather patterns, and likely fire spread-directions. This placement can significantly influence the scale of treatment needed to achieve objectives. If treatments are located to maximize their effectiveness in intercepting fire across the landscape, a sufficient scale and rate of treatment is 1–2% of the landscape per year, ideally reaching a condition where 20–40% can be maintained in a treated state (Finney et al., 2007). If treatments are located randomly, as may happen given other objectives and constraints, nearly twice as much area needs to be treated to achieve similar results to treatments optimally located to disrupt large fire growth (Finney et al., 2007).

Finney et al. (2007) also found that as much as a third of the landscape can remain in untreated reserves without substantially diminishing treatment effectiveness. However, this depends, in part, on the specific landscape and the location of reserves with respect to areas of high fire hazard and fire-spread potential.

The likelihood of any given treated area experiencing fire over the effective lifespan of a treatment is quite low on most landscapes, even those covered with fire-prone forests; Campbell, Harmon, and Mitchell (2012) estimate the probabilities of

## Spatial Strategies for Fuel Management

|  | Restoration of low severity fire regime in dry forests | Broad landscape protection | Localized protection | Protection of dispersed values | Restoration of mixed severity fire regimes | Strategic containment |
|---|---|---|---|---|---|---|
| *Spatial pattern of values* | High density, dispersed | Low density, dispersed | Variable density, clumpy | Clumpy | Any | Low or none |
| *Landscape goal* | Low hazard fire containers | Disrupt spread, facilitate containment | Localized defensible fuel breaks | Dispersed defensible fuel breaks | Restoration of dispersed natural fire barriers | Contain large fires at defensible locations |
| *Performance measure* | Area burned by prescribed and natural fire | Reduction in landscape burn probability | Local reduction in exposure near values at risk | Reduced exposure to fire | Landscape reduction in hazard and burn probability | Area burned by natural fire |
| *Treatment goal* | Reduce fire severity | Reduce fire spread rate | Facilitate suppression | Facilitate suppression | Reduce fire spread rate | Facilitate suppression |
| *Example map* | 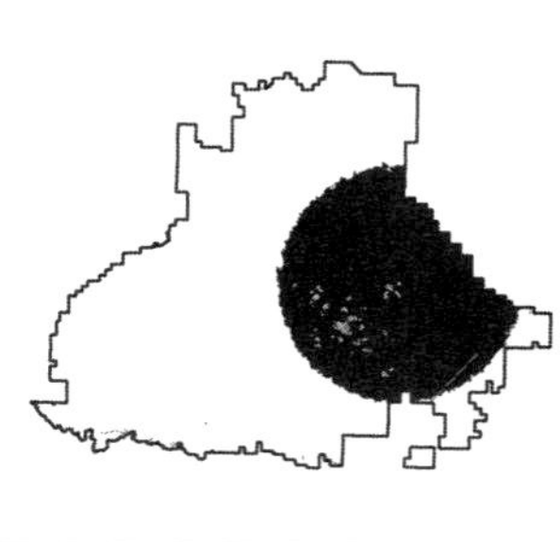 | 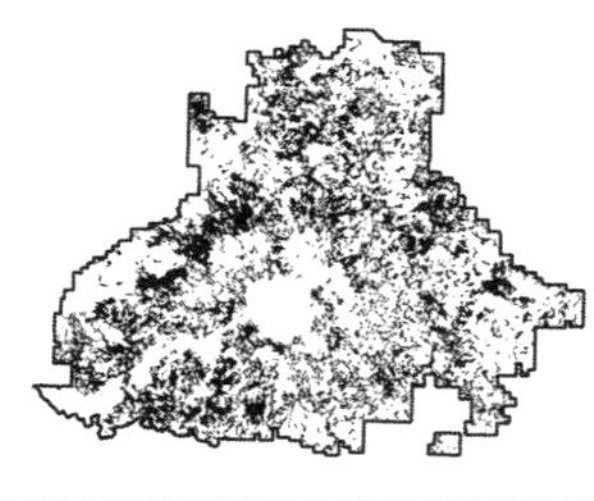 | 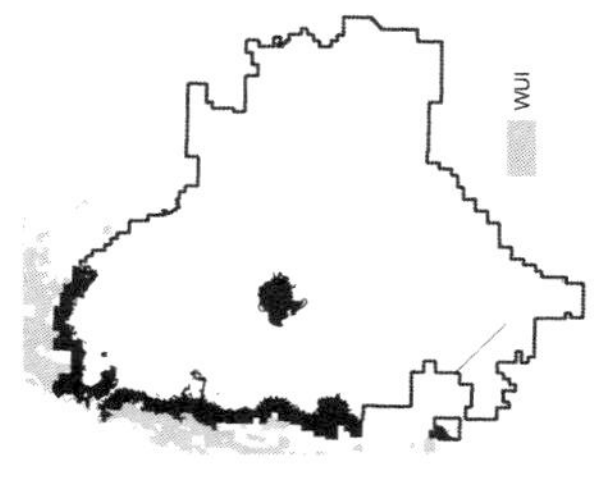 | 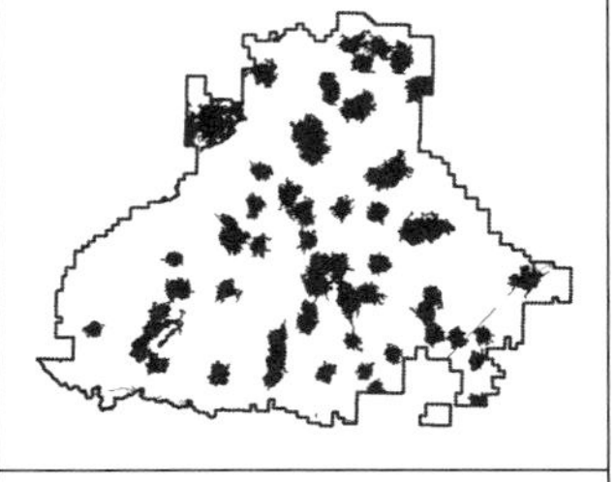 | 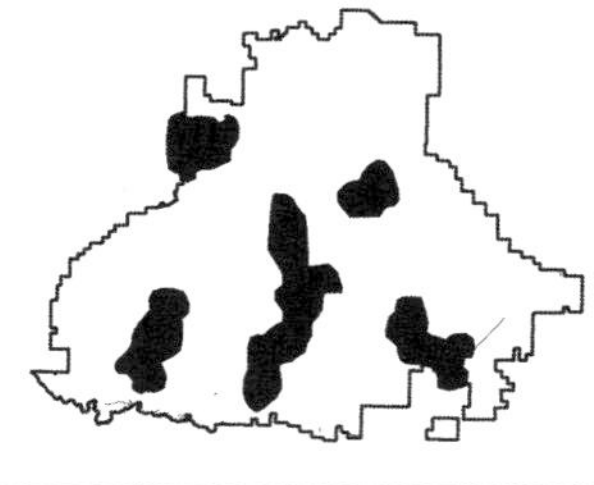 | 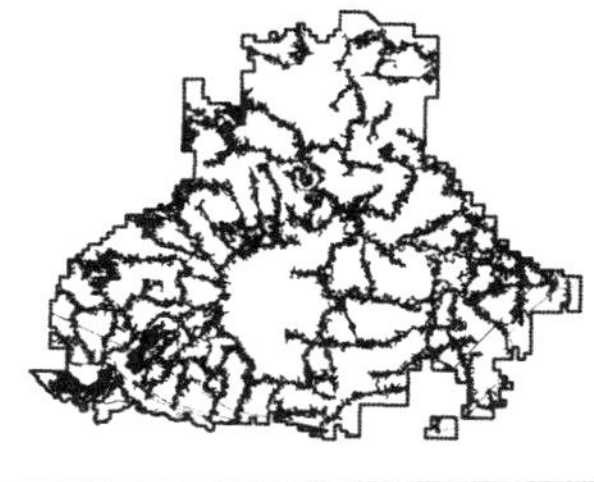 |

Figure 13.15 *Spatial strategies for fuel management. Fuel treatment areas are shown in black. (Source: USDA Forest Service, 2014)*

treated areas experiencing wildfire to be between 1–20%, depending on forest type and treatment longevity. Considering both temporal and spatial factors, though, can help managers increase the odds that treatment strategies will be successful. Regarding temporal factors, managers can ensure that treatments have a long, effective duration by treating at a sufficient intensity to meaningfully reduce fuel loads and investing in sufficient maintenance treatments through time when required; the longer a treatment is effective, the greater the odds of the treatment interacting with wildfire.

Vegetation recovers and fuels accumulate in previously treated areas, so that over time strategies may need to balance maintenance of previously treated units with treatment of new units (Finney et al., 2007). Managers therefore need to consider factors such as treatment intensity and site productivity in determining how treatment effects will

---

### Box 13.5 Fire modeling in action on the Deschutes National Forest

Modeling fire can also help evaluate the potential impact of alternative treatment strategies on fire spread and landscape-scale burn probabilities (e.g., Ager et al., 2013). An example of a recent application of fire modeling to evaluate fuel treatment impacts comes from the Deschutes Collaborative Forest Project (DCFP) on the Deschutes National Forest in Oregon (Thompson et al., 2013b). Figure 13.16 provides a map of the analysis area, along with project boundaries and proposed treatment unit locations. Nearly 50% of the DCFP landscape is scheduled to receive fuel treatment over the course of a decade-long planning horizon.

Fuel treatment objectives on the DCFP landscape vary according to forest type, at-risk resources, and other factors. In the drier forest types, treatment objectives include restoring natural fire regimes and creating trajectories to late-successional stages, which will be achieved by reducing stand density, reducing ladder fuels, and favoring large, fire-resilient trees. Priority areas for treatment include midsuccessional stands with closed canopies. Elsewhere in the wetter forest types, treatments are strategically located to inhibit fire spread driven by westerly winds. The primary treatment was thinning from below (mechanical) with surface fuels treated through a combination of hand-piling and burning, mowing, and prescribed fire.

Results of fire simulation modeling that evaluates fire growth potential and subsequent burn probabilities across the DCFP landscape indicate that many of the areas with the greatest reductions in burn probability are within fuel treatments. However, reductions in off-site burn probability are also evident, in particular on the eastern (lee) side of the treatments. Analyses like this example can help fire managers develop and evaluate risk-informed treatment strategies.

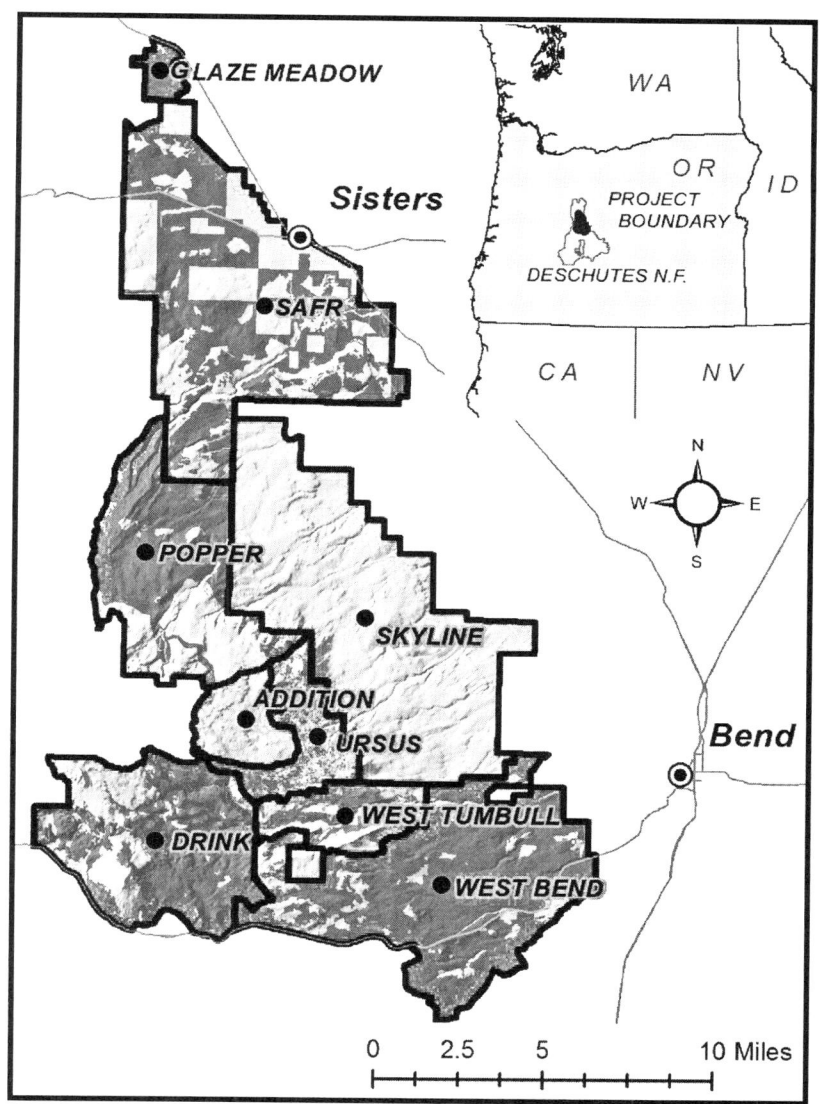

**Legend**

☐ Project areas

▨ Treatment units

Figure 13.16 *Map of Deschutes Collaborative Forest Project study area with project areas and treatment units highlighted (Reprinted from Thompson et al., 2013b, with permission of the Society of American Foresters)*

dampen through time and possibly require subsequent retreatment. Regarding spatial factors, managers can ensure that treatments are targeting areas of highest risk or areas that could most effectively limit spread across the landscape.

Fuel treatment success is also largely contingent on the weather conditions during the wildfire–treatment interaction, requiring managers to consider targeting particular weather conditions. At one end of the spectrum, a treatment designed to be effective only in very moderate fire weather conditions is unlikely to reduce loss, because loss rarely occurs under these conditions. Further, wildfire itself rarely grows to a large size under moderate conditions due to highly effective suppression efforts that typically contain all ignitions except those that occur under extreme weather conditions. These rare large wildfires typically account for less than 5% of all ignitions, but over 95% of all area burned (Short, 2014). To be successful, treatments must be designed for the more extreme conditions under which the treated area is likely to burn, recognizing, though, that neither treatments nor suppression efforts are likely to be successful under very extreme fire weather conditions.

In practice, treatments can range from highly effective to ineffective to potentially worsening fire behavior. Postfire analyses have shown that treatments can significantly reduce burn severity (Wimberly, Cochrane, Baer, & Pabst, 2009) and enhance suppression operations (Romero & Menakis, 2013). Where ineffective, treatments often were not designed with appropriate target weather conditions, did not apply prescribed fire or treat activity fuels, or were located more because of operational/financial considerations than wildfire hazard and risk (Graham et al., 2012).

## Fuel Treatments: The Many Constraints on Implementation

In addition to the identification of fuel treatment needs, as mentioned above, planning processes must also identify relevant objectives and constraints that could influence or limit implementation of treatment strategies. An important first step is identifying feasible management opportunities, which can be defined spatially (e.g., slopes suitable for mechanical treatment, restricted areas) as well as temporally (e.g., seasonal windows for prescribed burning).

Mechanical fuels treatments can be highly constrained by a variety of factors. Thus, their ability to modify fire behavior may be limited without the use of prescribed fire and managed wildfire (Box 13.6).

The application of prescribed fire in particular is significantly constrained in many locations. Questions of where and when to use prescribed fire can be highly complex, influenced by weather, fuel moistures, organizational capacity, air quality concerns, and the potential that the fire may escape control (Jain et al., 2012). Factors limiting application include

---

Box 13.6 **The limits of mechanical fuels treatment in the Sierra Nevada of California**

North et al. (2015b) analyzed the amount and distribution of constraints on mechanical fuels treatments on the national forests of the Sierra Nevada Bioregion in California. With the use of current standards and guides, feedback from practicing silviculturists, and GIS databases, they developed a hierarchy of biological (i.e., nonproductive forest), legal (i.e., wilderness), operational (i.e., equipment access, economics), and administrative (i.e., sensitive species and riparian areas) constraints on mechanical treatments. Of the 10.7 million acres of national forest studied, they found that 58% contained productive forest and 25% was available to mechanical treatment, with the national forests in the southern Sierra Nevada having higher levels of constraint due to more wilderness and steeper, more remote terrain.

North et al. (2015b) also evaluated different levels of operational constraints and found that increasing road building and operating on steeper slopes had less effect on increasing mechanical access than removing economic considerations (i.e., accessing sites regardless of timber harvest volume from the treatment). Constraints due to sensitive species habitat and riparian areas reduced productive forest access by 8%.

Further, they divided the Sierra Nevada Bioregion into subwatersheds and found that only 20% of these subwatersheds had enough unconstrained acreage to effectively contain or suppress wildfire with mechanical treatment alone. They concluded that mechanical treatment in most subwatersheds could be more effective as a fuel-reduced *anchor* from which prescribed and managed fire could be strategically expanded.

---

high rural housing densities, high fuel loads, risk-averse agency cultures, limited availability of experienced personnel, and laws/regulations related to air quality (North et al., 2012). Tragic events like the Lower North Fork Fire, which escaped control in Colorado and resulted in loss of human life and property, can lead to outright bans on prescribed fire. In comparison, significant success has been achieved with prescribed fire in the southern US (Box 13.2).

Financial realities also constrain implementation of fuel treatment strategies, as occurred in the Sierra Nevada (Box 13.6). In contrast to commercial timber harvests, fuel treatments on the federal forests of the US often generate little revenue from forest products, resulting in net costs. Limited budgets may prevent large-scale implementation even though high-cost treatments may emerge as worthwhile from an investment analysis perspective when considering the future benefits of reduced risk and increased resilience. Fuel management planning therefore needs to consider the economic viability of alternative strategies, incorporating factors influencing costs such as the logging system, the amount of merchantable material harvested, the end-use of harvested materials, available mills and market conditions, road system accessibility, and haul distances.

One option to increase the overall economic viability of treatment strategies is to package high-cost units with revenue-generating units by integrating fuel treatments as part of broader restoration efforts (see the Red Knight example below). On national forests, *stewardship contracting* is increasingly utilized to retain receipts from treatment harvests to subsidize other treatments that do not cover their costs.

With all these considerations, managers may have had difficulties treating significant portions of the landscape at any point in time, limiting the effectiveness of treatment strategies. Thus, managers must prioritize on the basis of costs and treatment effectiveness, as well as other factors

such as social license. With the limitations on mechanical treatments and prescribed fire, scientists and managers are increasingly looking to managed wildfire as a significant component in fuel reduction strategies (discussed in detail at the end of this chapter).

## Integrating Fuel Treatments into Forest Restoration

Recognizing the multifaceted goals for the federal forests in the United States, forest managers are increasingly framing their actions under the broad theme of forest restoration, especially in the frequent-fire forests that have seen a massive increase in stand densities with fire suppression. This approach folds fire-safe principles for stand treatments and landscape consideration and modeling of fire spread, as described earlier in this chapter, into a broader scheme of overall ecological restoration.

Toward that end, federal agencies managing frequent-fire forests often focus on retaining and improving the survivability of the remaining large and old trees (through clearing out fuels and competing vegetation around them), reducing stand densities, favoring fire-tolerant tree species, and creating spatial heterogeneity that reflects the historical clumpy patterns of these forests. With such a strategy, as an example, we would expect more spatial heterogeneity in the trees remaining after harvest, than occurred in the hazardous fuel reduction project shown in Figure 13.4, with clumps of different sizes interspersed with open areas containing scattered individual trees. Thus, managers increasingly take an ecological forestry approach, much as described for frequent-fire forests in Chapters 3 and 4 above.

At the landscape level, this restoration must accommodate many other resource goals, including protection of habitat for sensitive species, cover for big game, and special places, such as cultural sites and recreation areas. The landscape plan must also consider the funds that federal agencies have to spend on these efforts. Thus the landscape plan will seldom be optimal from a fuel hazard reduction standpoint but will rather reflect a suite of broader goals.

Red Knight, a 30,000-acre project in frequent-fire forests on the Fremont-Winema National Forest in south-central Oregon, provides an example of this integrated approach to landscape planning (Figure 13.17).

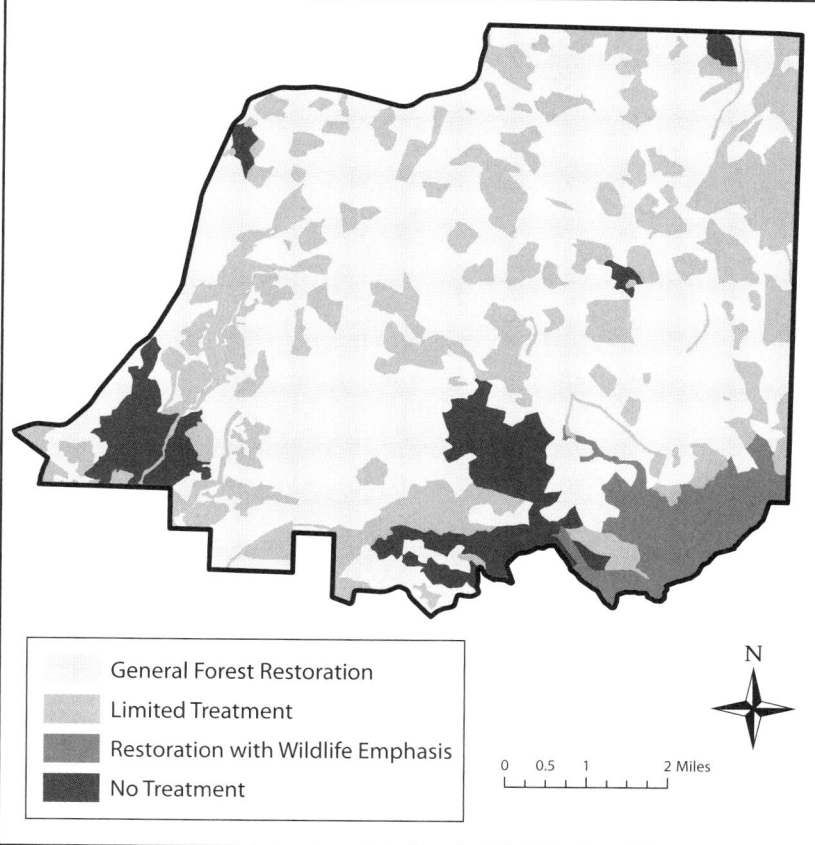

**Figure 13.17** *Landscape design for the Red Knight Restoration Project in the ponderosa pine and mixed-conifer forests of the Fremont-Winema National Forest. Treatments in the General Forest Restoration focus on restoring the historical composition and structure of these forests with a major emphasis on reducing fuels that have accumulated over the last 100 years, utilizing the ecological forestry principles described in Chapters 3 and 4. Restoration with Wildlife Emphasis has a similar focus while retaining habitat patches for the pileated woodpecker. Limited Treatment areas provide cover for big game (scattered patches) or are in recreation areas (long south-central patch); actions there focus primarily on clearing out around old trees or revitalizing hardwood patches, using funds generated in General Forest Restoration and Wildlife Emphasis areas.*

Ecological restoration is a primary goal within the General Restoration Area, including improving survivability of the remaining large and old trees, reducing stand densities, favoring fire-tolerant tree species, and creating spatial heterogeneity, but will be modified to varying degrees in the other allocations. "No Treatment" areas were identified as constraining critically important resources, and the forests surrounding them are a high priority for treatment. Old-growth trees, wherever they are found, have the highest priority for protection, which is typically achieved by removing ingrowth and other fuels around them.

## Leveraging Wildfires for Resource Benefits

Wildfire itself is a form of landscape-scale treatment, and managing wildfires for resource benefit and hazard reduction is a mechanism for increasing the spatial scale and benefit of hazardous fuels treatments (North et al., 2012). Wildland-fire use programs (managing fires) allow naturally ignited wildfires to burn and perform their ecological function, with reduced suppression activities (van Wagtendonk, 2007). These fires are allowed to burn during moderated fire weather conditions, where wildfires do not threaten other fire-susceptible resources or assets, and can produce desired fire effects. Areas that have in the recent past experienced wildland fire (i.e., wildfire and prescribed fire) can exhibit reduced severity and minimize or stop fire spread because fuels have already been consumed (Collins et al., 2009; Parks, Miller, Nelson, & Holden, 2013). These fire-on-fire interactions are complex and variable, influenced by burning conditions, incident response, and the location, extent, initial severity, site productivity, and age of the previous disturbances (Collins et al., 2009; Holden, Morgan, & Hudak, 2010). In many cases reestablishing frequent fire can reduce hazardous fuels so that subsequent fire events maintain resilient forests (Larson, Belote, Cansler, Parks, & Dietz, 2013), although burning more frequently than the historical regime can have the opposite effect (Enright, Fontaine, Bowman, Bradstock, & Williams, 2015).

Managing wildfires for resource benefits is another important tool in the wildfire management and ecological forestry toolkit. In fact, managing wildfires may be preferred over other fuel treatments for several reasons. First, mechanical treatments are often limited to a small portion of the landscape due to topography, critical wildlife habitat, potential impacts to highly-valued ecological and economic resources, and financial constraints (Box 13.6) (North et al., 2012). Second, wildfires currently impact a greater portion of the landscape than ongoing fuels management or restoration treatments, and therefore should be the focus of additional planning to mitigate undesirable fire effects while expanding their benefits. Lastly, policies

such as the Clean Air Act constrain treatment opportunities because of concerns over negatively impacting protected airsheds. Wildfires are not constrained by these same rules and liabilities, and don't observe topographic boundaries, and therefore wildfires offer an opportunity to achieve resource objectives when other treatments are not available.

As one should expect, there are many existing barriers to expanding the use of beneficial fire. At the most basic level, these include the presence of highly valued resources and assets, risk-averse managers, and extreme fire behavior. Additionally, there is often a desire for ecological restoration, through the use of mechanical treatment and prescribed fire to precede wildfires to best meet resource objectives, especially where past policies have led to a major buildup in fuels (Color Plate 13.1). At a more systemic level, agency incentives for aggressive suppression are pervasive as exemplified by limited controls on suppression costs or resource use in response to a fire incident (Thompson, 2014). Additionally, aggressive suppression response is often supported by some members of the public because of their aversion to increasing fire's presence on the landscape, especially with regards to smoke impacts. With all these considerations, fire managers tend to focus on short-term risk management at the expense of long-term risk reductions.

Some of these constraints can be overcome or effectively managed through pre-incident planning to develop effective spatial fire plans and objectives that integrate well with land and resource management plans (Meyer, Roberts, Wills, Brooks, & Winford, 2015). As new land and resource management plans are written or existing plans are revised there is an opportunity for zoning landscapes based on fire risk to multiple valued resources and assets, including identifying zones where fire is anticipated to provide a positive net value change (North et al., 2015a). As these plans are developed and fire management plans are written to support these efforts, the following principles should be adhered to as identified by Meyer et al. (2015). To be effective, spatial fire planning efforts should be:

- *Consistent and compatible*: plans shouldn't be contradictory or in conflict with land and resource management plans.

- *Collaborative*: Resource specialists and concerned stakeholders should have the opportunity to weigh in on fire management decisions.

- *Clear and comprehensive*: Fire management decisions are often time constrained; thus plans should be prepared in consultation with fire managers so objectives are clearly defined and all concerns have been addressed ahead of the incident.

- *Spatially explicit*: Plans should map highly valued resources and assets that may be impacted by fire, as well as landscape attributes (e.g., roads and ridgetops) relevant to fire operations.

- *Spatially and temporally scalable*: Plans should acknowledge the dynamic nature of fire through time.

- *Informed by best available science*: Plans should integrate the best available science and have mechanisms for integrating new information, in addition to acknowledging uncertainties to both incentivize new scientific research and effectively manage with uncertainty.

- *Flexible and adaptive*: Conditions are constantly changing throughout a wildfire event. Therefore, plans and managers need to be flexible and adaptive; otherwise status quo aggressive suppression will likely be pursued.

Despite all these efforts, managing beneficial fires will remain risky and fraught with uncertainty. The potential for occurrence of negative outcomes may limit social tolerance despite the long-term risk reduction or ecological benefits achieved (Calkin, Thompson, & Finney, 2015). The 1988 Yellowstone Fires provide an example of a negative response by the public to managing fires for resource benefit. Fortunately, as the forests regenerated, public attitudes about these fires have improved. Ultimately, land managers will have to decide how best to reduce long-term wildfire risk; however, it has become increasingly evident that managing wildfires must be part of this strategy combined with other tools available to resource managers (North et al., 2015a; Calkin et al., 2015).

## Ecosystem Resiliency as an Overarching Goal

Starting with Chapter 1, this book has emphasized the importance of restoring and maintaining resilient ecosystems with the capacity for adaptive change (Holling, 1973). The increasing focus on restoring and maintaining ecosystem functions comes about, in part, with the realization that the climate is changing and may lead to ecosystem adaptations that reflect these changed conditions. Thus, the goal of resiliency will be expressed through restoring and maintaining the functional capabilities of ecosystems rather than just restoring historical composition and structure (Millar et al., 2007).[1]

---

1 As discussed in Chapter 2, there are many ecosystem functions broadly encapsulated as habitat to sustain biological diversity, energy cycles or ecosystem productivity (carbon uptake, storage in the form of structures, and transfer), the hydrologic cycle (e.g., accumulation and melting of snowpack), and material cycles (conservation of critical nutrients, soil building and maintenance).

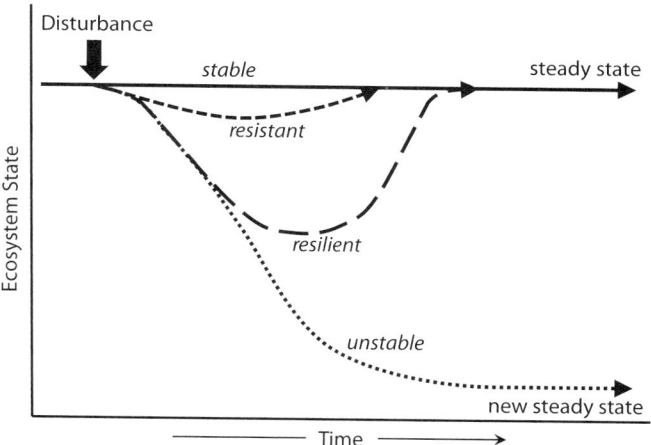

Figure 13.18 *Characterizing the relative stability of ecosystem functions (here referred to as the ecosystem state) according to how the ecosystem responds to a disturbance event over time. The resistant ecosystem remains stable regarding its functions (here referred to as the steady state). If the ecosystem is destabilized by the disturbance it may recover to an approximation of its original functional state, in which case it is viewed as resilient, or undergo change to a new functional state. (Source: reproduced from van Andel & Aronson, 2005, with permission of John Wiley and Sons, Inc.)*

In the absence of disturbance, a forest might be viewed as having stable ecosystem functions (Figure 13.18). Following a wildfire, these ecosystem functions may (1) remain stable—in which case it would be viewed as resistant; (2) undergo change but recover to an approximation of its pre-disturbance functional state, in which case it would be viewed as resilient; or (3) undergo change but not recover to an approximation of its pre-disturbance function condition and move to an alternative functional state (Figure 13.18).

Resistant ecosystems exhibit relatively little change in ecosystem function with disturbance and quickly recover. Frequent-fire forests that have retained or been restored to their historical structures can provide excellent examples of resistant ecosystems, such as longleaf pine forests that continue to experience low-severity fires at high frequency (see Chapter 3). Restored ponderosa pine forests also should be resistant to fire, drought, and bark beetle–related disturbances; however, in the ponderosa pine it may be desirable to reduce stand densities to levels in the lower portion of the historical range because the future climate is predicted to be hotter and drier than the historical climate.

Resilient ecosystems exhibit significant change following a disturbance but are adapted to these disturbances and over time will return to an approximation of their pre-disturbance functionality. As an example, the old-growth Douglas-fir–western hemlock forests of western Oregon that burn at high severity will go through a sequence of successional stages, each serving different functions until they achieve old-growth status again or a disturbance reoccurs.

Despite undergoing significant near-term change, resilience is maintained in these forests over time through ecological memory encompassed within biological legacies that can serve to restore functional capabilities and adaptation to arising climatic conditions (Johnstone et al., 2016).

Some forest ecosystems, on the other hand, have been altered sufficiently that when they are disrupted by a wildfire or other disturbance, they are no longer able to recover their pre-disturbance functionality and transition to another state (see Figure 12.23 for an example where a frequent-fire forest goes through a fire regime and species shift after wildfire, due to a long period of fire exclusion). Similar consequences may be observed when compounding disturbances impact an ecosystem, including the recurrence of severe fires at intervals shorter than necessary for the ecosystem to reestablish critical processes (Johnstone et al., 2016).

Increasingly federal forests in the United States and elsewhere are managing forests under the broad theme of restoring ecosystem resilience (and resistance), especially in the frequent-fire forests that have seen a massive increase in tree densities. Development of fire and fuel management strategies needs to expand beyond consideration of fire risk to include forest and ecosystem resiliency—indeed to consider the ecological integrity of these ecosystems. Whereas risk is focused on quantifying the likelihood and potential impacts from uncertain disturbances like wildfire, resiliency is focused on the ability of the ecosystem to absorb and recover from disturbance. When designing fuel treatment strategies, it is important to evaluate where treatments can increase resistance, resilience, or both, rather than just targeting areas of high risk (Ager et al., 2013). The fire-safe principles for stand treatments, landscape consideration, and fire-spread modeling, as described earlier in this chapter, are still very useful. However, they are most successful and beneficial when embedded in a strategy of restoring the resistance and resilience of these forests as described in Chapters 3, 4, and 5 and illustrated in the Red Knight example described above.

## The WUI Problem: Fire Management's Greatest Challenge?

The occurrence of wildland fire near human developments is a major fire management concern, and trends of increasing ex-urban residential development in fire-prone areas suggest that WUI fire challenges may increase (Theobold & Romme, 2007). First and foremost, wildland fires that burn into communities can threaten human life and safety, particularly in areas with limited evacuation options. These concerns extend to emergency first responders and firefighters seeking to protect human life and property, tragically exemplified by the loss of 19 firefighters on the Yarnell Hill Fire in 2013. Second, significant damage and loss of homes can occur, particularly in instances where homes are highly ignitable and firefighting capacity can be overwhelmed. This *WUI problem* has been and continues to be a major challenge to fire managers, consumes significant amounts of time and money, and leads to major questions over how best to reduce WUI loss. One representation of the WUI along the Colorado Front Range is depicted in Figure 13.19 along with recent large wildfire activity.

A conceptual model of the major risk mitigation actions and their ultimate effects in reducing risk to human communities allows us to further analyze the WUI problem (Figure 13.20). In this model the two primary determinants of risk of home loss are the probability of a home being exposed to flames and/or to burning embers (firebrands) from wildfire and the susceptibility of the home to loss if exposed to either. Boxes shaded in gray represent a hierarchy of objectives—one can move up the hierarchy of objectives by asking why and move down the hierarchy by asking how. For instance, reducing wildfire occurrence is important to achieve the subsequent objective of reducing home exposure to wildfire (the why), and reducing home exposure to wildfire can be accomplished by reducing wildfire occurrence among other actions (the how). Below the objectives are a set of potential actions that can be undertaken to mitigate risk to human communities (the what). Note that these risk mitigation actions vary in terms of which risk factor(s) they can affect, whether they occur before or during a wildfire, and lastly—and this is very important—who has primary responsibility for their implementation (the who).

An important consideration in treating forested areas in or near the WUI, particularly on federal forestlands, is to retain as much of their ecological functionality as possible, consistent with achieving objectives of reduced risk to life and property (See Color Plate 13.2 for a depiction of federal forests in the Colorado Front Range in and near the WUI that might focus primarily on protection of life and property). This has not received much explicit recognition in the literature on WUI management and needs to receive more. Fortunately, many aspects of these forest ecosystems can be retained consistent with protection of life and property (Box 13.7).

Land management agencies can reduce home exposure to wildfire through ignition prevention, fuels management, and suppression. In response to the growing WUI problem, land management agencies have invested significant resources in treating hazardous fuels in and around communities. Typically these treatments aim to reduce the likelihood of fire spread into the community and/or to enhance suppression effectiveness; a number of cases are documented where treatments likely did help save communities. In other instances, however, the design and implementation of treatments has been insufficient to change

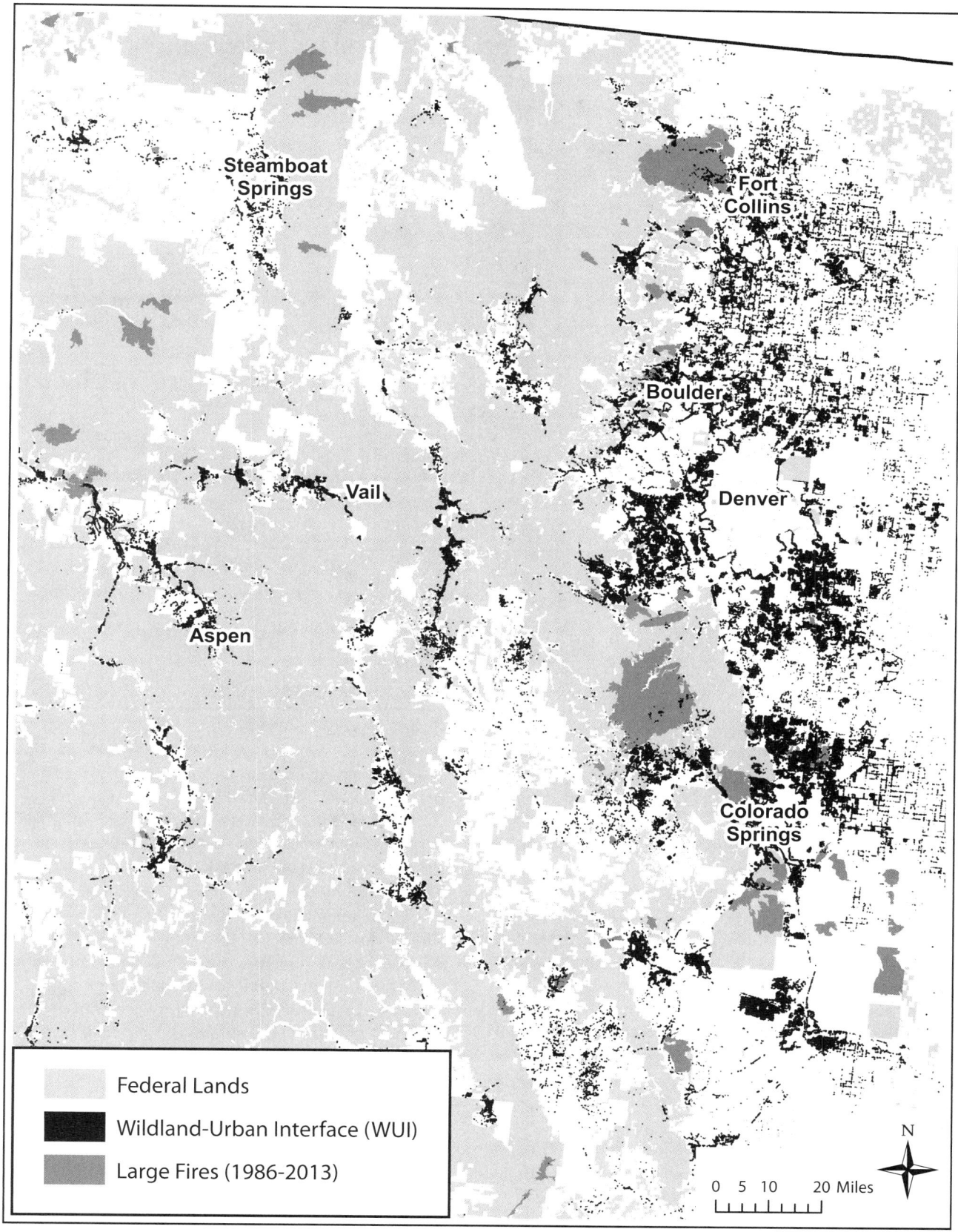

Federal Lands

Wildland-Urban Interface (WUI)

Large Fires (1986-2013)

Figure 13.19  *WUI along the Colorado Front Range, where the WUI reflects human development intermixed with flammable vegetation. One important point that shouldn't be overlooked is the transmission of fire from public lands to the WUI from miles away. Spatial fire planning can help public land managers understand the potential for this transmission to occur, and strategies can be developed to mitigate the associated risk, as described in the last section of this chapter, although that risk can never be fully eliminated.*

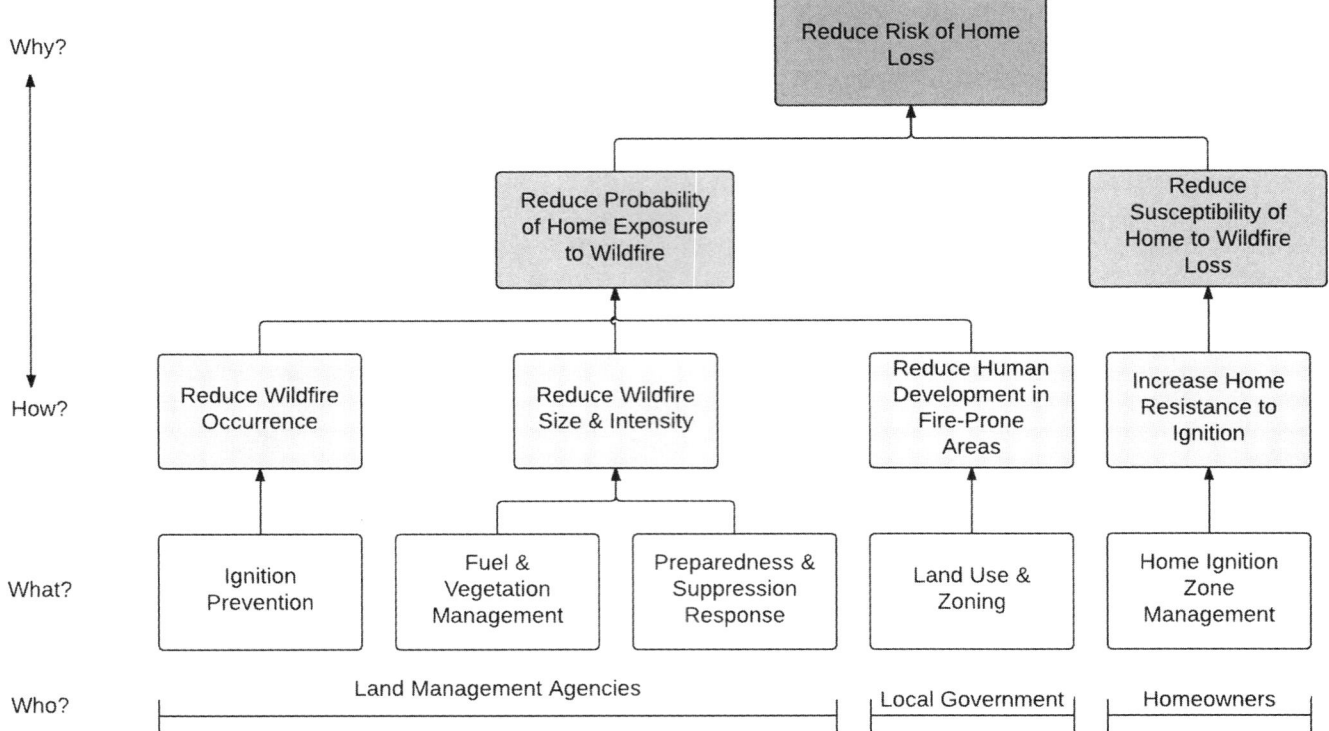

Figure 13.20 *Conceptual model of hierarchical objectives aimed at reducing the risk of home loss in the WUI, along with potential actions to reduce that risk and who bears primary responsibility for those actions.*
*(Source: Adapted from Calkin, Cohen, Finney, & Thompson, 2014)*

---

### Box 13.7  An ecological forestry approach to fuel treatments within and near the WUI

There is a tendency in thinking about forest treatments in or near the WUI to give consideration only to the safety of human life and property and to disregard impacts on the ecological values of forest ecosystems. Such a singular mindset is neither necessary nor desirable. Treatments of forests to reduce fuels and fire behavior and to provide safer conditions for fire fighters in the WUI can be designed to also maintain the ecological integrity of forests. Important elements of the forest that can be retained include structural and compositional features as well as key processes.

A number of features of ecological forest management in frequent-fire forests are also compatible with protection of life and property:

- Producing spatially heterogeneous, rather than uniform, structural outcomes. The widely spaced trees, clumps, and openings, a historical characteristic of western frequent-fire forests, inhibits the spread of crown fires as fires are forced back to the ground (Churchill et al., 2013). This heterogeneity is important from many ecological viewpoints, including the behavior of fire, bark beetles, and aspects of wildlife habitat (see Chapter 3).

- Retaining large and old tree structures of fire-resistant species, such as ponderosa pine and Douglas-fir; these

trees are the most fire-resistant component of these forests and are its structural backbone (see Chapter 3). Structural retention can also extend to large-diameter snags of short to medium height, which represent limited risk as fuels but are critical wildlife habitat.

- Creating and sustaining understories of native species—particularly those dominated by grasses and other herbaceous species—can contribute greatly to maintenance of ecological values. Prescribed burning can help create such understories, which, in turn, become excellent fuels for sustaining a prescribed burning program. Such programs can also help reduce existing tall shrubs and small trees, which represent undesirable ladder fuels. And, as odd as it might seem, there is perhaps no place where prescribed burning is a more appropriate activity than in or near the WUI!

Sustaining the integrity of forest ecosystems in or near the WUI needs to receive consideration as fuel loadings are reduced; it can be done without sacrificing the goals of reduced risk to life and property! This is a critical consideration for the large acreage of federal forestland in or near the WUI throughout the western United States.

fire behavior and reduce loss, especially under extreme fire weather conditions (Calkin et al., 2014) (Box 13.8).

The magnitude of the WUI problem is so large that agencies have not been able to afford the costs of treating or maintaining treated areas at a sufficient scale to protect all threatened communities. The challenge of treating enough area to change landscape-scale fire behavior is further complicated by dispersed residential development and coordination across mixed-ownership landscapes. It is therefore critically important to realize that treating hazardous fuels alone will not "solve" the WUI/wildfire problem. In fact, some have suggested deemphasizing broadscale wildland fuel treatments and instead targeting fuels in the immediate vicinity of homes and communities as a more efficient risk mitigation approach.

The entire spectrum of actions available to land management agencies is insufficient to fully reduce exposure (Figure 13.19); land and fire managers simply cannot reduce the likelihood of wildfire to zero. Instead, human development on private land in fire-prone areas is a significant determinant of the degree of exposure of these resources to fire. Controlling the pace and location of future WUI development is therefore key to success in reducing WUI exposure and ultimately WUI loss, which is a responsibility that falls on local governmental entities, such as zoning boards and county commissioners.

Equally, if not more important than exposure, is the susceptibility of homes to wildfire loss. Post-fire studies have determined that home loss can occur under a wide range of fire conditions and that the characteristics of the home itself and its immediate surroundings can primarily dictate home loss (Cohen, 2010). This point is illustrated in Figure 13.21, where the surrounding green vegetation indicates that the fire burned with low intensity in the adjacent trees. This home, along with more than 200 others, was destroyed by firebrand ignitions rather than wildfire burning through the residential development. When firefighters are overwhelmed or unavailable, even low-intensity or small fires can lead to devastation. Contrast Figure 13.21 with Figure 13.22, which shows a home that survived a high-intensity fire. This home survived the fire due to the resistance of the home ignition zone, and

Figure 13.21 *Home destroyed by the 2007 Grass Valley Fire in California. (Photo courtesy of Jack Cohen)*

---

## Box 13.8 Lessons from Fourmile Canyon Fire

High wind speeds and low relative humidity are common weather conditions associated with large wildfires along the Colorado Front Range foothills. Thus, recognition of these conditions is critical when developing fuel treatment prescriptions. However, the description and documentation of fuel treatments implemented in this area did not mention the weather conditions under which they were intended to be effective. The methods for maintaining surface fuels in a treated condition also were not identified. That is, the target conditions for the fuel treatments and supporting prescription elements were not identified.

If target fire weather conditions had been identified for the high-loss events typical along the Colorado Front Range, successful fuel treatments would have required considerably different arrangement, extent, and prescriptions. Fragmented, primarily private ownership resulting from mining claims interspersed with municipal and federal lands made large-scale treatment efforts difficult. The mechanical chipping of trees and brush used in the fuel treatments may have ultimately benefitted tree survival if it were followed by burning of the chip material after it was distributed across the ground surface. The narrow linear fuel breaks along roads (presumably intended to provide a defensive barrier) were ineffective under the regularly occurring target weather conditions of high winds and low humidity along the Colorado Front Range, resulting in long-range spotting of 1 km or more. Ultimately, existing treatments had no discernible influence on reducing fire spread or in aiding suppression effectiveness. See Calkin et al. (2014) for further details.

during the fire it provided shelter to the owner and several firefighters.

*Thus, effective management of the ignitability and survivability of homes is a prerequisite for reducing home loss, whether or not fuel treatments have also been implemented.* The burden for managing the ignitability of homes falls upon individual home owners and not land management agencies. Local governments can also play a role in ensuring that future development is risk-informed and responsible. Insurance companies can also contribute by inducing homeowners to manage home ignitability through premium adjustments in very fire-prone areas. Home loss will only be reduced through shared responsibility for WUI risk mitigation. In summary, land management agencies can play a vital role in helping to protect communities from wildfire through fuel treatments and other actions, but hold neither the only nor the primary responsibility for addressing the WUI problem.

Figure 13.22 *Home that survived a high-intensity fire during the 2003 Wedge Canyon Fire, Montana. This is the same home depicted in Figure 13.1. Note that being a wooden structure does not necessarily mean high susceptibility to fire; factors like roofing material, maintenance of gutters, and fuel conditions immediately adjacent to the home also play a crucial role. (Photo courtesy of Rick Trembath)*

## Strategic Zoning for Wildfire Response: An Integrative Approach

It may seem that this chapter has covered a number of important but somewhat disparate themes on how to address the issue of fire and fuels in our forests—fuel management through mechanical treatment and prescribed fire, managing wildfires for resource benefits, ecological forestry, restoration and maintenance of forest resilience, and protection of the WUI. Still, the question remains of how these themes will be integrated into a coherent vision.

At the beginning of this chapter, we stated that our focus would be mainly on the efforts of the US Forest Service to address fire and fuels issues. Thus, it seems fitting to end the chapter with an attempt to integrate these themes in the management of the national forests—especially into management of the frequent-fire forests of the western United States.

*Thompson et al. (2016) suggest that we focus on how wildfires are managed on the national forests as a key determinant of long-term socioecological resiliency of these forests and the ability to live with fire. Further, they argue that safe and effective response to fire requires prefire planning.* Utilizing recent advancements in spatial wildfire risk assessment—notably *in situ* risk and source risk assessment that capture fire effects within a defined geographic area and the spatial extent of fire ignitions that have the potential to reach the WUI—Thompson et al. integrate risk assessment results with additional geospatial information

to develop and map strategic response zones. As they also note, a given response category may encompass a range of protection and resource objectives.

Thompson et al. (2016) utilize *potential wildland fire operational delineations (PODs)* as the spatial unit of analysis for strategic response. PODs are "a spatial representation of an area useful for summarizing risk in a meaningful operational fire management context. PODs can also identify priority fuel treatment projects, within a given POD or along the boundaries between PODs with different risk levels and response categories" (Thompson et al., 2016, p. 11). This approach to PODs is useful for forest planning; a smaller scale may be needed for management of an actual incident.

Using results from a recent risk assessment performed on several National Forests in the southern Sierra Nevada area of California, USA, Thompson et al. (2016) illustrate how POD-level analysis of risk metrics can reduce uncertainty surrounding potential losses and benefits given large fire occurrence and how it lends itself naturally to the design of fire and fuel management strategies in forest planning. They describe three zoning categories that might be utilized on the federal forests (Thompson et al., 2016, p. 4):

1. *Protect:* Current conditions are such that *highly valued resources and assets (HVRAs)* are at high risk of loss from wildfire. Mechanical fuel treatments would principally be used to yield desired fire behavior conducive to more effective fire management, or in some instances retention of desired conditions for

natural resources. Prescribed burning would principally be used to maintain previously treated areas. The use of wildfire to increase ecosystem resilience and provide ecological benefits would be very limited.

2. *Restore:* Current conditions are such that HVRAs are at moderate risk of loss from wildfire. Wildfire could be used to increase ecosystem resilience and provide ecological benefits when conditions allow. Strategically located mechanical treatments and/or prescribed burning, where feasible, may be a necessary precursor to the reintroduction of wildfire to achieve desired conditions.

3. *Maintain:* Current conditions are such that HVRAs are at low risk of loss from wildfire, and many natural resources may benefit from fire. Due to low risk, wildfires are expected to be used as often as possible to maintain ecosystem resilience and provide ecological benefits when conditions allow. Mechanical treatments and/or prescribed burning, where feasible, would be used to complement wildfire to achieve desired conditions. Aggressive suppression to keep fires as small as possible would be limited and require justification because these types of actions generally are counter to land and resource management objectives.

They then illustrate this zoning with the Sierra National Forest in the Sierra Nevada Range of California (Figure 13.23). As they state (Thompson et al., 2016, p. 18):

*The spatial mosaic of POD response assignments tends to follow an easterly progression from "protect" to "restore" to "maintain" . . . Proximity to the wildland-urban interface along the western flanks of the Forest boundary clearly plays a strong role here. So too does the potential for "restore" PODs to act as a source of net loss to adjacent PODs within the "protect" category. . . . "Maintain" assignments by contrast tend to be the furthest from development, where the principal HVRAs impacted by fire are natural resources, and where fire can improve vegetation condition.*

This approach to federal forest zoning attempts to integrate public and agency concerns over wildfire response on and near national forests with fuel management strategies and achievement of ecosystem resilience. In addition, it identifies the types of tools that might be utilized to achieve management goals. While the distribution of PODS among the different zones will depend on the unique environment of each forest, this three-part zoning is a promising approach to integrating the many themes of this chapter into management strategies for the frequent-fire forests of the West.

As we have described throughout this chapter, an ecological forestry approach can prove useful in all three zones, employing the different tools to achieve both ecological and social objectives. Perhaps the greatest challenge here will be to integrate ecological forestry into the Protect Zone, where HVRAs are at high risk of loss from wildfire. Such an integration may require substantial change in implementation of fuel treatments and the way that people, communities, and institutions (including insurance companies) view the risk associated with the heterogeneous forest that remains after an ecological forestry treatment that has fuel reduction as one of its primary goals (see Box 13.7). However, given the probable extent of the Protect Zone in many parts of the West, such as in the southern Sierra Range of California (Figure 13.23) or the Front Range of Colorado (Figure 13.19; Color Plate 13.2), making such a shift can be important to providing ecological benefits from forests at the same time that people, communities, and property are protected.

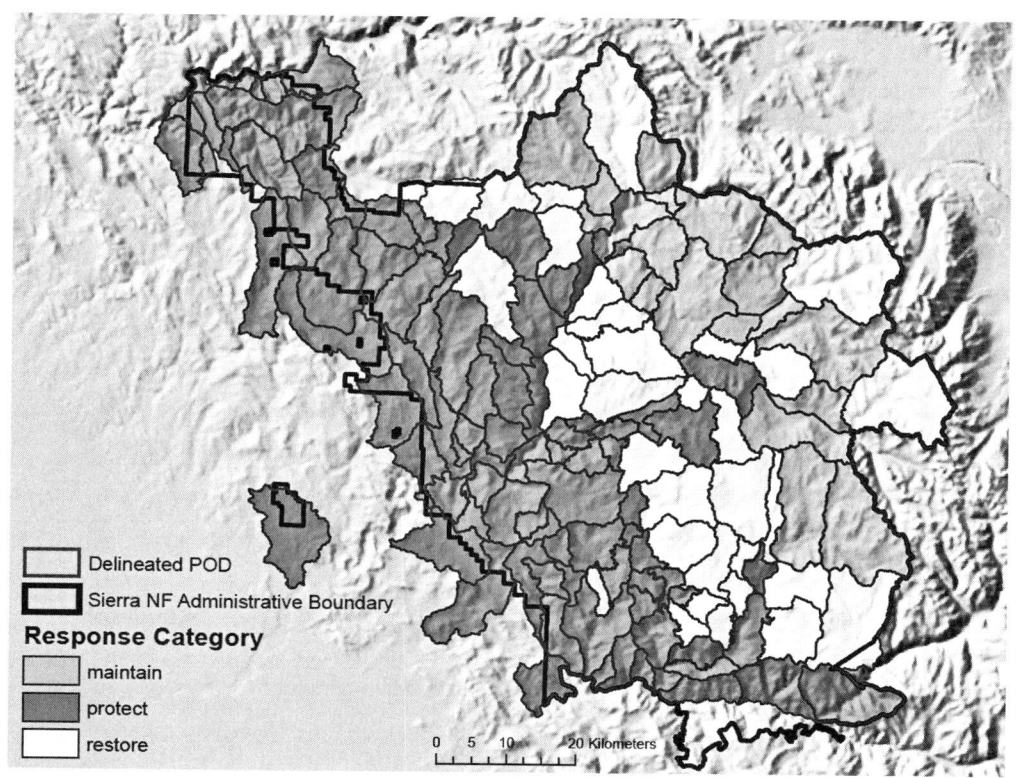

Figure 13.23 *A strategic zoning approach to wildfire response.*

## Appendix: A Brief Discussion of Fire Models

A number of fire and fuel modeling systems are available (Peterson, Evers, Gravenmier, & Eberhardt, 2007). These models typically vary across multiple dimensions, including their spatial and temporal resolution, the number of fire weather conditions considered, the number of fires considered, whether the models are deterministic versus probabilistic, and the types of outputs provided (Table 13.3). Many fire "models" are actually a composite of multiple models, for instance combining submodels for the frequency and location of ignitions, the spread of surface fire, and the initiation and propagation of crown fire.

We can organize fire models (roughly) into three categories:

- *Deterministic, nonspatial models* of fire behavior with an assumed set of ignitions and weather conditions (fuel moisture, wind speed and direction) that can influence fire behavior. By running the model multiple times with different inputs that managers can get a sense of the potential range of fire behavior.

- *Probabilistic, nonspatial models* whose results can be tied back to a particular location on the landscape with similar fuel conditions, but the actual growth of fires are not modeled. To illustrate why modeling fire growth can be important, consider fire growing as an ellipse elongated according to the predominant wind direction. All else being equal, fire behavior at the "head" of the ellipse (in the direction of the wind) will be the most intense; fire behavior at the rear of the fire (a "backing" fire) will be the least intense; and fire behavior along the flanks of the fire will be somewhere in between. The relative spread direction of fire as it moves across the landscape is therefore important in determining localized estimates of fire behavior and how fire spread is itself influenced by topography and fuel conditions across the broader landscape. Nonspatial models do not capture spread across the landscape and often assume that every location will burn under a "heading fire" scenario, in essence estimating near worst case burning conditions.

- *Probabilistic, spatially explicit models* that consider thousands of possible fires and model the growth of each fire across the landscape. Some spatial fire-spread models consider a limited set of user-defined weather conditions (often a single problem fire scenario) over a specific duration (often a single "burn period"), whereas others consider a wider range of weather conditions over a longer period of time. Spatial fire-spread models also vary according to whether they capture variability surrounding just the location of ignitions or the occurrence and location of ignitions; the latter is important to capture due to the fact that, in many areas, the occurrence of wildfire in any given year is relatively unlikely. Only the most complex of models consider variability around the frequency and location of ignitions, under a wide range of fire weather conditions, over the course of an entire fire season (Finney et al., 2011).

These more complicated modeling systems automate the process of modeling fire behavior and growth under a wide range of conditions, often by drawing from random scenarios according to historical patterns. As a result each simulated fire is analogous to a roll of the dice in a gambling game, hence the name Monte Carlo simulation. These Monte Carlo models provide a rich set of probabilistic results that can help managers evaluate which areas on the landscape are more likely to burn, or are more likely to burn at a given intensity. The clear trade-off is that although

Table 13.3 *Brief description of some commonly used and supported fire and fuel modeling systems. (See firelab.org and www.fs.fed.us/wwetac/arcfuels for additional information on these models; see Finney et al. [2011], and Scott et al. [2013] for descriptions of more advanced systems and tools typically used in research applications.)*

| Model Name | Description | Source |
| --- | --- | --- |
| *BehavePlus* | Collection of mathematical models to describe fire behavior, fire effects, and fire environment based on specified fuel and moisture conditions | Andrews (2014) |
| *FARSITE* | Computes wildfire growth and behavior for long time periods under heterogeneous conditions of terrain, fuels, and weather | Finney (2004) |
| *FlamMap* | Fire mapping and analysis system that creates raster maps of burn probability and fire behavior characteristics; often used to evaluate problem fire scenarios | Finney (2006) |
| *ArcFuels* | Streamlines fuel management planning and wildfire risk assessment system; interfaces with various forest growth and fire behavior models within an ArcGIS platform | Vaillant et al. (2013) |

the more complex models can allow for more detailed and comprehensive analysis, they can require significantly more time and effort to use appropriately.

Not all models are necessarily useful for every question fire and fuel managers may ask. Rather, the suitability of any particular model(s) will depend on the fuel treatment planning context:

- For prescribed burns, the potential spread of fire is less important since the size and shape of the burn are planned in advance and held by firefighters. In such cases, nonspatial, deterministic fire models that can estimate fuel consumption and smoke production under the target weather conditions may be most helpful.

- Nonspatial fire, probabilistic fire behavior modeling can be helpful for identifying stands that, under a given set of conditions, could burn with high intensity and lead to undesirable outcomes such as loss of legacy trees or destruction of habitat. This type of fire modeling can help in the design phase of treatment planning by identifying and prioritizing stands that present the greatest hazard. Nonspatial fire modeling can also be helpful for evaluating stand prescriptions; comparisons of fire modeling results under different posttreatment conditions can help identify the most suitable treatment type.

- Sophisticated probabilistic fire-spread modeling is most useful where managers are interested in changes to fire behavior within and outside of treated areas, measuring potential treatment effects on fire spread and subsequent patterns of fire likelihood and intensity across the landscape. Using interacting models of forest dynamics and wildfire spread allows researchers and fire managers to explore relationships between the scale, location, and treatment rates through time.

*Only the mountain has lived long enough to listen
objectively to the howl of the wolf.* — ALDO LEOPOLD

# CHAPTER 14

# Conserving and Restoring Biological Diversity

Cristina Eisenberg

In 1936 eminent forester and visionary Aldo Leopold wrote in his field journal, "To keep every cog and wheel is the first precaution of intelligent tinkering" (Leopold, 1993, p. 147). By this he meant that in managing any ecosystem, including forests, a basic rule of thumb is to prevent species from going extinct. He wrote those prescient words when the science of ecology was still young and about 50 years before the term biodiversity was coined.

Maintaining biological diversity is a basic principle of ecological forestry and is justified by both practical and philosophical considerations. The goal in this chapter is to provide forest stewards and stakeholders with an overview of biodiversity, its importance, and some of the challenges to sustaining it. The chapter has six sections that cover:

- The nature and importance of biodiversity, including discussion of its hierarchal levels and its measurement;

- Sustaining biodiversity as a part of ecologically based forest management at the forest and landscape scales;

- Species of special ecological importance, including top predators, such as wolves and lynx, and their potential cascading impacts on the ecosystems;

- The formative role of law in conserving biodiversity, using legal frameworks of the United States as our example;

- Combining ecosystem and species approaches to conserving biodiversity; and

- Summary conclusions on the relationship between biodiversity and ecological forestry.

*Wolf on an elk trail in Warrenton Lakes National Park, Alberta, Canada. (Photo courtesy of Parks Canada)*

# The Nature and Importance of Biological Diversity

## What Is "Biodiversity"?

What exactly is *biodiversity* and why does it matter? Biodiversity can be broadly defined as the variety of life and all of its processes. Ecologist W. G. Rosen coined the term in 1985 as a contraction of the phrase "biological diversity," and it emerged in the scientific literature in the book, *Biodiversity*, edited by ecologists Edward O. Wilson and Frances M. Peter (1988). Initially biodiversity referred to the number of species in a community or ecosystem (MacLaurin & Sternley, 2008), but it was soon expanded to include "the variety of living organisms, the genetic differences among them, the communities and ecosystems in which they occur, and the ecological evolutionary processes that keep them functioning" (Noss & Cooperrider, 1994, p. 389).

Hence, the term biodiversity is used most generally today to include all of the biota that are present and their interactions. This would include species and the various linkages among the biota, including mutualistic and competitive interactions. Food webs, as mentioned in Chapter 2, are an important example of the relationships among species. These are the nutritional linkages, which are typically composed of many species at different trophic levels, from green plants and their products through mammals and birds to a myriad of insects and other invertebrates and ultimately to fungi and microbial organisms that carry out the decomposition processes. These webs of "who eats who" represent common but important and highly structured linkages, which contribute significantly to sustaining functional attributes of ecosystems as well as dramatically expanding the number of species that an ecosystem can support.

Although biodiversity is not just about species, *species* remain the fundamental unit of biodiversity, defined as, "A population whose members are able to interbreed freely under natural conditions" (Wilson, 1999). Species matter for evolutionary reasons—to ensure that life in all its forms continues on this planet. However, as we shall see, not all species are created equal and simply enumerating species does not provide a particularly useful metric. Some species are abundant and weedy generalists, such as the dandelion (*Taraxacum officinale*), while other species have highly specific habitat requirements and may be relatively rare (e.g., the northern spotted owl [*Strix occidentalis caurina*]). Further, some species have extraordinary importance to ecosystem function and are recognized with labels such as "foundation" or "keystone." Other species appear to be simply "icing on the cake," with no apparent unique value or influence, but may, in fact, provide important sources of functional redundancy (where more than one species performs the same, or similar, role within an ecosystem) or an undiscovered source of some important chemical compound (as was the case with Pacific yew [*Taxus brevifolia*]).

When we think about species diversity we generally think first about larger and more conspicuous organisms—other vertebrates like ourselves—and those most useful to us as sources of food and shelter, like trees and shrubs. However, the concept of biodiversity includes small and relatively inconspicuous organisms, such as viruses, bacteria, fungi, protozoa, algae, and, most profoundly, invertebrates (Table 14.1). We generally give little attention to such organisms in our efforts to conserve biological diversity, including in forest management. Perhaps we think of them as being so universally abundant and mobile as to require little or no attention or, even worse, as being only pests and pathogens. In fact, these small organisms carry out much of the important work that goes on within ecosystems, second only to the green plants that capture solar energy.

## Why Is Biodiversity Important?

Biodiversity is fundamentally important to humankind because it makes it possible for human life to survive, to be reasonably predictable (stable), and to have a much richer experience than it might otherwise! Biodiversity creates and sustains life on earth, helps stabilize the life systems, and enriches and inspires human lives.

Biota are the organic "machines" that do *all* of the work needed to convert the physical elements of the environment—light, water, and nutrients—into ecosystems, including provision of the energy-rich carbon compounds needed to sustain those ecosystems and all of the life that they contain. As discussed in Chapter 2, ecosystems provide diverse functions, including production (capture of solar energy, its conversion to organic matter, creation of organic structures [e.g., trees!] and flows of energy/carbon through

Table 14.1 *Diversity of life on earth (developed following Hunter, 1999)*

| Category | Described Species | Estimated Species Richness |
|---|---|---|
| Viruses | 4,000 | 400,000 |
| Bacteria | 4,000 | 1,000,000 |
| Fungi | 72,000 | 1,500,000 |
| Protozoa | 40,000 | 200,000 |
| Algae | 40,000 | 400,000 |
| Plants | 270,000 | 320,000 |
| Arthropods | 1,065,000 | 8,900,000 |
| Other animals | 255,000 | 900,000 |

**Box 14.1  Trees, truffles, and red-backed voles (*Myodes californicus*): A web illustrating the complex and important mutualistic relationships among diverse biota that exist in forest ecosystems**

The symbiotic relationship between conifers and mycorrhizal-forming soil fungi in the Pacific Northwest provides an excellent example of how complex webs of diverse organisms sustain forest ecosystems. As discussed in Chapter 2, many species of fungi form intimate mycorrhizal associations with the fine roots of trees. Trees provide the fungi with nutrients in the form of carbohydrates from photosynthesis, and the mycorrhizal structures formed between the fungi and tree roots are critical in facilitating the uptake of water and nutrients by the trees.

In the 1970s, Jim Trappe, a mycologist, and Chris Maser, a mammalogist, described a mutualistic relationship between the western red-backed vole, truffles (*Tuber* sp.), and Douglas-fir (*Pseudotsuga menziesii*). Truffles are fungi that produce spore-bearing reproductive structures belowground rather than the mushroom-like structures that appear aboveground. Both types of fungi (truffle and mushroom producers) form mycorrhizal relationships with trees (see Chapter 2). Truffles are roughly round and brown (resembling tiny potatoes) and range from one half to three inches in diameter. Because they remain belowground, the primary means of spore dispersal is by animal consumption (mycophagy) and movement. The western red-backed vole depends almost entirely on truffles, which are also an important food source for other animals, such as the northern flying squirrel (*Glaucomys sabrinus*). After eating the truffles these animals disperse the indigestible spores in their feces throughout their travels. Ultimately some germinate and form new mycorrhizae with Douglas-fir

and other trees and shrubs. When a Douglas-fir dies and falls to the ground it gradually rots, providing habitat for the vole and creating a nutritious medium for truffle growth, completing this cycle (Maser, Claridge, & Trappe, 2008).

There are many other examples of important functional roles played by small mammals in forest ecosystems. For example, various species of chipmunks (*Eutamias* spp.), as well as the golden-mantled ground squirrel (*Citellus lateralis*), cache and consume the seeds of ponderosa pine (*Pinus ponderosa*) and bitterbrush (*Purshia tridentata*) in the frequent-fire forests of eastern Oregon. However, these small mammals fail to consume all of their caches and some of this forgotten seed germinates to produce small clusters of ponderosa pine and bitterbrush seedlings. This is a valuable outcome because these two species represent the dominant tree and shrub species in these forests and bitterbush is the most important browse for mule deer (*Odocoileus hemionus*). These small mammals also provide longer-term benefits for their own habitat with their seed-caching behavior by helping to regenerate future food sources (West, 1968).

Another example, which we will review later in more detail, concerns the contribution that wolves (*Canis lupus*) can make in helping to maintain diverse woody vegetation. By hunting elk and keeping them on the move, wolves can reduce browse pressure on hardwoods such as quaking aspen (*Populus tremuloides*), thereby enabling saplings to survive and grow, and eventually replace the older aspen that die.

food webs, including its eventual loss through respiration, decomposition, and combustion), regulation of hydrologic and geomorphic processes, development and conservation of soils and nutrient stocks, and provision of habitat for biological diversity. Intuitively the greater the diversity—the more different species supporting each of these various functions or processes—the more capable and resilient an ecosystem is likely to be.

**Biodiversity Helps Forest Ecosystems Function**  As we discuss throughout this book, forest structures and processes are vital to the survival of forest creatures, whether for shelter, food, warmth, or protection from predators. The reverse is also true—forest creatures (including microbial) are vital to the existence of forest structures and processes and to the functioning of whole forest ecosystems—they are the *creative agents*. There are many well-documented examples of this (see Box 14.1). We will come back to this theme throughout the chapter.

**Biodiversity Is Essential to Human Well-Being**  Maintaining biological diversity is a key focus in ecological forest manage-

ment; it is important to ensure that the forests will be: (1) more capable of generating the variety of ecological services and benefits that humans seek from forests (Lindenmayer & Franklin, 2002), and (2) more resilient to stresses such as drought and climate change. So, why are an abundance of species needed to accomplish these two objectives?

One could argue that a forest with multiple species of salamanders would not suffer if one or even several species became extinct. Why do so many seemingly functionally redundant species exist and why does the redundancy that they provide matter? The value of having many different species comes, at least in part, because the diversity makes a community more stable. For example, one may need only a single tree species to develop a forest structure but if that species is lost, the forest disappears. With multiple tree species, on the other hand, if one species is lost others are present that can continue to provide forest conditions. And, of course, the tree species will differ in their growth forms and in the kind of standing dead trees and down wood that they produce, providing a greater diversity in structural conditions within the forest. Thus, the redundancy provided by multiple species makes the forest stable and, also, more adaptable to changes in environmental conditions and introductions of new pathogens.

There are innumerable examples of the redundant value of multiple species. Two species of grouse in a forest, both of which may be eaten by coyotes (*Canus latrans*), may differ in terms of their ease of capture and seasonal and local occurrence and thereby provide alternative food sources for the coyote. This example illustrates that biodiversity helps maintain a more stable flow of energy through an ecosystem by sustaining ecological processes such as predation. Similarly, biodiversity helps sustain other ecological processes, such as pollination and decomposition (Hutchinson, 1959; Loreau et al., 2001). The abundance of fungal species that form mycorrhizae is an important example of the value of multiple species. Each of the typically numerous fungal species has different environmental optima. Hence, as environmental conditions change—over the seasons of a year, from year to year, over long-term succession, or with climate change—there is the potential for continuing adjustments in the dominant fungal species that are partnering with the mycorrhizae as needed to sustain optimal functionality.

Ecosystem services related to biodiversity include clean air and water, soil formation, pollution filtration, nutrient cycling, climate regulation, and recovery from disturbances. Biodiversity improves ecosystem processes, such as nutrient cycling (Hooper et al., 2005). An ecosystem in which nutrients are cycling vigorously and freely, via the carbon cycle and predation, will have sustained production of plant and animal biomass and higher nutrient retention in the soil than a less biodiverse system (i.e., one with fewer species of plants in it), and greater ability for the soil to regulate water quantity and quality. These ecological processes provide food, fiber, and fuel for humans. They also increase human well-being by supplying the basic materials for a good life, which include health, security, and recreational opportunities (Díaz, Fargione, Chapin III, & Tilman, 2006).

*The more biodiverse an ecosystem, the more resilient it is likely to be to disturbances of various types.* An ecosystem that has high biodiversity can better absorb the carbon dioxide and nitrogen produced by human activity and urbanization than one with low biodiversity (Mooney, Cushman, Medina, Sala, & Schulze, 1996). A system kept productive by multiple plant species has less risk of failing, because such communities have redundancies built into them (Peterson, Allen, & Holling, 1998). In the event that a disturbance (e.g., a fire) eliminates one of these species, another can fill its niche. Generally, as the number of species (called **species richness**) drops, ecosystem resilience declines along with energy cycling through a food web—also referred to as **food web efficiency** (Ives 2007; Naeem, Thompson, Lawler, & Lawton, 1994). *Increasing biodiversity is now viewed as one of the most important actions that can be taken to increase ecosystem resilience to climate change, primarily*

*as a risk-spreading strategy—i.e., the greater number of species present the less the risk that loss of species will result in significant loss in ecosystem function* (see Chapter 21).

Additionally, specific ecosystem services, such as carbon cycling through a forest, may be tied to a particular species found in a particular location, thereby making losses of such species more significant in terms of ecosystem function. For example, the lichen *Lobaria oregana* is found primarily in old-growth forests, where light and moisture conditions allow it to be abundant. It is one of the cyanolichens, which means that a cyanobacteria (see Chapter 2) is one of its three organismal components. Rain can leach nitrogen from the lichen, and nitrogen is also released when the lichen dies and decays, making nitrogen available to trees and other plants. *Lobaria* and other cyanolichens are scarce in young forests, reducing the amount of nitrogen available and potentially reducing forest productivity. This is another lesson in the importance of less conspicuous species, whether we currently understand the role that they are playing or not, and another reason why it is wise to *save all the pieces*, as recommended by Aldo Leopold (1993)!

## The Biodiversity Concept and Its Hierarchical Levels

Biodiversity is one of the most difficult concepts in ecology to define, because it is at once a multicontextual and hierarchical concept (Redford & Richter, 1999). The concept of biodiversity was created by scientists who worked within the discipline of **community ecology**, which is the study of the structure of ecological communities and how they vary in time and space in response to physical and biotic factors (Eisenberg, 2014). As mentioned above, biodiversity was initially identified with species diversity but quickly underwent broad expansion with a substantial boost from the 1986 National Forum on BioDiversity (Wilson & Peter, 1988). One of the most comprehensive definitional treatments of biodiversity is by Reed F. Noss (1990), who expanded its attributes to include structure and function as well as composition (species) and proposed a comprehensive set of monitoring indicators. Noss' (1990) organizational hierarchy is: *Regional Landscape, Community-Ecosystem, Population-Species, and Genetic.* Noss describes each of these levels in his nested hierarchy as:

- *Regional Landscape* emphasizes the spatial complexity of regions, with "Landscape" referring to "a mosaic of heterogeneous land forms, vegetation types, and land uses" (Urban et al., 1987, cited in Noss, 1990, p. 358). The spatial scale of a regional landscape might vary from a national forest or park and its surroundings up to the size of a physiographic region or biogeographic province.

- *Community-Ecosystem* emphasizes a more localized scale: *Community* comprises the populations of some or all species existing at a site while an *ecosystem* also includes the abiotic aspects of the environment with which the biotic community is interdependent.

- *Population-Species* can consider all populations of a species across its range, whether it is a metapopulation (populations of a species connected by dispersal) or a single, disjunct population.

- *Genetic* relates to the genetic variability within a species.

Noss (1990, p. 356) justifies his approach as follows:

*A definition of biodiversity that is altogether simple, comprehensive, and fully operational (i.e., responsive to real-life management and regulatory questions) is unlikely to be found. More useful than a definition, perhaps, would be a characterization of biodiversity that identifies the major components at several levels of organization. This would provide a conceptual framework for identifying specific, measurable indicators to monitor change and assess the overall status of biodiversity.*

Further, Noss utilizes Franklin et al.'s (1981) recognition of three primary attributes of ecosystems: composition, structure, and function, to help his indicators of the overall status of biodiversity. As Noss (1990, p. 357) says:

*Three attributes determine, and in fact constitute, the biodiversity of an area. Composition has to do with the identity and variety of elements in a collection, and includes species lists and measures of species diversity and genetic diversity. Structure is the physical organization or pattern of a system, from habitat complexity as measured within communities to the pattern of patches and other elements at a landscape scale. Function involves ecological and evolutionary processes, including gene flow, disturbances, and nutrient cycling.*

He then identifies indicator variables for assessing terrestrial biodiversity for each of the three attributes at the four levels of organization. As an example, some of his indicators of biodiversity at the regional landscape level are:

- *Composition*: Identity, distribution, richness, and patch (habitat) types and multipatch landscape types; collective patterns of species distributions;

- *Structure*: Heterogeneity, connectivity, spatial linkage, patchiness, porosity, fragmentation, patch size frequency distribution; and

- *Function*: disturbance processes, nutrient cycling, energy flow rates, past persistence and turnover rates.

Noss' approach in which he links biodiversity to the primary attributes of ecosystems (composition, structure, and function) relates well to the approach we take in ecological forestry, where we utilize these attributes to describe the goals of forest management actions. We rely on that linkage throughout this book.

A slightly different hierarchy is commonly utilized by scientists, or in projects, focused on individual species: Genetic (Species), Local Population, and Metapopulation (Box 14.2) This hierarchical structure is appropriately used, for example, in planning processes where conservation of a particular species, such as an at-risk species, needs to be addressed at a variety of landscape scales, from very small to very large (Soberón & Vázquez-Domínguez, 2000).

## How Can We Measure Biodiversity?

Biodiversity is measured in a variety of interrelated, hierarchical ways (Figure 14.2). Any attempt to measure biodiversity quickly runs into the problem that it is a multidimensional concept: it can't be reduced sensibly to a single number. **Alpha Diversity**, also called **species richness**, simply means the total number of different species in an area and is the simplest measure of biodiversity. However, managers and scientists often want to know how a particular management strategy, such as extending timber harvest rotations, or variable-retention harvest, will affect biodiversity. In order to know that, it becomes necessary to compare biodiversity between two different forest patches. **Beta Diversity** is the species diversity across the two patches, recognizing all the species found in them. Finally, **Gamma Diversity** is the overall diversity within a large region (Eisenberg, 2010).

Certain types of taxa are used to measure biodiversity, because they lend themselves well to surveys. Common taxa used for biodiversity surveys include songbirds and insects. Salamanders also can be used as indicators of biodiversity and ecosystem function in forested habitats. Due to their longevity, compact territories, fidelity to sites, propensity to occur in high densities, and the cost-effectiveness of surveying them, salamanders can be used to very effectively measure Beta Diversity. Thus, Welsh and Droege (2001) found salamander survey data more robust statistically than songbird, small mammal, or butterfly surveys to measure biodiversity.

## Sustaining Forest Biodiversity

Much of what is needed to sustain biodiversity in forest ecosystems can be done relatively easily as a part of managing forest properties for multiple values, including wood production. Conceptually it is simple—provide the variety of habitat elements that are needed by the biota, assuming there are not complicating issues such as invasive com-

petitors, illegal hunting, or introduced diseases or predators. Even where such complications are absent, providing the variety of habitat elements needed does require efforts over multiple spatial scales—considerations from logs to

---

### Box 14.2  Three hierarchical levels in consideration of a species

Three hierarchical levels are often recognized in dealing with a particular species: *genetic (species)*, *local population*, and *metapopulation* (Figure 14.1). Using lynx (*Lynx canadensis*) as an example, this species' unique set of genes represents the *genetic* level of diversity. Genetic diversity enables species to adapt to disturbance and change. For instance, if a lethal disease breaks out in a lynx community, diverse genetic makeup may allow some individuals to survive. The local population level for lynx would include all lynx living in an area of forest in northeastern Washington. This could consist of several female lynx and their kittens and some solitary males and females (lynx tend to be solitary except during mating and when females raise their kittens) (Eisenberg, 2014; McKelvey, Buskirk, & Krebs, 1999). Also called a *deme*, this local population level of diversity helps a larger population adapt to change. Finally, the metapopulation level of biodiversity would encompass all the lynx living in the Washington North Cascade Mountains. Broadly defined, a metapopulation is a group of local populations of a species separated by space where the spatially separated populations can interact as individual members and move from one population to another.

There are other contextual issues that need to be considered when dealing with individual species including the food web structure within ecosystems, i.e., where lynx fit into a food web, and their role within this framework; how they interact with other organisms, such as their primary prey, the snowshoe hare (*Lepus americanus*); and the link-

ages between ecosystem components in the geographic region. Lynx require mature forest with complex structure for denning and nearby early seral (preforest) plant communities for foraging.* Thus, lynx require that most forest stages be present.

Biodiversity concepts can feel inconsistent at the metapopulation level. Using grizzly bear populations in the northern Rocky Mountains as an example, the term metapopulation has been applied to: (1) the bear populations in Glacier National Park, Montana (Kendall et al., 2008); (2) the bear population in the region that encompasses Glacier National Park and the adjoining Great Bear Wilderness and Bob Marshall Wilderness (Kendall et al., 2009); and (3) the entire grizzly bear population in a region that includes northeastern Montana, the Idaho Panhandle, southeastern British Columbia, and southwestern Alberta, and includes Glacier National Park, the Great Bear Wilderness, and the Bob Marshall Wilderness (Proctor et al., 2012). All are useful applications of the term metapopulation and illustrate how management context influences the scales at which the term is used.

Resilience, or the ability of organisms to accommodate disturbances, accrues in part from the ability of plants and animals to move well within the area between local populations, called the *matrix*, thereby maintaining genetic diversity. A more permeable system for lynx, for example, is one in which lynx are more genetically diverse, due to the greater ease with which males disperse to establish new territories and breed (Figure 14.1). Genetic diversity makes this species more resistant to extinction (McKelvey et al., 1999). Taking the argument for diversity one step further means acknowledging that an ecosystem that has lynx in it is more diverse than one that does not, and therefore more resilient to ecological stressors due to the myriad of food web relationships connected to lynx presence. For example, by killing snowshoe hares, lynx presence reduces herbivory. This helps create a structural- and species-rich understory in early seral communities (Palomares, 2001). All of this suggests that to fully understand and conserve biodiversity, it is necessary to consider whole ecosystems, not just species.

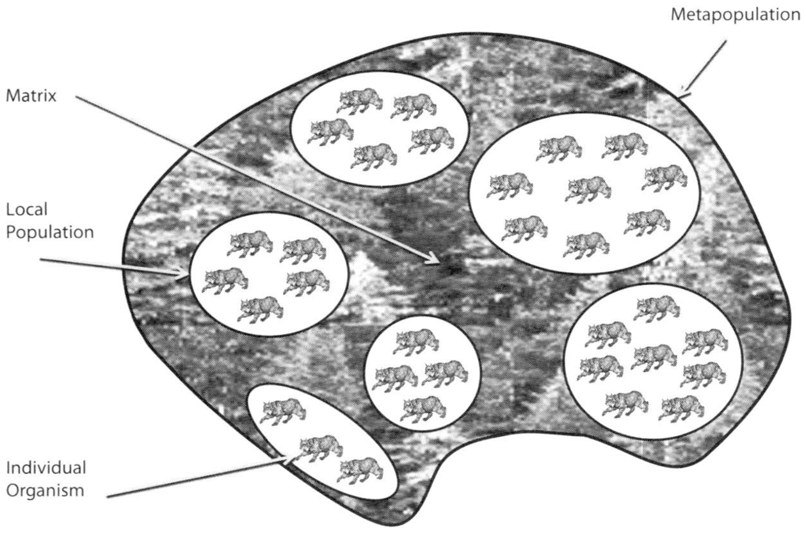

Figure 14.1 *Organization of a population of a species.*

---

* See Chapter 3 for definition and discussion of preforest (early successional) and mature forest ecosystems.

Figure 14.2 *Three measures of biodiversity in a typical landscape.*

landscapes! At the level of the stand, we need to provide the structures and structural complexity that are needed as habitat, such as for nesting and foraging—what Hunter and Schmiegelow (2011) call the "micro" approach. Structural needs may be related to individual structures, such as snags and logs, or to forest conditions that provide specific environments, such as temperature or moisture conditions. At larger spatial scales, providing habitat involves sustaining a diversity of stand conditions in the landscape, such as mixtures of open areas and closed-canopy forest—what Hunter and Schmiegelow (2011) call the "macro" approach. As we will see, both the micro and macro approaches are important in sustaining biodiversity in a managed forest landscape. In many ways, these two levels parallel the concepts of "coarse-filter" and "fine-filter" approaches to habitat conservation that we discuss later in the chapter.

## Providing Structural Elements within a Forest Stand

Sustaining biodiversity within a forest stand largely involves providing for a variety of structures and structural arrangements (Hunter & Schmiegelow, 2011). Live trees, standing dead trees (snags), and logs are all important structural elements. Mature and old live trees that have various kinds of decadent features, such as cavities and witches' brooms, as well as a variety of other specialized structures or niches are important structures for many organisms (see Chapter 2). Incorporating some hardwood trees in otherwise conifer-dominated forest stands can provide important habitat diversity. Snags were among the first of the dead wood structures identified as being important for wildlife, prob-

ably because they are related to habitat for a significant set of cavity-dependent or cavity-using vertebrates. Sustaining populations of snags can be challenging because of their transient nature. Snags were also historically exceedingly unpopular with foresters because of several hazards associated with their presence. Many birds rely on cavities in mature and old-growth trees in the forest for their nests. Silvicultural practices designed to maintain specific structural elements of mature stands (e.g., standing and down dead wood) can help sustain cavity-nesting birds on a landscape scale.

Down logs in various stages of decay are important for a very large number and diversity of species for a wide variety of functions, including as nesting habitat, sources of food, travel routes, and perches (e.g., Hunter & Schmiegelow, 2011; Spies, Franklin, & Thomas, 1988; Thomas, 1979). Salamanders provide a good example since many of these species require well-rotted, decayed logs. Harvests that remove all logs have been identified as a leading factor in local population declines and extirpation of salamander species in the Pacific Northwest and the Appalachians (Bunnell & Houde, 2010).

Large and old live trees are also very important structures because of the numerous niches that they provide, including large branch systems and many decadent features, such as cavities and witches' brooms created by dwarf mistletoes (*Arceuthobium* spp.). Brooms are another example of structures that are very important to wildlife but are an anathema to foresters focused on wood production.

## Sustaining a Diversity of Forest Stand Conditions

Sustaining the full array of biodiversity in forested regions requires the diversity of stand conditions that are associated with forested sites, including stands of different ages or structural conditions, varied composition, and early successional or preforest habitat areas (see Chapter 3). The diversity associated with different developmental stages has been recognized repeatedly in regional wildlife habitat management guides. The book, *Wildlife Habitats in Managed Forests [of] the Blue Mountains of Oregon and Washington* (Thomas, 1979), provides an early example of this approach. In this treatment, habitat needs for several hundred species of wildlife are associated with forest successional and stand developmental stages. A generic criticism of many of these attempts has been a failure to fully appreciate two important habitat features: (1) the importance of biological legacies that provide structurally rich habitat in preforest and young forest ecosystems, and (2) the importance of early successional habitat in forested landscapes (Box 14.3).

The developmental stages presented in Chapter 3 can be used to characterize the landscape-level heterogeneity that is needed to provide for the full array of forest-related biodiversity. In Chapter 3 we saw how a complete sere or forest development sequence could be described in four forest stages: preforest (PFS), young forest (YFS), mature forest (MFS), and old forest (OFS). When a forest experiences a disturbance that creates openings, vegetation development progresses through these stages sequentially unless another disturbance intervenes. The different developmental stages provide habitat for different sets of species (Figures 14.3a and 14.3b), with species richness often highest in PFS and OFS and lowest in YFS (Figure 14.3c).

The PFS is an initial period that lacks tree dominance. As described in Chapter 3 this results in development of a diverse plant-life-form community that is relatively rich in food resources and webs. Early seral communities also have important functional attributes, such as higher rates of nutrient mineralization and nitrogen fixation and accumulation than the forested stages. Because of the diversity of browse

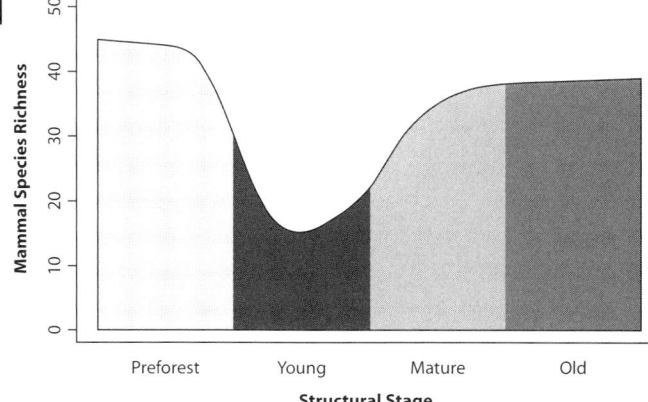

Figure 14.3  *(a) Examples of species associated with preforest. (left) Blacktailed deer* [Odocoileus hemionus columbianus] *(photo © Steve Reed); (right) American black bear* [Ursus americanus] *(photo courtesy of Chelsi Hornbaker/USFWS). (b) Examples of species associated with old forest in Douglas-fir–western hemlock sere. (left) Johnson's hairstreak butterfly* [Callophrys johnsoni] *(photo courtesy of David Nunnallee); (right) red tree vole* [Arborimus longicaudus] *(photo courtesy of Stephen DeStefano). (c) Mammal diversity (species number) in relation to the four major developmental stages in a Douglas-fir–western hemlock sere.*

in the PFS, such as that produced by sprouting and growth of disturbance-adapted herbs and shrubs (Figure 14.4), this is very good feeding habitat for ungulates (Romme, Turner, Wallace, & Walker, 1995). Songbirds that rely on more open habitat for nesting and feeding, including many neotropical migrant songbirds, also find this desirable habitat.

The YFS generally has the lowest biodiversity of the developmental stages. The YFS is strongly dominated by trees and is structurally simple. Habitat and food resources are typically very limited (see Chapter 3). Understory plant species diversity is generally very low, particularly relative to what it was in PFS, due to competition with trees for nutrients and light. YFS stands that have developed following natural disturbances (e.g., fire, windthrow) will generally have higher biodiversity than those produced by

clearcuts because they incorporate significant structural legacies, such as down trees, snags, and even live older trees (Franklin et al., 2002; Spies & Franklin, 1996).

The MFS represents a transitional stage between the relatively structurally simplified YFS and the structurally complex and niche-rich OFS (see Chapter 3). In the MFS, a major shift in patterns of mortality results in creation of canopy openings, which allow development of a richer forest understory and intermediate canopy layers. Death and damage of existing dominant trees also result in additions of snags and logs and increased decadence in live trees, increasing habitat for cavity-dwelling species and invertebrates (Spies & Franklin, 1996).

The OFS has the highest structural and species diversity of the forested stages (see Chapter 3). This is due to the diversity of structures and microenvironments that are present, which, for example, provides habitat for a greater variety of lichens and other epiphytes than in younger forest stages. OFS also provides habitat for species that require or prefer large decadent trees for nesting.

The linkage of individual species to a particular developmental stage should not be overly emphasized, however, as many species will actually be found in several of the stages, albeit at different levels of abundance (e.g., Ruggierro, Aubry, Carey, & Huff, 1991). This utilization is particularly the case in natural seres where there are significant biological legacies that enrich the YFS; this circumstance can, of course, be duplicated to varying degrees in areas subject to timber

Figure 14.4 *Vegetation response six weeks postfire in a northern Rocky Mountain aspen–conifer community.*

## Box 14.3  Build it and they will come: Biodiversity and forest structure

In the 1989 classic film, *Field of Dreams*, Kevin Costner plays the role of a farmer who builds a baseball diamond in his cornfield in response to a disembodied voice that tells him "If you build it they will come." Along with ghosts of baseball heroes, the diamond quickly draws hundreds of living people who find redemption and healing in that cornfield through baseball. Similarly, the Field of Dreams approach to forest management is based on the premise that if you manage a forest for structural diversity, species will come.

A foundational concept in ecological forestry is maintenance of structural complexity. Since the 1980s, forest community ecologists have observed a strong link between animal community composition and forest structure (Tews et al., 2004). However, these relationships are not linear. For example, the early successional ecosystem that develops immediately after a forest-replacing event may be more diverse than the old-growth forest that preceded it.

Ecosystems in the unsalvaged and unplanted portions of the blast zone north of Mount St. Helens developed and have sustained very high biodiversity during the first 35 years following the 1980 eruption; the majority of this area is still occupied by diverse early successional ecosystems (i.e., the preforest stage of development). As noted in Chapter 3, biodiversity during early succession on forest sites will often surpass that of the later stages of forest development, particularly if there are high levels of biological legacies. However, it is important to remember that every natural ecosystem is biologically diverse, but some more so than others. Even a highly modified ecosystem can contain much diversity, some of it hidden. Major examples of this phenomenon include the diversity that is found in the soil in terrestrial environments (Hobbs, Higgs, & Harris, 2009) and in the hyporheic zones of stream and river environments.

production, by providing for significant retention of biological legacies during harvests (see Chapter 4).

In addition, some species, like the lynx discussed above, rely on an intermixture of OFS and PFS. Others, as discussed in Chapter 5, rely on the edges between seres for productive foraging. Since species have evolved with the suite of development stages across the landscape, a risk-adverse conservation strategy would be sure to maintain different forest development stages even if we do not understand their function for a particular species.

We conclude this section by noting that there is an immense opportunity to conserve biodiversity associated with forests on forestlands used for wood production (Hansen, Spies, Swanson, & Öhmann, 1991). The key to this conservation is, in part, through creating managed forest landscapes that are, effectively, "shades of green" as described in Chapter 5.

## Species of Special Ecological Importance and Interest

### Focal Species

Resources are inadequate to assess the status of all species that occur in forests. Thus, scientists have turned to a *focal-species* concept, a comprehensive term referring to a species whose measurement provides substantial information beyond its own status (Committee of Scientists, 1999; Miller et al., 1999). The general idea is to monitor those species whose status allows inference of the status of other species, are indicative of the soundness of key ecological processes, or provide insights into the integrity of the overall ecosystem. This procedure is a necessary shortcut because monitoring and managing for all aspects of biodiversity is not possible.

---

### Box 14.4  From umbrellas to flagships: Categories of focal species

Scientists have identified five types of focal species, each of which serves a distinct function: *keystone, umbrella, flagship, indicator,* and *foundation* (Dayton, 1972; Miller et al., 1999):

- *Keystone species* are those whose effects are disproportionate to their number. Despite low abundance, they have strong effects on an ecosystem. Removing them creates changes that can result in loss of biodiversity. For example, removing large carnivores can cause a sharp increase in prey populations, which can have adverse effects on plant communities. Thus, their loss can weaken ecosystem resilience. Conversely, recovering keystone species provides an effective way to increase biodiversity, as in the case of recruitment of overbrowsed plant species. Single-species management is often based on the concept of keystone species, in that by restoring one species, managers hope to achieve a beneficial effect on the entire ecosystem.

- *Umbrella species* are those with large area requirements, whose conservation thus imparts a protective umbrella to many other coexisting species. Generally, umbrella species travel long distances and have large territories. The grizzly bear fits into this category, as its conservation implies the conservation of many other species (Figure 14.5).

- *Flagship species* are charismatic species with broad popular appeal. They are highly effective in outreach efforts that can build public support for conservation efforts. Often these species can trigger a strong emotional response, as is the case with the bald eagle (*Haliaeetus leucocephalus*).

- *Indicator species* are indicative of overall ecosystem function. Tied to a specific biotic community, they are generally associated with a particular set of circumstances. Wildlife managers often use indicator species as a shortcut to monitoring a whole ecosystem. Because these species will be vulnerable to ecological changes, protecting them is a way to ensure a specific desired effect on an ecosystem. The northern spotted owl (*Strix occidentalis caurina*) provides a classic example of an indicator species, as ensuring this species' survival means maintaining specific conditions (e.g. mature and old-growth forests) that have a beneficial effect on a biotic community.

- *Foundation species* are those that influence the structure and function of whole communities (Dayton, 1972). Typically trees, due to their architecture, physiology, and function are examples of foundation species and include Douglas-fir, whitebark pine (*Pinus albicauli*), and eastern hemlock (*Tsuga canadensis*) (Ellison et al., 2005).

Figure 14.5  *The grizzly bear is considered an umbrella species, because conserving it ensures that ecological connectivity will be conserved.*

No single species is adequate to assess biological sustainability. Thus, several species need to be monitored. For that purpose, a number of types of focal species have been identified (Box 14.4). The goal is to select a small number of focal species whose individual status and trends will collectively allow an assessment of ecological integrity and help guide ecosystem restoration. That is, individual species are chosen to provide complementary information and to be responsive to specific conservation issues and social interest.

The task is difficult. No body of knowledge currently exists to unambiguously guide the selection of focal species. Because of this uncertainty, the selection is often controversial and subject to change as new knowledge accumulates. Pragmatically, though, a reliable assessment of overall biodiversity needs to be attainable without assessing each species individually.

## Bottom-Up and Top-Down Effects and Trophic Cascades

To restore and conserve biodiversity, it is important to understand the *agents of biodiversity*. These agents influence ecological forces and flows of energy that can shape ecological communities. In this section, we highlight one type of agent that has gained much recognition and interest recently: keystone predators that drive trophic cascades.

Like most ecological communities, any forest type or developmental stage is influenced by a synergy of *bottom-up* (resources-driven) and *top-down* (predator-driven) processes that flow through food webs (Eisenberg, Seager, & Hibbs, 2013). A classical food web includes primary producers (plants) at the base of the web, primary consumers (such as herbivores), and secondary consumers (predators) at the top of the web. Predators can include keystone predators, defined as a carnivore species that dominate their trophic class and can have strong effects on other food web components (Soulé, Estes, Miller, & Honnold, 2005).

Bottom-up effects stimulate or limit vegetation growth. Lindeman (1942) described energy passing upward through trophic levels, which he envisioned as distinct and functionally homogeneous sets of green plants, herbivores, and primary carnivores. He referred to this as bottom-up control of ecological communities. Soil moisture influences plant growth. Nutrient (e.g., nitrogen, phosphorus) availability may increase after fire, also stimulating growth. Bottom-up effects include vegetation effects on herbivores, such as food resource availability (Murdoch, 1966). Anthropogenic modifications of plant communities also can cause bottom-up effects. For example, timber harvest can result in highly diverse early successional ecosystems (Swanson et al., 2010). Strong bottom-up effects prevail in all systems: While removing upper trophic levels leaves lower

levels intact, removing lower trophic levels leaves no system at all (Hunter & Price, 1992). Furthermore, the bottom-up effects present in all food webs may buffer top-down effects.

*Trophic cascades are ecological relationships in which a keystone predator produces a strong direct effect on its prey, which, in turn, results in significant changes in floral and faunal communities at other trophic levels (Paine, 1980)— the predator has a strong top-down effect.* Mills et al. (1993, p. 219) definition of keystone species includes two primary characteristics: "First, their presence is crucial in maintaining the organization and biodiversity of their ecological communities. Second, it is implicit that these species are exceptional, relative to the rest of the community, in their importance." Mills et al.'s keystone concept is fundamentally about species diversity—that the presence or absence of one of several key species influences the distribution and abundance of many other species. Also referred to as *strongly interactive species*, keystone species effects include habitat enrichment, mutualisms, predation, and competition (Mills et al., 1993; Soulé et al., 2005). Keystone species have great impact at low abundance relative to the other species in a community, and they do not need to be carnivores. The North American beaver (*Castor canadensis*) is an example of a noncarnivorous keystone species as is the gopher tortoise, the first building dams and creating ponds and the other creating significant burrows in soils used by many other species. (Figure 14.6).

Ecologists for a long time have observed that when keystone predators such as wolves are removed, their primary prey species increase significantly in numbers. This increase is termed an *irruption* (Leopold, Sowls, & Spencer, 1947) and it leads to intensive consumption of food resources and indirectly affects other species that depend on those plant communities (Bailey & Witham, 2002).

Trophic cascades are not uniform. They are typically stronger at the lower end of the productivity gradient, such as in arctic ecosystems (Oksanen, Fretwell, Arruda, & Niemela, 1981; Strong, 1992) and may be weak or nonexistent in closed-canopy Pacific Northwest forests, which characteristically have very high productivity and very little or no herbivory. Trophic cascades are also weaker or essentially absent in more species-rich ecosystems, such as native grasslands, where there are many more species of invertebrate predators, prey, and plants, than in agricultural systems (Halaj & Wise 2001; Schmitz, Hambäck, & Beckerman, 2000). Trophic effects are generally more complex and can be weaker in aquatic systems due to the higher number of trophic levels they contain, versus terrestrial systems (Power, 1990; Schmitz et al., 2000; Strong, 1992). These weak top-down effects have been termed *trophic trickles* (Kauffman, Brodie, & Jules, 2010; Power, 1990), i.e., a situation where a keystone predator is present but has limited indirect effects on vegetation.

Figure 14.6 *Examples of keystone species. (a) North American beaver (© jnjhuz CanStock Photo Inc.); (b) gopher tortoise (photo courtesy of the Joseph W. Jones Ecological Research Center); (c) gray wolf (photo courtesy of David Parsons).*

*The return of a keystone predator to an ecosystem can have both density-mediated (e.g., mortality) and behavior-mediated (fear-based) effects on prey* (Eisenberg, Hibbs, Ripple, & Salwasser, 2014) (Box 14.5). A behavioral trophic cascade was discovered between spiders and grasshoppers in a study of a reclaimed agricultural grassland or *old-field* system (Schmitz et al., 1997). The top predator—a nursery web spider (*Pisaurina mira*)—preferentially preys on a grasshopper (*Melanoplus femurrubrum*). Grasshoppers selected a diet composed almost entirely of grass rather than forbs where spiders are absent. In a famed experiment, Schmitz glued spiders' mouths shut to render them unable to prey on grasshoppers. Grasshoppers reduced their feeding time in the presence of these nonfunctional spiders and preferentially ate forbs, which provide greater cover and safety from predation. This shift from grasses to forbs resulted in a trophic cascade (Schmitz et al., 1997). One reason for the large response—in contrast with the trophic trickles described earlier in native grasslands—is probably because Schmitz's study was in an agricultural system, which had less biodiversity; this caused the trophic cascades to be more pronounced (Halaj & Wise, 2001).

In forest ecosystems, ecological context (e.g., spatial landscape heterogeneity and climate patterns) influences the relative importance of top-down and bottom-up effects. Such context may cause woody species recruitment to be more strongly influenced by bottom-up than top-down effects (Marshall, Hobbs, & Cooper, 2012). For trophic cascades to occur in a wolf → elk → hardwood food web, wolves must have a strong effect on elk, and elk must have a strong effect on hardwoods. If both effects do not occur simultaneously, then a trophic trickle or a system dominated by bottom-up effects can result.

The density-mediated and behavior-mediated effects of wolves on elk can release vegetation from intense herbivory, thereby enabling shrubs and saplings to grow into the lower forest canopy, providing habitat for taxa such as songbirds (Laundré, Hernandez, & Ripple, 2010; Figure 14.7). Some

species such as the American redstart warbler (*Setophaga ruticilla*) rely on these lower-canopy deciduous, early seral communities to nest and feed. In the Intermountain West this species has been declining, due to the decline of its habitat. Because of fire suppression, climate change, predator extirpation, and excessive herbivory, the mixed-age, mature

---

**Box 14.5  Ecology of fear: Effects of wolves on deer in northwestern Montana**

In the mid-1990s, my (Cristina Eisenberg's) family moved to a remote valley in northwestern Montana. The land we bought included some dense second-growth forest and a large meadow, where our hand-hewn log cabin stood. Undeveloped land surrounded ours, followed by a strip of state forest, then national forest administered by the US Forest Service (USFS), which included a roadless backcountry area and the congressionally designated million-acre Bob Marshall Wilderness. Our closest neighbor lived a half mile away and the nearest town (population 1,000 people) was ten miles away. After 20 years, the only major changes to our property were nearer neighbors (a quarter mile away) and a much wilder forest.

In the late 1990s wolves returned to our valley, and within five years we observed some significant ecological changes. We began to see changes in deer and elk behavior shortly after we saw a wolf pair hunting a white-tailed deer (*Odocoileus virginianus*) across our meadow. It was no longer safe for these herbivores to stand around boldly munching down shrubs and saplings with wolves present. They had to stay on high alert, taking quick bites and looking up frequently to avoid becoming prey. As a result, within five years of the wolves' return, the aspen on our land began to grow into the forest canopy, filling in the meadow and creating habitat for birds. These dramatic changes and the powerful relationships I witnessed between wolves, their prey, and the forest community made me deeply curious and inspired me to study wolves as a scientist.

Figure 14.7 *Recruitment gap in an aspen forest, Glacier National Park, Montana. The gap in tree ages between senescent trees and saplings matches the years when wolves were extirpated and did not occur in this system, and when they returned naturally, with wolves recolonizing this region from Canada.*

aspen stands with complex structure that once abounded in this region have been replaced by senescent, late seral stands lacking understory shrubs and young aspen (Seager, Eisenberg, & St. Clair, 2013). In areas where wolves have been allowed to return, and subsequent release in herbivory has been observed in aspen forests and shrub communities, species such as the American redstart have returned (Figure 14.8).

In Yellowstone National Park, ecologists William Ripple and Robert Beschta have linked wolf-driven trophic cascades to recovery of riparian cottonwood (*Populus* spp.) and willow (*Salix* spp.) communities (Ripple & Beschta, 2006). However, these effects have been investigated by David Cooper and others who have found further complexity, such as moisture and climate change, and wolf effects secondary to bottom-up effects (Hobbs & Cooper, 2013, pp. 179–194).

*As compelling of a biodiversity conservation concept as trophic cascade effects may be, it is important to recognize that keystone predator presence does not ensure that trophic cascades will occur.* While keystone species are defined as those that in low densities have powerful effects (e.g., two packs of wolves comprising a total of 16 individuals can exert strong impacts via predation and the threat thereof on a herd of 2,000 elk), there nevertheless exist thresholds to keystone effectiveness (Estes, Tinker, & Bodkin, 2010). These thresholds are contextual and in part are determined by bottom-up effects such as nutrient availability. However, below these thresholds, keystone predators may not be ecologically effective. *An ecologically effective popula-*

*tion of a keystone predator is defined as one sufficient to produce trophic cascades* (Soulé, Estes, Berger, & Martinez Del Rio, 2003). Returning keystone predators to ecosystems is not a silver bullet that will automatically fix them. A well-designed management framework, with clear objectives for keystone species density and distribution, and a plan to monitor these effects across trophic levels are also needed. An adaptive management framework is essential because trophic cascades will vary temporally and spatially based on bottom-up factors such as fire, drought, and human development (Box 14.6).

## The Formative Role of Law in Conserving Biodiversity in the United States

Historically, much of the scientific, social, and regulatory focus in the United States has been on species whose abundance and even survival seem problematic. Perhaps the buffalo (*Bison bison*) was the first of these species. By the turn of the last century, the aggregate effect of market hunting, human population growth, urbanization, and federal/Indian tribe struggles had decimated game populations throughout the US. Private organizations, such as the Boone and Crocket Club and the National Audubon Society, formed to reverse these trends. Implementing state hunting laws and closing hunting seasons for some species, such as buffalo, followed. Federal legislation, such as the Migratory Bird Act of 1913, attempted to protect migratory birds throughout North America. The federal government used a double-barreled approach of

Figure 14.8 *The author of this chapter conducting songbird point counts to measure songbird species richness in an area with active wolf predation. (Photo courtesy of Steve Eisenberg)*

creating wildlife refuges to conserve at-risk game species and developing programs to eliminate as many of the predators affecting game species as possible, even in national parks. This led to the recovery of game species such as deer and elk, but the effective elimination of predators resulted in irruptions of ungulates that damaged rangelands and forests by unsustainable herbivory (Dunlap, 1988, pp. 34–48).

However, until the 1940s, most Americans gave relatively little thought to conservation of the thousands of nongame species or to consequences of predator loss. Aldo Leopold, who initially advocated predator control, subsequently recognized its consequences and raised awareness of conserving predators in order to conserve biodiversity (Leopold et al., 1947). Other scientific insights emerged,

---

**Box 14.6 Fire, wolves, and trophic cascades in the northern Rockies**

Working in the northern Rocky Mountains, I (Cristina Eisenberg) found that even in an area with a high wolf population, it took fire to stimulate strong trophic cascades. Here the powerful nutrient and growth surge created in an aspen community by fire worked with the top-down effects of wolves via predation risk. Elk avoided areas that had burned severely and that had many aspen sprouts, due to the higher predation risk there (e.g., greater density of downed logs and other obstacles to detecting and escaping a coursing predator such as the wolf) (Eisenberg, 2014, pp. 37–60).

One interesting site in this study, a wolf den, lay in a very large aspen stand in an area that received a relatively high amount of rainfall (50 inches per year). Approximately half

of the stand had burned in 2003, and the other half hadn't experienced fire since the mid-1800s. Soil, aspect, slope, and moisture were the same throughout the stand, which had a high measured density of elk utilizing it. The portion of the stand that had burned had a low amount of elk herbivory and many young aspen vigorously recruiting into the forest canopy. The portion of the stand that had not burned had high elk herbivory and a relatively barren understory, with aspen sprouts reaching only a meter or so in height. Figures 14.9a and b depict the aspen forest dynamics at this site. These dynamics suggest that without fire, even a very active wolf pack was unable to drive a trophic cascade.

Figure 14.9 *Evidence of top-down and bottom-up effects at a wolf den. Panel (a) depicts the portion of the stand that has burned in 2003 and the strong recruitment of aspen saplings into the canopy at that site. Panel (b) depicts the portion of the stand that has not burned since the mid-1800s and shows evidence of high herbivory and little recruitment of aspen into the canopy.*

such as the Green World Hypothesis (Hairston, Smith, & Slobodkin, 1960), which argued for conserving all species, including predators. Perhaps, though, it was the book *Silent Spring* by Rachel Carson (1962), describing the detrimental effects of pesticides on birds and other native species, that provided the popular alarm that pushed America into a new conservation era.

This loss in biodiversity was among many other environmental concerns, such as water and air pollution, that led to the US Congress passing a suite of environmental laws in the late 1960s and early 1970s, of which three were foundational in protecting biodiversity. One, the Endangered Species Act (ESA), applies to all lands in the United States and its territories, although the Act's requirements are strongest on federal actions. The other two, the National Environmental Policy Act (NEPA) and the National Forest Management Act (NFMA), apply to federal actions and lands.

These laws are briefly discussed below in terms of their function in protecting biodiversity. (See Chapter 7 for a more expansive discussion of the Endangered Species Act and National Environmental Policy Act and Chapter 20 for a more detailed discussion of the National Forest Management Act.)

## Endangered Species Act

ESA is one of the most far-reaching and powerful environmental laws in the United States and is specifically focused on preventing the extinction of species. Under provisions of ESA, species (or other recognized taxonomic units, such as subspecies) can receive a scientific review to determine their current or future potential to become endangered. If such a potential exists throughout all or a significant portion of their range they are listed as "Threatened"; species in danger of extinction are listed as "Endangered." Collectively they are commonly referred as "T&E species," and it is recognized that they are to be conserved using a population-based approach.

ESA also contains language that links species to ecosystems, even though the primary focus has been on a population-based approach to preventing extinction of species. The opening lines of the Endangered Species Act of 1973 (as amended by 87 Stat. 884) state that one purpose of the act is "to **provide a means whereby the ecosystems upon which endangered species and threatened species depend may be conserved**" (§ 2(b), ESA, 1973; emphasis added). Also, the courts have established that protection of habitat upon which species depend is addressed in ESA in addition to the species itself, as is the case with the northern spotted owl (*Babbitt v. Sweet Home Chapt. Comms. For Ore.*, 515 U.S. 687, Supreme Court [1995]).

Species recovery and delisting decisions revolve almost exclusively around the question of whether demographically and genetically diverse populations can persist in the wake of delisting. However, maintaining an ecologically effective population of a species requires a population sufficiently large for the species to fulfill its ecological role, such as driving trophic cascades (Estes et al., 2010). Recovery requirements for wolves under the ESA (persistence) are generally not enough for them to have their historical ecosystem effects.

Thus, restoration of trophic cascade effects of threatened top predators, like the wolf, is not assured and generally unlikely where they conflict with humans. With the opening line of the ESA calling for "a means whereby the ecosystems upon which endangered species and threatened species depend may be conserved" (§ 2(b), ESA, 1973), an argument could be made for a different interpretation of the ESA for species that drive trophic cascades, but such an interpretation awaits future policy change.

## National Environmental Policy Act

The National Environmental Policy Act (NEPA, 1969) fundamentally changed the way the federal government makes decisions affecting natural resources. The law requires a federal agency proposing an activity to perform an interdisciplinary analysis of the environmental impacts of major proposed actions that could significantly impact the environment, to fully divulge the results of that analysis, and to engage the public in the process. While NEPA itself does not directly protect species, it does open up federal decisions to more consideration of ecological effects and public critique. Paired with the strong requirements for protection and recovery of these species in the ESA, the NEPA process can expose proposed practices that are unacceptable under the ESA.

## National Forest Management Act

The National Forest Management Act (NFMA) is intended to resolve controversies about US Forest Service timber management practices. This law is also the lynchpin of biodiversity protection on the national forests due to § 6 (g) (3) (B), which states that the Act shall "provide for diversity of plant and animal communities based on the suitability and capability of the specific land area in order to meet overall multiple-use objectives" (USDA, 1976). This NFMA provision is the most comprehensive commitment to sustaining biodiversity in federal legislation, and regulations that interpret this law have become a driving force in federal lands management. Collectively, the legal interpretations of NFMA and its associated federal regulations over time has shifted its focus from providing habitat for all vertebrate species in some representative areas on the national forests to providing habitat for all species (plant and animal) across the national forests (Box 14.7).

## Combining Ecosystem and Species Approaches to Conserving Biodiversity

As scientists, policy makers, and managers recognized that more and more species faced extinction, it became evident that a species-by-species approach to recovery would be insufficient. An approach that focused first on conserving ecosystems was needed (Franklin, 1993).

Both science and policy have coalesced around what are commonly known as "coarse-filter/fine-filter" approaches to sustaining native biodiversity (Hunter, 1990; USDA, 2012). These complementary ecosystem-level and species-level approaches to maintaining biodiversity pair an emphasis on conserving landscape structures and processes with a special consideration of species that are not adequately protected by such an ecosystem approach.

### The Coarse-Filter Approach

A coarse-filter approach considers ecological land units in terms of landscape processes and structures. More specifically, it involves managing or restoring forest ecosystems across the landscape to ensure that the habitat required by native species will continue to exist. Often the metric for judging success here is whether the landscape is within the *historical range of variability* for key measures of landscape integrity, the reasoning being that ecosystems managed in a manner consistent with the historical conditions to which organisms have adapted will be more likely to maintain their biological diversity. Management of fire regimes (or fuel reduction) in ponderosa pine forests to reflect historical disturbance processes exemplifies this approach.

In the 1990s, keeping forests within their historical range of variability was seen as the broad safety net for protecting biodiversity, especially on federal lands in the US. Climate change has upended this approach, to some degree, because this historical approach may cause managers to prepare landscapes for the conditions of the past rather than the conditions of the future (Miller, Stephenson, & Stephens, 2007), increasing the vulnerability of species to local extirpation and the possibility of extinction.

Still, information on historical range of variability can be a useful benchmark for assessing forests' potential to conserve native biodiversity (Keane, Hessburg, Landres, & Swanson, 2009). As an example, historical information on the structures of the frequent-fire forests of the western USA can help inform and guide efforts to reduce stand densities, but the coming increased temperatures associated with climate change may influence the setting of silvicultural goals to some degree. Recent planning directives for the national forests attempt to cope more comprehensively with changing climate by utilizing a *natural range of variability* that can change dynamically over time to maintain ecosystem

functions (USDA Forest Service, 2015). (See Chapter 20 for more discussion of this approach.)

In much of the eastern USA, on the other hand, relatively little of the historical forest still exists to serve as a guide. In many states, much of the forest was cleared for agriculture several hundred years ago and has now reverted back to forest, as we described in the New England case in Chapter 5. In such cases, landscape design often builds out from the documented habitat needs of particular groups of species. For example, using the size of snags needed by large cavity nesters in designing snag retention policies, such as leaving at least two large green trees per acre at harvest (for future snags), may also provide snags needed by smaller birds. Such approaches are also used in designing state forest practice rules and certification schemes for private landowners.

> **Box 14.7 Making diversity matter: The National Forest Management Act**
>
> NFMA (USDA, 1976) directs national forest managers to provide for the diversity of plant and animal communities consistent with the suitability and capability of the specific land area to meet overall multiple-use objectives. Working with the Committee of Scientists, also mandated by NFMA, the US Department of Agriculture (USDA) developed regulations that state: "Fish and wildlife habitat shall be managed to maintain viable populations of existing native and desired nonnative vertebrate species in the planning area. For planning purposes, a viable population shall be regarded as one which has the estimated numbers and distribution of reproductive individuals to insure its continued existence, well distributed in the planning area" (USDA, 1982). This clause, which required well-distributed populations, enabled NFMA to become a controlling provision for management of the national forests.
>
> However, as written, the clause provided direction only for vertebrates—a very small proportion of all species in national forests. As an example, the mature and old-growth (late successional) forests of the Pacific Northwest contain over 1,000 species, of which less than 5% are vertebrates, the rest being lichens, mosses, fungi, mollusks, and various plants (Forest Ecosystem Management Assessment Team, 1993). Scientists helping to develop a plan to conserve late successional ecosystems broadened their viability analysis to include all living things in these forests (including vertebrates and invertebrates). In ruling on the legality of applying the viability provision to invertebrates, the courts stated (*Seattle Audubon Soc. v. Lyons*, 871 F. Supp. 1291 [1994]), "The federal defendants were bound by law, and by the obvious fact of species interdependence, to consider the survival prospects of species other than vertebrates. Their chosen method of doing so was within the legitimate scope of their discretion."

## The Fine-Filter Approach

The fine-filter approach focuses on the habitat needs of selected species inadequately protected via a coarse-filter approach, such as the red-cockaded woodpecker (*Picoides borealis*), through development of a species-specific conservation plan. Generally, these are declining species about which there is strong social or legal concern. Often, the federal government has recognized the extinction risk these species face and has given them threatened or endangered status under the ESA, or identified them as candidate species for listing or species of conservation concern.

## Application in the NFMA Planning Rule

The revised NFMA planning regulations, released in 2012, illustrate this two-part approach to conserving biodiversity:

1. *Coarse filter:* "The plan must include plan components, including standards or guidelines, to maintain or restore the ecological integrity of terrestrial and aquatic ecosystems and watersheds in the plan area, including plan components to maintain or restore their structure, function, composition, and connectivity" (USDA, 2012, § 219.9[a]).

2. *Fine filter:* "The responsible official shall determine whether or not the plan components required by . . . [the coarse-filter provisions] . . . provide the ecological conditions necessary to: contribute to the recovery of federally listed threatened and endangered species, conserve proposed and candidate species, and maintain a viable population of each species of conservation concern within the plan area. If the responsible official determines that the plan components . . . are insufficient to provide such ecological conditions, then additional, species-specific plan components, including standards or guidelines, must be included in the plan to provide such ecological conditions in the plan area" (USDA, 2012, § 219.9 [b]).

## Conclusions

Sustaining native biodiversity is a basic principle of ecological forestry. This chapter has focused on providing: (1) the rationale for this principle, including the fundamental importance of biodiversity to sustaining the functionality of forest ecosystems so that they can continue to provide the services and goods sought by society; and (2) concepts and information on how sustaining biodiversity can be incorporated into management approaches using ecological forestry. Generally, sustaining biodiversity in ecological forestry will be accomplished by incorporating structural complexity into forest management objectives and practices and providing for a diversity of patch conditions, including different forest developmental stages, in regional forest landscapes. In addition, identifying and protecting ecologically significant areas, such as aquatic habitats, is important at multiple spatial scales. Species-based approaches will be used where necessary to sustain species of exceptional ecological and/or social significance or where habitat needs have not been provided under the general principles of ecological forestry. All of this is consistent with the ecosystem-level philosophy of Aldo Leopold, which he described as restoring and sustaining "the land" and, of course, the necessity of retaining all parts of the forest (Leopold, 1949, 1993; Leopold et al., 1947). Ecological forestry can help to conserve all these parts while meeting human needs.

*The era of procrastination, of half-measures, of soothing and baffling expedients, of delays, is coming to its close. In its place we are entering a period of consequences.* — WINSTON CHURCHILL, 1936

# CHAPTER 15

# Climate Change, Carbon, and Forests

Increases in carbon dioxide ($CO_2$) levels in the atmosphere have been identified as a major source of climate change. Because forests sequester $CO_2$, and are a primary terrestrial carbon sink globally, forest policies have been an important part of international discussions regarding climate change. Much of this discussion has been about slowing down or reversing deforestation of the world's forests, which has historically been a significant source of $CO_2$ emissions. Currently the international concern over deforestation focuses mostly on the tropics where, despite recent reductions in forest clearance rates, deforestation continues to influence emission trajectories. Thus, slowing or reversing deforestation in the tropics must be a major component of any comprehensive global forest strategy that seeks to provide cost-effective emission reduction pathways.

Our focus in this book, though, is on temperate forests and, to a lesser degree, boreal forests. While deforestation associated with land development for housing and communities continues to be a concern in temperate forests, as we saw in Chapter 5 on the future of forests in New England, much of the policy discussion on the role of forests in combating climate change addresses a somewhat different issue: whether forests make their greatest contribution to reducing atmospheric $CO_2$ by being left alone to grow and sequester carbon, or by providing wood products on a sustainable basis. In addition to sequestering $CO_2$, forests provide renewable building materials and woody biomass for energy; therefore, timber harvest has been a part of the policy discussions on reducing $CO_2$ emissions as well. These dual and somewhat conflicting roles that forests might play in addressing climate change have generated much technical and policy discussion and debate.

In this chapter, we attempt a reasoned discussion of these two roles. We first review anthropogenic greenhouse gas emissions and their role in climate change, highlighting $CO_2$ emissions. Then, we discuss the role of forests in the carbon cycle, covering the pathways by which forests function as sinks or sources, and carbon accounting. Next,

*A redwood tree in California.*

we cover the role of forestry in storing or releasing $CO_2$, considering both on-site and off-site effects. Finally, we use these principles and concepts to analyze the implications for atmospheric $CO_2$ under different forest policies.

Climate change has modified terrestrial and aquatic ecosystems in many ways, which have been documented in thousands of studies. We do not attempt to summarize these effects here (see IPCC 2014 for a comprehensive discussion of the myriad effects of climate change and Chapter 3 for a brief discussion of climate change effects on forest ecosystems).

## Part 1: Human-caused Greenhouse Gas Emissions and Their Role in Climate Change

### Greenhouse Gases

Greenhouse gases regulate Earth's surface temperature by absorbing and emitting solar radiation, making life as we know it possible. Three greenhouse gases, carbon dioxide ($CO_2$), methane ($CH_4$), and nitrous oxide ($N_2O$) have increased to levels far beyond those that would have occurred from natural processes (like volcanic eruptions) since the beginning of the industrial era (ca. 1750). These increases have altered Earth's energy balance and caused a rapid global warming trend that is unprecedented in Earth's geological record. Human-caused (anthropogenic) increases in carbon dioxide are due primarily to fossil fuel use and land use change, while increases in methane and nitrous oxide are largely the result of agricultural practices (Figure 15.1).

Greenhouse gases vary in the way they influence climate change because of differences in how they trap radiation and their persistence in the atmosphere. Carbon dioxide, the main greenhouse gas associated with human activities, moves through the ocean-atmosphere-land system; excess amounts that are not absorbed can remain in the atmosphere for hundreds of years. Carbon dioxide causes the greatest concern in the debate about climate disruption because of its concentration in the lower atmosphere, the rapid increase in this concentration, and the direct correlation between rising $CO_2$ concentrations and the rising mean surface temperature of the planet (Blockstein & Wiegman, 2010). Methane is much more efficient than carbon dioxide at trapping radiation and is the second most prevalent greenhouse gas associated with human activities, but its lifetime in the atmosphere is quite short (about 12 years). Nitrous oxide accounts for the smallest portion of emis-

sions from human activities, but its molecules can remain in the atmosphere for an average of 120 years.

Carbon dioxide concentrations in the atmosphere remained relatively stable at about 280 parts per million (ppm) for thousands of years until the 19th century, when people began burning increasing amounts of fossil fuels. It has been rising continuously since, and in 2013 reached the 400 ppm mark (Molina et al., 2013). Since 1880, average global temperatures have risen by 0.8 degrees Celsius (1.4 degrees Fahrenheit) (Earth Observatory, n.d.).

Although large fluctuations in carbon dioxide concentrations are visible in the geological record, reconstructed temperature data from Antarctic ice cores reveal that present carbon dioxide concentrations are well beyond the peaks of the natural oscillations that have occurred during the past 800,000 years (Figure 15.2). So significant are the human-induced changes occurring to Earth's biosphere that many scientists assert that a new geological epoch has begun and have named it the "Anthropocene" (Crutzen, 2006).

Future trajectories for carbon dioxide emissions are simulated using Representative Concentration Pathways (RCPs) scenarios, which are based on the level of *radiative forcing* that the scenario produces. Radiative forcing is a change in the balance between incoming solar radiation and outgoing infrared radiation. Without any radiative forcing solar radiation coming to the Earth would be about equal to infrared radiation emitted from the Earth. Greenhouse gases trap a fraction of infrared radiation (NOAA, 2017). As radiative forcing increases, global temperature increases. The RCPs scenarios can help forecast climate based on different assumptions about key variables like population, energy consumption, and land use. Results of a variety of global climate model simulations are displayed in Color Plate 15.1. Both the level of uncertainty associated with

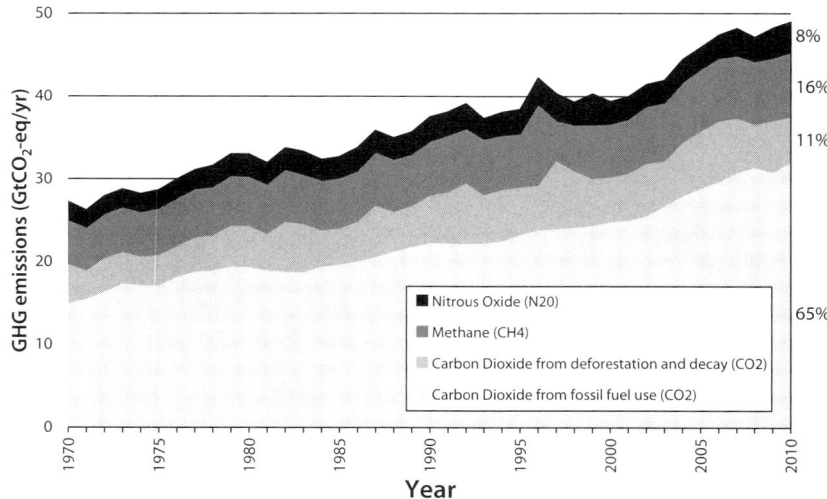

Figure 15.1 *Global annual emissions of anthropogenic greenhouse gas emissions (gigatonnes of $CO_2$-equivalent per year) for the period 1970 to 2010. (Source: IPCC, 2014)*

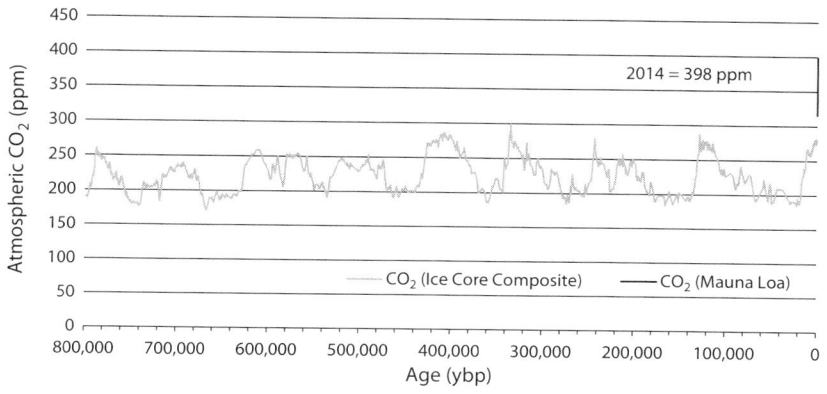

Figure 15.2 *Carbon dioxide levels are higher now than they have been for the past 800,000 years based on the analysis of air trapped in Antarctic ice (Lüthi et al., 2008) compared to $CO_2$ measured at Mauna Loa Observatory, Hawaii. (Data Source: NOAA)*

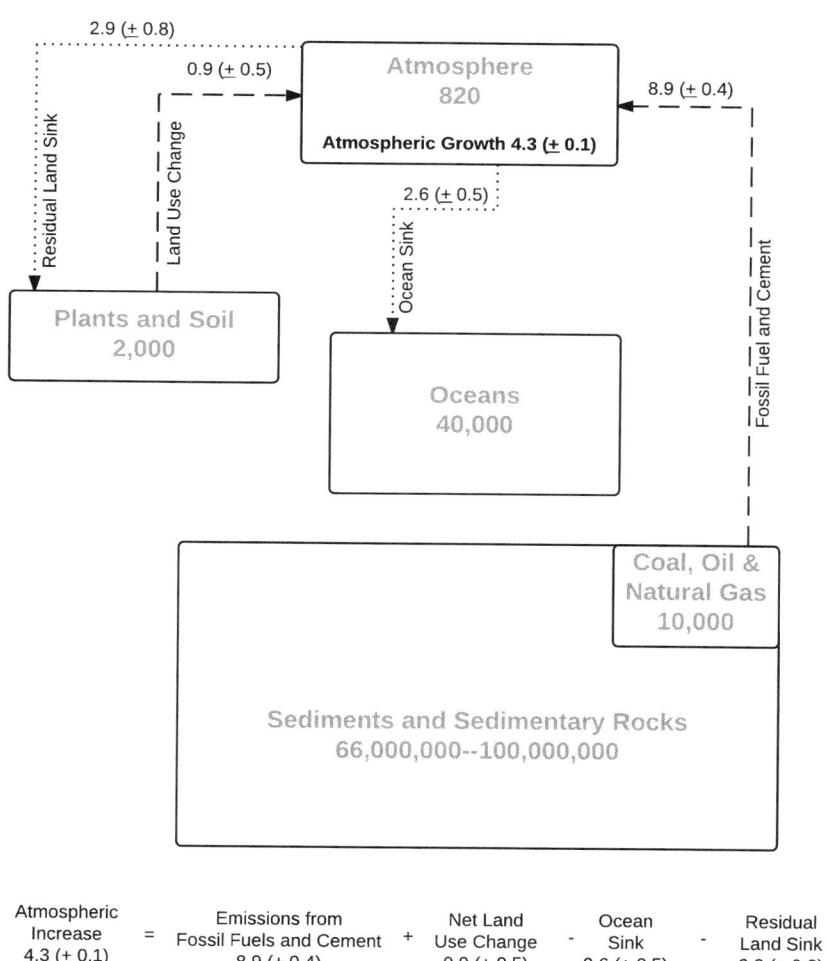

Figure 15.3 *Global carbon pools and perturbation of the global carbon cycle caused by anthropogenic activities averaged globally for the decade 2004–2013. The upward arrows represent emissions from fossil fuel burning and cement production, and emissions from deforestation and other land use change. The ocean and land sinks are the response to elevated carbon dioxide and changes in climate where the land sink is calculated as the residual of the other terms in the mass balance budget. Carbon pools (boxes) are in total gigatonnes of carbon, and fluxes (arrows) are in gigatonnes of carbon/year. (Source: Adapted from Le Quéré et al., 2015, and Ryan et al., 2010)*

future climate projections and the generally consistent upward trend of many scenarios are evident in the simulations.

In this chapter we discuss scenarios that use carbon units of measure. Therefore, before proceeding to the discussion of forests, we present information on carbon measures, including carbon content in different tree species (Box 15.1) for use throughout the chapter.

## Global Stocks and Flows of Carbon

The law of conservation of mass states that within a closed system mass cannot be created or destroyed—it can be rearranged in space or changed in form, but the total amount must remain constant through time. Earth is a closed system where matter is transported and transformed through biogeochemical cycles. We will examine the **carbon cycle** to help understand the role of $CO_2$ in regulating the Earth's climate, how increases in atmospheric carbon dioxide are warming the planet, and the mitigating role forests can play.

When carbon is added to the atmosphere (as carbon dioxide) faster than the natural processes can remove it, more solar radiation is trapped by the higher concentration of this greenhouse gas, causing global temperatures to rise.

***Carbon is stored in geologic, biologic, oceanic, and atmospheric pools.*** Of these four carbon pools, geologic carbon deposits are the largest. Compared to the geologic, biologic, and oceanic pools, the atmospheric pool is small, so relatively small changes in the other pools can have a large effect on atmospheric $CO_2$ and climate (Figure 15.3).

Carbon cycling associated with these pools is studied at two different time scales—geologic and biologic. The geologic carbon cycle is measured in the lifetimes of sedimentary rocks (millions of years). In contrast, the biologic carbon cycle is usually examined over time periods from less than a year to hundreds of years, and so within this time period it is possible to develop management scenarios that may help reduce anthropogenic carbon dioxide emissions, or increase carbon dioxide uptake.

In the geologic carbon cycle, carbon moves between the atmosphere, rocks, minerals, fresh water, and the oceans. Sedimentary rocks contain carbon in the form of **kerogen** (the soft-tissue remains of ancient plants and animals found in shales) and in the form of **carbonates** (the skeletal remains of ancient marine organisms that are the principal component of limestone); these rocks are broken down through a process called **weathering**. Kerogen slowly returns to the atmosphere as $CO_2$ (the natural analogue to burning fossil fuels), and carbonates are broken down by carbonic acid, which is formed when $CO_2$ is dissolved in water (Berner & Lasaga, 1989). In carbonate mineral weathering, all of the atmospheric $CO_2$ taken up is ultimately returned to the atmosphere (Berner & Lasaga, 1989).

Silicate minerals and rocks, like feldspars, granites, and basalts, are also weathered by carbonic acid and produce calcium carbonate, but in the reactions associated with silicate weathering only half of the $CO_2$ is returned to the atmosphere, which results in an important net loss of atmospheric $CO_2$. This loss is balanced by outgassing when the carbonates that are drawn into Earth's mantle by subduction are returned to the atmosphere as $CO_2$ in volcanic eruptions, or from soda springs (Berner & Lasaga, 1989).

---

### Box 15.1 Carbon units of measure

1 megagram (Mg) = 1 tonne = 1,000 kilograms

1 terragram (Tg) = 1 million tonnes = 1 megatonne (Mt)

1 petagram (Pg) = 1 billion tonnes = 1 gigatonne (Gt) = 1.1 million US short tons

1 tonne (t) = 0.984 imperial tons = 1.10 US tons

1 tonne of carbon stored = 3.67 tonnes of carbon dioxide ($CO_2$) equivalent

1 tonne per hectare = 892 pounds per acre

1 hectare (ha) = 2.471 acres = 10,000 square meters ($m^2$)

1 cu m/ha = 14.29 cu ft/ac

1 cu ft/ac = 0.06997 cu m/ha

1 cu m = 35.31 cu ft

How to estimate the amount of carbon in a cubic foot or meter of wood:

1. Look up the specific gravity of the wood species you are interested in.
2. Divide the specific gravity by the weight of a cubic foot (62.4 lbs) or cubic meter (1,000 kg) of water (because specific gravity = the weight of wood / the weight of the equivalent volume of water).
3. Multiply the resulting weight of wood by the percent carbon in that species of wood. This will result in the pounds or kilograms of solid carbon that can then be converted to megagrams (tonnes) of carbon, a common metric in carbon simulations (Table 15.1).

Table 15.1 *Examples of volume to carbon conversion factors*

| Species | Specific Gravity* | Percent Carbon† | Carbon (lbs/cubic foot) | Carbon (kgs/cubic meter) | Carbon (Mg/cubic foot) | Carbon (Mg/cubic meter) |
|---|---|---|---|---|---|---|
| Douglas-fir (Coast) | 0.48 | .512 | 15.335 | 245.76 | 0.007 | 0.246 |
| Douglas-fir (Interior West) | 0.50 | .512 | 15.974 | 256.00 | 0.007 | 0.256 |
| White fir | 0.39 | .512 | 12.460 | 199.68 | 0.006 | 0.200 |
| Western hemlock | 0.45 | .512 | 14.377 | 230.40 | 0.007 | 0.230 |
| Loblolly pine | 0.51 | .531 | 16.899 | 270.81 | 0.008 | 0.271 |
| Ponderosa pine | 0.40 | .512 | 12.780 | 204.80 | 0.006 | 0.205 |
| Sugar maple | 0.63 | .498 | 19.577 | 313.74 | 0.009 | 0.314 |
| American beech | 0.64 | .498 | 19.888 | 318.72 | 0.009 | 0.319 |
| Northern red oak | 0.63 | .498 | 19.577 | 313.74 | 0.009 | 0.314 |

* Specific gravity for 12% moisture content (USDA, 2010).
† (Birdsey, 1996).

In the biologic carbon cycle, carbon circulates between the atmosphere, the oceans, fresh water, and the terrestrial system, which includes forests and soils. Of these four reservoirs, oceans contain the largest amount of carbon and play a major role in regulating the concentration of carbon dioxide in the atmosphere. When $CO_2$ is dissolved in surface seawater, it is fixed by phytoplankton and shell-building organisms. Food web processes then move the carbon into the deep zones of the ocean. This process where carbon dioxide is exchanged across the sea–air interface and then transferred to deeper water is called *biological pumping* (Post et al., 1990).

The terrestrial part of the biologic carbon cycle begins with photosynthesis in which plants, algae, and cyanobacteria absorb $CO_2$ and combine with water to produce carbon-containing sugars and oxygen (Chapter 2). $CO_2$ is released by living organisms when they metabolize sugars and by dead organisms as they decompose.

While the biologic and geologic carbon cycles are distinguished by their vastly different time scales, they both depend on interrelated processes. Within the biologic cycle there are abiotic processes occurring, including fires, river and ocean transport, and turbulent mixing of ocean waters by waves. Living organisms are very important in the geological cycle, including the impact that root respiration has on mineral weathering; the organisms that make up kerogen, which yield oil and gas; and the skeletal fragments of marine organisms that make up most limestone.

## The Global Carbon Budget

The global carbon budget quantifies the input of $CO_2$ emissions to the atmosphere as a result of human activities, the increase in carbon dioxide concentrations in the atmosphere, and the resulting changes in the land and ocean carbon reservoirs (Le Quéré et al., 2015). Estimating $CO_2$ sources and sinks is a major effort that the carbon cycle research community reviews annually so that changes in human-induced climate change can be monitored. With information about the global carbon budget, the dynamics of the carbon-climate human system can be seen and meaningful ways to intervene can be evaluated. The combined components of the global carbon budget are displayed as a function of time in Figure 15.4; as $CO_2$ emissions from human activities increase, more $CO_2$ must be absorbed by the atmosphere, oceans, and land (Le Quéré et al., 2015).

Forest use has had a significant influence on forest carbon stocks over time in the US. These forests were a source of $CO_2$ emissions for almost 200 years, mostly because of forest clearing. More recently, they have become a sink as agricultural land was abandoned and the forest returned. However, that sink is projected to weaken over the next few decades (Box 15.2).

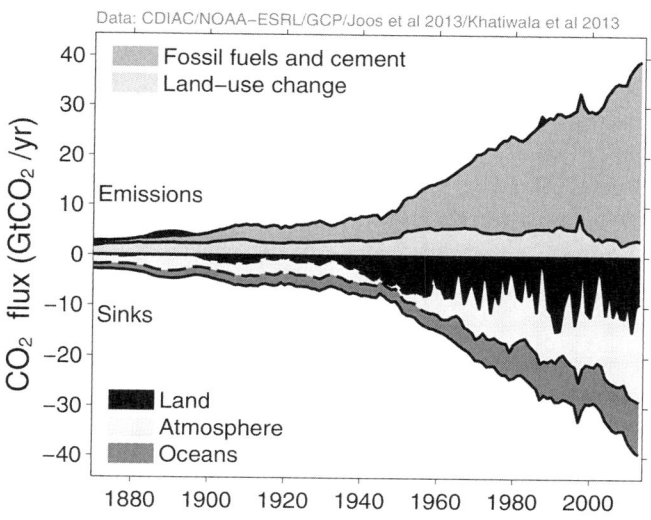

Figure 15.4 *The global carbon budget for anthropogenic $CO_2$ emissions as a function of time, for (top) emissions from fossil fuel combustion and cement production and land use change (deforestation), and (bottom) their partitioning among the atmosphere, land, and ocean. (Source: Le Quéré et al., 2015)*

## Part 2: The Role of Forests in the Carbon Cycle

While carbon dioxide gas from the combustion of fossil fuels is responsible for increasing temperature levels above the natural climate cycles, the same gas provides the foundation to life in forest ecosystems. Forest plants *sequester* carbon by converting $CO_2$ into solid forms through photosynthesis (see also, Chapter 2). Gross primary production (GPP) is the total amount of carbon assimilated by plants; this carbon is used to create biomass and maintain plant metabolism. Net primary production (NPP) is the amount remaining after subtracting what is used by plants for cellular respiration (autotrophic respiration). Total ecosystem respiration combines autotrophic respiration with heterotrophic respiration, which includes $CO_2$ released during the decomposition of organic matter by soil organisms, fungi, and other decomposers. In forests that are carbon sinks, total ecosystem respiration is lower than GPP. Management practices must increase GPP or decrease ecosystem respiration to increase carbon stores.

Carbon within the forest is distributed among the live trees (including above- and belowground components), standing and down dead trees, understory plants, forest floor litter and duff layers, and the soil (Figure 15.6). The proportion of carbon in each of these pools varies by forest type and age, but the largest pools are usually the live tree biomass and the soil, where carbon from decomposing organic matter accumulates. The distribution of carbon in a representative 75-year-old stand in four different forest types in the United States is illustrated in Figure 15.7.

The world's forests contain just over half of the carbon in terrestrial vegetation and soil pools (about 1,200 Gt [gigatonnes]). Although the total amount of stored carbon is higher in boreal forests than either tropical or temperate forests (Figure 15.8a), 80–90% of the carbon in boreal ecosystems is stored in the form of soil organic matter, whereas in most upland tropical forests the carbon is distributed more equally between vegetation and soil (Figure 15.8b). At lower latitudes, warmer temperatures usually lead to faster decomposition rates (FAO, 2001) whereas the cooler climates of the boreal forests have lower decomposition rates.

The warm tropical mangrove wetland forests do not follow this pattern, however. Although mangrove forests account for only a small percentage of the world's tropical forests, they are one of the most carbon dense forest systems in the world because of their complex particle-trapping root systems, which enable them to accumulate large amounts of soil organic matter (Figure 15.8b). They are also one of the most endangered forms of tropical forests (Box 15.3).

*Carbon flux* is the rate of exchange of carbon between pools. The amount of carbon stored is the result of a balance between the amount of carbon dioxide absorbed from the atmosphere and the amount released to the atmosphere. While there is only one process for carbon to enter the forest (photosynthesis), it can be released to the atmosphere through many different processes, such as respiration of plants, animals, and microbes; decomposition of dead organic materials; combustion; and oxidation. Accounting for all of the ways carbon leaves the forest is the most challenging aspect of understanding how much carbon a forest might sequester. This part of the problem is especially complicated in management strategies that generate pools of carbon stored in wood products and release carbon as $CO_2$ from the decomposition and combustion of wood products

---

## Box 15.2  United States forest carbon budget: Past, present, and future

The history of forest use in the United States (US) has influenced carbon flux over time (Figure 15.5) (Birdsey, Pregitzer, & Lucier, 2006). Settlement and forest clearing (mainly for agriculture) resulted in forests becoming a source of $CO_2$ emissions for much of the 1800s, which peaked in the early 1900s. Poor financial returns from farming, reduced soil fertility from repeated cropping, and major economic depressions led to the abandonment of much agricultural land and its return to forest, especially in the Northeast and Southeast. Forests in the US recently have become an important carbon sink as a result. In 2013, those two regions contained 65% of forest carbon in the conterminous United States and were the location of 78% of the forest sequestration that occurred each year (Wear & Coulston, 2015).

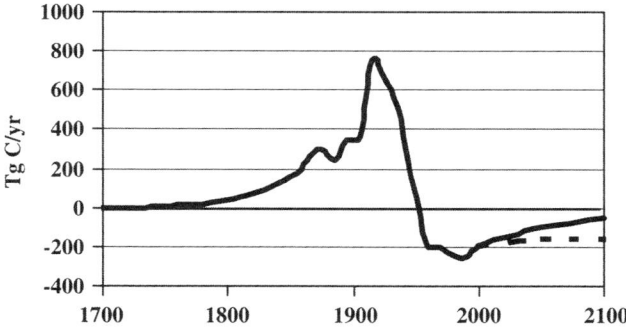

Figure 15.5 *Carbon emissions in the US from drain on the sawtimber stand, and sequestration from regrowth, 1630–2000. Projections from 2000–2100 show a continuation of current trends (solid line) and a possible alternate trend (dashed line) that reflects implementation of policies to increase carbon sequestration by the forest sector. (Republished with permission of Birdsey et al., 2006; permission conveyed through Copyright Clearance Center, Inc.)*

In a detailed study, Wear and Coulston (2015) confirm that sequestration of carbon in forests has partially offset $CO_2$ emissions in the US and might reduce overall costs of achieving emission targets. Using detailed forest inventory data for the conterminous US, the authors estimate that the current net sequestration of carbon in forests each year offsets 10% of the carbon in emissions from transportation and energy sources. Accounting for multiple driving variables, they project a gradual weakening in the forest carbon sink over the next 25 years, with important regional differences:

- The rate of sequestration in the East declines (weakens) gradually, largely due to forest conversion for homes and other developments;
- The rate of sequestration in the Rocky Mountain region declines rapidly, and forests in that region could become a source of $CO_2$ emissions because of disturbances like fire and insect epidemics; and
- The rate of sequestration in the Pacific Coast region stabilizes as forests harvested from public lands in previous decades regrow.

Simulated climate-induced productivity enhancement and afforestation (mostly land that is shifted from agriculture to forest) policies, which increase carbon sequestration rates, do not fully offset declines from forest aging and disturbances (both human and natural) (Wear & Coulston, 2015). By separating carbon transfers associated with land use changes from sequestration, the authors also clarified the role of forests in reducing net $CO_2$ emissions and demonstrated that retention of forestland is crucial for protecting or enhancing the strength of forest carbon sinks.

and harvest residues. A schematic of forest carbon pools (in live vegetation, dead vegetation, the soil, wood products, and landfills), solid carbon transfers between pools, and greenhouse gas ($CO_2$) flux is illustrated in Figure 15.10.

## Part 3: Carbon Accounting in Forest Management

*With the complexity of quantifying the net effects of forest management strategies on carbon sequestration and $CO_2$ emissions, it should not be surprising that carbon accounting protocols for such evaluations are at the center of an international discussion over how to credit forests and forestry with reducing the amount of $CO_2$ in the atmosphere.* Over the next two sections of this chapter, we will discuss this issue, starting with carbon accounting principles in this section and then moving on to the analysis of the effect on carbon sequestration and $CO_2$ emission of different management strategies in the next section.

Suppose landowners want some sort of financial reward for increasing carbon storage in their forests, thus compensating for $CO_2$ emissions from other sources. The reduction in $CO_2$ emissions or increase in carbon storage associated with a forestry project is often called an ***offset*** because it can

Figure 15.6  *Sources of carbon within forests.*

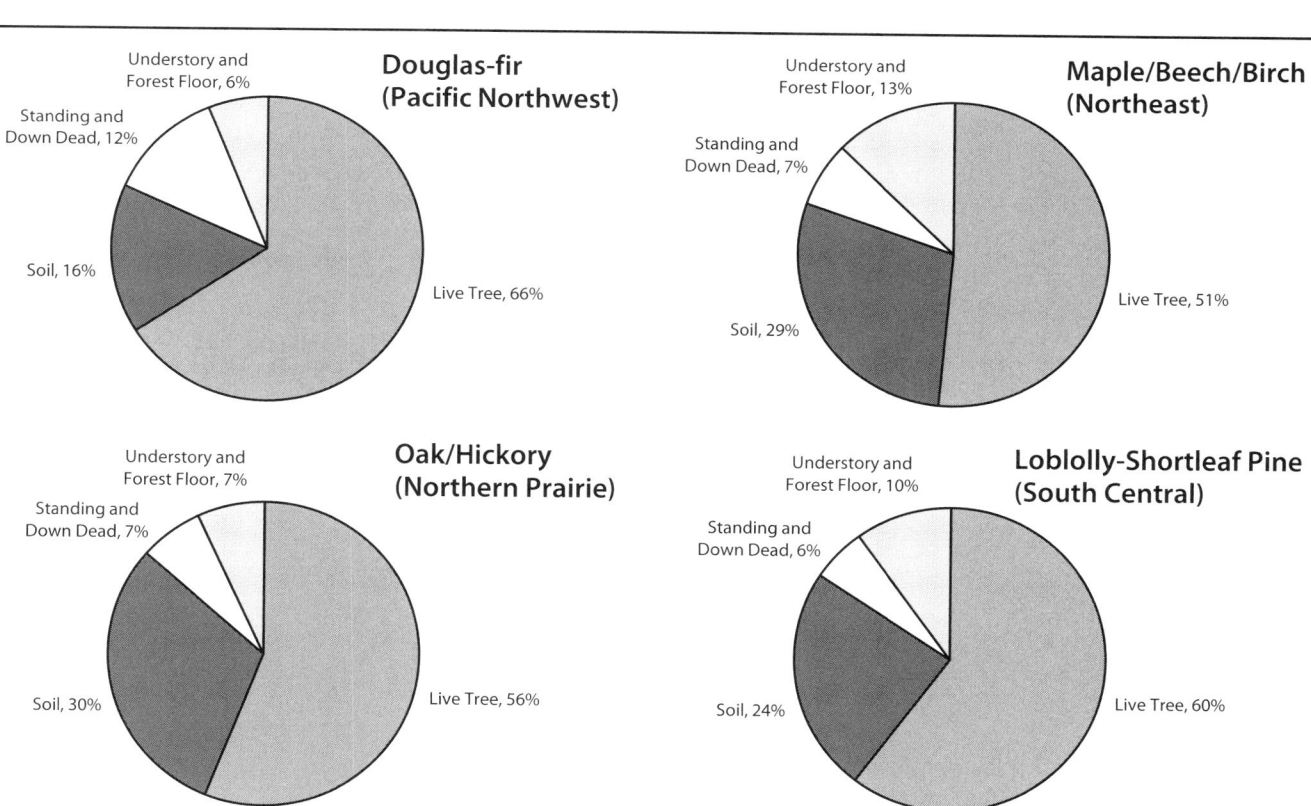

Figure 15.7  *Carbon distribution in a representative 75-year-old stand in four different forest types of the United States.*
(*Source: Smith, Heath, Skog, & Birdsey, 2006*)

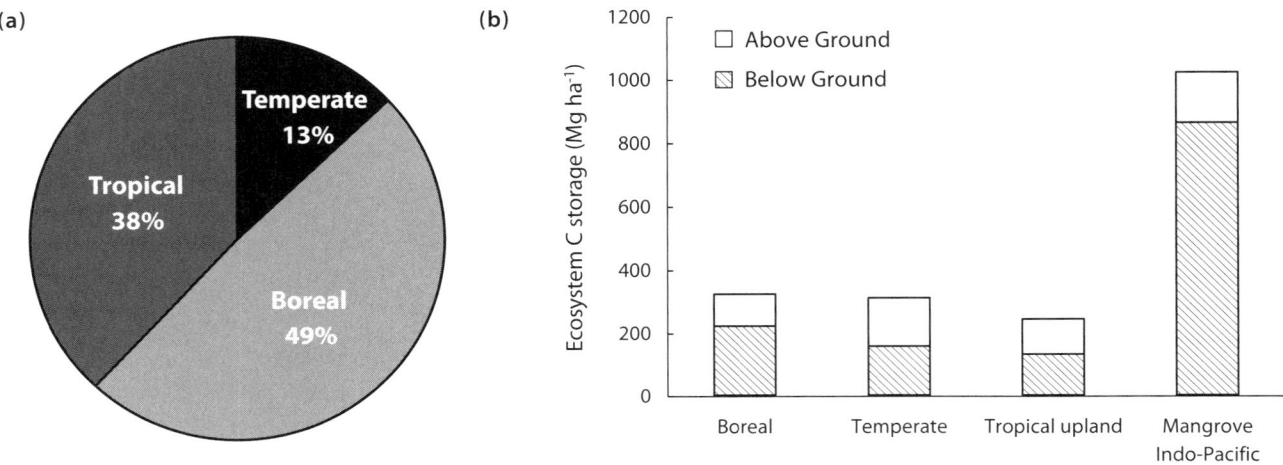

Figure 15.8  *(a) Carbon stocks by forest domain. (b) Comparison of mangrove carbon storage with major global forest domains. ([b] Source: Adapted from Donato et al., 2011)*

---

## Box 15.3  **The carbon footprint of a shrimp cocktail**

Mangrove forests rim the tropical oceans of the world. They are made up of complex communities of trees and shrubs that are adapted to fluctuating tidal saltwater levels, and provide habitat for an array of fish and wildlife species. An important feature of these swampy forests is their complex root systems, which slow down the movement of tidal waters, protecting coastlines from erosion and causing sediments to settle out of the water and build up (Figure 15.9).

The carbon-rich soils of mangrove forests that slowly accumulate in this warm, wet environment can be ten feet deep. Carbon stocks in these soils are effectively "locked up" because decomposition is inhibited by low-oxygen conditions and other factors (Pendleton et al., 2012), making them highly effective carbon sinks.

The areal extent of mangrove forests has declined up to 50% over the last 50 years because of coastal development, aquaculture, and overharvesting (Donato et al., 2011). Unlike the conversion of tropical upland forest to pasture where the majority of $CO_2$ emissions are from aboveground carbon pools, mangrove conversion also results in the release of large amounts of carbon from the soil carbon pools. Kauffman et al. (2017) estimated that 84% of $CO_2$ emissions from mangrove conversion came from declines in soil carbon. Mangrove deforestation generates as much as 10% of the total $CO_2$ emissions from global deforestation, even though these forests account for less than 1% of tropical forest area (Donato et al., 2011).

Shrimp farming is one of the greatest threats to mangrove forests because the shore zone where mangroves grow is a prime location for shrimp farms. Mangrove forests in many parts of Latin America and Asia are being converted to shrimp farms to satisfy the high demand for shrimp in the United States, the EU, and Japan.

Kauffman et al. (2017) have calculated the ecosystem carbon footprint of a shrimp cocktail based on typical shrimp farms in Southeast Asia created through mangrove conversion that are functional for nine years. A 100 gram (about 4-ounce) shrimp cocktail sourced from these farms represents the loss of 161 kilograms of carbon dioxide, which is equivalent to burning 69 liters (about 18 gallons) of gasoline.

Figure 15.9  *Root system of a mangrove forest in Thailand. (© olovedog—Can Stock Photo Inc.)*

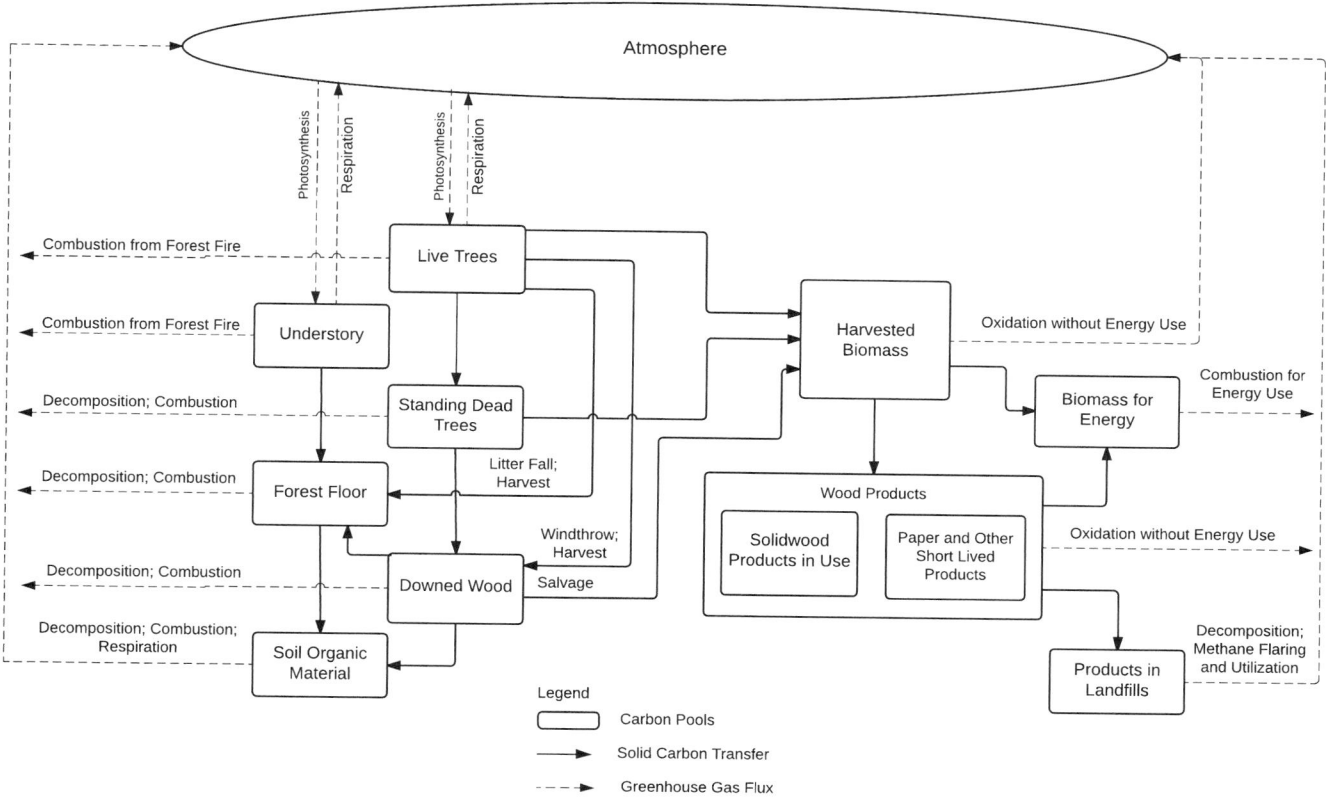

**Figure 15.10** *Forest carbon pools, carbon transfers, and greenhouse gas flux. (Source: Adapted from Hoover et al., 2014)*

compensate for $CO_2$ emissions that occur elsewhere.[1] How might you evaluate their request for a carbon offset? It turns out that such evaluations are fraught with complexities and controversies and intensely debated.

To help understand whether a forestry project increases carbon storage, people around the world rely on carbon accounting protocols that document and define credible accounting procedures (Hoover et al., 2014). While carbon accounting and reporting systems vary, they are generally based on a set of similar concepts and principles (Cathcart & Delaney, 2006):

1. *Baseline*: The baseline (also known as a *business as usual* scenario) represents the amount of carbon that would be stored in the forest and (perhaps) in harvested timber, without the prospective carbon offset project. It provides a reference level against which carbon storage following implementation of the forest carbon project can be compared. Estimating a realistic baseline can be challenging because it requires estimating what would have occurred in the absence of the forest carbon project.

2. *Additionality*: Carbon offset projects are only credited for increases in carbon storage above what would have occurred anyway. Carbon stored from voluntarily planting trees on marginal agricultural lands may satisfy the *additionality* requirement, whereas carbon stored from trees planted after harvest to meet reforestation laws would not.

3. *Leakage*: Carbon lost from actions outside the project as a result of project implementation is termed *leakage*. One type of leakage (sometimes called *activity shifting*) occurs when the person or organization receiving an offset then undertakes activities elsewhere that have a countervailing effect on carbon sequestration. As an example, suppose a forest landowner agrees to manage some of his lands on longer rotations than he normally would to accrue additional carbon, and then shortens harvests on other lands to make up the lost timber revenue. Another type of leakage (sometimes called *market effects*) occurs when projects influence competitive markets. As an example, consider a commitment by a landowner or government to lengthen rotations to increase carbon sequestration in forests. If that action results in log shortages and subsequent price increases, others may harvest more of their timber

---

1 Carbon offsets are often part of *cap and trade programs*. See the Appendix for more discussion on cap and trade and carbon offsets.

and reduce the net amount of sequestration that will occur. Leakage can be considerable (Box 15.4).

4. *Permanence*: The time scale of a sequestration project must be long enough such that removal of $CO_2$ from the atmosphere actually occurs. Permanence represents the amount of time that a project is obligated to continue, and can last up to 100 years or more. Without this assurance, forest-related carbon projects might be compromised by changes in ownership and/or land management. For example, while an original owner might agree to a long rotation, new owners may wish to harvest much sooner in order to pay down the purchase debt.

5. *Risk*: There is always a chance that anticipated carbon offsets are not realized during the project duration because of natural disturbances like fire, wind, or insect and disease problems, or because some of the initial assumptions used to calculate the offset values were incorrect. Also, proof that leakage will not occur is often difficult. As a result, carbon sequestration projects are often credited with less than the expected amount of sequestration.

6. *Measurement and monitoring*: Fundamental to the accounting system is an inventory of forest carbon in the project area, both initially and over time. Forest carbon estimates are often divided into six pools (Figure 15.6): live trees, understory vegetation, standing dead trees, the forest floor, downed wood, and soil organic carbon. The standards for measuring these pools and converting them to carbon vary. For live tree pools, as an example, tree volume estimates from a forest inventory are often first converted to biomass and then to an estimate of the carbon they contain.

7. *Reliability*: Since many forestry projects last for decades, reliability is the framework that ensures that a carbon project is properly implemented throughout its duration. A project may be considered *reliable* if it has the organizational infrastructure and long-term contractual structure to manage and monitor the project. Many accounting protocols incorporate estimates of management reliability into the project risk rating.

8. *Timing*: The attractiveness of a forestry carbon project may be influenced by the amount of time involved

---

Box 15.4 **The effect of carbon leakage on aggregate forest carbon sequestration**

Murray et al. (2004) combined analytic, econometric, and sector-level optimization models to estimate leakage from different forest carbon sequestration activities. They define leakage from forest carbon sequestration (p. 109) as "the amount of a program's direct carbon benefits that are undermined by carbon releases elsewhere" which, they point out, "depends critically on the ability of timber product consumers to substitute non-reserved timber for timber targeted by the program." Their empirical estimates for the US show that the leakage can be considerable, depending on the activity and region, suggesting that leakage effects should not be ignored in accounting for the net amount of greenhouse gas offsets from land use change and forestry mitigation activities.

Among the conclusions drawn by Murray et al. (2004) are:

- The carbon sequestration leakage associated with increased harvest elsewhere to make up for forests being reserved from harvest is highly conditioned by the relative carbon utilization efficiency in the forests involved. As an example, much of the reduction in harvest from reserving US Pacific Northwest (PNW) federal forests in the early 1990s was made up by increases in harvest on western and southern private lands and on Canadian lands. However, the carbon sequestration leakage was much less than might have been expected. As described by Murray et al. (2004),

this result occurred because of the lower carbon utilization efficiency in PNW forests compared to the forests where replacement timber was obtained. Setting aside old-growth forest in the PNW diverted harvests to other regions, such as the South, where the forests are typically younger and more uniform, with the result that the carbon loss per unit of harvest volume was much less. Therefore, carbon losses from the shift in harvest to regions outside the PNW were not nearly as large as were the carbon savings in the PNW.

- Preventing deforestation associated with the conversion of forest to agriculture may result in carbon sequestration leakage by shifting the pressure for land conversion to agriculture to other locations, with substantial variation among regions in the United States. Leakage in the Lake States was especially high, suggesting that protecting forest tracts from agricultural conversion in this region would divert forest clearing to other areas within and outside the region, thereby moderating net carbon gains.

- Afforestation in which land is shifted from agriculture to forests also results in carbon sequestration leakage. Regions that have had a history of large-scale shifts of land use from agriculture to forests had leakage ranging from 20% to 40%.

before offsets are actually realized. Some projects, like afforestation, may start out as a net source of $CO_2$ but become sinks over time as the forest becomes established. Other projects, like developing conservation easements to restrict development, can provide immediate emission reductions by preventing imminent conversion to a non-forest use.

Cathcart and Delaney (2006) provide a simple example of how additional carbon sequestered from a project might be estimated for an afforestation project with a fixed-length rotation (Figure 15.11). The initial carbon storage reflects the storage level without the project, and the average carbon storage increase over time gives an estimate of the additional carbon storage that would occur. Usually, as mentioned above, only a portion of that additional storage would be credited in a carbon offset project to allow for risk that the project might not succeed.

While policies that would increase carbon sequestration in forests are generally seen as effective in reducing the levels of $CO_2$ in the atmosphere, forest policies that encourage increased harvest or intensively managing forests for wood production in the name of combating climate change are more controversial. To put it another way, is there a role for timber harvest and wood production in the worldwide effort to reduce $CO_2$ in the atmosphere? Or are forests best left alone to grow and sequester carbon? The next two sections are devoted to addressing those questions and the controversies that surround attempts to answer them.

## Part 4: Forests, Forestry, and Carbon Storage

*To help us understand how different forest policies might influence the level of $CO_2$ in the atmosphere, we have divided our analysis into two parts: (1) on-site effects and (2) off-site effects. On-site effects* refer to the effects of forest policies on carbon storage within the forests being analyzed, such as changes in total ecosystem biomass per unit area. *Off-site effects* refer to the effects of forest polices on

carbon storage beyond the forests where the policies apply, such as effects on carbon storage in wood products, selection of building materials, and expansion, contraction, or alteration of forests elsewhere.

Some important differences in the consideration of on-site and off-site effects are:

- *People concerned with on-site effects tend to emphasize the importance of forests as carbon stores. People concerned with off-site effects tend to emphasize forests as "carbon pumps" that use atmospheric $CO_2$ to produce wood products that can substitute for more fossil-fuel intensive building materials.*

- Perhaps not surprisingly, ecologists often emphasize on-site effects, whereas economists often emphasize off-site effects.

- *For many strategies that propose to use forests to reduce $CO_2$ levels in the atmosphere, on-site and off-site effects work in different directions.* Policies that increase carbon storage on-site (in the forest being studied) tend to reduce carbon storage off-site, and vice versa. This type of relationship is made-to-order for policy confusion and conflict.

### Potential On-Site Effects of Growing and Harvesting Forests

Quantities of stored carbon in forest tracts change over time as a function of growth, decay, harvest, and natural disturbance, sometimes slowly and sometimes rapidly. In the absence of harvest or large natural disturbances, many forests can continue to store and accumulate carbon for long periods (Figure 15.12). Although there are limits to the amount of biomass that can accumulate in a forest, Luyssaert et al. (2008) found that many old-growth forests can continue to accumulate carbon and serve as important carbon sinks for centuries.

*On-site contributions of forests to reducing atmospheric $CO_2$ generally come from sequestering carbon as forest biomass. Disturbance events like wildfire, wind, and timber harvest alter the carbon storage trajectory of forest ecosystems, generally lowering the amount stored on-site.* With a commercial harvest, as an example, carbon is redistributed from live pools to dead pools, is emitted to the atmosphere as decomposition of residual biomass increases after harvest, and leaves the ecosystem as forest products (Figure 15.10).

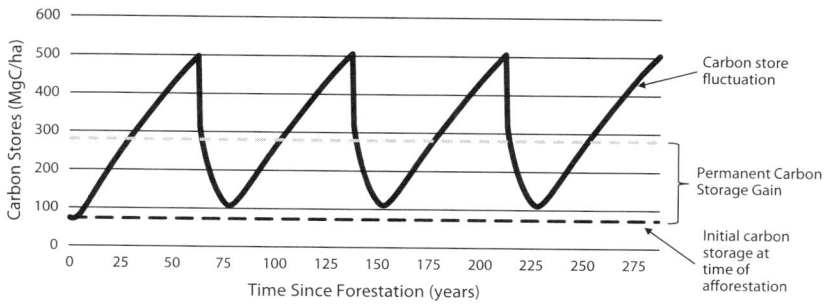

Figure 15.11 *Estimating the amount of carbon sequestered (live and dead) that is additional and permanent from an afforestation project. (Source: Adapted from Cathcart & Delaney, 2006)*

### Management Regimes and Carbon Stores

The effect of forest management on carbon stores depends, in part, on the management regime used. To illustrate this relationship, we will compare carbon storage over time for three management regimes for a productive Douglas-fir forest in the Oregon Cascade Range: (1) a 35-year rotation with minimal retention, (2) a 70-year rotation with minimal retention, and (3) a 70-year rotation with 33% retention.

To simulate carbon pools over time we used the Forest Sector Carbon Calculator (FSCC, 2014), which was rated among the best tools available to evaluate carbon dynamics in forests by Zald, Spies, Harmon, and Twery (2015). For each management regime, we calculate and display carbon stores over time in megagrams of carbon per hectare (MgC/ha), broken into two parts:

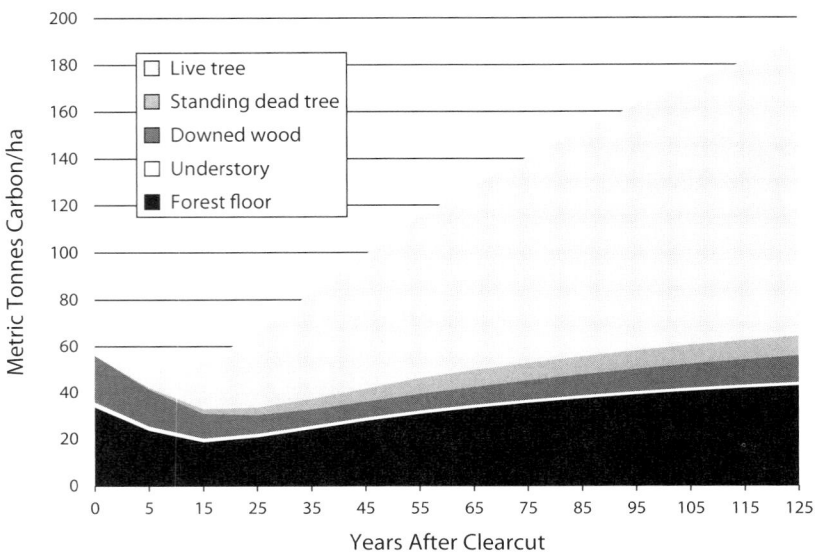

Figure 15.12 *Regional estimate of carbon stocks for spruce–balsam fir stands on forestland after clearcut harvest in the northeastern United States. (Source: Smith et al., 2006)*

- The live carbon pool, which includes all live vegetation parts: stems, foliage, branches, and roots; and

- The dead carbon pool, which includes all dead vegetation, including logs and snags that have not decomposed enough to be part of the soil carbon pool.

With land use conversion (such as through afforestation) or following the first harvest of a natural stand, soil carbon levels may change substantially. Neither of these cases applies in the examples we use here, and we will assume that soil carbon remains relatively stable over time from rotation to rotation.

At the stand level in all three instances we see the distinct fluctuation of on-site carbon stores associated with growth and harvest (Figure 15.13) as the live forest carbon pool declines sharply at harvest and then gradually builds again with stand growth until the next harvest event. The dead carbon pool increases significantly at harvest, reflecting the limbs, tops, roots, and other material left on-site at harvest. The dead wood pool gradually declines following harvest, until mortality from the maturing stand begins to contribute new material to this pool. Carbon storage levels of the longer rotations come closer to the levels associated with leaving the site unharvested, but still remain below it through time. Note that harvested wood is included in neither the live nor the dead wood stores shown in Figure 15.13, since it is removed from the site and is no longer part of the on-site forest carbon pool. We consider the fate of harvested wood later in this chapter in our discussion of the off-site effects of growing and harvesting forests.

Not surprisingly, the 70-year rotation results in a higher long-term average level of carbon storage in the forest than the 35-year rotation, and retention of one-third of the original stand at the time of harvest increases it still further

(Figure 15.14). This is similar to the results of Harmon and Marks (2002), who found that extending rotation age and using variable-retention harvest, which retains a significant portion of a forest's aboveground carbon on-site at all times, increased carbon stocks in the forest.

*In sum, forests generally are effective sinks for atmospheric $CO_2$. Harvest lowers carbon storage on-site and turns the site into a source of $CO_2$, as the post-harvest debris decays, until new growth reverses this process.*

**Additional On-Site Considerations**   Forestry projects alter not only carbon stocks but also energy partitioning, water cycling, and atmospheric composition (Zhao & Jackson, 2014). While these biophysical effects on climate might also be considered in the analysis of forestry projects, they are currently difficult to quantify.

One of the biophysical characteristics that forestry can alter is *albedo*, which is the portion of solar energy reflected from Earth back into space. Surfaces that reflect a large amount of incoming radiation (like bright snow and ice) have a high albedo, and dark-colored forests generally have a low albedo. Land management practices like converting croplands to forest can increase the amount of $CO_2$ being sequestered but can also increase the amount of solar absorption, warming the land and air. This warming effect may be countered by another biophysical characteristic— the evapotranspiration by trees, which cools near-surface air and contributes to the formation of clouds that reflect sunlight. Quantifying this one biophysical characteristic is complicated by the fact that the cooling caused by solar reflectance and the warming increases in atmospheric $CO_2$ occur on much different temporal and spatial scales.

Afforestation activities where the background albedo before landscape change is low, snow cover is minimal, cloud cover is high, and soil water availability is sufficient will have the greatest climatic benefits (Zhao & Jackson, 2014). Reforesting tropical areas while also reducing tropical deforestation may have the most positive climate effect of any forestry project. In addition to providing a large forest carbon pool, tropical forests have high transpiration rates that contribute to cloud formation, which reduces

both surface temperature and the amount of sunlight that reaches the Earth's surface (Anderson et al., 2011).

## Including Off-Site Effects of Growing and Harvesting Forests

Off-site effects of growing and harvesting forests on atmospheric $CO_2$ come primarily from the use of wood products in the broader economy and society or changes in the amount of harvest and investment in forests elsewhere. We have already discussed one potential off-site effect, leakage, which reduces the contribution to carbon sequestration that a forest project might otherwise have produced, as when a decrease in harvest on one forest results in an increase in harvest elsewhere. *Four off-site effects of wood products that could potentially reduce atmospheric $CO_2$ are: (1) turning logs into long-term wood products, which provide off-site carbon storage, (2) using wood products in construction rather than more energy-intensive materials, such as steel or cement, (3) increasing the revenue stream to forest owners, which could encourage them to keep their lands in forest (or perhaps expand their forest area) rather than converting their forestlands to other uses, and (4) using wood products instead of fossil fuels to produce energy.* We will examine these potential off-site effects below, and discuss how they may moderate the conclusions we might draw about the effect of harvest on atmospheric $CO_2$ if we focus solely on on-site effects.

Quantifying some of these off-site effects of timber production can be especially complicated and problematic, as assumptions must be made about how people will respond to changes in markets and policies. Many of the conclusions about off-site effects come from engineering studies rather than actual studies of human behavior; these two approaches can yield very different results (Box 15.5).

**Fate of the Harvested Forest**  For our purposes here, we divide our analysis of the fate of the harvest into two categories: (1) harvesting efficiency—the proportion of the biomass removed from the site for processing and (2) processing efficiency—the proportion of the biomass available for

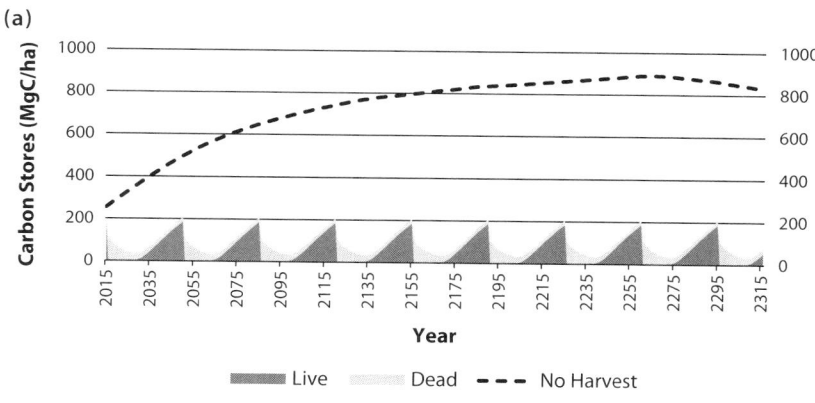
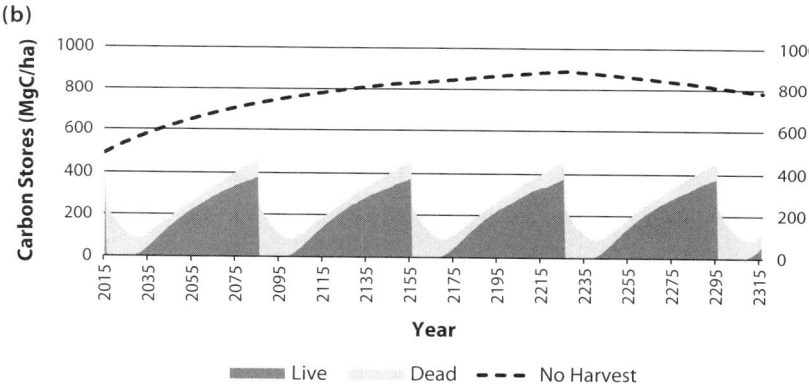
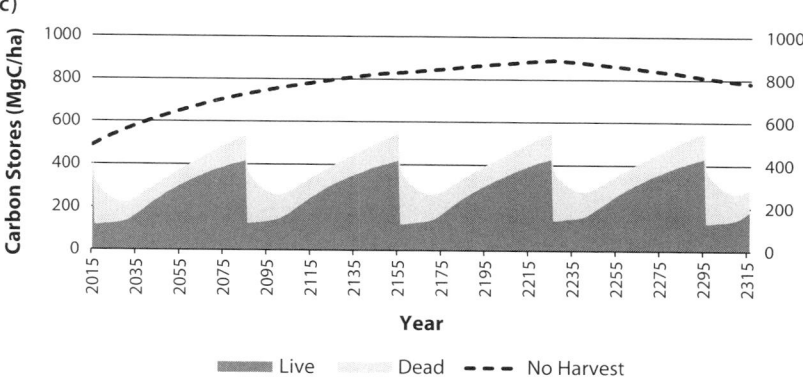

Figure 15.13 *On-site average carbon stores with growth and harvest on a Douglas-fir site in the Oregon Cascade Range were simulated with the stand-level module of FSCC (2014) under three different management regimes: (a) 35-year rotation with minimal retention, (b) 70-year rotation with minimal retention, and (c) 70-year rotation with 33% retention. Culmination of mean annual increment of biomass carbon (maximum average annual growth) peaks at about 50 years of age. The trajectory of the stand without harvest is shown for comparison.*

processing that is turned into wood products of various kinds. The proportion of biomass removed from the site through harvest and taken to the mill for processing depends on many factors, including forest type, stand age and condition, transportation distance to mills, and market conditions for prospective forest products. Also, use of the biomass available for processing, and its distribution among potential products, depends on many technical and economic factors. We will utilize information on harvest and processing efficiencies from recent studies, but the dependence of the study results on these factors should not be forgotten.

We will look at three examples of harvest utilization, one from the US Pacific Northwest, one from the southeastern US, and a third from southeastern Australia. All examples assume clearcut harvesting and no removal of biomass specifically for the purpose of bioenergy production.

Our example from the Pacific Northwest (Figure 15.15) models utilization of a Douglas-fir plantation that is approximately 35 to 45 years old. A certain proportion of the live biomass in the stand (above- and belowground) remains on-site as residual material in the form of limbs, tops, foliage, stumps, and roots. In this example, we assume that 40% of the live biomass will be left on-site, based on the work of Birdsey (1996) and Jenkins, Chojnacky, Heath, and Birdsey (2003). This material will decompose (or be burned), releasing carbon into the atmosphere. Thus, 60% of the live biomass (stem wood and associated bark) will be hauled off for processing as stem wood and associated bark (a harvesting efficiency of 60%).

Based on the work of Milota (2015), and assuming that 60% of live stand biomass is harvested and transported to the mill, we estimate that approximately 27% of the live stand biomass of a Douglas-fir plantation is made into structural lumber and 15% is made into chips for pulp and composite wood products (Figure 15.15). The remaining 18% is composed of planer shavings, sawdust, and bark, of which 8% is sent to the boiler to produce power for mill operations and 10% is processed as by-products. Thus, approximately 52% / 60% = 86% of the biomass brought to the mill is made

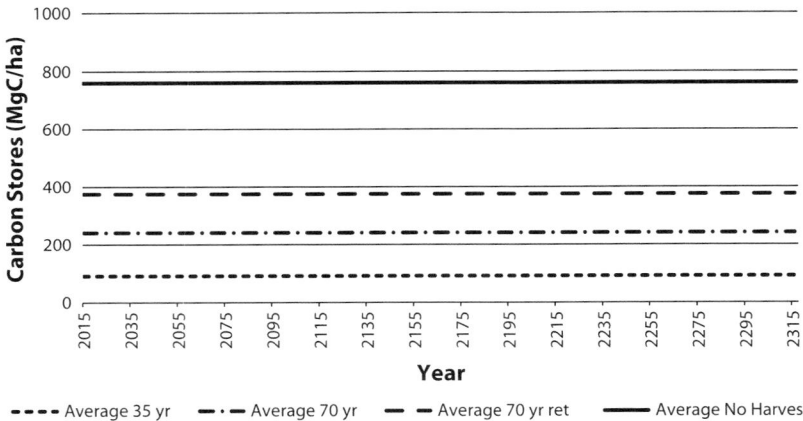

Figure 15.14 *Average carbon stores over time for a productive Douglas-fir site in the Oregon Cascade Range under three different management regimes simulated with the stand-level module of FSCC (2014): (a) 35-year rotation with minimal retention, (b) 70-year rotation with minimal retention, and (c) a 70-year rotation with 33% retention. Also, the average carbon stores without harvest are shown for comparison.*

---

Box 15.5  **The difficulty of engineering studies in capturing the elusiveness of human behavior**

The difficulty of predicting how people will respond to policies can be seen in a study of an energy-efficiency investment program reported in *The Wall Street Journal* (Ip, 2015). Energy efficiency has long appealed to political leaders trying to combat climate change. It holds out the promise of policies that reduce fossil fuel consumption while saving consumers money.

The Winterize Assistance Program (WAP) gave federal subsidies to households to "winterize their homes." The basic rationale behind WAP is that consumers are shortsighted when they fail to insulate their homes or buy more efficient appliances, and should be "nudged" in that direction with incentives. Based on engineering models, proponents of WAP projected a rate of return of almost 12% over 16 years. A recent field study in Michigan, which compared energy use by those who signed up for the program and those who did not, found that program participants reduced their energy use by less than half of what the engineering models predicted, resulting in a rate of return for those individuals of −2.2% (Fowlie, Greenstone, & Wolfram, 2015). Perhaps people do not always act like engineering equations!

Yes, but can't the WAP program be justified as a $CO_2$ reduction effort? Study scientists estimated that the energy efficiency subsidies cost $329 per tonne of carbon reduction, almost 10 times the White House estimate (at the time) of $38 per tonne as the social cost to society of a tonne of carbon, so the program can't be justified in this way either.

We will come back to the issue of predicting human behavior in response to policy change when we look at specific forest policies to help reduce atmospheric $CO_2$. How humans react to these policies in the general economy and society is often a key to whether they help or hurt the effort to lower the $CO_2$ level.

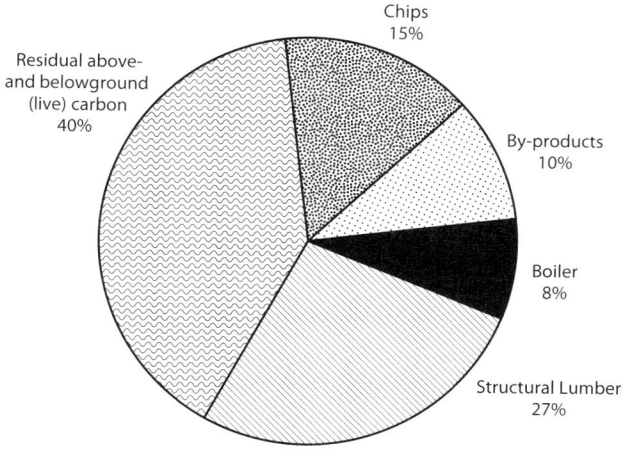

Figure 15.15 *Percentage distribution of live biomass (above- and belowground) following clearcut harvest, by use category, in the Douglas-fir region of the Pacific Northwest US. Source: based on data from Milota, 2015; Birdsey, 1996; and Jenkins et al., 2003)*

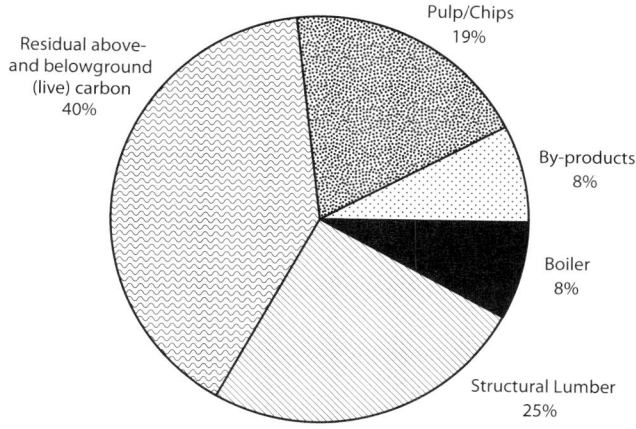

Figure 15.16 *Percentage distribution of live biomass (above- and belowground) following clearcut harvest, by use category, in the pine plantations of the southeastern (Source: US based on data from Milota et al., 2005; Birdsey, 1996; and Jenkins et al., 2003)*

into different kinds of wood products, with the balance going to the boiler. Chips, shavings, sawdust, and bark are intermediate products, however, and require further processing to turn them into final products like paper, oriented strand board, pellets, and bark dust. Assuming that secondary processing has the same proportionate losses as those experienced at the lumber mill, we estimate an aggregate manufacturing efficiency of 80%; that is, approximately 80% of the biomass brought to the mill will be made into final products. We will utilize an 80% processing efficiency in our simulations below.[2]

Our example from the southeastern US (Figure 15.16) represents a typical plantation of southern pine (e.g. loblolly, shortleaf, or slash pine) that is approximately 40 years old at the time of harvest. As with the example of the Pacific Northwest, we assume that approximately 40% of the preharvest live above- and belowground stand biomass remains on-site as residual material, with slightly less of the stand turned into lumber and more into pulp chips compared to the Pacific Northwest (Milota et al., 2005).

Both of these examples of the fate of the harvested forest illustrate relatively high harvest and processing efficiencies. These estimates can be subject to debate and criticism as to whether harvest and processing actually achieve these levels (on average), or whether these represent upper limits of efficient logging and processing. However, they do demonstrate the capabilities of modern harvesting and milling.

In contrast to the young, even-aged managed forests of the previous two examples, our third example is from native Eucalyptus forests in southeastern Australia that vary in age from approximately 75 to 250 years, most of

which had not been previously harvested. Unlike the data for the two examples from the United States, which are based on mill-survey data, these data were compiled from multiple studies by Keith et al. (2014). Although not a mill-utilization study, Keith et al. (2014) show a very different product mix, with 20% of total forest carbon going to pulp for paper products and 4% being used for structural lumber (Figure 15.17). It should be noted that comparison of utilization rates of the Australian example to that of the two US examples is difficult because this latter case includes dead biomass and soil carbon and partially comes from old forest. Still, these three examples do demonstrate differences in forest utilization efficiency and product mixes.

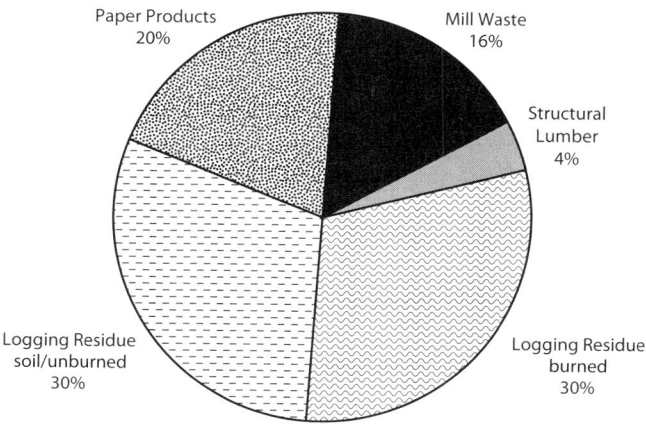

Figure 15.17 *Percentage distribution of live and dead biomass (above- and belowground) and soil carbon following clearcut harvest by use category in native Eucalyptus forest of southeastern Australia. (Source: Keith et al., 2014)*

2 Actual manufacturing efficiency will vary with the processing facility.

**Effect of Harvest on Carbon Sequestration over Time** What happens to forest carbon with harvest?

- Logging residues, such as foliage and branches, may be piled and burned after harvest, releasing carbon to the atmosphere immediately. Left to decompose on-site, this material will release stored carbon to the atmosphere more slowly than if it is burned, though still at a faster rate than logs, stumps, and roots.

- Biomass removed from the forest and turned into forest products release carbon into the atmosphere at different rates:[3]

  ○ Paper products, at the end of their useful life, may decompose rapidly in an open landfill, releasing carbon, or they may be recycled, partially delaying the release of carbon, or they may be stored in a sealed landfill where they might sequester carbon for centuries.

  ○ Structural lumber can have a longer life span than most other wood products; for example, some wood used in the construction of homes may sequester carbon for a period longer than the homes themselves if the original building materials are recycled. On the other hand, some structural lumber is used for pallets or forms for concrete that has a much shorter life span as useful products. Eventually, much of the lumber from all uses may end up in a landfill.

  ○ Mill waste may be burned for fuel, creating $CO_2$ emissions but at the same time offsetting emissions that might otherwise come from fossil fuel energy sources.

  ○ By-products, such as landscaping bark or animal bedding, may release carbon at an intermediate rate (five to ten years or so).

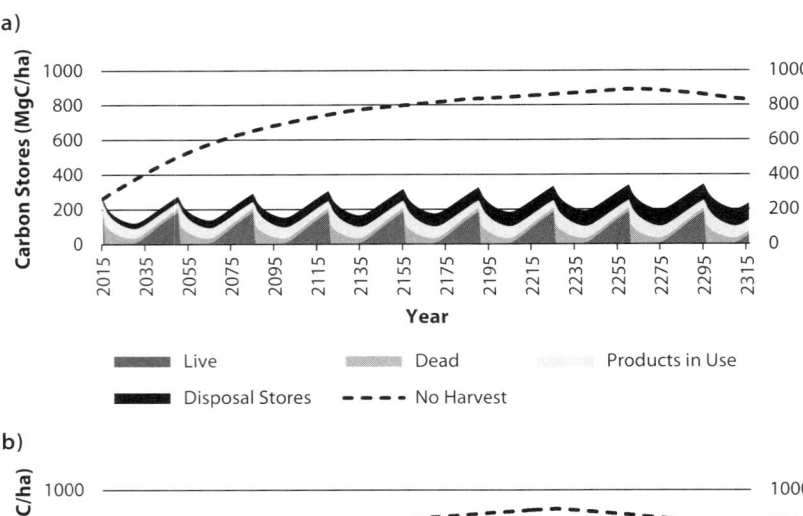

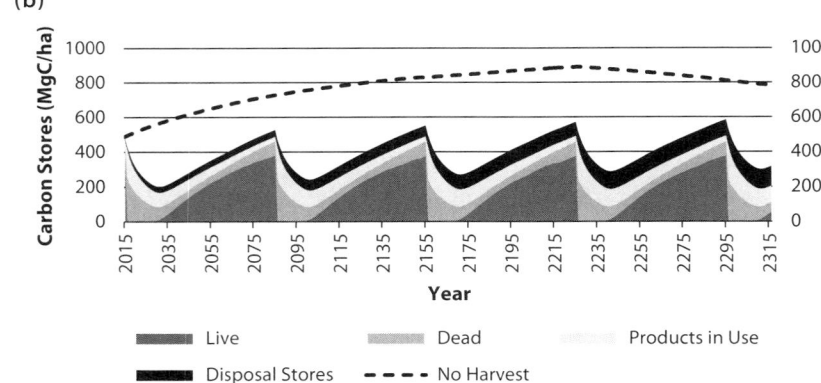

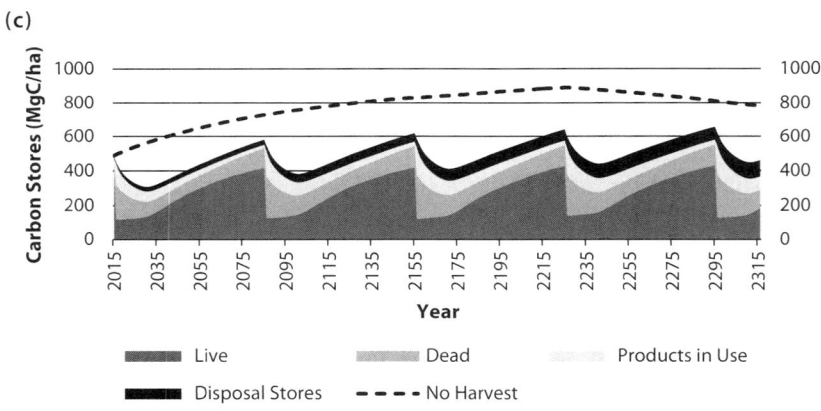

Figure 15.18 *On-site and off-site carbon stores with growth and harvest were simulated with the stand-level module of FSCC (2014) for a productive Douglas-fir site in the Oregon Cascade Range under three different management regimes: (a) 35-year rotation with minimal retention, (b) 70-year rotation with minimal retention, and (c) 70-year rotation with 33% retention.*

To recognize the contribution of wood products to carbon storage, we add two categories of carbon storage in our FSCC (2014) simulations:[4]

---

3 Decay rates for the harvested wood products have been studied extensively and provide vital information for models that estimate the effects that management alternatives have on the amounts of carbon sequestered in forests, and in forest products. For example, see Smith (2006).

4 We also need to acknowledge emissions from management, harvesting, log transport, and wood processing. According to Lippke et al. (2011, p. 310), these emissions "reduce the pre-harvest carbon storage by approximately 6%.... Approximately half of these emissions are currently offset by using internally generated mill residuals, such as bark, sawdust and trim as biofuel, displacing the need for fossil fuel."

- The product-in-use carbon pool includes all wood products such as lumber, paper, and composite wood products; this pool may include recycled materials.

- The disposal carbon pool includes all wood products that have been disposed of but still exist as a physical carbon pool (e.g., have not decomposed or been burned).

*We can then add these pools to those of on-site storage to simulate both on-site and off-site storage after adjusting the FSCC (2014) results for our assumptions about harvest and processing efficiency (Figure 15.18).*

Some notable results:

- Products-in-use declines most rapidly immediately after harvest, reflecting such components as paper and paperboard, which can have a half-life of less than three years. Over time, the remaining products in the pool decline much more slowly, reflecting housing that can have a half-life of greater than 80 years (Skog, 2008; USEPA, 2014).

- The disposal pool accumulates over time and can exceed the products-in-use pool after a number of rotations: the parameters we used for the FSCC model placed most disposed products in sealed landfills, which are assumed to store carbon longer than products-in-use and therefore accumulate more carbon over time than products-in-use.

- *Total carbon stores for the no-harvest alternative (Live + Dead) exceed the carbon stores plus timber product stores through the projection period for all management regimes. Again, the longer the rotation*

*and the greater the retention at harvest, the closer the active regimes came to the no-harvest regime.* Nunery and Keeton (2010) found similar results when examining the effect of harvesting intensity and post-harvest retention on forest carbon storage in mixed forests of hardwoods and conifers in the northeastern US. They found a clear gradient of increasing carbon sequestration (total carbon stocks) as forest harvest intensity went from high (clearcut) to low (individual tree selection or no-management). The no-management scenario had significantly higher mean carbon stocks than all other scenarios. Among the active harvest scenarios, those with high structural retention sequestered the greatest amount of carbon. Post-harvest structural retention significantly affected (increased) carbon sequestration, but longer rotations still resulted in the largest carbon stocks.

*Landscape carbon effects of alternative management regimes.* We will rely on the concept of a *regulated forest* to illustrate landscape carbon effects of alternative management regimes (Figure 15.19).[5] Here a regulated forest refers to a forest in which each age class covers the same number of acres. We can use FSCC to simulate the carbon stores in the live, dead, products-in-use, and disposal pools over a rotation for each of our three management regimes. Then we can calculate the average carbon storage on a hectare by adding up the carbon stores for each type of pool at each age up until the rotation age, and dividing by the rotation age (Figure 15.19). This approach works fairly well for the live and dead pools after the simulations are run for a few rotations to stabilize the amounts in those pools. On the other hand, the products-in-use pool and the disposal pool continue to gradually increase over time. We chose the levels associated with a rotation that was several rotations into the future for these results. Using an even later rotation would increase those pools somewhat but not enough to change the conclusions that we reach here.

Comparing the average stores with harvest to the average stores in a forest left unharvested can be challenging, since we do not have harvesting to act as a disturbance agent in the unharvested forest. Thus, we rely solely on the forest's natural disturbance processes to affect carbon stores. Here we represent that disturbance in the form of wildfire—the dominant disturbance process in the western Oregon Cascade Range. The FSCC model can incorporate a random wildfire regime into the analysis based on a specified fire-return interval. To begin to understand the variability, we used three fire-return intervals in the landscape module of FSCC (2014) for the no-harvest scenario for this episodically disturbed forest: (1) default, (2) 125 years,

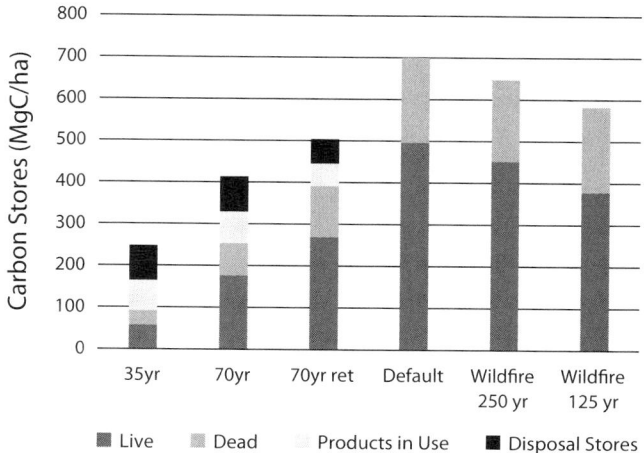

Figure 15.19 *Average carbon stores per hectare by category in a regulated forest under three management regimes compared to a forest left unharvested under three different fire regimes. Simulations were done with the stand and landscape module of FSCC (2014) for a productive Douglas-fir site in the Oregon Cascade Range.*

---

5 See Chapter 17 for a detailed treatment of the regulated forest.

(3) 250 years (Figure 15.19). Recent studies (Dalton, Mote, & Snover, 2013) suggest that the Western Cascades in Oregon will experience considerably more fire in the future as the climate changes. The shorter fire regimes attempt to model these changing conditions.

Some conclusions from this analysis:

- As with the stand-level analysis, total carbon stores (including wood products) are highest under the "no-harvest" scenario for all fire-return intervals. In fact, the 35-year regime contains approximately less than half of the carbon stores of the "no-harvest" scenario.

- *Considering both on-site stores and off-site wood product and disposal stores, this exercise lends support to the argument that replacing older forests with young, fast growing forests does not increase carbon stores.* As documented elsewhere, older forests are effective at sequestering and storing carbon (Harmon, Ferrell, & Franklin, 1990).

- Although wildfires may emit large amounts of carbon over short periods, only a small portion of total forest carbon is released, with the remaining carbon in forms that persist for a relatively long time (Box 15.6). The persistence of the dead carbon associated with the no-harvest regime is shown by the high proportion of the carbon stores through time in Figure 15.19 from dead material.

- As with the stand analysis, the longer the rotation and the greater the retention at harvest, the closer the active regimes came to the no-harvest regime.

- Fires might also occur in the managed forest. Even with salvage, such an occurrence would tend to lower overall carbon stores there.

*Calculating the carbon richness of alternative land allocation strategies.* We have calculated the average carbon stores and product-in-use per hectare in a regulated forest under a variety of management strategies (Figure 15.19). The analysis demonstrates that the management regime with the 70-year rotation with retention, which contains key elements of ecological forestry, stores the most carbon of regimes that harvest timber, considering both on-site storage and off-site wood products and disposal stores.

We might wonder how our results and conclusions change as we move to a landscape analysis. As an example, from a carbon storage standpoint, suppose we wish to know whether it would be better to partition the landscape into production forestry and reserves or use ecological forestry across the entire area. To help think through that issue, we can examine which landscape strategy is more carbon rich

from the standpoint of wood production, using the management regimes shown in Figure 15.19.

Toward that end, we need to determine the size of forest that would be needed under each regime, to produce the same amount of wood product (product-in-use). Under our analysis (Figure 15.19), a forest managed under the 35-year rotation or the 70-year rotation without retention produces about the same amount of wood product, so we would need about the same size forest for a given level of wood production. Since the 70-year rotation without retention stores more carbon per unit of wood produced, it would be the more carbon-rich strategy in aggregate. On the other hand, a forest managed under the 70-year rotation with retention produces less wood than does one managed under the 35-year rotation in our analysis (Figure 15.19). Thus, a larger forest would be needed under the 70-year rotation to provide the same amount of wood product. Let's assume that this additional forest, needed by the 70-year rotation with retention, could be allocated to a reserve status and left unharvested under the 35-year rotation, as it would not be needed to achieve the equivalent wood production level. Let's further assume that the carbon stores in the reserve are represented by the unharvested forest with the 250-year fire regime (Figure 15.19). To understand the aggregate carbon richness of these two land allocation alternatives for a forest of the same size, we need to credit the added stores from the reserve to those of the forest managed under the 35-year rotation. Under these assumptions, the forest managed under the 70-year rotation with retention has a higher aggregate level of carbon stores, although the advantage over the carbon stores associated with the equivalent-sized forest managed under the 35-year rotation with reserves has declined.

It should be noted that we have simulated a longer rotation and also retention of a substantial biological legacy, both key elements of an ecological forestry approach, but not delay in yield due to a lengthened preforest stage. With a more complete representation of the preforest stage, the carbon richness advantage of the longer rotation would diminish further. Of course, using the fire regime from the shorter (125-year) fire-return interval for the reserve would tilt the comparison back toward the longer rotation.

## Substituting Wood Products for More Energy-Intensive Building Materials

*Some studies assert that substituting wood products for more energy-intensive building materials, such as concrete and steel, can make a substantial difference in global carbon emissions and that carbon emissions avoided by such substitutions effectively create another carbon pool that adds to the ecosystem and forest products carbon pools (Lippke et al., 2011; Oliver, Nassar, Lippke, & McCarter, 2014;*

Upton, Miner Spinny, & Heath, 2008). These substitution pools become quite large over time in comparison to other carbon pools and have been used to make an argument for production forestry as a vehicle for reducing $CO_2$ emissions (Perez-Garcia, Lippke, Comnick, & Manriquez, 2005; Lippke et al., 2011).

## Box 15.6 Does wildfire immediately combust most of the carbon in a forest?

In 2002 the Biscuit Fire burned over 200,000 ha of mixed conifer forest in the Siskiyou Mountains of southwestern Oregon and northwestern California. The fire burned with a mixture of severities through forests characterized by a diversity of conifers and hardwoods, steep slopes, and strong climatic gradients (Figure 15.20).

Combustion factors were calculated based on inventory data that was collected from permanent plots before and after the fire. From this work (Table 15.2) we can see that even in the areas that burned at high severity only 18% of the forest carbon was lost through combustion (Campbell, Donato, Azuma, & Law, 2007). Although most or all of the trees may have been killed in the high severity portions of the fire, a large proportion of the carbon that was initially released by the fire came from litter, foliage, and small downed wood. Dead tree boles and large downed wood remained on the site, where they will gradually release their carbon through decomposition.

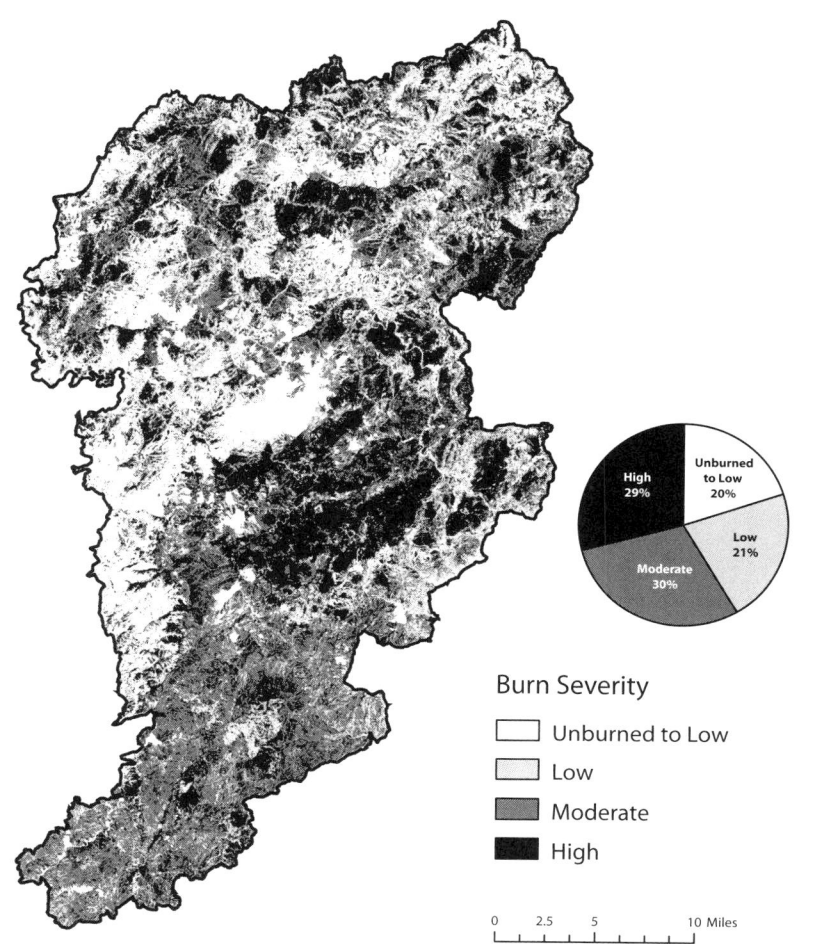

Figure 15.20 *Burn severity distribution in the Biscuit Fire.*
*(Source: Monitoring Trends in Burn Severity [MTBS] available online at www.mtbs.gov)*

Table 15.2 *Combustion factors for the Biscuit fire*

| Fuel Type | Pre-burn Density (Mg C/ha) | Pre-burn Density % | Combustion Factor by Burn Severity | | | |
|---|---|---|---|---|---|---|
| | | | High | Moderate | Low | Unburned/ Very Low |
| Live Foliage | 7 | 3% | 0.73 | 0.43 | 0.21 | 0.02 |
| Live Wood | 121 | 58% | 0.05 | 0.03 | 0.01 | 0.00 |
| Dead Wood | 20 | 10% | 0.33 | 0.21 | 0.16 | 0.13 |
| Litter | 9 | 4% | 1.00 | 0.76 | 0.75 | 0.70 |
| Soil & Roots | 52 | 25% | 0.19 | 0.10 | 0.10 | 0.07 |
| % Combusted | | | 18% | 11% | 9% | 6% |

*Source:* Campbell et al. (2007).

In accounting for $CO_2$ emissions (or other environmental burdens) associated with wood and wood substitutes, attributional life-cycle inventories (ALCIs) consider the direct inputs and outputs used to make a product (Lippke et al., 2011). In the case of structural lumber, as an example, inputs include logs, fossil fuels for logging and transportation, electricity for milling, lubricants, and water. Outputs include chips, bark, and shavings; structural lumber; and $CO_2$ emissions (Milota et al., 2005). An ALCI for steel framing studs might consider inputs such as iron, alloys, recycled steel, carbon, and fossil fuels, and outputs such as $CO_2$ emissions, waste materials, and steel framing studs.

A meta-analysis (analysis of many studies) of greenhouse gas displacement factors by Sathre and O'Connor (2010) estimated that each US ton of carbon in wood products substituted for non-wood products results in an average reduction in greenhouse gas emissions equivalent to 2.1 US tons of carbon. As Sathre and O'Connor summarize (2010, p. 104):

*A displacement factor can express the efficiency of using biomass to reduce net greenhouse gas (GHG) emission, by quantifying the amount of emission reduction achieved per unit of wood use. Here we integrate data from 21 different international studies in a meta-analysis of the displacement factors of wood products substituted in place of non-wood materials. We calculate the displacement factors in consistent units of tons of carbon (tC) of emission reduction per tC in wood product. . . . The average displacement factor value is 2.1, meaning that for each tC in wood products substituted in place of non-wood products, there occurs an average GHG emission reduction of approximately 2.1 tC. Expressed in other units, this value corresponds to roughly 3.9 t $CO_2$ eq emission reduction per ton of dry wood used.* [6]

While the live, dead, product, and disposal pools in our analyses represent direct physical attributes of the stand and its products, the substitution pool represents a reduction in fossil-based $CO_2$ emissions as a consequence of using wood products rather than more energy-intensive alternatives. Because wood can, in some instances, be used to substitute for products that require greater amounts of fossil fuel to produce, such as steel and concrete, the *emissions avoided* by using wood instead of a fossil-fuel intensive alternative are regarded by some experts as a *substitution carbon pool* that should be added to the total carbon storage of managed forest stands that produce forest products (Perez-Garcia et al., 2005; Lippke et al., 2011; Oliver, Nassar, Lippke, & McCarter, 2014).

Crediting a large and ever-growing carbon-storage substitution effect across multiple rotations can have a major influence on whether timber production is viewed as an effective vehicle for reducing $CO_2$ emissions as compared to leaving trees growing in the forest. We can demonstrate that effect using some of the information from our previous analysis of the carbon sequestration effects of different prescriptions. Six key assumptions determine the magnitude of the substitution effect through time:

1. *The amount of product-in-use created from the harvest.* Here we employ the harvest from the previous analysis.

2. *The displacement factor.* Here we employ the average displacement factor of 2.1 from Sathre and O'Connor (2010). It should be noted that Sathre and O'Connor (2010) and Lippke et al. (2011) found that this factor can vary greatly depending upon the particular type of construction being considered and other assumptions. Harmon (2016) argued for a much lower displacement factor.

3. *The percent of the harvest that will substitute for non-wood products like concrete and steel.* We focus on lumber, plywood, oriented strand board, and other wood products that could substitute for these other building materials. We simulated two levels of substitution: (1) 50% of product-in-use created from the harvest (most of the lumber from the harvest would substitute for energy intensive, non-wood products), and (2) 75% of product-in-use created from the harvest (almost all of the lumber and chip products would substitute). With the product mix (lumber, chips, and by-products) in our example, the 75% level might be viewed as the upper limit on the amount of substitution. Of course, a lower percentage might also occur.

4. *The cumulative nature of the substitution effect.* Here, we assume that the substitution effect is cumulative through time with the substitution pool credited each time the stand is cut, under the argument that a displacement occurs each time wood is used in place of concrete or steel (Perez-Garcia et al., 2005; Lippke et al., 2011). Others challenge this assumption (Harmon, 2016).

5. *The length of time that the substitution effect accumulates.* We look out 70 years (two harvests of the 35-year rotation [year 0 and year 35] and one of the 70-year rotation [year 0]). As we discuss below, the substitution ratio will undoubtedly change over time and most likely decline; accumulating the effect of the current substitution ratio for long periods can certainly be questioned.

---

6 Sathre and O'Connor (2010) assume that the carbon equivalent of wood is 50% of oven-dry weight.

6. *The effect on the average life span of buildings if wood is substituted for more fossil-fuel intensive building materials.* We assume no effect from using wood. If wood shortens the average life span, the substitution effect would be less.

*Under these assumptions, our results show that including the effect on CO2 emissions from using wood products instead of alternative building materials may bring the aggregate carbon "storage" of managing a stand to produce wood products on a sustainable basis close to the carbon storage of leaving the stand to grow and may even exceed it over a long simulation period* (Figure 15.21). At the higher (75%) level of product substitution and two harvests, storage under the 35-year rotation is still below that of leaving the stand to grow, but would approach and exceed it if the simulation continued. At the higher level of product substitution and one harvest, both 70-year rotations approach the storage over time of the regime that leaves the stand to grow, and would exceed it at both levels with the next harvest. While these results support the argument that sustain-

able harvest of forests can help fight climate change, some cautions are in order.

Sathre and O'Connor (2010, pp. 111–112) summarize the valid use of a displacement factor in the analysis:

*A displacement factor is valid only for wood used **instead** of non-wood materials. The displacement factors calculated here should not be misinterpreted to suggest that a GHG emission reduction will result from each and every piece of wood used, regardless of how it is produced and used. The use of wood in applications for which wood is typically used will not result in a GHG emission reduction, except to the extent that emission would have been greater if non-wood materials were used instead. Thus, depending on the context, a displacement factor can be a measure of either the GHG emission that is avoided because something is made of wood when it could have otherwise been made of non-wood materials, or of the potential reduction in GHG emission if something made of non-wood materials were instead made of wood.*

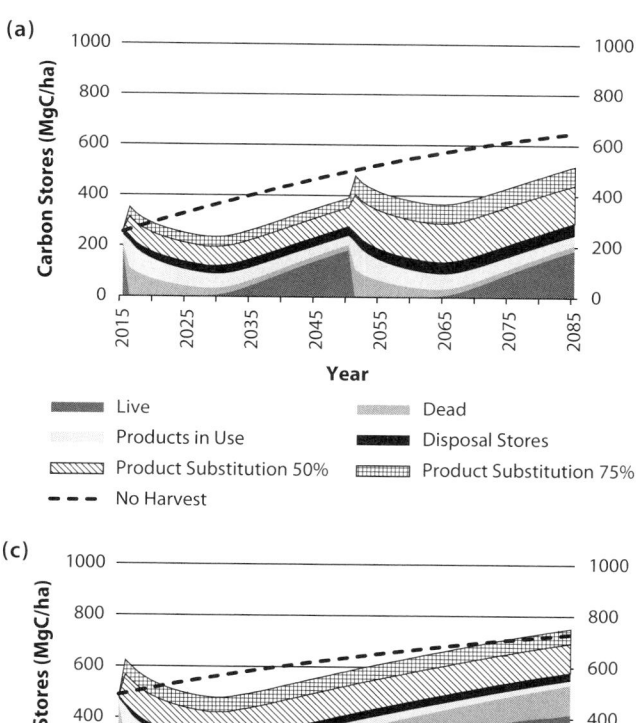

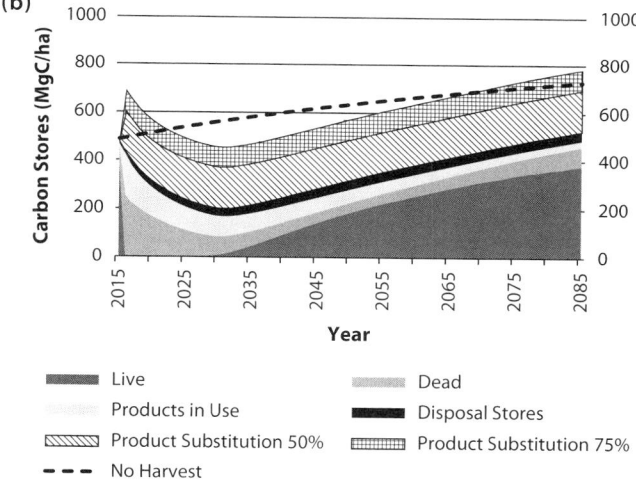

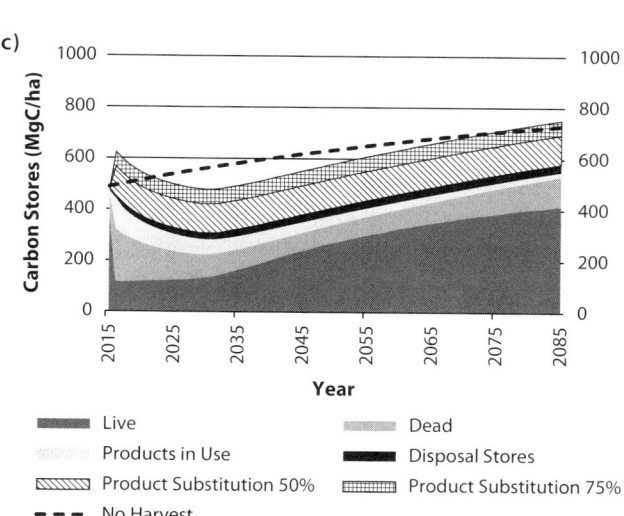

Figure 15.21 *On-site and off-site carbon stores over 70 years, along with credit for reduced emissions from substituting wood products for other building materials for two harvests of the 35-year rotation (year 0 and in 35 years) and one of the 70-year rotation (year 0). Growth and harvest were simulated with the stand-level module of FSCC (2014) for a productive Douglas-fir site in the Oregon Cascade Range under three different management regimes: (a) 35-year rotation with minimal retention, (b) 70-year rotation with minimal retention, and (c) 70-year rotation with 33% retention. For comparison, we credit both half and three-quarters of the product-in-use carbon, at time of processing, with substitution.**

\* Some authors provide an additional credit for displacement of fossil fuels from power generated from the burning of woody debris from processing (Lippke et al., 2011). Doing so here would provide another, comparatively small, substitution effect.

Harmon (2016; Harmon & Campbell, 2017) points out that claims for a large substitution effect from forest management, as we showed in Figure 15.21, must be tempered by a number of considerations:

- Market-driven carbon leakage can occur. Substitution ratios come from engineering studies—the validity of which we questioned earlier in the chapter as a guide to human behavior. These studies assume that the shift from cement or steel to wood will result in the unused fossil fuels "staying in the ground," i.e., they will not be consumed through other production processes. However, as the demand for these fuels for construction materials falls, their price should also fall, making them cheaper for other uses and potentially triggering a countervailing increase in use elsewhere. This phenomenon is another example of carbon leakage and limits the reduction in $CO_2$ emissions that would otherwise occur.

- Assuming fixed substitution ratios through long time periods is not realistic. Fossil carbon energy use for some non-wood construction materials, such as steel and brick, have been declining over time (Hammond & Jones, 2008). Changing manufacturing methods, such as the addition of fly ash to cement, can reduce embodied energy (Hammond & Jones, 2008). Increasing the use of recycled steel and concrete would reduce fossil fuel use in building construction (Tormark, 2002). Changing the mix of fossil fuels used to generate energy, such as switching from coal to natural gas, substantially reduces the amount of carbon released per unit of carbon consumed (Jaramillo et al., 2007). Moreover, concrete and steel industries are not oblivious to the need to become more $CO_2$ efficient in their manufacturing processes as part of global efforts to reduce $CO_2$ emissions. On the other hand, the carbon efficiency of wood production has increased over time as harvest has shifted from old-growth forests to plantations, and milling efficiency has improved. Overall, we expect a downward trend in the average substitution ratio through time.

- Harvest of old-growth forests is especially difficult to justify as a tool to reduce atmospheric $CO_2$, even with a substitution effect. Conversion of older, high carbon-store forests to short-rotation plantations would likely lead to more $CO_2$ being added to the atmosphere despite some of the harvested carbon being stored and production substitution occurring (Mackey et al., 2013).

*In sum, emission reductions from substituting wood for other building products are real, but their magnitude over time is somewhat uncertain and controversial.* Beyond the issue of uncertainty about their magnitude over time, taking credit for the reduction in $CO_2$ emissions associated with this substitution is fundamentally different from taking credit for the effect on atmospheric $CO_2$ from carbon storage in a forest, a wooden house, or a landfill. Rather, the substitution effect takes credit for not using fossil fuels—for keeping them in the ground, without guaranteeing that they will stay in the ground and not be used for some other purpose. The fate of this fossil fuel not used for concrete and cement, though, is a function of the supply and demand of a multitude of interacting goods and is influenced by social policy, consumer preferences, and many other factors. *Still, the positive effects on reducing $CO_2$ emissions by using wood in construction, instead of non-wood products such as concrete or steel, provide one more approach to reducing the worldwide dependence on fossil fuels. It also can provide political support for requiring that fossil fuels stay where they are.*

## Effects of Wood Product Income on Aggregate Area in Forest

Economists argue that revenue to landowners from wood products, whether it is lumber, paper, or biomass, creates incentives for landowners to keep their lands in forest, rather than converting them to other uses such as housing subdivisions or agriculture (Lubowski, Plantinga, & Stavins, 2008; USDA Forest Service, 2012). Such conversions can result in an immediate release in $CO_2$ and have a limited future carbon sequestration potential. In Oregon, as an example, Cathcart, Kline, Delaney, and Tilton (2007) demonstrated that conversion from forest to housing subdivisions results in a significant loss in carbon storage.

Miner et al. (2014) argue that the ability of landowners to increase their revenue stream from forests will cause landowners to keep more "forests in forest," rather than converting the area to some other use, such as agriculture. Indeed, *revenue may encourage owners to expand forest area. Such expansion was found in the southeastern US, where econometric simulations suggest that a robust biomass market can result in expansion of the area in forest, with more land being planted or being allowed to naturally regenerate to forest, thus adding to carbon stores* (Abt, Abt, Galik, & Skog, 2014). Based on this type of relationship, Miner et al. (2014) argue that we should consider the effect of biomass harvest revenue streams on aggregate forest area and the resulting positive effect on forest carbon sequestration. More generally, economic theory and econometric analysis suggest a link between the revenue stream to forest owners and their decisions about whether to maintain or increase the area in forests. However, the extent and magnitude of these effects can be difficult to verify.

## Using Woody Biomass for Energy

For millennia people have burned wood for energy, but in many parts of the world the emphasis on wood for energy has declined with the shift to coal, oil, and natural gas. Recently, a rebirth of interest in wood for fuel has occurred in the United States, Europe, and elsewhere as part of the larger consideration of biomass as a source of energy.

Initially, an argument was made that such use was *carbon-neutral by definition* since forests are renewable. However, it soon became clear that burning wood for fuel creates an immediate *carbon debt*, since woody biomass is less efficient, in terms of the amount of $CO_2$ released per unit of energy produced, than most fossil fuels (Table 15.3). This conclusion has raised many questions about their use, despite the promotion of woody biomass as *green energy* by many European countries.

As noted by Walker, Cardellichio, Gunn, Saahd, and Hagan (2013) there is wide variability in the magnitude of carbon debts across different biomass technologies. This is a function of the way specific life-cycle GHG characteristics of a bioenergy technology combine with the GHG

Table 15.3 *Excess biomass emissions as a percentage of total biomass emissions from the substitution of biomass for other fuel sources*

| Scenario | Coal | Oil (#6) | Oil (#2) | Natural gas |
|---|---|---|---|---|
| Electric | 31% | | | 66% |
| Thermal | | 8% | 15% | 37% |

*Source:* Adapted from Walker et al. (2013).

characteristics of the fossil fuel energy plant it replaces. Carbon debts for situations where biomass thermal capacity replaces oil-fired thermal capacity can be as low as 8%, whereas the debt when biomass replaces natural gas in large-scale electricity generation can range as high as 66% (Table 15.3).

On the other hand, forests regrow over time and, at least to some degree, offset the initial carbon debt incurred by using woody biomass instead of fossil fuels for energy. Such a countervailing effect is real, but how long it takes to repay the carbon debt, and whether it fully repays that debt, remains deeply controversial (Hudiburg, Law, Wirth, & Luyssaer, 2011; Walker et al., 2013) (Box 15.7).

Following Miner et al. (2014), we will divide the discussion of the $CO_2$ emission effects from forest biomass into two parts: (1) utilization of forest debris created during harvest from tops, branches, and unusable parts of the bole, and (2) use of roundwood (logs large enough to be made into solid wood products) from sustainably managed forests.

**Using Harvest Debris for Biomass Energy** Net biogenic $CO_2$ emissions from increased use of forest harvest residues for energy are highly dependent on whether the harvest residues used for energy production would have been burned in the forest or left to decompose (Miner et al., 2014). We will consider each of these instances in turn.

Large quantities of tops and branches are created during harvest (Figure 15.22). They are often left in a pile at the landing and burned, piled in the forest and burned (see Chapter 12 for examples), or sometimes broadcast burned across the harvest unit. Burning this biomass in a

---

### Box 15.7 Forest bioenergy production on the Pacific Coast of the United States

Hudiburg et al. (2011) used forest inventory data to assess annual net change of land-based forest carbon on the Pacific Coast (Washington, Oregon, and California) from three strategies that increased harvest to produce more biomass for energy. In terms of their current condition, the forests in this region are carbon sinks, especially in the wetter coastal areas. However, many interior forests have very low rates of sequestration due to a combination of relatively low growth rates and losses caused by wildfire and insects.

In their analysis, the authors compared current management to three other strategies: (1) fire prevention (fuel treatment), (2) economically feasible timber harvests, and (3) bioenergy production. They simulated the total amount of sources and sinks in these forests under each strategy to estimate their effect on emissions. They measured carbon sinks in terms of net ecosystem productivity, fossil fuel substitution associated with use of biomass, and added regrowth after harvest, and measured carbon sources such as fossil fuel use during harvest and processing, wood decompo-

sition, biofuel emissions, and fire emissions. They looked ahead 20 years, considering both harvest and growth.

Their simulations showed an increase in emissions in the alternative strategies, with the amount of increase correlated with the amount of harvest. Since biomass is generally less efficient than fossil fuels in terms of emissions per unit of energy produced, the emissions associated with energy production increased. The reduction in fire emissions and regrowth that occurred (from reducing fuels on the landscape) across the three Pacific states was not sufficient to offset the carbon debt created by switching from fossil fuels to biomass for energy production.

Hudiburg et al. (2011) noted that insect infestations, increased fire emissions, or reduced primary production could further weaken the forest carbon sink in eastern Oregon and eastern Washington, which might change their conclusions for that area. In that case, management schemes that emphasize bioenergy production might succeed in jointly reducing fire risk and carbon emissions.

biomass boiler rather than on-site at least gets some use-able energy from this material. In such cases, Miner et al. (2014) argue that net emissions of biogenic $CO_2$ associated with using forest residues for energy are zero, since the emissions would occur anyway and the benefits from displacing fossil fuel occur instantaneously. While that statement is reasonable, the fossil fuel cost of gathering and transporting the material to the biomass boiler must also be included. Still, a strong case can be made for the net $CO_2$ emission reduction from using woody byproducts for energy production that would otherwise be burned on-site, provided the collection and transport emission costs are modest. Of course, this begs the question of whether, from a carbon standpoint, the harvest should have occurred at all.

Perhaps, though, the debris will be left to decompose naturally either at the landing or in the forest. What are the potential $CO_2$ emission reductions from using them for bioenergy then? Miner et al. (2014) conclude that net benefits from using forest residues to produce electricity are generally observed in less than a decade or two under conditions representative of the eastern United States. Where decomposition rates are slower, such as in portions of the Pacific Northwest, longer time periods may be required to see net benefits. Again, the analysis would need to include the fossil fuel cost of gathering and transporting the biomass to reach definitive conclusions about particular sites.

**Using Roundwood for Biomass Energy**    Under the economic conditions studied by Miner et al. (2014), prices for logs used in energy production would need to be higher than for their use as sawlogs, which the authors suggested is improbable. Still, they simulate such an outcome for sustainably managed forests. They conclude that, depending on the fossil fuel being displaced and the timing of the investment response, net $CO_2$ emission benefits may be realized within a few decades where growth rates are relatively high and an investment response to the revenue stream from selling woody biomass is strong (in terms of maintaining or increasing forest area). Where tree growth is slow and investment response is lacking, they conclude that many decades may be required to see net emission benefits from using roundwood for energy. The off-site emission reduction from creating solid wood products that will be lost must also be considered, such as their functioning as long-term storage and as a source of building materials

Figure 15.22 *Many logging operations in the United States haul the entire tree to the landing where they process the trees and create "slash" piles from the branches and tree tops, which are then burned. Using this biomass to produce energy in place of fossil fuels can reduce net $CO_2$ emissions if transportation distances are moderate.*

with relatively low energy costs. Thus, shifting the use of sawlogs from solid wood products to biomass energy production can create a *reverse substitution effect* by reducing the availability of construction lumber, causing an increase in the use of fossil-fuel intensive alternatives, such as concrete and steel.

## The Potential for Wood Product Harvest to Reduce CO$_2$ Emissions

### On-Site Effects

- *Wood product harvest generally reduces forest carbon stocks (CO$_2$ storage) compared to leaving the forest alone*, both through removing biomass and increasing the decomposition rate of the biomass that remains.

- Exceptions to this conclusion can occur when harvest helps stabilize carbon stocks so that forests do not turn into a source of CO$_2$ due to the combined effects of drought, insect outbreaks, and wildfire.

### Off-Site Effects

- *Counting wood products as carbon stores (products-in-use or in disposal sites) causes only a modest increase in total stores* and is usually insufficient to make up for carbon losses associated with harvest.

- *Including the "carbon store" effect of substituting solid wood products for other building materials that emit more CO$_2$ during their manufacture increases aggregate carbon stores associated with harvest. Under some calculation assumptions, it can result in higher stores being associated with harvest than with leaving the forest alone. However, the magnitude of these effects has been challenged, as discussed above.*

- *Creating revenue streams for landowners through timber harvest may cause them to maintain or expand the land in forest, thus contributing to carbon stores.* Again, the magnitude and generality of these effects can be difficult to measure accurately.

## The Potential for Using Woody Biomass for Energy to Reduce CO$_2$ Emissions

- *In terms of CO$_2$ emitted per unit of energy produced, woody biomass is an inefficient source of energy compared to fossil fuels. Thus a "carbon debt" is created when woody biomass is used as a substitute for fossil fuels.*

- *For most forests, it is difficult to justify harvest solely for woody biomass as a CO$_2$ emissions tool as it would take many decades, if ever, for regrowth to make*

*up for both this carbon debt and the loss of on-site carbon stores, compared to leaving the forest alone.*

With respect to the potential for different components of a harvest to reduce CO$_2$ emissions through woody biomass energy production, we conclude that:

- *The strongest case can be made for using logging debris that would otherwise be burned in the forest*, as long as collection and transport emissions do not overwhelm the gains that would have otherwise occurred.

- *The next strongest case can be made for using logging debris that would otherwise deteriorate naturally, although the net benefit may take decades to appear.* Two caveats: (1) collection and transport emissions cannot overwhelm the gains that would otherwise occur, and (2) collection needs to avoid degrading forest productivity and biodiversity.

- A weaker case can be made for harvesting trees unsuitable for sawlogs that would otherwise be left to grow on the site. Any analysis must account for the disruption to the continued contribution they would otherwise make to carbon sequestration on-site.

- The weakest case is for using sawlogs for biomass energy production. Many conditions and relationships have to fall into place for this outcome to produce net emission benefits and, even then, the benefits may take many decades to appear.

Overall, the case for using forest biomass for energy to reduce CO$_2$ emissions is somewhat stronger when: (1) biomass use generates enough revenue to create a significant incentive for landowners to maintain or expand the area in forest, or (2) biomass harvest helps stabilize carbon stocks so that forests do not turn into a source of CO$_2$ due to the combined effect of drought, insect outbreaks, and wildfire—an especially important consideration in frequent-fire forests.

## Part 5: Forest Policies to Help Lower CO$_2$ in the Atmosphere

As we have shown throughout this chapter, forests generally are effective sinks for atmospheric CO$_2$. Harvest lowers carbon storage on-site and turns the forest into a source of CO$_2$ as the post-harvest debris decays, until new growth reverses this process. However that is only part of the story in terms of the effect of harvest on atmospheric CO$_2$. Three off-site effects of harvest that we will discuss here increase carbon storage or lower CO$_2$ emissions: (1) turning logs into wood products, which provides off-site carbon storage, (2) using wood products in construction rather than more energy-intensive materials, such as steel or cement, and (3) increasing the revenue stream to forest owners, which can encourage them to keep their lands in forest (or perhaps expand their forest area) rather than converting their forestlands to other uses. Also, use of forest biomass for energy can reduce $CO_2$ emissions over time in some situations as we discussed above.

*Forest policies often have countervailing on-site and off-site effects on $CO_2$ in the atmosphere, setting up potential conflicts over which effect should be given the most weight or has the greatest influence on policy and public understanding (Table 15.4). A singular exception to this conflict is afforestation, which helps to explain why it is the most widely accepted forestry strategy in temperate forests for reducing $CO_2$ levels.* As we have done elsewhere, we restrict our analysis to temperate forests.

We do not include old-growth forests in our analysis below. Stopping the harvest of old-growth forests can make a significant contribution to maintaining carbon stores of forests, along with many other benefits (Harmon et al., 1990; Harmon & Marks, 2002). Not only do old-growth forests generally contain high levels of carbon stores (they are carbon rich), but much wood is often left after the harvest of old-growth forests, which will decay and return $CO_2$ to the atmosphere. Any countervailing off-site carbon sequestration and emission reduction will be swamped by the negative impact that harvest has on these old-growth carbon stores. Therefore, we exclude old-growth forests from this analysis. In fact, many of these conclusions apply to many younger natural forests, too. Therefore, we will apply the analysis below to *previously harvested* forests—those that have received a harvest that removed a substantial amount of their volume and could be harvested again—a history that covers much of the forest that now exists in temperate regions.

We summarize below a variety of policy proposals for using these previously harvested forests to help reduce the amount of atmospheric $CO_2$. We divide our forest policies into four categories: (1) maintaining or increasing forest area, (2) reducing harvest, (3) increasing harvest, and (4) turning more of the harvest into solid wood products. We evaluate the contribution of each policy for reducing $CO_2$ levels in terms of both its on-site and its off-site effects, also noting whether these reductions make a sizeable contribution in the short run (next 20 years) or will mostly occur beyond that period (Table 15.4).

## Maintaining or Increasing Area in Forest

**Afforestation**   From the early days of global efforts to combat climate change, afforestation has been the most widely recognized way in which forestry can help reduce atmospheric $CO_2$ levels. In fact, it is the only policy on our list in which off-site effects potentially complement on-site effects: when these new forests are managed sustainably

for timber production, the increase in on-site carbon is complemented by off-site storage in the form of wood products. Thus, we would see both an expansion in forests and an increase in wood production. Four caveats: (1) most of the potential gains in carbon storage will occur in the longer run (beyond 20 years); (2) afforestation needs to be focused on farm pastureland with relatively low existing carbon stores, since converting natural grass and shrub lands to forest can create an immediate carbon debt by disturbing the existing rich carbon storage in the soil; (3) the potential exists for considerable leakage in carbon sequestration effects as discussed earlier (Box 15.4); and (4) the albedo effect of changing a white surface (from winter snow) to a dark one (with trees and their foliage) can offset a portion of the gain where snow blankets the ground for many months out of the year (Thompson, Adams, & Johnson, 2009).

**Reducing Deforestation**   While much of the global concern over deforestation has understandably been focused on the tropics, deforestation also occurs in temperate forests through land use conversion from forests to farms, rural residential areas, and other forms of commercial development (Wear and Coulston, 2015). Keeping forests in forest has become a battle cry for combating climate change (Cathcart et al., 2007). Reducing deforestation has positive short-term on-site effects, in terms of increasing sequestration and reducing $CO_2$ emissions. However, it can also have negative short-term off-site effects to the degree that maintaining these carbon stocks, by limiting land use conversion, reduces the short-term amount of available structural lumber, leading to greater use of fossil fuel-intensive alternatives. In the longer run, on the other hand, reducing deforestation can have positive off-site effects to the degree that sustainable harvests occur on these forests. Two caveats: (1) it is especially important to prevent deforestation of carbon-rich forests, and (2) significant leakage in carbon sequestration effects can occur if a policy to control deforestation in one place leads to more deforestation elsewhere.

## Reducing the Harvest Rate on the Area Maintained in Forest

Reducing harvest in a forest managed for wood products on a continuing basis generally results in increased carbon storage in the forest over time and reduced $CO_2$ emissions from post-harvest debris left on-site, with the benefits starting immediately. Reducing forest harvest also may increase off-site $CO_2$ emissions by causing an increase in the use of more energy-intensive building materials. Reducing harvest will also decrease the income of the affected landowners, which may lead to less interest of those landowners in keeping the land in forest.

Also, sizeable harvest reductions will likely trigger increased harvest elsewhere (i.e., leakage) as wood product prices rise, negating at least some of the carbon storage effects that would otherwise have occurred. However, as we noted in Box 15.4, a shift in harvest may result in much less than a proportionate leakage in carbon sequestration.

**Devoting Highly Productive Forests on Public Land to Carbon Sequestration**    Public forests contain some of the most productive forests in the temperate region of the world. As an example, the national forests of western Washington and Oregon and southwestern Alaska contain many of the world's greatest carbon banks. The same can be said for the crown lands of western British Columbia, other public lands in those areas, and the federal and state forests of Tasmania.

It is understandable that many voices call for devoting these forests to on-site carbon storage. It is also true that these forests, especially in North America, provide excellent construction lumber that can substitute for more energy-intensive materials.

In many places, these public forests contain remnant old-growth stands and also previously harvested stands that have been replanted densely with conifers. While these young stands contain modest levels of carbon stocks, they are rapidly growing. In the future, much of the debate concerning the fate of public forestry may focus on whether there is ecological and social value in harvesting some of these younger stands or whether they should be left unmanaged to sequester additional carbon.

**Lengthening Rotations on Production Forests**    With their emphasis on putting carbon in the plants that can store it the longest and creating conditions for rapid growth, tree farms are potential carbon engines. With a focus on return on investment, though, rotation lengths usually are short of, perhaps far short of, rotation lengths that maximize mean annual increment (maximum average growth rate). In some forests, such as the Douglas-fir region, a period of sustained growth and significant carbon sequestration can continue far beyond the financial rotation age.

Table 15.4 *Potential effect of polices for previously harvested forests, which could be harvested again, on atmospheric CO₂ in the temperate regions of the world*

| Policy | On-site effects of policy on atmospheric $CO_2$ (D = decrease [sink], I = increase [source])[#] | Off-site effects of policy on atmosphere $CO_2$ (D = decrease [sink], I = increase [source])[#] |
|---|---|---|
| *Maintain or increase forest area* | | |
| Afforest farm/pasture land | | |
| Manage as reserve | D[*] | NA |
| Sustainably harvest | D[*] | D[*] |
| Reduce deforestation | | |
| Manage as reserve | D | I |
| Sustainably harvest | D | (?) then D[*] |
| *Reduce harvest* | | |
| Devote highly productive forests on public land to carbon sequestration | D | I |
| Use longer rotations on production forests | D | I then D[*] |
| *Increase harvest* | | |
| Reduce fuels in frequent-fire federal forests | I then D(?)[*] | D (if commercial products) |
| Salvage after disturbance | I | D |
| Increase harvest on forests where harvest less than growth | I | D |
| *Increase proportion of long-term wood products from logs* | NA | D |

\# A significant portion of the effect occurs in the first 20 years unless otherwise noted.
\* Most of the effect occurs in the long run (beyond 20 years into the future).
NA—not applicable.
(?) Considerable uncertainty exists about the effect.

Thus, extending rotation lengths in production forests could significantly increase on-site carbon stores in those forests. It would also have a countervailing effect off-site by reducing the availability of construction lumber in the short-term. However, it would result in increased lumber availability in the long-term as stands mature. A requirement to lengthen rotation ages could also reduce the interest of corporate owners in keeping their land in forests, depending on how they were compensated for these restrictions.

## Increasing Harvest on the Area Maintained in Forest

**Reducing Fuel Levels in Frequent-Fire Public Forests**    Over the last few decades wildfires in frequent-fire public forests have damaged important forest values due, in part, to a buildup of fuels in these forests as a result of past policies (see Chapter 12). The smoke from those fires is often visible from space. Such dramatic displays of nature's power have led to calls for fuel treatments, such as broadcast burning and thinning to reduce fire risk and severity, as we described in Chapter 13.

Restoration treatments can reduce the potential for greenhouse gases to be released by large, high severity wildfires from restored areas; however, the treatments themselves will result in $CO_2$ emissions. Also, there is only a small probability in any year that a fire will occur on any particular acre of forest, as we discussed in Chapter 13, and the reduction in hazard from fuel treatments diminishes with time since treatment. Moreover, wildfire, if it occurs, will combust only a relatively small portion of the forest biomass (see Box 15.6). Thus, carbon is removed from the forest and $CO_2$ emissions are created to avoid an improbable future event (Campbell, Harmon, & Mitchell, 2011; Mitchell, Harmon, & O'Connell, 2009).

Some experts argue that using a series of forest restoration treatments to reduce fuel loads can keep emissions lower than would otherwise occur and can help stabilize carbon stocks in the hotter climates many

of these forests face in the future. As an example, removing many small trees in the Sierra Nevada forests of California would redirect growth resources and carbon storage into more stable forest stocks, such as large, long-lived, fire-resistant pines (Hurteau & North, 2009). Further, North and Hurteau (2011) found that wildfire emissions in untreated Sierra Nevada mixed conifer stands under long-term simulations were more than double the emissions from stands that had been treated with thinning and prescribed fire. However, they acknowledge that, in the short-term, emissions were higher in treated stands.

In summary, the case for reducing forest fuel levels as a means of reducing $CO_2$ emissions is relatively weak. As discussed throughout this chapter, though, an exception to this conclusion occurs where such reductions can prevent a forest from shifting from a sink to a source of $CO_2$ emissions due to the combination of fire, insects, and drought, such as may occur if climate change destabilizes frequent-fire forests. Also, numerous other ecosystem values may be enhanced by restoration treatments, including restoring the fundamental integrity of frequent-fire forest ecosystems.

**Increasing Timber Harvest on Forests where Growth Exceeds Harvest**   Growth exceeds harvest on many state and federal forests in the United States (USDA Forest Service, 2012) as well as in public ownerships in many other countries. Not surprisingly, the surplus of growth over harvest can lead to calls for national, provincial, and state efforts to increase harvest levels as a means to reduce atmospheric $CO_2$ through the off-site effects of wood products, particularly as building materials produced with lower energy requirements. It is also true that the immediate on-site effects of increased harvest would be to reduce carbon stores and to increase $CO_2$ emissions.

## Turning More of the Harvest into Long-Term Wood Products

As we have discussed throughout this chapter, the ability of timber harvest to help reduce atmospheric $CO_2$ is related to how much harvest is turned into wood products, especially into solid wood products that have a long life as off-site storage and can substitute for building materials that take more energy to manufacture. Some harvest operations, such as those in Tasmania, have a very small proportion of the harvest going into solid wood products (Figure 15.17). Others, such as those from the Pacific Northwest or from the Southeast in the US (Figures 15.15 and 15.16) produce more, although the proportion of the harvest that goes into solid wood products is still less than one-third.

In general, we would expect the product mix that results from a harvest to be a function of the interaction of stand condition, harvesting and milling technology, markets,

regulations, and local customs. A number of policy tools could be employed to shift the product mix, including subsidies and regulations. Also, this shift could be encouraged through indirect means such as a carbon tax, which would fall heavier on building materials that require higher levels of energy to manufacture and could increase demand for wood for construction materials.

## Conclusions

Forests are wonderful carbon sequestration machines—one of the best natural sinks we have for $CO_2$ at a time when we face a global emergency over increasing atmospheric $CO_2$ levels. Also forests can be a source of renewable materials that can replace nonrenewable materials. As we have shown, though, most forest policies discussed here have countervailing on-site and off-site effects on atmospheric $CO_2$, setting up a conflict over which effect carries the most weight in the development of forest carbon policy (Table 15.4).

Thus, a complicated relationship exists between forests, forestry, and atmospheric $CO_2$. From the standpoint of reducing the level of $CO_2$ in the atmosphere, a strong case can be made, in general, for retaining our old-growth forests as carbon stores and for other purposes, preventing deforestation, and afforesting farm and pasture land; these are the low-hanging fruit of the forest/climate discussion. Beyond that, though, as we get into the broader issue of whether forests, in general, make their largest contribution to lowering atmospheric $CO_2$ through carbon sequestration from continued growth rather than the harvest of wood products on a sustainable basis, a more nuanced, thoughtful analysis and discussion is needed. Similarly, the issue of whether we should use woody biomass rather than fossil fuels does not lend itself to absolutes and broad generalizations.

To help illustrate key concepts surrounding the debate about whether to leave forests to grow or to harvest them for wood products, we modeled a productive Douglas-fir forest of the Oregon Cascade Range. We did find that when managed with longer rotations and legacy retention—both key elements of ecological forestry—such forests sequester greater quantities of $CO_2$ than forests managed under our representation of a production forestry regime, considering carbon storage both on-site and in wood products. Including an extensive preforest stage in the ecological forestry regime would tend to moderate the gain in carbon storage attributable to that regime, however. Nevertheless, in aggregate, none of the regimes examined would store more carbon than simply allowing the forest to continue growing without management intervention. Inclusion of the "substitution effect"—the reduction in emissions that comes from substituting wood for more fossil-intensive building materials, such as coal and steel—substantially increases the carbon storage attributable to timber production, which under some assumptions can approach or exceed the carbon storage of an unharvested forest. However, we should remember that this conclusion is based on a suite of assumptions about harvest and manufacturing efficiency, product mix, product life cycles, displacement factors, substitutability, and market interactions, which make precise estimates difficult.

We end with two caveats regarding the issue of using forests to influence carbon balances, $CO_2$ emissions, and climate change. First, as it should now be obvious to the reader, the potential of forest harvest to reduce levels of greenhouse gases is a very complex topic. It is very easy for important aspects of the forest–carbon relationship to be incompletely analyzed or misrepresented. Be especially skeptical about simple, unqualified assertions.

Second, we have focused in this chapter on the carbon aspects of forests without significant consideration of other values. However, a principle of ecological forestry is that it is almost never appropriate to manage a forest ecosystem with a singular objective, such as maximizing carbon sequestration. *Whenever forests are managed for a single outcome, such as carbon sequestration, other ecosystem services and values are invariably marginalized or lost and the integrity of the ecosystem is degraded. We would argue, therefore, that any decisions about management of forest ecosystems for carbon benefits should not consider those benefits in isolation from other important ecosystem values.*

# Appendix: Forest Carbon Offsets in a Cap and Trade Program [7]

The increase in carbon storage associated with forest management can be quantified under an accounting protocol and, if part of a verified, standardized system, the resulting credit can be used as an *offset* to compensate for $CO_2$ emissions that occur elsewhere. Carbon offsets can be documented through a transferable certificate, note, or other form of documentation (like carbon units issued by a registry) and sold into a carbon market (Cathcart & Delaney, 2006). Such markets are seen as an important component of *cap and trade* programs. As of 2016, all 11 states of the US with binding $CO_2$ emissions reductions policies and the two Canadian provinces with cap and trade components of their climate policies have unified their forest carbon storage offsets under one protocol that is promulgated through the California Air Resources Board.

## The Basics of Cap and Trade

A *cap* is a legal limit on the quantity of greenhouse gases that can be emitted each year from certain, defined sources. Over time, regulators may lower the emissions cap until objectives for the reduction of greenhouse gas emissions are met. The *trade* portion comes into the mix when the state or province sells or gives away permits (allowances) for greenhouse gas emissions. *Permits or allowances* are distributed or auctioned to polluting entities: one allowance per tonne of $CO_2$, or equivalent of other greenhouse gases, such as methane or nitrous oxide. A company or utility may only emit as much carbon dioxide as it has allowances for. If a firm goes above the limit, it must either buy someone else's permits, become more efficient (in terms of $CO_2$ emitted per unit of production), or reduce overall production. By creating a market for pollution permits or allowances, a price is placed on pollution that should motivate businesses to find ways to trim greenhouse gases. Over time, as the cap is lowered, firms have further incentives to find ways to reduce these gases (USEPA, 2016).

The regulations governing cap and trade may allow entities with compliance obligations in the cap and trade market to lower their $CO_2$ emissions by buying the carbon credits associated with activities that result in increased net carbon sinks. These *carbon offsets* are a transferable certificate, note, or registry unit that quantifies a $CO_2$ emission reduction benefit from an eligible activity, practice, or policy, with these reductions measured in tonnes of $CO_2$ or its equivalent in other greenhouse gases. Each tonne of forest emissions reductions must be kept out of the atmosphere for many decades.

With the enormous capacity of forests to function as carbon sinks, (forests are the most expandable terrestrial carbon sink, globally) forests are a natural source of carbon offsets. In fact, forest landowners had great hopes that selling carbon offsets would provide another revenue stream from their forests—one that paid them for keeping their forests growing. Indeed, it is now standard forestry industry practice to have a carbon inventory, along with their timber inventory, as a way of accounting for their assets. While there are currently forest landowners in 28 states with projects developed for the compliance cap and trade market, and over 2 million acres of forest carbon projects providing offset supply, a whole-scale adoption of forest carbon projects has not occurred. This is partly because most countries, provinces, and states have not adopted cap and trade regulations, and partly because of stringent forest management requirements for project activities to qualify for carbon offsets. However, the role of forests both nationally and globally has been increasingly recognized as a vital tool in addressing climate change, with the adoption of the "Paris Agreement" in December 2015. Of the 195 countries that signed the agreement to lower $CO_2$ emissions levels sufficient to keep temperature rise to under 2 degrees C, 120 have identified forests as key to meeting their goals. A number of governments and states have begun cap and trade programs; in the United States, California has taken the role as the lead state in the cap and trade carbon market. The Regional Greenhouse Gas Initiative states of the Northeast and the province of Quebec have adopted the California system for accounting for cap and trade projects. California is now exploring opening its market—which accepts forest projects from 49 states (all except Hawaii)—to international projects under the REDD, or *Reduced Emissions from Deforestation and Forest Degradation*, rubric.

## Forest Carbon Offsets in the California Cap and Trade Program

California has enacted a mandatory cap and trade program and, in the process, established a compliance market and a price for carbon. Its Global Warming Solutions Act of 2006 requires California to reduce its greenhouse gas emissions to 1990 levels by the year 2020, approximately 15% below emissions expected under a *business as usual* scenario. This level is set to be further reduced by 2030 (30% below) and then 2050 (50% below). [8] Regulated greenhouse gas

---

7 This appendix was prepared with the assistance of the Pacific Forest Trust of San Francisco, CA, for which we are very thankful. However, we take full responsibility for any errors or omissions.

8 A recent news article credits the California program as providing 5 percent of the total United States contribution to reducing greenhouse gas emissions in 2025 under international agreements reached in Paris in 2015. http://www.nytimes.com/interactive/2016/12/08/us/trump-climate-change.html

emitters are allowed to satisfy a portion of their reduction compliance targets through offsets approved by the Air Resources Board (CARB) of the California Environmental Protection Agency. This has created a compliance market in which carbon offsets are purchased from approved projects (California Air Resources Board, 2014; Sample et al., 2015).

CARB has specified four offset protocols, of which forest management is one, that can generate compliance offset credits. These offsets are an approved set of activities designed to increase removals of $CO_2$ from the atmosphere, or reduce or prevent emissions of $CO_2$ to the atmosphere, through increasing and/or conserving forest carbon stocks. Forests must be native to the state and area where the project is undertaken, and must be managed to maintain natural forest functions. Permitted forest projects include (California Air Resources Board, 2014):

- Regenerating nonstocked land, which has been in that condition for at least 10 years, with suitable soils;

- Improving forest management and net forest carbon through practices like lengthening rotation age and improving stocking on understocked areas; and

- Preventing conversion to nonforest uses, where there is a demonstrated threat of conversion, and that conversion is worth at least 40% more than keeping the land in forest.

Forest project requirements under the California program include (California Air Resources Board, 2014):

- Meet all laws and regulations.

- Make a commitment for each tonne of $CO_2$ reduced to be maintained for 100 years, or, in the case of preventing conversion to the nonforest use, putting the forest into a permanent conservation easement.

- Maintain or increase standing, live carbon stocks over the project's life (exceptions are allowed for demonstrated need for forest health enhancement).

- Demonstrate that forests are managed under sustainable long-term harvesting practices (through certification, long-term management plan sanctioned by a public agency, or practicing uneven-aged management).

- Use or make progress toward using **natural forest management practices**, including promoting and maintaining a diversity of native species and providing a distribution of habitat/age classes and structural elements to support functional habitat for local native plant and animal wildlife species considered at multiple spatial scales.

- Demonstrate **additionality**—document that the project will sequester additional carbon beyond a standard

baseline and that which would otherwise occur under all relevant laws and regulations and given economic and physical feasibility. This assessment considers both carbon storage on-site and long-term storage associated with wood products. The protocols call for comparison of carbon storage associated with the project with business as usual to demonstrate additionality. As might be expected, it can often be difficult to understand what business as usual means for a particular landowner, especially in relation to improving forest management practices or preventing land conversions. Therefore the protocol uses a standardized quantification scheme that has two basic methodologies: (1) Forest stocks are compared with average carbon stocks (called the Common Practice Indicator) in a defined assessment area with similar forest types, drawn from USDA Forest Inventory and Assessment Program data; projects with higher carbon stocks can receive credit for the portion of carbon stocks that are above average while projects below average must demonstrate additionality by growing and maintaining more carbon stocks, following the second methodology. (2) All projects must model potential carbon stocks for the 100-year project period to quantify the carbon outcomes of forest management that meet regulatory and economic minimum feasibility (similar to a model of future cash flows used in a timberland).

Other stipulations include:

- Offsets are issued based on annual quantification of actual project carbon stocks in reference to the baseline.

- All projects rely on a rigorous on-site carbon inventory; whereas off-site quantification of forest products relies on USDA data for the carbon value of various products over 100 years.

- The quantification of all project baselines and carbon stocks must be verified by CARB-approved third-party verifiers.

Since 2014, when California's cap and trade program was launched, through March 2016, 34 forestry projects were verified with CARB, comprising about 23 million tonnes of offsets. An additional 155 projects are known to be in development. In total more than two million acres of forestland in 25 states are enrolled or in the process of enrolling in this initial period of California's compliance offset program. The great majority of these projects are for improved forest management, with avoided conversion projects being next; few reforestation projects have been completed so far. California has the most projects; however there are also many projects in North Carolina, South Carolina, Michigan, and Maine. A broad range of landowners are participating, including TIMOs, REITs, industrial, and nonindustrial owners, tribes, communities, and conservation organizations. A few examples include the original *early action* project registered in California under its voluntary system on redwood land developed by the Pacific Forest Trust on the Van Eck Forest; the Shannondale Tree Farm in Missouri, the oldest tree farm in that state; the old-growth longleaf pine Brosnan Forest owned by Norfolk Southern Railway Company in Georgia; lands of the Yurok, White Mountain Apache, and Round Valley Tribes; the Potlach Moro Big Pine property in Arkansas; and the Forestland Group's three projects in Michigan, Vermont, and Virginia. While many of these pioneering projects have conservation easements, many do not.

Perhaps not surprisingly, the forest project component of the California cap and trade system has encountered some implementation issues. As compared to the voluntary market that existed before the cap and trade regulations, the price for regulatory offsets has proven to be higher (over $10/tonne in 2016) and relatively stable due to the transparent price of carbon provided by the allowance market; however, the price is still not yet high enough to make every project economically feasible. In particular, the costs of the forest inventory and verification, required at regular intervals, tends to favor larger properties (greater than 1,000 acres) unless there are significantly above average carbon stocks. This, combined with the long time commit-ment to produce this verified carbon commodity, can make nonindustrial landowners reluctant to commit to an offset project. Also, landowners must cope with relatively complicated calculation procedures to determine the economic viability of the potential offset project. Further, the project baseline, which is calculated from regional averages based upon the USFS Forest Inventory Analysis (FIA), may not be representative of actual comparable conditions or forest types on private forests due to insufficient plots on private lands. Finally, the requirement to make progress toward natural forest management may necessitate changes in forest management that some landowners find unacceptable. Still, carbon offsets do provide a potential source of revenue from letting the forest stay as forest and grow, recognizing the public service that landowners provide through their forest conservation efforts.

Anderson et al. (2017) evaluated the California offset program described here. They found that California's forest offset program, comprising a small portion of the state's mitigation portfolio, does contribute to emissions reductions and supplies "meaningful carbon sequestration and multiple co-benefits." Some of those benefits include protection of the habitat of endangered species and of water quality. Overall, they conclude that "California's pioneering program demonstrates that forest-based offsets are feasible in a compliance market" (Anderson et al, 2017, p. 365).

*Forest certification has presented the world of policy analysis with one of the most provocative . . . institutional designs since governments . . . first began addressing the impacts of human activity on the natural environment.* — BEN CASHORE

# CHAPTER 16

# Forest Certification

Sustainable development has been defined in many ways, but a frequently quoted definition is from *Our Common Future*, also known as the "Brundtland Report" (World Commission on Environment and Development, 1987, p. 43): "*Sustainable development is development that meets the needs of the present without compromising the ability of future generations to meet their own needs.*" How do we achieve sustainable development, or in our case, achieve *sustainable forest management*? Certainly some people and groups will attempt to reach this goal on their own, and government mandates can help. Still, more may be needed.

In this chapter, we will examine a nongovernmental approach to sustainable forest management—governance through markets, or as Cashore, Auld, and Newsom (2004) call them, *nonstate, market-driven governance systems*. The clout of these systems comes not from government authority but from companies along the supply chain that make their own evaluations about whether to comply with the rules and procedures of these private governance systems. As Cashore et al. (2004) note, environmental groups and other nongovernmental organizations (NGOs) attempt to influence these company evaluations through economic carrots (the promise of market access or potential price premiums) and sticks (public and market campaigns that pressure companies to support certification).

What does it mean to *certify* a forest? In general, certification verifies that the party receiving the certification is able to make claims of meeting specified standards designed to represent *responsible forest management*. From a commonsense perspective, Meidinger, Elliott, and Oesten (2003) suggest that forest certification implies we understand what it means to take care of a forest properly, and that a trustworthy person assesses the work of the people who manage the forest and certifies to others that things are being done correctly.

*Forest Stewardship Council certified lumber in the United Kingdom. (Courtesy of FSC UK)*

## Emergence of Forest Certification on the International Scene

In the late 1980s and early 1990s a number of key forces coalesced to produce a growing interest in nonstate, market-driven governance systems in general, and within forestry specifically (Auld, 2014; Cashore et al., 2004; Meidinger et al., 2003; Perara & Vlosky, 2006).

Increased capital mobility, international trade, and foreign investment led both to concerns about environmental degradation around the world and to consideration of the potential to influence these processes at many points. Market-based campaigns were used by NGOs to increase governmental and firm-level environmental protection, an approach that seemed easier than attempting to influence domestic and international public policy formation. These attempts provided important lessons for environmental NGOs about the power of using market forces to shape policy responses.

Within the environmental community, efforts to address tropical forest destruction were pervasive. Boycotts were launched by various environmental NGOs, and a number of forest-products retailers paid increasing attention to better understanding the sources of fiber in their stores and whether their products were harvested in an environmentally friendly manner. These concerns led to creation of the International Tropical Timber Organization (ITTO) and to associated agreements, through which tropical exporting countries made commitments to promote conservation of tropical forest resources and their sustainable management, use, and trade. Product labeling entered the discussions of those interested in shaping global forest management, even though complete agreement could not be reached.

Interest in nonstate, market-driven environmental governance in the forest sector turned to action when the 1992 Earth Summit failed to produce a global forest protection agreement. The lack of progress at the Earth Summit convinced many environmental NGOs that international public policy alone would not achieve their goals for forest protection. Nevertheless, the Earth Summit provided a place where environmental NGOs from around the world could focus on forestry issues and provided a catalyst for forest certification and product labeling by laying out an action plan for forestry.

## Rise of the Forest Stewardship Council (FSC)

By the end of 1992, transnational environmental and social groups, led by the World Wildlife Fund (WWF), launched a private certification scheme for sustainable forests, which they called the Forest Stewardship Council (FSC) program. Meetings of environmental groups, social activists, retailers, and some forest companies solidified the FSC approach: forest landowners who practiced sustainable forest management according to FSC rules would be given an environmental stamp of approval through FSC's certification and labeling process.

FSC is an independent, nonprofit organization formed with the goal of establishing a global system for certifying that forest products come from well-managed forests. The mission of FSC is to promote environmentally appropriate, socially beneficial, and economically viable management of the world's forests (Forest Stewardship Council, 2015). FSC uses a two-pronged process that includes both a forestry performance audit and a chain of custody audit. FSC certification standards are based on ten principles (see below), and timber that comes from sources that meet the FSC standards is eligible to carry the FSC logo, which signifies that the product comes from well-managed forests.

FSC created a set of core international principles and evaluation criteria used in the certification process that address the sustainability of forests and the needs of forest-dependent communities. The FSC program also mandated creation of national and regional working groups to develop specific standards for their respective areas, based on the international principles and criteria. As an organization, FSC does not itself certify forests; rather, FSC recognizes qualified independent organizations, known as certification bodies, to carry out the on-the-ground evaluations and certification of managed forests.

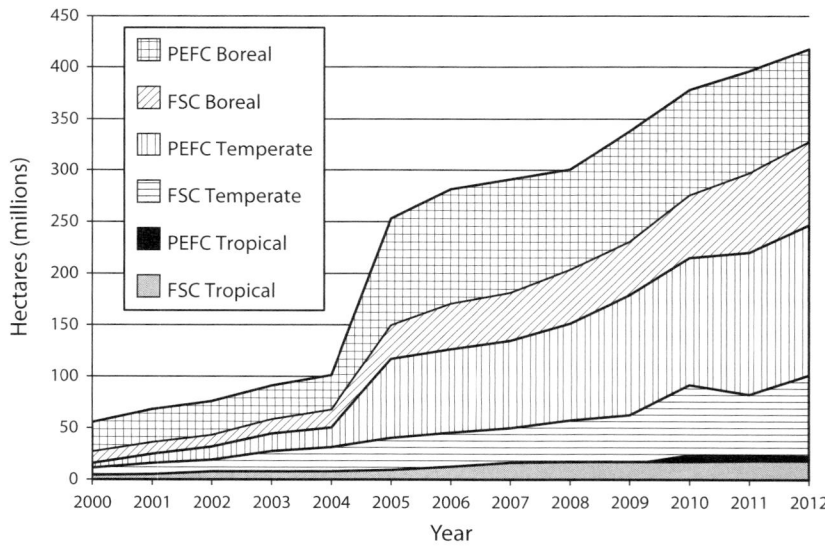

Figure 16.1 *Forest certification worldwide by certification system (FSC and PEFC) and bioregion through 2012.*
(*Source: http://www.bipindicators.net/forestcertification*)

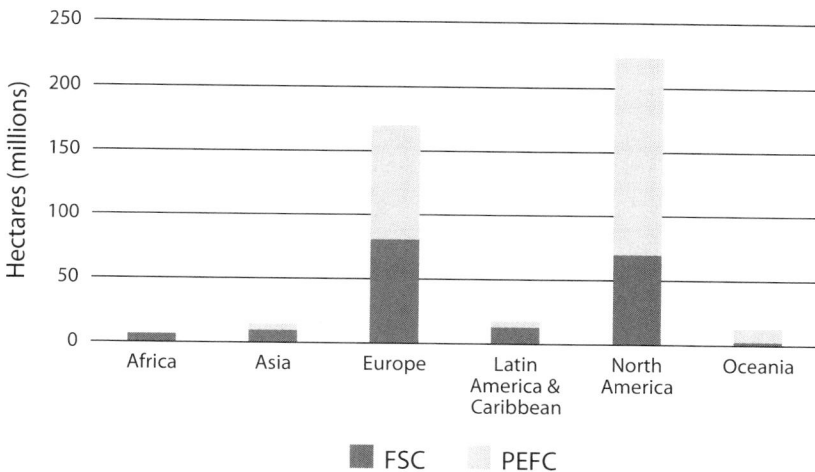

Figure 16.2 *Forest certification by certification system (FSC or PEFC) and continent in 2014. (Source: Forest Stewardship Council [FSC], 2014; Programme for the Endorsement of Forest Certification [PEFC], 2014)*

## Rise of FSC-Competitor Programs

The FSC certification program was quickly matched by forest industry and forest landowner programs developed in North America and in Europe. A number of industrial forestry companies in the United States rejected the idea of certification under the FSC as incompatible with their business model. In response, the American Forest and Paper Association launched its own Sustainable Forestry Initiative (SFI) to integrate responsible environmental practices with sound business practices. In general, SFI recognizes general principles of *sustainable forestry* and then relies heavily on the judgment of individual forest owners and managers in deciding how to apply them. We will study SFI, which is now an independent organization, in more detail below as a representative competitor to FSC.

In Canada, where the majority of forestlands are publicly owned, industry interests joined forces with government and other stakeholders to develop an alternative to FSC under Canada's national standards body, the Canadian Standards Association (CSA). This became the CSA Sustainable Forest Management certification system.

These certification schemes were generally aimed at medium and large forest ownerships and companies, leaving small, family forest ownerships without a similar mechanism. However, many family forest landowners had long been involved in the American Tree Farm System (ATFS). The ATFS developed its first certification standard in 1941 and focused on recognizing forest landowners who replanted after harvest. The ATFS has not historically fit the definition of forest certification as a market-based system with environmental labels and comprehensive requirements. However, more recently, it has worked to establish itself as a recognized certification system on par with the FSC, SFI, and others.

Also, a number of national FSC-competitor programs were developed in Europe. By the late 1990s, the Pan European Forest Certification Program (PEFC) created an umbrella program of the FSC-competitor programs in Europe. Most FSC competitors have joined the PEFC, which is now called the Program for Endorsement of Forest Certification. PEFC has become the international umbrella organization for FSC competitors around the world.

## Progress of Forest Certification around the World

By 2012, slightly more than 400 million hectares had been certified around the world, with most of this area in temperate and boreal regions (Figure 16.1). Thus, certification covers approximately 10% of the world's four billion hectares of forests, which produce 30% of the global industrial wood supply (Bettinger et al., 2017). Globally, approximately 60% of the area certified has been by the various members of PEFC, and the remainder by FSC (Figures 16.1 and 16.2). The large increase in area under PEFC certification between the years 2004 and 2005 came mostly from a major certification effort by Canada's forest industry.

By region, North America (mainly Canada and the United States) and Europe have over 90% of PEFC-certified hectares, and over 80% of FSC-certified hectares (Figure 16.2). In Europe, PEFC is the dominant certification system in Finland, Germany, and Sweden, whereas FSC is the dominant system in Russia.

Looking at the United States and Canada in more detail, Canada has much more certified forest than does the United States, with SFI having the largest share of certified hectares in both countries (Figure 16.3). Canada has more forest than the United States and also a much higher proportion of large ownerships, the traditional focus of certification schemes, so a higher certification acreage in Canada should not be surprising.[1]

## The Certification Process

*Certification schemes generally have three major components: (1) standards that are used as a basis to assess applicants, (2) a clearly defined certification process, along with rules regulating the use of certificates and labels, and (3) adequate institutional arrangements with qualified*

---

1 Looking at the number of landowners certified would reveal a somewhat different picture: FSC has certified many more small- and medium-sized landownerships than has SFI.

*human resources to implement the certification process.* Certification standards are set by the certification body, and accredited independent third-party auditors evaluate an applicant's adherence to the established standards (Perara & Vlosky, 2006).

A credible forest certification program should evaluate both the integrity of the producer's sustainability claim and the authenticity of product origin. Thus, to provide the necessary information to the final consumer, two essential components of a certification scheme are: (1) forest management certification and (2) product certification (Perara & Vlosky, 2006). Two types of certification have emerged to meet these needs:

1. Forest ownership certification—the process of verifying that an area of forest is managed to a defined standard.

2. Chain of custody certification— the process of verifying that mechanisms are in place to track wood from the certified forest to the final consumer.

## Forest Ownership Certification

Forest ownership certification involves site visits and the examination of records by certification auditors. Also, local stakeholders are usually interviewed. Topics covered during the certification process generally include management plans, silvicultural practices, timber harvesting, forest road construction, and environmental protection measures. All are assessed against predetermined standards. In addition, local economic and community relations may be assessed.

A common certification standard is that forest owners demonstrate their commitment to sustainability by developing and implementing a long-term forest management plan. Forest management plans must be consistent with the scale of forestry operations of the property and include items such as the owner's goals, maps describing stands and conditions, important features such as special sites, and management protections for designated fish and wildlife species.

The certification review will lead to a report outlining any deficiencies that have been found. Deficiencies generally fall into three categories:

1. Preconditions—problems that must be fixed before certification can be granted, such as the development of an allowable cut for the entire property.

2. Conditions—problems that must be fixed during the certification period as specified in

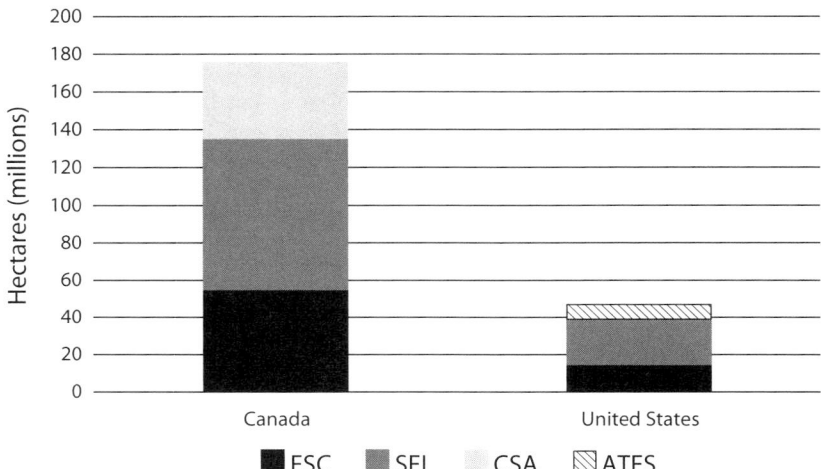

Figure 16.3 *Division of certification in the United States and Canada between FSC and the certification systems of PEFC (SFI and ATFS in the United States; SFI and CSA in Canada) in 2014. (Source: Forest Stewardship Council [FSC]), 2014; Programme for the Endorsement of Forest Certification [PEFC], 2014)*

the contract (before the next compliance audit), such as the establishment of coarse woody debris targets for all silvicultural prescriptions.

3. Recommendations—nonmandatory suggestions for improving environmental performance, such as suggestions on improved monitoring practices.

If all preconditions are met and agreement reached of the rate at which the conditions will be addressed, certification will be awarded and products from the certified forest can carry the logo of the certification program.

## Chain of Custody Certification [2]

Lumber or panels look the same whether they come from certified or noncertified forests. Product certification gives consumers confidence that when they buy certified wood products they are supporting well-managed forests. This process is known as *chain of custody* (CoC) certification. We will utilize the FSC approach to CoC to demonstrate how CoC works.

As originally envisioned, every company that takes legal ownership of certified wood in the process of moving the wood from the forest to the consumer (harvest, milling, fabrication, distribution, and sale) must be CoC certified and undergo an annual third-party audit to demonstrate segregation and accounting. For most exotic hardwoods, as an example, CoC means that certified material is harvested and segregated from noncertified material at each point in

---

2 Paul Vanderford, Sustainable Northwest, provided much of the information about FSC Chain of Custody Certification.

the supply chain. When a consumer buys product labeled as FSC 100%, as an example, the consumer is holding wood that grew on a certified forest. This process is called the *Transfer System*. The FSC 100% claim represented by the Transfer System has similarities to organic food certifications that require food to be grown in specific ways and segregated during processing to deliver a product, like an organic apple, to the customer.

However, in terms of markets, the main goal is to create a demand for certified wood. For many companies, segregation of individual logs or other wood inputs is impractical and cost prohibitive. Therefore, chain of custody offers systems that allow comingling of certified and noncertified product, such as the *Credit System* and the *Percentage System*.

Wood volumes handled on the Credit System operate like wind credits offered by utilities. Credits are earned when a company buys certified wood. Certified logs are put into production with noncertified logs and are no longer physically identifiable as certified. Wood products are sold as noncertified until a certified wood order comes in. When a certified wood sale is made, the company subtracts the volume sold as FSC Mix Credit from their credit account, ensuring the account is never overdrawn.

Under the Percentage System, inputs are tracked by percent. The X% represented on sales documentation on a product being sold represents that percentage of certified material in that product.

Comingling systems represented by the Credit and Percentage Systems allow consumers to support certified forests without requiring physical product segregation. Products offered to consumers under the comingled input systems can be found in stores labeled as FSC Mix Credit or FSC Mix X%. Paper, lumber, and plywood products are commonly sold under these labels.

SFI has similar approaches to accommodating situations where certified and noncertified logs are comingled. In addition, SFI has embraced a new variant of product certification called *Fiber Sourcing*—certification for organizations that do not own or manage land but do procure wood directly from forests. Participants must show that the raw material in their supply chain comes from legal and responsible sources, including use of *best management practices (BMPs)*, whether the forests are certified or not.[3]

In this chapter, we will focus on forest ownership certification, as that form of certification relates most directly to forest management.

# Government Regulation and Forest Ownership Certification: Similarities and Differences

In Chapter 7, we gave a brief summary of forest practice regulation around the world. It may be useful to reflect on the similarities and differences between government regulation and certification.

First and foremost, *forest practice regulation is government-based and certification is nongovernmental*. The maximum sanction for violating forest practice regulations would generally be civil or criminal penalties; the maximum sanction for violating certification standards would be decertification and potentially loss of public good will.

Forest practice regulation and certification differ in terms of their approach to compliance with regulatory standards. Forest practice regulations set minimum or maximum standards that must be met, such as the number of seedlings that must be planted, the maximum clearcut size, or the process for setting allowable cuts. Enforcement focuses on whether a landowner has met (stayed within) the prescribed levels or processes of these regulatory standards. Most certification schemes, on the other hand, have somewhat flexible (negotiable) standards linked to the *concept of continuous improvement*. A landowner might not entirely meet the desired level of some standard at time of certification but will make a commitment to improve over time. In addition, FSC (2015) tailors its requirements to the scale, intensity, and risk of the management unit being certified; it recognizes that ways of achieving compliance with requirements differs, depending on the scale and intensity of management activities and on the risk of negative impacts. As an example, more flexibility would be shown (other things equal) in certification of a small ownership using low-intensity management as compared to a large ownership using high-intensity management.

Forest practice regulation and certification can differ in terms of their focus. In many parts of the world, forest practice regulations focus on forest management activities, such as road building and harvest. Certification, on the other hand, focuses on the long-term management of the forest. There is still interest in individual activities, but the evaluation is much broader. In some places, like the state of California, forest practice regulation is increasingly calling for this more comprehensive view, diminishing the difference between government regulation and certification.

## Two Views of Forest Ownership Certification

*The two major certification approaches (FSC and PEFC) hold contrasting views about forest management, and about the appropriate structure and role of forest certification (Cashore et al., 2004). FSC emphasizes substantive*

---

3  Source: www.sfiprogram.org/sfi-standard/fiber-sourcing-standard/
Last accessed 5/12/16

*performance standards that promote ecosystem-based management, whereas PEFC programs tend toward process-oriented approaches that give forest owners and managers greater discretion in compliance and allow a wide variety of forestry practices, including production forestry.*

Throughout this chapter, we will use SFI, one of the certification groups in PEFC, to illustrate the more discretionary, owner-driven approach to sustainable forest management. We use SFI in our examples because SFI has certified more forest than any other certification program and because SFI recently (2015) released its latest standards, which are useful in comparing the PEFC approach to the FSC approach. It should be noted that the mandated use of BMPs by SFI, as we discuss below, may result in aquatic protection practices that go beyond that of other PEFC groups.

The contrasting conceptual frameworks of SFI and FSC have resulted in significant differences in their respective approaches to certification (Cashore et al., 2004). Three key differences between FSC and SFI relate to the (1) rule-making power structure, (2) types of standards, and (3) policy scope (Table 16.1).

## Rule-Making Power Structure

FSC has an especially complex rule-making process, both at the international level, where the general principles and criteria are created, and at the national and regional levels, where more localized interpretations of the criteria are made. Great effort is taken to ensure balanced participation by environmental, social, and economic interests in the rule-making process. SFI has a simpler process with one set of principles and criteria. It is now an independent organization with representation by all three types of interests.

## Types of Rules

As noted above, forest certification programs follow two basic approaches to defining sustainable forest manage-

ment (Cashore et al., 2004; Meidinger et al., 2003; Perara & Vlosky, 2006): (1) performance-based approaches, and (2) process-based approaches.

In performance-based approaches, a certification program sets substantive performance standards that must be met by all certified organizations. For example, suppose a certification system calls for protection of biodiversity. A performance-based approach might require a landowner to identify rare, threatened, and endangered (RTE) species on the forest management unit being evaluated and to protect habitat required by the RTE species.

Standards required under a performance-based approach may vary by forest type and ecoregion, such as the number of seedlings required for successful regeneration or the width of a stream buffer; this approach necessitates national or regional standards that reflect the requirements of different ecosystems across North America and the world. This can lead to inconsistencies between regional standards, though, and confuse landowners who have forests in multiple regions.

Since FSC began as an attempt by environmental NGOs to reform forest management, especially tropical forest management, it is not surprising that FSC emphasizes performance-based approach to ensure that desired changes are made as needed. International principles and criteria provide overall guides, but many standards are set at national and regional levels.

In process-based approaches, certification is based primarily on meeting procedural requirements. This approach is applied at the level of the business enterprise and requires firms to implement environmental management systems (EMS) that have defined organizational structures for planning, operations, monitoring, and corrective action. Process-based certification generally does not emphasize specific, on-the-ground standards for forest management and instead focuses on improved environmental planning. Substantive standards to which firms must conform are usually set by the firms themselves, although certified firms remain subject to governmental regulations, which may also require adherence to substantive standards. In general, the primary focus in

Table 16.1 *Two approaches to market-driven certification governance systems*

| Criteria | FSC | SFI |
|---|---|---|
| | **Certification Approach** | |
| Rule-making power structure | Environmental, social, and economic interests represented | Environmental, social, and economic interests represented |
| Standards—substantive | Generally nondiscretionary | Generally discretionary |
| Standards—procedural | To facilitate implementation of substantive rules | End in itself (procedural rules will result in desired effects) |
| Policy scope | Broader (facilitate forest, social, and economic sustainability) | Narrower (focus on mostly forest sustainability and its improvement) |

*Source:* Adapted from Cashore et al. (2004) with updates on SFI rule-making structure.

process-based approaches is on establishing an environmental management system with planning, operations, monitoring, and corrective actions. However, without the requirement for performance standards that ensure fulfillment of the principles of the certification scheme, this approach makes attainment of sustainable forest management more problematic.

SFI reflects this process-based approach in many of its certification standards, relying on environmental management processes as defined by the landowner. In general, SFI calls for certain procedures and steps to be instituted at the management level, leaving considerable latitude for the individual landowner to decide how to respond with on-the-ground practices.

In practice, both systems have elements of performance or process, but their primary orientation nevertheless sets them apart. As an example, both FSC and SFI call for forest management plans and monitoring (process-based standards). However, as we will see below, FSC has many more substantive performance requirements for judging whether sustainable forest management has been achieved.

## Policy Scope

From the beginning, FSC has encompassed all aspects of sustainable forest management—environmental, economic, and social. Thus, FSC is concerned with both sustainability of forest ecosystems and sustainability of the communities and economies around the forests. SFI takes a somewhat narrower approach, focusing on attaining, improving, and explaining sustainable forestry.

## Comparison of Certification Systems

We will compare certification systems in terms of the *principles* that guide these systems and the *standards* that must be achieved. In our use, principles are aspiration statements of what a certification system should achieve, such as "protect biodiversity." Standards are the levels of quality or attainment by which we can judge whether a principle has been fulfilled, such as "genetically modified organisms will not allowed" to protect biodiversity.[4] While the principles underlying these systems are relatively easy to find, locating the standards that measure attainment of the principles can be more difficult. As an example, SFI often lets the landowner set the standards for measuring achievement of its principles.

## Principles

As forest ownership certification systems have become more sophisticated in their approach to sustainability, their

principles have increasingly overlapped. With the most recent revisions, the principles of both FSC (2015) and SFI (2015) recognize a broad suite of values commonly associated with forest sustainability (Tables 16.2a and b):

- Both share a commitment to sustaining the many benefits of forests and protecting biodiversity— core principles of sustainable forest management as originally envisioned by the developers of FSC. However, as we will see below, SFI allows considerable discretion for the landowner to decide what these principles mean in practice.

- Both require adherence to all laws and regulations. In areas where enforcement of forest practice and conservation laws and regulations are lax, certification can be an important vehicle to ensure these laws and regulations are followed.

- Both call for protection of waterbodies and riparian areas and of water quality.

- Both call for recognition of the rights of indigenous peoples.

- Both call for continuous improvement in practices as documented through monitoring.

- Both call for recognition of places of special environmental and cultural significance.

Significant differences in principles, though, still exist (Tables 16.2a and b):

- *FSC makes a commitment to the social and economic well-being of forest workers and local communities. SFI focuses mostly on forest practices.*

- SFI highlights protection of water quality through *best management practices (BMPs)*. This term has meaning in both countries where SFI operates— United States and Canada. FSC uses more general language about protection of water quality in its international principles, relying on the development of specific language in its regional standards.

- FSC calls for maintaining or enhancing areas of High Conservation Value, such as concentrations of biodiversity and areas important to indigenous peoples. SFI does not make such a strong commitment to conserving these areas.

- Many of SFI's principles highlight *sustainable forestry* as the goal that SFI pursues, using the classic definition of sustainability of *meeting the needs of the present without compromising the ability of future generations to meet their own needs*. FSC principles do not mention sustainable

---

4 Standards, as the term is used here, are called criteria, indicators, or performance measures in the various certification systems.

forestry by name, although its principles suggest a similar overall definition of sustainability. Rather, FSC (2015) refers to *responsible forest management* and *sustainable forest stewardship* in describing its overall certification goal. *In this chapter, we refer generically to sustainable forest management to describe the overall goal of these two systems.*

## Standards

As forest ownership certification systems have become more sophisticated in their approach to sustainability, as mentioned above, it has become increasingly difficult to tell them apart solely by examining the principles of each

system. With the most recent revisions, FSC and SFI both recognize a broad suite of principles for sustainable forest management (Tables 16.2 a and b). We need to look beyond stated principles to assess fully what each certification system requires (Table 16.3, page 448).

In this comparison, we will utilize the most recent statement of standards for SFI (2015) and the most recent FSC United States statement of standards (Forest Stewardship Council, 2010), augmented by global standards on consideration of plantations in the recent FSC statement of principles and criteria for forest stewardship (FSC, 2015). While FSC overarching documents frame international principles, as we discussed above, we often have to go down to the national or regional level for standards. We will utilize the

Table 16.2a *Principles of FSC forest certification (Summarized from FSC July 2015, pp. 10–20)*

| |
| --- |
| 1. Comply with all laws and regulations |
| 2. Maintain or enhance the social and economic well-being of workers |
| 3. Identify and uphold indigenous peoples legal and customary rights of ownership, use, and management of land, territories, and resources affected by management activities |
| 4. Contribute to maintaining or enhancing the social and economic well-being of local communities |
| 5. Efficiently manage the forest to provide, maintain, or enhance economic viability and environmental and social benefits |
| 6. Conserve and restore ecosystem services and environmental values, and avoid, repair, or mitigate negative environmental impacts* |
| 7. Maintain an up-to-date long-term management plan with sufficient detail to guide staff, inform stakeholders, and justify management decisions |
| 8. Demonstrate progress toward management objectives, impacts of activities, and forest conditions through monitoring, assessment, and adaptive management |
| 9. Maintain or enhance High Conservation Values applying the precautionary approach† |
| 10. Select and implement management activities consistent with the organization's policies and objectives and with the FSC principles and criteria |

\* Includes criteria that call for conservation and restoration of critical ecosystem values such as threatened species and their habitats; naturally occurring biological diversity; natural waterbodies and riparian zones and water quality; and a mosaic of species, sizes, ages, spatial scales and regeneration cycles appropriate for landscape values.

† Includes criteria identifying many High Conservation Values, such as concentrations of biological diversity, landscape level ecosystems and mosaics, and sites of special importance to communities and indigenous peoples.

Table 16.2b *Principles of SFI forest certification (Summarized from SFI 2015, pp. 3/11–3/12)*

| |
| --- |
| 1. Practice sustainable forestry, to meet the needs of the present without compromising the ability of future generations to meet their own needs, by practicing a land stewardship ethic that integrates reforestation and managing, growing, nurturing, and harvesting trees for useful products and ecosystem services |
| 2. Maintain and improve long-term forest health and productivity |
| 3. Protect waterbodies and riparian areas and conform with forestry BMPs to protect water quality |
| 4. Protect and promote biological diversity including animal and plant species, wildlife habitats, and ecological or natural community types |
| 5. Consider visual impacts of forest operations and provide recreational opportunities for the public |
| 6. Manage lands that are ecologically, geologically, or culturally important sites in a manner that takes into account their unique qualities |
| 7. Ensure responsible fiber sourcing practices in North America by promoting sustainable forestry practices among other forest landowners |
| 8. Comply with all applicable laws and regulations |
| 9. Support advances in sustainable forest management through research, science, and technology |
| 10. Improve the practice of sustainable forestry through education and training programs |
| 11. Broaden the practice of sustainable forestry through community involvement, socially responsible practices, and recognition and respect for indigenous peoples' rights and traditional forest-related knowledge |
| 12. Broaden understanding of SFI forest certification |
| 13. Continually improve the practice of sustainable forestry through monitoring and reporting performance |

United States standards for FSC (FSC, 2010).[5] In the discussion, we emphasize standards for forest management; FSC also has extensive standards for maintaining or enhancing the economic and social well-being of workers and communities and protecting the rights of indigenous peoples.

We have broken the comparison of FSC and SFI into four categories: (1) the certification process, (2) the need to meet law, regulation, and best management practices (BMPs), (3) forest management process requirements, and (4) forest management practice requirements (Table 16.3). We signal whether and how a standard is recognized in a certification system with four codes: (1) yes (Y), (2) no (N), (3) strongly recommended (SR), and (4) goal recognized but discretion on how to achieve the goal left to landowner (O). As an example of the fourth symbol (O), SFI recognizes the value of special sites (ecologically, geologically, or culturally important sites) and calls for their protection. However, SFI generally leaves it to the landowner to determine the sites to consider in this category and how to protect them, rather than to establish performance standards as FSC commonly employs. As we will see, many forest practice requirements fall into this "O" category under SFI—discretion is left to the landowner in how to meet them.

Key points in this comparison are (Table 16.3):

- FSC and SFI now have similar certification processes (third-party certification and periodic recertification), as SFI over the years has moved toward FSC's approach.

- *Both FSC and SFI require that all laws and regulations be met.* In areas with lax enforcement, this requirement turns certification into a process that helps ensure that federal and state laws and regulations will be met. Even in the United States, the amount of funds, personnel, and political will to enforce laws and regulations may be limited. Thus, certification may function, in some ways, as the enforcement arm of the state. This is a somewhat surprising outcome for a nongovernmental approach to sustainability and provides a motivating force for landowner compliance with laws and regulations.

- *Both FSC and SFI require that BMPs recommended for forests by federal or state agencies be followed. Thus, certification can turn recommendations into requirements.* In the United States, BMPs designed to protect water quality under provisions of the federal Clean Water Act are developed by individual states

under guidance of the Environmental Protection Agency (see Chapter 7 for more detail). In some cases, BMPs developed by states may be voluntary and lack enforcement provisions. To be certified by FSC or SFI, these BMPs, which may include logging, road building, and stream buffer policies, must be employed.

- *FSC also calls for aquatic ecosystem protection that often goes beyond BMPs.* As an example, FSC requires stream buffers that go significantly beyond the requirements in the BMPs for Oregon (see Box 16.1, page 450).

- FSC and SFI have similar forest management process standards, including the need for a forest management plan, inventory, monitoring, and continuous adjustment, although the details of what is required differ somewhat. One difference is the degree to which species at risk must be inventoried, with FSC having more stringent requirements. Since the location of species at risk can lead to restrictions on action in places like the United States, this difference can be important.

- FSC and SFI both incorporate key elements of the internationally accepted International Organization for Standardization Environmental Management System (ISO/EMS) that includes standards for planning, implementation, monitoring, and improvement. In fact, the concept of continuous improvement is fundamental to FSC, SFI, and ISO/EMS. They all may certify forests whose management does not quite meet their certification standards, based on a commitment to positive change over time. Periodic audits then focus on whether these commitments have been met.

- Both FSC and SFI require that harvest stay within the long-term sustained yield capacity of a forest. In principle, this restriction limits timber harvest to the sustained yield level in keeping with historical approaches to ensuring forest sustainability. However, SFI leaves more of the determination to the landowner, such as allowing discretion in how to combine management units for comparison of the harvest level to the sustained yield capacity, and the length of time over which the comparison of harvest to sustained yield is made. With such discretion, the SFI approach to sustained yield could place much less restriction on capital flow than does FSC.

- Neither system allows genetically modified organisms (GMO) to be utilized as planting stock, in light of the controversies over such use.

5  FSC US management standard report (FSC, 2010) is an umbrella document that breaks the United States into 11 regions for more detailed standards like riparian buffer widths and harvest unit sizes. However, those regional standards generally conform to, and derive from, the national standards described here. We will utilize FSC regional standards for the Pacific Coast and the Southeast later in this chapter when we compare SFI and FSC requirements in two regions.

Table 16.3 *Comparison of forest management standards for the United States for FSC\* (FSC, 2010) and SFI (SFI, 2015) certification*[†]

| Standard | FSC | SFI |
|---|---|---|
| **Certification Process** | | |
| • Third-party certification required | Y | Y |
| • Periodic third-party audit required after certification | Y | Y |
| **Laws, Regulations, and BMPs** | | |
| • Meet all laws and regulations | Y | Y |
| • Meet or exceed BMPs (water resource related) | Y | Y |
| ***Specific Requirements Beyond General Stipulation to Meet Laws, Regulations and BMPs*** | | |
| **Forest Management Process Requirements** | | |
| *Inventory* | | |
| • Forest condition and growth | Y | Y |
| • Biological hot spots | Y | O |
| • High conservation value forests such as old growth | Y | O |
| • Rare, threatened, and endangered species | Y | O |
| • Cultural and spiritual sites | Y | O |
| *Planning and monitoring* | | |
| • Forest management plan | Y | Y |
| • Monitoring | Y | Y |
| • Continuous improvement | Y | Y |
| **Forest Management Practice Requirements** | | |
| *Forest cover* | | |
| • Restrict conversion of forest to other land uses | Y | O |
| • Reforest after harvest | Y | Y |
| • Afforestation limited to native species | N | N |
| *Production enhancement* | | |
| • Prohibit GMO planting stock | Y | Y |
| • Prohibit use of pesticides | N | N |
| • Phase out pesticides over time | SR | N |

| Standard | FSC | SFI |
|---|---|---|
| *Plantations* | | |
| • Restrict certification of management units containing plantations established on areas converted from natural forests after 1994 | Y | N |
| • Allow conversion of nonforest to plantations (afforestation) | Y | Y |
| *Sustained yield* | | |
| • Keep harvest within long-term sustained yield | Y | Y |
| *Even-aged harvest unit size* | | |
| • Limit size of harvest unit | Y | Y |
| *Natural disturbance and development processes* | | |
| • Retain biological legacies at harvest | Y | O |
| • Restore/maintain natural heterogeneity | Y | N |
| • Maintain/restore under-represented successional stages | Y | O |
| *Aquatic and watershed conservation* | | |
| • Retain riparian area buffers | BMP+ | BMP |
| • Control of roads/logging effects on sediment delivery to streams | BMP+ | BMP |
| • Control of cumulative effects at landscape level | SR | O |
| *Other biodiversity considerations* | | |
| • Protect habitat of rare, threatened, and endangered species | Y | O |
| • Protect high conservation forest such as old growth | Y | O |
| • Provide dead and down trees | Y | O |
| *Areas of special social significance* | | |
| • Conserve cultural areas | Y | O |
| • Conserve other social-important areas | Y | O |

\* FSC also specifies standards relative to the social and economic well-being of workers and communities.

† Y = Yes, N = No, SR = Strongly recommended, O = Goal recognized, but discretion on how to achieve the goal largely left to landowner, BMPs = Best Management Practices required to protect water quality, BMP+ = Standards to protect water quality beyond those required by BMPs.

- As our comparison of SFI and FSC moves into forest management performance standards, substantial differences between the systems appear:

  - *SFI allows conversion of forest to other uses, such as agriculture or development, with certification remaining with the forest that still exists. FSC strictly limits conversion.*

  - SFI generally allows conversion of natural forest to plantations. FSC will generally not certify plantations created from natural forests since the mid-1990s, even if management changes are made. [6] These limitations, combined with requirements to emulate natural processes, have reduced the interest of firms focused on intensive management of plantations for wood production in FSC certification, especially in the United States. However, it must be noted that FSC has certified millions of hectares of plantations around the world, including afforestation projects, which serve important conservation purposes.

  - *FSC anchors its forest management practices in emulation of natural processes and their effects. SFI generally does not ascribe to this goal.*

  - FSC calls for maintaining or restoring native plant diversity and underrepresented successional stages. SFI puts less emphasis on these policies.

- FSC pesticide restrictions are established at a higher level than US federal or state regulations. SFI requires compliance with federal/state laws, but FSC requires compliance with those PLUS their list of banned chemicals and specified tracking procedures. Atrazine is an example of a herbicide banned by FSC, but not by SFI. Also, FSC strongly advocates the reduction in the use of pesticides over time.

## Summary

Following deadlocked diplomatic efforts of world governments at the 1992 Earth Summit that failed to produce an agreement to protect the world's forests, FSC was created in 1993 by a broad range of nongovernmental stakeholders that included environmental NGOs, retailers, trade unions, and indigenous groups (Pattberg, 2005). The mission of FSC is to promote environmentally sound, socially beneficial, and economically prosperous management of the world's forests.

The ten principles upon which FSC certification standards are based not only include environmental protections but also require consideration of the rights and well-being of workers and communities, and recognize the rights of indigenous peoples to own, use, and manage their lands and resources (FSC, 2015). FSC employs a prescriptive, region-based approach to certification, which includes standards for forest cover, the protection of biodiversity, aquatic and watershed protection, and conservation of special places, and emphasizes principles of natural ecosystem processes and disturbance. Importantly, FSC distinguishes between plantation forests and natural forests, and favors the incorporation of natural ecosystem processes into forest management, while discouraging the conversion of natural forests to plantations. FSC has developed a palette of regional standards that reflect differing ecosystems and cultural needs across the world, which has led to some criticism of the consistency of standards. Recently, FSC has issued an international standard to improve consistency of regional guides (FSC, 2015).

SFI was created by a timber industry trade organization in response to negative public perceptions of the timber industry (Wallinger, 1995), the emerging desire for product certification by retailers and by the public (Lober & Eisen, 1995), and industry concerns about third-party certification as a new and unwelcome form of regulation (Ozanne & Vlosky, 1996). Rather than implementing new standards, SFI focuses on achieving or exceeding existing regulatory standards and BMPs by strengthening the institutional systems and processes used to achieve them. Thus, SFI has not proposed many environmental standards beyond the laws, regulations, and BMPs that currently exist. Such an approach might be seen as an attempt to enable landowners to maintain competitive rates of return and mobility of capital while fostering sustainable forest management and protecting environmental values; however, the lack of certification-specific environmental standards has led some critics to dismiss SFI as little more than industry-sponsored "greenwashing" of customary industrial forestry practices. SFI is now an independent organization, and with the latest revision of its principles (SFI, 2015), SFI supports many environmental values promoted by FSC. Nevertheless, with few exceptions such as limitations on clearcut size and use of GMOs, SFI generally leaves achievement of these environmental values—beyond those imposed by law and regulation and those recommended by BMPs—to the discretion of the landowner.

*In aggregate, FSC and SFI differ substantially on the role of ecological forestry in forest sustainability. With FSC's focus on reflecting natural processes, its principles and standards generally align with ecological forestry, while SFI principles and standards generally allow landowners to choose the type of forestry to employ, including production forestry, within law, regulation, and BMPs.*

---

6 FSC (2015) recognizes natural forests and plantations much like the FAO classification discussed in Chapter 6. Previously, some FSC classifications had recognized three categories of forest: (1) natural, (2) near-natural, and (3) plantations.

## Box 16.1   How certification can affect forest management: A comparative study

Mendell and Lang (2013) modeled the land base and timber harvest effects of management requirements under SFI and FSC certification on industrial land in the Pacific Northwest. In each case, they modeled four scenarios: (1) FSC-Natural, (2) FSC-Plantation, (3) SFI, and (4) a base case that generally corresponds to state timber harvest guidelines or regulations, along with voluntary measures implemented by landowners. FSC-Natural calls for managing to achieve native ecosystem attributes such as complexity, structure, and diversity, while FSC-Plantation does not attempt to maintain these attributes and is mainly employed with exotic species. We will represent FSC through the FSC-Natural scenario here.

Modeling the effects of the certification scenarios required large blocks of timberland with stand-level detail for harvest scheduling and map-based information for conducting spatial analysis associated with riparian management zones (RMZs) and harvest adjacency issues. Mendell and Lang (2013) found two industry cooperators for their research who shared detailed stand-level and spatial data about their respective ownerships: (1) approximately 210,000 acres of predominantly Douglas-fir–western hemlock located in western Oregon, and (2) approximately 110,000 acres of predominantly loblolly pine in Arkansas and Louisiana.

Mendell and Lang (2013) then developed scenarios based on their interpretation of the alternate forest certification programs as implemented in the US South and Pacific Northwest in 2013. While FSC and SFI cover a range of objectives and standards, the scenarios focus on five forest management guidelines in the certification schemes the researchers judged as economically sensitive for landowners:

- Riparian management zones (RMZs);
- Retention of trees after a harvest operation;
- Permanent set-asides of land;
- Harvest unit size restrictions; and
- Green-up interval (minimum time between harvest of neighboring stands).

See Figures 16.4 and 16.5 for examples of harvest on certified forests in western Oregon.

They assumed longer minimum rotations for the FSC options than for the SFI options (55 years of age vs. 45 for the Pacific Northwest), and required a nondeclining yield of timber harvest for a period equal to one industrial rotation (45 years in the Northwest and 35 years in the South).

### Land Base Impacts

Looking first at the land base impacts of certification in the Oregon case, SFI certification had no impact on land base, in large part because stream buffer requirements for BMPs are written into the Oregon Forest Practice Act (OFPA) regulations. FSC requires riparian buffers that go considerably beyond the OFPA requirements, which led to a significant reduction in land base in the study. However, the effect on timber harvest of this reduction was partly a function of Mendell and Lang's decision to model FSC riparian rules as withdrawals from the timber base; in practice, FSC (2010, p. 114) actually allows individual and group selection harvest in much of this added buffer area. Thus, the harvest impacts reported below for FSC certification in the Pacific Northwest are somewhat overstated.

Land base impacts of certification in the US South show a somewhat different relationship among the scenarios. Neither SFI nor FSC showed any reduction in land base, as the landowner involved in the study already exceeded the BMPs for riparian protection and also exceeded what FSC required.

### Harvest Impacts

In the Pacific Northwest, SFI certification does not cause a harvest reduction when compared to the base scenario, as the relevant SFI standards are already written into the OFPA regulations for Oregon. On the other hand, the analysis showed a reduction in harvest volume of approximately 30% with FSC certification compared to the base scenario, primarily due to the assumed reduction in land base associated with added stream buffers. Also the need to leave biological legacies, and smaller limits on harvest unit size contributed to the lower harvest. As described above, the actual reduction in harvest should be less than estimated here.

In the South, SFI certification resulted in a slight harvest reduction compared to the base scenario because of clearcut size requirements that are not required under state laws.

Figure 16.4 *A variable retention harvest unit in an FSC-certified forest in the coast range of Oregon managed by Ecotrust Forest Management (EFM, Inc.)—a private investment and advisory firm, which manages for improved forest health, enhanced carbon storage, reduced fire risk, and harvests steady amounts of timber and other forest products that support rural enterprises. Clearcuts shown in the background are on other ownerships. (Photo taken by Fitzpatrick Ecological Consulting. Photo courtesy of EFM, Inc.)*

FSC shows some added reduction in harvest due to smaller harvest unit size restrictions.

Our major conclusions from the case studies are:

- FSC and SFI differ in their effects on forest management, with FSC certification generally calling for more environmental protection, resulting in lower harvests.

- Changes in land base due to certification are a function of the assumed landowner baseline compared to the certification requirements. Where that baseline meets or exceeds law, regulation, and BMPs, very little reduction in land base occurs due to SFI certification. FSC generally requires more reserves or partial harvest areas than law, regulation, or BMPs would require, but the effect on the land base depends on the landowner's existing management.

- Reductions in harvest volume are also a function of the assumed baseline, although the impact of certification on harvest is more difficult to generalize due the complex interactions of land base inventory, minimum rotation

ages, and harvest scheduling limitations such as clearcut size and green-up requirements. Generally, though, the harvest over the first rotation will be lower under FSC than SFI, perhaps significantly lower. Also, harvest levels under FSC may rise over the long term as the larger inventories associated with the longer rotations under FSC become available; also the grade of the wood may increase making it more valuable.

Figure 16.5  *A harvest on an SFI-certified, corporate forest in the coast range of Oregon. (Photo courtesy of Deanne Carlson)*

## Potential Forest Certification Costs

There are both direct and indirect expenses (Figure 16.6) to becoming certified. We will use the FSC framework to describe these expenses; SFI certification expense categories are similar. Large landowners may hold an individual FSC certificate and bear the costs themselves, or a group entity, such as an owners' association (the most common approach to certify family forests), may address costs on behalf of group members. A land management organization seeking certification must hire a third-party auditor, and must prepare for and participate in audits that occur periodically. The audits examine administrative operations, as well as the organization's on-the-ground forest stewardship. As a result of these audits, landowners may receive *Corrective Action Requests (CARs)* that must be addressed to receive or maintain certification.

### Direct Costs

**External Audit Costs**   Auditing costs climb as a function of acreage, management intensity, and auditing difficulty but rapidly decline in cost per acre. Cubbage, Moore, Henderson, and Araujo (2009) found similar relationships

between ownership size and cost per hectare between certification systems: overall audit costs for FSC certification are on par with other forest certification systems, such as SFI, when size of the forest being certified is taken into account, although FSC costs average higher per hectare because the current certified land base includes smaller ownerships.

As an example, Cubbage et al. (2003) tracked the cost of the initial audit of the forests of the North Carolina Division of Forest Resources, Duke University, and North Carolina State University (Table 16.4). Those costs are for the initial certification. Annual surveillance audits and periodic recertification audits are additional costs that will again be charged to the landowner. Factors affecting costs included the size, location, and staff management of the three forests, which in turn affected the time spent by the auditors. Smaller tracts had greater costs per acre because the fixed costs of auditors were spread over fewer acres.

**Internal Audit Costs**   Landowners, or their staff, must prepare for audits, including organizing their records for review and participating in the audits. All these actions cost landowners both time and money, with the amounts very much owner-specific.

## Indirect Costs

There are also indirect costs of certification in terms of needed changes in planning or management. These are often called *compliance costs*.

Certification may require changes in management plans, inventory, and monitoring, with the rigor and extent of these requirements somewhat a function of ownership size and complexity. ***Perhaps most importantly, a comprehensive long-term management plan for the property must exist, or be created*** or improved. These changes can range from slight to extensive, depending on the landowner's existing situation and the certification scheme chosen.

Certification may require changes in management practices (Forest Stewardship Council, 2011; Cubbage et al., 2003). Examples of potential changes are:

- Conforming more completely with laws and regulations;

- Utilizing BMPs for water quality, such as fixing culverts so they will not wash out roads during storms and setting aside buffers along stream channels;

- Improving reforestation practices;

- Retaining a percentage of trees at harvest to function as wildlife habitat;

- Reserving some areas to protect endangered wildlife and plants;

- Using fewer chemical pesticides and tolerating ingrowth of some natural herbs, shrubs, or trees;

- Communicating with neighbors about property boundaries or anticipated harvests;

- Installing safety precautions, such as gates or signs, when appropriate; and

- Keeping records of harvests or a journal of management work.

Again, these changes can range from slight to extensive, depending on the landowner's existing situation and the certification scheme chosen.

## Group Certifications

Certification standards allow group certificates. Group certification helps landowners with small holdings access certified markets

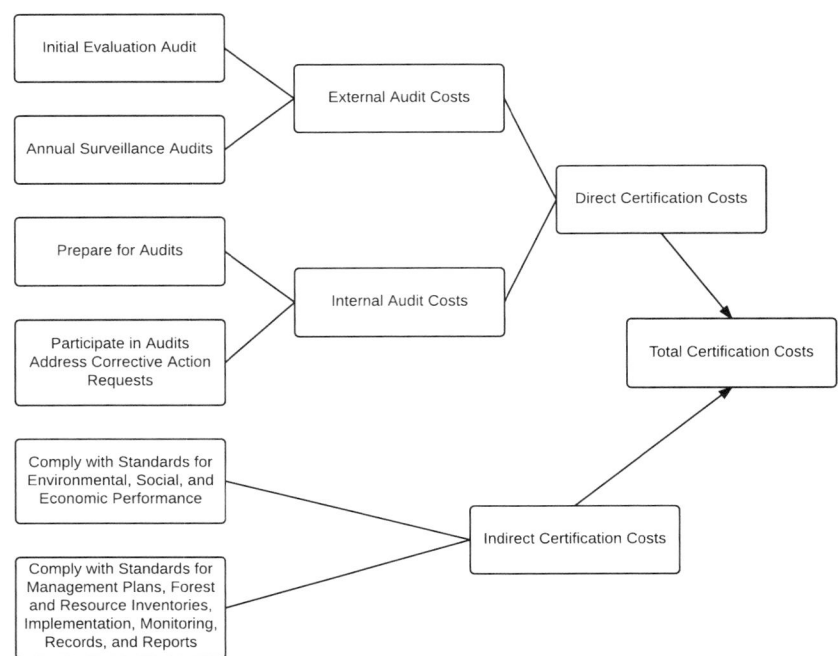

Figure 16.6 *Direct and indirect costs of certification. (Source: Adapted from Forest Stewardship Council, 2011)*

by reducing the difficulty and cost of certification. In a group certification program, a managing entity works directly with each landowner and contracts with a third-party auditing body. The managing entity's role is to stay abreast of changes in standards, create support documents and templates, and provide technical support directly to each member.

## Potential Forest Certification Benefits

Many claims have been made about the potential benefits of forest certification, including improved forest management, higher prices for wood products, improved market access, and demonstrating that properties are sustainably managed to skeptical critics. We review here a variety of studies of these potential benefits, starting with the perspective for forest managers of certified forests and then summarizing independent evaluations that have been made.

Table 16.4 *Comparison of certification audit costs for three forest ownerships in North Carolina, USA*

|  | Acres | SFI Per acre | FSC Per acre |
|---|---|---|---|
| North Carolina Division of Forest Resources[*] | 32,000 | $0.54 | $0.72 |
| Duke University | 8,000 | $4.18 | $2.92 |
| North Carolina State University | 4,500 | $9.32 | $5.47 |

[*] North Carolina Division of Forest Resources had 32,000 acres audited for SFI and 42,000 acres for FSC.

*Source:* Adapted from Cubbage et al. (2003).

## Forest Manager Perspective

Rickenbach and Overdevest (2006) surveyed FSC-certified forests in the United States. They found that managers regarded *signaling* to external stakeholders (activists, retailers, and governments) that their organization was meeting high forestry standards as the greatest benefit of certification. They also found that the managers believed that certification can help improve forest practices through *learning*. This learning can take two forms: (1) acting as a technology transfer device, exposing managers to new ecological concepts and business practices, and (2) encouraging forest managers to review the full scope of the consequences of their management and adapting management plans and practices accordingly. This learning process was the second most important benefit that landowners noted from certification.

Moore, Cubbage, and Eicheldinger (2012) utilized e-mail surveys of organizations that had received forest management certification under FSC in the United States and SFI in the United States and in Canada to assess forest manager satisfaction with certification. The researchers found that forest managers believed the advantages of forest certification were greater than the disadvantages, with SFI managers rating the benefits of forest certification higher than FSC managers. Most managers sampled felt certification helped them accomplish their objectives and were likely to recertify, indicating their endorsement of the process.

Organizations especially valued the benefits of certification in terms of public relations and their public image, in addition to the feeling that achieving certification was part of their corporate social responsibility (Table 16.5). They thought certification also helped with market access and improved their internal management. Audit and preparation costs were cited as the major disadvantages of certification.

In addition, forest managers were not overly troubled by other potential disadvantages of forest certification: cer-

tification did not result in too much openness, too much public interaction, more discussion than management, adversarial audit processes, negative changes in forest management, and undue limits on professional discretion.

The Moore et al. (2012) survey of FSC- and SFI-certified properties also asked companies whether forest certification led to changes in their forest management practices. On average, firms implemented 13 to 14 changes in forestry, environmental, social, and economic/system practices to obtain or maintain forest certification, out of a total of 54 potential changes in the questionnaire. Although the researchers found no statistical difference between FSC-certified and SFI-certified organizations in the total number of changes, they did find differences in implementation of specific forest practices, with FSC-certified firms required to make more environmental/forest management changes and SFI-certified firms required to make more economic/system changes.

In summary, Moore et al. (2012, p. 87) said: "Our research and burgeoning literature reviewed here confirm that forest certification is prompting many positive changes in forest management. For example, we found that certified organizations increased their forest management practices of writing forest management plans, implementing forest inventory programs, establishing geographic information systems, controlling exotic invasives, monitoring chemical use, using BMPs, and planning for biological diversity." It must be noted, however, that FSC and SFI standards differ significantly (Table 16.3). Relative to the perceived disadvantages of certification frequently mentioned, added costs for forest management and record keeping came just behind audit costs and time and preparation costs in importance for both SFI managers and FSC managers.

One potential additional advantage of certification, especially for public forests, is to reduce litigation. Many state forests in the US have been certified, as an example, which can reassure interested publics and the courts that they are practicing sustainable forest management. Given the ecological focus of many laws that are the source of litigation (see Chapter 7), FSC certification would seem of special value here.

In general, federal forests in the US have not been certified. It might seem logical that they be FSC certified since the goals for these forests seem to closely match those of FSC. For many years, federal foresters did not actively seek FSC certification. Also, while they continued to cut old-growth forests, they would not be eligible for FSC certification. We have argued elsewhere that third-party monitoring, such as would be provided by certification, could be a useful check on the sustainability of federal forest practices. Still, some environmental groups may feel

Table 16.5 *Perceived benefits (advantages) and perceived costs (disadvantages) of forest certification that received a median score of 4 (important) under both FSC and SFI certification systems*

| Benefits (advantages) | Costs (disadvantages) |
| --- | --- |
| Right thing to do/corporate social responsibility | Audit costs |
| Value in public relations | Preparation costs |
| Better organizational/professional image | |
| Strategic position of organization | |
| Retain/gain market access | |
| Better management systems and performance | |
| Better planning and implementation | |

*Source:* Moore et al. (2012).

that the federal lands now adhere to a higher standard than required for FSC certification and worry that this standard could be eroded through certification. Thus, as valuable as FSC certification might be in reassuring the people of the US that their federal lands are well managed, certification does not seem to be likely, at least in the near future.

## Independent Evaluation

As described above, Moore et al. (2012) found that those who have been certified generally have an overall positive view of certification and its impact on their operations and public perception. Questions remain, though, about how much difference certification has made in management and in economic, social, and environmental effects.

**Management Changes**   Newsom and Hewitt (2005) examined the reports on 129 FSC-SmartWood certification operations worldwide that were implementing FSC standards. They focused on changes required of clients by certification assessment teams. We highlight their findings on five environmental issues (Table 16.6). Improvements needed in roads and skid trails were required most often, followed by changes in regeneration practices. The identification of problems with land conversion in developing countries fits with the evidence on deforestation and conversion of forests to agriculture there. While this table does not reveal the scope or magnitude of the changes, the authors concluded that SmartWood certification for FSC did require changes in practices.

Newsom, Bahn, and Cashore (2006) examined conditions or preconditions that 80 FSC-certified forestry operations in the United States were required to address in order to obtain or maintain their certification. They found that system elements, such as forest management plans, monitoring, and inventory, most frequently required change (by 94%, 79%, and 71% of certified operations, respectively) followed by ecological elements, such as protection of high conservation value forests and retention of woody debris,

snags, and legacy trees (by 71% and 63% of operations, respectively). From these results, the authors concluded that early adopters of certification were required to make important changes as a result of the certification process.

Newsom et al. (2006) also found that the region of the United States where the operation was located significantly affected the types of concerns that the operation was required to address and the number of conditions specified during the certification assessment. In general, operations in the Southeast and Appalachia were given the most conditions and types of concerns to address, while those in the Pacific Coast and Northeast were given the least. Comparing the Pacific Coast with the Southeast, operations in the Pacific Coast were required to make more ecological improvements, while those in the Southeast were required to make more improvements in compliance with laws, regulations, and state BMPs, communication and conflict resolution, and worker safety. These differences in results are intertwined with the difference in standards required by FSC in the two regions (Box 16.1).

A recent in-depth study by Blackman, Raimondi, and Cubbage (2014) takes a somewhat more pessimistic view of the degree to which FSC certification resulted in improved management and environmental outcomes in the forests of developing countries. To answer the question of the benefits of certification, they analyzed over 1,000 corrective action requests (CARs) issued after third-party inspections of a diverse set of 35 forests in Mexico certified by the FSC. These CARs detail the changes in procedures and on-the-ground conditions that forest managers must make to either obtain or retain certification. Their analysis indicated that a relatively small proportion of CARs required major changes in on-the-ground environmental conditions, with the majority of the CARs focused on social and legal issues. Overall, most of the CARs called for only minor procedural changes.

Blackman et al. (2014) hypothesized that these findings were at least partly driven by the tendency of FSC certification to attract forests that already meet its standards and by the governance challenges of community forestry in

Table 16.6 *Percentage of SmartWood-certified operations in more developed and less developed countries required to make changes in management, relative to different forest management issues, during their certification assessment*

| Issue | Operations in more developed countries (%) | Operations in less developed countries (%) |
|---|---|---|
| Roads and skid trails | 55 | 73 |
| Regeneration and reforestation | 48 | 64 |
| Chemical use and disposal | 40 | 55 |
| Exotic species and pests | 40 | 9 |
| Conversion to nonforest uses | 3 | 27 |

*Source:* Newsom and Hewitt (2005).

developing countries. They concluded that policy makers using FSC certification to generate environmental benefits may want to target forests with less-than-stellar management—particularly in the case of Reduced Emissions from Deforestation and Degradation (REDD) initiatives that emphasize improvement beyond business-as-usual—and build the community and legal institutions needed for sustainable forest management.

It should not be surprising that interest in certification may be partly a function of how much management practices must change for certification to occur. On the Pacific Coast of the US, as an example, the cost of FSC certification (in terms of changes in management practices required), is higher in Oregon than in California for many owners because California has higher protection standards in its forest practice rules. Thus, less change would be needed for landowners currently managing at minimum standards and, other things equal, we would expect more FSC certification in California over time.

**Economic effects**   Past surveys have identified a number of economic reasons why companies and landowners seek certification (Cashore et al., 2004; Stevens, Ahmad, & Ruddell, 1998). We will focus on three that are commonly mentioned as very important: (1) increased market prices for certified products, (2) market access, and (3) being recognized for environmental responsibility.

*Obtaining a price premium.*   Originally, certifiers and landowners hoped that the appearance of certified wood products in markets would be met by customers willing to pay more to know their wood was grown in sustainable forests, perhaps much more (Cashore et al., 2004). A model for this effort was organic food, where people have been willing to pay a premium for healthier, more sustainable, foods. However, certified wood products have not met similar acclaim in the market place.

Numerous *willingness to pay* studies, such as Aguilar and Vlosky (2007) have documented consumers' willingness to pay a premium for certified wood. However, that intent and willingness has been difficult to translate into actual behavior. Studies using a variety of different methods (Anderson, Laband, Hansen, & Knowles, 2005; Hartsfield & Ostermeier, 2003; Perera, Vlosky, Dunn, & Hughes, 2008; Rickenbach & Overdevest, 2006) found that certification generally did not improve producer prices. Recent meta-analyses on the producer benefits of forest certification have confirmed these findings (Blackman & Rivera, 2011; Chen, Innes, & Tikina, 2010).

In Oregon, for example, Anderson and Hansen (2004) performed an experiment at two Home Depot stores in Oregon, with the intent of measuring consumer-purchasing behavior with respect to eco-labeled forest products. In one experiment, they asked customers how much more they would pay for wood certified as coming from sustainable forests. Approximately two-thirds said they would pay at least 10% more. In the second experiment, consumers were offered a choice between virtually identical eco-labeled and non-eco-labeled plywood products. They found that the eco-labeled product outsold the non-eco-labeled product, 2 to 1, so long as the price of plywood in each bin was equal. When the eco-labeled plywood was priced at a small premium, the ratio was reversed: the non-eco-labeled product outsold the eco-labeled by almost 2 to 1. The authors noted that plywood is a **commodity product** and therefore price is the most important consideration for purchase. The researchers note that this exploratory study focused on a limited geographic area, involving a single forest product, and thus we must be cautious about broader inference. Still it does provide an interesting case about the interest of consumers in eco-labeled products.

Other studies have identified price premiums for **specialty products** from certified forests, such as higher-quality tropical hardwoods. For example Nebel, Quevedo, Bredahl Jacobsen, and Helles (2005) found a 5–50% premium for the majority of exported certified products from Bolivia. Also, Yamamoto, Skinkuma, and Takeuchi (2014) found a price premium of 4% for cedar in Japan, a highly prized wood there.

These results, and others like them, have led **big-box** retailers, like Home Depot, to provide certified commodity products in the United States without a price premium (Chen et al., 2010). We can speculate as to why these results are so different from those of organic food. First, these retailers base much of their advertising on their low prices, so it may not be surprising that many of their customers do not want to pay more for certified wood. Second, lumber and plywood take lots of room in a store, whereas fruits and vegetables do not. Thus, grocers can play to niche markets by providing both nonorganic and organic vegetables, charging more for the latter. Retailers who sell lumber generally do not have sufficient room to carry two types of each product. If they choose certified wood and charge more, they may lose business from the majority of people who will not pay higher prices for certified wood. Third, certified wood products generally do not suggest potential health benefits as organic vegetables do to some people.

However, these results do not tell the whole story. In fact, they suggest a niche for certified wood for those who will pay more, especially where they are not directly competing with the big box stores. Sustainable Northwest, a Pacific Northwest conservation group focused on natural resources and job creation, specializes in the development of markets for FSC-certified wood. They created a wood warehouse that sells FSC-certified wood and deliver a premium to over 34 family-owned wood producers in the region. The Sus-

tainable Northwest Wood Warehouse has discovered some interesting certified wood market trends:[7]

- Certified wood markets are more stable. Consumers that select certified wood are more likely to stick with a product that they have proactively chosen versus a product they chose because of low price. This allegiance continued during the 2008 recession: certified wood products held market better than noncertified wood markets.

- Consumers that buy into the story of where their wood comes from are willing to pay more. Having and sharing a wood sourcing story is critical to impacting consumer behavior.

Sustainable Northwest also runs a group certification that enables 71 Chain-of-Custody businesses access to certified wood markets. In 2014, businesses in the group sold over $13 million in certified wood. Annual member surveys consistently find that most businesses in the network receive a price premium. Premiums, however, are not evenly experienced throughout the supply chain; that is, they are strong in the retail side of the supply chain but more rarely seen by the landowner.

**Improving market access.** Forestry companies view certification as an opportunity to maintain existing markets and/or expand into more lucrative niche markets (Chen et al., 2010). Thus, certification can be an effective way to enter environmentally sensitive niche markets, such as those created by governments and public bodies where procurement policies require purchase of certified products, or markets created by large retailers or buyers who are increasingly specific about the nature and origin of the products they buy (Cashore et al., 2004; Chen et al., 2010).

Public procurement policies, which specify the use of certified wood, are becoming a driver to ensure the legality and sustainability of wood sources and wood products especially in Western Europe, the United States, and Japan (Chen et al., 2010; Durst, McKenzie, Brown, & Appanah, 2006;). Also, buyer groups have become an important player in the demand for certified products, especially in the United States and Europe. These groups are independent associations of businesses that are committed to purchasing and/or stocking certified forest products (Ozanne & Vlosky, 2003). Large retailers, such as Home Depot in the United States, have also stated their preference for certified wood (Auld, 2014).

In comparison to American and European markets, though, certification has not gained a meaningful market

---

7 Personal communication, May 2016, Paul Vanderford, Sustainable Northwest

share in principal Asian markets such as China (Perara & Vlosky, 2006). It should be noted that countries in Asian markets are among the leading importers of tropical timber (International Tropical Timber Organization, 2012).

***Public recognition of environmental responsibility.*** Few studies have been made of how much certification actually improves the public image of a company. However, many companies believe it does so and put it very high on the list of certification benefits as previously noted by Moore et al. (2012) and Rickenbach and Overdevest (2006).

**Environmental effects**  Relatively few scientific studies have been done on the positive environmental effects of certification. There are numerous explanations for this dearth of studies. As discussed above, researchers have used certification audit reports and surveys to document the large number of changes required during certification as evidence of environmental improvement, and FSC prides itself on modeling its standards after the latest research about how to sustain ecosystems and the species within them. Thus, one line of reasoning is that following those standards should automatically lead to improvements in the restoration and protection of ecosystems and species. Also, studies of how certification actually affects the environment can be difficult and costly to conduct. Still, a few studies have been done as documented by Blackman and Rivera (2011). They conducted a meta-analysis of studies of producer-level benefits of sustainability certification, and they highlighted four studies of environmental effects, including those by Gulbrandsen (2005), Kukkonen, Rita, Hohnwald, and Nygren (2008), and Nebel et al. (2005) that focused on environmental benefits. Overall, Blackman and Rivera (2011) concluded that certification can improve forest practices but, generally does not, by itself, reduce deforestation or prevent land conversion.

More recent studies have reached more optimistic conclusions about the positive effect of certification, especially FSC, on environmental and social sustainability. We summarize two below.

Miteva et al. (2015) used temporally and spatially explicit village-level data on environmental and socioeconomic indicators in Kalimantan (Indonesia) to evaluate the performance of the FSC-certified timber concessions compared to noncertified timber concessions. They found that, between 2000 and 2008, FSC certification reduced aggregate deforestation by 5% and the incidence of air pollution by 31%. In addition, FSC certification reduced firewood dependence and respiratory infection. Also, they found that the effect of FSC certification of logging concessions on biodiversity was less clear, with some bird species benefiting from the partial harvest that occurred and some species doing less well, suggesting that the impact of FSC certification will likely depend on the conservation goal (a few target species vs. overall species richness).

Because the success of FSC certification largely depends on the involvement of the local communities, Miteva et al. (2015) emphasized the importance of the program generating benefits to them. Toward that end, they found that FSC generated positive benefits to local communities (e.g., reduced disease incidence and fuelwood dependence, and increased private funding) compared to villages in noncertified forests.

Miteva et al. (2015) cautioned that FSC has some limitations in terms of protecting biodiversity and providing ecosystem services such as carbon sequestration, and presents some hurdles to certification such as certification cost. Given the compatibility of REDD and FSC requirements, though they argued that FSC certification can be used as the stepping stone to receiving carbon payments that can be used to subsidize certification and make it accessible to more firms.

Heilmayr and Lambin (2016) examined three nonstate, market-driven governance (NSMD) regimes in Chile relative to reducing the conversion of natural forest to plantations: (1) an NGO-inspired agreement with Chilean forest industry firms to stop conversions, (2) a national certification scheme later endorsed by PEFC, and (3) FSC certification. Using quasi-experimental methods, they demonstrated that Chile's NSMD governance regimes were successful in reducing natural forest conversion to plantations by 2–23%. Of the three governance regimes evaluated, the multistakeholder FSC certification standard achieved better environmental performance than either the industry-led certification standard or the NGO-inspired moratorium.

Further, Heilmayr and Lambin (2016, p. 2910) found that "the more collaborative governance systems studied [such as FSC] achieved better environmental performance than more confrontational approaches. Whereas many government conservation programs have targeted regions with little likelihood of conversion, we demonstrate that NSMD governance has the potential to alter behavior on high-deforestation properties."

## Summary of Forest Certification Potential Costs and Benefits

### Evaluation of Potential Costs

- *Direct costs of certification can make certification expensive for companies and/or individuals with relatively small holdings.* FSC and some PEFC certification groups are attempting to deal with this issue by expanding their emphasis on group certification.

- *Indirect compliance costs, in terms of needed changes in management, can be significant, with the costs varying depending on the baseline management and the certification scheme chosen.* These costs can weigh heavily in decisions regarding the certification route to choose, with some form of PEFC certification often less costly than FSC certification for organizations interested in production forestry (see comparison of SFI and FSC certification in Box 16.1).

## Evaluation of Potential Benefits

- *Forest managers in certified organizations, at least in the United States and Canada, appear relatively happy with certification and believe it has improved the quality of management, even though some of its hoped for benefits have not been realized.*

- *Certification audits generally require a number of changes in management before certification can occur, giving indirect evidence that certification is shifting the practices of firms and landowners management toward sustainable forest management.* These numbers, though, do not give information on the depth of changes required for certification.

- *Retailers, and occasionally landowners, can attain a price premium in certain specialty markets. However, premiums are generally unavailable for commodity products* in most developed countries; findings of a willingness to pay more for certified wood by an environmentally-sensitive portion of the public have generally not been captured in purchasing behavior.

- *Maintaining or improving market access is another potential benefit of certification.* As we discuss below, this force is likely to increase in the future.

- *Companies in North America generally believe that certification improves their image as a protector of the environment and thus reduces stakeholder conflict. In fact, this outcome is rated by firms as perhaps the greatest benefit of certification.* Through the signal of certification, an enterprise can address concerns of key stakeholders who might otherwise oppose forest management. *However, the evidence that these perceptions by the public vary with certification scheme (FSC or PEFC) is weak.*

- *Relatively little research has been done on the ecological benefits of certification.* Research that has been done suggests that positive changes in forest management may result. However, findings about the ability of certification to prevent deforestation or land conversion are mixed, with FSC certification showing the most promise.

- Since certification is voluntary, we would expect it would be chosen first by those who need to make the least changes to comply, both in terms of whether to certify and the certification scheme to choose. Thus certification may be as much a way to recognize sustainable forest management as to bring it about.

## Emerging Issues and Trends in Forest Certification

Forest certification has gained wide acceptance since its introduction in the early 1990s. The concept has gained the support of many environmental NGOs and has been accepted, modified, and adopted by much of the forest industry in North America and Europe. Despite its promising role as a market-based mechanism in support of sustainable forest management, many unresolved issues remain.

### Uncertain Source of Future Certifications

As of 2014, a modest proportion of the world's forests were certified by either FSC or PEFC, and the total number of hectares certified is only slowly increasing (Figure 16.1). The United States, Canada, and Europe have been the source of most of the certification acreage so far. Perhaps that market is becoming saturated. Thus, the rate at which certification will capture more hectares in the future is uncertain.

**Slow Progress of Certification in Tropical Forests**    Forest certification was initially introduced by FSC, in large part, to reduce deforestation and destructive forest management in the tropics. Yet, the vast majority of certifications at present have occurred in Europe and North America, while developing countries, where most tropical forests lie, contribute less than 10% to the total acreage of certified forests (Figures 16.1 and 16.2).

The seminal study of Ebeling and Yasue (2009) comparing forest certification success in Ecuador and Bolivia sheds light on keys to certification success in tropical countries. Bolivia has a higher proportion of forest under certified forest management than Ecuador, and significantly more certified products. The study's authors note that the difference in success between the two countries is particularly notable because Bolivia is a poorer country than Ecuador and suffers from widespread corruption. They found, though, that Bolivia has stronger government enforcement of forestry regulations, which increased the cost of illegal logging and enabled larger management units and higher vertical integration in the timber processing chain. They also found that forestry laws in Bolivia are highly compatible with certification requirements, and the government provides significant tax benefits to certified producers. As Ebeling and Yasue (2009, p. 1145) summarize:

*Certification can be successful in countries where governments have limited governance capacity. However the economic incentives for certification do not only arise from favorable market conditions. Certification is likely to be more successful where governments enforce forestry laws, provide financial incentives for certified forestry, and provide land security, and where large-scale and vertically integrated forestry operations are commercially feasible. For this reason, at present, there are few developing countries where forest certification is likely to achieve widespread success.*

It is not surprising that there is little interest in sustainable forest management where land tenure is uncertain and deforestation and illegal logging are tolerated and profitable. Efforts to address these issues have become integrated into the global movement to combat climate change and have moved to other policy tools such as the REDD program of the United Nations. Also, work to combat illegal logging has moved to national and international trade laws and regulations, such as recent revisions to the Lacy Act in the United States, which prohibits the import of illegally sourced wood products (Chen et al., 2010). The degree that forest certification can be part of these efforts remains to be seen. Whether other countries that import tropical woods, like China, will develop or adhere to trade restrictions could be an important determinant in its success.

**Difficulties in Certifying Family Forests**   The certification of forests owned by small landowners has been given less attention by most of the leading forest certification schemes over the years, and as a result, small landowners are generally underrepresented in forest certification programs. Some certification programs have recently targeted forests owned by small landowners and taken measures to assist them in meeting challenges by introducing programs such as group certification to help bring down the cost of certification.

## Confusion Caused by Multiple Certification Schemes

Certification, as envisioned by FSC, would ensure retailers and customers that the wood they stocked or bought meets a set of environmental standards that protect and enhance forest sustainability. FSC's emergence on the international scene was met almost immediately with a counter move by the forest industry and some landowners to provide certification without many substantive environmental standards beyond meeting those in laws and BMPs.

With multiple eco-labels claiming to support sustainable forest management, many consumers may not be capable of differentiating among these labels or may just be confused. The confusion associated with multiple certification

schemes is heightened by the interest of each scheme in convincing the sources of demand for certification (retailers and the public) that it covers all aspects of sustainability. Knowing whether there is substance to these claims requires a closer look, as we have done in Table 16.3. *While certification has been rightly trumpeted as a nongovernmental approach to sustainability, it is also true that such an approach means we do not have government-induced standards that must be met by a certification scheme.* The term *caveat emptor* (let the buyer beware) applies.

Since it is not clear which certification schemes will become globally accepted in the future, forest owners and wood-based manufacturers face a difficult choice when it comes to selecting a certification scheme. Internationally, the schemes have shaken out into two major groups: FSC and most of the rest blended together under PEFC (including SFI, ATFS, and CSA). The battle continues between the two groups, with supporters of PEFC schemes devoted to getting PEFC recognized by markets, retailers, builders, and policy makers as equal to FSC in ensuring sustainable forest management, and supporters of FSC devoted to preventing that outcome from happening. For example, a fierce battle rages over whether PEFC, especially SFI, should be recognized as equivalent to FSC in *green building* codes as we discuss below.

Some ownerships, such as the states of Wisconsin, Michigan, and Minnesota in the US, have responded to this dilemma by seeking certification of their state forests by both FSC and a PEFC affiliate (SFI). However, not everyone has the resources to do that!

## Role of Plantations in Sustainable Forest Management

Certification of intensively managed plantations has long been at the heart of the battle for dominance in certification of sustainable forest management in the United States and other places. Historically, FSC understandably has been reluctant to certify landowners who convert natural forests into intensively managed plantations to produce their wood. *Since plantations managed to achieve an acceptable rate of return is the dominant paradigm of corporate forestry in the United States, it is not surprising that this group largely rejected FSC certification and developed its own certification scheme (SFI).*

However, FSC has certified millions of hectares of plantations around the world as its approach has evolved. FSC has certified afforestation projects in many different countries, including in the United States, under the argument that forest expansion should be rewarded. Also, some firms, especially outside the United States, covet the attainment of FSC certification for their plantations as a demonstration that they practice sustainable forest management—to protect themselves from criticism, public censure, and lawsuits and to gain access to particular markets. That assurance is worth the changes they must make in their management, especially where recent or continued conversion of native forest is not an important component of their forest management and the laws, regulations, and BMPs of the country in which the forest sits already meet some of the FSC standards.

Some authors have questioned whether the path to forest sustainability, regionally or globally, is to force owners to abandon intensively managed plantations. Through their use, they argue, much of the world's demand for wood fiber can be met using only a small proportion of global forest area (Sedjo & Botkin, 1997). Such an approach potentially reduces wood-production pressures on the remaining forests, leaving those forests for management strategies that could, in theory, consider a multitude of values. On the other hand, competition from such plantations can make it more difficult for other landowners to obtain the economic return needed to retain and manage their forests.

## Certification as a Public Good

It can be argued that we all benefit from the sustainable forest management that flows from certification, whether or not we contribute to its costs. Further, it appears that landowners who seek certification, and perhaps change management to receive it, are unable to monetize many of these benefits. Goods and services with these characteristics are often called **public goods**. Because the people incurring the cost cannot obtain the benefits, economists often argue that they will be underproduced (Cubbage, O'Laughlin, & Peterson, 2017). In such cases, governments sometimes step in to subsidize the production of these benefits, as is done in the United States to encourage reforestation and habitat protection on family forests. If certification is recognized as a public good, the direct and indirect costs of certification might be subsidized by governments. Of course, that might get governments into the battle over which certification schemes to endorse!

## Certification's Role in Market Access as a Key to Its Future

Market access will likely drive certification in the future, both in terms of total hectares certified and the certification system chosen. Access to four different types of markets will be key: (1) wood-product markets, (2) green building markets, (3) carbon markets, and (4) biomass markets. As we describe below, governments may be much more involved in certification determinations than in the past.

**Wood-Product Markets** Although forest certification was largely built on a market-driven mechanism, with environmentally concerned consumers sending price signals through the supply chain to the forest industries and forest managers, this ideal relationship has generally not developed, except for niche products. Whether consumers will demand that retailers in the future more generally limit their products to certified wood remains to be seen.

Governments can play a key role in determining market access through their trade policies. Much internationally traded wood still flows through markets that do not require certified products, especially in Asia. Until that changes, much of the world's forests, especially tropical forests, may remain noncertified without penalty. Further, whether markets that require certified products discriminate among certification systems, especially between FSC and PEFC systems, can have a substantial effect on how certification affects forest management and also on the future of different certifiers.

**Green Building Markets** Recently, certification has spread to the buildings themselves, with many cities in the US and elsewhere now requiring green building certification. The prominent building certification program in the US is the LEED system (Leadership in Energy and Environmental Design), introduced in 2000 by the US Green Building Council. LEED provides four levels of certification: *Certified, Silver, Gold,* and *Platinum.* To become certified at any level, projects must first meet all required standards, such as achieving energy efficiency and water conservation baselines. Provided a building project meets these required standards, the *level* of certification is based on attaining a minimum number of discretionary credits awarded to the project for achieving other certification standards (USGBC, 2017). Until recently, LEED awarded credit for using a minimum percentage of FSC-certified wood in construction, but offered no such credit for wood from PEFC certification programs, such as SFI, CSA, and ATFS. In 2016 LEED implemented a pilot "alternative compliance path" that awards credit for using a minimum fraction of wood from "legal, responsible, and certified" sources, which includes PEFC certifications, resulting in protest from FSC supporters and praise from SFI supporters (Melton, 2016). Going forward, a key question will be whether the LEED alternative compliance path will continue to be eligible for credit or whether credit, once again, will be awarded only for FSC-certified wood. Recognition by LEED as a sustainable source of forest products carries both prestige and market value, and the battle for that recognition will likely be a source of contention for years to come.

**Carbon Markets**[8]    As stated in the Fourth Assessment Report of the Intergovernmental Panel on Climate Change, "In the long term, a sustainable forest management strategy aimed at maintaining or increasing forest carbon stocks, while producing an annual sustained yield of timber, fibre or energy from the forest, will generate the largest sustained mitigation benefit" (Nabuurs et al., 2007, p. 543). How will sustainable forest management be determined? Will certification play a role? Such decisions could substantially affect access to markets related to reduction of $CO_2$ emissions.

The potential of forest sinks as carbon offsets in cap-and-trade markets could certainly affect the pace of certification. If certification of a forest as sustainable is the gateway to carbon-offset markets, and forest carbon gains considerable value, interest in certification may significantly increase. When certification is needed for entry into these markets, the next question will be whether both FSC- and PEFC-certified forests will gain access.

**Woody Biomass Markets**    Woody biomass is a potential source of energy, and a number of governments are looking to it as a potential source of renewable power. As an example, the European Union treats power from forest biomass as renewable and has mandated that significant and increasing proportions of power in its member countries or states must come from renewable sources. The resulting demand for forest biomass by Europe has resulted in extensive biomass markets developing on the East Coast of the United States and elsewhere. Key questions are whether this demand will be limited to biomass from certified forests and whether any preferences among the certification schemes will occur.

Also the Environmental Protection Agency (EPA) in the United States, the primary body overseeing the federal response to climate change, has waffled over whether to count forest biomass as renewable energy, like solar and wind, and whether to limit such an acknowledgement to woody biomass from sustainably managed forests. Such an outcome might push the US government into the certification business.

## Certification and Ecological Forestry

*The philosophy, goals, and forest management practices of FSC closely match those of ecological forest management, with the focus in FSC on emulating natural processes and maintaining ecosystem integrity. Among the different certification systems we have reviewed, FSC comes the closest,* *by a significant margin, to fully reflecting ecological forestry as described in this book.* However, one of the significant challenges for FSC certification will be to stay current with scientific discoveries and management experience. Such currency in knowledge and practice is intrinsic to ecological forestry, with its emphasis on adaptive management. Ecological forestry and FSC certification have much to learn from each other. Books like this one attempt to describe the latest scientific thinking on ecological forestry and can help guide revisions in FSC national and regional standards and other ecologically based certification systems that emerge. Conversely, forest management activities conducted under FSC certification standards can provide global real-world experiences of the potential and practical realities of ecological forestry.

*SFI, on the other hand, does not fully align with ecological forest management, especially in the lack of reliance on natural processes as a management guide (such as in retention of substantial biological legacies within stands at harvest). However, by requiring the use of BMPs and endorsing many of the same environmental goals as FSC, SFI certification does advance the application of some ecological forestry principles and practices, especially where there is relatively little forest practice regulation.* The southern US, as an example, has a long history of landowner freedom to manage their forests as they wish with only modest state oversight. SFI certification of industrial forests combined with adherence of manufacturing plants to SFI Fiber Sourcing standards turn voluntary BMPs that states develop to help implement the Clean Water Act into requirements. In this way, protection of aquatic systems, one of the most significant conservation responsibilities of private landowners (Chapter 5), can be advanced across both corporate and family forest ownerships (Wilent, 2017). In addition, calling for landowners to protect biodiversity can alert them to these values, although decisions of how they will recognize the values in their management practices are left largely to discretion of the landowner.

*More broadly, we hope that all involved in forest management understand and adopt practices consistent with the goal of restoring and maintaining the integrity of forest ecosystems, no matter what certification system they choose or support.* We encourage the broad adoption of the philosophy and goals of ecological forest management across the spectrum of landowner and societal goals and situations: every aspect of ecological forest management implemented in a forest stand or landscape contributes to the application of ecological forestry.

---

8  See Chapter 15 for more on climate change, forests, and carbon, including the role of carbon offsets and woody biomass in reducing $CO_2$ emissions.

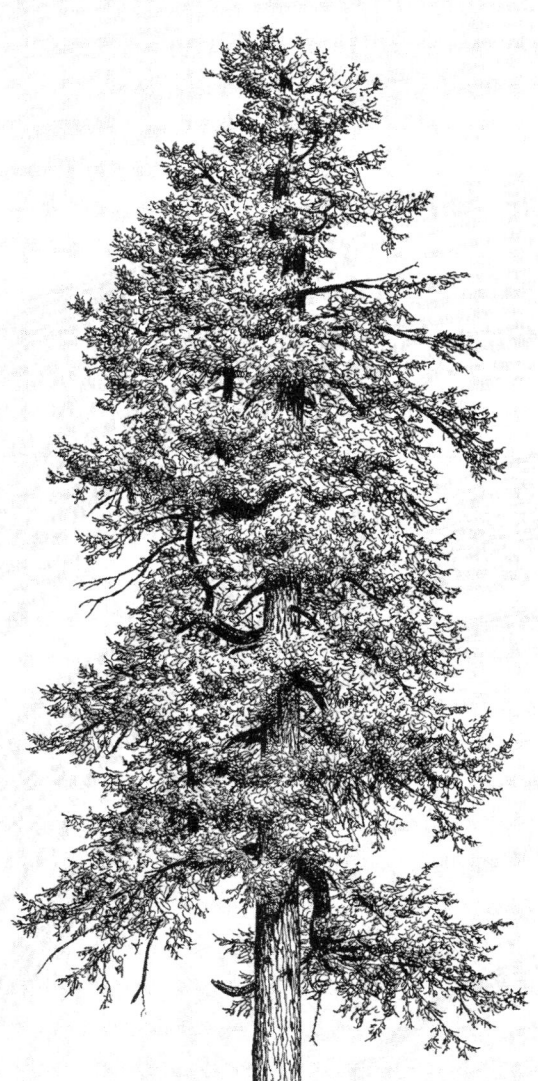

# Part *IV*
## Forest Planning

*The task of forest regulation is to build up, put in order, and keep in order a forest business.* — FILIBERT ROTH

# CHAPTER 17

# Classical Forest Regulation: Its Relevance to Ecological Forestry

*Dr. Filibert Roth, University of Michigan, talking to his forestry summer camp class in 1903. (© Bentley Historical Library, University of Michigan)*

Forest planning, as conceived in this book, focuses on examining alternative strategies for the management of forests. To do this type of analysis, foresters many centuries ago realized they would need to look far into the future. This need for a long-term view comes from three fundamental aspects of forestry.

First, compared to many other biological resources, trees take a long time to grow to maturity—from decades to hundreds of years depending on the species and the measure. Thus forest planning has always looked many decades into the future. In fact, this approach to planning sets forestry apart, in many ways, from other arenas of resource planning. Time is a crucial dimension in almost all forest planning problems and the need for consideration of future ecological, economic, and social conditions permeates forest planning.

Second, damage to the forest can take a long time to repair, arguing for careful consideration before we act. Our ability to change forests is asymmetric—they are easy to destroy but difficult to create—a biological and economic reality that we sometimes forget. Often we must wait through one or two human lifetimes to achieve the desired result. This is hard to accept in an impatient political and social world.

Third, foresters have long been interested in providing a sustainable supply of timber. Toward that end, foresters historically focused on the idea of a *regulated forest* in which growth equaled harvest and a constant supply of timber could be delivered forever. Concern about achieving a regulated forest has long been a hallmark of professional forestry—one of the organizing principles of classical forest conservation. In the eyes of early foresters, the regulated forest became a guiding star, perhaps never achieved but always providing a way forward.

In a historical context, the regulated forest provided a conservation framework for forest planning, with its focus on conservative use and the maintenance of forest productivity and growth over time. It provided a distinct alternative to the *cut and get out* mentality originally practiced in many of America's forests. The use of regulated forests as a conservation framework today is limited, as we take a broader, more nuanced view of conservation, but we should not forget the positive role it played in forest conservation in the formative days of professional forestry in the United States.

While goals for our forests have now broadened beyond providing a sustained yield of timber harvest volume, the concern for the long term remains a defining feature of forestry. Thus, foresters have been, by necessity, some of the first futurists—an approach necessitated by the resources they manage and their desire for sustaining those resources. In this chapter, we revisit the classical approaches foresters took to meet their sustainability responsibilities as they saw them at the time, starting with classical decision rules for forest management, especially the focus on achieving and maintaining a regulated forest. Along the way, we will cover the two major approaches to move an *unregulated forest* to a regulated condition—*area control* and *volume control*, along with attempts to combine these two approaches.

We then will discuss the relevance to ecological forestry of key concepts derived from classical forest regulation, such as achieving a regulated forest and providing a sustained yield of timber harvest. It turns out there are parallels to these concepts in ecological forest planning!

There are two good reasons to read this chapter. First, you will hear mention of the regulated forest, area control, volume control, and long-term sustained yield if you hang around forestry and foresters much. In fact, we utilized the concept of the regulated forest in Chapter 15 to help us examine the long-run implications of alternative carbon storage policies for a forest. Second, some of these concepts and tools apply to the planning problems of ecological forestry, too. Thus, it is helpful to know about them.

## Forestry's Classical Decision Rules

As mentioned above, professional forestry came into being in the United States, in large part, to stem the rapid liquidation and destruction of our forests. The specter of timber famine was immediate and real. In those early days, professional foresters utilized a series of relatively simple decision rules to aid them in forest planning (Table 17.1). Many were developed to implement the classical tenets of faith described in Chapter 1, focused on the sustained production of wood products over long periods. Even with the commitment to a regulated forest, many decisions were needed such as desired harvest flow, best rotation age, and

Table 17.1 *Some classical forestry decision rules*

| |
|---|
| Achieve a regulated forest (a balance of harvest and growth) as quickly as possible. |
| Keep harvest at or below the long-term sustained yield. |
| Cut the same number of acres every year. |
| Cut the same amount of volume every year. |
| Set the target rotation age at the age of maximum average growth. |
| Cut the oldest (stands or trees) first. |
| Cut the slowest growing (stands or trees) first. |

which stands to cut first. These decision rules enabled foresters to quickly settle on their desired harvest schedule in an almost intuitive fashion.

While forestry professionals focused on the goal of a regulated forest in which harvest equaled growth and the stability of timber supply was assured in perpetuity, forests in the United States in the early 1900s were quite different from the idealized regulated forest. Either the forests had been largely liquidated in a short period of time without concern for regrowth, as in Maine, the Lake States, and parts of the South, or they were primarily covered with old, slow-growing forest, as in the West. In either case, the forests were far from regulated. Thus foresters sought *conversion* of the existing forest to the idealized regulated forest as a major component of their overarching mission. They were mindful, though, that they needed to do that conversion at a rate that would enable the stability of wood flow wherever possible. Thus they developed many techniques to meet these dual objectives. We will study some of them in this chapter.

Reflecting the classical approach, we will divide forests into *even-aged* and *uneven-aged* for discussion of the regulated forest and methods to achieve it. It should be noted though, that these names refer more to the management regime that will be imposed than the condition of the stands at the beginning of regulation period. Also, we will conduct our discussion without consideration of biological legacies, heterogeneity, or similar ideas from ecological forestry. Later, we will come back to these ecological concepts when we discuss the relevance of classical approaches to ecological forestry.

## The Regulated Forest

The organization of a forest property to provide a sustained yield of timber products forms the heart of classical forest management, one of our first examples of landscape planning. To understand why the idea of sustained yield is so firmly embedded in forestry thinking and literature, we must trace the intellectual history of forestry in the United States back to its roots in Europe.

European foresters in the 1800s, especially German foresters, emphasized the notion of a forest organized to produce a sustained yield of timber to deal with their particular situation. Their forests were often commonly owned and had been continuously cut for hundreds of years. Wood product uses change slowly. Self-sufficiency in timber production was a primary goal in each country's wood product policies, and stability was the overriding economic tenet of the day. All of these factors helped create the psychological climate in which organizing a forest to provide a sustained yield of timber volume became a guiding ideal in Europe's forest management (Davis & Johnson, 1987).

Our early forestry leaders—Fernow, Schenck, Roth, Pinchot—were educated in Europe. Most went to German schools where forest regulation was at its zenith as an idea around which forestry could be organized. Not surprisingly, this idea was transferred virtually intact to the United States. Fear of a future timber famine made this country ripe for embracing the European idea of a forest organized to produce an even flow of timber forever. Such a fear helped bring the forestry profession into existence, slowed the movement of public domain forestland into private ownership, and helped to generate political pressure for creation of the national forests. Organizing a forest to produce a continuous flow of wood served as an intellectual rallying point for the new forestry profession just as the creation of the national forests served as a political rallying point for laypersons concerned with overcutting and a future timber shortage (Davis & Johnson, 1987).

## Traditional Virtues

As described by Filibert Roth in the first forest management book published in the United States, a regulated forest had many virtues (Roth, 1925, p. 113):

a) *Yearly cut of about equal volume.*

b) *Yearly cut of about the same age, size, and quality of timber, and hence a yearly income of about the same amount.*

c) *Growth and income secured on a capital no larger than is necessary, and therefore this regularity assures the largest percent interest on the capital.*

d) *Best growth under given conditions of site, species, and rotation.*

e) *Greatest degree of safety from fire and other dangers, since the forest is never made up entirely of young or of old stuff.*

In short the forest is in a properly regulated or 'normal' condition.

In summary, Roth says (1925, p. 113): "Regulation of the cut, then, should prevent overcut as well as undercut in the forest."

## Characteristics [1]

How is a forest organized for continuous production? To answer that question, we will focus on how the forest looks and behaves when the regulated structure is fully attained. Even though this idealized structure is rarely achieved, its description will help us understand what is meant by a "regulated forest" and visualize the standard by which forest management progress was traditionally measured.

*The essential requirement of a fully regulated forest is that its age or size classes are represented in such proportion and growing at such rates that an approximately equal annual or periodic yield of products of desired size and quantity can be obtained in perpetuity.* A progression of age or size classes must exist such that an approximately equal volume and size of harvestable trees can be regularly scheduled for harvest.

### Regulation in Even-Aged Management

Classical even-aged management was keyed to the periodic establishment and harvest of stands as determined by rotation age (Figure 17.1a). For this discussion, we will define an even-aged stand as a stand of trees composed of a single age class in which the range of tree ages is generally within

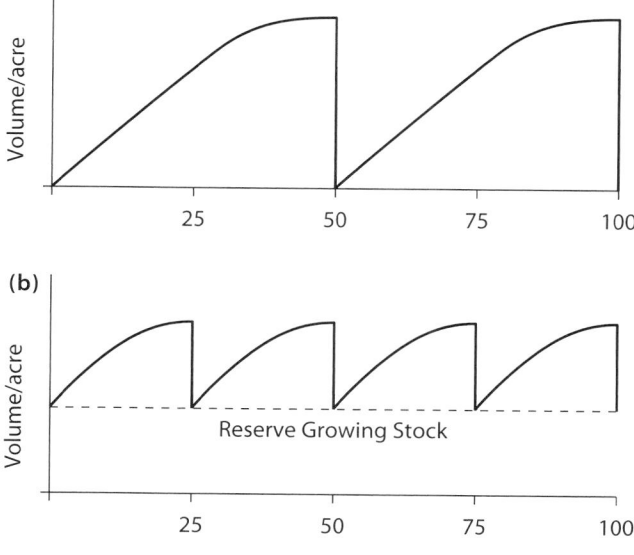

Figure 17.1 *(a) Volume/acre in a stand in a regulated even-aged forest managed on a 50-year rotation. (b) Volume/acre in a stand in a regulated uneven-aged forest managed on a 25-year cutting cycle.*

---

1 Adapted from Davis & Johnson (1987).

20% of the mean age (Helms, 1998) and an even-aged forest as one that is composed of even-aged stands. As noted previously, this characterization of stand structure may refer more to the goal of management than existing stand condition; that is, the existing forest may contain many acres with stands that do not fit the even-aged description, but the goal of management is to convert them to it.

We will start with a very simple case: a forest containing one species growing on one productivity (site) class managed under one silvicultural regime. Let $A$ be the number of acres in such a forest or planning unit and $R$ the selected rotation length. In this classical regulated forest, the acres in the forest are distributed such that A/R acres are in each age class from 1 to R years. The acres in the oldest age class are harvested and regenerated each year, becoming the acres in the youngest age class in the following year. All other acres move up one age class each period. With each age class having equal acreage, the structure of the forest stays constant from year to year, the same number of acres is cut in each year, the same harvest volume is produced each year, and harvest ($H_R$) equals growth ($G_R$). A fully regulated forest!

Table 17.2 *Yield of even-aged loblolly pine of site index 90 (cu ft/ac)*

| Age (years) | Yield (cu ft/acre) |
|---|---|
| 10 | 700 |
| 20 | 1800 |
| 30 | 3500 |
| 40 | 4300 |
| 50 | 4700 |
| 60 | 5100 |
| 70 | 5300 |
| 80 | 5600 |

*Source:* Adapted from Meyer (1942).

The idea that the acres to harvest in a year in a fully regulated forest can be represented by A/R is one of the organizing ideas of classical forestry. We will illustrate it with a 300-acre loblolly pine forest that grows at a rate to produce the yields shown for in Table 17.2, using a rotation of 30 years that is the age of maximum average growth (CMAI).

Table 17.3 *A regulated even-aged forest of 300 acres of loblolly pine stands on a 30-year rotation using the yields of Table 17.2 and 10-year periods;\* each period (here decade) we would harvest all acres*

| Period/ Inventory status | Age (years) | Acres | Inventory Volume per acre cu ft (thousands) | Total volume cu ft (thousands) | Periodic Harvest Acres | cu ft (thousands) | Periodic Growth Acres | cu ft (thousands) |
|---|---|---|---|---|---|---|---|---|
| **Period t** | | | | | | | | |
| Before harvest | 30 | 100 | 3.50 | 350 | | | | |
| | 20 | 100 | 1.80 | 180 | | | | |
| | 10 | 100 | .70 | 70 | | | | |
| | 0 | 0 | 0 | 0 | | | | |
| | Total | 300 | | 600 | | | | |
| | | | | | 100 | 350 | | |
| After harvest, | 30 | 0 | 3.50 | 0 | | | | |
| before growth | 20 | 100 | 1.80 | 180 | | | | |
| | 10 | 100 | .70 | 70 | | | | |
| | 0 | 100 | 0 | 0 | | | | |
| | Total | 300 | | 250 | | | | |
| | | | | | | | 300 | 350 |
| **Period t+1** | | | | | | | | |
| After growth, | 30 | 100 | 3.50 | 350 | | | | |
| before harvest | 20 | 100 | 1.80 | 180 | | | | |
| | 10 | 100 | .70 | 70 | | | | |
| | 0 | 0 | 0 | 0 | | | | |
| | Total | 300 | | 600 | | | | |

\* Calculation of harvest, growth, and inventory for a regulated 300-acre loblolly pine forest on site 90 managed on a 30-year rotation. Ten-year periods are used and harvest occurs every 10 years. At the beginning of each period, cut A/R × years in a period = 300 acres/30 years × 10 years = 100 acres and then grow. Harvest priority rule: Cut the oldest stands first.

Table 17.4 *Calculation of growth over a period (here a decade) in a regulated forest*

| Starting Stand Age | Ending Stand Age | Acres | Starting Volume/ac | Ending Volume/ac | Forest Growth[*] |
|---|---|---|---|---|---|
| (years) | | | Thousands of cubic feet | | |
| 0 | 10 | 100 | 0 | .70 | 70 |
| 10 | 20 | 100 | .70 | 1.80 | 110 |
| 20 | 30 | 100 | 1.80 | 3.50 | 170 |
| Total | | | | | 350 |

[*] Growth = 100 × (.7 − 0) + 100 × (1.8 − .7) + 100 × (3.5 − 1.8) = 70 + 110 + 170 = 350

Further let us assume that we wish to manage this forest on a 30-year rotation. Using our formula, we would harvest A/R = 300 acres/30 years = 10 acres/year. However, assume that we wish to harvest the forest only once a decade (use a period length of 10 years). Then the formula to calculate the acres to harvest in a period becomes: A/R × number of years in a period = 300 acres/30 years × 10 years = 100 acres.[2] Each decade, we enter the forest and harvest 3.5 thousand cu ft/ac on 100 acres for a total harvest volume of 350 thousand cu ft from an inventory of 600 thousand cu ft. That harvest leaves an inventory of 250 thousand cu ft, which will grow back to 600 thousand cu ft by the beginning of the next decade, and so on forever (Table 17.3).

Since we said $H_R = G_R$, we should also be able show that growth over a decade in our example will be 350 thousand cu ft. We can make this demonstration either by comparing the forest inventory before and after growth (250 thousand cu ft after harvest in a period, grow to 600 thousand cu ft in the next period in Table 17.3), or calculating the growth age class by age class (Table 17.4).

In addition, we can calculate growth in yet another way. We specified a 30-year rotation. Over 30 years, the average stand will produce 3,500 cu ft/ac for an average growth/year of 3,500/30 = 116.67 cu ft/ac/yr. Multiplied by the number of acres in our forest, we obtain 116.67 × 300 = 35,000 cu ft/yr or 350 thousand cu ft/decade—the growth and harvest per decade we calculated for our perfectly regulated forest.

The spatial relationship of the different age classes across the landscape does not influence these calculations—each age class can be in one large block or in many small ones (Figure 17.2a and b).

Our simple assumptions about a uniform site quality, one species, and one silvicultural regime can be eased with-

**(a)**                                    **(b)**

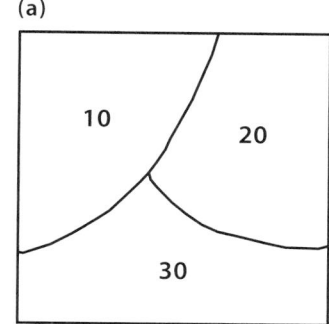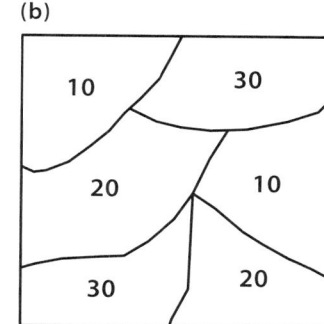

Figure 17.2 *(a) Map of our 300-acre regulated forest of 3 age classes (10, 20, 30) divided into 3 irregular areas of equal size. (b) Map of our 300-acre regulated forest of 3 age classes broken into smaller irregular blocks.*

out loss of the regulated forest idea. More generally, we would divide the forest into acreages of equal productivity (in terms of timber volume) under the species and sites in use. They can be in single blocks or scattered. If rotation ages vary greatly among different land allocations, separate regulated forest calculations may be needed; that is, the areas devoted to long-rotation forestry can be regulated separately from the areas devoted to intensive timber management on shorter rotations. Then the equilibrium harvest volumes from the two allocations would be added to get total harvest for the regulated forest. In sum, the regulated forest concept can remain functional in a more complicated forestry world!

## Regulation in Uneven-Aged Management

Classical uneven-aged management was keyed to the partial harvest of stands on a regular cycle (Figure 17.1b). For this discussion, we will define an uneven-aged stand as a stand of trees with three or more distinct age classes, either intimately mixed or in small groups (Helms, 1998).[3] Again, it should be noted that this characterization of stand structure may refer more to the goal of management than existing stand

---

2 Both the 30-year rotation age and the grouping of the forest into 10-year age classes were chosen so that the example will easily fit on a textbook page. Further, we will assume that the forest is entered at the beginning of each 10-year period. Thus, we will harvest one-third of the area at each entry from a regulated forest composed of three different age classes. The same concepts and procedures discussed here apply if we utilize age classes of one year, five years, 10 years, or some other consistent time interval.

---

3 In this context, a ***multiaged*** (multicohort) stand is defined as a stand with two or more age classes or cohorts.

condition; that is, the existing forest may contain many acres with stands that do not fit the uneven-aged description, but the goal of management is to convert them to it.

In the simplest case, a regulated uneven-aged forest is composed of one species growing on one productivity (site) class managed under one silvicultural regime. Let A be the acres in such a forest and *CC* be the *cutting cycle*—the number of years needed to harvest the forest. Each year an acreage equal to A/CC is cut, reducing the inventory on that area back to a residual growing stock, with the volume cut equal to the growth that occurred on the forest that year.

We can use a similar table to that employed for an even-aged regulated forest to demonstrate an uneven-aged regulated forest (Table 17.5). Rather than identifying a stand by its age, we identify it by years since the last partial cut. As before, we use 10-year periods. Thus, the acres to cut each period = A/CC × years in the period = 300 acres/30 years × 10 years = 100 acres. The same number of acres is cut

each period (100 ac/decade), the same harvest volume is produced each period (350 thousand cu ft/decade), and volume growth is the same in each period (950 − 600 = 350). Harvest ($H_R$) equals growth ($G_R$). A fully regulated forest!

Of course, most uneven-aged forests are not of a single site and species. Thus regulation of a forest to provide a stable harvest over time is usually more challenging than discussed here. As described under the even-aged case, we could recognize acreages of equal productivity to harvest every period and also separately regulate land allocations with very different management regimes. But the principles of forest regulation still hold!

## The Regulated Forest and Long-Term Sustained Yield

Provision of a sustained yield of timber products in the long run was a foundational tenet of classical forestry. *Sustained*

Table 17.5  *A regulated uneven-aged forest of 300 acres of loblolly pine stands on a 30-year cutting cycle based on a hypothetical inventory and growth and 10-year periods.* Notice that the stands are identified by time since last harvest instead of age and that harvest removes 77% (3.50/4.50) of the volume per acre in the stands being harvested

| Period/ Inventory status | Time since last harvest (years) | Inventory | | | Periodic Harvest | | Periodic Growth | |
|---|---|---|---|---|---|---|---|---|
| | | Acres | Volume per acre cu ft (thousands) | Total volume cu ft (thousands) | Acres | cu ft (thousands) | Acres | cu ft (thousands) |
| **Period t** | | | | | | | | |
| Before harvest | 30 | 100 | 4.5 | 450 | | | | |
| | 20 | 100 | 3.0 | 300 | | | | |
| | 10 | 100 | 2.0 | 200 | | | | |
| | 0 | 0 | 0 | 0 | | | | |
| | Total | 300 | | 950 | | | | |
| | | | | | 100 | 350 | | |
| After harvest, before growth | 30 | 0 | 0 | 0 | | | | |
| | 20 | 100 | 3.0 | 300 | | | | |
| | 10 | 100 | 2.0 | 200 | | | | |
| | 0 | 100 | 1.0 | 100 | | | | |
| | Total | 300 | | 600 | | | | |
| | | | | | | | 300 | 350 |
| **Period t+1** | | | | | | | | |
| After growth, before harvest | 30 | 100 | 4.5 | 450 | | | | |
| | 20 | 100 | 3.0 | 300 | | | | |
| | 10 | 100 | 2.0 | 200 | | | | |
| | 0 | 0 | 0 | 0 | | | | |
| | Total | 300 | | 950 | | | | |

* Calculation of harvest, growth, and inventory for a regulated 300-acre loblolly pine forest to be managed on a 30-year cutting cycle. Ten-year periods are used. At the beginning of each period, cut A/CC × years in a period = 300 acres/30 years × 10 years = 100 acres, and then grow. Harvest priority rule: Cut the stands that have grown the longest without harvest.

*yield* became the watchword of professional forestry in the US, both as a goal and a cap on short-term harvest levels, and calculation of *long-term sustained yield* became a central feature of forest planning. Those terms have similar definitions (Helms, 1998):

> *Sustained yield*— . . . (1) the yield that a forest can produce continuously at a given intensity of management—*note* sustained yield management implies continuous production so planned as to achieve, at the earliest practical time, a balance between increment and cutting, (2) the achievement and maintenance in perpetuity of a high-level annual or regular periodic output of the various renewable resources without impairment of the productivity of the land. (p. 181)

> *Long-term sustained yield (LTSY)*—the highest uniform wood yield that may be sustained under a specific management intensity consistent with multiple-use objectives on lands being managed for timber production. (p. 109)

Construction of a fully regulated forest automatically provides an estimate of the long-term sustained yield (LTSY) for that forest[4]—it is the equilibrium harvest ($H_R$) and growth ($G_R$) associated with the regulated forest.

In a fully regulated forest: $LTSY = H_R = G_R$.

## Achieving a Fully Regulated Forest

The *regulation* problem that traditionally faced forest managers was how to *convert* the existing forest over time into the desired forest. How do we get from here to there? And how long will it take?

Given the existing forest and the desired fully regulated forest, classical *harvest scheduling* addressed the question of how many acres and how much volume should be cut over time to move the existing forest to the desired forest. Classical methods generally fell into one of two categories:

1. Area control—focus on the area harvested.
2. Volume control—focus on the volume harvested.

### Area Control

The principle of area control is very simple: harvest a set number of acres each year or period. The resultant volume harvested is determined by the timber on the area scheduled for cutting each year. Here we are interested in cutting the number of acres per year that will move the forest toward a regulated condition.

**Application to Even-Aged Management**    Area control is the quickest way to attain a regulated forest in even-aged management. As before, suppose we have a forest of 300 acres and our desired regulated forest would put those acres on a 30-year rotation as shown in Table 17.3. Using area control, we would schedule 300 ÷ 30 = 10 acres for harvest and regeneration each year or 100 acres per decade—the same number of acres per year we would harvest in a regulated forest. Through this process, we would achieve a balanced age-class distribution (a regulated forest) in one rotation of 30 years. Applied to a forest that is initially irregular in age-class structure or volumes per acre, though, area control can yield a fluctuating timber harvest volume while regulation is being achieved.

To illustrate the use of area control to convert an unregulated forest into a regulated forest, lets utilize the even-aged loblolly pine forest from Table 17.3 above while assuming that it now has 200 acres of 40-year-old timber with an average volume per acre of 2.5 thousand cu ft/acre and 100 acres of timber with an average volume of 1.8 thousand cu ft/acre. The older stands (age 40) had never been harvested; not surprisingly these natural stands contain lower timber yields than we would expect from the future managed forest of the same age. On the other hand, the younger stands (age 20) have been previously harvested and then planted; they are growing at the rate we would expect in the future forest.

We wish to achieve a regulated forest managed on a 30-year rotation with area control. As expected, a regulated forest is achieved in three periods (30 years) (Table 17.6 and Figure 17.3). Also, as expected, harvest of an equal acreage in each of those three periods produced a somewhat irregular harvest volume (Figure 17.4).

**Application to Uneven-Aged Management**    Area control can also be used to guide the amount of acreage entered for harvesting each year in an uneven-aged forest. We saw earlier that once an uneven-aged forest is fully regulated, an equal area would be entered each year of the cutting cycle, removing an equal volume. For the unregulated forest, however, cutting an equal area per year does not guarantee achievement of the regulated forest in one cutting cycle as the residual growing stock we leave each time may not have the capability to grow into the desired condition after only one harvest. Thus it may take more than one cutting cycle to achieve a regulated forest. As with even-aged stands, applying area control as a way of bringing an unregulated uneven-aged forest into a regulated condition over one or more cutting cycles may cause irregular volume flows.

---

4 In analysis of a fully regulated forest, multiple-use objectives would be considered, as needed, in selecting the forest available for timber production and the management intensity to apply.

Table 17.6 *Achieving a regulated forest in one 30-year rotation using area control*[*]

| Period/ Inventory status | Age (years) | Inventory | | | Periodic Harvest | |
|---|---|---|---|---|---|---|
| | | Acres | Volume per acre cu ft (thousands) | Total volume cu ft (thousands) | Acres | Volume cu ft (thousands) |
| **Period 1** | | | | | | |
| Before harvest | 40 | 200 | 2.5 | 500 | 100 | 250 |
| | 20 | 100 | 1.8 | 180 | | |
| | | | | 680 | | |
| After harvest, before growth | 40 | 100 | 2.5 | 250 | | |
| | 20 | 100 | 1.8 | 180 | | |
| | 0 | 100 | 0 | 0 | | |
| | | | | 430 | | |
| **Period 2** | | | | | | |
| Before harvest | 50 | 100 | 3.0 | 300 | 100 | 300 |
| | 30 | 100 | 3.5 | 350 | | |
| | 10 | 100 | .70 | 70 | | |
| | | | | 720 | | |
| After harvest, before growth | 30 | 100 | 3.5 | 350 | | |
| | 10 | 100 | 0.7 | 70 | | |
| | 0 | 100 | 0 | 0 | | |
| | | | | 420 | | |
| **Period 3** | | | | | | |
| Before harvest | 40 | 100 | 4.3 | 430 | 100 | 430 |
| | 20 | 100 | 1.8 | 180 | | |
| | 10 | 100 | 0.7 | 70 | | |
| | | | | 680 | | |
| After harvest, before growth | 20 | 100 | 1.8 | 180 | | |
| | 10 | 100 | 0.7 | 70 | | |
| | 0 | 100 | 0 | 0 | | |
| | | | | 250 | | |
| **Period 4** | | | | | | |
| Before harvest | 30 | 100 | 3.5 | 350 | 100 | 350 |
| | 20 | 100 | 1.8 | 180 | | |
| | 10 | 100 | 0.7 | 70 | | |
| | | | | 600 | | |
| After harvest, before growth | 20 | 100 | 1.8 | 180 | | |
| | 10 | 100 | 0.7 | 70 | | |
| | 0 | 100 | 0 | 0 | | |
| | | | | 250 | | |

[*] Calculation of harvest, growth, and inventory from a 300-acre loblolly pine forest on site 90 to be managed on a 30-year rotation under area control. Ten-year periods are used. At the beginning of each period, cut A/R × years in a period = 300 acres/30 years × 10 years = 100 acres and then grow. Harvest priority rule: Cut oldest stands first. Growth can be calculated by comparing the inventories in adjacent periods.

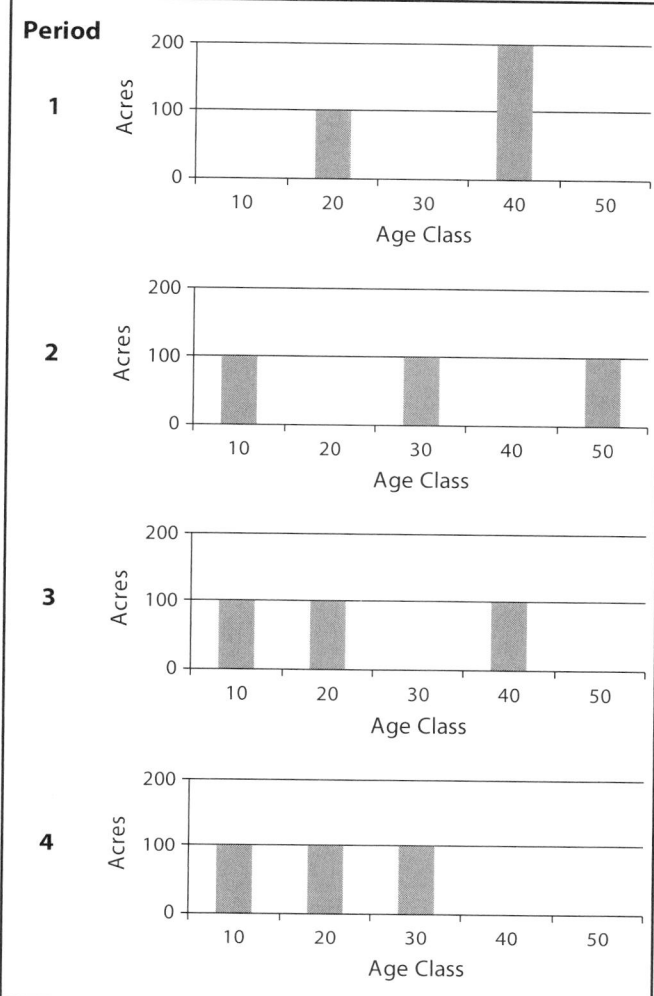

Figure 17.3 *Acres by age class on a 300-acre loblolly pine forest, before harvest in each period while achieving a regulated forest in one 30-year rotation using area control.*

## Volume Control

In volume control, we focus on how much volume to cut each year. The acres to cut are then chosen to satisfy this volume. Classical approaches generally focused on analysis of the amount and distribution of the growing stock and its increment, with foresters creating numerous formulas for approximating the volume to harvest that would enable a stable harvest volume during the conversion period (Bettinger, Boston, Siry, & Grebner, 2017; Davis & Johnson, 1987).

The ability of volume control to provide a quick estimate of a stable harvest level for an unmanaged forest made it a popular way to calculate the *allowable cut*. On the old-growth national forests of the western US, volume control techniques found much use in even-aged management. Also, they were applied widely with uneven-aged management—the explicit adjustment of growing stock inherent in uneven-aged management proved a natural application. However, lack of formal control on area cut per year made it difficult to quickly move a forest to a regulated condition.

## Combining Area and Volume Controls

Because forest planners generally had both area and volume goals, they developed approaches for considering them both, such as *area-volume check*, that would enable them to better control both aspects of the harvest scheduling problem. We can illustrate area-volume check with the loblolly pine forest to which we previously applied area control to achieve a regulated forest (Table 17.6). In that application, our simulation resulted in an irregular harvest volume—one that starts below the long-term sustained yield, rises above it, and then falls back to it. (Figure 17.4). Foresters generally found a projected harvest decline as counter to their commitment to a sustained yield of timber harvest. Therefore, they would test *even-flow* harvest volumes at or below the long-term sustained yield to assess whether these volumes could be maintained over a rotation and still (perhaps approximately) achieve the age-class distribution of the acres that they sought.[5]

Let's try a harvest level equal to the long-term sustained yield (350 thousand cu ft/decade). We can maintain that harvest for three 10-year periods (one rotation),

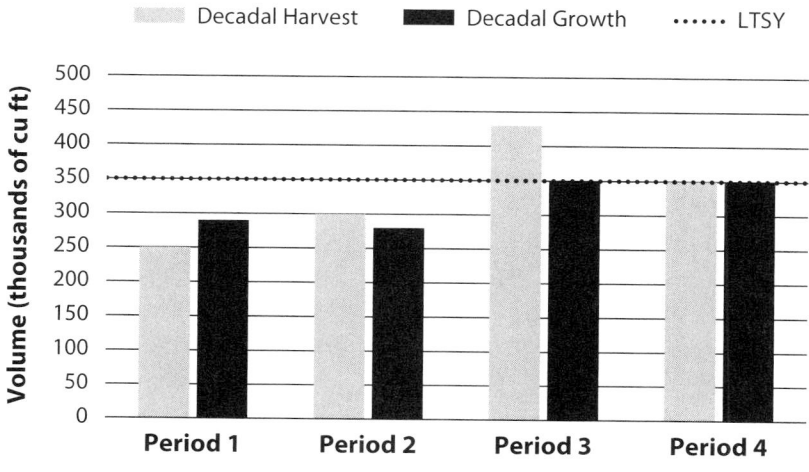

Figure 17.4 *Inventory, harvest, and growth on a 300-acre loblolly pine forest in each 10-year period while achieving a regulated forest in one 30-year rotation using area control (LTSY = long-term sustained yield).*

---

5 This irregular harvest could be smoothed by shifting some of the harvest to the younger age class and also allowing an increase in harvest over time. Foresters generally were reluctant to shift harvest to the more rapidly growing, younger stands; modeling an increasing harvest over time was possible, but the pencil and paper techniques of those days made such refinements difficult.

Table 17.7 *Simulating an even-flow harvest level equal to the long-term sustained yield*[*]

| Period/ Inventory status | Age (years) | Inventory | | | Periodic Harvest | |
|---|---|---|---|---|---|---|
| | | Acres | Volume per acre cu ft (thousands) | Total volume cu ft (thousands) | Acres | Volume cu ft (thousands) |
| **Period 1** | | | | | | |
| Before harvest | 40 | 200 | 2.5 | 500 | 140 | 350 |
| | 20 | 100 | 1.8 | 180 | 0 | 0 |
| | | | | 680 | 140 | 350 |
| After harvest, before growth | 40 | 60 | 2.5 | 150 | | |
| | 20 | 100 | 1.8 | 180 | | |
| | 0 | 140 | 0 | 0 | | |
| | | | | 330 | | |
| **Period 2** | | | | | | |
| Before harvest | 50 | 60 | 3.0 | 180 | 60 | 180 |
| | 30 | 100 | 3.5 | 350 | 48.6 | 170 |
| | 10 | 140 | 0.7 | 98 | 0 | 0 |
| | | | | 628 | 108.6 | 350 |
| After harvest, before growth | 30 | 51.4 | 3.5 | 180 | | |
| | 10 | 140 | 0.7 | 98 | | |
| | 0 | 108.6 | 0 | 0 | | |
| | | | | 278 | | |
| **Period 3** | | | | | | |
| Before harvest | 40 | 51.4 | 4.3 | 221.0 | 51.4 | 221.0 |
| | 20 | 140 | 1.8 | 252.0 | 71.7 | 129.0 |
| | 10 | 108.6 | 0.7 | 76.0 | 0 | 0 |
| | | | | 549.0 | 123.1 | 350.0 |
| After harvest, before growth | 40 | 0 | 4.3 | 0 | | |
| | 20 | 68.3 | 1.8 | 122.9 | | |
| | 10 | 108.6 | 0.7 | 76.0 | | |
| | 0 | 123.1 | 0 | 0 | | |
| | | | | 198.9 | | |
| **Period 4** | | | | | | |
| Before harvest | 30 | 68.3 | 3.5 | 239.1 | | |
| | 20 | 108.6 | 1.8 | 195.5 | | |
| | 10 | 123.1 | 0.7 | 86.2 | | |
| | | | | 520.8 | | |

[*] Calculation of harvest, growth, and inventory from a 300-acre loblolly pine forest on site 90 under a harvest of 350 thousand cu ft/period for three periods. Ten-year periods are used. At the beginning of each period, cut 350,000 cu ft and then grow. Harvest priority rule: Cut the oldest stands first. Growth can be calculated by comparing the inventories in adjacent periods.

but at the cost that our age-class structure has not achieved the desired age-class distribution of 100 acres in each of the three 10-year age classes after three periods of harvest (Table 17.7, Figure 17.5)—we have fewer acres in the older age class and more acres in the younger age classes than desired. Thus, we leave the forest in a depleted condition, without the ability to maintain a harvest equal to the long-term sustained yield in the immediate future. Looking at these results, foresters might then lower the harvest level somewhat and do the simulation again and again until they found a result that balances their volume and area goals.

With the advent of computer-based algorithms, analysts developed a wide variety of harvest scheduling models that allowed rapid simulation of harvests and age-class structures for many rotations. (See Davis et al., 2001, and Bettinger et al., 2017, for a detailed examination of these approaches.) We will use some of these techniques in Chapter 19 to explore creation of a harvest schedule under ecological forestry.

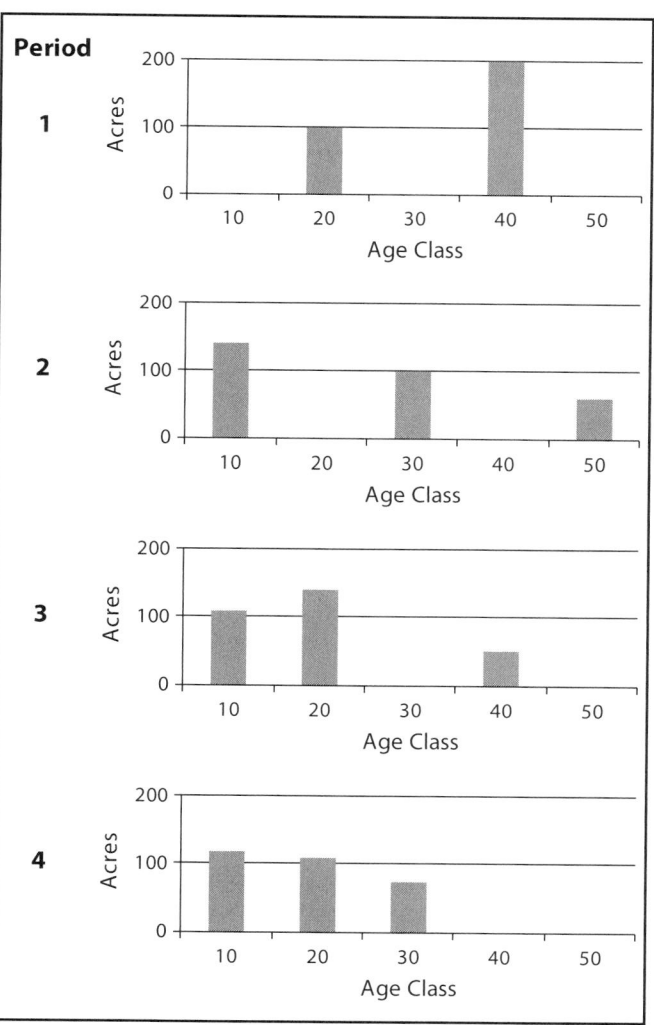

Figure 17.5 *Acres by age class on a 300-acre loblolly pine forest before harvest in each period while harvesting the long-term sustained yield.*

## Relevance to Ecological Forestry

Foresters developed the ideas of the regulated forest, area control, and volume control with the best of intentions—to sustain the benefits of forests in the long run. True, the approach was timber dominated and assumed a stable, unchanging future. Still, it began in the United States as a courageous attempt to change forest exploitation into forest conservation. It certainly can be argued that foresters continued to apply these classical rules after their usefulness was exhausted, but we should not forget the beginnings and purpose of these techniques and their importance to the forestry profession in its early days.

As we have expressed in this book, we now anchor our thinking about forest conservation and management in ecosystem complexity, disturbance processes, and a world of change and uncertainty. Thus, methods anchored in concepts of timber primacy, few disturbances, and a stable world may not have the appeal they once did.

Relatively fewer landowners now focus on achieving a regulated forest, in the classic sense, as their primary objective. Large corporate owners, such as TIMOs, increasingly focus on maximizing net present value, playing the markets as best they can. Family forest owners have a multitude of objectives as we discussed in Chapter 6. Our national forests generally focus more on achieving ecological objectives as we will discuss in Chapter 20. States and Indian tribes often do calculate harvest levels with methods that have strong linkages back to volume control through their adherence to sustained yield, but that objective is often subsumed within many other ecological, economic, and social goals.

Still, at a more abstract level, ecological forestry is faced with issues similar to those of classical regulation. First, ecological forestry embraces the idea of maintaining a balanced mixture of forest structural conditions or developmental stages over time (see Chapters 3 and 5). While the ideal is rarely the perfectly regulated forest described above, the general goal of achieving a distribution of forest structural conditions or developmental stages still holds. Second, the relationship between short-term harvest levels and the sustained yield that the forest might produce in perpetuity (the long-term sustained yield) is often of interest in ecological forestry. However, the function of the long-term sustained yield in controlling harvest is more problematic, especially where forest restoration is a primary goal. Third, whether ecological forestry "pays" remains an enduring issue, and timber harvest is still a primary way in which revenue is produced for the landowner. Thus, estimating likely harvests and associated revenue over time is an important activity under ecological forestry. We expand on these ideas below and provide a detailed example of their application in Chapter 19.

## The "Regulated Forest" and Ecological Forestry

The *fully regulated forest* concept emphasizes maintaining a variety of age classes or structural conditions to ensure a flow of benefits over time. This idea is valuable for ecological forestry, even if the desired structural conditions are different from those of the past and an equal acreage of each condition is not sought.

As we noted in Chapters 2 and 14, maintaining a variety of structural stages of the different forest types in a forest is the foundation of providing for biodiversity. Thus, the idea of a *balanced distribution of age classes or structural stages* has value in ecological forestry. But what does balance mean here? Some might argue for the distribution of structural stages that will enable the flow of ecological benefits from a forest, using history to provide information on "what worked" in the past. While this is only a starting point, estimates of historical structural-stage distributions do provide an invaluable context for evaluating the appropriate balance.

Wimberley (2002) developed such a historical distribution of age classes/structural stages for the Oregon Coast Range from simulations of wildfire disturbance processes, as we discussed in Chapter 5. Compared to historical conditions, the contemporary landscape in the province has much less old forest and diverse early preforest and much more young, simplified forest. From an ecological standpoint, we would probably want to conserve and protect any remaining mature and old forest while directing harvest toward that simplified young forest, being careful to encourage the development of diverse early seral ecosystems in openings created along the way. In this manner, we would have a set of age/structural benchmarks to help guide management—in some ways, they are conceptually similar to the classical approach of moving the existing forest to the regulated forest!

Further, as we also discussed in Chapter 14 on biodiversity, managers may wish to focus on providing specific structural stages or combinations of stages to help conserve species of interest. Whether we are interested in diverse early seral for ruffed grouse or mature forest for the red cockaded woodpecker, managers of large forests often need a representative amount of the different structural stages. Also, providing stand-level complexity, including cohorts of different ages and biological legacies at harvest, can help meet biodiversity goals.

## Sustained Yield Management and Ecological Forestry

A commitment to sustained yield management is deeply engrained in forestry. In addition, it has intuitive appeal to the public. Not surprisingly, the US Congress has made sustained yield management a foundational element of federal lands management: a commitment to sustained yield appears in the Multiple-Use Sustained Yield Act, the National Forest Management Act, the Federal Land Management and Policy Act, the Oregon and California Lands Act, and many other laws.

Duerr and Duerr (1975, p. 38) illustrated the appeal of sustained yield to public forest managers:

> Suppose you are at the head of a government bureau which manages public forestland. Consider your obligations respecting the timber resource. You are charged with the awesome responsibility for husbanding and servicing and bringing into use a vast stock of growing timber. . . . You are faced with the obligation to decide how much of your timber you will make available for harvest, decade by decade, into the future. How will you go about making such a decision?
>
> You can cling to the security of the faith you learned at your mother's knee, that is, at the knee of the Founders. You can do what virtually every public forest administrator in the Western world has done for the past few centuries: take shelter in a policy of sustained yield. Under this policy, you will manage the forest to the goal of producing the same, hopefully large, physical quantity of wood period by period into the indefinite future. Under this policy, you will find peace with yourself.

Many states in the US practice sustained yield forestry on their own lands, as mentioned above, making sure that they can sustain their harvests into the distant future. Also, federal forestry in the US has historically embraced this approach.

Looking internationally, McDermott et al. (2010) evaluated limits placed on harvest around the world, that is, limits placed on the volume of timber that may be harvested over time from a specific area. In the cases we reported (Table 7.3), most public forests have a requirement that the harvest stay within the sustained yield capacity, some with an added requirement of a projected nondeclining yield of harvest. Requirements for private forests are more variable.

In addition, certification schemes, such as the Forest Stewardship Council and the Sustainable Forestry Initiative, call for limiting harvest to the sustained yield capacity. However, as we noted in Chapter 16, the Forest Stewardship Council calls for a tighter set of controls on both harvest and calculation of sustained yield capacity than does the Sustainable Forestry Initiative.

## Calculating Long-Term Sustained Yield in Ecological Forestry

The calculation of a long-term sustained yield (LTSY) for a forest—*the sustained yield capacity*—was closely linked to the regulated forest in our initial discussion of this concept above. However, a forest goal of equal acres or productivity in each age class up to some rotation age may be inconsistent with other ecological and social objectives, especially given the current condition of the forest. Thus we need to dig deeper to identify core elements of LTSY.

Calculation of LTSY, under classical definitions, has three core requirements:

1. a commitment to long-term timber production, without which calculation of LTSY is not possible since it is not clear what role that harvest will play in management;

2. a description of the silvicultural system and management intensity that will be utilized; and,

3. an ability to calculate a yield curve that reflects the designated silvicultural system and management intensity so that growth and yield can be calculated.

We will provide a few examples of these calculations for a hypothetical 500-acre forest that will be managed for timber production as one of its goals using ecological forestry prescriptions.

### For Forests with Infrequent, High Severity Disturbances

Assume that we wish to emulate natural stand development over time as the best approximation of what our ecological forestry prescriptions will produce. Further, we conclude that a 100-year rotation would be needed for the forest to develop the structural characteristics we seek. To estimate the yields from such a future forest, we might look to existing natural stands of 90–110 years of age to approximate likely stand volumes under ecological forestry prescriptions, or to historical information on natural stand yields, or to a growth simulator to approximate these yields.

We will need to account for the legacy structures that we will leave. Let's assume we will leave 30% of the stands we harvest as a legacy, mostly in aggregated retention, but also some individual trees as dispersed retention.

We can then calculate the LTSY as either annual growth or annual harvest:

Acres = 500

Rotation age = 100

Percent of stand volume removed at final harvest = 70%

Average of natural stand yields at age 100 = 10,000 cu ft/ac

LTSY/yr as harvest on the forest = 10,000 cu ft/ac
× 500 ac/100 years × .7 = 35,000 cu ft/yr

LTSY/ac/yr as growth = 10,000 cu ft/ac/100 years
× .7 = 70 cu ft/ac/yr

LTSY/yr as growth on the forest = 70 cu ft/ac/yr
× 500 ac = 35,000 cu ft/yr

One complaint with our approach could be that we have not accounted sufficiently for the growth effects on the future stands of leaving the biological legacy. Two responses to that could be: (1) we would expect existing or historical natural stands to have these kinds of legacies so their growth effects should already be built into estimates that use those sources, and (2) we would expect that aggregate retention, suggested here as the primary retention strategy, would limit those growth-suppressing effects as compared to dispersed retention. Still, we may decide to apply an additional yield reduction. In sum, we believe that this type of calculation provides a strong foundation for the LTSY estimate.

**For Frequent-Fire Forests**   Assume we wish to emulate historical structures and densities of frequent-fire forests but also wish to use harvest as a tool to help achieve them; that is, we want to harvest periodically the trees that grow into the stand under and around the mature and old-growth trees. Further, looking at growth rates in natural stands in the area with a full complement of mature and old-growth trees, we find that the growth rate of younger trees in these stands averages approximately 50 cu ft/ac/yr. We also plan to run fire through the stands after harvest and assume that will consume (on a yearly average) 10 cu ft/yr. In addition, we want to leave 10 cu ft/ac/yr for trees that will replace the mature/old growth as it dies, leaving an average removable growth of 30 cu ft/ac/yr.

LTSY/year for the forest = 30 cu ft/ac/yr
× 500 ac = 15,000 cu ft/yr

Of course, we will not visit every acre every year, but we will visit each acre once during the cutting cycle, removing the accumulated growth, net of what we wish to leave and what we expect to kill with prescribed fire.

Are these calculations rough and approximate? Yes they are, but they do make an honest attempt to estimate LTSY. And they can be revealing about the long-run implications of our plans for the forest. Isn't that the major purpose of forest planning anyway?

## A Place for Classical Approaches in Ecological Forestry

Suppose you wish to develop a forest plan using the principles of ecological forestry. How might you use area and volume control in this planning effort? Let's demonstrate these ideas for an infrequent, high-severity landscape continuing the example above where we wish to manage the forest on a 100-year rotation (Box 17.1). On the average, we would need to harvest approximately 1% of the forest area per year or 10% per decade. In addition, we might seek to use the LTSY as the upper bound on harvests through time. We could apply something like area-volume check, illustrated by Table 17.7, to our forest inventory with the goal of harvesting approximately 10% of the forest per decade while providing a volume at or below the LTSY. In addition, we might want the harvest volume to be fairly stable or increasing through time. Fortunately, we now have computer models that make the balancing of all these goals and constraints relatively easy, as we demonstrate in Chapter 19.

## Limits of Classical Approaches under Ecological Forestry

The classical regulation approach of limiting harvest to the LTSY of the future forest is still part of forest regulations in many parts of the world (Chapter 7). However, this calculation and use of LTSY may unduly limit restoration goals in some ownerships for at least two reasons:

- It may be desirable, from an ecological standpoint to rapidly restore a degraded landscape, with the result that the harvest exceeds the LTSY in the short run, and then declines to a lower level in the long run once the landscape has been restored. This situation may often occur on public lands that focus on restoration goals.

- Relatively little of the restoration landscape may be committed to long-term timber production. Harvest may be a tool to achieve restoration in the short run without allocation of much of the landscape to timber production goals. Since the classical approach to calculating LTSY applies to lands that have timber production as a goal, that calculation in this case may produce a very low LTSY compared to desired short-term harvest. As in the first reason, this situation may often occur on public lands that focus on restoration goals.

For these reasons, the classical use of LTSY as a cap on harvest over time, as a core element of sustainability, may be limited under ecological forestry. In Chapter 19, we will examine management of a family forest in which the owners focus on forest condition, diversity, and financial value of the forest at the end of their planning periods as their measures of sustainability. In Chapter 20, we will examine the revised approach to planning adopted by the Forest Service for the national forests in which they focus on ensuring ecological integrity as its core element of sustainability, reinterpreting how LTSY and harvest flow restrictions interact with forest restoration.

In addition, the approaches to forest planning discussed in Chapters 19 and 20 and in Box 17.1 simulate activities and outcomes for two to five decades into the future—a fairly short simulation period as compared to recent, computer-based applications of classical approaches (Davis et al., 2001). The uncertainties of the future that we have discussed throughout this book, including climate change,

make us question the usefulness of multi-rotation projections of growth, yield, and harvest, along with associated projections of economic, social, and environmental conditions, to ensure sustainability.

These long-term projections can be especially troublesome when a goal is applied that links projected levels of some input or outcome across planning periods. As discussed in Chapter 9, when we analyzed the implications of requiring a nondeclining amount of capital through time, such linking relationships have the benefit of increasing the importance of the future in considering what should be done in the short term. They also have the effect of increasing the importance of uncertain assumptions about the way the world will function in the future on what should be done in the short term. As an example, assumptions

---

## Box 17.1  Applying classical approaches in forest planning under ecological forestry

Bureau of Land Management (BLM) forests in western Oregon were formed mainly from lands given by the federal government to a railroad company as part of an agreement to build a rail line through western Oregon and northern California. The lands were reclaimed from the company after it violated the terms of its agreement. Then, in 1937, Congress passed the O&C Act calling for the BLM to provide a sustained yield of timber harvest from these lands that would contribute to the economic vitality of local industries and communities. Meeting this mandate while also meeting other federal laws, such as the Endangered Species Act, makes BLM's forest planning especially challenging. Many pieces of legislation have been introduced in Congress over time to clarify how the BLM balances all the requirements they face. Some of them have mandated ecological forestry, and Norm Johnson has worked with the agency to model activities, age classes, and harvest levels over time under ecological forestry for *moist forests*—those associated with an infrequent, high-severity fire regime—using the agency's computerized harvest simulator.

First, we wanted to estimate LTSY along the lines described above, assuming a 100-year rotation and significant retention at harvest. Toward that end, we examined existing natural stands nearly 100 years of age in the BLM inventory and found that their average growth rate was slightly more than 600 bd ft/ac/yr over their life. Multiplying that growth rate times the portion of the stand we would remove (.67) times the total acres allocated to timber production (approximately 400,000 acres) enabled us to estimate (roughly) the LTSY associated with the application of this strategy:

$$600 \times .67 \times 400{,}000 = 160 \text{ million bd ft/yr}$$

We used this LTSY as both a goal and upper limit on the harvest level through time. We then set the requirement of harvesting 10% of the available forest per decade or 40,000

acres, based on an area control approach (A/R × number of years in a period = 400,000 acres/100 years × 10 years = 40,000 acres/decade). Some questions about this approach might be:

***What kinds of stands were available for harvest?*** The 400,000-acre inventory contained stands up to 80 years of age. Mature and old-growth stands were excluded from the harvest calculations, recognizing the ecological importance and shortage (compared to history) of these older stands. Most of the stands under 80 years of age were the result of past clearcuts.

***What stands were selected for harvest?*** Ideally, we would harvest stands near the desired rotation age of 100 years. However, initially, we have only stands 80 years or younger available for harvest. Therefore we allowed the harvest to come from stands 60 years or older, selecting stands with a variety of ages and volumes/acre to ensure a stable or rising harvest. By the fifth decade, stands 90–110 years of age provided most of the harvest.

***How far into the future did the simulation look?*** We looked out 50 years. Traditionally, we would look out at least one rotation and perhaps more to make sure the harvest could be sustained far into the future. However, given the uncertainties of the future, we believe we are fooling ourselves to think we can do quantitative simulations with any accuracy for hundreds of years. Rather, we used a combination of a LTSY cap, a limit on acres harvested per decade, and a check on the inventory after harvest at year 50 to make sure that we were not leaving the forest in a depleted condition. If the inventory was in a depleted condition at the end of our simulation, as we found with our example of area-volume check (Table 17.7 and Figure 17.5), we could reduce the acres harvested per decade and try again.

about growth and yield in the distant future in harvest scheduling simulations will include assumptions about the effect of coming climate change that can have a significant impact on what volume might be harvested in the near term. While we can do sensitivity analysis, in which we change assumptions about the future we expect and redo the analysis, the variety of uncertainties that we may need to address as we move out beyond a few decades can be formidable.

The difference between our view of forest planning and the classical view of it can be at least partially captured by the difference between seeing the problems as a mystery and seeing them as a puzzle, as we described in Chapter 1. When you can proceed under the assumption of a stable and unchanging future, which is implicit, at least to a significant degree, in the classical approach, you can view forest planning as a puzzle in which the challenge is to find all the pieces and figure out how to fit them together. On the other hand, when you work under the assumption of an uncertain and potentially chaotic future, as we do here, we believe you might be better served by viewing forest planning as a mystery in which judgment is needed as much as knowledge. In the latter case, you might be better served by undertaking detailed projections for only a short time into the future, where you have some confidence in relationships, and focus on leaving the forest at the conclusion of that projection period in a condition such that it can provide a robust response to what might come beyond that time.

We have taken this latter view of forest planning as a mystery in which judgment plays a central role in Chapter 19 where we provide a detailed application of forest planning for ecological forest management. In this approach, we develop a set of long-term goals for the forest and simulate activities and harvests associated with moving toward those goals for only a few decades. Inevitably, this approach requires judgments, including how to achieve a forest by the end of the simulation period that can produce a multitude of desired ecosystem services into the distant future, given the many uncertainties about the future. Toward that end, we suggest a combination of four types of controls or checks: (1) a variety of restrictions on the activities and harvests during the simulation period, such as limiting the acres harvested, the volume harvested, and the amount that can be removed from particular structural stages, (2) certain conditions that must be attained by the end of the simulation period, such as the amount of inventory volume or value that must be left on the forest or the structural conditions that must be attained, (3) assessing the resulting forest at the end of the simulated period about whether we would leave it in a depleted condition relative to its ability to provide ecosystem services, as we did in our analysis in this chapter, and (4) embedding the overall analysis in the tenets of ecological forestry.

We also find a variant of this approach to forest planning in Chapter 20 on planning the national forests of the US. That approach limits the detailed simulations to a shorter period than historically used and employs a variety of guides and controls to achieve a forest that, at the conclusion of the simulation period, will be in a better condition to deal with both expected changes and uncertainties of the future.

## Conclusions

*In many ways, the perfectly regulated forest and the methods of achieving it reflects the view that foresters can completely control their forest environments, happily focus on timber production, and live forever in a world of great stability*—the classical tenets of faith in forestry. Such an approach may seem badly out of step with the problems and uncertainties of forest sustainability we face today.

*When we move to a higher level of abstraction, though, many of the classical ideas still provide a useful framework.* They highlight the importance of seeking long-run goals, understanding where these goals lead in terms of desired structures and developmental stages, developing a strategy to achieve them, calculating the timber harvest and other ecosystem services that the management strategy will produce for a time, and checking to ensure that we will leave the forest in a better condition at the end of the planning periods.

*Moreover, we need to embed these ideas in the tenets of ecological forestry* that we described in Chapter 1:

1. *Restore and sustain the integrity of forest and associated ecosystems.* Ecosystems, in all their complexity and variety, are the source of the ecosystem services that we seek and upon which we depend. This is a fundamental principle of ecological forestry. In this book, we embed the retention of complexity and integrity of ecosystems in our approaches to forest management planning—even while acknowledging the daunting nature of this task.

2. *Develop policies and management practices that consider and sustain a broad array of ecosystem services.* We need to emphasize policies that perform well in a variety of ecological and social environments rather than maximize some singular good, service, or income—that is, emphasize policies that provide multiple benefits even if they are "inefficient" in regard to any single benefit.

3. *Be attentive and adaptive to new scientific and technical developments and to changes in societal goals, priorities, and concerns.* Goals, knowledge, and social context will undergo continued change and "once and for all" solutions are not possible. Constant learning will be needed for adaptation and survival.

4. ***Choose management approaches that reduce risks to forest assets and increase future options.*** Change, uncertainty, and surprise will likely dominate the future. Managers can help prepare for this uncertainty by selecting management approaches that will reduce risks to the forest and increase future options. Heterogeneity at multiple spatial scales, creating redundancy, and increasing resistance and resilience in the face of potential disturbance will help forests survive and adapt in the face of risk and uncertainty. Managing forests to increase options will likely be served by many of the same approaches that are undertaken to reduce risks—by maintaining structurally and compositionally diverse forests.

We will utilize these tenets in Chapter 19 when we illustrate forest planning under ecological forest management.

*The intuitive mind is a sacred gift and the rational mind is a faithful servant* — ALBERT EINSTEIN

# CHAPTER 18

# Making Decisions: Naturalistic and Structured Approaches

Imagine that you and your brothers and sisters have just inherited your father's 2,500-acre forest. Your father knew the forest well and had been gradually harvesting some of the trees but did not have much of a written plan. You went there as a child but have not been there since. The deed requires that you keep the forest intact but has few other stipulations except to manage the forest on a sustainable basis. You and your siblings would like some income from timber harvest on this forest, among many other values that you find in it. Thus, you could face a myriad of decisions about how to conserve and manage this forest (Table 18.1). What should you do? How will you sustain the forest and its benefits? Perhaps as important, how will you and your siblings decide what you should do?

We all make decisions on a regular basis. Few hours go by without the need for decisions both large and small: what to wear, where to eat lunch, whom to marry, which car or house to buy. How do we make those decisions? When can detailed analysis help? Both of these questions will be addressed in this chapter.

We would not survive with our sanity intact if we had to submit each decision we make in our lives to a detailed evaluation of objectives, alternatives, and implications, as is often prescribed in books on decision making. Thus, people have developed informal rules to help them get through the day. Table 18.2 offers a collection of such aphorisms, and, whether you see them as pithy, wise, or thoroughly disheartening, you'll probably recognize their guiding power. We reviewed a similar set of decision rules for classical forest management in Chapter 17 (Table 17.1).

In this chapter, we will review two different approaches to decision making that move beyond these informal rules: (1) *naturalistic decision-making* approaches that we employ every day as we encounter difficult decisions, relying on our knowledge, mental agility, intuition, and worldview, and (2) *structured decision-making* approaches that can be useful in situations of high informational and social complexity.

*A forester advising a forest owner in the southern United States ca. 1960. (US Forest Service photo courtesy of the Forest History Society, Durham NC)*

Table 18.1 *Examples of types of decisions needed in the conservation and management of forests*

| Type of decision | Examples |
| --- | --- |
| Management emphasis for different parts of the forest | Big game habitat, songbird and butterfly habitat, timber production, scenic protection, wildness |
| Types of activities allowed | Timber harvest, use of prescribed fire, hunting, fishing, hiking |
| Structure of forest | Acreage in different age classes or development stages |
| Size, shape, and spatial pattern of harvests | Small units versus large units; concentrated versus dispersed; overall heterogeneity |
| Regeneration harvest timing | Rotation age or cutting cycle length |
| Rate and pattern of timber harvest and associated revenue | Even flow or a fluctuating flow |
| Emphasis on revenue production | Break even or make a profit |

Naturalistic approaches have value in many situations, and we can increase their power through practice and application. Much of this chapter and the next, though, will be spent studying structured approaches, as they have dominated forest planning for many decades. Most generally, structured approaches involve the construction and use of quantitative models of the forest and the ecosystem services they can provide over time. These models can both help and hurt effective forest planning; thus, we will spend time discussing how to maximize the chance they will be helpful. Throughout, we want to emphasize that the two approaches to decision making are connected: structured forest planning enables us to test and improve our intuitive powers to understand how different planning alternatives (also called options or scenarios) relate to our objectives. We need both approaches to be successful in ecological forest management!

## Naturalistic Decision-Making Approaches [1]

We all have decision processes that quickly integrate our objectives, choices, and outcomes in an intuitive, almost unconscious way. How can we do that? A decision making model, called *naturalistic decision making*, has emerged through research that examines people who are making real decisions under typical conditions. This research looks at decisions by experienced decision makers under conditions of time pressure, high stakes, limited information, ill-defined objectives, poorly defined procedures, and dynamic conditions—exactly the context for many decisions in ecological forestry (Table 18.3) (Lach & Duncan, 2007).

Naturalistic decision making researchers have identified several strategies of effective decision making by studying decision makers in multiple settings (Lach & Duncan, 2007). It turns out that expert decision makers typically do not identify the range of possible alternatives, as prescribed by classical decision making—this is hard work and takes a lot of time. Instead, their experience allows them to characterize situations as familiar and identify a reasonable reaction. This strategy has been labeled *satisfying* by Simon (1957). Instead of optimizing across choices, he found that expert decision makers evaluate each choice on its own merits, rather than comparing it to other options—they may cycle through several iterations of choices as they determine the best fit, but they assess each choice based on its own characteristics. All of this happens quickly for expert decision makers, almost unconsciously, as they search for the right choice.

## The Power of Intuition and Mental Simulation

What are decision makers doing when they're quickly searching for and assessing options? One of the most pow-

Table 18.2 *Some informal rules for decision making*

1. Shoot first and ask questions later.
2. A bird in the hand is worth two in the bush.
3. Don't rock the boat.
4. It's now or never.
5. It's easier to seek forgiveness than ask permission.
6. An ounce of prevention is worth a pound of cure.
7. Go wisely and slowly. Those who rush, stumble and fall. [1]
8. When you come to a fork in the road, take it. [2]
9. What doesn't kill you makes you stronger. [3]
10. Between two evils, I generally pick the one I never tried before. [4]

---

1 The discussion on naturalistic decision making relies heavily on the ideas of Lach and Duncan (2007).

1 Shakespeare   2 Yogi Berra   3 Friedrich Nietzsche   4 Mae West

Table 18.3 *Characteristics of naturalistic tasks and settings*

| |
|---|
| Complex decisions |
| Ambiguous and uncertain information |
| Large quantity of information to consider |
| Poorly structured problems |
| Shifting, poorly defined, or competing objectives |
| Iterative outcomes due to ongoing evaluation |
| High stakes and consequences for decision makers |
| Involvement of organizational objectives and norms |
| Dynamic decision-making environment |
| Time constrained |

*Source:* Lach & Duncan (2007); Zsambok & Klein (1997).

erful decision skills turns out to be what is commonly called *intuition*, using our experience to recognize key patterns that indicate the dynamics of a situation (Klein, 1999). In a *New York Times* bestseller called *Blink*, Malcolm Gladwell (2005) described how these decisions happen: Expert decision makers are able to size up a decision and almost immediately know how to respond; based on their experience with similar situations, they are able to ascertain what is critical, what objectives to seek, what to expect, and how to respond. And it all happens in the blink of an eye—so quickly that it's hard to think of it as conscious consideration (Box 18.1)!

We can't usually tell someone how we used our experience to recognize patterns in a situation, as it seems almost

---

**Box 18.1  Chess anyone?**

An article on chess in the *New Yorker* magazine provides an intriguing mathematical perspective on decision making:

"With about $10^{128}$ possible unique games—vastly more than there are atoms in the known universe—chess is one of mankind's most complex activities. In an average arrangement on the board, white has thirty-five moves and black has thirty-five replies, yielding twelve hundred and twenty-five potential positions after one full turn. With subsequent moves each of these positions branches out exponentially in further lines of play—1.5 million positions after the second turn, 1.8 billion after the third—forming a gigantic map of potential games.

"How human beings confront this complexity and seize on a few good moves remains a mystery. Experienced players rely on subconscious faculties known variously as pattern recognition, visualization, and aesthetic sense. All are forms of educated guesswork—aids to making choices when certainty through exhaustive calculation is impossible—and may be summed up in a word: intuition" (Mueller, 2005, p. 64).

---

accidental and peripheral to our analytical thinking. Actually, intuition can play a major role in our decision making in many instances, helping us to quickly anticipate the consequences of good and bad decisions. People, whether they realize it or not, often use intuition—they inherently look for and retain or discard patterns in assessing the future consequences of their decisions—with that intuition activated long before they are aware of making decisions (Bechara et al., 1997).

In addition, expert decision makers are able to simulate future scenarios in their heads—to engage successfully in *mental simulation*. Albert Einstein's theory of relatively grew largely out of his *thought experiments* in which he could imagine the effect on time and space of being in one moving object (a train) and seeing another (Isaacson, 2008). Experienced forest and wildlife scientists can often simulate outcomes from actions with very little external assistance—in fact, we often count on that when we ask for an *expert opinion* (Box 18.2).

As a variation on these more informal decision processes, Charles Lindblom (1959) argued that decision makers *muddle through* problems, with only small policy changes resulting. They come up with satisfying solutions, after looking informally at incremental changes from the existing policy, and move on to the next problem without ever clearly articulating objectives or the full range of choices. Lindblom argued that this incremental decision making is probably the smartest way of doing things because it is so difficult to evaluate the consequences of more radical decisions.

In sum, intuition and mental simulation are two approaches employed by expert decision makers (Lach & Duncan, 2007). They see situations as patterns and relationships that grew out of past choices and understand how they can grow into the future. Thus they see many things that are invisible to the rest of us:

- Patterns the rest of us miss;
- Events that did not happen but should have;
- Individual parts as elements in a bigger picture;
- Mental models of the way things work;
- Opportunities and ways to improvise; and
- Events that either have already happened or are likely to happen soon.

Most of us, for better or worse, make many decisions with a combination of informal decision rules, intuition, and mental simulation, taking advantage of our background knowledge and our experience. Not surprisingly then, it is possible to help people become more expert decision makers relative to some issue or problem of interest—to be able to think and learn like experts by expanding their experience base, making decisions in many different situations, and developing realistic scenarios for practice in sizing up numerous situations. People and groups can also become more adept at mental simulations through decision premortems or imagining what the future looks like with their decision in place (Lach & Duncan, 2007).

## Group Decision Making

How does decision making in a group context, such as the collaborative approach described in Chapter 8, fit into naturalistic decision making? It appears that the value of group decision making is linked to the complexity of the problem. In particular, the more difficult the problem to be solved, the more beneficial it may be to work in a group (Lach & Duncan, 2007).

In fact, as tasks and problems become more complex and multilayered, it may be critical to move to a group decision process (Wilson, Timmel, & Miller, 2004). In *The Wisdom of Crowds*, Surowiecki (2004) reviews the research and experiences people have with group decision making. He describes how diversity among the decision makers is critical to good group decisions: if you can bring together a diverse group with varying degrees of knowledge and insight, "you're better off entrusting it with major decisions rather than leaving them in the hands of one or two people, no matter how smart those people are" (Surowiecki, 2004, p. 31). Lindblom (1959) also argued that redundancy—having many decision makers working on a problem at the same time—helps produce better decisions. He used "The Manhattan Project," which led to the creation of the atomic bomb, to illustrate how a team of scientists offset individual

---

**Box 18.2  Evaluating alternative old-growth protection strategies for the federal forests of the Pacific Northwest: A grand experiment in mental simulation**

In the summer of 1989, lawsuits over the adequacy of protections for the northern spotted owl halted old-growth timber harvest on federal lands in the Pacific Northwest (PNW). At the time, these harvests provided almost 20% of the softwood lumber in the United States and employment for tens of thousands of people. The Forest Service had been working for a decade to craft plans that would protect the northern spotted owl and other species, while at the same time providing sustainable timber harvests near historical levels. These lawsuits and resulting court decisions suggested that a forest planning approach, heavily reliant on classical harvest scheduling models, would not be successful.

To cope with this impasse, the chief of the Forest Service and other agency heads asked Dr. Jack Ward Thomas, a senior wildlife biologist, to develop a "scientifically credible conservation strategy for the northern spotted owl" for the millions of acres of its range. Toward that end, Thomas gathered around him a cadre of scientific experts, called the Interagency Scientific Committee (ISC). After months of deliberation, the ISC built a conservation strategy founded on the fundamentals of conservation biology. The strategy called for creation of a system of reserves, large enough to contain self-sustaining populations of owls, and located close enough together so that owls could disperse between them. The ISC also suggested new conservation rules for the federal forest between reserves, which was an innovative alternative to the traditional approach of corridors, and concluded that such a system would give the northern spotted owl a reasonably high probability of survival.

Old-growth forests, though, contain hundreds of species. When the US Congress subsequently dealt with the PNW forest issue, two committees of the House of Representatives asked four senior scientists—Jack Ward Thomas, Jerry Franklin, Norm Johnson, and John Gordon—to develop

alternatives for the conservation of old-growth forests in the Pacific Northwest and to estimate the implication of each alternative for risks to forest species and impacts on timber harvest levels. They also asked that the alternatives deal with habitat for at-risk anadromous fish stocks and requested that the scientists complete this task in three weeks.

The four scientists gathered together hundreds of specialists to help them map the location of old-growth forest and to develop conservation alternatives. They ended up with alternatives for federal lands that varied in the size and extent of reserves and in management options for the nonreserve forests and stream systems. They then assessed the risks to species and ecosystems of each alternative, in terms of five risk measures, and estimated likely timber harvest for the millions of federal acres in their study. Much of the risk assessment for the different alternatives was done with pencil and paper over a few days, with the scientists and specialists visualizing the future forest under each alternative—truly an exercise in mental simulation. The harvest estimates were only slightly more elaborate.

The four scientists (known as the *Gang of Four*) took six weeks to complete their assignment rather than the three weeks they had originally been given. They presented a report to Congress, where it was accepted with little criticism, even though it clearly showed that it was not possible to conserve species associated with old-growth forests and to maintain historical levels of timber harvest. The Gang of Four effort was followed two years later by a much more elaborate effort called FEMAT (FEMAT, 1993), which led directly to the Northwest Forest Plan. FEMAT (FEMAT, 1993) covered much of the same ground as the Gang of Four report and reached similar conclusions, although with much greater analysis and documentation. (Adapted from Lach & Duncan, 2007.)

Table 18.4 *A generalized comparison of world views of those whose frame of reference is managed forest systems as compared to those whose frame of reference is natural forest systems*

| Category | Emphasis on managed systems | Emphasis on natural systems |
|---|---|---|
| *Greatest threat* | Disruption of production | Loss of species and ecosystems |
| *Attitude toward disturbances* | Suppress | Emulate |
| *Effect of human actions on natural processes* | Nature generally robust | Nature somewhat fragile |
| *Belief in technical progress to solve problems* | Relatively high | Relatively low |
| *Uncertainty about effect of human actions on outcomes* | Relatively low | Relatively high |
| *Burden of proof* | On those who want to stop actions that might harm species and ecosystems | On those who wish to undertake actions that might harm species and ecosystems |

Adapted from Johnson (2007).

perspectives and errors through the inbuilt redundancy and diversity of a group decision process.

We discussed the power and use of group decision making through collaborative processes in Chapter 8. It has increasingly become one of the mechanisms through which we try to channel and integrate different knowledge, insight, intuition, and judgment.

## The Influence of Worldview on Decision Making

In Chapter 1, we highlighted classical forestry's tenets of faith that foresters used to help make decisions in the face of massive uncertainty, which focused on timber primacy and a sustained yield of timber harvest. A set of decision rules grew out of these tenets that greatly eased the decisions of foresters (Table 17.1), much like the decision rules in Table 18.2 help us as we go about our lives. However, the classical tenets rested, more deeply, on a way of thinking about the world; they, by and large, reflected a worldview: "the overall perspective from which one sees and interprets the world, a collection of beliefs about life and the universe held by an individual or a group."[2]

Worldviews, as related to the sciences, ethics, arts, politics, and religions, are integral parts of all cultures. They have a strongly motivating and inspiring function. A socially shared view of the whole gives a culture a sense of direction, confidence, and self-esteem. As summarized by Johnson (2007), six key components of worldviews are: (1) theories and models for describing the phenomena we encounter, (2) an understanding of how the world functions and how it is structured, (3) explanations of why the world is the way it is, (4) descriptions of more or less probable future developments, (5) values addressing what is good and what is evil, and (6) descriptions of how we should act to solve practical problems.

Using the federal forests of the Pacific Northwest as our example, we will illustrate how the worldviews on managing these forests, and of the professionals who implement these views, fundamentally affect management. Toward this end, we will describe the change in worldviews that accompanied the shift in the primary focus of national forest planning from sustained timber production to protection of biodiversity.

As the new ecological perspective took hold in the early 1990s, foresters lost their dominance in national forest planning. New science and new kinds of professionals were needed, and ecologists and conservation biologists answered the call. This changing of the guard, from foresters to ecologists and conservation biologists, is apparent in the appearance and domination of new policy players, new kinds of policy reports, and the staffing of the federal agencies (Cashore & Howlett, 2006).

The change, though, was much more than a change in objective from commercial timber harvest to protection of ecosystems and species. Rather, Johnson (2007) argues that we saw an almost complete replacement of one worldview by another. One way to represent these differing worldviews described in Johnson (2007) is to compare the perspectives of those who tend to emphasize managed systems (like many foresters) to those who tend to emphasize natural systems (like many ecologists, wildlife biologists, and environmental groups) (Table 18.4).

While it might be argued that some of the differences in worldview described in Table 18.4 were due to evolving legal requirements, such as, the elevation of threatened species to a preeminent policy position, we argue that there is more at work here. The differences described in the table go significantly beyond differences in overall goals or analytical procedures, as important as those may be. More fundamentally, they relate to differences in worldview—in theories and models for describing the world, in our under-

2 www.thefreedictionary.com/worldview

standing of how and why the world functions and how it is structured, in descriptions of probable future developments, in values addressing what is good and what is evil, and in describing how we should act to solve problems. While the characterization here of the worldview of each group may be somewhat of a caricature and only roughly accurate, it should be clear that worldview can greatly affect how professionals approach forest planning.

One key to how the differences in the worldviews displayed in Table 18.4 affect forest management decisions is the framework that each provides for acting in the face of uncertainty about potential environmental outcomes. Consider the *precautionary principle*, which came into prominence with the rise of the ecological perspective. It was famously stated in the United Nations Rio Declaration on Environment and Development (United Nations, 1992, p. 4) as "Where there are threats of serious or irreversible damage, lack of full scientific certainty shall not be used as a reason for postponing cost-effective measures to prevent environmental degradation." Over time, the concept shifted beyond being limited to "threats of serious or irreversible harm" to more general decision criteria about actions affecting the environment. As articulated by New Jersey Governor Christine Todd Whitman (later director of the Environmental Protection Agency) "policymakers need to take a precautionary approach to environmental protection. . . . We must acknowledge that uncertainty is inherent in managing natural resources, recognize it is usually easier to prevent environmental damage than to repair it later, and shift the burden of proof away from those advocating protection toward those proposing an action that may be harmful" (Appell, 2001, p. 18).

Applying these ideas to forestry, we face the question about who should have the burden of proof about whether proposed actions (cutting trees, etc.) will harm the environment—the person proposing the action or the person who wishes to stop it? With the shift in the intellectual framework for managing the national forests, we saw a comparable shift in the burden of proof about whether actions are likely to harm species. This is most readily seen in the application of the Survey and Manage provisions of the Northwest Forest Plan for management of species about which little is known—especially fungi, lichens, and mollusks. These species were not known to be at-risk; rather we lacked knowledge about their habitat needs. Under the Survey and Manage provisions, planners assumed that timber harvest might harm the habitat for these species, and put the burden of proof that it would not harm them on the proponents of harvest. This shift reversed previous approaches that put the burden of proof on those who wanted to prevent the harvest and made achieving projected timber harvest levels significantly more difficult.

The precautionary principle is but one example of how worldview can influence the approach taken to forest man-

agement. When combined with other tendencies shown in Table 18.4 for those who emphasize natural systems, such as an emphasis on the relatively high uncertainty of the effects of human actions, a worldview can have a dominant effect on management decisions.

The potential impact of worldview on decisions also suggests that the intuitive approach to decision making that we have discussed earlier in this chapter may reflect worldview as much as it reflects knowledge and experience. It also gives more depth to the idea of *wicked problems* that we described in Chapter 1, where there is little agreement on the problem or even the context in which issues are being discussed and debated.

At times, we may want a decision-making approach in which underlying assumptions are more transparent. Some transparency may be provided through group decision making, as we discussed previously and in Chapter 8, especially if different worldviews are present and given space and time to surface as can happen through collaborative processes. However, we may want a still more systematic, analytical approach. And to that we now turn.

## A Role for Systematic Decision Making

For many decisions, a combination of simple decision rules, intuitive decision processes, and mental simulation can suffice. Sometimes, though, we need more. Perhaps we want an organized way to look at more than small policy changes. Perhaps our bosses or client groups want to see the evidence on why our proposed plan is best. Perhaps we wish to surface the underlying assumptions and worldviews behind different proposals. Or perhaps the problem is so complicated that we feel systematic analysis is needed. In those situations, we may want to take a deeper, more systematic look, seeking to use what Benjamin Franklin so elegantly dubbed *moral algebra* where he divided a sheet of paper into two columns, wrote Pro over one and Con over the other, filled in ideas under the different heads to clarify thinking, and then crossed out items of comparable weight on each side until one side or the other prevailed (Johnson & Gordon, 2007).

Gordon (2006) and Johnson and Gordon (2007) argue that as complexity increases, so might the usefulness of such moral algebra. Their approach poses complexity in at least two dimensions: (1) the social dimension relates to how complicated and contentious are the people and groups who are involved in the decision, and (2) the informational dimension relates to how technically complicated is the decision, especially in terms of estimating the consequences of different alternatives. Figure 18.1 provides examples in each dimension. Those authors suggest that, as either or both of these dimensions increase in complexity, the need and call for systematic and transparent analysis will also increase.

| Social Complexity | | | |
|---|---|---|---|
| **High** | Whether to remove geese from the city pond | | Reintroducing grizzly bears into Montana Wilderness |
| **Low** | Which kind of bird seed to use in a feeder | | Where a private firm puts harvest units over the next few decades to distribute deer forage across the landscape |
| | *Low* | | *High* |
| | **Informational Complexity** | | |

Figure 18.1 *Examples of different levels of social and informational complexity. (Source: Adapted from Gordon, 2006).*

## Principled Negotiation to Address Social Complexity

We describe here three approaches to systematic decision analysis: (1) principled negotiation to address social complexity, (2) resource optimization to address information complexity, and (3) structured decision making to address both types of complexity.

The existence of social complexity suggests a potential need for bargaining and negotiation to reach decisions. As we discussed in Chapter 8, much in life involves bargaining and negotiation. Many decisions about how best to conserve and manage forests are the result of negotiations. Whether we are at the kitchen table of a family deciding what to do with their farm woodlot, at a meeting of the board of directors of a large private firm, at the annual public meeting of a state forest trust, or at a mediation process to resolve a dispute about management of a national forest, negotiation is often the order of the day.

Over 25 years ago a little book called *Getting to Yes: Reaching Agreement without Giving In* introduced the idea of **principled negotiation** (Fisher & Ury, 1991; Fisher et al., 2011). This concept entails ideas that have dominated thinking about negotiation ever since, appearing, in one form or another, in almost all recent books about negotiation in business, government, and natural resources.

Fisher and Ury (1991) and Fisher et al. (2011) suggest four negotiation principles (see Chapter 8 for more details):

1. *People: Separate people from the problem; focus on relationships.* A basic fact about negotiation is that we are dealing with human beings, not with abstract representatives. People (including us) have emotions, deeply held values, and different backgrounds and viewpoints. People are also unpredictable. Thus, the human aspect of negotiation can be either helpful or disastrous. We need to recognize these aspects of negotiations and try to avoid entangling the problem with our relationships. In addition, we generally need to avoid damaging relationships with those with whom we negotiate. Frequently we see our negotiating partners over and over as we work together to decide ways to conserve and manage a forest; we may need their help in the future, and damaging relationships certainly does not serve this purpose.

2. *Interests: Focus on underlying interests, not positions.* A position is what you say you want. It is a preformed idea of your ideal outcome. Interests are the needs, hopes, fears, concerns, and desires that underlie positions. To make progress in negotiations, we need to surface the underlying interests. Interests are likely to be broader than positions; thus, we have a better chance of finding outcomes that satisfy interests than ones that satisfy positions.

3. *Options: Invent options for mutual gain.* Figuring out a way that all parties can have their interests met is at the heart of mutual gain negotiation— brainstorming on different options for advancing the diverse interests that have been expressed.

4. *Criteria: Use objective criteria in evaluation.* Developing objective criteria, reflective of the interests of the parties involved in the negotiation, enables everyone to evaluate the options being considered.

## Resource Optimization to Address Informational Complexity

As information complexity increases, we may quickly come face-to-face with the question of whether to use systematic, perhaps quantitative, resource analysis. Foresters have built models to help develop forest management plans for hundreds of years, often organized around the achievement of a regulated forest (see Chapter 17). As with the "muddling through" approach described earlier, these efforts rarely separated the goals from the policies. Rather, the goals implied by the classical tenets of faith described in Chapter 1, including the primacy of timber production, were generally accepted, whether they were expressed or not.

Forest planning tools for much of the last century focused on setting allowable cuts while recognizing the growth dynamics of forests and maintaining the harvest over time.

Foresters often broke the forest into stands or groups of stands, each with a set of choices for when and how to harvest. They found that such calculations quickly become complicated. For example, a forest of 200 stands and a 10-decade planning horizon and two types of harvest could result in $200 \times 10 \times 2 = 4{,}000$ choices to consider in setting the allowable cut. And 200 stands is a very small forest!

In addition, forest planning almost always encounters constraints on what can be done. There is only so much land, so much capital, so many people to help out. There are only so many spatial patterns of activity that satisfy multiple goals. More fundamentally, forest management focuses on sustaining forests and the benefits that flow from them, which requires constraints on our use so that we do not deplete the resource.

A single-minded focus on the allowable cut has waned, while interest has increased in a broader notion of sustainability on public lands and in financial performance on private lands. These issues and concerns have often driven landowners, boards, managers, and interested groups to consider detailed modeling of alternatives and their implications.

Over the last 40 years, forest analysts have shed much blood, sweat, and tears on representing forest management decision problems as optimization problems. Two intersecting developments helped push along this approach to forest management planning. First, managers of both large private forests and public forests were increasingly challenged to justify their decisions. Second, high-speed computers and associated decision algorithms were developed that could solve quantitative decision problems.

A common approach to setting up these optimization models is to:

1. Identify the decision maker and the resource and policy constraints;

2. Outline the goals that will guide the analysis;

3. Establish criteria to measure goal attainment;

4. Develop a quantitative model that represents the goals and constraints; and

5. Utilize the model to help develop efficient alternatives for meeting the goals while satisfying the constraints.

In many forest management books, such as Davis and Johnson (1987), Davis et al. (2001), and Bettinger et al. (2017), the authors utilized these optimization models to solve timber harvest scheduling problems. They approached forest management planning as an exercise in quantitative economic analysis. Thus, they used techniques, such as linear programming, to portray alternatives, solutions, and trade-offs, and emphasized finding efficient solutions—that is, solutions that achieved the highest level for a particular goal (such as timber production) given specified levels for

others (such as recreation opportunity and wildlife habitat). With some reformulation, these efficiency analyses can be of great value in ecological management as they help minimize the trade-off in achieving different goals. We will discuss further and demonstrate these ideas later in the chapter.

In reality, development and use of such quantitative planning models is generally a back-and-forth negotiation with the people involved in the decision, whether these people are family members, business associates, interest groups, or policy makers. At its best, the model-building process contributes to brainstorming in both evaluating existing alternatives and helping us think of new ones.

## Structured Decision Making to Address Both Types of Complexity

Recently, a number of authors (Gregory et al., 2012; Thompson et al., 2013a) have suggested a decision-making approach called *structured decision making*, which integrates major elements of both principled negotiation and resource analysis. Gregory et al. (2012) break structured decision making into six key steps:

1. *Clarify the decision context*—describe the problem or problems being addressed, decisions needed, decision makers, participants, general range of alternatives, constraints on actions, and analytical tools that may be needed. This initial problem structuring stage lays out a road map for the deliberations that follow, so that all parties understand what will happen and when. A key technique at this point is *decision sketching*—working quickly to clarify what the decision is about and what will be needed to make an informed choice.

2. *Identify objectives and performance measures*—surface what people hope to achieve through the decision and the metrics that will be used to gauge how well any proposal responds to these objectives. Together, objectives and performance measures play two critical roles: (1) they drive the search for creative alternatives, and (2) they form a consistent and transparent framework for comparing them. While key stakeholders may attach different importance to different objectives, the objectives and performance measures (in aggregate) must be accepted as adequate to evaluate the alternatives—they need to be accepted by the participants as clarifying what matters and what needs to be addressed in developing and comparing alternatives.

3. *Develop alternatives*—outline comprehensive sets of actions that address the problem or problems being studied in different ways. Identifying, comparing, and refining alternatives is the heart of structured decision making, with the goal of presenting the decision maker with real choices.

4. *Estimate consequences*—assess the effect of the alternatives on the performance measures. Technical experts often take the lead here— scientists, environmental professionals (such as hydrologists and wildlife biologists), silviculturists, logging engineers, economists, planners, and local or traditional knowledge holders (e.g., local foresters, ranchers, or tribal members). Qualitative or quantitative models may be built to aid in the analysis. Gregory et al. (2012) describe the importance of participants in the structured decision-making process developing a common understanding of what constitutes the best available information for assessing consequences. Also, they stress that honest and accurate representation of uncertainty is essential, along with attempting to reduce uncertainty through the gathering of information, using predictive modeling tools, eliciting judgments on outcomes from recognized experts, and creating alternatives that directly address it. Finally, they suggest that a *consequence table*, summarizing the consequences of the alternatives—a matrix with alternatives across the top and performance measures down the side can be extremely valuable (much like Benjamin Franklin's moral algebra).

5. *Evaluate trade-offs and select the best alternative*— compare and contrast alternatives in terms of how well they do on different performance measures. Does improved protection from wildfires in a rural community offset losses in forest biodiversity that would result from proposed wildfire management actions? Does the increase in diverse early seral habitat offset the loss of young forest that will be harvested to create this habitat? Choosing a preferred alternative involves value-based judgments, about which reasonable people may disagree. Gregory et al. (2012) argue for approaches to making choices that allow participants to state their preferences for different alternatives based on credible technical information about estimated consequences.

6. *Implement, monitor, and learn*—promote learning and build management capacity to make better decisions in the future. With the uncertainties that surround most environmental decisions, an emphasis on learning over time, accompanied by a formal commitment to review the decision when new information is available, can be the key to reaching agreement on a controversial management strategy.

According to Gregory et al. (2012), structured decision-making approaches most often are used to structure decisions involving a group of 10–20 people who agree to work iteratively and collaboratively through the structured

decision-making steps in a sequence of five to ten meetings. There may also be additional technical working groups or expert panels who provide input to the main group. Furthermore, there may be public meetings or sessions with other people or groups to gather information, but there is the assumption that a core group gets together repeatedly to work through a complex problem.

## Comparing the Three Approaches: Similar Steps but Differing Emphases in Implementation

The three approaches discussed above—principled negotiation (Fisher et al., 2011), resource optimization (Davis & Johnson, 1987; Davis et al., 2001), and structured decision making (Gregory et al., 2012)—show many similarities in the steps they use for environmental problem solving and decision making, although they use somewhat different language (Table 18.5). They also display substantive differences. Principled negotiation does not specifically address trade-offs in advancing the different interests, which may not be surprising since trade-off analysis can heighten conflict by highlighting gains and losses. The resource analysis of Davis and Johnson (1987) and Davis et al. (2001) emphasizes trade-off evaluation and the role of efficiency analysis in reducing trade-offs. Structured decision making alone emphasizes adaptive management, which is not surprising as the other two approaches were developed largely before adaptive management came to the fore.

At each step, principled negotiation emphasizes relationships among people while resource optimization emphasizes quantitative analysis and modeling. With structured decision making, we attempt to integrate these two well-tested approaches.

## Structured Decision Making for Ecological Forest Management

For our approach to systematic forest planning and decision making in the context of ecological forest management, we will generally utilize the steps of structured decision making described by Gregory et al. (2012), augmented by aspects of collaboration described in Fisher et al.'s *Getting to Yes* (2011), and the forest management planning modeling and efficiency analysis described in Davis and Johnson (1987) and Davis et al. (2001) (Box 18.3). We describe a seven-step decision-making process below, adding one step (development of an engagement strategy) to the six-step process (Gregory et al., 2012) that we summarized. We added this step to emphasize the importance of the involvement of people and groups in decision making about forests. We also, and perhaps most importantly, embed the philosophy, principles, and tenets of ecological forest management into this decision-making structure.

Table 18.5 *Comparison of three approaches to decision making in addressing an environmental problem*

| Topic | Principled Negotiation (Fisher & Ury, 1991; Fisher et al., 2011) | Resource Optimization (Davis & Johnson, 1987; Davis et al., 2001) | Structured Decision Making (Gregory et al., 2012) |
|---|---|---|---|
| *Context* | Separate people from the problem/focus on relationships | Identify decision maker and resource and policy constraints | Clarify the decision context |
| *What is sought* | Identify interests | Identify goals | Identify objectives |
| *Measure* | Establish objective criteria | Establish criteria for goal attainment | Establish performance measures |
| *Choices* | Develop options to advance interests | Develop alternatives to achieve goals | Develop alternatives to achieve objectives |
| *Consequences* | Estimate consequences using criteria | Estimate consequences using criteria | Estimate consequences using performance measures |
| *Uncertainty* | | Conduct sensitivity analysis | Consider and reduce uncertainty throughout analysis |
| *Trade-offs* | | Assess trade-offs utilizing efficiency analysis | Assess trade-offs |
| *Adaptation* | | | Implement, learn and adapt |

Below, we provide an explanation of each step in Box 18.3. Also, we discuss incorporation of uncertainty into both development and evaluation of alternatives and the important role of efficiency analysis in reducing trade-offs.

We want to emphasize, though, that the process is rarely as linear as presented in Box 18.3. Rather, this planning process often has numerous feedback loops especially among steps four and five (creating alternatives and estimating their consequences) (Figure 18.2). Assessing the consequences of one or more alternatives that were initially specified often (almost always) leads to the desire (demand) for more alternatives. In fact, if the planning process is working as the free-flowing brainstorming and learning process that we hope for, the initial assessment of alternatives will result in a request for alternatives that more completely integrate the different objectives. Many rounds of alternative creation and assessment may follow. These two steps are so tightly coupled in forest planning that we have merged them together in the example of structured decision making provided later in this chapter.

When a set of alternatives has been developed that the participants in the decision think illustrates the choices as well as they can, the process moves on to evaluation of trade-offs and selection of the forest plan. Here again the discussion and negotiation that will occur among the group engaged in the decision can easily lead to a request for more alternatives (Figure 18.2).

The decision process of Figure 18.2 may jump back to an earlier step at any step along the way as more is learned. Such a return to an earlier box should not be seen as a defeat as long as the process leads to a decision within an acceptable time. In fact, recognizing the need for these feedback loops can greatly strengthen the decision process.

We will discuss our seven-step decision-making process in the context of developing a *strategic forest plan*—a long-term plan for a forest. We will then provide an example of the application of these steps to a relatively simple forest planning problem. Also, Chapter 19 is devoted to applying the seven-step decision process to a much more complex forest planning problem.

## Step 1: Frame the Problem (Overview and Decision Context)

Decision making for ecological forest management starts with a general description of the decision problem at hand. Whose land is this? Who will make the decision? What type of problem is this person or group trying to address?

---

**Box 18.3 Structured decision making for ecological forest management**

**Step 1.** Frame the problem: Overview and decision context (ecological, human use, economic, social, and legal).

**Step 2.** Develop an engagement strategy.

**Step 3.** Identify objectives and performance measures, including the approach to sustainability and conservation of critical natural capital and special places.

**Step 4.** Create alternatives: Delineate different solutions to the problem being studied.

**Step 5.** Estimate consequences: Assess how the alternatives score on the performance measures.

**Step 6.** Evaluate trade-offs and make a decision.

**Step 7.** Implement, monitor, and adapt.

As an example, are they deciding where to put a particular harvest, designing a prescribed fire, or developing a comprehensive, long-term forest plan? What are the limits on the choices that can be considered? Will logging be allowed? Might a conservation easement be sought? While the general problem definition may change and multiply as the decision analysis unfolds, a first attempt at *framing the problem* is essential to kick things off.

As part of this framing, there is a need to provide a detailed context for ecological forest planning from many different dimensions:

- **Identifying the underlying ecological processes and structures that have historically occurred in the forest.** Setting the context for the decision requires a description and an understanding of the underlying historical ecological processes and resulting structures of the forest being studied. This includes identifying the major disturbance processes that have historically shaped the forest landscape (see Chapter 3 for disturbance processes).

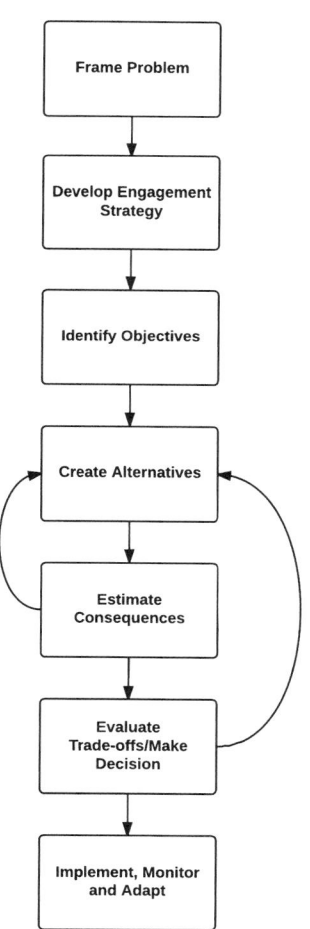

Figure 18.2 *The multistep process of structured decision making with two of the most likely feedback loops.*

- **Understanding human use of the area.** Most forests have experienced significant human occupancy and use over time, starting with aboriginal peoples. More recently, significant harvest and associated road building have greatly modified many forests. Understanding this history is part of understanding the forest that now exists.

- **Assessing economic possibilities.** Revenue from forest products is usually essential to successful forest conservation and management. Thus, investigating markets for different types of forest products will be needed.

- **Identifying social considerations and networks.** From neighbors to environmental groups to local collaboration groups, the social environment will need to be understood, in part, to avoid or minimize potential conflicts.

- **Surfacing responsibilities under federal and state environmental law and regulation.** In the United States, this includes the federal Endangered Species and Clean Water Acts (for all landowners), state land use and forest practice laws (for state and private forests), and the National Forest Management Act (for the national forests).

## Step 2: Develop an Engagement Strategy

Once you have developed an understanding of the decision context for your forest planning problem, a crucial next step is to craft a process for the involvement of others in decision making. With the assessment of the social context, you can begin to identify who has a stake in the decision and their interests. How might they be involved? Should they be part of the group that describes the objectives and performance measures and develops alternatives? Or should you just check with them at the beginning to understand their interests and then seek their reaction to the alternatives you develop or to the decision you make? Or should you proceed without their involvement? Thinking through these questions can save much trouble down the road!

Toward that end, you might employ a *spectrum of engagement* in decision making (Table 18.6) in deciding how you would like to involve others in planning your forest. At the *Inform level*, you keep interested parties aware of your activities. At the *Consult level*, you keep interested parties aware of your activities, solicit their input, and consider their concerns and suggestions as you develop your forest plan. At the *Involve level*, you work closely with interested parties and try to address their concerns to the extent consistent with your objectives. At the *Collaborate level*, you work with interested parties to reach agreement throughout the planning process.

## Step 3: Identify Objectives and Performance Measures, Including Approach to Sustainability and Conservation of Critical Natural Capital and Special Places

Identifying objectives is an exceedingly important task in structured decision making, but it can be difficult. Often the families who own a tract of forestland or a small forest products company are also active decision makers who can help define the objectives for forest management. In larger companies, however, the owners are the stockholders and are represented by the company's board of directors and executive officers. Many forest-level decisions are made by forest managers well down in the company hierarchy, who know company objectives and policies only indirectly through written guidelines and who accumulate a sense of those objectives through years of meetings and interactions.

Delineating objectives for a public forest is perhaps the most difficult task for forest managers because they are hired hands for the real owners: the citizens. More than their private counterparts, public managers typically have poorly defined guidance on the nature and relative importance of the many different objectives for the many different people and groups interested in the public lands. Often citizens do not speak up or communicate directly with the manager. Rather, they rely on organized groups to make their case, and may threaten to, or actually use, political or legal intervention to change, prevent, or reverse decisions of public forest managers.

**Types of Objectives** *Gregory et al. (2012) emphasize the need to separate objectives into fundamental or ends objectives and means objectives. Fundamental objectives are the basic things that matter, the outcomes you care about regardless of how they are achieved. Means objectives refer to ways of meeting the fundamental objectives.* While fundamental objectives are usually fairly set, means objectives may be more flexible and subject to imaginative revision. Also fundamental objectives are often somewhat abstract, so we often focus in forest planning on achieving means objectives (Table 18.7).

It should be noted that the things that matter—the outcomes we seek regardless of how they are achieved, and to which we refer to here as fundamental objectives—are often called "goals." In fact, we have used the term goals to describe the outcomes we seek earlier in this book and in this chapter (when we discussed the qualitative resource analysis of Davis and Johnson [1987] and Davis et al. [2001]). We use the term *fundamental objectives* for Chapters 18 and 19 in describing and implementing structured decision making to be consistent with the terminology of Gregory et al. (2012) and because it creates a helpful connection between ends and means.

Gregory et al. (2012) also describe process objectives and strategic objectives. Process objectives generally relate to how the decisions will be made, including who should be involved and how they should be involved. Strategic objectives relate to broader organization concerns such as maintaining public trust and avoiding illegal activities. In this chapter we focus mainly on fundamental, means, and process objectives. Other parts of this book focus on strategic objectives such as maintaining public trust (Chapter 8).

**Selecting Performance Measures that Reflect Objectives** *Performance measures* are the quantitative or qualitative indicators of how alternatives score relative to achieving specified objectives. For an objective to be an operational guide, we must be able to devise a performance measure that measures its achievement:

- *Objective:* To maintain the entire forest sere

- *Performance measure:* The number of acres in each development stage on a forest

- *Objective:* To provide a variety of recreational experiences

- *Performance measure:* The number of acres in each class of the recreation opportunity spectrum

- *Objective:* To provide a sustained yield of timber harvest

- *Performance measure:* The even-flow level of timber harvest associated with a management plan

*The existence of a performance measure to represent an objective is a test of its operational significance.*

Gregory et al. (2012) describe a number of characteristics of a good performance measure: *Complete*—they cover the range of relevant consequences under all reasonable

Table 18.6 *A spectrum of engagement for involving interested parties in environmental decision making. Note: each type of engagement includes all commitments in types that came before it*

|  | Inform | Consult | Involve | Collaborate |
|---|---|---|---|---|
| *Commitment* | Will provide information | Will consider concerns and suggestions | Will incorporate concerns and suggestions into plan consistent with your objectives | Will work to find mutually-agreeable solutions |
| *Goal* | Keep informed | Understand their concerns | Address their concerns to the extent feasible | Create a plan that has broad agreement |
| *Example* | Describe new plan at local meeting | Get their ideas early in the planning process and report back to them when plan is finished | Modify plan to incorporate their ideas | Work with them throughout the planning process to find common ground |

Adapted from *Council of Environmental Quality* (2007).

Table 18.7 *Examples of fundamental objectives and means objectives in forestry*

| Fundamental objective | Related means objective |
| --- | --- |
| Maintain ecosystem integrity | Provide the entire sere (preforest, young, mature, old) |
| | Retain biological legacies at harvest |
| | Keep all old trees in harvest units |
| Maintain community economic health | Provide employment in the nearby forest |
| | Provide a steady supply of logs for local processing |
| | Provide a variety of recreational experiences on the forest |

alternatives; *Unambiguous*—a clear, accurate, and widely recognized relationship exists between the measures and the consequences they describe; *Understandable*—they can be understood clearly and consistently by different people; and *Operational*—the information required by the measure can be obtained within the limits of the planning process.

Gregory et al. (2012) also describe different types of performance measures: *Natural*—measures that report directly on the objective of interest, such as dollars per year to measure income; *Proxy*—measures utilized when natural measures are not available, such as habitat utilized as a proxy for species abundance or welfare; and *Constructed*—specially crafted measures utilized when natural and proxy are not available.

*In forest planning in this book, we systematically link performance measures to means objectives to ensure that those objectives are represented in the planning process. The performance measures are then used to help develop and evaluate forest plan alternatives. We may also use them in the monitoring associated with the plan, along with more integrative measures of plan effectiveness.*

**Approach to Sustainability, Including Conservation of Critical Natural Capital and Special Places** Ensuring the sustainability of forests and the benefits they provide has been a focus, perhaps the central focus, of forest planning for hundreds of years. We have seen how that concern was addressed in classical forestry, with its emphasis on sustained yield and movement to a regulated forest. Also, as we have seen (Chapter 7), assessing the continuity of timber harvest volume over time is still an important part of ensuring forest sustainability around the world.

To sustain forest ecosystems and the services that flow from them, ecological forestry emphasizes providing the full range of developmental stages in managed landscapes, creating and sustaining structurally complex and biologically rich managed stands, and recognizing and maintaining important specialized habitats in managed landscapes such as riparian areas and old-growth patches.

These forest conditions and characteristics, which are critically important elements of ecological forestry, provide the foundation of ecosystem sustainability in both the current climate and the changing and uncertain climate to come, as we have discussed elsewhere in this book.

To put it another way, these conditions and characteristics constitute much of the ***critical natural capital*** that underlies the provision of ecosystem services we seek from forests. As such, other forms of capital cannot substitute for them.[3] They are needed for the forests to function as natural systems. In addition, we often need to maintain and restore habitats of selected species, whose continued survival is not assured by ecosystem planning. Critical natural capital that may need consideration in forest planning comes in many forms. We highlight three here: (1) old-growth groves, old trees, wet meadows, riparian areas, and other special ecological structures and sites, which will be reserved or treated with great care to maintain their essential elements, (2) biological legacies that will be left after harvest through aggregate or dispersed retention, and (3) representative amounts of different development stages that will be maintained or restored across the forest through time.

In the modeling associated with forest planning, we usually simulate forest structure and ecosystem services for a number of periods into the future as we will see in the next chapter. Beyond maintaining the elements of ecological systems critical to providing ecosystem services on a continuing basis, we often put limits on the flow of ecosystem services over time, especially on timber harvest value or volume, and on the underlying forest structures and complexity needed to provide desired levels of these services such as wildlife populations. The actual levels chosen of these performance measures depend somewhat on how their achievement interacts with the levels of other performance measures of interest; understanding those trade-offs is generally the focus of forest planning.

During the modeling process, we also need to specify the forest we wish to attain by the conclusion of the simulation to make sure that we maintain options for the future. Those ending conditions become ever more important as we shorten the simulation periods due to the difficulty of predicting future forest dynamics and desired forest structure in the context of changing and uncertain climate, economic system, and societal demands.

In addition, we need to recognize special places—features of the landscape of special importance to those who will be involved in the decision. These special places could

---

3 See Chapters 1 and 9 for a detailed discussion of "critical natural capital."

be a favorite stream, an old-growth grove, a sacred mountain, or a historical site. Planning needs to acknowledge their importance and consider them and their protection in the analysis.

In sum, we have moved in forest planning from a very few measures of sustainability, centered on ensuring sustained timber production, to a multitude of diverse measures, some of which may be built into the prescriptions and choices we consider for forests, others that we recognize formally as controls, and still others that we evaluate by looking at the entire forest plan. We will demonstrate these measures in our forest planning example below and, more extensively, in the next chapter.

## Step 4: Create Alternatives [4]

So how will you achieve the objectives that you have identified? Here is where the real brainstorming begins. What strategies should you test? What strategies can you undertake to advance specified objectives and comply with any constraints you have set? At their best, these strategies reflect analysis and ingenuity—they are a key creative part of the problem-solving process. They may be an attempt to emulate natural disturbance processes in management, new and experimental ways to combine forest fuel reduction with the protection of spotted owl habitat, or portray many other ideas. Our goal here is to turn these ideas into alternatives for managing the forest.

By alternative, we mean a solution to a given problem that can be directly compared to other proposed solutions (Gregory et al., 2012). What constitutes an alternative is context dependent. For example, if a forestry office can fund one restoration project for the year, then the individual candidate projects are the alternatives. If the department will fund multiple restoration projects up to some budget limit, then the alternatives are different combinations of projects that could be funded.

**Why Alternatives Are Needed**    Development and evaluation of alternatives is the heart of forest planning and decision making. Perhaps we should just select a plan, estimate its consequences, and see if it is acceptable to people. Gregory et al. (2012), though, make a strong argument for systematically developing alternatives as part of planning:

- We learn by generating and exploring alternatives and their implications.

- A set of alternatives helps decision makers and stakeholders think about how the different alternatives affect attainment of their objectives.

- The presence of alternatives provides context for people to evaluate choices—judgments about what is acceptable can be more easily made with knowledge of what is possible.

- A well-developed set of alternatives helps make the process of choosing and decision making more transparent.

We will demonstrate these ideas in the example of forest planning below and (especially) in the case study in the next chapter.

**Characteristics of a Good Alternative**    With the importance of alternatives to effective decision making, we need to think about what is a *good* alternative. Most importantly, a good alternative is one that provides a meaningful solution to the problem at hand. Toward that end, Gregory et al. (2012) outline a number of characteristics of good alternatives:

- *Complete and comparable:* they must address the key aspects of the problem over the same time period, using the same underlying assumptions about events or conditions beyond the influence of the decision at hand.

- *Value focused:* they must be designed to address the fundamental values of importance in the decision—the things that matter as defined by the objectives and their performance measures.

- *Fully specified:* they must be defined in sufficient detail so that their consequences can be evaluated. As, an example comparing prescribed burning alternatives is difficult without information on weather conditions, time of year, and other information.

- *Internally coherent:* the combination of elements that make up an alternative, when considered together, need to be both feasible and logical.

**Incorporating Uncertainty into Development and Analysis of Alternatives**    Uncertainty infuses virtually every aspect of environmental decision making, whether it relates to how nature functions and reacts to human actions or to the host of sociopolitical influences that can affect both planning and plan implementation. In addition, the sheer difficulty of communication among different members of a forest planning team (often called *linguistic uncertainty*) can create significant uncertainties relative to a common understanding of the problems and solutions under discussion (see Gregory et al., 2012).

---

4 In planning over time, alternatives, as described here, have a close relationship to scenarios, which can be defined as: "a sequence of events especially when imagined; especially: an account or synopsis of a possible course of action or events" https://www.merriam-webster.com/dictionary/scenario. We introduce scenario planning at the end of this section.

Many articles and books have been dedicated to analytical treatment of uncertainty. Usually, though, the suggested techniques are relevant for only a subset of the uncertainties affecting environmental decision making (Gregory et al., 2012). Following the lead of Gregory et al. (2012), we focus here on providing an overview of some useful ways of approaching uncertainty in decision making for ecological forest management, without resorting to sophisticated quantitative models.

With the approach to structured decision making for ecological forest management described in this chapter, we have two complementary foundations for accommodating uncertainty:

1. As we have discussed throughout this book, starting in Chapter 1, we utilize a set of tenets for ecological forest management to guide plans and actions in the face of uncertainty. They are:

   a. *Restore and sustain the integrity and complexity of forest and associated ecosystems*, embedding such an approach in forest management planning.

   b. *Develop policies and management practices that consider and sustain a broad array of ecosystem services*, emphasizing policies that perform well in a variety of ecological and social environments.

   c. *Be attentive and adaptive to new scientific and technical developments and to changes in societal objectives, priorities, and concerns*, recognizing that objectives, knowledge, and social context undergo continual change.

   d. *Choose management approaches that will reduce risks to forest assets and increase future options*, including providing heterogeneity at multiple spatial scales, creating redundancy, and increasing resistance and resilience in the face of potential disturbance.

2. The process of structured decision making can help in surfacing, highlighting, and reacting to uncertainties. By making explicit the assumptions and relationships utilized in decision making, structured decision making can help increase the common understanding of the problem being studied and the options for addressing it, and thus reduce linguistic uncertainties among those involved in planning and decision making.

   Also, as pointed out by Gregory et al. (2012), a variety of approaches have been suggested for creating alternatives in structured decision making that provide managers with defensible approaches to managing under uncertainty:

   a. *Precautionary approaches:* The precautionary approach, which we introduced previously, is generally interpreted as placing the burden of proof about whether actions will cause environmental damage on those proposing the action rather than those questioning it. With high levels of uncertainty, such an approach, taken literally, may bring potential actions to a complete halt. While Gregory et al. (2012) recognize the value of precaution, as an overall principle, they also note that it is difficult to be simultaneously precautionary relative to all ecological and social considerations. As such, Gregory et al. (2012) feel that precautionary approaches provide only limited guidance in choosing among alternatives, but have considerable value in development of alternatives, where alternatives with different degrees of precaution relative to ecological and social outcomes of interest can be developed and compared. We add that the value of precaution as a decision guide should be keyed to the likelihood of serious or irreversible damage. As an example, the precautionary principle is (understandably) often invoked as a decision guide for endangered species.

   b. *Adaptive approaches:* These approaches encourage learning and are flexible enough to enable planners and decision makers to respond to that learning over time, as we covered in Chapter 11. Key uncertainties are highlighted as plans are developed. Actions are seen as experiments and information is gathered as the actions are taken, especially relative to these key uncertainties, to understand whether the actions have the expected effect.

   c. *Robust approaches:* These approaches identify alternatives that are expected to perform reasonably well over a range of uncertainties and plausible future conditions. "The concept follows from the observation that sometimes alternatives that are preferred under most probable conditions perform particularly badly should less likely conditions occur—their performance is said to be brittle, or extremely sensitive to key assumptions" (Gregory et al., 2012, p. 145). The idea behind robustness here is to assess performance of alternatives over a set of potential scenarios, beyond just the most probable one, to find alternatives that do reasonably well over many of them.

Gregory et al. (2012) emphasize that the synergy of robust and adaptive approaches provides more resilient, complex systems—one of the key goals of ecological forest management.

*Sensitivity analysis* and *scenario planning* are two well-recognized ways to assess and improve the robustness and adaptability of a proposed solution to an environmental problem:

- Sensitivity analysis is often identified with testing the effect on the results from a quantitative decision model by varying model parameters or constraints (Davis et al., 2001; Bettinger et al., 2017). As an example, suppose you have built a forest planning model in which you simulate the timber harvest compatible with maintaining habitat for a set of wildlife species. You might then vary the representation of habitat relationships in your model, about which you are uncertain, to assess how that will affect the resulting timber harvest schedule, including where and when to harvest and the resulting volume and income levels. To the degree that the resulting changes to the harvest schedule are modest, you would say that your harvest schedule is robust under these different representations of the habitat relationships. Perhaps, though, varying the habitat relationships results in major changes in the harvest schedule. That result would demonstrate considerable sensitivity of the harvest to the habitat uncertainties and would suggest the need for greater understanding of the reasons for this sensitivity and (perhaps) for a search for a harvest schedule that performs better under the different habitat relationships.

- While sensitivity analysis can be very useful, it is often limited to testing the existing modeling framework. Scenario planning is much broader. The term "scenario" was created by a famous futurist named Herman Kahn due to "its Hollywood association as a detailed outline of a future movie that was fictional, reinforcing his assertion that he did not make accurate predictions, but stories to explore" (Van der Heijden, 2005, p. 3). Scenario analysis is used to translate complex and uncertain relationships into understandable narratives for consumption by a broader audience. Scenarios assist with the examination of potential complex and fundamental changes in ecological, economic, and social conditions. They are developed to help us understand how the future might unfold and how it might be different from current or past conditions (Johnson et al., 2016; Bettinger et al., 2017). Thus, scenario planning focuses on the changing context within which decisions are made, both the internal organizational context and, perhaps more importantly, the external context within which an organization exists and attempts to survive and prosper. It attempts to surface the alternative futures that a firm or family might face so that they can evaluate how well their solutions to the problems might fare, consider whether they might want to change their proposed solutions, and prepare the firm or family for changes that may be needed in the future if a particular scenario comes to pass.

We will demonstrate both sensitivity analysis and scenario planning in our forest planning example later in this chapter.

## Step 5: Estimate Consequences

In many ways, suggesting alternatives is easy compared to evaluating their consequences. Thus, much of the effort in environmental decision making focuses on assessing how alternatives score on the different performance measures that have been developed. We certainly see that focus in forest planning with its emphasis on quantitative forest planning models that enable trade-off analysis.

**The Role of Forest Planning Models**   In forestry, we often use quantitative forest planning models to test the effectiveness of alternatives as part of planning the long-term conservation and management of forests (see Davis et al., 2001; Bettinger et al., 2017). This interest in models has occurred, in part, because of the information complexity involved in modeling alternatives for management of a forest, especially once we recognize individual stands or stand groups and a number of time periods. As an example, the OSU College Forest planning problem described in Box 18.5 (a moderate-sized forest planning problem) recognized 500 stands with three prescriptions and 10 periods for a total of 500 × 3 × 10 for 15,000 potential choices. Beyond the constraints on the land available for each stand, more than 50 other constraints were recognized to maintain an even flow of income and harvest, and to provide other conditions over the 10 planning periods.

Thus, forest planning models can be infuriatingly large and complex. On one hand, models like these can be just the ticket to aid the brainstorming that you hope occurs during negotiations over the future of a forest; on the other hand, they can overwhelm and derail creative activities. We cover model building and model use to evaluate consequences of forest plan alternatives, in detail, through our case example of forest planning in the next chapter. Also, we have a section below (after an introductory example of forest planning) that describes how these models can help or hinder forest planning, along with recommendations for effective use.

**Delineating Trade-offs in Achieving Multiple Objectives**
Assume you are managing a forest and are interested in harvesting a sustainable volume over time while also retaining legacy structures when harvest occurs. Some retention might not lower timber volume level at all if the trees left are largely noncommercial (perhaps too misshapen or branchy), but as the level of retention increases, the sustainable harvest level will gradually fall. As you move between alternatives, the decrease in harvest associated with the increase in reten-

tion is called a *trade-off*. Whether the tool used is a page of "moral algebra" of Benjamin Franklin or the "consequence table" of Gregory et al. (2012), people often find it useful to make a tabular or graphical comparison of the alternatives in terms of the performance measures of interest—to help measure the trade-offs as they move between alternatives.

People passionately care about forests and see them in many different ways for many different purposes. Thus, multiple, competing objectives almost always surface in forest planning, whether they be owls and timber or retention of legacy structures and income. Identifying trade-offs in achieving different objectives, that is, how much we have to give up of one objective to achieve another, is an important part of forest planning.

Generally, in delineating trade-offs, we want to ensure that we give up the minimum amount of achievement of one objective to increase achievement of another—we want to ensure that our analysis provides *efficient solutions*. Finding the least-cost way (in terms of trade-offs) to reach our objectives is important to policy making and management planning for at least two reasons: (1) inefficient solutions can result in needless conflict as the protagonists believe that the trade-offs are higher than they really are, and (2) the higher the costs of achieving an objective (in terms of reduced achievement of another objective) the less likely it is that decision makers will choose high levels of that objective.

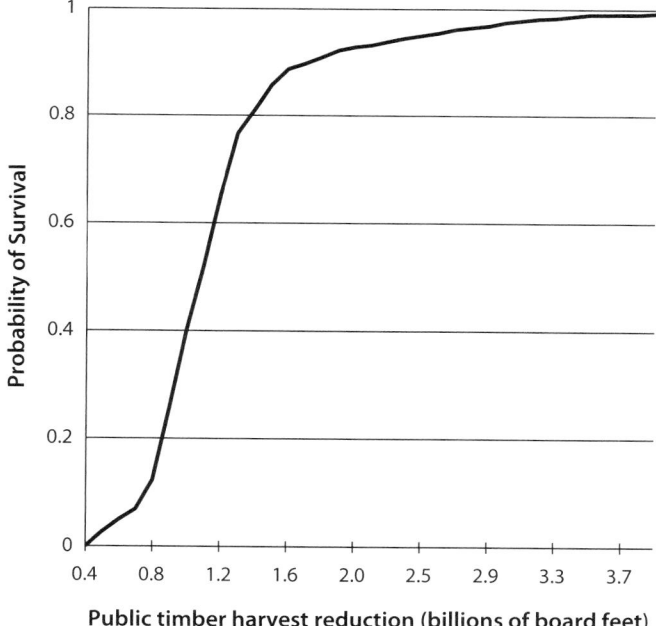

Figure 18.3 *An estimate\* of the probability of survival for northern spotted owl as a function of public timber harvest reduction from national forest plan levels. (Source: C. Montgomery, Oregon State University, personal communication, 2000)*

\* This estimate did not include the negative effects of barred owl (*Strix varia*) competition.

Minimizing trade-offs is especially important in ecological forest management: making sure you minimize any extra costs or revenue reductions is an important ingredient in getting people to consider ecologically grounded approaches to forestry. To put it another way, we often want to understand how much money it is possible to make while still achieving ecological forestry objectives. After all, the money that is made might pay for treatments, achieve other worthwhile conservation objectives, or be returned to the landowners or shareholders. Thus, efficiency analysis can help make sure we do not shortchange the potential of ecological forestry.

To help better understand the role of efficiency analysis in resource decisions, consider the issue of conservation of scarce wildlife habitats and ecosystems in the Pacific Northwest. Montgomery, Brown, and Adams (1994) synthesized a number of analyses into a trade-off curve reflecting the simultaneous pursuit of two outcomes: (1) protection of the northern spotted owl, and (2) timber harvest volume (Figure 18.3). In the Pacific Northwest, the debate over how much protection to give the northern spotted owl had raged for many years. The intensity of that debate was intimately related to how much this protection would cost, with the cost generally measured in terms of reduced timber harvest on federal forests in the region. For each level of protection of the spotted owl, efficiency analysis can help find the minimum cost (measured here in terms of lost timber harvest) of achieving a stated level of owl protection.

The curve in Figure 18.3 was derived from information in Montgomery et al. (1994). It is often called an *efficiency frontier* in that it provides the locus of points for which it is impossible to achieve more of one objective or outcome of interest (say owl protection) without having less of another (say timber harvest). All points inside (southeast) of the curve represent forest management strategies that are inefficient in that more of one objective or outcome can be obtained without having less of the other. All points outside (northwest) of the curve are infeasible in that they cannot be achieved. Put another way, efficient solutions give us the maximum of one objective or outcome for a specified level of another.

Development of efficiency frontiers can be useful for many types of natural resource problems (Box 18.4), in helping to minimize the potential conflict in achieving multiple objectives. We will utilize this concept in our examples of structured decision making in forest planning later in this chapter and in Chapter 19.

We do, though, offer two cautions about a focus on delineation of efficiency frontiers as the basis for decision making: (1) political or managerial pressure to underestimate the trade-offs, and (2) risks of managing on the efficiency frontier. We will cover each caution in turn, using trade-off analysis from the development of the Northwest Forest Plan as our example.

**Box 18.4  Simultaneously helping conserve grizzly bears and wolverines: The value of efficiency and trade-off analysis**

Dilkina et al. (2017) studied how to improve the efficiency of designing conservation corridors for at-risk species. As they note, "conservation biologists recognize that a system of isolated protected areas will be necessary but insufficient to meet biodiversity objectives. Current approaches to connecting core conservation areas through corridors consider optimal corridor placement based on a single optimization objective: commonly, maximizing the movement for a target species across a network of protected areas" (p. 192). They show that designing such corridors for single species leads to linkages that are suboptimal from both ecological and economic perspectives for multispecies connectivity objectives.

To overcome these problems, Dilkina et al. (2017) developed algorithms for optimizing corridors for multispecies use given a specific budget for land acquisition. To delineate potential wildlife corridors, Dilkina et al. (2017) used spatial analysis tools to develop landscape-resistance surfaces in which each parcel or pixel is associated with a value that indicates the resistance to movement, dispersal, or gene flow through particular landscape features for a given species. These types of models are based on the assumption that a path of higher total resistance corresponds to a more difficult or less likely route for the animals to take. Using this information and potential information on land acquisition costs on the path of any corridor, they devised an optimization framework for a budget-constrained corridor design problem that simultaneously incorporates spatially explicit models of species-specific resistances and spatially heterogeneous economic costs of conservation actions.

Dilkina et al. (2017) applied their approach in western Montana and evaluated trade-offs in connectivity for two species (grizzly bears [*Ursus arctos*] and wolverines [*Gulo gulo*] [Figure 18.4]) with different habitat requirements, different core areas, and different conservation values. They found that "incorporating a budget constraint and jointly optimizing for both species resulted in corridors that were close to the individual species movement-potential optima but with substantial cost savings" (p. 192). Their approach produced corridors that were within 14% and 11% of the best possible corridor connectivity for grizzly bears and for wolverines respectively, and saved 75% of the cost for the corridors. As they say, "Our results demonstrate economies of scale and complementarities conservation planners can achieve by optimizing corridor designs for financial costs and multiple species connectivity jointly" (p. 192).

Thus, Dilkina et al. (2017) were able to identify cost-effective corridors for both wolverines and grizzly bears simultaneously

(Figure 18.5). For each budget level, they outlined an efficiency frontier in which they found the minimum resistance for one species for a stated level of resistance for the other species. For a budget of $4.5 million, as an example, they found that a cumulative resistance of 70 for wolverines was the minimum resistance feasible for a resistance of 50 for grizzly bears and vise-versa (50 was the minimum resistance for grizzly bears for a resistance of 70 for wolverines). Points to the right and above the efficiency frontier would be called **inefficient** in the context of this budget level, in that resistance can be lowered for one species without an increase in resistance from the other. In the language of economics, such potential efficiency gains through shifting to the efficiency frontier are known as **Pareto-type improvements**.

Figure 18.4  *Wolverine. (© Can Stock Photo / Jamenpercy)*

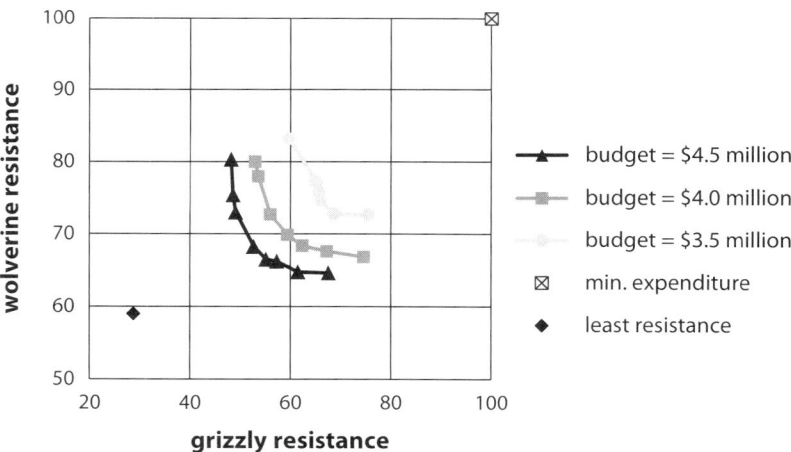

Figure 18.5  *Trade-off curves between the cumulative resistances for wolverines and grizzly bears at different budget levels (each curve is generated by varying the relative prioritization of the two species; different curves correspond to different budgets). Minimum-expenditure corridor regardless of habitat quality and least-resistance corridor regardless of cost are extreme solutions and contain no between-species trade-offs; therefore, they are represented as points in the resistance trade-off. (Republished with permission of Blackwell Publishing Inc. from Dilkina et al. 2017; permission conveyed through Copyright Clearance Center, Inc.)*

Realizing that the presence or absence of the northern spotted owl was an imperfect measure of late-successional (mature and old-growth) forest ecosystems at risk, the Forest Ecosystem Management Assessment Team (FEMAT, 1993) developed an analytical structure that recognized the habitat needs of hundreds of vertebrate and invertebrate species that use late-successional forests. The team then developed a summary trade-off curve reflecting the simultaneous pursuit of two objectives: (1) protection of habitats for the multitude of species that inhabit late-successional forests, and (2) acres of late-successional forest that would be available for harvest over time (Figure 18.6).

There was intense political pressure on the analysts to create a relatively flat trade-off surface in Figure 18.6, one in which little loss in species protection occurs with increasing area of late-successional forest available for harvest. The president of the United States was going to select one of the alternatives as his forest plan, and he wanted a choice that both protected nature and provided abundant timber harvests to support local communities. *Especially in high-level public policy decisions, pressures abound to exaggerate what is possible and overlook what is not!* Maintaining the integrity of the analysis in the face of these pressures can prove immensely challenging to an analysis team.

Let's assume for a moment that Figure 18.6 does represent the maximum amount of late successional forest that can be available for harvest for each level of species protection. That should raise questions about how risky it might be to manage on the edge of the feasible region. Perhaps some inefficiency (managing inside the feasible region) is needed to buffer risks. Thus, delineating the efficiency frontier is an important part of trade-off analysis, but it is only one ingredient in decisions; judgment is still needed.

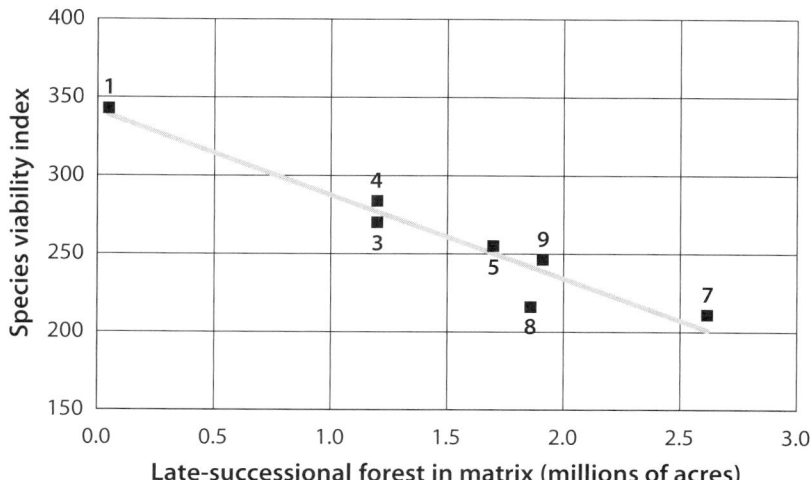

Figure 18.6  *Estimated number of late-successional species protected in relation to acres of late-successional forest available for harvest (in the matrix) for seven alternatives (nos. 1, 3, 4, 5, 7, 8, and 9) for management of the federal forests of the Pacific Northwest. (Source: FEMAT, 1993)*

## Step 6: Evaluate Trade-offs and Make a Decision

Once you have exhausted your creativity in developing alternatives, evaluating their consequences, and implementing your engagement with interested parties, it is often useful to organize the results into a *consequence table* or chart, such as shown in Figures 18.3, 18.5, and 18.6, to help you select the best choice for your forest plan, as we demonstrate below and in the next chapter. You probably will have discarded many alternatives along the way as you find others that seem to do better on all or almost all performance measures (alternatives that *dominate* others) or are more robust in the face of different potential futures. In the consequence table, you can summarize how well each alternative does against your performance measures. It is also helpful to summarize information like how robust each alternative might perform under different futures. Actually, you may construct a number of rounds of consequence tables, as seeing the information organized in this way may inspire you to create alternatives that combine the best features of a number of them.

Through this process, you may have discovered that one alternative is superior to all others on all performance measures. Or perhaps one is superior to all others on almost all measures, such that it is still seen as the best upon reflection and comparison to each of the other choices. That is a happy day indeed! However in the complicated world of forest planning, with multiple objectives and performance measures, that is not always the case. Now what?

While there are many ways to explore trade-offs, Gregory et al. (2012) suggest two basic approaches to selecting the best alternative: (1) direct ranking and (2) weighting techniques. With direct ranking, alternatives are ranked in their entirety. Assuming that a group of people are involved in the decision, their rankings can then be compared.

With weighting techniques, an overall score is developed through aggregating the scores of the different performance measures and weighting them by their importance. Since the performance measures are in different units (dollars, acres, etc.) their levels must be normalized, such as given a score of 1, 2, or 3 based on the level of the performance measure in an alternative. Then each of the normalized performance indicators for an alternative are weighted by their importance, perhaps again on a 1, 2, or 3 weight, and an aggregate score is attained. Thus, the overall score for an alternative would be:

Overall score for an alternative = $W_1X_1 + W_2X_2 + W_3X_3 + \ldots$

Where $X_1$ is the score given to performance measure 1 and $W_1$ is the weight or importance assigned to measure 1, and so on.

We will demonstrate this weighting technique for evaluating alternatives in the case study in the next chapter.

Where such approaches are needed by a group of people trying to reach agreement on an alternative to suggest to a decision maker, Gregory et al. (2012, p. 220) recommends using both weighting and ranking approaches as follows:

1. The group reviews and confirms understanding of the objectives, performance measures, alternatives, and consequences.

2. Each participant directly ranks and scores the alternatives.

3. Each participant weights the performance measures; scores and ranks are then calculated for each alternative for each participant.

4. Each participant reviews their individual results and examines inconsistencies across the two methods.

5. The group reviews aggregated results. Areas of agreement and difference among individuals are identified and discussed.

6. Each participant provides a final ranking of alternatives based on what they have learned.

7. The group clarifies key areas of agreement and disagreement in the rankings and provides reasons for any disagreements.

Gregory et al. (2012) stress that this approach is not intended to hand decision making over to a formula. Rather, it is intended to deepen people's understanding of the choices and to help them move away from positions and toward performance-based or value-based deliberations. In that way, the approach has considerable similarities to the principled negotiation approach of Fisher et al. (2011) that was the foundation of the collaboration discussion in Chapter 8.

## Step 7: Implement, Monitor, and Adapt

As we pointed out in Chapter 11 on adaptive management, forest management is fraught with uncertainties as to how forest plans will be implemented and whether they have the intended effects. Thus, monitoring, learning, and adapting is an essential part of forest planning. In Chapter 11, we suggested how that might be done as we briefly outline below.

Our focus here will be on implementation and effectiveness monitoring and resulting adaptation. This process can be seen as having four key elements:

1. *Identify key uncertainties.* Adaptive management starts with an acknowledgement of the uncertainties surrounding proposed actions. Both social uncertainty (such as whether old trees will be left at harvest as planned) and scientific uncertainty (such as whether the effects on goshawk habitat will be as assumed) may exist. Identifying key uncertainties— those suppositions crucial to achievement of plan objectives about which you are unsure—is a critical step in successful adaptive management. Further, it is useful to group key uncertainties into a few major categories, such as (1) implementation (Were the actions preformed as designed?), and (2) effectiveness (Were the objectives achieved?). In our examples here, the issue about whether old trees were left as planned would be an uncertainty about implementation and whether the effects on goshawk habitat was as assumed would be an uncertainty about effectiveness.

2. *Develop testable hypotheses about treatment success.* We need to turn the key uncertainties into testable hypotheses by reframing them as testable statements (as needed) and by adding two attributes to each statement: (1) determining what will be measured to assess the validity of the hypothesis, and (2) determining what standard (expectation) will be used to judge whether the hypothesis should be accepted or rejected. As an example, the uncertainty that timber harvest will retain old trees becomes a testable hypothesis by adding how this supposition will be measured (number of live trees over 200 years of age at diameter breast height will be cut) and the standard (expectation) by which the hypothesis will be judged (an average of less than one tree/acre over 200 years of age will be cut). As another example, the assumption that goshawks would continue to use a landscape after a restoration harvest becomes a testable hypothesis by adding a measurement approach (average number of nests that produced young/year) and a standard (at least as many successful nests in the area as before harvest).

3. *Search for information to test the hypothesis or hypotheses.* Relevant information can range from informal observations by professional resource specialists, to results of the latest formal research projects, to formal replicated experimental design; however, all approaches require a commitment to assess the validity of the proposed hypotheses.

4. *Develop mechanisms that ensure monitoring results and methodologies will undergo periodic, fair-minded review, with the goal of revising policies that are not working.* Bella (1992) emphasized the difficulty that people and organizations have in admitting that policies in which they are invested have failed to achieve

their intended objectives. This makes it important to create mechanisms that will increase the probability that management success and failure will be fairly considered and that policies can be altered as a result.

The results of the reviews of monitoring results, of course, may cause reengagement of the structured decision-making process, perhaps from the beginning but more likely from Step #5 (development of alternatives). See Chapter 11 for more detail on this process of monitoring and adaptation.

## Structured Decision Making for Ecological Forestry: An Example

Ultimately, crafting a strategic (long-term) forest plan requires extensive use of judgment. However, experience, imagination, and consistent and careful use of the concepts and procedures of structured decision making can hone your skills at successfully completing this task. They also will help improve your intuition and mental simulation ability to evaluate alternatives on the fly! Practice, though, is necessary to achieve this competence. In this section, we present an introductory problem to demonstrate planning and decision making in ecological forest management, emphasizing model building and analysis. A more sophis-

ticated and complete demonstration of structured decision making applied to forest planning, including planning over multiple time periods, can be found in Chapter 19.

### The Patch/Individual Tree Problem

**Step 1: Frame the Problem**    Debora Lee Hanson (Figure 18.7) and her family (two teenagers) own 200 acres of pine forest in the foothills of the Rockies (Figure 18.8). They built a small cabin on the property, where they stay on weekends. They love their forest but have trouble keeping up with the taxes on it. Debora Lee sees residential developments springing up around her but feels selling parts of the forest for home sites is a last resort. At a family council, she suggests they may have to start cutting some of their trees to enable them to keep the property intact. Also, Debora Lee points out that reducing stand density could help moderate the effects of a future wildfire.

At first that idea does not sit well with her daughters, but they finally agree that harvest might be acceptable if the harvest emulates nature. Debora Lee and her children also begin to make a list of worthy projects for any money they make from the harvests not needed for taxes, such as removing invasive plants that are taking over their meadow and rocking a road that is impassible in the winter.

In speaking with the local extension agent, Debora Lee learns that, historically, her forest probably burned periodically, with the fires killing scattered individual trees and, occasionally, small groups—a frequent-fire forest similar to those described in Chapter 3. That information gives them an idea of what a "natural forest" would look like.

**Step 2: Develop an Engagement Strategy**    Debora Lee knows that she will not have peace in the family if she adopts a plan that her children do not accept, so she wants to find a plan that reflects their wishes too, as long as she can make enough money to pay the taxes. Thus, we might say that she chooses an engagement strategy that we called "Involve" in Table 18.6: she will accommodate the desire of her children for a natural forest to the degree that it does not prevent making enough income from the forest to pay the taxes, and possibly do some other good works.

**Step 3: Identify Objectives and Performance Measures** What are the fundamental objectives and the means objectives? We might view the desire to keep the forest in the family (not having to sell the forest due to the taxes on it) and the desire for a natural forest are the fundamental objectives—they are not a means to other objectives but important in their own right. Further, receiving income from timber harvest and achieving or maintaining the fine-grained nature of the spatial pattern of the forest and the old and gnarly trees might be viewed as means objectives—

Figure 18.7 *Debora Lee at work in her forest.*

Figure 18.8 *Leave tree marking for a forest restoration project (individual tree) in the Colorado Front Range. (Photo courtesy of Tony Cheng)*

they are ways to help achieve the more fundamental objectives at the heart of the problem.

With this knowledge of the natural history of the forest, the family settles on two possible management strategies to provide the net income/year to pay the taxes: (1) Debora Lee's kids want to take out carefully marked individual trees, because they believe this form of harvest will best maintain the natural character of the forest; (2) Debora Lee wants to cut small patches (up to an acre in size) because she thinks it will make more money. In both cases, they plan to leave all old-growth trees and gnarly wildlife trees alone (as critical natural capital). Also, Debora Lee agrees to recognize the 20 acres around their cabin as a special place and use the individual tree strategy there.

They next form a table summarizing their fundamental objectives, means objectives, and performance measures (Table 18.8). The performance measures reflecting means objectives of income from harvest and keeping the old trees come easily; they also settle on a measure for maintaining the forest's fine-grain character.

**Steps 4 and 5: Create Alternatives and Estimate Their Consequences**   Debora Lee plans to supervise their harvests and have her children do the marking, sale layout, and planting on their weekend trips to the property—she thinks that will be good for their understanding of forestry and a way for them to earn money. Debora Lee estimates that her children each have about 225 hours available/year for this project. Also, she estimates it will take her children about one hour/year for each acre allocated to the patch strategy and about three hours/year for each acre allocated to the individual tree strategy to implement the plan.

Debora Lee's kids insist that they replant openings, and the local seedling nursery told her they could provide up to 3,600 seedlings each year. Debora Lee estimates she will need about 20 seedlings/year for each acre she allocates to the patch strategy to reforest the portion of those acres she cuts each year. Also, she estimates she will need about 10 seedlings/year for each acre she allocates to the individual tree strategy to do some spot planting after harvest.[5]

Debora Lee works with a forestry consultant to estimate the likely net income from an acre managed under each strategy—about $25/year for each acre managed under the patch strategy and $20/year for each acre managed under the individual tree strategy.

Finally, as mentioned previously, Debora Lee agrees to make sure that 20 acres around their cabin are allocated to the individual tree strategy.

With this information as background, Debora Lee and her children want to understand how much money they might make from their forest and how much land would be allocated to each of the two management strategies. To do that analysis, Debora Lee creates a simple two-variable planning model relating a selected performance measure (called the *objective function*) to the constraints on its achievement through the available activities (called the *decision variables*).

---

5 The per acre coefficients are the average/year incurred on an acre allocated to the patch or the individual tree strategy. In each year only a portion of the area allocated to the strategy will be harvested. We will explicitly represent time in forest planning problems in the next chapter.

**Table 18.8** *Objectives and performance measures for the patch/individual tree problem*

| Fundamental objective | Means objective | Performance measure |
|---|---|---|
| Keep the forest in the family | Make enough money from harvest to pay the taxes | Net income/year |
| Have a natural forest | Achieve or maintain the fine-gain character of the forest and the old and gnarly trees | Proportion of the forest managed using the individual tree strategy or left unharvested. Proportion of old and wildlife trees retained |

Decision variables:

$X_1$: Acres allocated to patch strategy

$X_2$: Acres allocated to individual tree strategy

Objective function: maximize net income/year

Maximize $25X_1 + 20X_2$
where:

$25 = net income/year from each acre allocated to patch strategy

$20 = net income/year from each acre allocated to the individual tree strategy

Constraints:

a) Land: 200 acres available to be allocated among the two harvest strategies

or

$1X_1 + 1X_2 \leq 200$

b) Seedlings: 3,600 seedlings/year available to support the two strategies

20/acre for each acre allocated to the patch strategy

10/acre for each acre allocated to the individual tree strategy

or

$20X_1 + 10X_2 \leq 3,600$

c) Labor: 450 hours/year available to support the two strategies

1 hour/acre for each acre allocated to the patch strategy

3 hours/acre for each acre allocated to the individual tree strategy

or

$1X_1 + 3X_2 \leq 450$

d) Individual tree objective: A minimum of 20 acres must be allocated to individual tree strategy

or

$X_2 \geq 20$

In summary form, her model is:

Maximize $25X_1 + 20X_2$
where:

$X_1$ = acres allocated to patch strategy

$X_2$ = acres allocated to individual tree strategy

Subject to the constraints:

a) Land    $1X_1 + 1X_2 \leq 200$

b) Seedlings    $20X_1 + 10X_2 \leq 3,600$

c) Labor    $1X_1 + 3X_2 \leq 450$

d) Individual tree    $X_2 \geq 20$

She uses an approach called **linear programming** to find an "efficient" solution to this problem—the allocation of acres among the two strategies that yields the highest annual net income given other objectives and limitations. Linear programming is a solution technique for problems that can be expressed as linear equations. Since its development in World War II, linear programming has been employed in thousands of applications in business, government, and natural resources. (See the Appendix for a detailed presentation of the analysis done here.)

The solution to Debora Lee's problem yields the following results: acres of patch strategy = 160; acres of individual tree strategy = 40; and annual net income = $4,800. Since the individual tree strategy produces less income/acre allocated to it than the patch strategy, she is surprised that more than 20 acres are devoted to it. She then realizes that a solution of 160/40 uses up all the seedlings 160 × 20 + 40 × 10 = 3,600. Any more acres allocated to the patch strategy would require more seedlings than allowed under the seedling constraint.

She then takes these results to a family meeting. Debora Lee is happy that they might be able to pay the taxes on the property and have enough money left to do other projects. Her children, on the other hand, are disappointed with how little forest is devoted to the individual tree strategy. They think the objective function pursued should reflect their desire to minimize the amount of forest allocated to the patch strategy. Toward that end, Debora Lee says that she will redo the analysis with the objective of minimizing the acres allocated to the patch strategy at different income

Table 18.9 *Solution values and binding constraints for five variations of the patch/individual tree problem, in which the acres allocated to the patch strategy are minimized subject to different required levels of income (ITS = individual tree strategy)*

| Alternative | Minimum income ($) | Solution values for decision variables | | | Binding Constraints |
| | | Patch strategy (acres) | ITS strategy (acres) | Reserved (acres) | |
| --- | --- | --- | --- | --- | --- |
| 1 | 4,800 | 160 | 40 | 0 | Land, Seedlings, Income |
| 2 | 4,500 | 100 | 100 | 0 | Land, Income |
| 3 | 4,000 | 54.5 | 131.8 | 13.7 | Labor, Income |
| 4 | 3,500 | 27.2 | 140.9 | 31.9 | Labor, Income |
| 5 | 3,000 | 0 | 150 | 50 | Labor, Income |

levels[6] from \$3,000 (the minimum to pay the taxes) to \$4,800 (the maximum possible given the constraints). Thus the model formulation is now:

Minimize $X_1$

   where:

   $X_1$ = acres allocated to patch strategy

   $X_2$ = acres allocated to individual tree strategy

   Subject to the constraints

   a) Land    $1X_1 + 1X_2 \leq 200$

   b) Seedlings    $20X_1 + 10X_2 \leq 3,600$

   c) Labor    $1X_1 + 3X_2 \leq 450$

   d) Min. income/yr    $25X_1 + 20X_2 \geq R$,
      where R = 3,000, 3,500, 4,000, 4,500, or 4,800

The children are pleased with the resulting simulations (Table 18.9) and plan to use them to lobby for allocating fewer acres to the patch strategy when they meet to decide on the mix of harvest strategies they will employ.

An important aspect of this type of analysis is that it reveals which constraints are limiting attainment of the objective function; these are referred to as **binding constraints**. This information helps display the sensitivity of the solution to different levels of these controls. As an example, Debora Lee notices that the ability to shift away from the patch strategy, which uses less labor/acre than the individual tree strategy, is increasingly dependent on the amount of labor available as the income requirement is lowered; at the lower income levels, labor replaces land as a binding constraint and not all the land is needed for harvest (some of it can be reserved).

That relationship becomes very important when her oldest child announces that she is thinking of going to Oregon State University to study forestry the following year and might not be available to work in the family forest. What

would happen to Debora Lee's analysis and trade-offs if the available labor was halved to 225 hours? To find out, she can rerun her alternatives at this lower amount of available labor (Table 18.10).

These alternatives are just the tip of the iceberg of choices that Debora Lee and her kids might consider. They do, though, begin to illuminate some possibilities and their implications, and also show how complicated a seemingly simple problem can become.

Of course, these two formulations are only a partial statement of Debora Lee's problem. Many objectives and considerations are implicit in how we set up the problem— in the example here, large clearcuts and sale to developers were not allowed, old-growth and wildlife trees were retained, and labor came only from the family. Also, the satisfaction associated with many other objectives and considerations can't be easily quantified—the value the Hanson family feels in walking through their forest, their desire to provide homes for a multitude of animals, and their wish to hand down the forest from generation to generation, among many others. Still, crystallizing some of the objectives and constraints can help us think through management of this forest, so long as we do not forget these other equally important considerations.

**Step 6: Evaluate Trade-offs and Select a Forest Plan**    After Debora Lee and family exhaust themselves with this analysis, they still will need to make decisions. This analysis does not do that. At its best, the analysis portrays the implications of alternatives for the multiple objectives, using methods that minimize the trade-offs that must be made. A decision must still be made.

To help Debora Lee and her daughters make a decision, they have created Tables 18.9 and 18.10 and Figure 18.9 showing the consequences of their alternatives under different potential futures (different levels of available labor). From these tables and figures, they can assess the trade-offs as they move between alternatives. Some relationships jump out at them (Tables 18.9 and 18.10 and Figure 18.9):

---

6  Minimizing the area allocated to the patch strategy is the same as maximizing the area allocated to the individual tree strategy + reserves.

Table 18.10 *Solution values and binding constraints for five variations of the patch/individual tree problem, after a halving of the available labor, in which the acres allocated to the patch strategy are minimized subject to different required levels of income (ITS = individual tree strategy)*

| Alternative | Minimum income ($) | Solution values for decision variables | | | Binding Constraints |
| | | Patch strategy (acres) | ITS strategy (acres) | Reserved (acres) | |
| --- | --- | --- | --- | --- | --- |
| 1 | 4,800 | ------ | ----- | ----- | Infeasible |
| 2 | 4,500 | 163.6 | 20.5 | 15.9 | Labor Income |
| 3 | 4,000 | 136.4 | 29.5 | 34.1 | Labor, Income |
| 4 | 3,500 | 109.1 | 38.6 | 52.3 | Labor, Income |
| 5 | 3,000 | 81.8 | 47.7 | 70.5 | Labor, income |

- With both children available to work, they can raise the area in the individual tree strategy from 40 to 100 acres, equal to those in the patch strategy, if they will drop the needed income by only $300 (from $4,800 to $4,500).

- With only one child able to work, an income of $4,800 is not attainable.

- Some of the forest is not needed for a required income at or below $4,000 at both labor levels; land is no longer a binding constraint as shown in the last column of Table 18.9 and Table 18.10 and some forest can be reserved. Rather, labor becomes the key restriction. And at an income of $3,000, with both children able to work, the forest can be managed through a combination of the individual tree strategy and reserves.

- Labor is a key to minimizing trade-offs (Figure 18.9): with sufficient labor, Debora Lee can have both a relatively high income and a forest mostly allocated to individual tree selection—an outcome that should make the entire family happy. If her oldest child does leave for college, she might want to rethink her reluctance to use outside labor.

So what will Debora Lee do? With this simple problem, she may not need to resort to the alternative weighting approach for Step 6 discussed previously, but she still might find it useful to have each person rank the alternatives under both futures. Also, many of the elements of naturalistic decision making, discussed earlier, may come into play as she chooses among these alternatives.

We earlier introduced two ways in which people assess and improve robustness and adaptability of their forest management decisions: (1) sensitivity analysis and (2) scenario planning. Examining the implications of reduced availability of labor, due to Debora Lee's oldest daughter going off to college, provides an example of a sensitivity analysis that highlights the potential vulnerability of her assumption that she will use only her children for labor. Thus, Debora Lee might begin assessing other potential sources of labor.

Also, Debora Lee might step back and engage more broadly in scenario development and planning. We will consider two scenarios here: (1) the development scenario and (2) the fire scenario. Both reflect potential changes in future environmental, economic, and social conditions that might substantially affect Debora Lee's ability to successfully manage her forest:

- The development scenario: Pressures for development might accelerate, with a substantial increase in property tax, to the degree that some combination of the patch and individual tree strategies will no longer suffice. How might consideration of this scenario affect her management? As an example, she might work with the children to locate

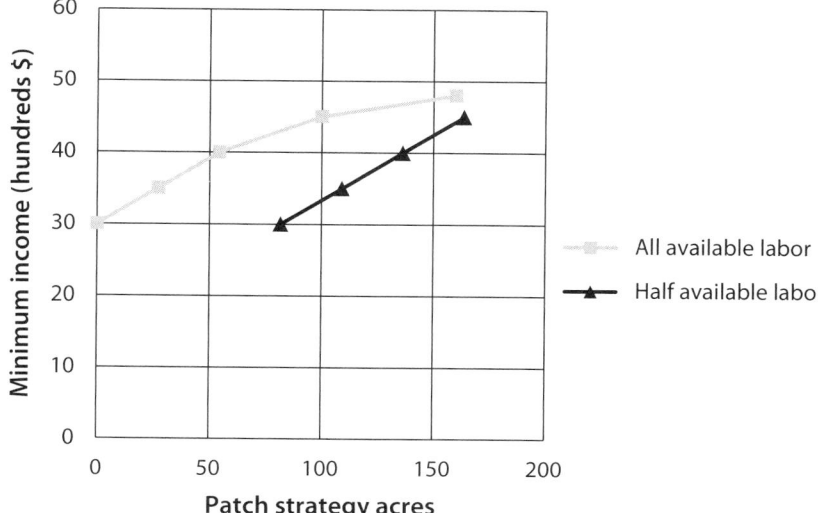

Figure 18.9 *Trade-off between acres allocated to the patch strategy and the income required under two different levels of labor availability.*

the portion of the forest they would be most willing to part with—probably the part farthest from their cabin. She also might investigate the possibility of a Conservation Easement in which she sells her development rights, as we discussed in Box 10.4, and is then assigned a lower property tax. She also might harvest more trees. At a minimum, she should probably begin to think through how to react to a situation where her tax payment strategy does not suffice.

- The fire scenario: Debora Lee's forest is in an area of Colorado that has experienced numerous wildfires in the past decade, but her patch/individual tree strategy should help reduce the potential for a crown fire in her forest. Also, her neighbors have been managing their forests to reduce fuel hazards. However, they have suggested they might sell their forests. What if the new owners manage their properties as reserves, allowing a buildup of fuels and not maintaining their roads for access for fire fighters? That would increase the chance that a fire could roar though their property as a crown fire, putting her forest at risk. Perhaps putting a road or fire break at the edge of the property would help. Also, she might work with the neighbors to jointly reduce fuels at the property boundaries. With some chance of wildfire on or near her property over the next decade, she might be worried enough to immediately talk to whomever buys the property about a joint strategy.

These two examples are intended to provide a brief introduction for how scenario planning might help in decision making. The subject has a very rich and deep literature, with Van der Heijden (2005) a good introduction.

**Step 7: Implement, Monitor, and Adapt**   As we described earlier, implementation and effectiveness monitoring can be seen as having four key elements (Table 18.11):

1. *Identify key uncertainties.* After discussion with the extension agent and her children, Debora Lee decides to focus on one implementation uncertainty and two effectiveness uncertainties:

   a. *Implementation uncertainty:* whether the harvest will leave the old trees in the forest. Those trees have the highest financial return of any trees and her children are skeptical as to whether they will be retained.

   b. *Effectiveness uncertainties:* (1) whether the management plan will provide the projected income and (2) whether the forest will retain its natural appearance where individual tree harvests occur.

2. *Develop testable hypotheses about treatment success.* We need to turn the key uncertainties into testable hypotheses by reframing them as testable statements (as needed) and by adding two attributes to each statement: (1) determining what will be measured to assess the validity of the hypothesis, and (2) determining what standard (expectation) will be used to judge whether the hypothesis should be accepted or rejected (Table 18.11).

3. *Search for information to test the hypothesis or hypotheses.* Debora Lee and her children will gather relevant information to assess the validity of the proposed hypotheses (Table 18.11).

Table 18.11 *Sample monitoring outline as part of the adaptive management plan for the patch/individual tree problem*

| Key uncertainty | Hypothesis | Measure | Standard (Expectation) | Monitoring method |
|---|---|---|---|---|
| *IMPLEMENTATION* | | | | |
| Whether harvests will harm old trees | Treatments will not cut old trees | # of trees cut over 100 years of age | An average less than one tree cut per acre | Post project survey by the children |
| *EFFECTIVENESS* | | | | |
| Implementing the management plan will produce the projected income | Allocating XX acres to patch strategy and YY acres to individual tree strategy will produce the projected income | $/year over five years | Average income over five years will be at least 95% of projected | Annual accounting by Debora Lee |
| Forest allocated to the individual tree strategy will retain its natural appearance | Acres allocated to the individual tree strategy will still seem like a forest after harvest | Proportion of the harvested acres in the individual tree allocation that do not appear "cutover" | More than 90% of these acres pass the test | Annual survey by Debora Lee's children |

Table 18.12 *How forest planning models (FPMs) might help or hinder forest planning*

| An FPM can help by | An FPM can hinder by |
|---|---|
| Enabling consideration of detailed and complex information and relationships | Committing the organization to a system beyond its capability |
| Surfacing nonobvious results | Creating a slow, expensive, cumbersome process |
| Providing a mechanism to help organize and channel thinking | Restricting creative thinking |
| Providing a consistent framework for implementation and further analysis | Focusing effort on the wrong problems |
| Providing an institutional memory for adaptive management | Deemphasizing unknown or poorly known (but important) aspects of a system |
| Improving the information base | Creating the illusion of certainty and knowledge |
| Increasing understanding and value of modeling among stakeholders | Creating a modeling priesthood |
| Improving transparency and credibility with stakeholders/public/policy makers | Causing a feeling of powerlessness that discourages participation |

*Source:* Adapted from Johnson & Gordon (2007).

4. *Develop mechanisms that ensure monitoring results and methodologies will undergo periodic, fair-minded review, with the goal of revising policies that are not working.* Debora Lee and her children agree to meet once a year to compile and interpret their monitoring results, with the extension forester who advised them on developing the plan also present to give an outsider's perspective.

## Forest Planning Models: Help or Hindrance?[7]

Sooner or later, most forest managers face the question of whether to use a sophisticated forest planning model (FPM) to help them understand the implications of different alternative management strategies for their forest. There are a number of software *decision aids* available[8] to assist in this task. In addition, they might think about building their own!

As we discuss here, FPMs have earned a mixed reputation, with many pros and cons (Table 18.12). We cover some of the ways they may help or hinder forest planning below, along with examples of where they have helped forest management planning (Box 18.5) and where they have hindered it (Box 18.6). We then offer some suggestions for getting the most that you can from your efforts.

## How an FPM Can Help Problem Solving and Decision Making

In our discussion, we will elaborate on points from Table 18.12 about how FPMs can help forest planning, utilizing an example from the OSU College Forest (Box 18.5).

### Points to Consider about the Potential Helpfulness of FPMs

*Enabling consideration of detailed and complex information and relationships*   Earlier in this chapter, we discussed the strengths of human decision makers, including their impressive capability for pattern matching and mental simulation. Still, many forest management problems consider many objectives, involve thousands or millions of acres, and look decades into the future—simply too much analytical complexity for mental simulation. Computer models can be an excellent complement to people in this situation. In planning the OSU College Forest, as an example, the planning team built a harvest scheduling model to coordinate the management of 500 stands over ten planning periods to achieve a stable harvest and high revenue, to distribute harvest across zones, and to demonstrate a variety of harvest methods to provide examples for instructional use by the college.

*Surfacing nonobvious results*   Complex models are sometimes criticized because they incorporate so many interacting uncertainties. How can one possibly claim that they have any accuracy (or relevance) when they contain so much embedded uncertainty? We believe the point of modeling

---

7  This section relies heavily on the ideas of Johnson & Gordon (2007).

8  As an example, *Woodstock* by Remsoft Inc. is a widely used mathematical programming system in forest planning, with both linear and nonlinear programming capability. www.remsoft.com/forestry.php

is not so much to enhance accuracy as it is to bring forward outcomes that otherwise would have escaped our view. What might happen given the interaction of all these various elements—developments that our mental simulations alone may have trouble with?

Patterns and processes not immediately apparent to the decision makers emerge from the results of modeling exercises. If these emergent properties make sense (are believable), those involved in the modeling exercise have learned something new that may be useful to their collective decisions. In the case of the OSU College Forest, modeling quickly revealed a cash flow crunch in the first few analysis periods that became a focus of problem-solving efforts.

*Providing a mechanism to help organize and channel thinking (build capacity)*   Group decision making is often chaotic and plagued by differing worldviews, knowledge, and interests. Especially if deliberation is ongoing or arduous, it can be difficult to keep a group focused and to bring their expertise together in some common framework. The structure of a modeling effort, and the models themselves, can be a powerful integrative force.

A major use of these models is to test the consistency of assumptions that people make about the management of forests, thus enabling assessment of the many ideas that managers and stakeholders have. In the case of the College Forest, a key question was: can we proceed with the use of

---

**Box 18.5  When FPM Helped: FORPLAN and the Oregon State University College Forest (adapted from Johnson & Gordon, 2007)**

In the early 1990s, the dean of the College of Forestry (COF) at Oregon State University (OSU) wanted a forest plan developed for the OSU College Forest—a 12,000-acre Douglas-fir forest in the foothills of the Coast Range near Corvallis, Oregon. First, faculty worked with a variety of stakeholders to illuminate the concerns, future vision, and possible objectives for the forest. Then the dean formed a faculty committee to construct the forest plan itself—a plan that would describe the long-term forest condition that would be sought and the activities (especially harvests) that would occur in the next 10 years, reflecting the objectives suggested in the stakeholder discussions and those developed during further conversations between the dean and faculty.

The faculty team met three hours every week for five months as they solidified a vision of forest management that would best meet the different objectives that had been identified earlier. As part of that effort, the team wanted an estimate of the types of harvest that would occur and the harvest volume and revenue that would result. To do that, they used a quantitative decision support system (FORPLAN) and worked back and forth with the modelers and the dean to solidify a plan that would best meet the agreed-upon objectives.

Once the faculty team settled on a plan that seemed reasonable, the team explained the proposed plan to a broader group of faculty and staff and then took it to leaders in the community for advice and consultation, which generated several further adjustments to the plan. Upon its public announcement and description, the local press, which had initially been hostile to the effort, became enormously supportive, and the plan was implemented and largely followed for the next decade.

The OSU College Forest Plan was developed and approved in 1994, and then implemented over the period 1994–2003—one of the few public forest plans successfully implemented in Oregon during the 1990s. FORPLAN, a timber harvest scheduling FPM, was successfully used in this planning effort. What were the keys to that success?

We can identify at least five reasons for the usefulness of FORPLAN in this effort, potentially instructive for any organization that might choose to use an FPM:

1. FORPLAN was a mature, well-tested system, and an experienced FORPLAN user and forest planner was at the controls.

2. FORPLAN was not the focus of the planning effort, nor was it the final answer; rather, FORPLAN was used as a mechanism to try out ideas in a back-and-forth discussion about the implications of different proposed plans, and to help the college faculty refine their intuition about how the forest worked—an ideal use of a decision support system.

3. The FORPLAN analysis targeted one crucial aspect of forest planning on the OSU College Forest: the harvest level and associated revenue for the next decade, in the context of sustaining that revenue through time. While the problem definition changed slightly as the analysis was done, information on harvests and revenues remained an important element in the analysis during the entire planning process.

4. Proposed harvest sites and silvicultural methods for the first decade were mapped and shown to policy makers, managers, faculty, and the operations (implementation) crew, which triggered revisions and subsequent improvements to the forest plan.

5. The FORPLAN analysis was deeply embedded in a social process of plan revision. From the initial discussion with stakeholders, to the numerous meetings of the faculty team, to the check-ins with the dean, to the review with the community, to the interaction between the planners and the implementation crew as they poured over maps of the harvest schedule, the plan was developed through a process of analysis, debate, challenge, and compromise.

the forest for teaching, research, and extension projects while still producing sufficient revenue to cover costs and produce income for the College of Forestry? As you might expect, the college faculty had many opinions here, and the FPM provided a tool that could help sort through this issue.

***Providing a consistent framework for implementation*** FPMs can capture a group's knowledge in such a way that it is accessible to a wide variety of people in the organization. It can also document what type of management is to occur where, integrating a variety of factors such as variable stream-buffer widths and special forest types. Before foresters plan operations, they can check the modeling results to make sure the operations are compatible with their overall land use plan. This can help provide the organizational coordination and control needed to meet regulatory demands and public expectations. The harvest scheduling map that resulted from interaction of the faculty with the modeling effort for the College Forest, for example, proved invaluable in directing management over the decade.

***Providing an institutional memory for adaptive management*** Assessments based on expert opinion can be difficult to document. How exactly did a group of experts arrive at a particular conclusion? One or two years later, when an assessment is being considered for another decision, no one might be able to recall. Using an FPM provides an explicit statement of how the assessment was done, and the model can be updated as new data and knowledge come into play. In general, this type of dynamic institutional memory resembles adaptive management in that it allows decisions to be viewed as hypotheses, which then can be supported, rejected, or refined as new information becomes available. It also greatly eases plan revision, as it did for the College Forest, by functioning as a repository of the information and relationships underlying the forest plan.

***Improving the information base*** FPMs tend to be data hungry, meaning they require considerable data about the problem at hand, such as forest inventories, habitat classifications, or species–habitat relationships. FPMs can help organize available information in a decision-relevant

---

Box 18.6 **When FPM Hurt: FORPLAN and the National Forests (adapted from Johnson & Gordon, 2007)**

In early 1977, the USDA Forest Service announced that FORPLAN, the timber harvest scheduling FPM discussed in Box 18.5, would be used as the primary analysis tool (decision support tool) for forest planning as the Forest Service developed new forest plans under the recently enacted National Forest Management Act. Forest Service leaders wished to have a standard approach to considering alternative management strategies for managing the national forests—an understandable goal. With this announcement, the Forest Service committed itself to a single decision support system for all 120 administrative units covering 190 million acres.

Thus began a futile 15-year odyssey of the Forest Service, which consumed hundreds of millions of dollars and untold human resources, to develop the optimal timber harvest schedule for each national forest. In the end, few of the plans developed using FORPLAN analysis were implemented, and many, many people became disenchanted with decision support models for forest planning.

Use of FORPLAN was unsuccessful for at least six reasons; these reasons my be instructive for any organization that might choose to use a decision support system:

1. FORPLAN was not a finished or widely understood system before the Forest Service staff attempted to use it. The developers continued its testing and repair as it was being implemented—a fairly reliable recipe for disaster.
2. Forest planners were required to use FORPLAN as their central analysis tool. This created enormous

resentment because the planning teams did not have the freedom to pick the decision support methods that best fit the problems they were expected to address.
3. FORPLAN was exceedingly difficult to understand. Thus, harvest schedules were produced without planners being able to explain why these solutions were "best" or where they came from. This created a sense of powerlessness and frustration among the Forest Service planning teams and the public.
4. Many wildlife habitat considerations of interest had important spatial dimensions that were difficult to represent in a planning model like FORPLAN. These spatial issues were especially important for protection of at-risk species like the northern spotted owl—it was not only the amount of habitat that was important but also how that habitat was distributed across the landscape.
5. Use of FORPLAN assumed that the central resource planning problem on the national forests was to find a sustainable harvest level within environmental constraints. But, as we now know, it turned out that the central resource planning problem was to find scientifically credible conservation strategies for at-risk species, and for biodiversity in general.
6. FORPLAN was embedded in a technical, rather than a social, planning process. Thus, planning was viewed as a technical analysis, rather than a social negotiation.

framework and identify missing information needs. Such was the case in the OSU College Forest effort.

***Increasing understanding and value of modeling among stakeholders***   At its best, the iterative use of FPMs in brainstorming can increase the understanding and appreciation of planning teams and stakeholders in FPMs as planning aids, along with the improved ability to think in terms of objectives, constraints, and trade-offs. In the OSU College Forest case, the ability to immediately assess the faculty team's latest ideas and compare them to their previous ideas proved the worth of these types of models to them, and provided a framework that they could relate to for thinking through the forest planning problem.

***Improving transparency and credibility with stakeholders/ policy makers***   Scientific and technical analyses tend to have privileged roles in decision making. FPMs can reflect this type of thinking and so may enhance the credibility of the decision processes in which they are used. The ability to trace the path from assumptions to results should not be underestimated as a way to provide understanding and improve credibility. The OSU modeling helped enormously in providing a believable process for assessing the implications of choices.

## How an FPM Can Hinder Problem Solving and Decision Making

In our discussion, we will elaborate on points from Table 18.12 about how FPMs can hinder forest planning, primarily utilizing an example from planning on the national forests of the US (Box 18.6).

### Points to Consider about the Potential Hindrances of FPMs

***Committing the organization to a system beyond its capacity to implement***   If you take the FPM plunge, it's likely you will need at least one person to devote significant time to modeling forest planning alternatives. In practice, model documentation can be poor, knowledgeable people scarce, and learning curves steep. In addition, the ability to collect the data needed for the modeling represents a very important and sometimes overlooked aspect of capacity. Common data needs are land-cover maps, forest inventories, and species–habitat relationships, locations of special places, and information reflective of the interests, values, and preferences of decision makers and stakeholders. The Forest Service use of FORPLAN proved to be a classic case of commitment to a system beyond the capacity of the organization to implement.

***Creating a slow, expensive, cumbersome process***   Even if your organization has the capacity to do modeling, it is likely that it will take significant time and effort. Time is needed to complete the analysis, and this must be reconciled with the decision environment. In our experience, use of an FPM requires many months, in part because of the data that must be gathered or organized to populate the models that will be used. In addition, successful use of an FPM will undoubtedly require back-and-forth discussion and revision as people begin to understand the results. Modeling is not like building a bridge, where the work is done and the ribbon is cut. You can expect that a significant portion of the modeling time will be spent revising alternatives people thought they wanted, but that changed once they saw where they lead. Wildly unrealistic planning deadlines combined with inadequate computational support for FORPLAN led to repeated slippage of timelines.

***Restricting creative thinking***   Although FPMs can help bring forward nonobvious results, they also may restrict creative thinking. Each type of modeling comes with its own assumptions and limitations. Further, once time and effort have been sunk into an FPM, it becomes the default conceptual framework for understanding how the world works and the consequences of different decisions. In the end, FORPLAN's harvest scheduling focus greatly inhibited the brainstorming of planning teams.

***Focusing effort on the wrong problem***   As mentioned in Box 18.6, Forest Service use of FORPLAN addressed the wrong resource planning problem: sustainable harvest levels were not the key issue in forest planning to policy makers, or to the courts; rather, it was credible conservation strategies to protect species at risk, and biodiversity in general. The use of FORPLAN delayed this realization.

Many decision making processes are fast moving and fragmented; the primary criteria for decision making can literally change overnight. The Chesapeake Forest Project is one example from cases documented by Gordon (2007) in which the center of attention changed radically. The FPM focused on trade-offs between timber production and habitat for the endangered Delmarva fox squirrel but, when the process was opened for public comment, few were interested in this problem. Public access to the forestlands for hunting game species quickly came to dominate the discussion, something that the Chesapeake FPM did not address at all.

***Deemphasizing unknown or poorly known aspects of a system***   FPMs will tend to focus efforts on the aspects of the problem for which the most data are available, but these areas may not actually be the most important relative to the objectives. Expert opinion and local qualitative knowledge may become much more important than the quantitative information typically used in an FPM; in such cases, a process for incorporating this nonquantitative knowledge is needed. This can be especially true in the conservation of at-risk species, where habitat needs often are imperfectly quantified in the scientific literature.

***Creating the illusion of certainty and knowledge*** Computer models are generally associated with precision, and outputs from FPMs typically have an appearance of certainty. Tables, graphs, and maps all exhibit vast amounts of orderly information, one value per cell. But much of the information going into an FPM is likely to be imprecise. Further, these imprecise data are combined using our inexact knowledge about their relationships. This illusion of certainty can sometimes be addressed by quantifying uncertainty, but this is too rarely done. Even if done, such meta-analyses may be difficult to understand and are consequently ignored. Certainly the harvest schedules that poured out of FORPLAN gave the illusion of certainty that was hard to argue against.

***Creating a modeling priesthood*** Developing and using analytical models usually requires specialized expertise and is therefore restricted to a few specialists with this knowledge. The rest of the participants in the problem-solving process may have little idea of how the model works. Everyone may have to go through these analysts to get their ideas vetted and rely heavily on modeling specialists for formulating alternatives to fit within the model framework. Then, it may be difficult for anyone other than the analysts to understand and explain the results. Such an insulation of modelers from the rest of the world, especially from their planning team, is a recipe for disaster as it does not enable the social processes of planning to work effectively. FORPLAN analysis provided ample evidence of this difficulty, with the most critical person in planning the future of a national forest often a young and inexperienced planning analyst.

***Causing a feeling of powerlessness that discourages participation*** Many of the potential disadvantages can generate a feeling of powerlessness and discourage participation. An organization might take on a modeling project beyond its capacity and end up feeling that it simply cannot solve the problem (instead of realizing that the modeling approach needs to change). Participants may feel that the wrong problem is being addressed but that they cannot change the focus because the modeling approach has been set. Or, even if the focus is useful, they may feel that their ideas must be filtered through an unsympathetic "priesthood" of analysts. If such a process gets drawn out by time-consuming analyses, it should not be surprising that participation is likely to wane.

## Improving the Chances that an FPM Can Help Decision Making

Whoa! That is a pretty daunting list of hindrances. How do we get back to the helpful side of modeling? Well there is no magic formula, but here are a few ideas. First, read back through how FPMs can help forest planning and the positive experience on the OSU College Forest (Box 18.5). FPMs can provide invaluable support for forest planning, but success takes thought, effort, and persistence in the face of difficulty. Second, learning about potential pitfalls should help you be alert for them and be more prepared to overcome them. Third, you should remember:

- Forest planning is a social process with some technical calculations, not the reverse. At its best, forest planning is an improvisational learning process for all involved—an open, welcoming approach will work wonders here.

- If users (that is, people who use the FPM results, not just the users of the software) are involved in the application from the beginning, they can be empowered in decision making.

- Forest planning is inherently nonlinear, even if it does use linear programming as a simulation tool. Expect and encourage feedback loops and a roller-coaster ride for all.

- Forest planning can be an exciting, surprising voyage of discovery with many "aha" moments. Have fun and keep your spirits up!

## Integrating Naturalistic and Structured Decision Making

Forest conservation and management decisions almost always involve both naturalistic and structured decisions, and much negotiation along the way. Think back to Debora Lee's problem. She immediately ruled out selling the land for development. That decision happened after relatively little analysis but reflected deeply held beliefs of her family. Then she undertook a structured analysis of her forestry problem and began discussions with her family about the results she had found. That resulted in a reformulation of her original thinking and also the development of scenarios that reflected some of the uncertainties she faces.

At their best, models should be seen as tools for informing debates, dialogues, and deliberations. Modeling can open new avenues of thought, stimulate learning and encourage deliberation, and uncover multiple aspects of the problems under consideration. In this sense, modeling can help engage and improve the intuition and mental simulation skills so important to the decisions we make.

## Appendix: Developing Efficient Alternatives with Linear Programming[9]

We used linear programming to create internally efficient alternatives for Debora Lee's patch/individual tree problem—a type of mathematical programming often used in forest planning. However, linear programming is a tool to inform debate, not a tool to end debate. Efficient solutions provided by linear programming do not by themselves give answers; they do, however, provide a systematic and quantitative process for estimating the consequences of alternatives that reflect specific objectives and constraints.

To build a linear programming model, we need to specify an objective function to guide the solution, decision variables that we can manipulate to achieve the objective, and a set of constraints on the activities that can be selected, as we did for the patch/individual tree problem. We then solve the model repeatedly, varying the level of constraints or the performance measure selected for the objective function. In this way, we can delineate a wide variety of efficient alternatives, which will enable us to assess trade-offs implicit in achieving objectives and to recognize the constraints controlling the solution.

Components of a linear programming formulation of a resource problem include:

- *Decision variables (activities) to achieve our objectives:* We need to delineate what can be done to achieve our objectives, such as cutting trees, reserving a wilderness, or building a trail. Linear programming solutions select a level for each of these decision variables that, collectively, helps us best achieve the maximum (or minimum) value of the objective function given the constraints that we also specify. In the patch/individual tree problem discussed earlier in the chapter, the two decision variables were the acres allocated to the patch strategy and the acres allocated to the individual tree strategy.

- *An objective function to guide the analysis toward our objectives:* We generally select a performance measure for one of the means objectives to serve as the objective function.[10] In the patch/individual tree

problem, we first identified annual net income as the objective and utilized a performance measure of dollars/acre/year realized from allocating an acre to a particular silvicultural strategy (patch or individual tree) to represent that objective in the objective function. We then reanalyzed the problem with acres allocated to patch strategy as the objective function.

- *Constraints:* Constraints limit achievement of an objective function; they are invariably present and need to be identified. Constraints generally arise from three general sources: (1) resource limitations, (2) externally imposed policies or regulations, and (3) multiple objectives.

  - *Resource constraints:* Physical, human, technological, and economic restrictions limit the amount and kind of decision variables that can be selected. Available budgets, land, workforce, and labor are common limits on production inputs. In the patch/individual tree problem, we have resource limitations on land, labor, and seedlings.

  - *Policy and regulatory constraints:* Laws, regulations, political necessity, and other external influences can impose a second set of constraints. Many such constraints set minimum or maximum required levels on certain outcomes. Perhaps the woodlands manager has a contract for a monthly quota of wood that must be supplied to the mill, company policy does not allow wood sales to foreign buyers, all available deer winter range by law must be protected on state forest lands, more than 10% of a watershed cannot be cut in any one decade, or a local politician decrees that a particular campground must be built.

  - *Objectives as constraints:* Many problems have more than one objective that we wish to represent in the analysis. Sometimes we may want to maintain big game habitat and provide an even flow of timber harvest or revenue. Other times we may seek to minimize the acres treated, subject to achieving habitat objectives. Since we generally specify one performance measure as the objective function, we formulate others as constraints if they are to be formally incorporated into the problem. In the patch/individual tree problem, Debora Lee's kids wanted at least 20 acres to be allocated to the individual tree strategy (the area surrounding the cabin), so that was represented as a constraint when she pursued a net income objective. Then we can vary the level specified for the objective represented as a constraint to delineate the trade-off between the two objectives. As an example, we might study the

9 We utilized the mathematical programming package called What's Best! to solve the alternative formulations of the patch/individual tree problem. www.lindo.com

10 A form of linear programming called *goal programming* enables the use of multiple objectives to guide the solution by associating penalty functions with the nonachievement of specified levels of the objectives. This approach can be somewhat difficult to use in forestry applications. See Davis et al. (2001) for a discussion of this approach.

trade-off between net income/year and the amount of acres allocated to the patch strategy as Debora Lee did (Tables 18.9 and 18.10 and Figure 18.9).

## The Patch/Individual Tree Problem as a Linear Program

We illustrate the components of a linear programming problem with our patch/individual tree problem from earlier in the chapter.

In summary form, we can represent Debora Lee's original problem as follows:

Maximize $25X_1 + 20X_2$
where:

    $X_1$ = acres allocated to patch strategy

    $X_2$ = acres allocated to individual tree strategy

Subject to the constraints:

a) Land   $1X_1 + 1X_2 \leq 200$

b) Seedlings   $20X_1 + 10X_2 \leq 3{,}600$

c) Labor   $1X_1 + 3X_2 \leq 450$

d) Individual tree   $X_2 \geq 20$

e) Non-negativity   $X_1 > 0, X_2 \geq 0$

After seeing the results from the first set of runs, Debora Lee decided to minimize the acres allocated to the patch strategy while still earning at least a specified net income/year. In the next set of model runs, her minimum net income/year can be expressed as a constraint, while the objective function can be to minimize the amount of acres allocated to patch cuts.

In summary form, we can represent Debora Lee's revised problem formulation as follows:

Minimize $X_1$
where:

    $X_1$ = acres allocated patch strategy

    $X_2$ = acres allocated to individual tree strategy

Subject to the constraints

a) Land   $1X_1 + 1X_2 \leq 200$

b) Seedlings   $20X_1 + 10X_2 \leq 3{,}600$

c) Labor   $1X_1 + 3X_2 \leq 450$

d) Min. income/yr   $25X_1 + 20X_2 \geq R$,
    where R varied from \$3,000 to \$4,800.

e) Non-negativity   $X_1 > 0, X_2 \geq 0$

## The Detached Coefficient Matrix

Writing out problem formulations as equations is instructive, but as the problems become larger, there is a great deal of repetition in writing the same decision variable symbols over and over again. A detached coefficient matrix organizes the equation into the rows and columns of a matrix, with each column representing a different decision variable and each row representing an equation (an objective function or a constraint). We will use such a representation later in the book. We can demonstrate it here with the original formulation of the patch/individual tree problem in which Debora Lee maximized net income/year subject to constraints on land, seedlings, labor, and minimum acres of the individual tree strategy:

| | $X_1$ | $X_2$ | Sign | Right Hand Side (RHS) |
|---|---|---|---|---|
| Obj. function | 25 | 20 | = | Max |
| Seedlings | 20 | 10 | $\leq$ | 3,600 |
| Labor | 1 | 3 | $\leq$ | 450 |
| Land | 1 | 1 | $\leq$ | 200 |
| Min. individual tree | | 1 | $\geq$ | 20 |

The requirement that decision variables are greater or equal to 0 is implicit in this representation.

## Graphical Solutions to the Patch/Individual Tree Linear Programming Formulation

The formulation in which Debora Lee maximized net income/year can serve as an example of how linear programs find quantitative solutions. Since there are only two decision variables ($X_1$, $X_2$), we can represent graphically the processes utilized by linear program solvers to determine the level of acres to allocate to each of the harvest strategies. When the objective is to maximize some variable, as it is in this formulation, the program will choose infinite levels of our two decision variables unless somehow constrained. Thus, we first delineate the feasible region to illuminate the problem solutions that meet (are consistent with) the constraints that have been specified.

As an example, up to 200 acres are available in Debora Lee's problem to be allocated between the patch strategy and the individual tree strategy. The combinations of the two strategies that fit this description can be shown graphically as an area defined by the gray area in Figure 18.10, which is delineated by $X_1 + X_2 \leq 200$, $X_1 \geq 0$, $X_2 \geq 0$. Given that the acres of each strategy contribute positively to achieving the objective, combinations of the two strategies that maximize the objective function can be found on the upper boundary of the shaded figure in Figure 18.10—the line connecting 200 $X_2$ to 200 $X_1$. This boundary delineates the most land that we can have of $X_2$ for each level of $X_1$, or (to put it another way) the most land we can have of $X_1$ for each level of $X_2$.

Similarly, we can represent the feasible region defined by all four constraints for Debora Lee's problem (Figure 18.11), along with the acreages of the two strategies associated with constraint intersections. As we will see, the mathematically optimal solution will be found at one of those intersections.

We can also graph different combinations of the acres allocated to the two harvest strategies for each level of net income/year (Figure 18.12). To obtain these lines, we solve the equation $25X_1 + 20X_2 = R$, were R takes different values such as \$2,000, \$3,000, and so on.

Then we can combine the graph of the different levels of net income/year possible (Figure 18.12) with the feasible region identified by the constraint set (Figure 18.11) to determine the "optimal" solution for this objective function and constraint set (the highest objective function value that touches the constrained area) (Figure 18.13).

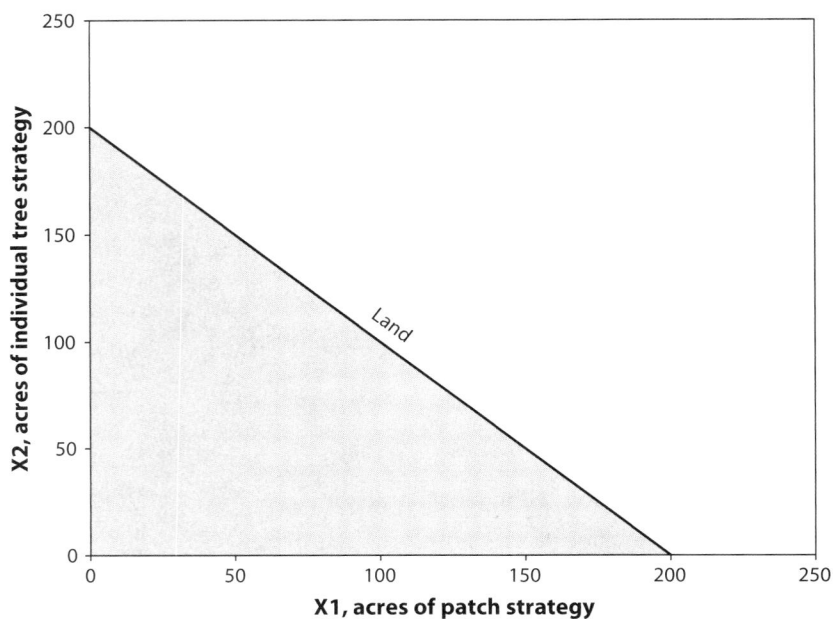

Figure 18.10 *Combinations of acres of the patch strategy and acres of the individual tree strategy that might be selected (shown in gray) considering the amount of land available.*

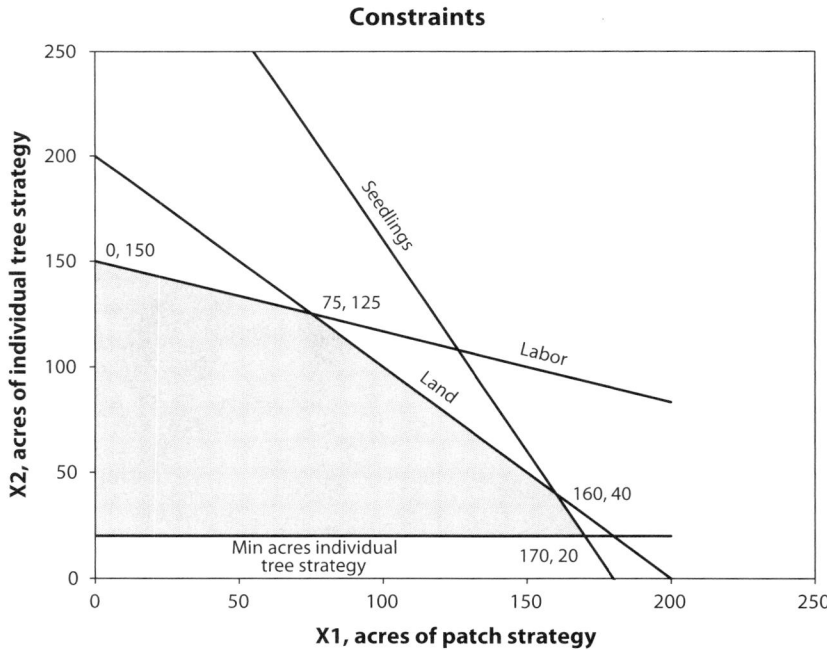

Figure 18.11 *Combinations of acres of the patch strategy and the individual tree strategy that might be selected (shown in gray), considering all the constraints from the original formulation of the patch/individual tree problem, along the allocation of acres among the two strategies at constraint intersections.*

**Objective Values**

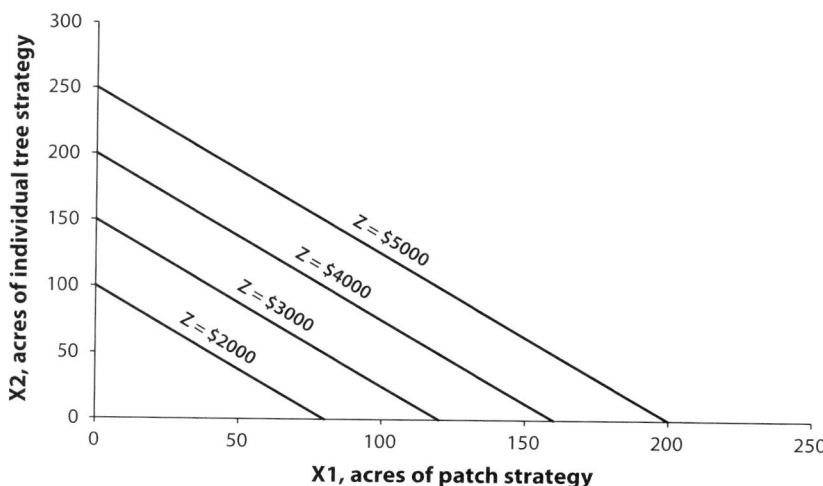

Figure 18.12   *Combinations of acres of patch and individual tree strategies that provide different levels of net income/year, with a net income of $25/year for each acre allocated to the patch strategy and $20/year for each acre allocated to the individual tree strategy.*

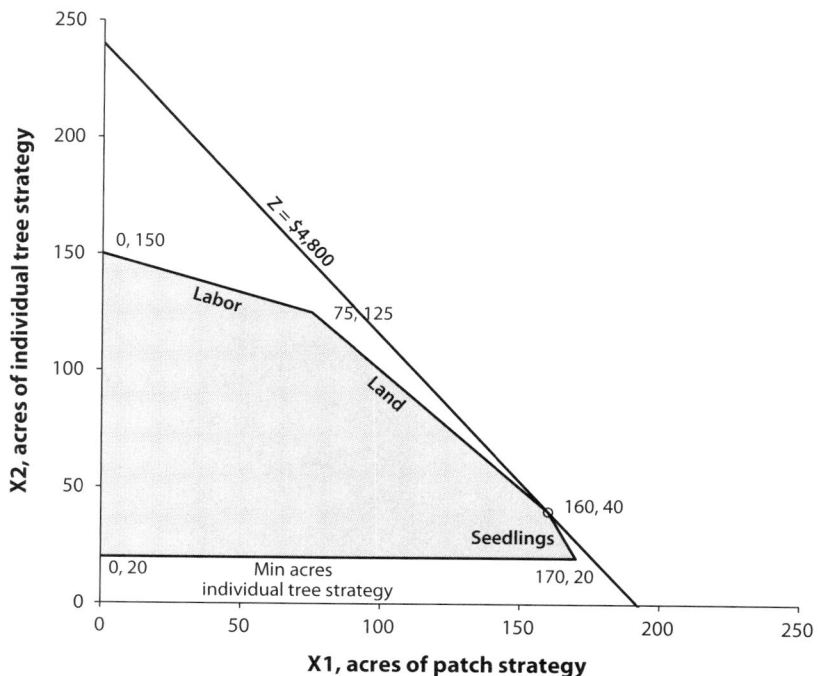

Figure 18.13   *Maximum objective function value ($4,800) and associated values of acres of patch and individual tree strategies ($X_1 = 160$, $X_2 = 40$) for the original formulation of the patch/individual tree problem.*

*Planning is bringing the future into the present
so that you can do something about it now.* — ALAN LAKEIN

# CHAPTER 19

# Forest Planning under Ecological Forestry

*A mature red pine forest with red oak and paper birch in the understory. (Courtesy of Brian Palik)*

Almost all forest planning problems have more than one objective. A landowner may wish to conserve or restore certain habitats, sustain a particular harvest level, produce revenue over time, or retain a forest that their grandkids will be proud of when they grow up. Quite likely, landowners want to do most or all of these things. Thus we need approaches that help us sort through ideas for managing forests, considering these objectives in an integrated fashion. In this chapter, we suggest structured approaches to forest planning with multiple objectives, and illustrate them with a detailed application on a forest of our imagination that we call the *Pine Hill Forest*.

In Chapter 18 we summarized a general seven-step approach to structured decision making for ecological forest management (Box 19.1). We will employ it here.

---

**Box 19.1 Structured decision making for ecological forest management**

**Step 1.** Frame the problem: Overview and decision context (ecological, human use, economic, social, and legal).

**Step 2.** Develop an engagement strategy.

**Step 3.** Identify objectives and performance measures, including approach to sustainability and conservation of critical natural capital and special places.

**Step 4.** Create alternatives: Different solutions to the problem being studied.

**Step 5.** Estimate consequences: Assess how the alternatives score on the performance measures.

**Step 6.** Evaluate trade-offs and make a decision.

**Step 7.** Implement, monitor, and adapt.

# Forest Planning: The Pine Hill Forest Example [1]

## Step 1: Frame the Problem (Overview and Decision Context)

Debora Lee Hanson, along with her brother and sister, recently inherited a 2,500-acre forest on Pine Hill in northeastern Wisconsin from her father Emil Hanson—the place where she was raised. Before he died, Debora Lee had told her father that she would like to retire and move to Pine Hill and manage the forest, utilizing experience gained managing her pine forest in Colorado. Emil agreed and named her forest manager in his will, along with the proviso that the forest be managed for the benefit of the entire family (Debora Lee and her children and her brother and sister and their children).

Debora Lee has now retired and moved from Colorado to Pine Hill to live on the family homestead. She would like to develop a management plan to guide activities on Pine Hill Forest for a number of years into the future. She has seen pictures of the forest from the distant past when it was dominated by large pines, and she would like to bring back that type of forest. Her children and those of her brother and sister like to walk through the woods and see all kinds of birds and animals, along with picnicking in the few remaining patches of intact old growth. Many in the family fish and swim in headwater streams that run through the property. Also, the family hopes that income from the forest can help defray the upcoming cost of college education for the children. Their forest plan will need to reflect these many values.

**Ecological Background**    What is the natural history of these forests? Major disturbance elements? Predominant forest types? Proportions of mature, young, and preforest? As we discussed in Chapters 2 and 3, the underlying disturbance regimes provide a template for management practices that help ensure ecological sustainability. From the stories of her father, her reading, and discussions with the county extension agent, Debora Lee has been able to reconstruct the natural history of this forest: This is northern dry mesic forest as classified by the Wisconsin Department of Natural Resources. The vegetation prior to Euro-American colonization likely was dominated by red and white pine, with some red oak and red maple, and some aspen and birch. These forests were occasionally disrupted by wildfire, with surface fires occurring on the order of every 30–50 years and more severe canopy-disturbing fire occurring every 200–300 years. Small gap-to-patch scale wind disturbances

also occurred periodically. While the proportion of the forest in each structural stage cannot be fully known, it seems likely that, on the average, perhaps one-third to one-half was in mature and old forest and less than one-tenth was occupied by a preforest community.

**Land Use and its Effects**    Much of the forest has been harvested in different ways and at different times in the past, by both her parents and her grandparents. In the early 1950s logging began on the property, focused on selectively removing large overstory pines. At first, logging concentrated on removing the large pines with clear boles, which resulted in a forest of increasingly scattered mature pines of lesser log value. This also resulted in considerable hardwood encroachment, especially of sugar and red maples, due to the canopy openings.

As time went on, the harvest shifted to clearcutting, as the log market accepted trees of lower and lower commercial quality, and clearcutting became popular in forestry across the United States. Where site preparation and planting of pines after harvest did not occur, much of the forest cut in this way became dominated by aspen, paper birch, red maple, red oak, and sugar maple, with only occasional young pines—a *young hardwood/pine forest* (Figure 19.1a), as pine seed sources were greatly reduced and aspen sprouted and spread vigorously after slash fires. Where site preparation, planting of pines, and hardwood suppression did occur after clearcutting, *pine plantations* resulted—a legacy of Debora Lee's father's foray into high-yield forestry in the 1970s (Figure 19.1b).

By the 1980s, the family requested that clearcutting stop, and Debora Lee's father reverted to selectively logging again the areas that had not been clearcut, focusing on harvest of the remaining large pines. Those parts of the forest now have a remnant pine overstory averaging 6–8 large pines per acre—remnant *pine/hardwood forest* (Figure 19.1c and d). Most of the remaining large pines there have relatively low commercial value, having been passed over for harvest at least twice.

Approximately 15 years ago, Debora Lee's father decided to greatly reduce the harvest to help build up the timber inventory as part of his bequest to his children. Crucial to that decision was his ability to greatly reduce his property tax for the Pine Hill Forest. Toward that end, he enrolled the forest in Wisconsin's Managed Forest Law that gives property tax reductions to owners of forestland who agree to adopt a plan to periodically log timber from the land. [2] This 1985 law was aimed at encouraging commercial timber production, protecting habitat, and increasing opportunities for outdoor recreation. In exchange for paying much

---

1 The data for this problem originated with the "Daniel Pickett" problem from Davis and Johnson (1987) and Davis et al. (2001).

2 Wisconsin DNR. 2016. Wisconsin Managed Forest Law: A Program Summary. dnr.wi.gov/files/pdf/pubs/fr/fr0295.pdf

Figure 19.1 *(a) Young hardwood/pine forest, the result of removal of the pine overstory. (b) Pine plantation created after removal of the pine overstory and intensive management. (c) Landscape view of a remnant pine/hardwood forest. (d) Group of remnant pines in the remnant pine/hardwood forest. (Courtesy of Brian Palik and Tony D'Amato)*

lower property taxes, the owners must keep the land in timber production and allow citizens to use the land for hunting, fishing, hiking, sightseeing and other recreational uses. Also, the law allows landowners to set aside a portion of the property for private use. Debora Lee's father reserved 160 acres near the homestead for use by himself and his family, while allowing nonmotorized use by the public on the rest of the forest. He also wrote a rudimentary management plan that committed his forest to sustainable timber production.

**Economic Possibilities**   Debora Lee has talked to the local extension service about markets for different types of forest goods and services she might sell. She found that strong markets for softwood and hardwood logs exist in the local area for both lumber and pulpwood depending on log size and quality. She also asked about the values to place on other ecosystem services the Pine Hill Forest provides, including clean water for downstream users, summer range for a migratory deer herd, and habitat for many birds and small animals. The extension agent agreed with Debora Lee that these goods and services have value and that society should pay landowners for sustaining them. However, beyond the property tax reduction from allowing public access for nonmotorized recreation, she would receive money only for timber delivered to the mill. The extension agent did add that carbon markets might develop in the future, at which time she might receive money from letting the forest grow.

Also, Debora Lee checked into the local labor force to log and reforest Pine Hill. She found that loggers and reforestation contractors were available if she was relatively flexible about when she needed help.

**Social Considerations and Networks**   Debora Lee's family does not know nearly as much about professional forestry as she does, but they have a vital interest in and passion for this forest. Thus, they want a major say in the forest management plan that will be adopted.

The Pine Hill Forest borders other family forests to the north and to the east. She has met those families, and their main concern about her management relates to their streams that originate on Pine Hill. Their worries include stream sedimentation and herbicide drift. Debora Lee promised to be very careful near those streams and to discuss the Pine Hill forest management plan with them before she implements it. She also assured her neighbors that she does not plan to broadcast spray herbicides; any herbicide use would be targeted applications on invasive plants. In addition, Debora Lee knows it would help her to be able to use some of her neighbor's roads while logging and that her logging costs could be lower if she and her neighbors harvested at the same time. Thus she is especially interested in staying on good terms with them.

The Pine Hill Forest is adjacent to state forestland on two sides. Debora Lee has met the state forest manager, who also has a special interest in stream protection on the Pine Hill Forest.

**Legal Requirements**   The Wisconsin Department of Forestry (Holiday & Wagner, 2010) distributes a booklet on *best management practices (BMPs)* for road building and logging near streams; these practices have been accepted by the federal Environmental Protection Agency as adequate to meet the requirements of the Clean Water Act. While these BMPs are voluntary, Debora Lee intends to use them in her own road building and logging as do her neighbors.

No populations of threatened or endangered species have been found on Pine Hill, but the state has declared two fish species in her streams as *sensitive*. Again, that points out the need for special care of those headwater streams.

## Step 2: Develop an Engagement Strategy

Rarely does one person make unilateral decisions about conserving and managing a forest, isolated from the rest of humanity. Debora Lee's case is no different as we discussed above. Her kids and her brother and sister and their kids have strong views about management of this forest—they see it as theirs, too. Also, her downstream family forest neighbors and adjacent state forest manager have concerns about conserving the stream systems, and she would like to cooperate with them in logging operations.

Debora Lee knows that she will need family agreement on a forest plan for the Pine Hill Forest for the plan to be viable. Thus, she has taken time on the family's holiday visits to talk through their values and interests in the forest (some of which we highlighted at the beginning of the chapter).

At their initial meeting on the forest plan, the family and Debora Lee agreed that they will help her develop objectives, performance measures, and management alternatives, and then she will model the implications of these alternatives and bring them back to the family for evaluation. Once the family settles on an alternative they all like, she will share it with the neighbors and the state forest manager to hear any concerns they have that may need further consideration. In the engagement classification of Chapter 18 (Table 18.6), Debora Lee plans to *collaborate with her family and to consult with her neighbors.*

## Step 3: Identify Objectives and Performance Measures, Including Approach to Sustainability and Conservation of Critical Natural Capital and Special Places

The meetings Debora Lee held with the family about their hopes and dreams for the Pine Hill Forest were very lively. At the meetings, she emphasized her desire to shift the forest toward its historical conditions and the family's need for a steady stream of revenue to help defray the children's college expenses; her brother and sister and her kids emphasized the majesty and wonder of the big trees, dark old-growth patches, variety of birds, and cold, clear streams for fishing and swimming—the memories of their summer visits. Also, they like the squirrels and raptors that live in the remnant pine/hardwood forest. Finally, they dislike clearcutting and hope that Debora Lee will emulate nature to the greatest extent possible in her harvests.

How does she move from these broad aspirational statements to recognizing the actual possibilities and potential conflicts? She realizes that she needs to develop more definitive objectives, develop performance measures to evaluate how well different management alternatives meet them, and then model these alternatives.

An extension agent helped her summarize the results of family meetings in terms of fundamental objectives (basic things that matter to the family—outcomes they care about regardless of how they are achieved) and means objectives (objectives that help achieve the fundamental objectives)

(Table 19.1). As might be expected, the fundamental objectives reflect a variety of family interests—some ecological, some social, and some financial.

*Selection of means objectives is vitally important as these objectives drive the forest planning analysis that follows*; they identify the ways in which you will try to achieve the fundamental objectives. As such, they deserve considerable thought.

Some of the means objectives contribute to more than one fundamental objective and some of the fundamental objectives have more than one means objective associated with them—common and somewhat complicating occurrences in forest planning. As an example, the means objective of providing income relates to fundamental objectives of keeping the forest in the family and assisting in the education of the children, and the fundamental objective of restoring the historical forest has multiple means objectives associated with it.

Many fundamental objectives, and their associated means objectives, help address the sustainability of the forest and the ecosystem services it can provide. We will highlight two:

Table 19.1 *Relating means objectives to fundamental objectives for the Pine Hill Forest decision problem*

| Fundamental objectives | Means objectives |
| --- | --- |
| Protect special places. | Reserve old-growth remnants and wet meadows. |
| Protect the stream. | Maintain buffers along streams and have sizeable culverts whenever a road crosses a stream. Maintain the wet meadow. |
| Restore the historical forest. | Harvest in a way that encourages the return of pine dominance with a hardwood understory. Protect any old pines or other old trees during harvest. Leave biological legacies at harvest. (See Chapters 3 and 4 for examples of the many ways in which this can be done.) Focus actions on the forest that is the most degraded. Maintain or restore representative elements of the historical sere over time (preforest, young, mature, old), with immediate emphasis on preforest and complex young forest. Emphasize the clumpy, gappy nature of the forests. |
| Provide for biodiversity across the forest. | (All means objectives listed above for the fundamental objective of restoring the historical forest apply here.) Reserve old-growth remnants, wet meadows, and stream buffers. Retain a portion of the remnant pine/hardwood forest. |
| Maintain a "natural-appearing" forest. | Leave biological legacies at harvest. Keep all old trees at harvest. Provide for a preforest stage after harvest. Emphasize the clumpy, gappy nature of the forests. |
| Ensure that the forest stays in the family. | Provide a steady income from harvest to pay property taxes. |
| Assist in college education of children. | Provide a steady income from harvest for college tuition. |
| Provide for the long-term economic productivity of the forest. | Leave at least as much timber value in the ending inventory as is in the beginning inventory. |

1. The family wishes to restore historical forest conditions, as best they can. Toward that end, they develop a number of means objectives, including harvesting in a way that encourages return of the pines, protecting all old trees, leaving biological legacies at harvest, and attaining a representative amount of the development stages that naturally occurred here. Needless to say, this fundamental objective has profound implications for the management of the forest.

2. The family has a deep interest in maintaining the long-term economic productivity of the forest for their children and grandchildren. Toward that end, they will utilize a means objective that the financial value of the ending inventory at the planning horizon equals or exceeds the financial value of the beginning inventory. They considered focusing on the ending volume as their measure of long-term economic productivity, but it is likely that the different types of forest will yield different revenues per unit of volume harvested. When that occurs, focusing on the ending volume would allow exploitation of higher-valued types. (See Box 9.3 in Chapter 9.) Thus, focusing on the ending financial value instead of ending volume as a sustainability check makes sense with a fundamental objective of maintaining the long-term economic productivity of the forest.

Next, Debora Lee and the extension agent link one or more performance measures to each of the means objectives to help develop and evaluate alternatives (Table 19.2).

Table 19.2 *Relating performance measures to means objectives in the Pine Hill Forest decision problem*

| Means objectives* | Performance measures |
|---|---|
| **Permanent designation objectives** | |
| Reserve old-growth remnants and wet meadows. | Maintenance of these areas without human disturbance |
| Maintain buffers along streams. | Utilization of state-recommended BMPs |
| **Prescription objectives** | |
| Harvest and reforest in a way that encourages the return of pine dominance with a hardwood understory. | Species composition and structure in post-harvest forest |
| Protect any old pines during harvest. | Proportion of old pines retained after harvest |
| Leave biological legacies at variable-retention harvest. | Amount and placement of retention at harvest, especially to protect biological hotspots |
| Provide for a preforest stage after variable-retention harvest. | Numbers and abundance of native early seral plants present within five years after harvest |
| Emphasize the clumpy, gappy nature of the forest. | Tree distribution in post-harvest forest |
| Place correctly sized culverts whenever a road crosses a stream. | Utilization of state-recommended BMPs for culverts |
| **Harvest scheduling objectives** | |
| Provide a steady income from harvest to pay property taxes and assist with college tuition. | Level and stability of net income per year from harvest<br>Distribution of harvest across forest types in a period<br>Stability of harvest volume over time |
| Leave at least as much timber value in the ending inventory as is in the beginning inventory. | Financial value of the harvestable ending inventory compared to the financial value of the harvestable beginning inventory |
| Focus actions on the forest that is the most degraded. | Amount of restoration in young hardwood/pine forest and pine plantation in the near future |
| Retain a portion of the remnant pine/hardwood forest. | Amount of remnant pine/hardwood left unharvested over the planning periods |
| Restore representative amounts of the historical sere over time (preforest, young, mature, old). | Amount and stability of preforest and amount of complex young forest[†] |

* In the terminology and concepts of this book, many of these means objectives are "critical natural capital" (fundamental elements of ecological systems critical to providing ecosystem services the family desires on a continuing basis), including old-growth groves, wet meadows, stream buffers, old pines, biological legacies, spatial heterogeneity at harvest, and some amount of preforest, complex young forest, mature forest, and remnant pine/hardwood forest. Some of these elements also qualify as "special places" themselves, such as the old-growth groves and the streams. Also, special care would be taken around the family homestead.

† As we will see, Debora Lee will plan in detail for 20 years, too short a time to restore mature forest.

Toward that end, they organize the means objectives into three categories:

1. *Permanent designation objectives*—objectives that call for particular forest allocations;

2. *Prescription objectives*—objectives that guide development of prescriptions for each forest type; and

3. *Harvest scheduling objectives*—objectives that guide development of the harvest schedule over the planning periods.

Finally, Debora Lee needs to decide how far into the future to plan. After talking with the extension agent, Debora Lee decides to plan for 20 years, feeling that a 20-year planning horizon is a long enough period of time to get a good understanding of the direction the forest is going and the benefits it can provide. Also, she is uneasy with the accuracy of projections beyond that time period and into the distant future.

## Step 4: Create Alternatives

Now the fun begins. What sort of alternatives will Debora Lee's family wish to examine? In the alternatives they will pursue the means objectives of Table 19.2 in three different ways:

1. Reserve remnant old-growth patches, wet meadow, and take special care of stream buffers.

2. Embed the prescription objectives in the silvicultural guidance that will be developed for each type of forest as we describe below.

3. Create alternative harvest schedules that vary the emphasis on achievement of different harvest scheduling objectives.

Within that framework, Debora Lee wants to focus on restoration of the young hardwood/pine forest and of the pine plantations over the next 20 years, as they are the most degraded. Toward that end, the extension agent recommends that she concentrate on variable-retention harvest (VRH) in the young hardwood/pine forest and variable-density thinning (VDT) in the pine plantations. In addition, the extension agent notes that restoration of the remnant pine/hardwood forest is also needed, to reduce the major increase in hardwoods that has occurred and encourage pine regeneration. He recommends that with any harvest there be a VRH that retains all overstory pines along with selected hardwoods. After reading the literature, the extension agent suggests retaining at least 15% of the forest being harvested as a biological legacy in all VRH with most of it in aggregated retention—enough of a legacy to help provide the environment in which a variety of native wild-

life can survive and thrive. Accepting that advice, Debora Lee has the silvicultural building blocks for the alternatives she and the family will consider: VRH in the young hardwood/pine forest and remnant pine/hardwood forest and VDT in the pine plantations.

The family is very interested in, and somewhat apprehensive about, whether this proposed restoration strategy for the forest will produce enough revenue. Debora Lee expects to simulate many different combinations of these prescriptions to assess their impact on income and the other harvest scheduling objectives.

After a conference, the family settles on a set of requirements on prescriptions and harvest scheduling that the alternatives must meet. All will utilize the VRH and VDT prescriptions described above. Also, given the interest in restoring the most degraded forest, they will require that all acres of the young hardwood/pine forest and the pine plantations receive one restoration harvest over the 20-year planning horizon. Finally, all alternatives will be required to have as much timber value in the ending inventory as they have in the beginning inventory and a stable or rising revenue over the planning periods.

Within these requirements, the family selects two initial alternatives to consider to help *benchmark* their possibilities: (1) Maximize sustained net income and (2) Concentrate harvest on the most degraded forest in the first 10 years. Once they understand the implications of these two alternatives for performance measures, the family feels they will undoubtedly want to craft additional alternatives to simulate and assess.

## Step 5: Estimate Consequences

Given what she has done so far, Debora Lee has to admit that she does not know how much of each type of forest to harvest in each period under her family's multiple objectives, including the revenue that harvest will provide over time. For that information she will need to build a forest planning model in which to simulate different amounts and combinations of harvest in her three types of forest. To create such a model, she will need to gather and organize information on the forest resources of Pine Hill, develop detailed prescriptions along with choices for their time of implementation, and relate these choices to the performance measures. She will then need to build a planning model containing all this information, and controls on the flow of income over time and the ending timber value, in which she can simulate the implications of different alternatives.

**Organize Information about Forest Resources** The 2,500 acre Pine Hill Forest is a wonderfully complex place, with watersheds, streams, roads, and a wide variety of tree species and forest conditions. You might say that every acre is unique as in most forests, but representing every acre in this analysis would overwhelm Debora Lee and bury her in data. What should she do? How much detail should she recognize?

Given the importance of the watersheds and streams, she will want to highlight her stream systems and the special protection she will give them (Figure 19.2a). Luckily, roads built to access the property when it was first logged are in the uplands and cross only one stream (the connector road to the county road system [Figure 19.2b]), so sedimentation from roads should not be an appreciable source of stream pollution. After some consultation with the managers on the adjacent state lands about temperature and sediment protection and the natural delivery of wood to streams, Debora Lee decides to use 150-foot buffers on all of her streams. Harvest will not be regularly scheduled in these buffers, but some activities might be scheduled in the future, to meet ecological objectives, after the family has a better understanding of managing the uplands.

To help her decide how to break up the forest for analysis, Debora Lee works with a forestry consultant. He recommends that they start with a relatively simple classification—the minimum number of groupings that will reflect the family's objectives and restoration needs. In addition to the old-growth patches and the wet meadow, they map the three types of conditions that now cover much of the forest: (1) remnant pine/hardwood forest, (2) young hardwood/pine forest, and (3) pine plantation.

After an inventory, Debora Lee finds that most of her acres are in either remnant pine/hardwood forest or in pine plantations, along with a scattering of young hardwood/pine forest (Figure 19.2c and d, and Table 19.3). Also the forestry consultant has mapped two small remnant old-growth patches and a wet meadow near one stream. Once they calculate the acres in stream buffers, they can estimate the upland acreage in each forest type (Table 19.3).

**Create Prescriptions**   As mentioned above, the forestry consultant suggests Debora Lee consider variable-retention harvest (VRH) for the young hardwood/pine type and remnant pine/hardwood type and variable-density thinning (VDT) for the pine plantations.

The prescription will vary by forest type:

- VRH of the young hardwood/pine type, focused mostly on reducing hardwood dominance:
  - Create openings while retaining some legacy structure;
  - Retain any remaining pines in openings that will be created;
  - Leave some hardwood overstory, especially aspen; keeping aspen legacies can help reduce aspen suckering by providing shade and competition; and
  - Plant native pine species where the resulting openings lack pine seedlings or saplings; most harvested patches will have only a few pine seedlings, so planting of pine will generally be needed, but at levels low enough to enable the full preforest compositional diversity.

- VDT of the pine plantations:
  - Thin across the diameter classes;
  - Retain the few hardwoods that now grow there; and
  - Create spatial complexity.

- VRH of the remnant pine/hardwood forest:
  - Create openings while retaining the legacy structure of mature and old-growth pines and targeting hardwood concentrations for harvest; and
  - Consider planting pines where hardwood competition is likely, but at levels low enough for preforest to flourish.

The consultant estimates that the VRHs under these prescriptions should result in preforest habitat for about a decade following harvest.

After some discussion, the forestry consultant and Debora Lee decide to break the 20-year detailed simulation period for her plan into four five-year periods. Thus their analysis

Table 19.3 *Types recognized on the Pine Hill Forest and associated acreage**

| Forest Type | Riparian Acres (within 150 ft of stream) | Upland Acres | Total Acres |
|---|---|---|---|
| (A) Remnant pine/hardwood | 96 | 853 | 949 |
| (B) Young hardwood/pine | 30 | 447 | 477 |
| (C) Pine plantation | 30 | 969 | 1,000 |
| (OG) Old-growth pine | 1 | 37 | 38 |
| (WM) Wet meadow (forbs, sedges, and willows) | 23 | 14 | 37 |
| Total | 181 | 2,319 | 2,500 |

* Totals may be slightly off due to rounding.

will calculate how much of each prescription to implement in each five-year period.

**Define Land Allocation Choices**   With the help of the consultant, Debora Lee develops a set of choices for the three forest types outside of riparian buffers that she will consider harvesting (Table 19.4). She sets up choices for a VRH in each of the four periods for Type A (remnant pine/hardwood) and Type B (young hardwood/pine). Also, she

sets up a choice for Type A that allows it to remain unharvested over the 20 years, as the family would like to retain some remnant pine/hardwood forest over the 20 years. Finally, she sets up choices to reflect a VDT in Type C (pine plantation) in each of the four periods.

She identifies each prescription/timing choice in Table 19.4 by three symbols: (1) the type of forest (A, B, C), (2) the type of harvest—a VRH which is indicated by a "V" or a VDT which is indicated by a "T," and (3) the period of

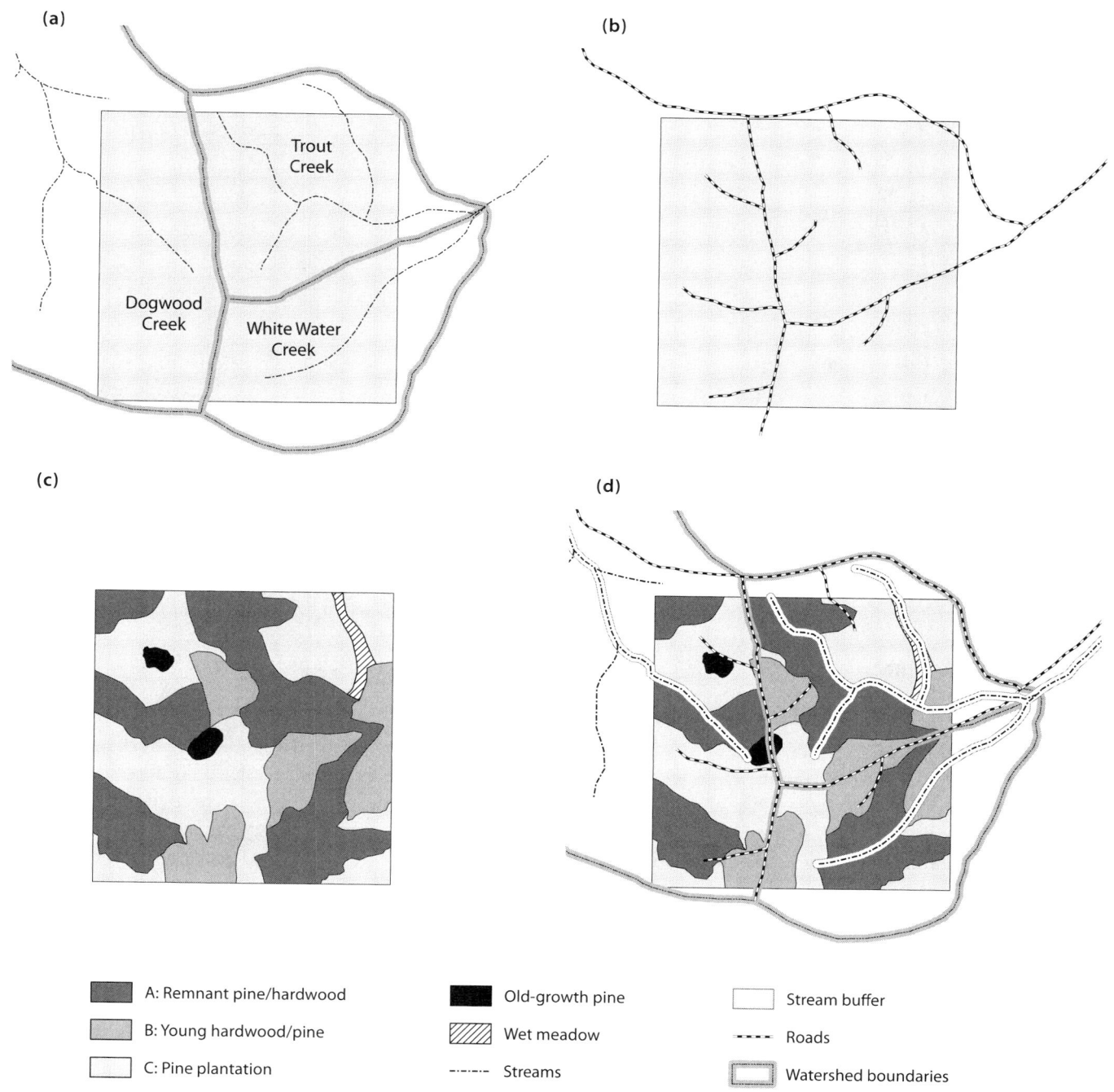

**Figure 19.2** *The Pine Hill Forest (a) streams and watersheds, (b) roads, (c) forest types, and (d) streams, stream buffers, watersheds, roads, and forest types all on one map.*

Table 19.4 *Land allocation choices for upland areas in the three major forest types (A, B, C) on the Pine Hill Forest with kind of harvest indicated in the period in which it will occur. (V = variable-retention harvest, T = variable-density thinning, U = left unharvested)*

| Period | A | | | | | B | | | | C | | | |
|---|---|---|---|---|---|---|---|---|---|---|---|---|---|
| | $V_1$ | $V_2$ | $V_3$ | $V_4$ | U | $V_1$ | $V_2$ | $V_3$ | $V_4$ | $T_1$ | $T_2$ | $T_3$ | $T_4$ |
| 1 | V | | | | | V | | | | T | | | |
| 2 | | V | | | | | V | | | | T | | |
| 3 | | | V | | | | | V | | | | T | |
| 4 | | | | V | | | | | V | | | | T |

Table 19.5 *Preforest (P), simplified young forest (Y), complex young forest (Yc), and remnant pine/hardwood forest (M) associated with the land allocation choices for three forest types*

| Period | A | | | | | B | | | | C | | | |
|---|---|---|---|---|---|---|---|---|---|---|---|---|---|
| | $V_1$ | $V_2$ | $V_3$ | $V_4$ | U | $V_1$ | $V_2$ | $V_3$ | $V_4$ | $T_1$ | $T_2$ | $T_3$ | $T_4$ |
| 1 | P | M | M | M | M | P | Y | Y | Y | Yc | Y | Y | Y |
| 2 | P | P | M | M | M | P | P | Y | Y | Yc | Yc | Y | Y |
| 3 | Yc | P | P | M | M | Yc | P | P | Y | Yc | Yc | Yc | Y |
| 4 | Yc | Yc | P | P | M | Yc | Yc | P | P | Yc | Yc | Yc | Yc |

harvest (1–4). Thus, $BV_1$ signals a VRH will occur in Type B during period 1, and $CT_2$ signals that a VDT will occur in Type C in period 2. A "U" represents the area of the type that will be left unharvested over the 20 years.

We call a planning model that defines the choices as shown in Table 19.4 a *land allocation* model, in which we frame the forest planning problem as how to allocate land among different choices for forest management. Often, choices are also developed that recognize different prescriptions for each forest type, in addition to recognizing a different time of implementation for a particular prescription as we have done here.

Specification of the land allocation choices implies constraints on the actions that will be considered. As an example, Debora Lee requires that all of Type B have a VRH over the four planning periods and requires that all of Type C have a VDT over those periods. Thus, she requires that all acres in Types B and C receive one restoration harvest over the four planning periods. On the other hand, including land allocation choice AU in Type A (remnant pine/hardwood forest) allows the possibility that some or all of the remnant pine/hardwood forest may be left unharvested over the planning horizon.

At the beginning of the analysis, care should be taken not to unduly constrain the alternatives by limiting the choices that can be considered.[3] Additional restrictions can be added to create new alternatives as you go.

**Estimate Impact of Land Allocation Choices on Performance Measures** Debora Lee next needs to estimate how each land allocation choice will affect her ability to achieve the harvest scheduling objectives described in Table 19.2 (left column), utilizing the performance measures associated with these objectives (Table 19.2, right column) to measure that achievement. Toward that end, she is especially interested in the acres that will be harvested from the three forest types in the four planning periods, associated harvest volume and net harvest revenue, the acreage in preforest, young forest (simplified and complex), and remnant pine/hardwood forest in each planning period, and the volume and value of the beginning and ending timber inventory.

*Development stages over time* Since Debora Lee is interested in the amount of preforest, young forest (simplified and complex), and remnant forest over the 20-year planning horizon, she needs to keep track of the development stage associated with each land allocation choice in each period (Table 19.5). To simplify this tracking, she adopts the convention that an acre receiving a harvest switches to the next logical development stage in the period of harvest. As an example, an acre receiving a VRH switches entirely to preforest in the period of harvest.

Tracking the development of complex young forest can be challenging. Currently, the young hardwood/pine forest and the pine plantations both qualify as simplified young forest. Complex young forest can develop as a result of a VDT in the pine plantations and as a result of a VRH in the other two types. An acre receiving a VDT switches to

---

3 We have greatly limited the choices here to fit within the confines of a textbook page.

Table 19.6 *Timber harvest volume in hundreds of cubic feet per acre and net stumpage revenue in hundreds of dollars per acre for each land allocation choice for the three major types on Pine Hill Forest. Assumes harvest in the middle of the 5-year period. Beginning inventory is calculated as the volume and value that would be available for harvest in the middle of the first period; ending inventory is similarly calculated as the volume and value that would be available for harvest in the middle of the fifth period (one period of growth after the four period simulation)*

| | $AV_1$ | $AV_2$ | $AV_3$ | $AV_4$ | AU | $BV_1$ | $BV_2$ | $BV_3$ | $BV_4$ | $CT_1$ | $CT_2$ | $CT_3$ | $CT_4$ |
|---|---|---|---|---|---|---|---|---|---|---|---|---|---|
| Period 1 | 16/9 | | | | | 10/3 | | | | 5/2 | | | |
| Period 2 | | 18/10 | | | | | 12/4 | | | | 5.5/2.5 | | |
| Period 3 | | | 20/11 | | | | | 14/5 | | | | 6/3 | |
| Period 4 | | | | 22/12 | | | | | 16/6 | | | | 6.5/3.5 |
| Beginning Inventory volume/value | 16/9 | 16/9 | 16/9 | 16/9 | 16/9 | 10/3 | 10/3 | 10/3 | 10/3 | 14/6 | 14/6 | 14/6 | 14/6 |
| Ending Inventory volume/value | 7/2 | 5/1 | 2/0 | 0/0 | 24/13 | 7/2 | 5/1 | 2/0 | 0/0 | 15/7 | 16/7.5 | 17/8 | 18/8.5 |

complex young forest in the period of harvest and an acre receiving a VRH switches to complex young forest after two periods of preforest. As an example, land allocation choice $AV_2$ refers to a variable retention harvest in period two in the remnant pine/hardwood forest. Thus, the remnant pine/hardwood forest occupies the site in period one, preforest occupies it in periods two and three, and complex young forest occupies it in period four (assuming that preforest lasts two periods as we will do here).

***Timber harvest volume and value*** To develop an understanding of timber harvest volume and value associated with each land allocation choice, the forestry consultant conducts a timber inventory of the forest. He then uses a forest growth simulator to project harvest volume under each choice and uses Wisconsin state information on stumpage prices for different sizes, grades, and species of timber to estimate the harvest value.

All VRHs will leave a structural legacy (approximately 15% of the volume) that emphasizes the remaining large, old pines where they exist. The legacies will be placed in biodiversity hotspots, to the degree possible, such as around accumulations of large wood. VDT in the pine plantations will encourage compositional and structural diversity by harvesting from a range of diameters in a complex spatial mixture of heavy thinning and light thinning. Larger trees from the harvests can be sold for sawtimber, while smaller trees can be sold for pulp chips.

Pulling all of that information together, Debora Lee and the consultant estimate the timber yields and net stumpage revenues associated with different land allocation choices (Table 19.6). While wood in the local area is usually sold as pulpwood measured in cords or tons and sawtimber measured in board feet, for simplicity we will represent all wood

volume in terms of hundreds of cubic feet/acre (cunits). Similarly, we will aggregate the stumpage revenue from the different products into a single net revenue per acre in hundreds of dollars, after deducting costs associated with preparing the harvest and reforesting the site after harvest.

**Construct a Model to Simulate Different Management Alternatives** Debora Lee needs some way to simulate the implications of different alternatives—a model that will provide a systematic process to link the land allocation choices (Table 19.4) to the family's objectives and performance measures. In the common terminology of forest planning (Davis et al., 2001), we will utilize both ***decision variables*** and ***policy variables***.

***Defining decision variables and policy variables*** As we described in Chapter 18, identifying the kinds of actions that Debora Lee will undertake to achieve her family's objectives (defining her decision variables) is a first step in model building.[4] In this case, she already had a good start on that definition when she developed land allocation choices for the different types (Table 19.4). Thus, she measures her decision variables in terms of how many acres are allocated to each of them.

---

4 An introductory model building example is covered in Chapter 18 in which Debora Lee analyzes how she might manage a ponderosa pine forest in Colorado, and a more detailed explanation of decision variables and policy variables is given in the Appendix to Chapter 18. As with that example, we will employ an analysis tool called linear programming to solve the different formulations of the Pine Hill Forest problem that we consider here. We used the What's Best software (Lindo Systems, Inc.) to solve the linear program. What's Best is an add-in to Microsoft Excel that allows you to build optimization models in a free form layout within a spreadsheet (www.lindo.com/products/wb/). An introduction to linear programming is given in the Appendix to Chapter 18.

In addition, it will help her to define policy variables that add up outcomes of interest, such as harvest volume and value, beginning and ending inventory value and volume, and amount of preforest, simplified young forest, complex young forest, and remnant pine/hardwood forest (outside of riparian buffers) (Table 19.7). This recognition of policy variables of interest will make their levels easy to see and to control.

Debora Lee can now begin to populate her model with information on development stage and on harvest volume and value, and on relationships among decision variables and between decision and policy variables.

***Limiting resources available to decision variables*** As we saw in the patch/individual tree problem in Chapter 18, we need to limit the amount of resources available to the decision variables in this type of problem formulation. In that problem, constraints were developed on the amount of land, labor, and seedlings available. Here the major resource constraint is the amount of land available. To make sure she does not allocate more land among the land allocation choices for each type than is available, Debora Lee sets up equations that limit the number of *upland acres* that can be distributed among the choices of each forest type:

$$AV_1 + AV_2 + AV_3 + AV_4 + AU = 853 \text{ acres}$$

$$BV_1 + BV_2 + BV_3 + BV_4 = 447 \text{ acres}$$

$$CT_1 + CT_2 + CT_3 + CT_4 = 969 \text{ acres}$$

It should be noted that these limitations are often represented as upper limits (such as the amount of budget available) rather than equalities as shown here. In this case, Debora Lee wishes to ensure that all acres available for harvest are allocated among these choices, so she utilizes equalities.

In addition, sometimes she may wish to limit the amount of a type harvested in a period:

Acres harvested in a forest type must equal at least XX in a period:

$$AV_i \geq XX \text{ for } i = 1\text{--}4$$

$$BV_i \geq XX \text{ for } i = 1\text{--}4$$

$$CT_i \geq XX \text{ for } i = 1\text{--}4$$

Acres harvested in a forest type must not be more than XX in a period:

$$AV_i \leq XX \text{ for } i = 1\text{--}4$$

$$BV_i \leq XX \text{ for } i = 1\text{--}4$$

$$CT_i \leq XX \text{ for } i = 1\text{--}4$$

***Relating policy variables to decision variables*** Once all the land allocation choices are related to resource limits, the next step is to relate them to the policy variables. To help do that, Debora Lee will first set up accounting equations that define the relationship between the land allocation variables and the policy variables of interest.

In a land allocation model, policy variables like habitat distribution, harvest level, net revenue, and inventory accumulate as a function of how acres are allocated across the allocation choices. For example, Debora Lee's three potential sources of revenue in period one are from a VRH in Type A, a VRH in Type B, and a VDT in Type C (Table 19.6). She estimates that allocating an acre to prescription/timing choice $AV_1$ will produce \$900 of revenue in period one and similarly allocating an acre to prescription/timing choice $BV_1$ will produce \$300 in period one, and allocating an acre to prescription/timing choice $CT_1$ will produce \$200 in that period. Thus, she can set up an equation to define that relationship: $R_1 = 9AV_1 + 3BV_1 + 2CT_1$. In a similar fashion, she can relate other policy variables to the decision variables:

Revenue in each period (100s of \$):

$$R_1 = 9AV_1 + 3BV_1 + 2CT_1$$

$$R_2 = 10AV_2 + 4BV_2 + 2.5CT_2$$

$$R_3 = 11AV_3 + 5BV_3 + 3CT_3$$

$$R_4 = 12AV_4 + 6BV_4 + 3.5CT_4$$

Table 19.7 *Description of variables used in the Pine Hill Forest planning model*

| | Description |
|---|---|
| **Decision Variables** | |
| $AV_1$–$AV_4$ | Acres of VRH in Type A in periods 1–4 |
| AU | Acres in Type A that do not receive a harvest |
| $BV_1$–$BV_4$ | Acres of VRH in Type B in periods 1–4 |
| $CT_1$–$CT_4$ | Acres of VDT in Type C in periods 1–4 |
| **Policy Variables** | |
| $R_1$–$R_4$ | Net revenue in 100s of dollars, periods 1–4 |
| $H_1$–$H_4$ | Harvest in 100s of cubic feet, periods 1–4 |
| SI\$ | Beginning inventory value in 100s of dollars |
| EI\$ | Ending inventory value in 100s of dollars |
| SIV | Beginning inventory volume in 100s of cubic feet |
| EIV | Ending inventory volume in 100s of cubic feet |
| $P_1$–$P_4$ | Preforest in periods 1–4 (acres) |
| $Y_1$–$Y_4$ | Simplified young forest in periods 1–4 (acres) |
| $Yc_1$–$Yc_4$ | Complex young forest in periods 1–4 (acres) |
| $M_1$–$M_4$ | Remnant pine/hardwood forest, periods 1–4 (acres) |

Beginning and ending inventory value (100s of dollars)

$$SI\$ = 9(AV_1 + AV_2 + AV_3 + AV_4 + AU) + 3(BV_1 + BV_2 + BV_3 + BV_4) + 6(CT_1 + CT_2 + CT_3 + CT_4)$$

$$EI\$ = 2AV_1 + 1AV_2 + 0AV_3 + 0AV_4 + 13AU + 2BV_1 + 1BV_2 + 0BV_3 + 0AV_4 + 7CT_1 + 7.5CT_2 + 8CT_3 + 8.5CT_4$$

Harvest volume in each period (100s of cubic feet):

$$H_1 = 16AV_1 + 10BV_1 + 5CT_1$$

$$H_2 = 18AV_2 + 12BV_2 + 5.5CT_2$$

$$H_3 = 20AV_3 + 14BV_3 + 6CT_3$$

$$H_4 = 22AV_4 + 16BV_4 + 6.5CT_4$$

Beginning and ending inventory volume (100s of cubic feet):

$$SIV = 16(AV_1 + AV_2 + AV_3 + AV_4 + AU) + 10(BV_1 + BV_2 + BV_3 + BV_4) + 14(CT_1 + CT_2 + CT_3 + CT_4)$$

$$EIV = 7AV_1 + 5AV_2 + 2AV_3 + 0AV_4 + 24AU + 7BV_1 + 5BV_2 + 2BV_3 + 0BV_4 + 15CT_1 + 16CT_2 + 17CT_3 + 18CT_4$$

Amount of upland preforest in each period (acres):

$$P_1 = AV_1 + BV_1$$

$$P_2 = AV_1 + AV_2 + BV_1 + BV_2$$

$$P_3 = AV_2 + AV_3 + BV_2 + BV_3$$

$$P_4 = AV_3 + AV_4 + BV_3 + BV_4$$

Amount of upland simplified young forest (acres):

$$Y_1 = BV_2 + BV_3 + BV_4 + CT_2 + CT_3 + CT_4$$

$$Y_2 = BV_3 + BV_4 + CT_3 + CT_4$$

$$Y_3 = BV_4 + CT_4$$

Amount of upland complex young forest (acres):

$$Yc_1 = CT_1$$

$$Yc_2 = CT_1 + CT_2$$

$$Yc_3 = AV_1 + BV_1 + CT_1 + CT_2 + CT_3$$

$$Yc_4 = AV_1 + AV_2 + BV_1 + BV_2 + CT_1 + CT_2 + CT_3 + CT_4$$

Amount of upland remnant pine/hardwood forest (M) in each period (acres):

$$M_1 = AV_2 + AV_3 + AV_4 + AU$$

$$M_2 = AV_3 + AV_4 + AU$$

$$M_3 = AV_4 + AU$$

$$M_4 = AU$$

***Relating policy variables to objectives***  The policy accounting equations sum the implications of the land allocation choice for the policy variables of interest. That is very helpful, as it enables both the reporting and limiting of the levels of those policy variables. Here are some examples of limits on policy variables and relationships between policy variables that Debora Lee might utilize in her analysis:

Acres of preforest (P), simplified young forest (Y), complex young forest (Yc) or remnant pine/hardwood (M) must at least equal XX in a period:

$$P_i \geq XX \text{ for } i = 1\text{–}4$$

$$Y_i \geq XX \text{ for } i = 1\text{–}4$$

$$Yc_i \geq XX \text{ for } i = 1\text{–}4$$

$$M_i \geq XX \text{ for } i = 1\text{–}4$$

Acres of preforest (P), simplified young forest (Y), complex young forest (Yc), or remnant pine/hardwood (M) must be not more than XX in a period:

$$P_i \leq XX \text{ for } i = 1\text{–}4$$

$$Y_i \leq XX \text{ for } i = 1\text{–}4$$

$$Yc_i \leq XX \text{ for } i = 1\text{–}4$$

$$M_i \leq XX \text{ for } i = 1\text{–}4$$

Harvest volume must be constant over time (often called "even-flow"):

$$H_2 - H_1 = 0$$

$$H_3 - H_2 = 0$$

$$H_4 - H_3 = 0$$

Harvest volume must be constant or rising over time (also called "nondeclining yield"):

$$H_2 - H_1 \geq 0$$

$$H_3 - H_2 \geq 0$$

$$H_4 - H_3 \geq 0$$

Revenue must be constant over time:

$$R_2 - R_1 = 0$$

$$R_3 - R_2 = 0$$

$$R_4 - R_3 = 0$$

Revenue must be constant or increasing over time:

$$R_2 - R_1 \geq 0$$

$$R_3 - R_2 \geq 0$$

$$R_4 - R_3 \geq 0$$

Ending inventory volume equals or exceeds beginning inventory volume:

EIV – SIV ≥ 0

Ending inventory value equals or exceeds beginning inventory value:

EI$ – SI$ ≥ 0

It is often convenient to display the decision and policy variables and their relationships in a *detached coefficient matrix*[5][6] (Table 19.8).

## Simulation Results

All alternatives utilize the land allocation choices described above in the context of three requirements:

1.  All of forest types B and C will receive a restoration harvest during the four planning periods;

2.  The harvest must provide a nondeclining net revenue over the four periods; and

3.  The financial value of the ending inventory must equal or exceed that of the beginning inventory.

It should be noted that the requirement for the restoration harvest of types B and C is met through specification of the land allocation choices for them (leaving these types unharvested over the planning horizon is not an option) and that the requirements for nondeclining net revenue and the financial value of the ending inventory are met through explicit constraints.

Also, all alternatives have the objective function of maximizing net revenue, given the other requirements, to minimize the trade-off between providing net revenue from harvest and achieving other objectives as specified in the constraints.

As we discussed under creation of the alternatives, the family decided to start with two benchmark alternatives: Alternative #1—the objective function and requirements listed above—and Alternative #2—the objective function and requirements of Alternative #1 with the additional requirement of completing the restoration harvest of the young hardwood/pine forest (with a VRH) and the pine plantation (with a VDT) in the first two periods.

---

5 See the Appendix of Chapter 18 for a description of a detached coefficient matrix

6 In this formulation, which we will use throughout this section of the chapter, constraints are placed on the flow of net revenue over time and on the relationship between beginning and ending inventory value. Harvest and inventory volume, on the other hand, are tracked but not constrained. In addition, the accounting variables and equations for $P_1$–$P_4$, $Yc_1$–$Yc_4$, $Y_1$–$Y_4$, and $M_1$–$M_4$ are not shown due to lack of space.

Alternative #1 produces a relatively high net revenue (Figure 19.3a) by focusing on harvest of the remnant pine/hardwood first (the acres of $AV_1$ in Alternative #1 in Table 19.9) and thus immediately reducing the amount of this type (Figure 19.4a), putting off harvest of the young hardwood/pine forest and the pine plantation, which are increasing more rapidly in value growth, until later periods (Figure 19.4b). This harvest schedule delays creation of complex young forest (Figure 19.4c). Also, lack of smoothing requirements other than a stable revenue results in somewhat irregular amounts of preforest (Figure 19.4d) and harvest volume (Figure 19.3b) over time.

Alternative #2, with the added requirement of focusing on the harvest of the young hardwood/pine and the plantation acres in the first two periods, results in a reduction in net revenue by almost 20% (Figure 19.3a), but also substantially accelerates creation of complex young forest (Figure 19.4c) and preforest (Figure 19.4d) while leaving more of the remnant pine/hardwood unharvested until later in the planning periods (Figure 19.4a). Again, lack of smoothing requirements other than a stable revenue results in somewhat irregular amounts of preforest (Figure 19.4d) and harvest volume (Figure 19.3b) over time.

Looking at these alternatives, the family is most concerned that the harvest is not spread across the different forest types in each period. This harvest diversity strategy is one of their hedges against uncertainty. In addition, they are somewhat dissatisfied with the fluctuation in harvest volume from period to period, which can make it difficult to establish a continuing relationship with local loggers. Achieving some stability here is another of their hedges against uncertainty. To help spread the harvest among the forest types in a period, they decide to focus on stabilizing the harvest of young hardwood/pine forest and the pine plantation, requiring that at least 20% of each of these two forest types must be harvested in a period. They hope that will stabilize the harvest level too. Thus, Alternative #3 is the same as Alternative #1, with the added requirement that at least 20% of the two forest types are harvested in each period.

Alternative #3 does smooth the harvest rate of the three forest types (Table 19.9 and Figure 19.4a and b), the harvest volume (Figure 19.3b), and the amount of preforest (Figure 19.4d). Net revenue is only slightly below that of Alternative #1 (Figure 19.3a), while the amount of remnant pine/hardwood diminishes more slowly than under Alternative #1, with most of that type left unharvested over the planning horizon.

The family thinks Alternative #3 has promise but the kids would like more of the remnant pine forest left after four periods of harvest. Thus, they create Alternative #4, which adds a requirement of leaving 600 acres of upland remnant pine/hardwood forest unharvested over the planning periods. Alternative #4 has many of the harvest scheduling

Table 19.8 *The Pine Hill Forest planning model represented in terms of a detached coefficient matrix.*

| | $AV_1$ | $AV_2$ | $AV_3$ | $AV_4$ | $AU$ | $BV_1$ | $BV_2$ | $BV_3$ | $BV_4$ | $CT_1$ | $CT_2$ | $CT_3$ | $CT_4$ | $R_1$ | $R_2$ | $R_3$ | $R_4$ | $EI\$$ | $SI\$$ | $H_1$ | $H_2$ | $H_3$ | $H_4$ | $EIV$ | $SIV$ | |
|---|---|---|---|---|---|---|---|---|---|---|---|---|---|---|---|---|---|---|---|---|---|---|---|---|---|---|
| Acres rem pine/hard | 1 | 1 | 1 | 1 | 1 | | | | | | | | | | | | | | | | | | | | | = 853 |
| Acres young hard/pine | | | | | | 1 | 1 | 1 | 1 | | | | | | | | | | | | | | | | | = 447 |
| Acres plantation | | | | | | | | | | 1 | 1 | 1 | 1 | | | | | | | | | | | | | = 969 |
| Period 1 Rev | 9 | | | | | 3 | | | | 2 | | | | −1 | | | | | | | | | | | | = 0 |
| Period 2 Rev | | 10 | | | | | 4 | | | | 2.5 | | | | −1 | | | | | | | | | | | = 0 |
| Period 3 Rev | | | 11 | | | | | 5 | | | | 3 | | | | −1 | | | | | | | | | | = 0 |
| Period 4 Rev | | | | 12 | | | | | 6 | | | | 3.5 | | | | −1 | | | | | | | | | = 0 |
| End Value | 2 | 1 | 0 | 0 | 13 | 2 | 1 | 0 | 0 | 7 | 7.5 | 8 | 8.5 | | | | | −1 | | | | | | | | = 0 |
| Begin Value | 9 | 9 | 9 | 9 | 9 | 3 | 3 | 3 | 3 | 6 | 6 | 6 | 6 | | | | | | −1 | | | | | | | = 0 |
| Cubic ft Harvest P1 | 16 | | | | | 10 | | | | 5 | | | | | | | | | | −1 | | | | | | = 0 |
| Cubic ft Harvest P2 | | 18 | | | | | 12 | | | | 5.5 | | | | | | | | | | −1 | | | | | = 0 |
| Cubic ft Harvest P3 | | | 20 | | | | | 14 | | | | 6 | | | | | | | | | | −1 | | | | = 0 |
| Cubic ft Harvest P4 | | | | 22 | | | | | 16 | | | | 6.5 | | | | | | | | | | −1 | | | = 0 |
| Ending Volume | 7 | 5 | 2 | 0 | 24 | 7 | 5 | 2 | 0 | 15 | 16 | 17 | 18 | | | | | | | | | | | −1 | | = 0 |
| Begin Volume | 16 | 16 | 16 | 16 | 16 | 10 | 10 | 10 | 10 | 14 | 14 | 14 | 14 | | | | | | | | | | | | −1 | = 0 |
| Nondeclining Rev P1–P2 | | | | | | | | | | | | | | −1 | 1 | | | | | | | | | | | ≥ 0 |
| Nondeclining Rev P2–P3 | | | | | | | | | | | | | | | −1 | 1 | | | | | | | | | | ≥ 0 |
| Nondeclining Rev P3–P4 | | | | | | | | | | | | | | | | −1 | 1 | | | | | | | | | ≥ 0 |
| End Value ≥ Begin Value | | | | | | | | | | | | | | | | | | 1 | −1 | | | | | | | ≥ 0 |

characteristics of Alternative #3, except for leaving more of the remnant pine/hardwood forest unharvested (Figure 19.4a) and providing a lower net revenue, the lowest of any alternative (Figure 19.3a). Alternative #4 is the only alternative that leaves more harvestable value than required at the end of the planning periods (1.60 million); the first three alternatives leave the same harvestable value in the ending inventory as is available in the beginning inventory (1.48 million).

Many more alternatives might be created. However, the modeling of these four alternatives provide an illustration of the consequences that can be portrayed for forest planning alternatives, the dynamics of alternative creation, and insights that can be gained (Box 19.2).

## Step 6: Evaluate Trade-offs and Select a Forest Plan

Given the information described above about the consequences of the alternatives, how might the family go about selecting their forest plan beyond simply a majority vote of the family after some discussion? As we learned in the last chapter, a variety of methods exist. One of the most common is to score each alternative by each performance measure (such as the measures as described in Table 19.2), weight the importance of each measure, and develop an aggregate score.

Debora Lee develops such an aggregate score for the four alternatives in the Pine Hill Forest Problem (Box 19.3) using the harvest scheduling performance measures from Table 19.2, a one to three ranking to indicate how well the alternative did under the measure, and a simple summation of these rankings under each performance measure to

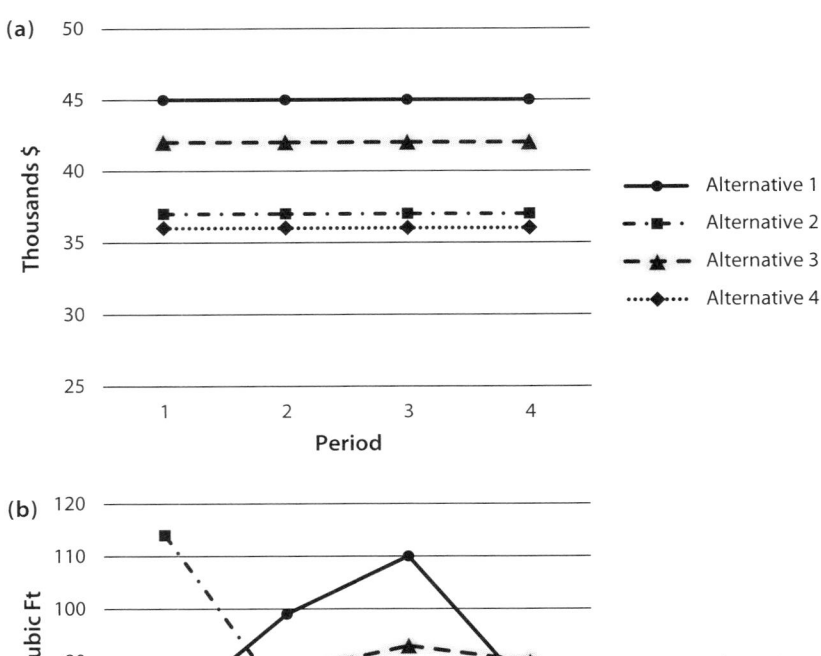

Figure 19.3 *(a) Annual net revenue in each period under the four alternatives, and (b) annual harvest volume in each period under the four alternatives.*

create an aggregate score (Table 19.10). These scorings and weightings are inherently subjective and should not be the sole arbiter, but they do provide one more perspective on the best alternative for the family.

Not surprisingly, Alternatives #3 and #4 scored highest, as the family developed them after they saw the results from the two benchmark alternatives. More than anything else, Alternatives #3 and #4 present a trade-off between

Table 19.9 *Land allocation of the harvestable area by forest type under each alternative, where each land allocation choice is portrayed in terms of the forest type (A = remnant pine/hardwood, B = young hardwood pine, and C = pine plantation), harvest type (V = VRH, T = VDT), and the period in which the harvest takes place. U = unharvested*

| Alternative | Land Allocation Choice (acres) | | | | | | | | | | | | |
|---|---|---|---|---|---|---|---|---|---|---|---|---|---|
| | $AV_1$ | $AV_2$ | $AV_3$ | $AV_4$ | AU | $BV_1$ | $BV_2$ | $BV_3$ | $BV_4$ | $CT_1$ | $CT_2$ | $CT_3$ | $CT_4$ |
| 1 | 250 | 148 | | | 455 | | 193 | 254 | | | | 326 | 643 |
| 2 | 8 | | 169 | 155 | 521 | 447 | | | | 224 | 745 | | |
| 3 | 160 | 125 | 71 | | 497 | 89 | 89 | 148 | 121 | 193 | 193 | 193 | 390 |
| 4 | 130 | 99 | 24 | | 600 | 89 | 89 | 89 | 180 | 193 | 193 | 370 | 213 |

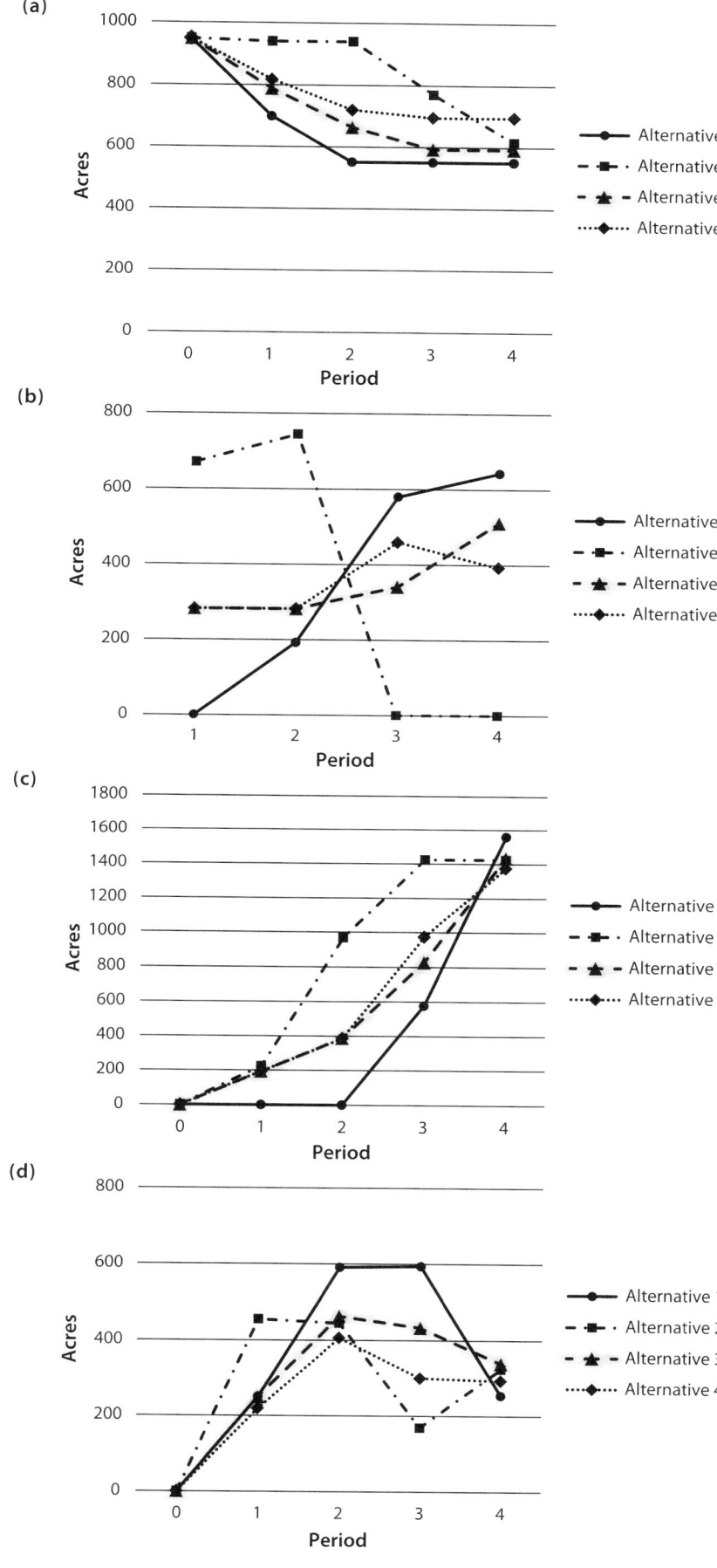

revenue produced during the 20-year planning horizon and amount of remnant pine/hardwood left after harvest in the last period. To look at it another way, the family has the choice of a higher revenue during the planning periods or more acreage and harvestable value in the remnant pine/hardwood after completion of the planning periods (Figures 19.3a and 19.4a). As we described above, all the alternatives were required to have as much harvestable value in the ending inventory as in the beginning inventory. However, the value of the ending inventory in Alternative #3 exceeds what is required due to the need to maintain 600 acres of upland remnant pine/hardwood.

While the family likes the safeguard that they must not deplete the value of the harvestable inventory, they are reluctant to go beyond that requirement, as they also feel the need for scholarship money for the children over the next 20 years. *Therefore, they choose Alternative #3 for their forest plan*.

## Step 7: Implement, Monitor, and Adapt

The family is happy that they now have a forest plan, including the projected forest structure that they will develop on the forest under their forest plan (Figure 19.5). They have come a long way.

Still, Debora Lee tells her family that they have one more step: they need to develop a monitoring plan to assess whether they are faithfully implementing the plan they have selected and whether the plan is effective in meeting the objectives they set for it. As we discussed in Chapters 11 and 18, implementation and effectiveness monitoring can be seen as having four elements:

1. Identify key uncertainties—implementation uncertainties and effectiveness uncertainties.

Figure 19.4 *(a) Total area of remnant pine/hardwood forest (Type A) after harvest in each period under the four alternatives; (b) harvest in types B and C in each period under the four alternatives (c) area of complex young forest in each period under the four alternatives; and (d) area of preforest in each period under the four alternatives.*

2. Develop testable hypotheses about treatment success.

3. Search for information to test the hypotheses.

4. Develop mechanisms that ensure monitoring results and methodologies will undergo periodic, fair-minded review, with the goal of revising policies that are not working.

Debora Lee asks her family about their greatest uncertainties about the plan they have just adopted, requesting that they relate these uncertainties to the table of fundamental objective and means objectives they put together when they started the planning effort (Table 19.1). In other words, she asks them which of the objectives in that table they are most concerned about attaining. After much discussion, it turns out that they are worried about whether the prescription objectives will be met or whether the VRH harvest will revert to the clearcuts of old. More specifically they worry whether the old pines will be retained, whether biological legacies will be left at harvest, especially over the designated biodiversity hot spots they will help select, and whether, overall, VRH units will still resemble clearcuts. Also, they are concerned about whether the hoped-for abundance of native butterflies and birds will appear in the preforest that is created. For her part, Debora Lee is

---

**Box 19.2  Some lessons from the Pine Hill Forest analysis**

This relatively simple analysis demonstrates a number of important concepts and relationships:

- *The multiple objectives of many landowners, such as those of Debora Lee's family, do not lend themselves to maximization of any particular ecosystem service or to representing the value of all these services through a single dollar figure or net present value.* Rather, the multiple objectives of landowners require approaches where they can explore the effect of emphasizing certain objectives on the suite of objectives they have. We have done so in this example, especially relative to the objectives of restoration, maintaining some remnant pine/hardwood forest, and risk-spreading through distributing the activities among the forest types.

- *Forest planning at its best is a continuous, improvisational learning experience with many feedback loops.* While we showed planning as a series of steps (Box 19.1), this case suggests the back-and-forth nature of forest planning as alternatives are developed, evaluated, and revised.

- *The differences in outcomes between alternatives illustrate how emphasizing certain objectives through policy constraints can influence the outcome of an alternative.* By varying constraints that represent various levels of a performance measure, such as the amount of remnant pine forest left unharvested, Debora Lee got a better idea of their effect on other objectives.

- *The implicit assumptions and decisions made prior to formulating the problem may influence the outcomes in unknown ways.* As an example, we did not include land allocation choices that allowed some area of Types B and C (young hardwood/pine and pine plantations) to remain unharvested through the 20-year planning horizon. Thus, we lack information on how the addition of those choices might alter the

results. Debora Lee could gain that information by adding those choices and altering the constraints.

- *Performing these analyses can help reveal emergent properties of the relationships implicit in the problem formulation that might not be obvious.* As an example, this analysis revealed the sensitive relationship between revenue generation and the temporal distribution of harvest in the young hardwood/pine forest and the pine plantations.

- *Sensitivity analysis through selection of objectives, constraint levels, and predictions about future forest conditions can add important information* for making decisions and can be a testing ground for how well the modelers understand the model they have built. Much more of this type of analysis could be done in this example problem.

- *Trade-offs are inherently present when managing for multiple objectives* as we have seen here. It is important to surface these trade-offs and try to minimize them, rather than relying on techniques that identify an "optimal" solution.

- *With the multiple sources of uncertainty inherent in planning for the future, an adaptive management component is an essential element of a forest plan.* Forest plans should be seen as indicative of future possibilities rather than fully predictive, as hypotheses rather than solutions. Monitoring and the willingness to change as evidence accumulates are fundamental to successful conservation and use of forests.

- Finally, modeling can help *sharpen intuition and mental simulation ability, helping to integrate naturalistic and systematic decision making.* Even with these few simulations, patterns and relationships begin to appear and strengthen the ability of the people involved in predicting the consequences of potential alternatives before they are simulated.

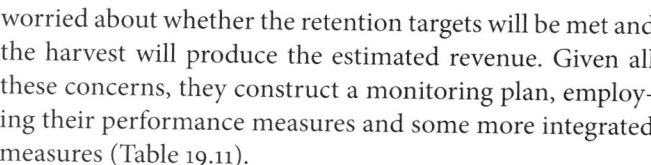

> **Box 19.3  Pine Hill Forest alternatives**
>
> All alternatives maximize first-period net revenue subject to restoration harvest of all area of forest types B and C, a nondeclining net revenue from period to period, and an ending inventory with a timber harvest value at least equal to that in the beginning inventory.
>
> **Alternative 1.**  No additional objectives are represented as constraints.
>
> **Alternative 2.**  Types B and C must receive a restoration harvest in the first two periods.
>
> **Alternative 3.**  Types B and C must each receive at least 20% of their harvest in each of the four periods.
>
> **Alternative 4.**  Types B and C must each receive at least 20% of their harvest in each of the four periods *and* at least 600 acres of Type A must be reserved from harvest.

worried about whether the retention targets will be met and the harvest will produce the estimated revenue. Given all these concerns, they construct a monitoring plan, employing their performance measures and some more integrated measures (Table 19.11).

As part of the monitoring, family members plan to drive and hike the forest each summer to assess the status of biodiversity hot spots designated for aggregated retention patches and gain a visual impression of the harvests that have occurred, and to walk the harvest units to see if any old pines have been harvested. In addition, they agree to keep a record of the birds and butterflies they see in preforest areas. Finally, the entire family agrees to have a forest planning reunion in five years to compare notes on how well the plan is working and assess what needs to be modified.

## Summary

With the description of the monitoring and adaptive strategy for the Pine Hill Forest plan, we have completed an initial demonstration of the application of structured decision making to forest planning under ecological forest management. In this demonstration, we attempted to incorporate considerations of uncertainty throughout. In selection of the relatively short time before potential revision (five years) and the number of years in the simulation (20), we implicitly acknowledged the uncertainty of the future. In building natural complexity and variety into the prescriptions, distributing harvests in a period across the harvest types, and requiring that we maintain the financial value of the forest capital, we

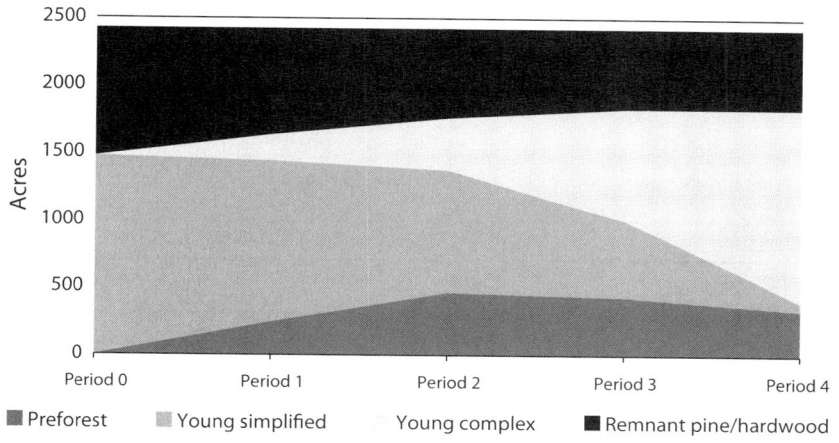

Figure 19.5 *Projected forest structure over the 20-year planning horizon for the alternative chosen by Debora Lee's family, categorized by preforest, young (simplified), young (complex), and remnant pine/hardwood. Acres can become young (complex) in two ways: (1) two periods after a VRH, or (2) immediately after a VDT. Riparian buffer acres of the three forest types are included, but old-growth pine and wet meadow are not shown.*

Table 19.10 *Aggregate performance score for the four alternatives in the Pine Hill Forest Problem using harvest scheduling performance measures from Table 19.2 and simulation of the consequences (a score of 3 is highest and 1 is lowest)*

| Harvest Scheduling Performance Measures | Alternative | | | |
|---|---|---|---|---|
| | 1 | 2 | 3 | 4 |
| 1. Annual net income (higher is better) | 3 | 1 | 2 | 1 |
| 2. The amount of harvest in types B and C in the first period (more is better) | 1 | 3 | 2 | 2 |
| 3. Harvest distribution across forest types in each period (more evenly distributed is better) | 1 | 1 | 3 | 3 |
| 4. Remnant pine/hardwood forest reserved across all four periods (higher amount is better) | 2 | 2 | 2 | 3 |
| 5. Development of complex young forest (faster is better) | 1 | 3 | 2 | 2 |
| 6. Preforest stability (more stable is better) | 1 | 2 | 3 | 3 |
| 7. Harvest volume stability (more stable is better) | 2 | 1 | 3 | 3 |
| 8. Ending inventory value exceeds the beginning inventory value (higher amount is better) | 1 | 1 | 1 | 2 |
| Total | 12 | 14 | 18 | 19 |

attempted to build a forest plan that would be robust in the face of alternative futures. In constructing an adaptive management plan, we attempted to create an early warning system to alert us as to where the plan may not be living up to expectations. In sum, we tried to follow the recommendations of Gregory et al. (2012) that environmental planning integrate robust and adaptive approaches in the face of an uncertain future.

## Linking Forest Planning to Implementation: The Importance of Spatial Analysis

The family next turns to where the harvest will occur in the first five-year period, since everyone in the family has their favorite place on the forest and worries about its fate under the selected forest plan. Debora Lee recognizes that her analysis has not determined the location of the harvest for the next five years, beyond estimating the acres of each type that will be harvested. Thus she begins to explore various approaches for determining more exactly where the harvest will occur.

If all acres in a type are scheduled for harvest in a single period, Debora Lee would know the location of that harvest. However, when fewer than all the acres in a type on the forest are selected for harvest in a period, she needs to determine where to undertake the harvest from among the acres of the type scattered over the forest. As an example, 160 acres of Type A (remnant pine/hardwood) would be harvested in period 1 under Alternative #3 (Table 19.9), out of 853 acres available for harvest. Where would that harvest occur in Type A? The analysis done so far does not provide that information. Thus, questions may arise about how *implementable* an alternative might be, that is, whether Debora Lee can successfully apply the prescriptions for the different types at the levels of harvest specified in Alternative #3.

Debora Lee could use her extensive knowledge of the forest to select the harvest location, considering the many factors that are difficult to model. She might also want to utilize historical disturbance patch sizes for these forests as a guide, as we discussed in Chapter 5. Or she might seek a more analytical approach. Planners are often called upon to

Table 19.11 *Sample monitoring outline as part of the adaptive management plan for the patch/individual tree problem*

| Key uncertainty | Hypothesis | Measure | Standard (Expectation) | Monitoring method |
|---|---|---|---|---|
| *IMPLEMENTATION* | | | | |
| Whether harvests will retain old pines | Treatments will not cut old trees | # of old pine stumps due to harvest | No old pine stumps from harvest | Post project survey by the children walking through harvest units |
| Whether marked retention aggregates covering biodiversity hot spots will be retained | These marked retention aggregates will be left unharvested | Proportion of these retention patches retained | Over 90% retained undisturbed | Pre project selection by family. Post project survey by Debora Lee and family |
| Whether the designated amount of retention will be left | Average retention will meet the requirement | Average % retention | At least 15% retention | Post project survey by Debora Lee |
| *EFFECTIVENESS* | | | | |
| Whether post VRH environment will function as preforest | Post VRH harvest units will attract early seral birds and butterflies | Variety of native birds and butterflies seen on each visit to harvest units | Uncertain | Family members who visit harvest units keep track of what they see and give the record to Debora Lee |
| Whether VRH units will look like clearcuts | Post-harvest units will not look like clearcuts | # of VRH units that pass the visual test | All VRH units pass the test | Post project visit by designated family members |
| Whether implementing the forest plan will produce the projected net revenue | Implementing the forest plan will produce the projected net revenue | $/year over five years | Net revenue will average at least 95% of the projected level | Annual accounting by Debora Lee |

Table 19.12 *Forest type acres by watershed*[*]

| Watershed | Forest Type | Riparian Acres (within 150 ft of stream) | Upland Acres | Total Acres |
|---|---|---|---|---|
| *Dogwood Creek* | A | 22 | 328 | 350 |
| | B | 0 | 57 | 57 |
| | C | 9 | 488 | 497 |
| | OG | 1 | 30 | 31 |
| | WM | 0 | 0 | 0 |
| | Subtotal | 32 | 903 | 935 |
| *Trout Creek* | A | 51 | 293 | 344 |
| | B | 12 | 179 | 191 |
| | C | 19 | 320 | 339 |
| | OG | 0 | 7 | 7 |
| | WM | 23 | 14 | 37 |
| | Subtotal | 105 | 813 | 918 |
| *White Water Creek* | A | 24 | 232 | 256 |
| | B | 18 | 211 | 229 |
| | C | 2 | 161 | 163 |
| | OG | 0 | 0 | 0 |
| | WM | 0 | 0 | 0 |
| | Subtotal | 44 | 604 | 648 |
| | Total | 181 | 2,320 | 2,501 |

* Totals may be slightly off due to rounding.

recognize more spatial detail in scheduling where harvests and other treatments will occur, especially in the short run. We will discuss two commonly used approaches to giving a harvest schedule more spatial resolution: (1) subforest types and (2) individual harvest units.

## Subforest Types

Major subdivisions of a forest, such as watersheds, can be recognized in a forest planning analysis. This enables both improved spatial resolution of where harvests or other treatments will occur in a time period and control of cumulative effects at the subforest level.

In the case of the Pine Hill Forest, people may be concerned about the amount of activity in a particular watershed during a time period, both in terms of aggregate sediment effects and the possibility of flooding during downpours if too much of the forest is opened up through harvest.[7] Thus, Debora Lee might want to rec-

ognize and control the level of activity by watershed on the Pine Hill Forest.

To consider a watershed as an organizing vehicle in the analysis, Debora Lee would need to estimate the area in her forest types in each of the three watersheds in the Pine Hill Forest (Table 19.12). She then would need to recognize land allocation choices by watershed. Looking back at Table 19.4, Debora Lee and her consultant recognized 13 land allocation choices across the three types where harvest might occur (five for Type A, four for Type B, and four for Type C). Since these three types occur in all three watersheds, recognizing watersheds in the analysis would triple the number of land allocation choices.

In describing the land allocation choices, Debora Lee would need to add an additional symbol to name each choice specific to each watershed, such as a "D" for Dogwood Creek. Also, each watershed would have its own controls on acres of each type available for harvest over the planning periods. Using the Dogwood Creek watershed as the example, equations on the amount of land available in each of the three types in the watershed would become:

7 See Chapter 5 for a discussion of cumulative effects associated with different types of weather events.

$$DAV_1 + DAV_2 + DAV_3 + DAV_4 + DAU = 328 \text{ acres}$$

$$DBV_1 + DBV_2 + DBV_3 + DBV_4 = 57 \text{ acres}$$

$$DCT_1 + DCT_2 + DCT_3 + DCT_4 = 488 \text{ acres}$$

Let's assume Debora Lee wishes to control the acres of VRH in a watershed in a period to limit potential cumulative watershed affects. Again using the Dogwood Creek watershed as the example, she could establish those controls by forming constraints on the acreage of VRH in each period:

$$DAV_1 + DBV_1 \leq XX$$

$$DAV_2 + DBV_2 \leq XX$$

$$DAV_3 + DBV_3 \leq XX$$

$$DAV_4 + BV_4 \leq XX$$

where XX is the acceptable upper limit on the acres of VRH in the Dogwood Creek watershed in a period.

Debora Lee now has the ability to account for, and control, the level of activity by watershed. However, unless an entire type is scheduled for harvest in a period, she still would need to rely on other analysis and judgment to determine where the specified harvest for a type in a period would occur in each watershed.

## Representing Individual Patches

With the increasing social emphasis on controlling the spatial aspects of the many positive and negative effects of timber harvest, forest planners have increasingly turned to breaking the forest into harvest (or other treatment) units for their forest plan modeling. Especially in the last two to three decades, we have seen a significant increase in these approaches to forest planning. Sometimes they are utilized as a forest planning tool on their own; at other times they are utilized to test the feasibility of implementation for a few periods of the results obtained from a model like the one we have used so far in forest planning. We devote the remainder of the chapter to these dynamic spatial planning models.

## Modeling Dynamic Spatial Objectives in Forestry

The approach to forest planning analysis we outlined above, in which we build a quantitative model of our planning problem as a set of linear equations and then solve it for a schedule of harvests and other treatments, has proven to be a powerful mechanism for developing modern forest plans. The requirements for specification of input constraints and resource objectives and for quantification of relationships have helped mightily in the development of internally consistent plans. Through sensitivity analysis, this approach has also helped people think through the implications of different assumptions, policies, and management strategies.

Increasingly, though, managers and stakeholders have become interested in modeling dynamic spatial relationships through time, and it may be difficult to represent such relationships as a set of linear equations, such as we have employed in our example of planning models thus far. Bettinger et al. (2003), for example, assigned thinning and group selection harvests in a complex spatial arrangement to facilitate development of mature forest structure while maintaining minimum levels of nesting, roosting, and foraging habitat for northern spotted owls. Other applications of spatial modeling to solve environmental problems include limiting adjacent clearcut harvests until the older units have regrown (Boston & Bettinger, 2006), designing compact and contiguous reserve networks (Nalle et al., 2002), modeling joint production of wildlife and timber (Bettinger et al., 1997; Bettinger et al., 1999; Nalle, 2004), and maintaining and restoring large old-growth forest patches (Öhman, 2000; Toth & McDill, 2008).

One particularly challenging spatial problem comes from the Wallowa-Whitman National Forest in eastern Oregon (Davis et al., 2001). Wildlife management objectives there call for maintaining an integrated spatial arrangement of

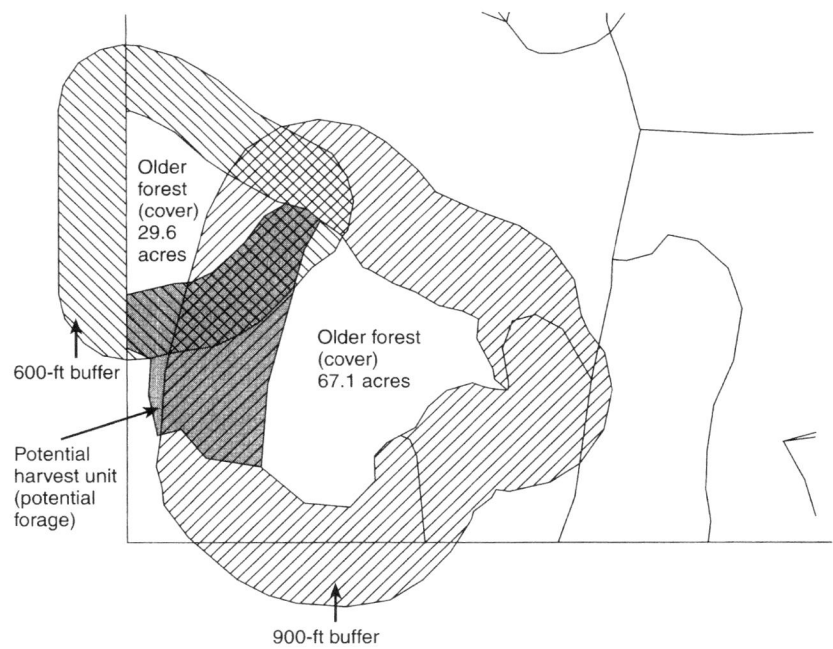

Figure 19.6 *A problem in the spatial arrangement of elk habitat on the Wallowa-Whitman National Forest. (Source: Davis et al., 2001)*

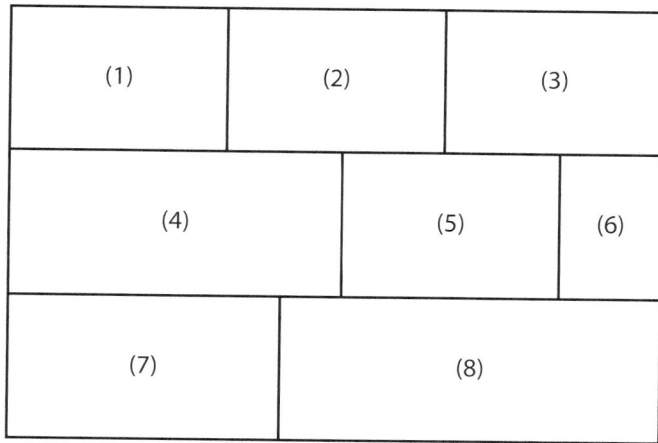

Figure 19.7 *Hypothetical landscape divided into eight planning units. Values in parentheses represent unit number.*

cover and forage: provide at least 80% of the forage area in elk summer ranges within 600 feet of a cover patch at least 10 acres in size and provide at least 80% of the forage area in elk winter ranges within 900 feet of a satisfactory cover patch of forest at least 40 acres in size (Figure 19.6). To include these types of objectives in a planning problem, we need to track not only the size of cover patches but also their spatial relationship to forage patches that might occur naturally or be created through harvest or prescribed fire.

These desired elk habitat relationships are an example of a broader group of wildlife models for particular species, often called habitat suitability index (HSI) models, in which the spatial arrangement of habitat components can be an important element in judging overall habitat quality. Because forests grow and change, it is difficult to designate once and for all what will be cover and what will be forage. Rather, we would like to be able to dynamically evaluate and control habitat quality over time for the multitude of species whose habitat we wish to conserve.

Managing explicitly for spatial considerations requires knowledge of where treatments occur on the landscape. Thus it is not sufficient to model the proportion of a type that will be assigned to a harvest or other treatment in each period, as we did earlier in this chapter. *Rather, we need to divide the landscape into spatial planning units and assign a planning unit to a management choice in its entirety* (Figure 19.7). In the nomenclature of quantitative planning, we will recognize the choices for each planning unit as integer variables (a planning unit is assigned to a particular treatment or it is not).

*Adjacency* is a fundamentally important concept for representing landscape conditions in spatial modeling. Though it can be defined differently depending upon the problem at hand, *adjacency generally refers to spatial planning units that share a common boundary or edge*. In Figure 19.7, as an example, unit 1 is adjacent to units 2 and 4, unit 2 is adjacent

to units 1, 3, 4, and 5, and so on. Knowing whether units are adjacent allows us to evaluate the spatial arrangement of forest conditions that result from treatments. For example, to determine if a plan could maintain or restore large contiguous patches of remnant pine/hardwood forest, we need to know the condition of all units adjacent to each remnant pine/hardwood planning unit, as well as the condition of units adjacent to those units, and so on. As another example, locating units of desired forest conditions next to each other, often called *complementary patches*, requires spatial information on unit arrangement.

Perhaps the most common spatial planning problem in forestry limits the size and distribution of harvest units across the landscape, especially when harvest creates openings such as clearcuts. Many forest practice regulations around the world impose adjacency (*green-up*) constraints to limit the size of clearcuts, as we discussed in Chapter 7. In Oregon, as an example, clearcuts are limited to 120 acres. Adjacent units cannot be harvested until regeneration in harvested units is at least four feet high or the harvested unit was reforested at least four years previously and the trees in it are free to grow. Also, FSC and SFI certification requires limitations on clearcut size, which can reduce both harvest volume and harvest revenue, as shown in the case study from Box 16.1 on southern industrial forests.

Using discrete decision variables (each planning unit is assigned in its entirety or not) results in what are called *combinatorial problems*. Addressing these combinatorial problems in forest planning has led researchers and practitioners to utilize solution techniques beyond the linear programming technique we used earlier in the chapter. As an alternative to exact optimization approaches, such as linear programming, *heuristics* have become a popular way of dealing with difficult spatial/temporal planning problems. Heuristics are *seeking or finding methods* that attempt to locate good solutions to problems at a reasonable cost (e.g., in terms of time and effort). Advantages of heuristics include their ability to handle integer variables and nonlinear relationships among variables. On the other hand, they cannot guarantee they will find the optimal solution to the mathematical problem being addressed. They can, though, find feasible and generally efficient solutions in reasonable amounts of time.[8]

## Solving Dynamic Spatial Problems on the Pine Hill Forest

To demonstrate the capabilities of spatial modeling, let's revisit the Pine Hill Forest problem. In terms of habitat,

---

8 See the Appendix to this chapter for a brief introduction to heuristic solution techniques for these unit assignment problems. For a more detailed discussion, see Davis et al. (2001) and Bettinger et al. (2017).

Debora Lee will focus on maintaining both preforest and remnant pine/hardwood forest stages—two important and potentially conflicting stages of forest development. With the achievement of these habitat objectives in mind, she will utilize prescriptions for the Pine Hill Forest that emphasize VRHs for the planning units, which will create preforest habitat. Also, Debora Lee utilizes a set of land allocation choices that allow Type B (young hardwood/pine) and Type C (pine plantation) to grow for one or two periods before being considered for harvest and that allow the possibility that all planning units of a type might not be harvested over the four periods (Table 19.13). With these considerations and the condition of the types, she creates the following land allocation choices:

- Remnant pine/hardwood—consider a VRH in each period for each planning unit in Type A and also leaving the planning unit unharvested. For period one, consider two harvest sequences: (1) VRH in period one, and (2) VRH in both periods one and four.

- Young hardwood/pine—consider a VRH in periods two through four for each planning unit in Type B, which will yield mostly hardwood pulpwood, and also leaving the planning unit unharvested.

- Pine plantation—consider a VRH in periods three through four for each planning unit in Type C and also leaving the planning unit unharvested.

Table 19.13 *Land allocation choices for the planning units of the three forest types (V = variable-retention harvest, U = leave the unit unharvested)*

|  | A | | | | | | B | | | | C | | |
|---|---|---|---|---|---|---|---|---|---|---|---|---|---|
| Period | 1a | 1b | 2 | 3 | 4 | U | 2 | 3 | 4 | U | 3 | 4 | U |
| 1 | V | V |  |  |  |  |  |  |  |  |  |  |  |
| 2 |  |  | V |  |  |  | V |  |  |  |  |  |  |
| 3 |  |  |  | V |  |  |  | V |  |  | V |  |  |
| 4 |  | V |  |  | V |  |  |  | V |  |  | V |  |

Table 19.14 *Preforest (P), young forest (Y) and remnant pine/hardwood forest (M) associated with land allocation choices for the three forest types*[*]

|  | A | | | | | | B | | | | C | | |
|---|---|---|---|---|---|---|---|---|---|---|---|---|---|
| Period | 1a | 1b | 2 | 3 | 4 | U | 2 | 3 | 4 | U | 3 | 4 | U |
| 1 | P | P | M | M | M | M | P | P | P | P | Y | Y | Y |
| 2 | Y | Y | P | M | M | M | P | Y | Y | Y | Y | Y | Y |
| 3 | Y | Y | Y | P | M | M | Y | P | Y | Y | P | Y | Y |
| 4 | Y | P | Y | Y | P | M | Y | Y | P | Y | Y | P | Y |

* As before, we assume that the acres of a type shift to preforest in the period of a VRH.

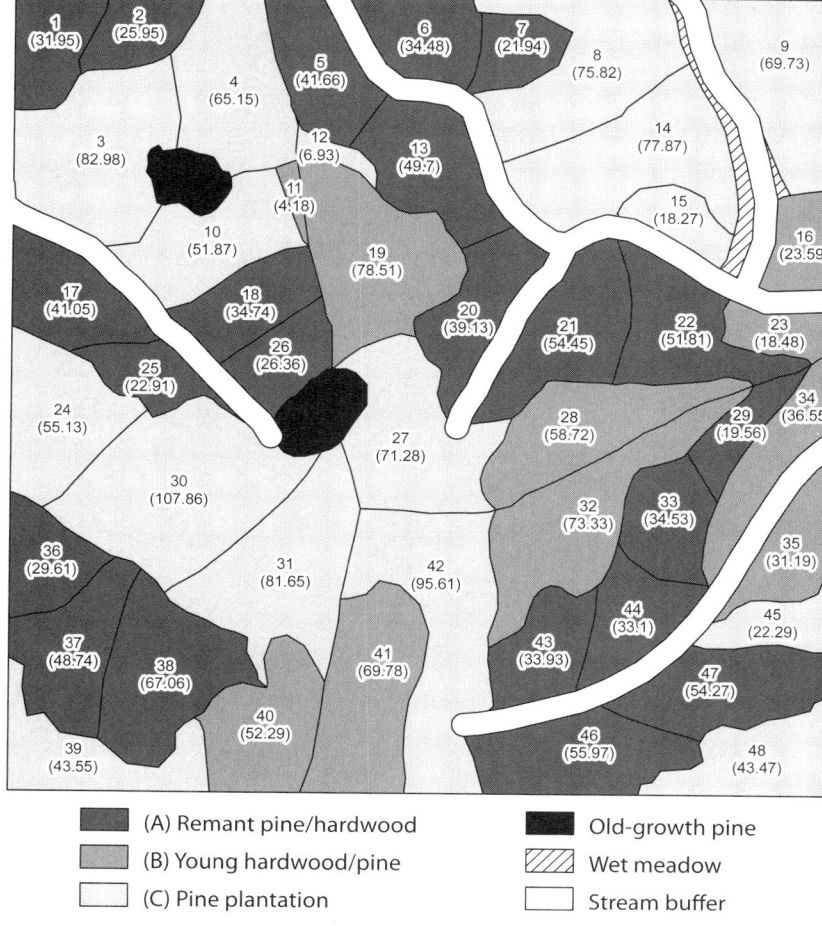

**Figure 19.8** *The spatial planning units recognized on the Pine Hill Forest, identified by forest type. The 48 planning units that can be harvested are indicated by number and acreage.*

Legend:
- (A) Remant pine/hardwood
- (B) Young hardwood/pine
- (C) Pine plantation
- Old-growth pine
- Wet meadow
- Stream buffer

from the problem formulation in the first part of the chapter have been partitioned into multiple planning units. Patches demarcated as old growth (OG) and wet meadow (WM) are off-limits from harvest, as are designated stream buffers. Therefore, Debora Lee has 48 planning units that she can schedule for harvest to achieve her family's objectives.

In the analysis, planning units from a forest type may be combined with adjacent planning units of the same types or other types over time as needed to meet designated objectives. In other words, patch boundaries can be dynamically modified through time to reach objectives, as planning units are treated in combination with adjacent planning units of like or unlike types. Also the boundaries of planning units may be retained intact for a period of time. We will see examples of these possible outcomes in the simulations.

**Modeling Dynamic Spatial Alternatives** As we discussed in the previous sections, Debora Lee's family wants to harvest the forest in a way that will produce continuing revenue over the next 20 years and into the distant future, while providing wildlife habitat and regaining many of the features these forests historically contained. To ensure a sustained revenue, Debora Lee again constrains forest revenue to stay the same or increase over the 20-year planning horizon and leave at least as much harvestable timber value in the forest after harvest in the last planning period as she has now. As before, all alternatives have the objective of maximizing net revenue, given the other requirements, to minimize the trade-off between providing net revenue from harvest and achieving other objectives. [9]

From a wildlife diversity standpoint, Debora Lee is most focused on remnant pine/hardwood forest and preforest through time. To get started in learning about this type of analysis, Debora Lee decides to require that at least 100 acres of both remnant pine/hardwood forest and preforest exist on the forest in each period after harvest.

Previously we assumed that the preforest stage lasts two periods (10 years). Here, we will assume that the preforest stage lasts one period (5 years), enabling us to focus concerns and interests in preforest on the period in which the harvest occurs. Also, we will assume that recent harvests in the young hardwood/pine type have left a very heterogeneous forest with numerous openings. Thus we will count it as preforest in period one, and it grows into young forest in period two. Given these assumptions, Debora Lee can utilize the prescriptions/timing choices (Table 19.13) to estimate the forest development stages through time if they are chosen (Table 19.14).

To perform spatial analysis, Debora Lee must partition the landscape into discrete spatial planning units that she can then combine into different configurations to meet her spatial objectives. Debora Lee, with the assistance of a forestry consultant, identifies 53 planning units, based upon physical land characteristics (such as the watershed in which they lie), type, and the desire to create harvest flexibility (Figure 19.8). Notice that many of the patches

9 Matthew Thompson did the spatial analysis. It uses slightly different yields and revenues than the formulation of the Pine Hill problem introduced earlier in the chapter, which have the effect of reducing the amount of remnant pine/hardwood needed to be left to meet the ending inventory constraint.

***Dispersing harvests***    Consider first a policy to disperse harvest openings by limiting their maximum size. That is, assume that Debora Lee wants to solve an ***area-restricted*** model, perhaps to achieve certification or to adhere to forest practice regulations. For this problem the maximum size of a VRH in any given five-year period is 120 acres. Additional constraints, as described above, include nondeclining net revenue, requiring an ending inventory timber value at least equal to the beginning inventory value, and having at least 100 acres in preforest and remnant pine/hardwood forest in each period.

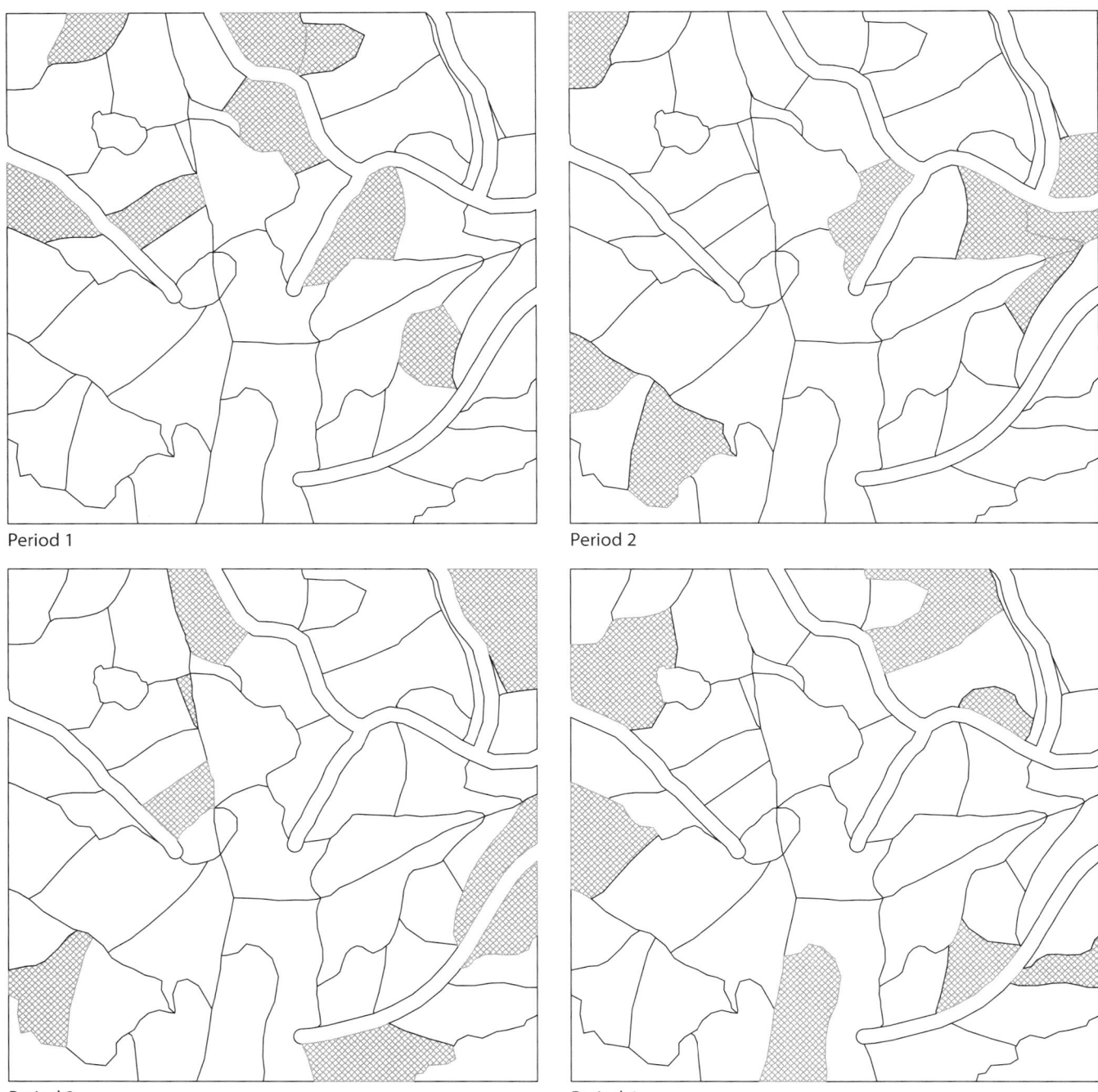

Period 1

Period 2

Period 3

Period 4

Figure 19.9 *Dispersing Harvests. Spatial distribution of harvests in each period under requirements to disperse VRH harvests by limiting maximum opening size to 120 acres and to maintain at least 100 acres of preforest and remnant pine/hardwood forest. VRHs are cross-hatched.*

Figure 19.9 displays the locations of harvests across the landscape, by period, for this alternative, while Figure 19.10 displays the distribution of forest development stages by period, as a result of growth and/or harvest. Note the shifts in location and distribution of preforest over time (Figure 19.10), reflecting the harvest pattern. By the end of the fourth period, little remnant pine/hardwood forest remains, and it is highly fragmented. Because the harvests have been dispersed, so is the subsequent preforest.

***Clustering harvests***   Next, Debora Lee considers a policy to cluster harvests as a way to reduce fragmentation of the

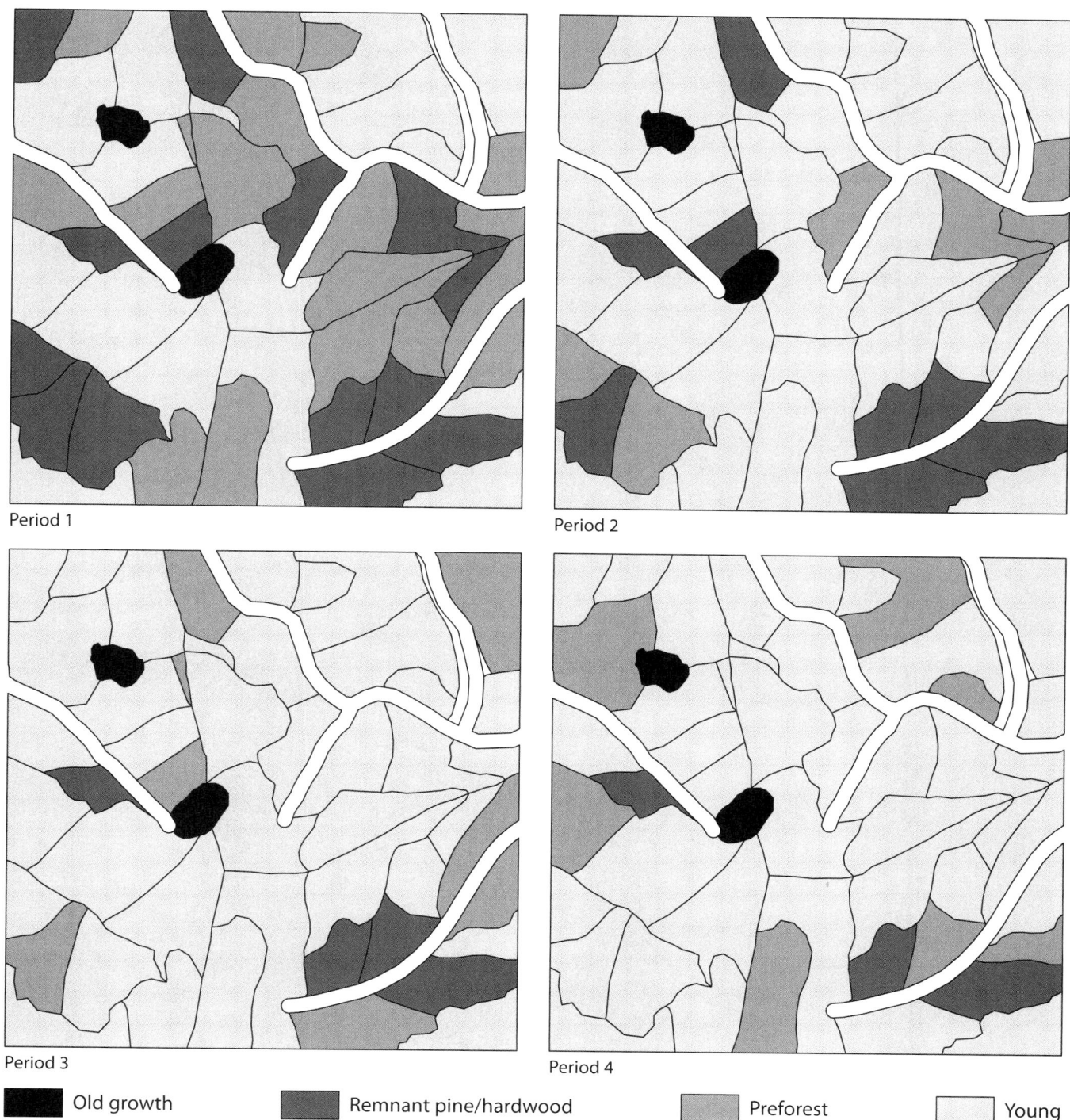

Period 1

Period 2

Period 3

Period 4

◼ Old growth      ▨ Remnant pine/hardwood      ▧ Preforest      ▫ Young

Figure 19.10 *Dispersing Harvests. Spatial distribution of forest development stages after harvest in each period under requirements to disperse harvests by limiting maximum opening size to 120 acres and to maintain at least 100 acres of preforest and remnant pine/hardwood forest.*

landscape. To solve this formulation, the planning model is modified to require minimum sizes on harvest openings, rather than maximum sizes. Specifically, a VRH must cover at least 80 acres, with other constraints as in the previous problem (Figures 19.11 and 19.12). Now, in contrast to the previous policy that limited maximum harvest size, both

preforest and remnant pine/hardwood forest are retained in larger areas, with multiple contiguous planning units sometimes harvested together to achieve the minimum size objectives by forming complementary patches. As an example, in period two, adjacent planning units of Type A and Type B are harvested (planning units 22, 23, 29, 34 in

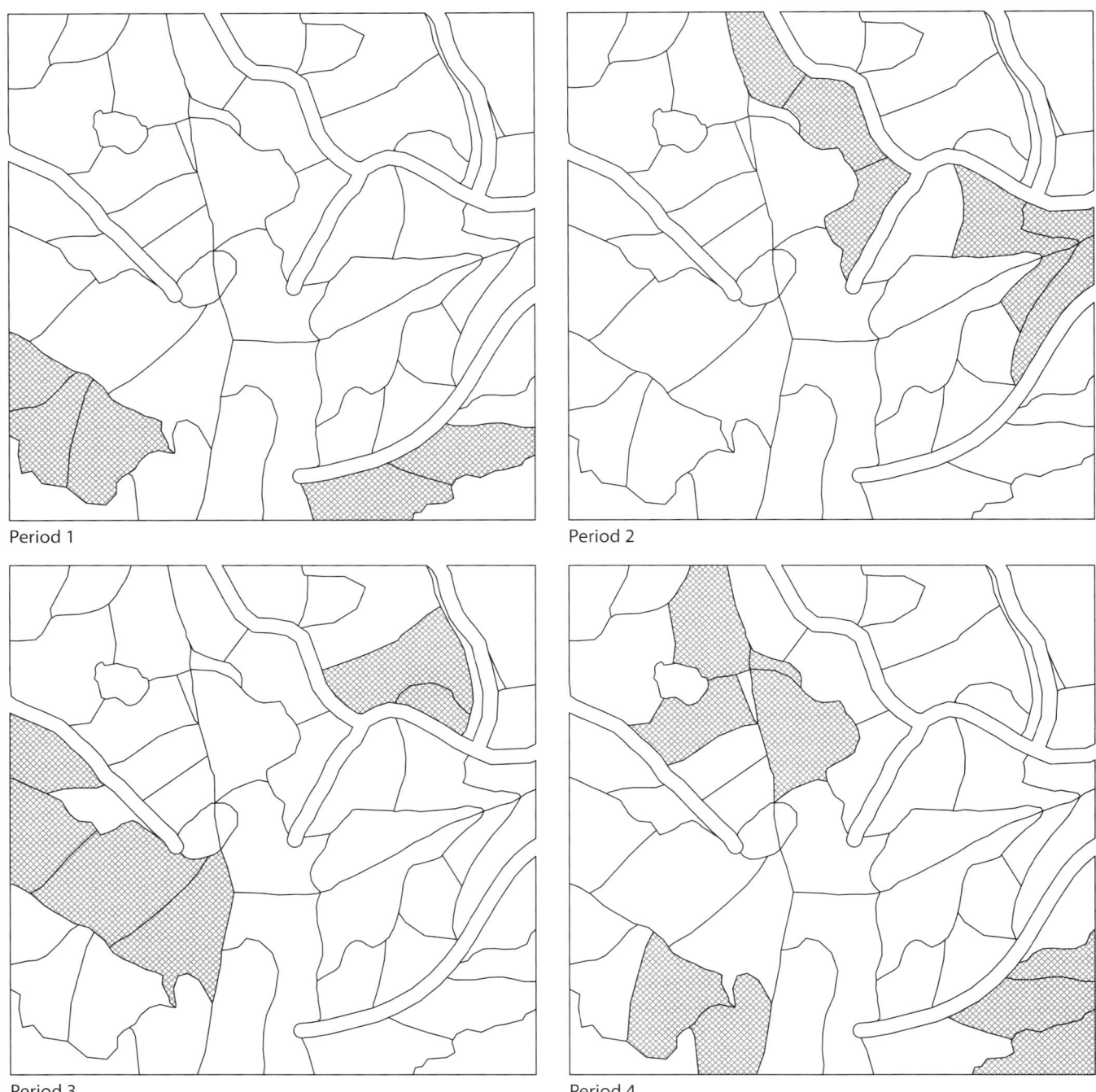

Period 1

Period 2

Period 3

Period 4

Figure 19.11 *Clustering Harvests. Spatial distribution of harvests in each period under requirements to cluster VRH harvests by setting a minimum harvest opening size of 80 acres and to maintain at least 100 acres of preforest and remnant pine/hardwood forest. VRHs are cross-hatched.*

middle-right of top right panel of Figure 19.11). Comparing Figures 19.10 and 19.12, we see that clustering the harvest has the serendipitous effect of retaining more remnant pine/hardwood forest over time as compared to the previous simulation that dispersed the harvest.

***Maintaining contiguous habitat*** Certain wildlife on the Pine Hill Forest may prefer larger contiguous patches of suitable habitat. To represent that situation, Debora Lee now considers a policy that seeks to expressly ensure contiguous patches of preforest or remnant pine/hardwood forest: she stipulates that a patch of preforest or remnant

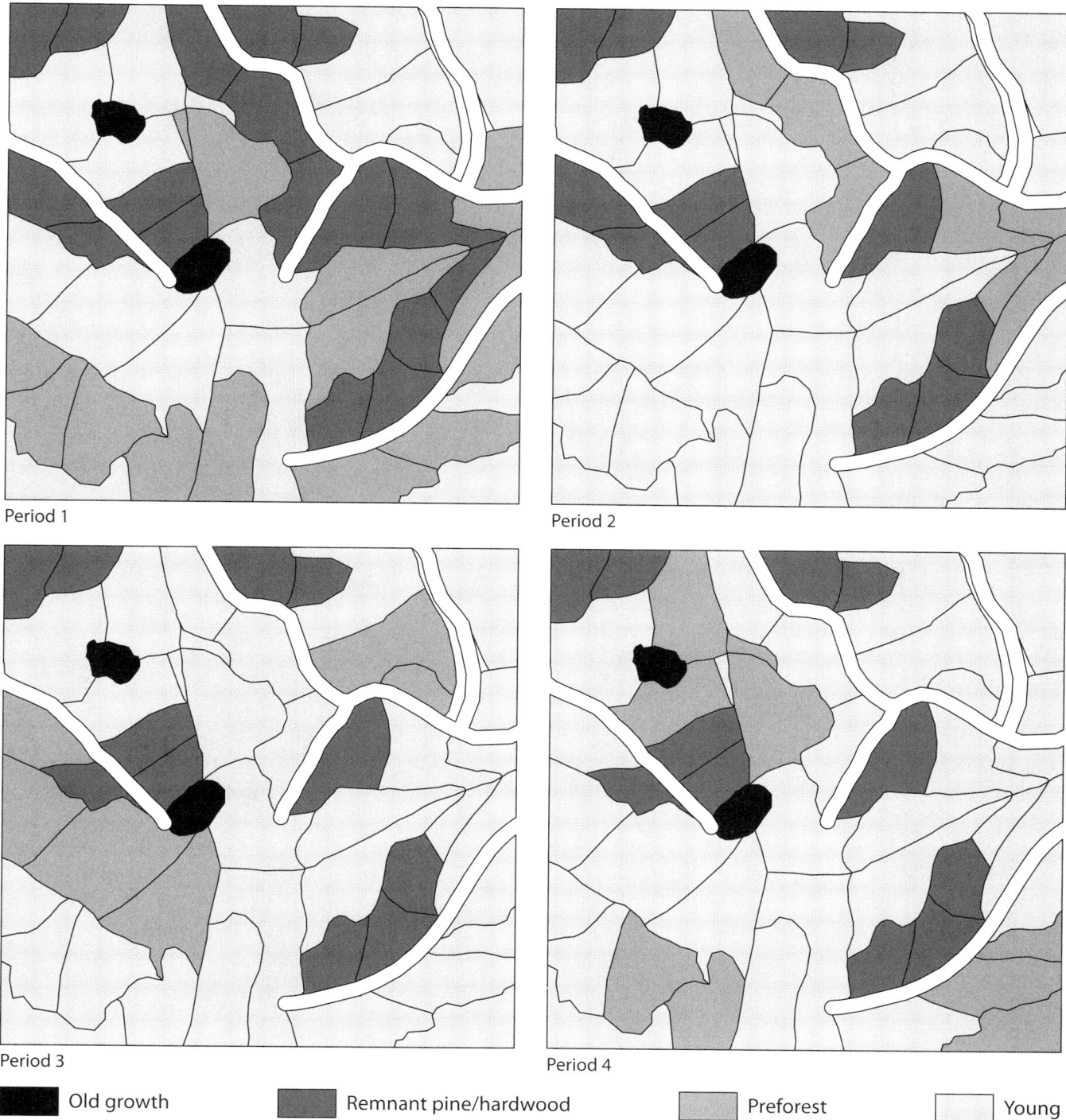

Period 1

Period 2

Period 3

Period 4

■ Old growth    ■ Remnant pine/hardwood    ▨ Preforest    □ Young

Figure 19.12 *Clustering Harvests. Spatial distribution of forest development stages after harvest in each period under requirements to cluster VRH harvests by setting a minimum harvest opening size of 80 acres and to maintain at least 100 acres of preforest and remnant pine/hardwood forest.*

pine/hardwood forest must be greater than some minimum size to be counted as suitable habitat. This prevents small isolated patches from counting towards the habitat objective. Here she requires that at least 200 acres of preforest and remnant pine/hardwood forest be maintained over time in patches of at least 50 acres in size.

Because Debora Lee is now explicitly addressing the spatial nature of habitat, she removes the requirement to cluster harvests and instead adopts the constraint from the first problem that places an upper limit on opening size of 120 acres. This maximum size constraint reflects legal standards in many provinces, states, and countries, as well as

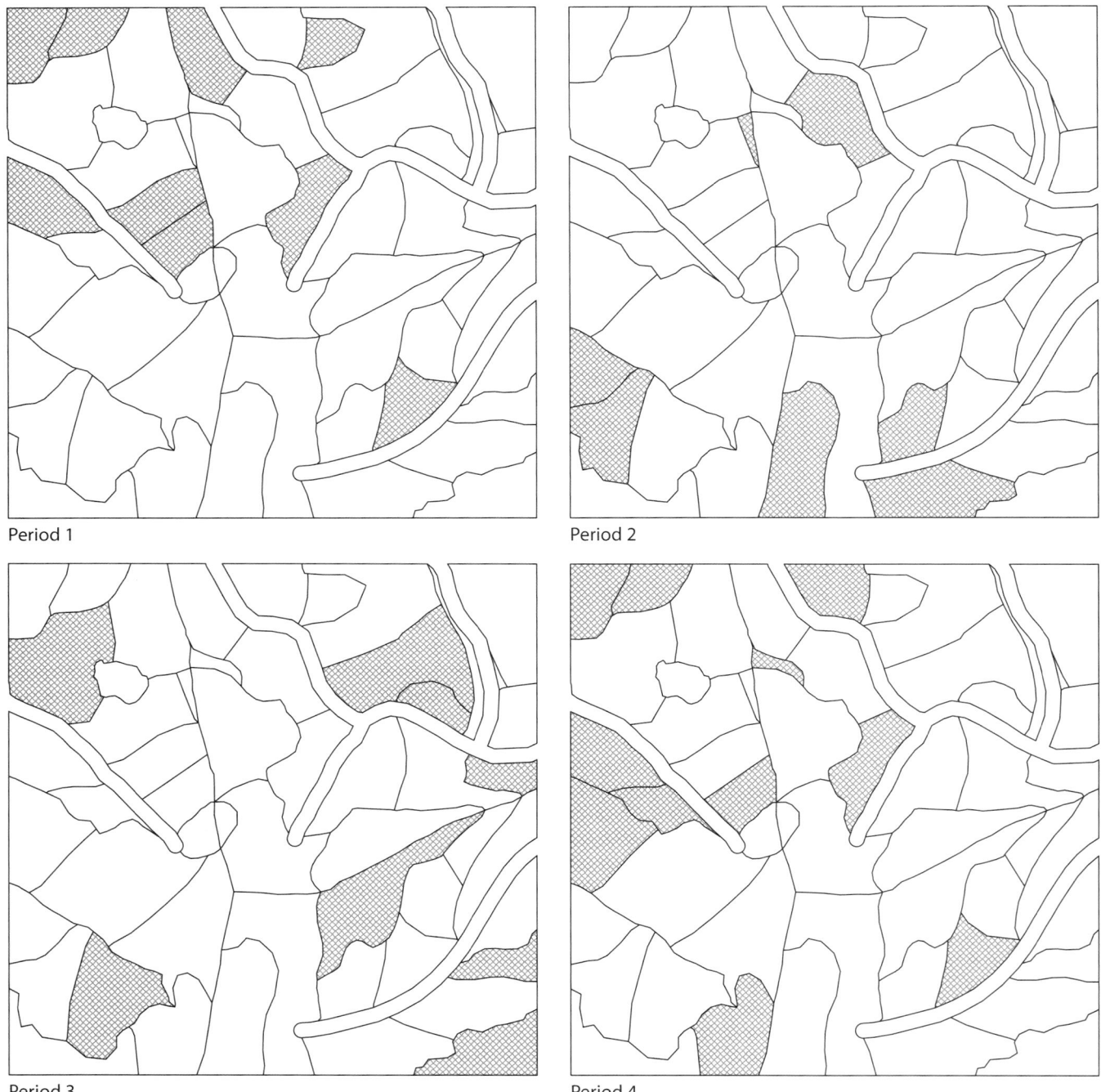

Period 1

Period 2

Period 3

Period 4

Figure 19.13 *Maintaining Contiguous Habitat. Spatial distribution of harvests in each period, under requirements to limit VRH harvests to less than 120 acres and to maintain at least 200 acres of preforest and remnant pine/hardwood forest in patches of at least 50 acres in size. VRHs are cross-hatched.*

the requirements of some certification systems. Constraints on nondeclining net revenue and ending inventory remain. The results are displayed in Figures 19.13 and 19.14. Here she has competing objectives: the harvest size limit requirement disperses the preforest created through harvest, while the habitat objective tends to aggregate them.

After carefully evaluating the results in Figure 19.14, Debora Lee is concerned that this policy does not actually protect as much remnant pine/hardwood forest as she would like. Fewer acres of remnant pine/hardwood forest remain after harvest in period four than provided by the cluster harvest alternative and significantly fewer acres than

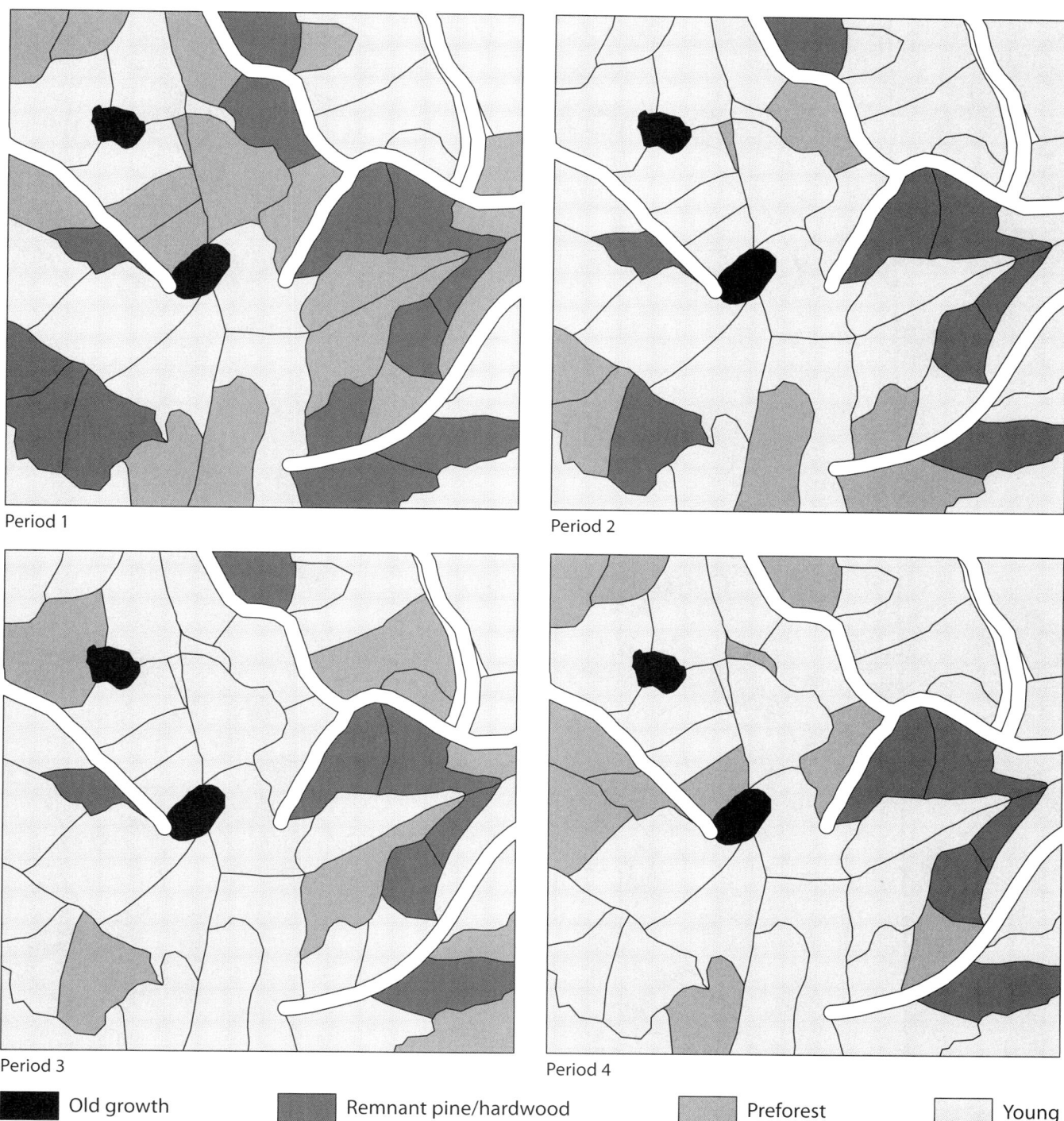

Period 1

Period 2

Period 3

Period 4

■ Old growth    Remnant pine/hardwood    Preforest    Young

Figure 19.14 *Maintaining Contiguous Habitat. Spatial distribution of patches among development stages after harvest in each period under requirements to limit VRH harvests to less than 120 acres and to maintain at least 200 acres of preforest and remnant pine/hardwood forest in patches of at least 50 acres in size.*

initially present. Also, most of the remnant pine/hardwood forest that remains after harvest in period four is contained within a single large patch on the right side of the landscape. Debora Lee instead decides to consider a policy that requires at least 400 acres of preforest and remnant pine/ hardwood forest in each period (Figures 19.15 and 19.16). As a result, more remnant pine/hardwood is maintained through time, and what remains is located in patches across the landscape rather than in a single large patch.

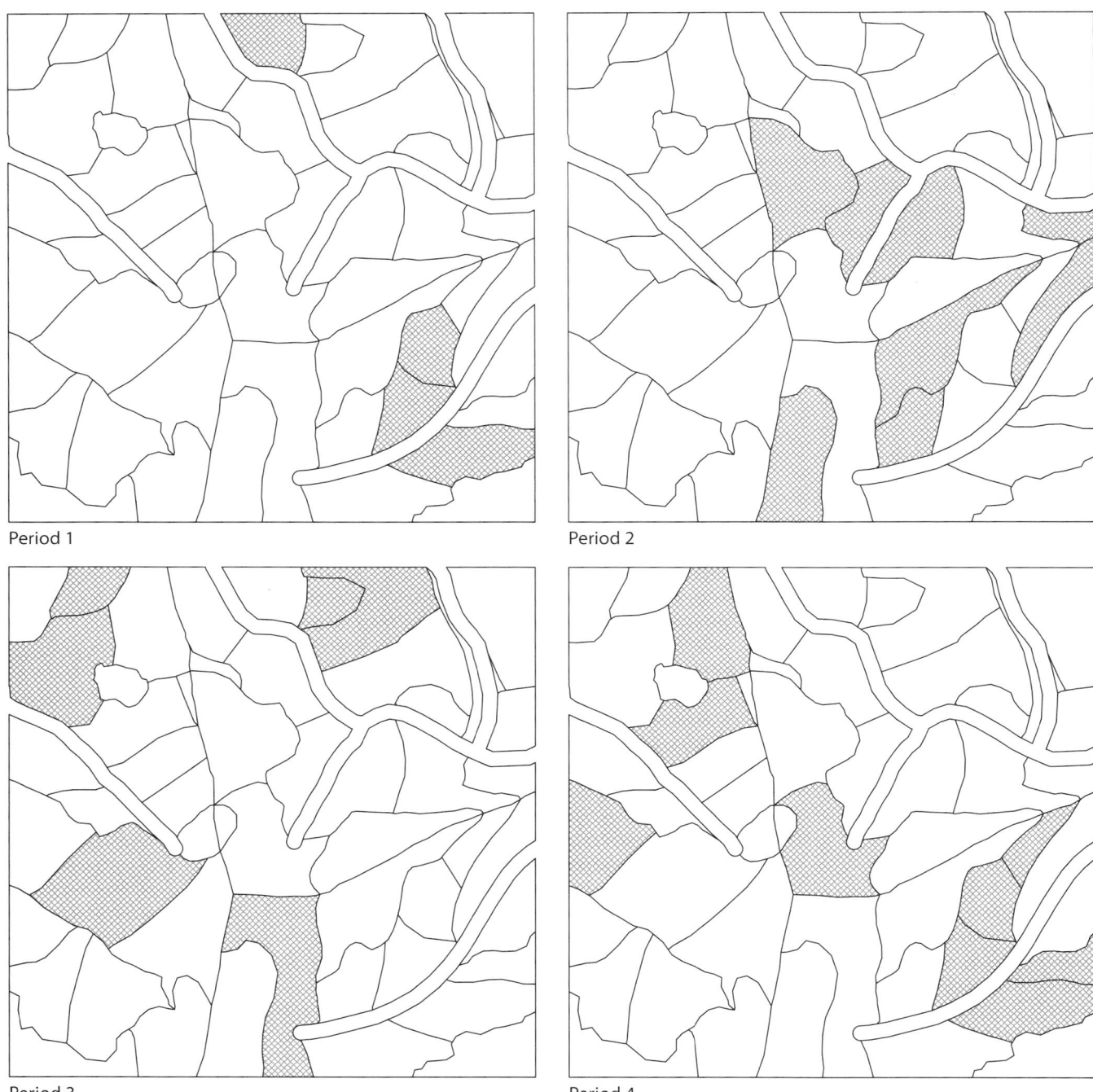

Period 1

Period 2

Period 3

Period 4

Figure 19.15 *Maintaining Contiguous Habitat with Additional Requirements. Spatial distribution of harvests in each period under requirements to limit VRH harvests to less than 120 acres and to maintain at least 400 acres of preforest and remnant pine/hardwood forest in patches of at least 50 acres in size. VRHs are cross-hatched.*

## The Role of Modeling in Forest Planning

With this brief tutorial, Debora Lee can see the capability of spatial modeling systems to help her access the feasibility of implementing her forest plan. Should she take that

next step and utilize the detailed spatial modeling shown here? Unlike the linear programming approaches discussed earlier in the chapter, these heuristics often must be tailor-made for a forest problem, which increases their cost and difficulty of use. (We discuss some technical details about

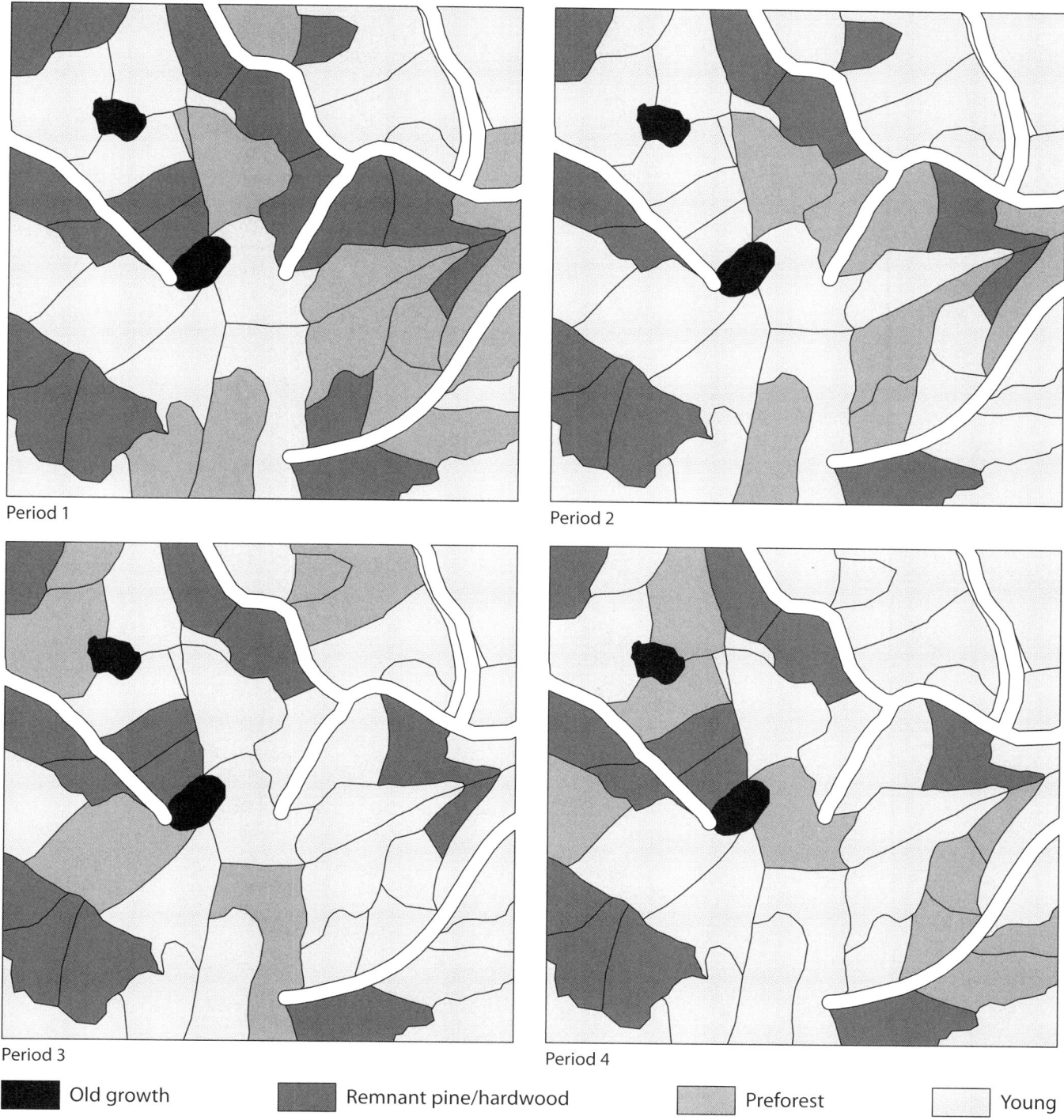

Period 1

Period 2

Period 3

Period 4

■ Old growth    ▧ Remnant pine/hardwood    ▨ Preforest    ☐ Young

Figure 19.16 *Maintaining Contiguous Habitat with Additional Requirements. Spatial distribution of patches among development stages after harvest in each period under requirements to limit VRH harvests to less than 120 acres while maintaining at least 400 acres of preforest and remnant pine/hardwood forest in patches of at least 50 acres in size.*

these heuristics in the Appendix to this chapter.) At a minimum, though, Debora Lee should consider representing different watersheds in her analysis to help give a finer spatial resolution as to where activities can occur.

We hope this chapter has demonstrated the considerable utility of quantitative forest planning analysis in practical applications of ecological forest management to forest properties. In fact, because ecological forest management typically involves much greater complexities in its efforts to integrate environmental, economic, and social objectives,

forest planning analysis may have appreciably greater utility in ecological forestry than in production forestry.

Thinking back to Chapter 18, *forest planning, at its most useful, integrates naturalistic and structured decision making. Modeling can help test our understanding and refine our intuition, improving our ability to mentally simulate the implications of alternatives for our forests. Also, our intuition can serve as a check on erroneous modeling results. Both approaches to decision making are needed for successful forest planning!*

# Appendix

## Heuristics for spatial scheduling of forest activities

Heuristics are "seeking" or "finding" methods that attempt to locate good solutions to problems at a reasonable cost (time, effort). They generally use relatively simple decision rules to guide a search process such *as choose the activity that increases the objective function value the most or ignore the activity if it leads to an infeasible solution.* They often begin with some ordering of the data and then utilize a process for choosing activities for planning units (Figure 19.17). As each new choice is made, the resulting solution is evaluated. If the new solution is found to be better than any other solution the search process has found, the new solution is saved as the *best* solution and compared against all future solutions. Once the search process has fulfilled its mission, or has been allowed to run for as long as the user specified, the best solution is reported. While this procedure sounds relatively simple, some heuristics have complex rules to define how the search process will be carried out (Davis et al., 2001; Bettinger et al., 2017).

Heuristics range from modifications of exact approaches (e.g., Lagrangian relaxation) to orchestrated interactions between local improvement procedures and overarching strategies designed to facilitate exploration and avoidance of local optima. The latter approach is known as a *meta-heuristic* (Glover & Kochenberger, 2003), and includes such techniques as tabu search, simulated annealing, threshold acceptance, great deluge, genetic algorithms, evolutionary algorithms, ant colony optimization, particle swarm optimization, and hybridizations. Meta-heuristics guide the search process and can include special operators designed to preserve diversity in the search, escape from local optima, and intensively search the solution space near high-quality solutions.

Three common types of meta-heuristic techniques used in forest planning are simulated annealing (SA), tabu search (TS), and genetic algorithms (GAs). SA and TS generally only examine a single current solution by evaluating a *neighborhood* of solutions, with a neighborhood defined as the set of possible solutions that can be obtained by changing the value of one or more decision variables. GAs are a special class of the broader field of evolutionary algorithms that model the process of natural selection to *evolve* high-quality solutions through various operations and methods, (i.e., maintain a population of solutions and examine alternate solutions by mating and mutating existing solutions). All three methods can be employed on the dynamic, spatial problems found in forestry. The strengths of SA tech-

niques include that they are easier to develop and they are generally fast algorithms. TS and GAs are more difficult to develop and are somewhat slower due to the vast number of computations they require, with the trade-off that they may provide a more robust search of the solution space. See Davis et al. (2001) and Bettinger et al. (2017) for more detail on these meta-heuristics.

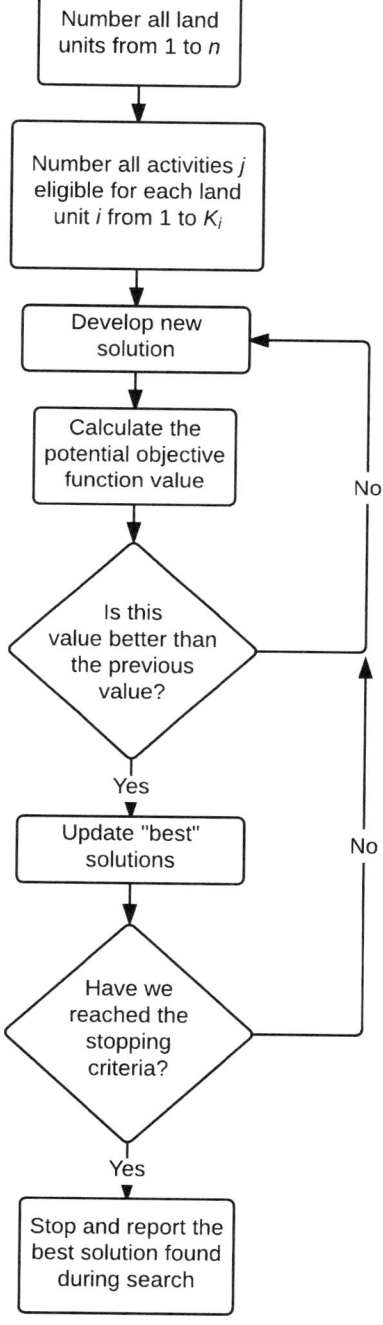

Figure 19.17 *General flowchart for a heuristic for dynamic spatial harvest scheduling. (Source: Davis et al., 2001)*

*The days have ended when the forest may be viewed only as trees and trees viewed only as timber. The soil and the water, the grasses and the shrubs, the fish and the wildlife, and the beauty of the forest must become integral parts of the resource manager's thinking and actions.* — HUBERT HUMPHREY, 1976

# CHAPTER 20

# The Greatest Good:
# Planning the Future of US National Forests

The national forests of the United States are a grand experiment in the collective ownership of almost 200 million acres of forest and associated wildlands (Figure 20.1). In many ways their management by the US Forest Service has set the standard for landscape planning on public lands. However, this planning has proven very difficult for the agency since passage of the National Forest Management Act (NFMA) in 1976, which fundamentally reformed its planning processes. Plans created under that Act took up to a decade to finish as they became the battlefield on which the further direction of these forests was fought. In addition, the resulting plans were overtaken, in many instances, by conservation mandates in other environmental laws, such as the Endangered Species Act, the interjection of scientists into planning processes, and the evolving interests of the American people in these forests. Over the past few years, the Forest Service has attempted to develop an approach to planning on the national forests that reflects the emerging mandates and interests. This chapter reviews the history of forest planning on the national forests, compares this new approach to past efforts, suggests ideas for its implementation, and discusses the potential role of ecological forest management in that effort.

## History

In the early days of the United States, most of the nation, outside of the original 13 colonies along the eastern seaboard, was *public domain*—federal land that the United States had accumulated through purchase and conquest. In general, the United States had a national policy of shifting lands in this public domain to private ownership. Environmental restrictions on land use generally did not exist. Markets would determine the uses of these forests and who received the benefits. By the late 1800s, scientific and conservation groups became concerned that forests passed into private ownership were being cut too rapidly,

*Norm's mother at Dark Lake in the Eldorado National Forest, California.*

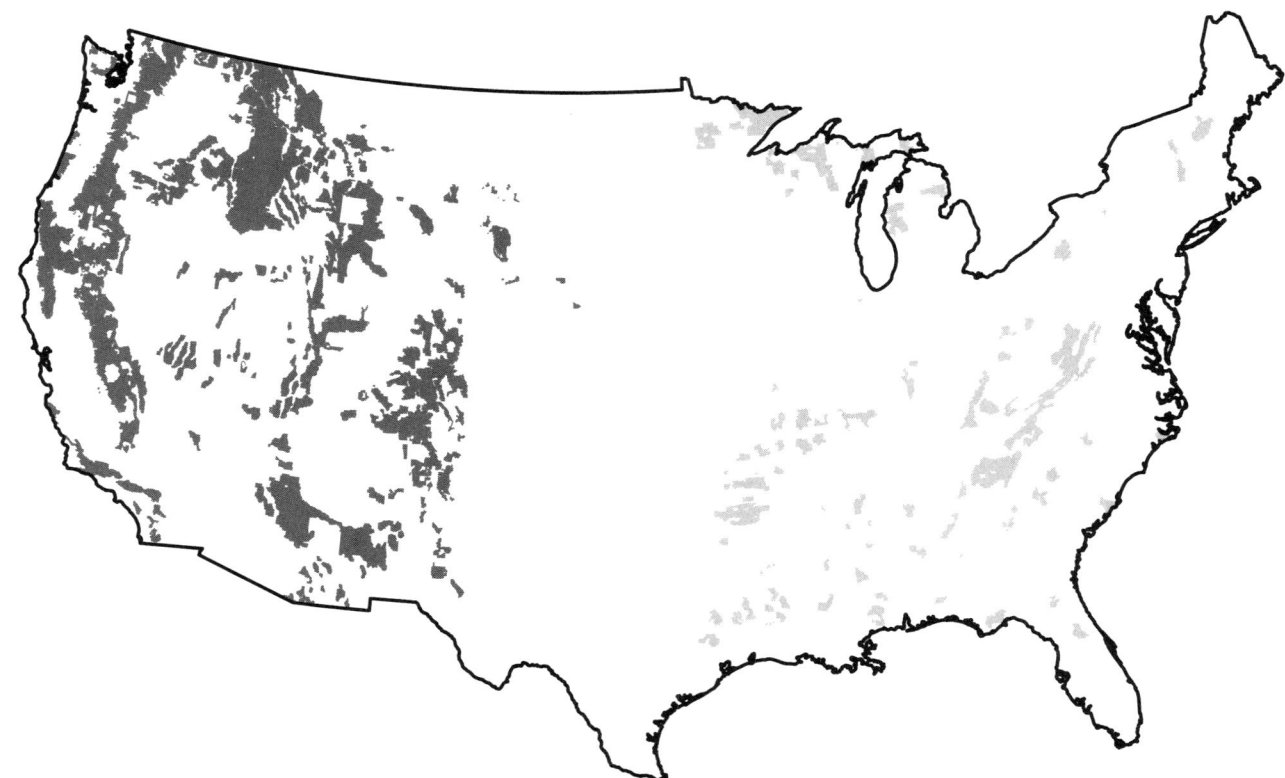

Figure 20.1 *The national forests of the United States. Western national forests (dark gray) were largely created out of the public domain. Eastern national forests (light gray) generally were passed from the public domain into private hands and then were repurchased by, or given to, the federal government after much of their commercial value had been removed.*

with inadequate protection of water resources and little provision for future wood supplies. These concerns led to the creation of a system of national forests in the western United States out of lands that were still in the public domain (Figure 20.1), with protection from wildfire a major early concern (Figure 20.2). Later, federal legislation enabled the repurchase of forests that had been shifted into private hands and largely harvested, with a special focus on obtaining lands in the eastern United States that would help protect watersheds there (Figure 20.1).[1]

Under guidance of Gifford Pinchot, the first chief of the Forest Service, and under subsequent chiefs, sustained yield forestry (as described in Chapter 17) became a guiding principle for management of the national forests (Box 20.1). Almost all forestland that could produce commercial crops of trees was included in the calculation of the sustainable harvest level. Until World War II these calculations were largely theoretical, since private timber was able to satisfy most of the demand for wood products. With the coming of World War II, though, national forest timber harvests began to increase, and pent-up demand for housing in the United States after the war created a growing market for softwood timber that the national forests helped fill (Figure 20.3).

Until the 1960s, the Forest Service largely controlled its own destiny, with few laws that impeded implementation of what the agency thought best. Passage of the Wilderness Act in 1964, though, foretold a changing attitude of the public toward the national forest management, a change that would increasingly limit Forest Service discretion in managing these forests. With a shrinking land base for timber production combined with ideas from the forest industry and research on improving timber productivity, the Forest Service often adopted intensive management practices, including clearcutting, planting dense stands of conifers, and suppressing hardwood competition. As these practices rolled out of the Pacific Northwest and across the nation, they were applied more and more to national forests that had not experienced them before, resulting in a nationwide public outcry against clearcutting that led to the passage of the NFMA in 1976 (Dana & Fairfax, 1980).

## The National Forest Management Act

The clearcutting controversy on the national forests, which began in West Virginia towns and valleys, the Bitterroot

---

1 See Dana & Fairfax (1980) for an outstanding history of forest and range policy of the United States.

Figure 20.2  *Ranger Griffin locating distant forest fires on the map, by means of compass, prominent peaks, and rivers from the top of Silcox Lookout Station on the Cabinet National Forest, Montana in 1909. (Photographed by W. J. Lubken. US Forest Service photo courtesy of the Forest History Society, Durham, NC)*

Valley of Montana, and western Wyoming in the 1960s, became a national issue in the 1970s. Congressional action to control clearcutting through discretionary guidelines did lit-

Figure 20.3  *Timber harvest volume on the national forests over time. (Data source: www.fs.fed.us/forestmanagement/documents/sold-harvest/documents/ 1905-2012_Natl_Summary_Graph.pdf)*

tle to satisfy critics, as the guidelines retained Forest Service discretion to select the silvicultural techniques to use, such as clearcutting. Some West Virginians, as an example, were still unsatisfied. Thus a local chapter of the Izaak Walton League brought suit in 1973 to halt clearcutting on the Monongahela National Forest, a national forest in West Virginia that had been created through purchase of private lands. The suit was not brought under National Environmental Policy Act (NEPA), the Endangered Species Act (ESA), or other recently created environmental laws. Rather, it alleged that Forest Service harvesting practices violated the Organic Act of 1897 (Fairfax & Achterman, 1977).

The Organic Act of 1897, which established the purposes of the national forests and associated management authorities, authorized the Forest Service to sell **"dead, matured, or large growth of trees."** It also

**Box 20.1  The Pinchot-Wilson letter: Setting the course for professional forestry in the United States**

In 1905, Congress passed legislation transferring the *forest reserves* from the Department of the Interior to the Department of Agriculture, where they became the national forests and were put under the Division of Forestry, then led by Gifford Pinchot (Figure 20.4). These forests had previously been reserved from the public domain, where they otherwise would have been claimed by private settlers. On the same day that President Roosevelt signed the legislation shifting the lands between cabinet departments, Secretary of Agriculture James Wilson sent Pinchot a letter (largely authored by Pinchot himself) outlining the principles and policies to be followed in management of these national forests. These principles guided management of the national forests and set the tone for professional forestry for much of the 20th century. The letter in part says:

*In the administration of the forest reserves it must be clearly borne in mind that all land is to be devoted to its most productive use for the permanent good of the whole people, and not for the temporary benefit of individuals or companies. All the resources of the reserves are for use, and this use must be brought about in a thoroughly prompt and businesslike manner, under such restrictions only as will insure the permanence of these resources. The vital importance of forest reserves to the great industries of the Western States will be largely increased in the near future by the continued steady increase in settlement and development. The permanence of the resources of the reserves is therefore indispensable to continued prosperity, and the policy of this department for their protection and use will invariably be guided by this fact, always bearing in mind that the conservative use of these resources in no way conflicts with their permanent value.*

*You will see to it that the water, wood, and forage of the reserves are conserved and wisely used for the benefit of the home builder first of all, upon whom depends the best permanent use of lands and resources alike. The continued prosperity of the agricultural, lumbering, mining, and livestock interests is directly dependent upon a permanent and accessible supply of water, wood, and forage, as well as upon the present and future use of their resources under business like regulations, enforced with promptness, effectiveness, and common sense. In the management of each reserve local questions will be decided upon local*

grounds; the dominant industry will be considered first, but with as little restriction to minor industries as may be possible; sudden changes in industrial conditions will be avoided by gradual adjustment after due notice; and where conflicting interests must be reconciled the question will always be decided from the standpoint of the greatest good of the greatest number in the long run.*

*These general principles will govern in the protection and use of the water supply, in the disposal of timber and wood, in the use of the range, and in all other matters connected with the management of the reserves. They can be successfully applied only when the administration of each reserve is left very largely in the hands of the local officers, under the eye of thoroughly trained and competent inspectors. (Dana & Fairfax, 1980, p. 82)*

Figure 20.4  *(a) Gifford Pinchot, first chief of the US Forest Service, at his desk ca. 1890–1910 (Photograph by Francis Benjamin Johnson); (b) Pinchot visiting students attending the Yale School of Forestry summer camp in 1910. Pinchot is with his dog in the front center of the photo. (Photos courtesy of US Forest Service)*

In these three short paragraphs, Gifford Pinchot expressed the principles that would guide management of the national forests for most of its first hundred years:

- All resources are *for use* under such restrictions as will ensure their permanence; conservative use will not interfere with their permanent value.
- A continued supply of wood, water, and forage from these forests will provide an essential contribution to continued prosperity.
- Local questions will be decided on local grounds, with the dominant industry considered first and sudden changes avoided.
- Administration of each reserve is left in the hands of the local officers, under the guidance of thoroughly trained and competent inspectors.
- Conflicting interests must be reconciled *"from the standpoint of the greatest good of the greatest number in the long run."*

In implementing these principles, the new Forest Service endorsed sustained yield forestry, control of grazing, protection of watersheds, and a cooperative relationship between local Forest Service rangers and dominant industries. Forests were for use rather than preservation, as long as that use retained a long-run view, assuring that these forests could provide wood, water, and forage on a continuing basis.

Over all these emphases and directions came the overriding dictate that decisions should be made from the "standpoint of the greatest good of the greatest number in the long run." Perhaps this phrase was not as much of an operational decision rule as the other instructions, but it certainly conveyed an aspirational goal that inspired generations of foresters and gave them discretion to determine what was "the greatest good."

required that such timber be *marked and designated* prior to sale and that it be *cut and removed under federal supervision.* The argument before a US district court centered on the meaning that Congress, originally and in subsequent legislation, intended with the words dead, matured, large growth, marked and designated, and cut and removed. The interpretation of these words underlay all federal timber harvesting practices, not just clearcutting (Fairfax & Achterman, 1977).

The court's findings were restricted to this narrow point. It held that by cutting immature and unmarked trees, and frequently not removing them, the Forest Service had exceeded its authority. Clearcutting was not specifically banned by the decision, although it is difficult to see how it could occur while meeting the provisions of the Organic Act (Fairfax & Achterman, 1977). With much national forest timber harvest coming from clearcutting, the Forest Service predicted dire consequences for rural communities throughout the western United States where sawmills were located that processed federal timber.

## How the NFMA Developed

Congressional leaders rejected the notion of a *quick fix* approach that simply negated the clause at issue in the Organic Act and instead began to entertain comprehensive approaches to resolving persistent problems and ambiguities in national forest management. Much of the work was done in the Senate where two different approaches were merged: (1) a prescriptive reform approach ("use uneven-aged management on eastern national forests," for example) and (2) a process reform approach (such as "use integrated

planning"). In the end the NFMA as passed by Congress (Act of October 22, 1976; P.L. 94-588; 16 U.S.C. §§ 1600–1614) included components of both approaches.

## Provisions of the NFMA

The NFMA reaffirmed congressional intent that multiple use and sustained yield were to remain foundational purposes of national forest management, 16 U.S.C. § 1604(e): "In developing, maintaining, and revising plans . . . the Secretary shall ensure that such plans . . . (1) provide for multiple use and sustained yield of the products and services obtained therefrom in accordance with the Multiple-Use, Sustained-Yield Act of 1960, and in particular, include coordination of outdoor recreation, range, timber, watershed, wildlife and fish, and wilderness; . . ."

The Multiple-Use, Sustained-Yield Act (P.L. 86-517; U.S.C. §§ 528–531) defined these two purposes, in part as (Sec 4):

- Multiple use—"management of all the various renewable surface resources of the national forests so that they are utilized in the combination that will best meet the needs of the American people,"

- Sustained yield—"the achievement and maintenance in perpetuity of a high-level annual or regular periodic output of the various renewable resources of the national forests without impairment of the productivity of the land."

By themselves, these definitions were interpreted by the courts as allowing the Forest Service to balance different uses and set harvest levels as it saw fit. In fact, the courts noted that the Multiple-Use, Sustained-Yield Act "breathes discretion at every pore" (Dana & Fairfax, 1980).

Much of the NFMA language attempted to provide further congressional definition of what these terms meant, especially with regard to timber production and timber harvest. Thus, most requirements of the NFMA focused on reining in timber production and harvest, either by changing planning processes or by stipulating substantive restrictions, which we outline below.

In terms of the planning process, the NFMA calls for an integrated approach to national forest planning, employing the process prescribed a few years earlier under the National Environmental Policy Act:

- "Provide for public participation in the development, review, and revision of land management plans" (16 U.S.C. § 1604[d]);

- "Form one integrated plan for each unit of the National Forest System" (16 U.S.C. § 1604[f][1]);

- "Be prepared by an interdisciplinary team" (16 U.S.C. § 1604[f][3]).

Previously, the Forest Service had created resource plans individually with little interdisciplinary or public involvement; now they would provide for public participation, create one plan for each national forest, and have the plans prepared by an interdisciplinary team.

Congress also mandated a number of directives in the NFMA to be utilized in this planning to better integrate timber production with other resources and uses. For example:

- Harvesting practices

  ○ "Insure that timber will be harvested only where— (i) soil, slope, other watershed conditions will not be irreversibly damaged; (ii) there is assurance that such lands can be adequately restocked within five years after harvest; (iii) protection is provided for streams . . . where harvests are likely to seriously and adversely affect water conditions or fish habitat" (16 U.S.C. § 1604[g][3][E]);

  ○ "Insure that clearcutting . . . and other cuts designed to regenerate an even-aged stand of timber will be used as a cutting method on National Forest System lands only where—(i) for clearcutting, it is determined to be the optimum method . . . to meet the objectives and requirements of the relevant land management plan; . . . (iv) there are established . . . maximum size limits for areas to be cut in one harvest operation . . . ; (v) such cuts are carried out in a manner consistent with the protection of soil, watershed, fish, wildlife, recreation, and

aesthetic resources, and the regeneration of the timber resource" (16 U.S.C. § 1604[g][3][F]).

These provisions put previous congressional guidance into legislation, while still leaving significant discretion to the agency.

- Marginal lands

  ○ "The Secretary shall identify lands within the management area which are not suited for timber production, considering physical, economic, and other pertinent factors to the extent feasible . . . and shall assure that, except for salvage sales or sales necessitated to protect other multiple use values, no timber harvesting shall occur on such lands" (16 U.S.C. § 1604[k]).

The Forest Service traditionally had included forests in its allowable cut base without consideration of whether harvest would cover its costs, including the cost of building roads to the site. The issue of **below cost sales** had become controversial during the 1970s, and much discussion ensued during the passage of the NFMA over how to remove economically marginal lands from timber production. The NFMA's wording expressed congressional intent while still leaving considerable discretion on interpretation. With the shift to an emphasis on ecosystem restoration across the landscape, though, these words and permissions have gained importance in another way: much of the restoration work that involves timber harvest may occur on lands declared *"not suited for timber production"* in the forest plan. The wording above allows such actions if they are taken to *"protect other multiple use values."*

- Culmination of mean annual increment (CMAI)

  ○ "Prior to harvest, stands of trees throughout the National Forest System shall generally have reached the culmination of mean annual increment of growth. . . . Provided, That these standards shall not preclude the use of sound silvicultural practices, such as thinning. . . . Provided further, That these standards shall not preclude the Secretary from salvage or sanitation harvesting of timber stands which are substantially damaged by fire, windthrow, or other catastrophe, or which are in imminent danger from insect or disease attack; . . . exceptions to these standards for the harvest of particular species of trees in management units after consideration has been given to the multiple uses of the forest including, but not limited to, recreation, wildlife habitat, and range and after completion of public participation processes" (16 U.S.C. § 1604[m][1 & 2]).

Congress was concerned that the national forests might be pressured to adopt rotation ages for even-aged management similar to those of the forest industry, which would result in harvest ages below those of maximum average growth over time. This clause attempted to prevent that strategy by mandating a practice largely already in place. Requiring that stands reach culmination before harvest, of course, continued the traditional focus of regeneration harvest on older forest, unless the exceptions were employed.

- Limitations on timber removal

  - "The Secretary of Agriculture shall limit the sale of timber from each national forest to a quantity equal to or less than a quantity which can be removed from such forest annually in perpetuity on a sustained-yield basis: Provided, that, in order to meet overall multiple-use objectives, the Secretary may establish an allowable sale quantity for any decade which departs from the projected long-term average sale quantity that would otherwise be established" (16 U.S.C. § 1611[a]).

As softwood supplies were depleted on private lands in the West, some western policy makers clamored for the national forests to harvest above their sustained yield level until private lands regrew a commercial crop. With this clause, Congress put limits on that strategy, requiring that the harvest stay at or below the sustained yield capacity of the forest, unless a case could be made that a departure was needed to meet multiple use objectives. The regulations implementing this direction interpreted it as endorsing existing *nondeclining yield* policy, as we discuss later. Departures were rarely sought.

- Diversity

  - "Provide for diversity of plant and animal communities based on the suitability and capability of the specific land area in order to meet overall multiple-use objectives" (16 U.S.C. § 1604[g][3][B]).

This clause provides a broad mandate to conserve biodiversity—described here as "diversity of plant and animal communities." As written, with its linkage to achieving overall *multiple-use objectives*, the clause leaves considerable discretion to the agency. However, as we discuss below, the regulations implementing the NFMA called for maintaining viable populations of native vertebrates, with enormous implications for management of the national forests.

Many of these provisions dealt with technical issues on which Congress could give only general guidance. Congress therefore deferred to the executive branch, with its substantial expertise, to develop the specifics: "the Secretary [of Agriculture] shall promulgate regulations . . . that

set out the process for the development and revision of land management plans, and the guidelines and standards" (16 U.S.C. § 1604[g]). In addition, the NFMA mandated that a committee of scientists assist the secretary in this task: "In carrying out the purposes of subsection (g) of this section, the Secretary of Agriculture shall appoint a committee of scientists who are not officers or employees of the Forest Service. The committee shall provide scientific and technical advice and counsel on proposed guidelines and procedures to assure that an effective interdisciplinary approach is proposed and adopted" (16 U.S.C. § 1604[h][1]).

The Committee of Scientists appointed by the secretary of Agriculture had an enormous impact on the 1979 regulations implementing the NFMA, both because the committee interpreted its charge broadly and because the Secretary of Agriculture deferred to their judgment. The committee suggested a planning approach based largely on the economic welfare concept of *maximization of net public benefits*, which included calculation of maximum resource potentials, benchmarks set through net present value calculations, and detailed trade-off analysis. However, the committee also prescribed environmental safeguards to help limit and direct national forest management, with the most important provision calling for sufficient habitat to be provided to maintain viable populations of native vertebrates in the planning area. Thus, under guidance from the Committee of Scientists, the NFMA regulations first issued in 1979 mandated *a major new goal for the national forests: maintaining habitat for viable populations of native vertebrates in the planning area*. This requirement was updated in 1982 (USDA, 1982), again with the committee's assistance, to explain that *a viable population was one that was well distributed in the planning area*, clarifying that the viability requirement could not be satisfied solely by providing habitat in a few isolated areas on a national forest. [2]

## National Forest Planning under the NFMA

As the national forests began to develop forest plans under the NFMA during the 1980s, much of the effort focused on estimating nondeclining harvest levels over time under different sets of assumptions, utilizing a timber harvest scheduling model called FORPLAN as the central forest planning tool. FORPLAN provided a computerized update of classical forest planning approaches to estimate sustainable harvest levels.[3] This multiyear effort to find a harvest level that met

---

2 USDA, 1982, p. 43048. "Fish and wildlife habitat shall be managed to maintain viable populations of existing native and desired nonnative vertebrate species in the planning area. For planning purposes, a viable population shall be regarded as one which has the estimated numbers and distribution of reproductive individuals to insure its continued existence is well distributed in the planning area."

3 See Chapter 17 for a discussion of classical harvest scheduling methods.

all of the NFMA requirements, the requirements of other environmental laws (e.g., the Endangered Species Act and the Clean Water Act), and the interests of stakeholders and political leaders, in the end, proved largely unsuccessful.[4]

As protection of biodiversity became a dominant concern for many national forests, conflicts arose with the prior emphasis on high levels of commercial timber harvest. Many factors contributed to this new attention to nontimber values, including the NFMA regulations mandating habitat for viable populations of native vertebrates, the importance of national forests in federal recovery strategies for threatened and endangered species, environmental litigation over habitat and biodiversity issues, public pressure for a broader interpretation of the multiple-use mandate, and the diminishing economic importance of federal timber in the West. Collectively, these forces fundamentally altered public and political expectations for the national forests. Few forest plans were implemented as written, and timber harvests from the national forests plummeted (Figure 20.3).

## Providing Habitat for Viable Populations of Native Species: An Overarching Goal

The inability of the national forests to navigate these troubled social and political waters led to a call for scientists, especially ecological and wildlife scientists, to help develop new management frameworks. In this process, the *viability rule* from the NFMA planning regulations became especially dominant as a mechanism to ensure sustainability. As an example, scientists who helped develop the scientific basis of the Northwest Forest Plan (NWFP) for federal forests within the range of the northern spotted owl used provision of habitat for viable populations of native species as the foundation of sustainability (FEMAT, 1993). In lawsuits about the legality of the NWFP, interpretation of the diversity clause as requiring viable populations of native vertebrates was challenged as drifting too far afield from the intent of Congress. Judge Dwyer (*Seattle Audubon Soc. v. Lyons*, 871 F. Supp. 1291 [W.D. Wash. 1994]) rejected this claim, citing previous court decisions: "When a statute authorizes an agency to issue legislative regulations, 'Congress entrusts to the Secretary, rather than the courts, the primary responsibility for interpreting the statutory term.' *Batterton v. Francis*, 432 U.S. 416, 425, 97 S. Ct. 2399, 2405, 53 L. Ed. 2d 448 (1977). Regulations thus adopted have 'legislative effect' and are 'entitled to more than mere deference or weight.' *Id.* At 425-26, 97 S. Ct. at 2405-06."

In addition, the scientists who helped develop the NWFP broadened the interpretation of the viability require-

ment to include invertebrates, such as fresh water mussels, bryophytes, fungi, lichens, and families of insects. While this interpretation was not specifically authorized by regulations, Judge Dwyer found: "The federal defendants were bound by law, and by the obvious fact of species interdependence, to consider the survival prospects of species other than vertebrates. Their chosen method of doing so was within the legitimate scope of their discretion."

A focus on individual species can turn ecosystem plans into species-by-species plans, and this happened, to a degree, in development of the NWFP (Thomas, Franklin, Gordon, & Johnson, 2006). As noted, scientists developing the NWFP broadened their viability analysis to include all living things in mature and old-growth forests (plant, animal, and otherwise). After evaluating whether proposed plan alternatives would protect these species, scientists identified a subset of species for which they could not conduct a viability analysis because their distribution and habitat requirements were largely unknown. This subset became the *Survey and Manage* species list for which the NWFP carried specific survey and management requirements. These requirements were not based on evidence that these species were at risk, but rather on lack of knowledge about their distribution and habitat requirements (Thomas et al., 2006).

## Summary

The many-year odyssey to implement the mandates of the NFMA on the national forests through integrated forest planning ultimately produced intense frustration, as planning teams spent a decade or more developing plans that were not implemented in any comprehensive manner. While congressional direction in the NFMA appeared to give an important role to timber production on the national forests, the increasing importance of habitat provision and changing public expectations limited attainment of that role. Attention turned to rewriting the regulations implementing the NFMA, with a series of US presidential administrations attempting to achieve this goal. None were successful until the Obama administration published a new final planning rule in 2012 (USDA, 2012). We will discuss this new rule below after we briefly cover how the national forests attempted to fulfill their mission over the last few decades in the face of seemingly conflicting direction.

## National Forest Planning in the 21st Century

### The Challenge

In a brilliant book on the governance of the western public lands, Martin Nie (2008) devotes a chapter to describing why there is so much conflict about public land and

---

4 See Box 18.6 for a detailed discussion of why the use of FORPLAN in national forest planning did not succeed.

resource management. He begins his explanation with a distinction between wicked and tame policy problems (Nie 2008, p. 11):

> *Scientists and engineers are often given a clear mission and asked to solve tame policy problems in which there is a right or wrong answer. The task at hand may be difficult and certainly complex but is nevertheless tame. Not only is the problem well defined but eventually the problem solver knows whether the problem has been solved. Wicked problems, however, as the term's originators explain, as "distinguished from problems in the natural sciences, which are definable and separable and may have solutions that are findable, the problems of governmental planning—and especially those of social or policy planning—are ill-defined; and they rely upon elusive political judgment for resolution. (. . . Social problems are never solved. At best they are only re-solved—over and over again.)"*[5]

Nie (2008) next highlights key characteristics of **wicked problems**:

- They do not have a definitive formulation. "In fact, the formulation of a wicked problem is the problem!—because those who get to define the problem have the upper hand in advancing their proposed solution." (Nie, 2008, p. 11).

- They have no stopping rule, meaning the problem solver never quite knows when the job is done.

- Their "solutions" are neither true nor false but good or bad depending on interests, values, and ideologies.

- They are each unique, making standardized approaches problematic.

- They can each be seen as a symptom of another problem. Generally, the search for an explanation of the problem being studied reveals important connections to lower-level and higher-level problems. At what level should the problem be tackled? As Rittel and Webber (1973, p. 165) explain: "the higher the level of a problem's formulation, the broader and more general it becomes; and the more difficult it becomes to do something about it. On the other hand, one should not try to cure symptoms; and therefore one should try to settle the problem on as high a level as possible."

Then, Nie (2008) outlines why federal natural resource-based conflicts in the United States are so often intractable by describing their dominant drivers, after acknowledging that these drivers are both "wicked by nature," in that their context essentially promises political conflict, and "wicked

by design," in that political actors, institutions, and decision-making processes compound them. We highlight here some of the drivers identified by Nie:

- *Scarcity*—controversy and conflict will most probably increase as the natural world becomes more endangered. As more of the national forests have been roaded and harvested, the battle over the remaining natural forest increases.

- *Public land law*—"the vague, contradictory, and problematic language found in public land law drives and perpetuates many conflicts and often turns them into prolonged and complicated legal battles" (Nie, 2008, p. 33).

- *Agency budgets*—budgets drive agency actions both in terms of what they can do and what they need to do to survive, and policies designed with problematic budgetary incentives perpetuate many natural resource conflicts. As an example, as Nie (2008) points out, the Knutson-Vandenberg Act of 1930 required timber purchasers to pay a portion of timber sale costs into a fund that the US Forest Service can use for reforestation, wildlife habitat improvement, and recreation, thus creating the incentive to cut timber to receive funds for other purposes. This use of timber receipts to pay for other services has been repackaged more recently in stewardship contracts, but it can still create similar types of potentially counterproductive incentives.

- *Scientific disagreement and uncertainty*—"Public land management is increasingly characterized by a type of conflict in which the contested role of science plays a large part . . . where judges increasingly rule on scientific grounds . . . this means that conflicts often have a particularly American flavor, combining our faith in science and technology with our love of litigation" (Nie, 2008, p. 28).

- *Surrogate issues*—policy problems can turn ever more wicked when they are used by political actors to debate larger and more controversial issues. In some ways, the northern spotted owl was a surrogate for larger issues about preservation of wildlands and federal timber management policies, drawing the attention of a wide variety of groups and agencies with their own motives and goals.

- *Spiritual meanings*—Public land issues have spiritual dimensions making them exceedingly difficult to resolve. Whether the issue is old growth or wolves, the sacred nature of these natural resources to many people make compromise exceedingly difficult.

---

5 The interior quote is from Rittel & Webber, 1973, p. 160.

- *Differing policy frames*—people differ greatly in how they frame conflicts, what is important, how they interpret evidence, and their explanation of how the world works and what the future holds— they hold different worldviews as we discussed in Chapter 18. While all may want a healthy forest, what they mean by healthy can differ mightily!

- *Lack of trust*—lost or diminished trust in our federal agencies often plays a primary role in undermining constructive debate and public inquiry. "It is a certainly a major obstacle in finding common ground or working compromises and in advancing innovative and experimental approaches to problem solving" (Nie, 2008, p. 38).

There is little doubt that the Forest Service under the NFMA viewed its planning problem as it had historically—a technical analysis in which it would estimate the sustainable timber harvest level for each national forest consistent with conservation responsibilities. Certainly, it was recognized by the agency as a difficult and complex task, but one that was nevertheless tame in the classification above with a well-defined problem. When that problem definition began to fray, first with the need for regional plans for species conservation and then with litigation that questioned the adequacy of those plans, the agency lacked the understanding and ability to adjust their planning process to accommodate the new reality. Rapidly, the planning problem transformed into the wicked problem that we have today.

## Responses

With the collapse of classical sustained yield forestry, and the associated well-defined planning problem, as a guide for the national forests, individual national forests, and ranger districts within them, took the initiative to craft an approach that would enable needed action. Much of this innovation for these activities has occurred outside the forest planning process, often involving ad hoc local individuals and groups (sometimes through collaborative efforts) working with individual ranger districts (Figure 20.5). This approach has a number of characteristics:

- It deals with local, immediate problems, such as reducing fire hazard or thinning plantations, around which people and groups of different backgrounds and interests can rally.

- It relies on repeated, often face-to-face, interaction between the agency and its public.

- It involves the agency sharing power with this public.

As described in Chapter 7, the approach is perhaps best seen in the attempt to involve the public early and often in project planning. From initial scoping trips to informal discussions to comments on draft environmental assessments, such a process has often enabled the Forest Service to learn what is acceptable and what is not.

In many ways, this approach is a throwback to the early days of the Forest Service utilizing Gifford Pinchot's admonition of "local questions decided on local grounds." However, this effort was often undertaken within a regional conservation framework provided by ad hoc groups of scientists commissioned by the agency, court settlements between the agency and environmental groups, or recovery plans for federally listed species. In addition, the resulting projects had the additional conservation safeguards provided by the consultation process for federally listed species, the NEPA process, and the potential for litigation over project effects.

To be effective, these collaborations had to move beyond the gridlock of traditional forest industry/environmentalist

Figure 20.5 *Stakeholders working with the Forest Service to develop restoration projects. (Photos courtesy of the Blue Mountains Forest Partners)*

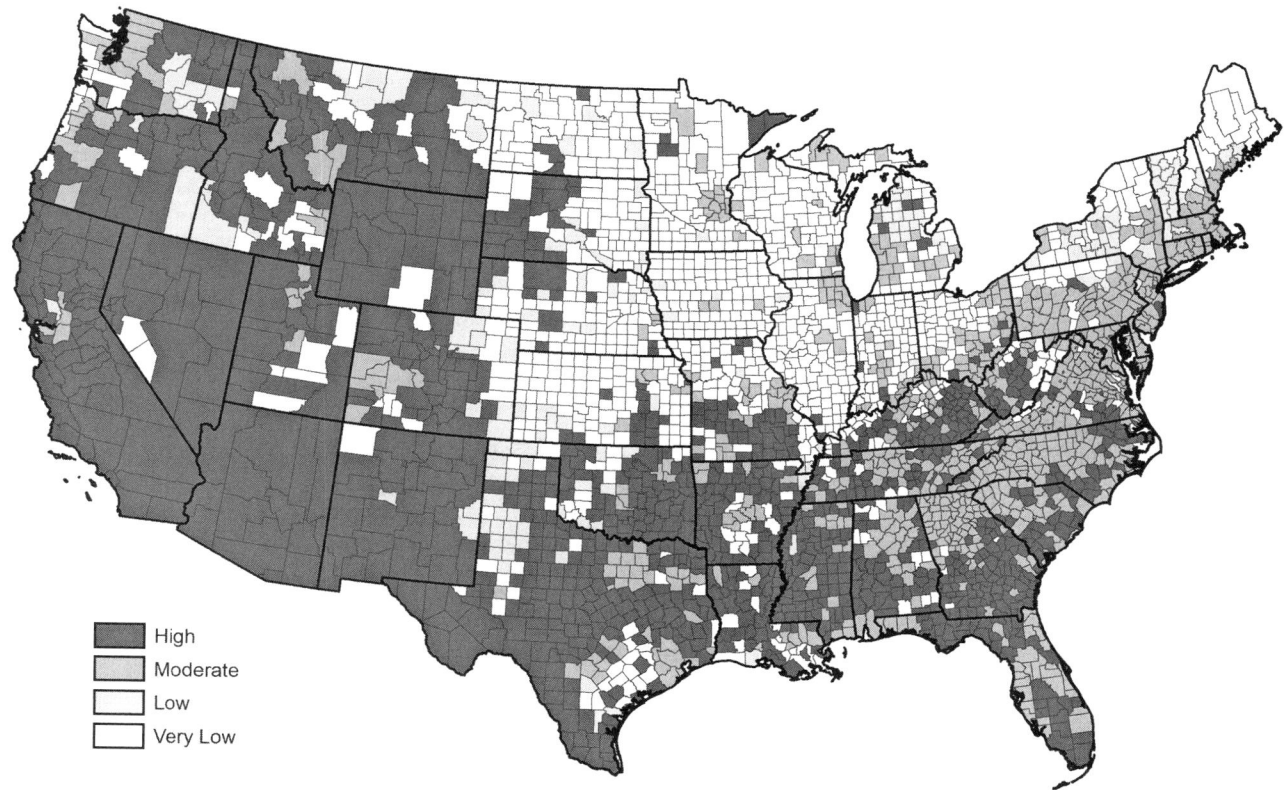

**High**
**Moderate**
**Low**
**Very Low**

Figure 20.6 *National priorities for community planning and coordination under the National Cohesive Wildland Fire Management Strategy. (Source: USDA-USDI, 2014)*

battles over timber harvest to approaches that accommodate diverse interests. Moreover, recent legislation has encouraged or required a collaborative approach to landscape and project planning, including the Healthy Forests Restoration Act of 2003 and the Collaborative Forest Landscape Restoration Act of 2009 (Title IV of Omnibus Public Land Management Act of 2009).

Two general themes emerged for project-level goals that resonated with a broader public: (1) protecting lives and property at risk from wildfire in the *wildland–urban interface (WUI)*, and (2) restoring forest ecosystems beyond the WUI.

**Protection of Lives and Property in the WUI**    Living near or adjacent to national forests is seen as highly desirable by many people. However, the presence of homes in these areas increases the risk that they will be threatened by wildfire, especially where a combination of fire suppression and past harvest has resulted in a substantial increase in forest fuels and their continuity. The increasing number of large fires occurring near communities and homes since the early 2000s has made this threat all too real, and national forest activities have turned increasingly to altering the amount and structure of fuels in the WUI. (See Chapter 13 for more details, especially the need for coordinated action by homeowners, communities, and the Forest Service.)

To help in this effort and to assist fuel treatments across the national forests, Congress passed the Healthy Forests Restoration Act of 2003. This Act contains a variety of provisions aimed at expediting the preparation and implementation of hazardous fuels reduction projects on federal land, as well as provisions meant to assist rural communities, states, and landowners in restoring healthy forest and watershed conditions on state, private, and tribal lands. It also mandates maintenance and restoration of old-growth stands, and retention of the large trees contributing to old-growth structure, during fuel reduction projects—the first such protection in federal legislation. Title I (Hazardous Fuel Reduction on Federal Land) provides for expedited environmental review, a predecisional Forest Service administrative review process, and other measures on National Forest and Bureau of Land Management (BLM) lands that are at risk of uncharacteristically severe wildfire. It especially focuses attention on the WUIs of at-risk communities for this expedited review.

Additionally, the National Cohesive Wildland Fire Management Strategy (USDA-USDI, 2014) identifies national priorities for community planning and coordination. Counties characterized by higher-than-average annual area burned, structures lost, and homes exposed within the WUI (especially in the West, South, and Southeast) are assigned the highest priority for community action (Figure 20.6).

**Forest Restoration outside the WUI**   Restoration of structural complexity and biological diversity in simplified forest systems has become a major focus on national forests, with restoration defined primarily in terms of restoring degraded ecosystems and landscapes. Restoration prescriptions have taken different forms depending upon the natural history of the forests—for example, whether they were characterized by infrequent episodic disturbances or by frequent fire (see Chapter 3). In the case of episodically disturbed forests where many hundreds of thousands of acres have been converted to even-aged plantations by previous harvesting, restoration typically has taken the form of various types of thinning or partial-cutting treatments. One major goal of these treatments has been to stimulate the development of greater structural complexity and biological richness (see Chapter 4 for details). In the case of frequent-fire forests and landscapes, many initial restoration efforts concentrated on reducing fuel loadings and modifying landscape patterns as a way to influence fire behavior and aid fire suppression. Often, simplified forests were the result of these efforts. More recently, restoration in frequent-fire forests has moved toward increasing the resistance and resilience of forest stands to disturbance (e.g., wildfire, insects, and disease) by modifying forest structure and composition in ways that retain their complexity (see Chapters 4 and 13 for more details). In general, forest restoration has become the major goal for much forest management that occurs on the national forests (USDA Forest Service, 2012c).

The success of collaborative restoration approaches on many national forests led to passage of the Collaborative Forest Landscape Restoration Act in 2009. This Act calls for collaborative groups working with the Forest Service to propose landscape-level forest restoration plans, which then receive special funding and other resources. Multiple collaborative efforts under the Act are now underway throughout the United States, with a special emphasis on those that address wildfire risk (Butler et al., 2015).

*History as a guide*   With the rise of forest restoration as the watchword for actions on the national forests also came the call for explanation of how restoration might be accomplished and what would be the overall goal. As we have discussed in Chapter 1 and elsewhere in this book, restoration has generally been associated with helping to recover degraded ecosystems and landscapes. Often that degradation has been measured in terms of how much those landscapes have changed in composition, structure, and function due to Euro-American colonization, policies, and exploitation. The argument here is that natural ecosystems and the native species within them flourished in the historical landscapes. Thus, if ecological restoration is a goal, history can provide much useful guidance (Box 20.2).

*The historical range of variability*   The desire to use history as a guide created interest in tools to estimate historical conditions. A concept known as the *historical range of variability (HRV)* is often used in restoration efforts to help describe the historical range of conditions on a landscape as a basis for evaluating how much the current landscape has changed from those conditions. That comparison helps in the assessment of whether the current landscape needs restoration and in developing the restoration prescription.

HRV is an estimate of the range of variation in physical and biological conditions in some period of the past as a function of natural climatic fluctuations and disturbance regimes, and is often used as a benchmark for conditions that describe functional ecosystems (Davis et al., 2001; Keane et al., 2009; Landres, Morgan, & Swanson, 1999; Morgan et al., 1994). Numerous plans and projects since 1990 have employed HRV concepts to identify a desired condition for a landscape or area, and projects have used desired conditions based on HRV as a guide for project activities. Examination and understanding of HRV have helped to quantify the ideas of resistance, resilience, and structural complexity in the natural world (Box 20.3).

Some have questioned whether HRV is a viable concept for managing lands in the future because of expected climate warming (Millar et al., 2007). HRV certainly provides a valued benchmark, but its use to set goals should be tempered by many other considerations, including recognition that the future will not be entirely like the past. Thus, the focus may shift to achieving ecological conditions that sustain critical ecological functions over time to provide ecosystem services. HRV analysis can still help in setting restoration prescriptions, but a future viewpoint will be needed. We will discuss this issue again below when we review how the Forest Service has tried to broaden HRV into a concept called the *natural range of variation* under the expectation that the future may be different from the past.

## Revision of the NFMA Planning Rule

Very little forest plan revision occurred during the first decade of the 21st century, even though forest plans developed in the 1990s had exceeded their expected life span of 15 years. To many, plan revision under the 1982 planning rule did not seem useful, since its focus on economic analysis and timber production seemed to collide with the Forest Service's emerging conservation responsibilities. While an update of the NFMA might have been a logical approach for providing new management direction for the national forests, lack of congressional consensus on natural resource issues prevented this approach. Instead, revision of the NFMA planning rule by the executive branch provided

## Box 20.2 Restoring the ponderosa pine forests of the southwestern USA: History as a guide

The largest forest restoration effort in the United States, called the "Four Forest Restoration Initiative," is occurring in the ponderosa pine forests of Arizona, USA.* It covers 2.4 million acres of ponderosa pine and pine/oak forest types south of the Grand Canyon and across the Mogollon Plateau, within the boundaries of four national forests (Coconino, Apache-Sitgreaves, Kaibab, and Tonto) (Hampton et al., 2011).

Figure 20.7 *Dr. Wally Covington.*

The Four Forest Restoration Initiative draws heavily on the ecological restoration concepts developed by Dr. Wally Covington (Figure 20.7) and his colleagues at the Ecological Restoration Institute of Northern Arizona University after years of research on their forests (Covington et al., 1994, Covington et al., 1997, Covington, 2000).

As Covington et al. (1997) note, previous research by Cooper (1960) and Covington and Moore (1994) had established that forests of ponderosa pine in the Southwest were much more open before Euro-American colonization. "Until the 1870s, light surface fires every two to five years, along with grass competition and regular drought, maintained an open and parklike landscape dominated by grasses, forbs, and shrubs with scattered groups of ponderosa pine trees. After Euro-American colonization, heavy livestock grazing,

fire suppression, logging disturbances, and climatic events favored dense ponderosa pine regeneration, and the open parklands closed" (Covington et al., 1997, p. 23).

Their research and subsequent recommendations were guided by the general premises that both restoration of ecosystem structure and reintroduction of fire are necessary for restoring rates of decomposition, nutrient cycling, and net primary production to natural levels consistent with the evolutionary environment of long-needled pine ecosystems, and that the rates of these processes will be higher in an ecosystem that approximates the natural structure and disturbance regime (Covington et al., 1997; Covington, 2000). That led them to study treatment regimes that combined thinning, forest floor fuel manipulation, and prescribed burning (Figure 20.8). Key elements of their approach include:

- Preserving all old-growth trees (those predating Euro-American colonization);

- Using old-growth stumps and other evidence (e.g., old-growth windthrow, pit and mound, etc.) to guide location and density of post-settlement trees to be left after thinning;

- Thinning and removing excess trees (trees other than those needed to restore ecological restoration reference conditions plus extra trees needed for other resource values such as wildlife habitat or sustainable wood harvesting); and

- Burning on an approximately natural interval as determined by fire regime analysis.

The Forest Service faced significant challenges if it wished to implement these forest restoration concepts and findings.

Figure 20.8 *Illustration of forest restoration using the principles of Dr. Covington and his colleagues at the Ecological Restoration Institute, Northern Arizona University, at the G. A. Pearson Natural Area seven miles north of Flagstaff. (a) before treatments and (b) four years after understory thinning and prescribed fire treatments. (Photos courtesy of Dr. Wally Covington)*

*(continued)*

Commercial timber harvest had largely stopped on those forests by 2000 and most facilities capable of processing the timber had closed. Influential local groups were skeptical that harvest would contribute to restoration goals and were prepared to litigate to prevent a return to logging. Massive severe wildfires, such as the 2002 Rodeo-Chediski Fire—at the time, the largest wildfire in Arizona's recorded history—galvanized public support for active and broadscale forest restoration activities. Broad stakeholder agreement on acceptable treatment levels had to be reached, however, before action could be taken (Hampton et al., 2011).

In 2006 an ad hoc group was convened of agency forest restoration professionals, environmental organizations, community forest partnerships, and academic scientists from Arizona and New Mexico to determine how to move forward. Concurrently, the governor of Arizona formed a task force to advance forest restoration. Many sharply focused stakeholder meetings were held to forge the consensus on where restoration would occur and what types of treatments would be used. The work by Dr. Covington and his colleagues was instrumental in providing a scientific foundation for the decisions made during the restoration planning process.

Debate focused on where mechanical treatment would be appropriate. After much deliberation, the stakeholders reached a consensus on treatment of the following percentages of the 2.4-million-acre area (Hampton, 2011):

- That 41% of the area was appropriate for mechanical thinning; and

- That 26% of the area was inappropriate for mechanical thinning.

In addition, a majority of stakeholders believed that mechanical thinning was acceptable or necessary in an additional 33% of the area. A minority did not agree on these areas, especially in Mexican spotted owl habitat, municipal watersheds, and wildlands.

There also was significant debate over the size of trees that could be harvested, with some stakeholders reluctant to allow harvest of trees more than 16 inches in diameter. The issue of harvesting of larger trees is significant because smaller trees have lower value and are more expensive to process than larger trees. Also, most of the larger post-settlement trees tend to occur in portions of the forest that were natural openings before fire exclusion. Leaving all large post-settlement trees prevents restoration of natural patterns of openings surrounding groups of older trees. Nonetheless, as a political compromise, harvest has generally been limited to the smaller trees, except in the wildland–urban interface.

Since World War II, the US Forest Service has found itself at the center of a passionate debate on the uses of the national forests, particularly timber harvesting. The development of broad-based collaborative groups that recommend management on millions of acres has been an unprecedented event for the agency. Hence, it was not surprising that some local national forest leaders needed time to adjust to this new concept of adopting proposals developed by a group of collaborating citizens.

The 4FRI Collaborative Stakeholder Group formed in 2009. In 2015, the NEPA process was completed and a Record of Decision signed by the Forest Service to support the proposed restoration. A 10-year stewardship contract has been awarded to treat 50,000 acres per year. This was quite an accomplishment! However, many challenges remain, especially rebuilding the infrastructure for logging and processing and finding markets for small ponderosa pine trees.

---

* For more details on the initiative, see https://www.fs.usda.gov/4fri and 4fri.org. For a comprehensive history of the 4FRI (1980–2010), see https://cdm17192.contentdm.oclc.org/digital/collection/p17192coll1/id/617/rec/1

new direction—another example of action in the outer ring of the policy arena as discussed in Chapter 6.

After 30 years and many attempts at revision by previous administrations, the Department of Agriculture adopted a new planning rule in 2012 (USDA, 2012). This new rule built on a report issued by a second Committee of Scientists, which had updated the science underlying forest planning (Committee of Scientists, 1999; Johnson et al., 1999b). Additional planning direction was issued in 2015 as a set of planning directives (USDA Forest Service, 2015). The 2012 planning rule and 2015 planning directives revamped national forest planning, attempting to bring the purpose and mechanics of planning into synchrony with emerging themes and practices.

We review the 2012 planning rule and associated planning directives in depth below, comparing some of its key elements to those in the 1982 rule. We follow that review with a discussion of remaining challenges.

## Fundamental Architecture

The revised national land management planning (LMP) process for the national forests calls for a three-phase framework: (1) assessment, (2) plan development, and (3) implementation and monitoring, embedded in the NEPA decision-making

## Box 20.3   **The historical range of variability as a guide to ecological restoration**

Citing a variety of sources, Keane et al. (2009) summarized the argument for the usefulness of HRV, which they define as the variation of historical ecosystem characteristics and processes over temporal and spatial scales appropriate for management application. For effective ecosystem management, managers require a reference or benchmark to represent the conditions that fully describe functional ecosystems. Contemporary conditions can then be evaluated against this reference to determine status and change, which enables managers to design treatments that return declining ecosystems to a more natural or native condition. That is, HRV provides land-use planning and ecosystem management with a spatial and temporal foundation for planning and implementing treatments to improve ecosystem integrity.

As scientists have pointed out, the full range of ecological characteristics are critical criteria in the evaluation and management of ecosystems; this variability helps to ensure continued health, self-organization, and resilience of ecosystems and landscapes across spatiotemporal scales (Holling, 1992).

As Keane et al. (2009) note, comprehensive quantification of HRV demands temporally deep, spatially explicit historical data, which are rarely available and often difficult to obtain. We used simulation data to provide that information in the landscape assessment of the Oregon Coast Range discussed in Chapter 5 (see Tables 5.1 and 5.2 and associated discussion). That work highlights that HRV is a function of scale: in general, the larger the area, the smaller the range of variability as disturbances in different areas over time offset each other (Figure 20.9).

In another study, Tucker et al. (2016) combined information from presettlement trees found in General Land

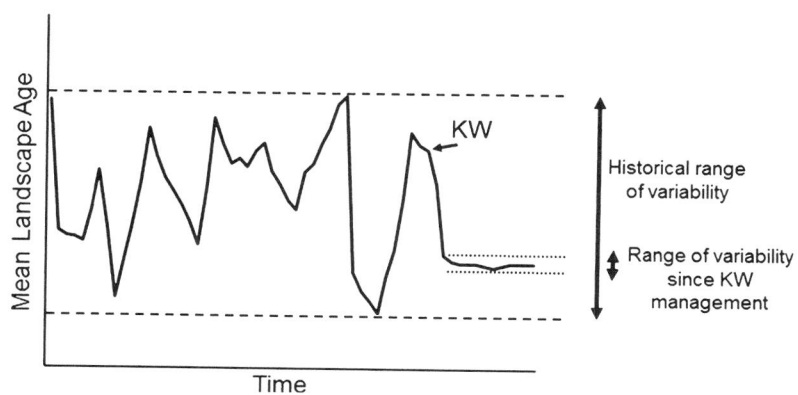

Figure 20.10 *Conceptual representation of the historic range of jack pine stand-age variability in northern Lower Michigan (USA), illustrating the effects of warbler habitat management on the temporal variability of stand age-distributions. "KW" indicates the beginning of Kirtland's warbler habitat management using plantations. Representation of landscape age prior to warbler management is hypothetical based on the periodic occurrence of large wildfires of variable size and timing on a 59-year rotation. (Republished with permission of Springer-Verlag Dordrecht, from Tucker et al. [2016]. Permission conveyed through Copyright Clearance Center Inc.)*

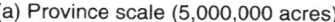

(a) Province scale (5,000,000 acres)

(b) National forest scale (600,000 acres)

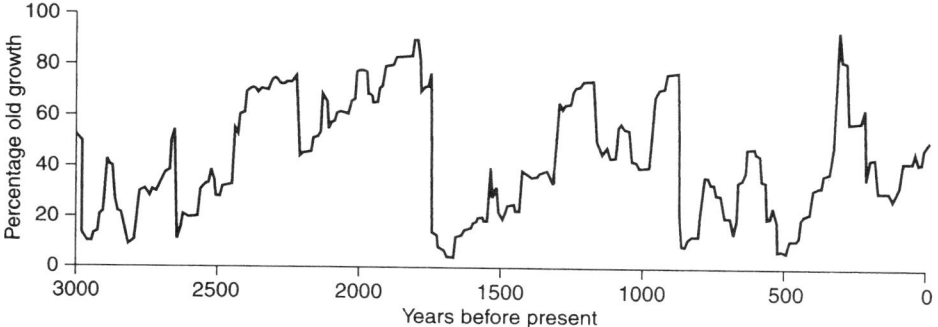

Figure 20.9 *Variability in the percentage of the landscape in old growth from a single 3,000-year simulation of the fire history of the Oregon Coast Range, summarized at two spatial scales. (Source: M. Wimberly and T. Spies, personal communication, 2000)*

*(continued)*

Office survey notes with simulation to estimate the historical range of jack pine stand-age variability in Michigan, USA, for comparison to stand-age distributions over time on jack pine forests managed for Kirtland's warbler (Figure 20.10). As discussed in Chapter 4, Tucker et al. concluded (2016, p. 2445): "Landscape metrics suggest the current landscape is younger and more fragmented than the pre-European landscape." (See Figure 4.10 and associated discussion about shifts in management of these forests that can provide a fuller set of forest structures to protect a wider range of forest biota.)

Another HRV data source is to substitute space for time by collecting data from forests over a large geographic region under the argument that in similar biophysical environments with similar disturbance and climatic regimes, a representative cross-section of variation may be observed. Differences in space are viewed as equivalent to differences in time, and inferences may be drawn regarding variation in spatial pattern that might occur at a single location over time.

Table 20.1 *Mean and standard deviation in the number of trees per hectare in different diameter classes from historical and current inventories of ponderosa pine and mixed conifer forests in southwestern Oregon*

**Ponderosa Pine and Mixed Conifer**

|  | 1916–1924 Trees/ha | 2014 Trees/ha |
|---|---|---|
| 15–53 cm dbh | 38 ±23 | 274 ±151 |
| 53–81 cm dbh | 23 ±11 | 19 ±19 |
| ≥ 81 cm dbh | 9 ±6 | 3 ±4 |

*Source:* Hagmann et al. (2017).

As an example of this latter approach, Hagmann, Johnson, and Johnson (2017) and Hagmann et al. (2013, 2014) have used historical inventories over large areas of the eastern Cascades of Oregon to describe historical forest structure in ponderosa pine and mixed conifer forests, using the mean, standard deviation, and range of observations (Figure 20.11). They also used current inventory information to describe contemporary structure. All studies showed similar characteristics—a major increase in small trees and a decrease in very large trees. Focusing on the small trees from the 2017 study (Table 20.1), we see the range over which two-thirds of the observations lie (15–61 trees/hectare historically and 123–425 trees per hectare currently). This information suggests that a major reduction in small tree density is needed to return these forests to their historical range of variability. The authors also suggest that contemporary densities were rarely seen historically.

Figure 20.11 *Dr. Keala Hagmann explaining her research.*

process (Figure 20.12).[6] Generally, an environmental impact statement will be required for plan revision.

The forest planning process begins with an assessment that "evaluates existing information about relevant ecological, economic, and social conditions, trends, and sustainability and their relationship to the land management plan within the context of the broader landscape" (36 CFR 219.5 [1]). This assessment helps set the stage for the needs and concerns

that forest planning will address. The 2012 planning rule emphasizes creating an integrated set of plan components beginning with the identification of desired conditions for the plan area. Desired conditions are defined as:

*A desired condition is a description of specific social, economic, and/or ecological characteristics of the plan area, or a portion of the plan area, toward which management of the land and resources should be directed. Desired conditions must be described in terms that are specific enough to allow progress toward their achievement to be determined, but do not include completion dates.* (36 CFR 219.7[e][1][i])[7]

---

6 Structured decision making, as we discussed in Chapter 18 and applied in Chapter 19, fits well with the planning process shown in Figure 20.12; step 1 of structured decision making (frame the problem and set the decision context) largely matches phase 1 of the LMP process (assessment phase). Steps 2–7 of structured decision making can provide the detail of phase two of the LMP process (plan development), and the last phase of both planning approaches focuses on implementation, monitoring, and adaptation.

7 All references to 36 CFR 219 refer to the planning rule of USDA, 2012. While the 1982 planning rule is also under 36 CFR 219, we will refer to it by page number.

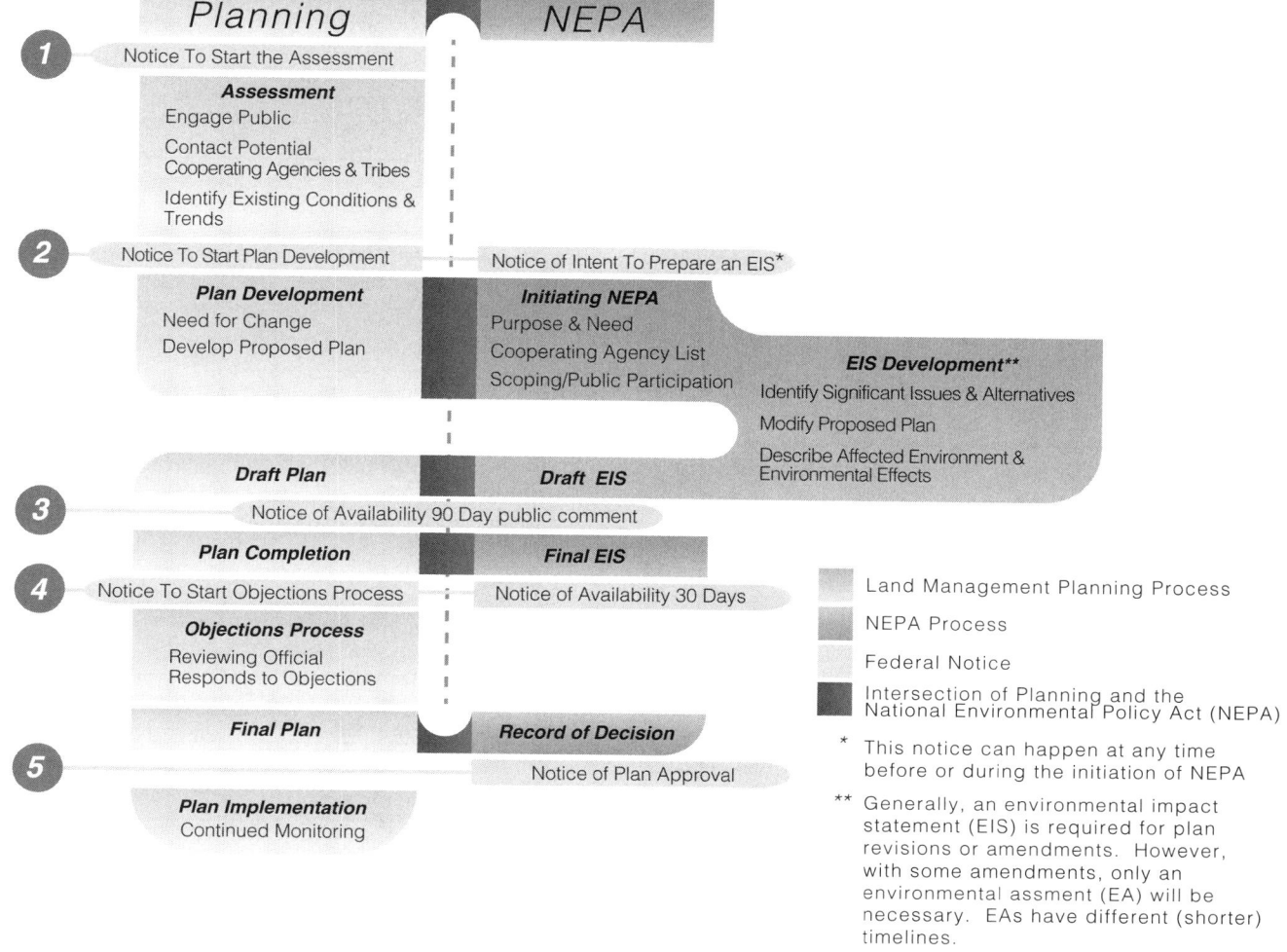

Figure 20.12 *The land management planning process for the national forests embedded in the NEPA decision-making process (Source: USDA Forest Service. June, 2016a)*

Desired conditions are to be informed by scientific information with participation from the public, and set forth the desired landscape of the future, while the other plan components give guidance on how to get there. They need to be specific enough to allow progress toward their achievement to be determined (USDA Forest Service, 2015).

The other required plan components, objectives, standards, guidelines and suitable lands, are developed to achieve the desired conditions identified for the plan. They are defined as (36 CFR 219.7[e][1][ii–v]):

- **Objectives.** *An objective is a concise, measurable, and time-specific statement of a desired rate of progress toward a desired condition or conditions.*[8] *Objectives should be based on reasonably foreseeable budgets.*

- **Standards.** *A standard is a mandatory constraint on project and activity decision making, established to help achieve or maintain the desired condition or conditions, to avoid or mitigate undesirable effects, or to meet applicable legal standards.*

- **Guidelines.** *A guideline is a constraint on project or activity decision making that allows for departure from its terms, so long as the purpose of the guideline is met.*

- **Suitability of lands.** *Specific lands within a plan area will be identified as suitable for various multiple uses or activities based on the desired conditions applicable to those lands. The plan will also identify lands within the plan area as not suitable for uses that are not compatible with desired conditions for those lands.*

Consistency with these plan components is used to determine consistency of projects with the plan.

We will utilize the recently released Draft Revised Forest Plan for the Flathead National Forest (USDA Forest

---

8 This is a different use of the word "objective" than found in our discussion of structured decision making in Chapter 18. In the discussion in that chapter, the terms "fundamental objective" and "means objective" referred to objectives to guide planning. Here the term "objective" refers to specific actions to be undertaken to implement a plan.

Box 20.4 **Examples of desired conditions, objectives, standards and guidelines from the Draft Revised Forest Plan for the Flathead National Forest**

Table 20.2 *Desired conditions forestwide for coniferous forest dominance types (percent of forest in the dominance type)*

| Forest dominance type[a] | Current estimate[b] (%) | Desired range (%) | Desired trend from current condition |
|---|---|---|---|
| Ponderosa pine | 0.4 (0–1.0) | 1–5 | Increase, with focus on sites currently dominated by Douglas-fir. |
| Douglas-fir | 18 (16–21) | 15–25 | Trend downward on sites that support ponderosa pine and/or western larch |
| Western larch | 5.7 (4.2–7.3) | 8–15 | Increase, with focus in areas currently dominated by lodgepole pine or Douglas-fir |
| Lodgepole pine | 15 (12–18) | 10–20 | Trend downward in areas that support western larch or ponderosa pine |
| Subalpine fir/ Engelmann spruce | 43 (39–47) | 20–45 | Maintain near current condition in Canada lynx habitat; trend downward elsewhere |
| Grand fir/ Western red cedar | 1 (0.4–1.6) | 0.5–2 | Trend upward in areas that would support long-term development and persistence of large-diameter western red cedar |
| Whitebark pine | 2.4 (1.4–3.4) | 2–7 | Trend upward, particularly in areas best suited for species success (less competition) |

a. Dominance type reflects the most common tree species in the stand.
b. Estimated mean across all Flathead NFS land. Lower and upper bounds at 90% confidence interval. Data source: Dominance Mid 40 classes, R1 Summary Data Base, from data produced from the Forest Service's Inventory and Analysis (FIA) program.

*Source:* USDA Forest Service (2016b, p. 29).

Objectives (USDA Forest Service, 2016b, p. 43):

- "Vegetation management treatments (e.g., timber harvest, planned ignitions, thinning, planting) on 62,000 to 174,000 acres forestwide to maintain or move towards achieving desired conditions for coniferous forest types and associated wildlife species."

- "Vegetation management treatments (e.g., timber harvest, planned ignitions, thinning, planting) on 500 to 5,000 acres of forest to contribute to restoration of diverse native hardwood forest types and associated wildlife species."

- "Vegetation management treatments (e.g., planned ignitions, slashing, control of non-native, invasive plants) on 1,500 to 5,000 acres to promote persistence of grass/forb/shrub plant communities, focusing on key habitats for big game species and pollinators, to improve conditions for native establishment and growth and reduce non-native plants (e.g., planned ignitions)."

Standards (USDA Forest Service, 2016b, pp. 44–45):

- "Within the . . . primary conservation area, all proposed vegetation management projects shall be evaluated for their effects on grizzly bears and their habitat."

- "In old-growth forest, vegetation management activities must not modify the characteristics of the stand to the extent that the stand would no longer meet the definition for old growth. . . . Vegetation management within old growth shall be limited to actions that:

1. "Maintain or restore old-growth habitat characteristics and ecosystem processes;

2. "Increase old-growth forest resistance and resilience to disturbances or stressors that may have negative impacts on old-growth characteristics (such as drought, high severity fire, bark beetle infestations);

3. "Reduce fuel hazards adjacent to private property or other exceptional values at risk; or

4. "Address human safety."

Vegetation management activities that may be used to meet these requirements include (but are not limited to) planned or unplanned low to mixed severity fire; removal of hazard trees in developed campgrounds; commercial or non-commercial thinning to reduce tree density; or treating insect and disease infestations through integrated pest management strategies."

Guidelines (USDA Forest Service, 2016b, p. 46):

- "Within the NCDE primary conservation area, vegetation and fuels management activities should be restricted in time and space if needed to reduce the potential for adverse grizzly bear disturbance/displacement, as determined by site-specific analysis. Note: Management activities such as pre-commercial thinning, burning, weed spraying, and implementation of road best management practices other than instream work may need to be completed during the spring time period in order to meet objectives (especially if needed to prevent resource damage), but should otherwise be restricted in time or space, if needed to reduce the potential for adverse grizzly bear disturbance/displacement."

Service, 2016b) to illustrate these ideas (Box 20.4). Many tables in that plan describe desired conditions, in terms of the current estimate of the condition, the desired range (based largely on estimates of the natural range of variation), and (sometimes) the desired trend. As an example, the table on desired conditions for coniferous forest dominance types (Box 20.4) shows that the ponderosa pine and western larch forest types are below their desired range, and the forest plan will try to trend their percentages upward. The Draft Revised Plan also contains objectives for the first decade to move toward the desired conditions for conifer forest dominance and many other measures. These objectives are summarized into terms of the amounts of vegetative treatments to achieve during the plan period that comes from detailed analysis (Box 20.4). Also, the Draft Revised Plan provides standards and guidelines to guide actions, both forest-wide and for particular land allocations (Box 20.4). Other topics covered include determination of lands suitable for timber production and estimation of desired harvest levels, which we will discuss later in this chapter.

Some (Matonis, Binkley, Franklin, & Johnson, 2016) have questioned the wisdom of stating the desired conditions in such detail as shown in Table 20.2, because it creates an illusion of knowledge and control beyond what can be achieved. They argue that these precise statements of the desired conditions overestimate our understanding of these systems, relative to how achievement of those conditions would affect achievement of plan goals. Also, this detailed statement of desired conditions implies a degree of control over these natural systems considerably beyond our abilities, especially with regard to climate change. Finally, they may discourage managers if they remain unattainable. Just as the regulated forest was a far-off goal rarely achieved, these desired conditions may provide general guidance but not a precise final state, especially since the desired conditions will, most probably, shift from plan to plan.

Matonis et al. (2016) argue instead for focusing on *undesirable conditions* that we should move away from. In some ways, it can be argued that achievement of the objectives for the plan period in the Draft Revised Plan will do just that to the degree that they focus on restoring degraded forests that do not now achieve the desired conditions (Box 20.4).

As important as these planning processes are, here we want to understand more deeply the concepts and principles that the Forest Service will use to navigate through their planning process. Thus, we emphasize the concepts and principles below.

## Key Elements

We have identified 11 important elements of national forest planning in the 2012 planning rule and associated planning directives.

**1. The 2012 Planning Rule Calls for an Ecological Way of Thinking**   The language, concepts, and principles of ecology permeate the planning rule with its focus on ecological integrity, as well as on the composition, structure, function, resistance, and resilience of ecosystems. The economic optimization approach of the 1982 regulations with its focus on maximizing net public benefits, net present value calculations, and associated timber harvest scheduling has largely disappeared. The ecological approach of the 2012 planning rule establishes a more solid foundation for forest planning to provide a wide variety of ecosystem services from the national forests.

**2. Under the 2012 Rule, the National Forests Must Be Managed in an Ecologically Sustainability Manner**   "Plans will guide management of NFS lands so that they are ecologically sustainable and contribute to social and economic sustainability" (36 CFR 219.1[c]).

The 2012 planning rule commits the Forest Service to managing the national forests to provide for ecological sustainability, through maintaining or restoring the ecological integrity of terrestrial and aquatic ecosystems and watersheds in the plan area as we discuss below. The sustainability discussion (36 CFR 219.8) begins with this commitment and then describes the different types of contributions to social and economic sustainability that could be made. The commitment is limited only by the authority of the Forest Service and the inherent capability of the land.

The 1982 planning rule attempted to integrate the agency's earlier emphasis on providing sustainable timber supplies with consideration of environmental limits and other values. Ecological sustainability was not specifically recognized as a concept or requirement, although the absolute nature of the viability requirement in the rule gave it priority over timber production.

*Implications: The national forests will be managed to provide for ecological sustainability under the 2012 planning rule. Important contributions to economic and social sustainability will be made within that context.*

### 3. The 2012 Rule Achieves Ecological Sustainability through Maintenance and Restoration of Ecological Integrity

"The plan must include plan components, including standards or guidelines, to maintain or restore the ecological integrity of terrestrial and aquatic ecosystems and watersheds in the plan area, including plan components to maintain or restore structure, function, composition, and connectivity" (36 CFR 219.8 [a][1]).

Further, the 2012 planning rule defines ecological integrity as "The quality or condition of an ecosystem when its dominant ecological characteristics (for example, composition, structure, function, connectivity, and species composition and diversity) occur within the natural range of variation and can withstand and recover from most perturbations imposed by natural environmental dynamics or human influence" (36 CFR 219.19).

This definition of ecological integrity has two interrelated parts:

1. The *dominant ecological characteristics* should be maintained within the natural range of variation. Focusing on natural range of variation is a well-accepted concept for sustaining ecosystems and the species within them (Seymour & Hunter, 1999). However, if the range is identified with the historical range of variability, which we discussed earlier, this formulation might be impractical as it would utilize historical information that might not be applicable to future conditions: historical ranges of variation as standards or guidelines for restoration may be inappropriate in the face of changing conditions brought about by climate change (Millar et al., 2007). Thus, the natural range of variation may need a dynamic formulation that takes expected ecosystem change associated with climate change into account, providing ecological conditions to sustain functional ecosystems based on a future viewpoint. We discuss this concept in more detail later in this chapter.

2. These dominant ecological characteristics should be able to withstand and recover from most perturbations imposed by natural environmental dynamics and human influence. This part of the definition reflects two desirable characteristics

of ecological systems: that they can both resist disturbances and recover from them. Of course, these desirable features are closely associated with the natural range of variation; in fact, maintaining ecosystems within their natural range of variation can be seen as a way to ensure they will be able to resist and recover from disturbance.

*Implications:* This focus on ecological integrity, and its associated direction of maintaining ecosystems within their natural range of variation with the ability to withstand and recover from most perturbations, clearly requires an ecosystem approach to ecological sustainability. In comparison, an ecosystem approach was largely lacking from the 1982 rule, which focused primarily on protections for individual species.

### 4. The 2012 Rule Takes a Two-Phase Coarse-Filter/Fine-Filter Approach to Conserving Biodiversity

As discussed in Chapter 14 on biodiversity, this approach starts with an ecosystem plan and then adds additional species-specific protections as needed:

- Coarse filter: "The plan must include plan components, including standards or guidelines, to maintain or restore the ecological integrity of terrestrial and aquatic ecosystems and watersheds in the plan area, including plan components to maintain or restore their structure, function, composition, and connectivity" (36 CFR 219.9[a]).

- Fine filter: "The responsible official shall determine whether or not the plan components . . . [the coarse filter provisions mentioned above] . . . provide the ecological conditions necessary to: contribute to the recovery of federally-listed threatened and endangered species,[9] conserve proposed and candidate species,[10] and maintain a viable population of each species of conservation concern[11] within the plan area. If the responsible official determines that the plan components . . . are insufficient to provide such ecological conditions, then additional, species-specific

---

9 See Chapter 7 for requirements of the Endangered Species Act.

10 Candidate species for US Fish and Wildlife Service are plants and animals for which the US Fish and Wildlife Service (FWS) possesses sufficient information on vulnerability and threats to support a proposal to list them as endangered or threatened, but for which no rule has been published. National Marine Fisheries Service has a similar category for species under their purview (36 CFR 219.19).

11 A species of conservation concern is a species, other than federally recognized threatened, endangered, proposed, or candidate species, that is known to occur in the plan area and for which the regional forester has determined that the best available scientific information indicates substantial concern about the species' capability to persist over the long-term in the plan area (36 CFR 219.9c).

plan components, including standards or guidelines, must be included in the plan to provide such ecological conditions in the plan area" (36 CFR 219.9 [b]).

As explained by Forest Service staff: [12]

*The premise behind the coarse-filter approach is that native species evolved and adapted within the limits established by natural landforms, vegetation, and disturbance patterns prior to extensive human alteration. Maintaining or restoring ecological conditions similar to those under which native species have evolved therefore offers the best assurance against losses of biological diversity and maintains habitats for the vast majority of species in an area, subject to factors outside of the Agency's control, such as climate change. The final rule recognizes the importance of maintaining the biological diversity of each national forest and grassland, and the integrity of the compositional, structural, and functional components comprising the ecosystems on each NFS unit.*

*For example, by maintaining or restoring the composition, structure, processes, and ecological connectivity of longleaf pine forests, national forests in the Southeast USA provide ecological conditions that contribute to the recovery of the red-cockaded woodpecker (Picoides borealis) (an endangered species) and conservation of the gopher tortoise (Gopherus polyphemus) (a threatened species), in addition to supporting common species that depend on the longleaf pine ecosystem. Species-specific plan components provide the fine-filter complement to the coarse-filter approach. For example, while coarse-filter requirements to restore longleaf pine ecosystems may provide most of the necessary ecological conditions for the endangered red-cockaded woodpecker, additional fine-filter, species-specific plan components may also be needed, such as a plan standard to protect all known red-cockaded woodpecker cavity trees during prescribed burning activities.*

*Implications:* The 2012 planning rule formally adopts a two-step approach to sustaining ecosystems and the biodiversity within them that reflects both scientific thinking and practical necessity: (1) develop plan components that maintain or restore ecological integrity, and (2) develop species-specific plan components in cases where the ecosystem plan does not sufficiently protect threatened, endangered, or candidate species, or species of concern. [13] This approach

is somewhat different from the 1982 planning rule, which focused primarily on species-specific viability planning. Also, this new approach put more emphasis on the responsible official (the forest supervisor or regional forester) for determining when species-specific plans are needed. It must be said, though, that the balance between ecosystem and species planning in practice is still unfolding.

**5. The 2012 Planning Rule Describes the Many Ways in which the National Forests Can Contribute to Economic and Social Sustainability**    "The plan must include plan components, including standards or guidelines, to guide the plan area's contribution to social and economic sustainability, taking into account:

1. "Social, cultural, and economic conditions relevant to the area influenced by the plan;

2. "Sustainable recreation; including recreation settings, opportunities, and access; and scenic character;

3. "Multiple uses that contribute to local, regional, and national economies in a sustainable manner;

4. "Ecosystem services;

5. "Cultural and historic resources and uses; and

6. "Opportunities to connect people with nature" (36 CFR 219.8 [b]).

*Implications:* The planning rule calls for the national forests to contribute to economic and social sustainability in a myriad of ways beyond the contributions made by well-functioning ecological systems. It must be said, though, that the rule has fewer standards for assessing whether that contribution is being made than it has for judging whether ecological sustainability has been achieved.

**6. The 2012 Planning Rule Emphasizes an Outward-Looking Approach in Assessment and Planning**    National forest planning has traditionally been inward looking, as it concentrated on providing sustainable harvests for local industry and communities, and the 1982 planning rule largely reflected this perspective. However, the 1982 rule also called for regional guidance for national forest planning, which required consideration of conditions and actions beyond national forest borders, especially to ensure the viability of wide-ranging vertebrates or species federally listed as threatened or endangered. This simultaneous call for both inward-looking and outward-looking approaches to planning created another source of the confusing direction that muddled national forest planning under the 1982 rule.

The 2012 rule, on the other hand, clearly calls for an outward-looking approach in assessment and planning:

---

12 Personal communication with Director Chris French, Ecosystem Management Coordination, USDA Forest Service 4/11/2016.

13 The responsible official (usually forest supervisor or regional forester) can also provide (at his or her discretion) "habitat conditions, subject to the requirements of § 219.9, for wildlife, fish, and plants commonly enjoyed and used by the public; for hunting, fishing, trapping, gathering, observing, subsistence, and other activities" (36 CFR 219.10 [5]).

- Assessments that underlie plan development must "consider and evaluate existing and possible future conditions and trends of the plan . . . , in the context of the broader landscape" (36 CFR 219.5[a][1]).

- Restoration and maintenance of the ecological integrity of terrestrial and aquatic ecosystems and watersheds in the plan area must consider:

  - "Contributions of the plan area to ecological conditions within the broader landscape influenced by the plan area" (36 CFR 219.8[a][1][ii]).

  - "Conditions in the broader landscape that may influence the sustainability of resources and ecosystems within the plan area" (36 CFR 219.8[a][1][iii]).

*Implications:* As the national forests have increasingly become the backbone of regional conservation efforts, including recovery of threatened and endangered species, an inward-looking approach to achieving sustainability is no longer sufficient. Rather, planning will focus on what national forests can contribute to sustainability given what others in the broader landscape are likely to do (Box 20.5).

**7. Planning Directives for the 2012 Planning Rule Interpret the Provision on the NFMA Limitations on Timber Removal in Ways that Will Significantly Lessen that Provision's Control on Timber Harvest Levels**   The NFMA states that "The Secretary of Agriculture shall limit the sale of timber from each national forest to a quantity equal to or less than a quantity which can be removed from such forest annually in perpetuity on a sustained-yield basis" (36 U.S.C. § 1611[a]). These limitations on timber removal are interpreted differently in the two planning rules:[14]

- The 2015 planning directives that interpret the 2012 planning rule define the *sustained yield limit* of the NFMA as the "amount of timber that could be produced on all lands that *may be suitable* for timber production, assuming all of these lands were managed to produce timber without considering other multiple uses or fiscal or organizational capability" (USDA Forest Service, 2015, Ch. 60, p. 33). Except for *departures*, which the handbook describes as "rarely used," the planning directives require that "the projected timber sale quantity must be equal to or below the sustained yield limit for each decade of the plan" (p. 34).

- The 1982 planning rule defines the *long-term sustained yield timber capacity* as "the highest uniform wood yield from lands managed for timber production that may be sustained under a specified management intensity consistent with multiple-use objectives" (USDA, 1982, p. 43039). Except for departures, which were rarely proposed, the 1982 rule required that "the planned sale for any future decade shall be equal to, or greater than, the planned sale for the preceding decade, provided that the planned sale is not greater than the long-term sustained yield capacity consistent with the management objectives of the alternative" (p. 43047). This constraint on harvest flow was known as the *nondeclining yield* requirement and the resulting permitted sale level under the forest plan was known as the *allowable sale quantity*.

These two approaches to interpreting the NFMA limitations on timber removal differ in a number of ways:

- *Terminology.* The 1982 planning rule and the 2015 planning directives use slightly different terminology to describe how to meet the NFMA provision on timber removal limitations that reflect their different approaches to meeting the limitation. The 1982 rule relates the *planned sale schedule* to the *long-term sustained yield capacity*, while the 2015 planning directives relate the *projected timber sale quantity* to the *sustained yield limit*. The expected duration of the forest plan is approximately 15 years under both planning rules and is here called the *plan period*.

- *Wood harvest included.* Both approaches include timber that is sold and meets utilization standards, except for salvage or sanitation harvest after major disturbance. Firewood and similar wood products that may be sold but don't meet utilization standards are excluded, though they are reported under the 2015 planning directives. However, the 1982 rule includes only timber harvested on national forestlands allocated to timber production in the limitations on timber removal, while the 2015 planning directives include timber harvested on any national forestlands, whether or not these lands are allocated to timber production.

- *Harvest scheduling analysis required.* To ensure compliance with the limitations on timber removals, the nondeclining yield sale level was projected for at least one and one-half rotations (usually 10 decades or more) into the future in implementing the 1982 planning rule. Depending on the inventory characteristics of the forest being analyzed, either the long-term sustained yield capacity or the nondeclining yield requirement would constrain

---

14 The 1982 planning rule included detailed procedures for interpreting the NFMA limitations on timber removal, while the 2012 planning rule calls for including those procedures in the Forest Service Directive System (219.11 [d] [6]). Therefore, we compare the procedures in the 1982 planning rule to those in the 2015 planning directives.

the sale level for the plan period (Figure 20.13). The 2015 planning directives take a different approach requiring "estimates in the plan of . . . the annual projected timber sale quantity for each of the first two decades" (USDA Forest Service, 2015 Ch. 60, p. 34).

- *Interpreting the resulting sale level.* The allowable sale quantity under the 1982 rule set the maximum sale level for the plan period from lands suitable for timber production. Additional timber could be offered from lands not suitable for timber production to achieve multiple-use objectives or as salvage. The projected timber sale quantity in the 2015 planning directives is an estimate of the sale level for the duration of the forest plan from all lands, whether or not they are suitable for timber production (except for salvage and sanitation harvest after major disturbance). The actual sale level can be higher (up to the sustained yield limit) or lower.

*Implications: The reinterpretation of the limitations on timber removal in the 2015 planning directives should* *greatly reduce the impact of this NFMA provision on the projected timber sales for the plan period (15 years) for two reasons:*

1. *The sustained yield limit calculated under the 2015 planning directives, which sets a cap on the harvest level of each forest planning alternative, will generally be much higher than the long-term sustained yield capacity calculated under the 1982 rule.* Two changes cause most of this difference:

   a) The sustained yield calculation in the 2015 planning directives includes all lands that may be suitable for timber production, a constant over all alternatives, while the calculation in the 1982 rule includes only lands allocated to timber production in the alternative being analyzed. Using the 2016 Revised Forest Plan for the Flathead National Forest as an example (USDA Forest Service, 2016b), 737,400 acres *may* be suitable for timber production (Box 20.6). Out of that total, 43–68% of those acres

---

**Box 20.5  The Siuslaw National Forest: Conservation responsibilities in a multi-owner landscape**

The Siuslaw National Forest, situated in the Oregon Coast Range, contains mostly low elevation Douglas-fir–western hemlock and Sitka spruce forests, and is physiologically similar to the corporate, state, BLM, and family forests that surround it (Color Plate 5.2). Historically, the Siuslaw National Forest was managed in a manner similar to these other landowners, with an emphasis on intensive timber management with clearcutting, albeit on a slightly longer rotation.

This national forest lies within the range of numerous federally listed threatened species, including the northern spotted owl, marbled murrelet, and coho salmon. During development of the Northwest Forest Plan, scientists and agency professionals were charged with developing alternatives that would sustain species and ecosystems of mature and old-growth forests, along with their associated aquatic ecosystems. They were given explicit instructions to have the federal lands shoulder the responsibility for protecting these resources and not to put additional responsibilities on state and private lands beyond existing state and federal requirements.

Federal lands, in particular Siuslaw National Forest lands, represent a relatively small fraction of Coast Range forests. Thus, it should not be surprising that this mandate resulted in a major shift on the Siuslaw National Forest from timber production to the protection of threatened species and the ecosystems in which they live. Extensive reserves were created, covering over 90% of the national forest, and the projected harvest dropped over 90% as well. Private forest management proceeded in a largely unchanged regulatory structure. In sum, the Siuslaw National Forest (and also nearby BLM lands) adopted a new primary mission—protecting species and ecosystems—while private landowners were largely free to pursue their timber production (and other) goals.

However, this asymmetric partitioning of conservation responsibilities works better for some species than others. For example, streams in the Coast Range run through both private and federal lands, and some of the best coho salmon habitat is privately owned, especially in the lowlands. The unavoidable need for stream protection on private lands remains a key element in the recovery of coho salmon (a species federally listed as threatened) and is a continuing source of tension between private landowners, federal regulators, and state officials responsible for forest and agricultural practices on private lands there.

The large area of forestland on the Siuslaw National Forest that was placed in reserves meant that the projected harvest, calculated for the small amount of forest that could be devoted to timber production, was relatively low. Thinning younger plantations within reserves is allowed as a way to increase the structural and compositional diversity of these stands, although no timber volume target from reserves is calculated, since harvest is a function of ecological needs. By concentrating on harvest within reserves that serves the purpose of ecological restoration, the Siuslaw National Forest has been able to harvest more volume than calculated for its timber production lands, has received the support of a collaborative group, and has won public acclaim! In sum, management of the Siuslaw National Forest has shifted sharply toward assisting in the recovery of threatened species in the Coast Range, while surrounding landowners make modest contributions to species protection (as required by law) and pursue their own goals.

are suitable for timber production depending on the alternative. Thus the 2015 planning directives include 47–133% more acres in the sustained yield calculation, depending on the alternative, than would have been included in the 1982 rule.

b) The sustained yield calculation in the 2015 planning directives assumes that these lands will be managed solely for timber production, while the calculation in the 1982 rule adjusts (lowers) timber yields for the actual management regime under the alternative. Very few acres are managed solely for timber production under the 2012 planning rule and the 2015 planning directives, due to consideration of other values and constraints, with the result that the estimated timber production levels will generally be considerably below that which would occur if timber production was the sole objective. Looking again at the Revised Forest Plan for the Flathead National Forest, the sustained yield limit is almost five times the projected timber sale quantity of any alternative (Box 20.6), even though these sale levels include timber from all lands, not just those allocated to timber production. It would have been very rare in the forest plans developed under the 1982 planning rule to have the long-term sustained yield capacity even double projected sale levels. In some cases, this limit could constrain sale levels for the plan period (Figure 20.13b).

In sum, these two changes in calculation procedures for estimating the sustained yield limit, between the 1982 planning rule and the 2015 planning directives, will result in the calculation of a sustained yield limit much higher than the projected sales level under an alternative—to a level unlikely to constrain projected timber sale quantity for the plan period.

2. *The requirement in the 1982 planning rule that the sale level estimated for the plan not exceed the*

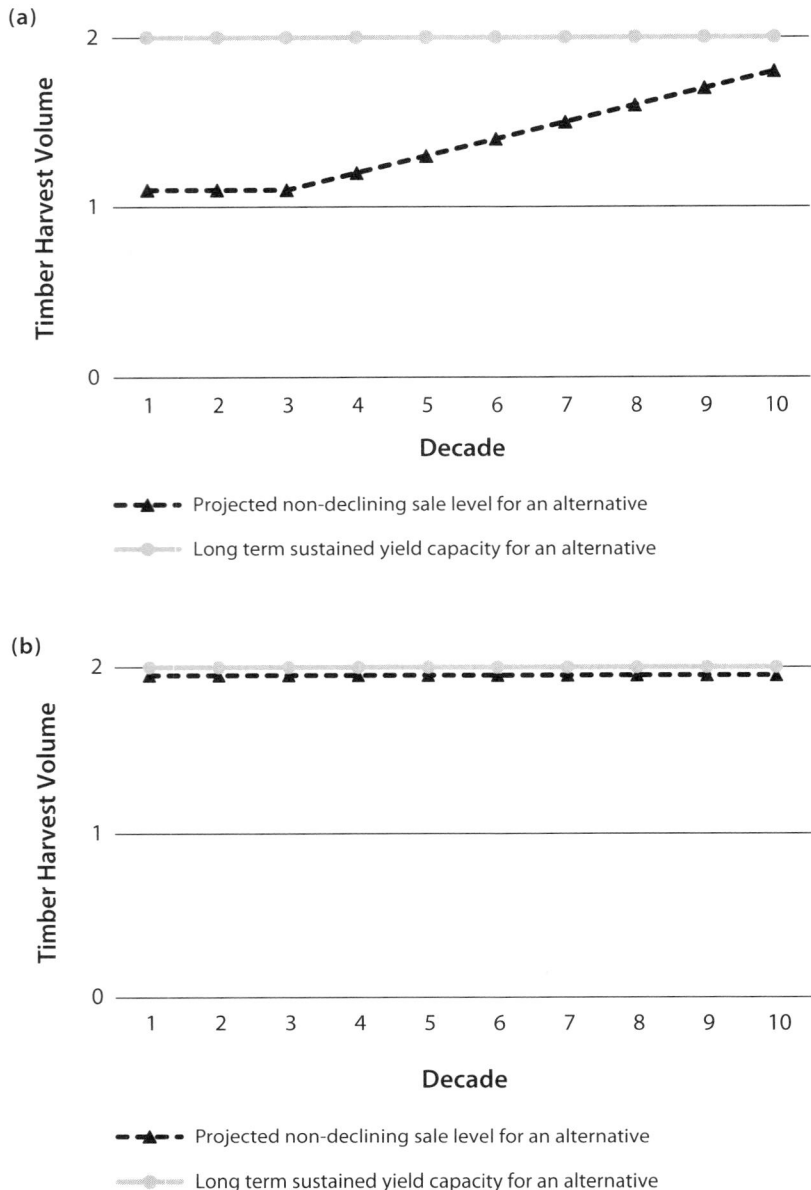

Figure 20.13 *The 1982 rule interprets the NFMA limitations on timber removal to require that the projected planned sale for any future decade shall be equal to, or greater than, the planned sale for the preceding decade, provided that the planned sale is not greater than the long-term sustained yield capacity consistent with the management objectives of the alternative. Harvest schedules calculated under this requirement generally demonstrated one of two relationships between the projected nondeclining yield sale schedule and the long-term sustained yield capacity (Davis and Johnson, 1987): (1) the projected sale schedule started below the long-term sustained yield capacity and moves up to it over time (called the deficit inventory case—the more common situation) (Figure 20.13a) and (2) the projected sale schedule started at the long-term sustained yield capacity (called the surplus inventory case) (Figure 20.13b). In the former case, the nondeclining yield requirement constrained the timber removals for the plan period; in the latter case, the long-term sustained yield capacity constrained them. Neither type of harvest scheduling constraint, associated with implementation of the 1982 rule, will generally limit timber removals for the plan period under the requirements of the 2012 planning rule.*

*nondeclining yield level projected for many future decades beyond the plan period has been dropped.* This change has two parts: (1) As we described above, the length of time over which planners must project sale levels has been greatly contracted from ten or more decades to two decades, and (2) A nondeclining yield projection even for those two decades is no longer required (USDA Forest Service,

2015, p. 43 [65.2 Exhibit 01]). Under the 2012 planning rule and directives, the projected timber sale quantity can go down between the two decades projected for the plan period (without requiring a departure).

*This revised interpretation of the NFMA limitations on timber removal was greatly needed and should assist the Forest Service in successfully revising national forest plans:*

---

Box 20.6 **Timber production suitability classification and projected timber sale quantity in the Draft Revised Forest Plan for the Flathead National Forest**

The 2012 planning rule and 2015 planning directives require "identification of lands that are suited and not suited for timber production, based on several factors that include legal withdrawal (e.g., timber production prohibited due to statute, executive order, etc.), technical factors (nonforestlands, geology or soil conditions, etc.), and compatibility with desired conditions and objectives stated in the plan" (USDA Forest Service, 2016b, p. 79). Suitability calculations for the Flathead National Forest Plan resulted in 43–68% of the lands that may be suited for timber production actually selected for timber production (13–21% of the Flathead National Forest) in the alternatives considered (Table 20.3).

Also, the 2015 planning directives call for the forest plan to calculate and state the sustained yield limit (SYL), the projected timber sale quantity, and the projected wood sale quantity for the plan period (Table 20.4) (USDA Forest Service, 2016b, p. 79):

*The SYL . . . is the volume that could be produced in perpetuity on lands that may be suitable for timber production. . . . The calculation of the SYL is not limited by land management plan desired condition, other plan components, or the planning unit's fiscal capability and organizational capacity.*

The Flathead Forest Plan describes the intended timber program in two ways: (1) the projected wood sale quantity (PWSQ) and (2) the projected timber sale quantity (PTSQ). The PWSQ is the estimated output of timber and other wood products, such as fuelwood, firewood, and biomass, expected to be sold during the plan period for any purpose (except for salvage harvest or sanitation harvest). The PTSQ is the portion of PWSQ that meets applicable utilization standards (here sawtimber standards). They both are based on expected budgets and organizational capacity. The PTSQ must remain at or below the sustained yield limit—here that limit is 4–6 times the PTSQ of the alternatives (Table 20.4).

Table 20.4 *Projected timber sale quantity (PTSQ) and projected wood sale quantity (PWSQ) (sustained yield limit = 25.4 millions of cubic feet/year)*

| Alternative | PTSQ/year in millions | | PWSQ/year in millions |
|---|---|---|---|
| | Cubic feet | Board feet | Cubic feet |
| B | 5.5 | 27.4 | 6.3 |
| C | 3.9 | 18.0 | 4.5 |
| D | 5.9 | 29.2 | 6.8 |

Source: USDA Forest Service (2016b, pp. 79–80).

Table 20.3 *Timber production suitability classification*

| Land Classification Category | Alt B | Alt C | Alt D |
|---|---|---|---|
| A. Total National Forest System lands in the plan area | 2,392,800 | 2,392,800 | 2,392,800 |
| B. Lands not suited for timber production due to legal or technical reasons | 1,655,400 | 1,655,400 | 1,655,400 |
| C. Lands that may be suited for timber production (A minus B) | 737,400 | 737,400 | 737,400 |
| D. Total lands actually suited for timber production in an alternative because timber production is compatible with the desired conditions and objectives established by the plan | 499,100 | 317,300 | 500,400 |
| E. Percentage of lands that may be suited for timber production that are selected for timber production in an alternative | 68 | 43 | 68 |
| F. Percentage of National Forest System Lands suitable for timber production | 21 | 13 | 21 |

*Source:* Adapted from USDA Forest Service (2016b, p. 79).

- Assessing the land suitable for timber production and estimating the nondeclining yield of timber sales from those lands formed the heart of forest planning analysis under the 1982 rule, continuing the tradition of focusing on a sustained yield of timber harvest for the assurance of sustainability. However, the timber sale limits were rarely reached; most forests fell far short of them as other sustainability issues, most commonly protection of biodiversity, became more controlling.

- As the concept of sustainability has broadened, so has the focus of forest planning, shifting from the analysis of timber harvest scheduling that consumed forest planning under the 1982 planning rule to the analysis of ecological integrity and contributions to economic and social sustainability under the 2012 planning rule.

- With the shift in focus toward forest restoration as envisioned in the 2012 planning rule, the move away from a commitment to nondeclining yield of timber sales over time, within the long-term sustained yield capacity of the future forest, seems both desirable and inevitable for many reasons:

  ○ It may be desirable, from an ecological standpoint to rapidly restore a degraded landscape, allowing the harvest to decline to a lower level in the long run once the landscape has been restored. Prohibiting that decline could have the unintended effect of delaying needed restoration activities.

  ○ Relatively little of the restoration landscape may be committed to long-term timber production, but harvest may be a tool to help in restoration. Restricting the sustained yield limit to the area committed to long-term timber production could result in a very low estimate, again delaying needed restoration.

- Calculating timber harvest quantities for 20 years into the future, a very short time compared to classical methods, fits well into the approach to planning described in the 2012 planning rule and throughout this book. The uncertainties of the future make longer, more detailed projections problematic. Also, projections of long-term harvest levels can rekindle debates about the long-term management of these landscapes, debates that are not needed to make progress on short-term restoration. Thus the short-run focus should enable the national forests to proceed with restoration of degraded landscapes, while leaving

potentially contentious issues about long-term management to another time (see Box 20.7).

*In sum, the assurance of sustainability moves away from demonstrating sustainable timber harvest levels under the 2012 planning rule and the 2015 planning directives. Rather the assurance of sustainability will focus on maintaining ecological integrity and providing additional protections to individual species as needed. Important contributions to ecological and social sustainability will also be made.*

It will likely take many years for the flexibility of this revised approach to limitations on timber removal to be fully expressed in forest planning, much as it took many years to sort out the implications of the 1982 planning rule. As an example, the analysis of harvest levels in the Draft Revised Forest Plan for the Flathead National Forest (USDA Forest Service, 2016b) utilized the revised approach, discussed above, to estimate a sustained yield limit, but continued the 1982 planning rule requirement of nondeclining yield over many decades. Still, this new interpretation of the NFMA limitations on timber removal signals major changes in how national forest planning will address sustainability.

**8. The 2012 Rule Requires Assessment of Climate Change Effects and Existing Carbon Stocks**    The 2012 planning rule requires responsible officials to identify and evaluate information on climate change and other stressors relevant to the plan area, along with a baseline assessment of carbon stocks for comparison with the carbon stocks over time associated with any alternative plan (36 CFR 219.6[b]). In the discussion published with the planning rule, carbon stocks are defined as "the amount of carbon stored in the ecosystem in living biomass, soil, dead wood, and litter" (USDA, 2012, p. 21200). In addition, the planning directives state, "A baseline assessment estimates existing carbon stocks and recent changes in carbon stocks on the land and in harvested wood products" (USDA Forest Service, 2015, Ch. 10, p. 30). Thus it appears that this assessment will account for both forest carbon and wood product carbon created from harvesting the forest.

There was no mention of climate change or carbon stocks in the 1982 planning rule.

*Implications:* With the increasing national focus on reducing $CO_2$ emissions, the effect of a forest plan alternative on carbon stocks could be an evaluation touchstone. Some managers or stakeholders may push for choosing the alternative that maximizes carbon stock accumulation. Focusing on only one value from these forests, though, is generally inconsistent with the multiple-use mandate of the national forests and, in many ways, would represent a return to the simpler times of the past with carbon now substituted for timber as the forest commodity of interest.

**9. The 2012 Rule Requires Use of the Best Available Scientific Information**   While the NFMA required the secretary of Agriculture to utilize a scientific committee in developing the initial regulations, the 1982 regulations did not specifically require use of the *best available science* nor was science or scientific information emphasized in the regulations. The 2012 planning rule requires: "The responsible official shall use the best available scientific information to inform the planning process. . . . In doing so, the responsible official will determine what information is the most accurate, reliable, and relevant to the issues being considered." Agency officials must also document "what

information was determined to be the best available scientific information, explain the basis for that determination, and explain how the information was applied to the issues considered" (36 CFR 219.3).

*Implications:* The 2012 planning rule makes the use of "best available scientific information" a requirement for national forest planning. However, both NEPA case law and the Administrative Procedures Act's prohibition of *arbitrary and capricious* decisions by federal agencies already implicitly require consideration of available scientific information along with its documentation and discussion of conflicting scientific information. Thus, this provision may signal

---

Box 20.7   **How forest planning can ease the search for common ground in management of the national forests**

As pointed out in Chapter 8 (Box 8.6), two alternative visions for the national forests have been paramount in battles over their management. One emphasizes the use of those forests for goods and services, like timber harvest and range forage for livestock, that contribute to economic development and local community sustenance. Another emphasizes the preservation of wildness and natural processes in those forests. These alternative visions help drive the political battles over our national forests to this day. With such differences, how can people come together on a forest plan? We believe three attributes of a forest plan increase the chances for such a success. All are present, at least to some degree, in the 2012 planning rule and the 2015 planning directives.

- First, the *desired conditions* that are specified should be general enough to embrace the possibility of both paradigms. As an example, the desired condition for frequent-fire forests could be stated in terms of the composition and structure that will enable these forests to be resistant, resilient, and adaptive in the face of disturbances and expected climate change. Timber harvest would be allowed to achieve these conditions, but the reliance on it as a management tool in a restored landscape could be left for future debates.

- Second, specific objectives for the plan period (15–20 years) should support the potential to achieve both visions. The focus in the planning rule on ecosystem restoration will help here, as it turns attention to *unnatural or degraded* conditions, whether it be the buildup in fuels due to fire suppression and past logging and grazing practices in frequent-fire forests or the plantations that were created after natural forests were clearcut in episodically disturbed forests (see Box 8.6 for examples). Immediate actions may be proposed to put these stands on a trajectory to develop into more *natural* forests that also produce wood products. In fact, Matonis et al. (2016) suggest that focusing on "undesirable conditions" as the basis for action is the

key in coming together in management of the national forests. As an example, fuel buildups that enable crown fires in frequent-fire forests may be targeted as an "undesirable condition" requiring action, as can dense plantations in episodically disturbed forests.

- Third, analysis of the detailed activities needed to achieve the desired conditions should focus on the short run, such as 15 or 20 years, a period of time over which restoration activities can be the dominant task, leaving the details of the potentially contentious issue of how to maintain restored ecosystems to future planning. Many may support mechanical treatments that supply wood products as part of restoration of degraded, overly dense frequent-fire forests. Once these forests are restored, those who wish to emphasize wildness may wish to use only prescribed fire to maintain dry forests. Many may support harvest to accelerate the transformation of tree farms, created after past harvest, into more natural forest conditions. Once they are restored, though, those who wish to emphasize wildness may want them left alone.

A key to a successful plan, as noted in Chapter 8, is not to fight the *final battle* over the actions that will be used to achieve the desired conditions in the long run. The 1982 planning rule interpretation of the NFMA clause on "limitations on timber removal" required simulation of nondeclining harvest levels over long time periods, ensuring that such a battle would be fought. The 2012 planning rule and the associated planning directives' interpretation of "limitations on timber removal," on the other hand, require detailed quantitative harvest modeling only for the plan period (approximately 15–20 years). Thus, national forest planners, if they wish, can leave the issue of the role of timber harvest, after the forests are restored, to future planning efforts to resolve. The changed interpretation of how to implement the NFMA requirement for "limitations on timber removal" can assist in developing a forest plan that has wide agreement.

less of a change than it seems (Green & Garmestani, 2012). However, it is clear that science and scientific results are now formally a part of national forest planning. It also signals that scientists, especially federal scientists, may play a significant role in national forest planning in providing and interpreting scientific information, as well as helping to integrate this information into planning frameworks.

### 10. The 2012 Rule Commits the National Forests to Comprehensive Public Engagement throughout the Planning Process

- "The responsible official shall provide opportunities to the public for participating in the assessment process; developing a plan proposal, including the monitoring program; commenting on the proposal and the disclosure of its environmental impacts in accompanying NEPA documents; and reviewing the results of monitoring information" (36 CFR 219 [4a]).

- "The responsible official shall engage the public . . . early and throughout the planning process" (36 CFR 219.4[a][1]).

This commitment to public engagement throughout the planning process goes considerably beyond the NEPA requirements for public involvement, which were embedded in the 1982 planning rule. Also, the commitment to involving the public in developing the monitoring program and allowing the public to see the monitoring results may help with one problem that has traditionally hampered monitoring programs—the tendency to bury bad news about whether policy and plans are achieving policy goals (as discussed in Chapter 11).

The 2012 planning rule also calls for "using collaborative processes where feasible and appropriate" (36 CFR 219.4[a][1]). Collaboration or collaborative processes are defined as "A structured manner in which a collection of people with diverse interests share knowledge, ideas, and resources while working together in an inclusive and cooperative manner toward a common purpose" (36 CFR 219.19). Collaboration was not mentioned in the 1982 regulations, which defaulted to standard NEPA approaches for public participation. More and more, though, collaborative processes have become the standard operative procedure on many national forests around the United States as they try to find enough consensus from their varied publics to successfully develop and implement projects (Chapter 8). Two caveats, though, should be recognized about the direction in the 2012 planning rule with respect to collaborative efforts:

- The planning rule and the planning directives do not contain standards or requirements that the Forest Service must meet to honor this commitment to use "collaborative processes where feasible and appropriate." Rather, the rule and directives leave it up to the Forest Service to determine when and how to utilize collaborative processes.

- The Federal Advisory Committee Act (P.L. 92-463; 5 U.S.C. §§ App. 2) requires a formal process for nonfederal employees to advise national forest managers, including appointment of the FACA committee, notice of all meetings (which must be open to the public), and documentation of discussion and recommendations. This requirement can limit the ability of collaborative groups to advise the Forest Service and often results in an *arms-length* relationship between the Forest Service and local collaborative groups (Butler, 2013).

*Implications:* With this strong commitment to public engagement, and to collaborative approaches where feasible and appropriate, the Forest Service acknowledges that it will need the public's help throughout the planning process to successfully revise forest plans. It also recognizes and embraces successful collaborative approaches to decision making pioneered on many different national forests (and ranger districts within them) over the past 10–20 years.

### 11. The Rule Emphasizes Adaptive Management and the Need for Adaptive Capacity in Forests and in Forest Planning

The 2012 planning rule and directives place great emphasis on adaptive management of the national forests. While the 1982 planning rule did call for monitoring land management activities, the planning process itself was focused on developing long-term plans under the assumption of a relatively stable physical and social environment. The 2012 planning rule and directives recognize that forest plans take place in a rapidly changing world headed toward an uncertain future. As discussed above, the 2012 planning rule and directives implicitly recognize the futility of long-term timber harvest estimates, given these uncertainties. They also recognize the potential for unprecedented changes in ecosystem conditions with respect to historical ranges of variability (or the closely related natural ranges of variation). Finally, they recognize the need for an early warning system to detect problems with ecosystem sustainability. Thus the 2012 planning rule contains a substantial section on monitoring (36 CFR 219.12), broken into forest plan monitoring (directed by national forest personnel) and broader scale monitoring (directed by the regional forester).

*Implications:* The 2012 planning rule puts an emphasis on adaptive management, as it should in this rapidly changing world. Still, we noted in Chapter 11 that the bureaucratic tendency to suppress evidence of failure is the Achilles heel of many monitoring programs. The 2012 planning rule addresses this problem to a degree in calling for biennial evaluation of monitoring information, including public disclosure of this evaluation (36 CFR 219.12 [d]). Such reporting is a good first step to creating a transparent process for assessing both policy successes and failures; it is too early to tell how well it will work in fostering adaptive management.

## Some Remaining Questions

**Will the 2012 Planning Rule Make National Forest Planning Relevant Again?**  In the past 20 years, many national forest managers have functioned without an up-to-date forest plan developed through the forest planning process prescribed by the planning rule. Rather, as described above, they have relied on regional conservation frameworks from a variety of sources combined with local actions to address immediate problems that gained support from a broad group of interests in the community and beyond. In this effort, the US Forest Service has muddled through, finding out what was acceptable and what was not through trial and error.

The NFMA was designed to address the traditional national forest problem of providing environmentally sound, sustainable timber harvests for local communities and interests. With such a problem, a national forest was a logical planning unit. In many ways, we live in a different planning world now. Three major hurdles exist that must be surmounted for forest plans to be the central planning documents envisioned for them at the time the NFMA was passed:

1. *Providing an integrative function when the national forest is no longer the logical planning unit for many of the issues facing the national forests.* With many ecological, economic, and social issues at scales other than a national forest, recognizing the multiscale nature of national forest planning will be central to success. The 2012 planning rule definitely moves planning in that direction, but a successful multiscale approach remains largely to be invented.

2. *Recognizing that planning architecture and wonderful technical analysis will not, by itself, tame this wicked problem.* The casual observer might look at the desired conditions, objectives, standards, and guidelines and conclude that the Forest Service has decided that the right architecture and analysis can "solve" its forest planning problem. While, at its best, this approach can provide tools that can help shepherd the forest planning process down a productive path, it would be foolhardy to think it will fundamentally change the nature of the problem.

3. *Ensuring forest planning does not damage relations with individuals and groups that have made a good-faith effort to help ranger districts and national forests find their way through the political minefield of federal forestry.* For the last 10–15 years, these people have provided energy, creativity, and friendship on many national forests when the Forest Service badly needed it. Forest planning has the potential to diminish their importance and sense of purpose, and losing them would be a major setback.

**Who Will Provide Regional Guidance for Issues that Span Many National Forests?**  The 1982 planning rule required that a regional guide be developed for each administratively-designated Forest Service region. These regional guides provided standards and guidelines for addressing major issues and management concerns at the regional level to facilitate forest planning. As an example, the Regional Guide for the Pacific Northwest Region (USDA Forest Service, Pacific Northwest Region, 1984) attempted to address conservation of wide-ranging vertebrate species, such as the northern spotted owl, through a regional network of small reserves across the national forests of the region. Also, this regional guide set specific standards for timber harvest methods for different forest types, harvest opening sizes, and management intensities and utilization standards. The regional guides were considered "major federal actions significantly affecting the quality of the human environment," and an Environmental Impact Statement and associated public review was required for each of them.

Regional guides were not referenced in the NFMA; rather, they were entirely a creation of the 1982 planning rule. They became a flashpoint of controversy in the 1980s and early 1990s, and much litigation ensued over them since they were viewed as decisions in a NEPA sense. As an example, the litigation over protection of the northern spotted owl began with a challenge to the guidance on the northern spotted owl in the Regional Guide for the Pacific Northwest Region (USDA Forest Service, Pacific Northwest Region, 1984). It is therefore understandable that agency planners would not retain the regional guides in the 2012 planning rule, which neither requires nor mentions them. However, the *outward focus* of the national forests expressed in the 2012 planning rule would seem to demand a more comprehensive view than can be attained by an individual forest. Even more important, many environmental issues that forest plans must address, such as water quality and conservation of at-risk species, cover large areas that far exceed that of an individual national forest. Hence it appears that guidance will be needed at a larger spatial scale. Whether such guidance can be provided without being viewed as an agency decision requiring an environmental impact statement, as was the case with the regional guides, remains to be seen.

## Box 20.8 Scientifically credible conservation strategies: Linchpin of national forest planning

Forest plans developed in the 1980s under the 1982 planning rule had to meet the standard that "Fish and wildlife habitat shall be managed to maintain viable populations of existing native and desired nonnative vertebrate species in the planning area. For planning purposes, a viable population shall be regarded as one which has the estimated numbers and distribution of reproductive individuals to insure its continued existence, well distributed in the planning area" (USDA, 1982, p. 43050). Management strategies to meet this standard were initially developed by agency personnel and managers in the context of the dominant goal of sustaining timber production. For many species, especially at-risk species, the strategies proved largely inadequate in the sense that they could not survive litigation or the threat of litigation.

In the late 1980s, this issue came to a head when the courts rejected repeated attempts by the Forest Service to construct a management strategy that would ensure the viability of the northern spotted owl. In frustration, the chief of the Forest Service turned to a science team of northern spotted owl experts, totally separate from agency managers. Unlike previous attempts that were focused on limiting the impact on timber harvest, this effort set the goal of *developing a scientifically credible conservation strategy for the northern spotted owl* (Thomas et al., 2006). With the goal of a scientifically credible conservation strategy, national forest planning changed in two fundamental ways: (1) forest planning had a conservation standard to meet despite its impact on timber harvest levels, and (2) the protection strategy had to be scientifically credible, which meant that it had to have the approval of scientific experts on the species at issue.

After months of work, the team of owl experts created a new planning framework based on the principles of island biography, modified for a terrestrial organism. This plan led to efforts by other scientific teams, who broadened the scope of analysis to include other species and also ecosystems. This work culminated in creation of the Northwest Forest Plan, which contained scientifically credible conservation strategies for protecting key at-risk species such as the northern spotted owl, coho salmon, and marbled murrelet and also old-growth and aquatic ecosystems. Federal agencies in the Pacific Northwest have lived within the planning framework created by scientists ever since, although it has recently been modified by the recovery plan and critical habitat designation for the northern spotted owl by the USFWS, which drew heavily on the scientific contingent within that agency.

The development of scientifically credible strategies for species conservation, especially for at-risk species, has become central to national forest planning, whether the species is the California spotted owl (*Strix occidentalis occidentalis*), the Canada lynx (*Lynx canadensis*), or the Indiana bat (*Myotis sodalis*). Where a species is federally listed as threatened or endangered, regulatory agencies, such as the USFWS, lead the development of conservation strategies. However, keeping species off that federal list is generally a goal of national forest planning efforts. Thus the Forest Service will undoubtedly expend great energy attempting to create scientifically credible strategies for at-risk species that are not listed as threatened or endangered, such as the California spotted owl and the Canada lynx. Forest planning can then proceed within the conservation framework that has been developed.

In addition to frameworks for conservation of at-risk species, the new overarching ecological sustainability goal in the 2012 planning rule, to maintain and restore ecological integrity, will necessitate the development of scientifically credible conservation strategies for maintaining and restoring the ecological integrity of the ecosystems of the national forests. These conservation strategies, combined with any additional needed conservation strategies for at-risk species, will become a framework within which achievement of other goals will be sought. Scientists will be needed to help develop or vet the scientific credibility of the strategies that are developed.

Some overall observations about the development of scientifically credible conservation strategies that underlie forest plans and planning are:

1. The 2012 planning rule calls for maintaining or restoring ecological integrity and also calls for the use of best available scientific information, but it does not provide a mechanism to connect these two crucial aspects of forest planning.
2. Creating scientifically credible conservation strategies can require more than scientists passing their studies to national forest planning teams or writing white papers synthesizing those results, as valuable as that may be.
3. Creating these strategies requires the conversion of scientific findings and syntheses into planning frameworks, whether they are a system of reserves and matrix management for the California spotted owl, a landscape management plan for the Canada lynx, or a general conservation strategy for aquatic ecosystems. Creating these strategies without heavy involvement of the scientific community is fraught with peril as we saw in the foundering of national forest plans in the late 1980s.
4. Until now, these conservation strategies have been largely developed outside the forest planning process, whether in science teams working with Forest Service personnel or regulatory agencies, or scientists working on their own.
5. These conservation strategies can sharply constrain forest plan choices. Yet they receive very little acknowledgement in Forest Service descriptions of the forest planning process.
6. At a minimum, the need for these scientifically credible conservation strategies and the important role they play in national forest planning should be acknowledged. Better yet, institutional mechanisms should be developed that bring this key facet of forest planning into the forest planning process.

A degree of regional guidance is provided by the National Marine Fisheries Service (NMFS) and the US Fish and Wildlife Service (USFWS), the regulatory agencies implementing the ESA by means of the recovery plans they develop for federally listed threatened or endangered species. Through species recovery planning, these agencies have taken over much of the regional planning for biodiversity across the United States, where wide-ranging species have been federally listed as threatened or endangered; national forest planners will need to draw heavily on recovery plans developed by NMFS and USFWS for their ecological sustainability frameworks.

Guidance by the NMFS and the USFWS recovery plans notwithstanding, more regional guidance will likely be necessary for many at-risk species and for the ecological processes that support these species. These include federally listed species without recovery plans, candidate species for federal listing, and species designated by regional foresters as being of conservation concern. Where these species are wide ranging, it is difficult to imagine how the planning process on an individual national forest can develop a credible conservation strategy. This issue has haunted national forest planning for decades, and the 2012 planning rule does not appear to resolve it.

A related, and perhaps even more difficult issue concerns how to ensure that any conservation strategies for species and ecosystems that are developed by the Forest Service can withstand scientific scrutiny. These strategies, which often have been created by ad hoc teams of scientists working alone or in cooperation with agency specialists, have both upended and assisted forest planning. While the planning rule calls for the use of the best available science, it is not clear how scientifically credible strategies will or should be created or updated (Box 20.8).

**How Will the "Natural Range of Variation" Be Interpreted under a Changing Climate?** As we discussed above, the 2012 planning rule commits the Forest Service to maintaining and restoring the ecological integrity of national forest ecosystems, where ecological integrity is defined as "the quality or condition of an ecosystem when its dominant ecological characteristics (for example, composition, structure, function, connectivity, and species composition and diversity) *occur within the natural range of variation and can withstand and recover from most perturbations imposed by natural environmental dynamics or human influence*" (36 CFR 219.19, emphasis added). While it can be argued that maintaining forests within their natural range of variation would enable them to withstand and recover from disturbance in a stable environment, what about disturbances that occur in a changing world, such as a world with a changing climate? In this situation, some scientists have argued that identifying "natural" with "historical"

will not be helpful as a guide to sustainability (Millar et al., 2007), while others have argued that we should utilize the future range of variation to temper our reliance on the historical range (Stine et al., 2014). The 2015 planning directives attempt to find a pathway through this debate.

The planning directives emphasize maintenance and restoration of ecological integrity. However, the directives also acknowledge the complexity of achieving these goals in a changing world (USDA Forest Service, 2015, Ch. 20, p. 58, emphasis added):

- "In light of possible changes in species composition under the effects of climate change and with a focus on restoration," *the Forest Service will design "plan components to provide ecological conditions to sustain functional ecosystems based on a future viewpoint. Functional ecosystems are those that sustain critical ecological functions over time to provide ecosystem services."*

- "Functional restoration may be necessary to restore the abiotic and biotic processes in degraded ecosystems. Functional restoration focuses on the underlying processes that may be degraded, regardless of the structural condition of the ecosystem. As such, *a functionally restored ecosystem may have different structure and composition than the past reference condition."*

Interdisciplinary teams developing forest plans are directed to design plan components that (to the degree it is within the Forest Service capability) (USDA Forest Service, 2015, Ch. 20, p. 59):

- "Provide ecological conditions to restore, establish, and maintain functioning ecosystems on National Forest System land that can support multiple uses and provide a broad range of goods and services."

- "Restore, establish, and maintain functional ecosystems that will have greater adaptive capacity to withstand stressors and recover from disturbances, especially changing and uncertain environmental conditions and extreme weather events."

- "Provide ecological conditions to sustain ecosystems that maintain the diversity of plant and animal communities and the persistence of native species in the plan area."

- "Take into account the effects of a changing climate in these designs."

The planning directives emphasize the importance to planning of the concept of natural range of variation as described above (USDA Forest Service, 2015, Ch. 20):

- It provides an understanding of how ecosystems are dynamic and change over time.

- It is fundamental in strategic thinking and planning about ecological integrity, even if restoration to historical conditions is not the management goal, or even possible on parts of the plan area.

- It helps managers understand an ecosystem's likely future character, based on projections of climate regimes.

- It provides guidance on how to restore an ecosystem's structural and functional properties that will enable it to persist into the future, providing an ecosystem (coarse-filter) approach to maintaining the persistence of native species.

Further, the 2015 planning directives call for the interdisciplinary team to consider the role of the natural range of variation as follows:

- "In general, where appropriate, the Interdisciplinary Team should design plan components aimed at maintaining or restoring the natural range of variation of specific key ecosystem characteristics needed to promote ecosystem integrity in the plan area" (USDA Forest Service, 2015, Ch. 20, p. 59).

- "For specific areas within an ecosystem, the Responsible Official may determine that it is not appropriate, practical, possible, or desirable to contribute to restoring conditions to the natural range of variation" (USDA Forest Service 2015, Ch. 20, p. 60). Examples of these situations include (USDA Forest Service, 2015, Ch. 20, p. 60):

  ○ "The system is so degraded that restoration is not possible."

  ○ "The system is no longer capable of sustaining key ecosystem characteristics identified as common in the past based upon likely future environmental conditions."

  ○ "Conditions that rarely or never occurred in the past, but that can be managed for in the future, will better contribute to long-term ecosystem sustainability and adaptation to the effects of a changing climate."

- If past conditions relative to the natural range of variation are not appropriate, practical, possible, or desirable approaches, interdisciplinary teams should "design plan components based on a general scientific and ecological understanding of the conditions that would sustain key ecosystem characteristics and sustain at-risk species" (USDA Forest Service, 2015, Ch. 20, p. 60).

Here we have one of the biggest quandaries facing national forest planning: how to deliver on a commitment to maintain and restore natural ecosystems when the underlying conditions under which these systems exist are changing in ways that we can only now begin to understand. *However, the commitment by the Forest Service to provide ecological conditions to sustain ecosystem functions based on a future viewpoint is an insightful approach to addressing this very difficult problem.* Much will need to be learned and an adaptive approach will be essential, but the Forest Service is off to a good start.

**Is Ecological Forest Management Compatible with the Provisions of the NFMA?** At first glance at the provisions of the NFMA, a number of questions can be raised as to whether the Act and the associated planning rule allows ecological forest management, as we have described in this book, to be practiced on the national forests. Three NFMA provisions could be seen as problematic relative to the application of ecological forest management:

1. 16 U.S.C. § 1604(m): "Prior to harvest, stands of trees throughout the National Forest System shall generally have reached the culmination of mean annual increment of growth." Intended to limit regeneration harvest in young stands, this provision could be interpreted to prevent the creation of preforest conditions in stands that have not reached culmination—the most likely source of these activities, given the protected status of most older forests. Fortunately, this clause allows exceptions to this standard "after consideration has been given to the multiple uses of the forest." The 2012 planning directives further state that the provision does not apply to "harvesting of trees on lands not suited for timber production because the type and frequency of harvests are driven by the need to protect multiple use values other than timber production." Also the directives state that a plan may provide for earlier even-aged regeneration harvest where such an exception would "contribute to the plan's desired conditions or objectives. . . . For example, it may be appropriate for a plan to establish shorter even-aged rotations to maintain levels of early seral stages sufficient for wildlife that depend on such habitat conditions" (USDA Forest Service. 2015, Ch. 60, p. 30).

2. 16 U.S.C. § 1604(g)(3)(E)(ii): "There is assurance that such lands can be adequately restocked within five years after harvest." If this clause was interpreted to mean stocking that would enable the establishment of dense stands of conifers, the provision would seem to preclude the long preforest stage important to ecological forest management. However, the planning

directives state that stocking standards "should be based on . . . the desired conditions and objectives of the plan" (USDA Forest Service, 2015, Ch. 60 p. 21), allowing the determination of whether a site is adequately stocked to be related to the goals of the prescription.

3. 16 U.S.C. § 1604(g)(3)(F): "There are established . . . maximum size limits for areas to be cut in one harvest operation." The 2012 planning rule establishes regeneration harvest unit sizes of 40–80 acres for most forest types (36 CFR 219.11[d][4]), reflecting concern about the potential for large clearcuts or other even-aged harvests. However, these limits can be out of sync with the size of historical disturbances, especially in forest types that historically had large, infrequent, high-severity wildfire. Emulating these disturbances might best be done with much larger harvest units, which incorporate significant amounts of grouped and dispersed retention. Fortunately, the responsible Forest Service official may allow for openings larger than the maximum limits described above if that official "determines that larger openings are necessary to help achieve desired ecological conditions in the plan area" (36 CFR 219.11 [d][4][i]).

Thus, we conclude that the provisions of the NFMA do not preclude ecological forest management. We also acknowledge that there may be a significant learning and demonstration process for all of these interpretations and exceptions to be fully implemented.

## Summary

The 2012 planning rule adopts an ecological approach to forest planning that replaces the economic approach of the 1982 rule. The 2012 planning rule makes ecological sustainability

the foundation of national forest planning, builds on that foundation to provide economic and social benefits, views management actions from an ecosystem perspective, and emphasizes public engagement in decision making. Equally important, the regulations call for the Forest Service to consider their actions in the context of the larger landscape in which each national forest is situated.

This new interpretation of the NFMA in the 2012 planning rule and the associated planning directives enables the Forest Service to chart a new path while increasing its discretion to do so. The dominance of the classical sustained yield forestry model is gone. Ecosystem planning with a restoration focus will guide the Forest Service's contributions to sustainability in the context of the larger landscape, and public engagement throughout the planning process will be the order of the day.

In many ways, the 2012 planning rule and associated directives catch up with the evolution of national forest management at the local level across the United States. National forest planning may be able to express a coherent vision for these lands for the first time since passage of the NFMA in 1976 (Box 20.9).

## A Role for Ecological Forest Management in Future National Forest Planning

The management objectives for national forests, as laid down in the 2012 planning rule, are highly congruent with the principles and practices of ecological forestry. Indeed, we would argue that the only way that those objectives can be achieved is by utilizing ecologically based management approaches! Both the planning rule and ecological forestry view forests as ecosystems rather than simply as stands of trees, and both share the objective of restoring and maintaining ecological integrity. At the same time, both

---

**Box 20.9** Sustainability in national forest planning—the evolution of a central idea

Looking back through the history of planning on the national forests, we see an evolution of approaches to ensure the sustainability of forests and the benefits they provide. During the first two-thirds of the 20th century, the Forest Service emphasized sustained yield timber harvest and achievement of the regulated forest as the way to sustain forests and the benefits they provide (to provide for sustainability in all its facets—ecological, economic, and social sustainability in modern terminology). The 1982 planning rule portrayed national forest planning as balancing three aspects of sustainability (ecological, economic, social) (see Figure 1.1, left-hand figure), especially meshing ecological considerations with achievement of economic and social goals. Sustainable timber supplies were seen as an important vehicle for achieving the integration of ecological, economic, and

social goals, and trade-offs among achievement of the three aspects of sustainability were the focus of forest planning. As indicated by the degree of each circle outside the area of overlap, much analysis was done without concern for compatibility with the other facets of sustainability. For example, the 1982 rule called for analyses that maximized different resource outputs without concern for their ecological effects. This approach created the illusion of choices that did not exist and created political pressures that greatly retarded the acceptance of realistic plans. In the 2012 planning rule, ecological sustainability might be viewed as the foundation of the benefits people seek from the national forests. Building on this foundation, contributions to economic and social sustainability are made (See Figure 1.1, right-hand figure).

acknowledge the importance of activities that achieve economic and social as well as environmental goals.

The 2012 planning rule and ecological forestry have similar landscape-level perspectives. A credible interpretation of the planning rule is that it seeks to create landscapes that are *shades-of-green* in which all elements of the landscape patchwork on a national forest contribute to ecological function, as discussed in Chapter 5. The planning rule emphasizes a coarse-filter approach to conservation of biological diversity with species-specific (i.e., fine-filter) elements added when the coarse-filter approach is judged inadequate. Again, this is very much in the spirit of ecological forestry, where the conservation of biological diversity—habitat needs and connectivity—is integrated into an ecosystem-based plan.

Finally, both the 2012 planning rule and ecological forestry emphasize an adaptive management approach. National Forest plans are to be periodically updated to incorporate management experience and new scientific knowledge as well as to accommodate changing social objectives.

In sum, we believe that ecological forestry can help the Forest Service navigate many issues facing our national forests. We highlight some of these issues below, and discuss the role ecological forestry might play in addressing them.

## Addressing Widespread Concerns about Wildfires and Utilizing Their Beneficial Effects

Wildfire risk to communities and homes near national forests has become a major social issue, as we discussed earlier in this chapter. It is also becoming increasingly clear that mechanical treatment and prescribed fire will be inadequate to address the backlog of restoration needs on the forests of the Interior West, especially in designated Wilderness, roadless areas, and other relatively inaccessible parts of these forests (North et al., 2015b). Occurrence of large wildfires is a near certainty. Forest planning can play an important role here through zoning the forest relative to how fire will be managed, and providing guidance on risk assessment and operational standards.

Historically, strategic zoning on the national forests focused on distinguishing between lands suited for timber production and lands that were unsuitable. This division was codified in the NFMA, and was a centerpiece of national forest planning under the 1982 planning rule. While the 2012 planning rule also calls for this division, its importance has greatly diminished, and significant restoration harvests could potentially occur on lands managed for other values and uses.

Recognizing the importance and many risks of wildfire management, some national forests have begun (at least informally) to delineate three zones that require different approaches to wildfire management in frequent-fire forests as we illustrated in Chapter 13 (Figure 13.23):

1. A zone closest to communities and homes, where planning focuses on project design, and fuel treatments are prioritized to reduce fire intensity, fire extent, and ignition of homes and other structures. This planning often covers both federal and nonfederal lands through community fire plans. Both mechanical treatment and prescribed fire may be used in fuel treatments; wildfires are usually extinguished immediately.

2. A zone in the backcountry far away from communities and homes, covering designated wilderness, roadless, and other inaccessible areas. In these areas, forests are restored through managed wildfire, if at all.

3. An area between these two zones, where forest restoration is the goal, but all three tools may be employed—mechanical treatment, prescribed fire, and, very sparingly, managed wildfire.

As another example of this zoning, consider the federal lands of Colorado, where WUI areas are interwoven with the federal lands (Color Plate 13.2). Many Colorado counties show up as high priority for fuels management and for community wildfire planning and coordination efforts (Figure 20.6), and a number of large wildfires have occurred there in recent years (Color Plate 13.2).

In many states, fuel treatments near communities and houses are well underway, in part because of broad community support for such efforts. From an ecological forestry standpoint, however, these prescriptions often leave much to be desired, with a focus on classic fuel reduction strategies—wide and fairly uniform spacing of residual trees and felling of snags. Alternative approaches that integrate ecological principles into fuel reduction, such as creating spatially heterogeneous outcomes and retaining old trees, should be considered more widely. (See Box 13.7 for more discussion).

Restoring forest resistance is a major restoration need in national forestlands between the community/residential zone and the backcountry. In many instances, this effort has shifted from fuels reduction to forest restoration with a fuels component (see Chapters 12 and 13) to better reflect the overall emphasis on restoration across the landscape. Ecological forestry provides a natural vehicle for addressing restoration goals here, using a combination of mechanical treatment and prescribed fire. However logical, we can safely assume that debates will continue over where and how ecological forestry should be applied, especially where such treatments would generate substantial quantities of commercial products.

Managed wildfire is potentially one important tool in restoration efforts, especially in the more remote areas; at this stage, though, it might best be called a work-in-progress—

officially encouraged,[15] but difficult to broadly implement. Suppression to contain and, if possible, to extinguish fire, when possible, is still predominant on the national forests (North et al., 2015a). Many considerations favor such actions. People in the path of the fires argue for quick actions, and the negative health effects of smoke limit the ability to allow fires where their smoke can drift into population centers. Also, public reaction to the escape of a managed wildfire leads to risk-averse management, and the long history of fire suppression has deeply embedded the need for such action in fire-fighting personnel (North et al., 2015a; Caukin et al., 2015).

However, policies regarding fire suppression on national forests have been undergoing significant change, and wildfires often do burn large acreages on the national forests, such as occurred in the West in 2017. Allowing wildfires to burn in wildland areas is increasingly done intentionally these days, a trend that is often necessitated by the needs to prioritize use of limited fire-fighting resources elsewhere and to reduce safety risks for fire fighters. Resources are often insufficient to aggressively attack multiple wildfires, which may be underway simultaneously, due to regional weather conditions or major lightning storms. The priority in such cases is using fire-fighting resources to halt the spread of fires into homes, communities, critical infrastructure, and municipal watersheds. Suppression of backcountry fires typically has a lower priority under those circumstances. In *fire years* when scores of fires are burning simultaneously, *managed wildfire* may consist mostly of *tending* or *herding* wildland fires to keep them from endangering people, damaging infrastructure, or destroying vital natural resources while allowing fire to move through the backcountry at will.

Whether such policies contribute to restoration objectives will depend upon the forest type, restoration goals, and burning conditions associated with the wildfire. For example, moderate- to high-severity wildfire behavior in forests subject to episodic disturbances can provide conditions for development of high-quality early successional ecosystems

(the preforest stage), if left unsalvaged. In frequent-fire forest landscapes wildfires can have varying effects. Low- to moderate-intensity wildfire behavior in frequent-fire forest ecosystems can help reduce tree densities and fuel loadings and favor fire-tolerant species—restoration objectives. On the other hand, intense stand-replacement fire in such forests can eliminate critical structures, such as old-growth trees. With regard to frequent-fire forests it is important to note that the wildfires that are likely to contribute most to restoration are usually going to be the easiest wildfires to suppress. We would conclude that with lengthening fire seasons, managed wildfire will, of necessity, become increasingly important in forest restoration efforts; hence, restoration goals will need to be given more attention in suppression strategies.

## Developing a Comprehensive Post-fire Salvage Policy

With the expectation of increased future wildfire, the issue of post-fire salvage will become increasingly important in federal forest management. The occurrence of severe wildfires in areas planned for restoration significantly alters the ecological circumstances and introduces questions about salvage logging and its potential effects on ecosystems.

In general, salvage is carried out primarily to recover economic values, and makes little direct contribution to ecological recovery (Lindenmayer, Burton, & Franklin, 2008). The burned forest provides habitat for a variety of animal species, such as black-backed woodpeckers (*Picoides arcticus*), and retains significant ecological values, including the structural and functional legacies of snags and down logs, which can persist for the many decades that pass before the forest again generates large dead wood. Salvage may eliminate much of this legacy, disrupt vegetative recovery, and cause damage to soils and streams (Lindenmayer et al., 2008).

Conversely, contemporary wildfires in densely stocked stands in what were historically frequent-fire forests often generate substantially more dead woody fuels than would have existed historically. Such an event would create *novel forest conditions* with little historical precedent. The dead fine fuels disappear relatively quickly, but significant amounts of the dead medium and larger fuels persist for decades, making it difficult to conduct prescribed burns due to high fuel loads. Hence, some removal of fire-generated fuels may be ecologically justified (Franklin & Agee, 2003). Under an ecological forestry approach, large and old ponderosa pine, western larch, and Douglas-fir snags generally should be retained because of their persistence and long-term value as wildlife habitat, along with any structural features that normally would have been retained as part of a restoration treatment of a green forest.

15 The National Cohesive Fire Management Strategy encourages the selective use of managed wildfire to accomplish ecological objectives. Managing wildfire for resource objectives and ecological purposes refers to a strategic choice to use unplanned ignitions to achieve resource management objectives. As pointed out in USDA-USDI (2014): "Federal fire policies traditionally restricted use to Federal wilderness areas, national parks, or other remote areas under specific conditions or circumstances. These restrictions were intended to reduce risk and avoid potentially negative impacts or consequences to lands of other ownership. Guidance issued in 2009 has led to expanded application of this method to manage wildland fuels. In contrast, most state and local jurisdictions are statutorily constrained to provide full wildfire suppression due to values at risk, human-caused fires, and protection of private lands. Like prescribed fire, allowing wildfires to burn for the purposes of ecosystem restoration or hazard reduction has inherent risk. These risks must be balanced with the potential benefits on an individual incident basis, which requires both pre-incident planning at the landscape scale and sophisticated incident management."

If a decision is made to salvage dead trees, a first principle under an ecological forestry approach is to minimize impacts to ecological values. As an example, approximately the same quantity and type of dead wood should be retained on-site that would have existed had a stand-replacing wildfire occurred in a historical or restored stand; that is, the larger and more decay-resistant trees (snags) should be retained. Material removed in the salvage would be small and medium-sized stems of more decay-prone species (e.g., grand/white fir). Salvage needs to occur promptly to capture the economic value of such material, which emphasizes the importance of having policies and contingency plans in place that cover post-disturbance activities. *Developing a comprehensive post-fire salvage policy is one of the most important issues that forest planning can address.* Of course, any salvage operation needs to limit negative impacts on soil and aquatic values.

Finally, landscape-level perspectives are essential in salvage planning. Landscape considerations include provisions for wildlife species that require standing and down dead wood as habitat, and the retention of large wood as integral structural components of terrestrial, riparian, and aquatic ecosystems and geomorphological processes (e.g., sediment retention). Such considerations are likely to necessitate the retention of significant unsalvaged areas. It is also critical to assess the distribution of various types of legacies, such as large snags and dense snag patches, across the burned landscape. Because of economic concerns, salvage efforts may be focused on limited areas within the landscapes that have high levels of dead wood legacies. This may result in the burned landscape being *cherry picked* for big wood; from an ecological perspective, *high-grading* the burned landscape for its best dead wood legacies is counterproductive, and should be avoided.

## Conserving Old Trees and Forests

As we have emphasized throughout this book, old trees provide the structural backbone of many forest ecosystems. Their importance to the ecological integrity of federal forests should be acknowledged and their conservation made a first priority of forest management. The scientific knowledge and management guidelines needed to identify old forests and old trees now exists, so there are no major impediments to recognizing old trees as a part of routine management.

Conservation of old forests and trees requires fundamentally different approaches in the different forest archetypes, as discussed in Chapters 3 and 4. In forests created historically through infrequent, severe disturbances, remnant patches of old forests should be reserved; further harvest of such forests is difficult to justify ecologically. In frequent-fire forests that still have a population of older trees, removal of some younger trees may be needed in order to restore more resistant (and characteristic) forest conditions, a key component of which is older trees. Old trees should be retained in restoration activities in both live and dead forms for both ecological and social reasons (Franklin & Johnson, 2012; Franklin et al., 2013).

Many existing old forests where infrequent or episodic severe disturbances have dominated (see Chapter 3) have not been substantially modified in composition or structure by modern human management. Silvicultural treatments of such forests are not required to sustain them, and their diminished abundance argues for their conservation, including efforts to suppress wildfires. In general, treatments to reduce fuel loadings are not ecologically justified, since they alter the fundamental ecological character of these stands.

Frequent-fire forests containing populations of old trees, on the other hand, typically have been immensely changed due to modern human activities, including elimination of fire as well as by extensive grazing by domestic livestock, timber harvesting, and establishment of plantations. Due to their density, composition, and fuel loadings, many of these forests are currently at high risk of uncharacteristic stand-replacement wildfire, as well as drought and insect outbreaks. Accelerated large-scale programs to restore resistant conditions in these forests should be a high priority. Such approaches are completely consistent with actions to prepare these forests for expected climate change, which includes increased temperatures, drought, and wildfire.

Many forests fall between these two archetypes, as we discussed in Chapter 3. Such circumstances can be recognized and accommodated by accepting that these intermediate types—from an ecological perspective—can be appropriately managed by a mixture of these approaches, depending on circumstances. The potential impacts of climate change, which will make these forests drier and more prone to drought and fire, argue for leaning toward approaching them as frequent-fire forests in order to increase their resistance and resilience.

## Providing Diverse Early Successional Ecosystems and the Biodiversity They Sustain

Much of the biodiversity associated with forest landscapes depends on high-quality early successional habitat, whether this habitat is in the pine barrens of New Jersey, the subalpine forests of the Rocky Mountains, or the Douglas-fir forests of the Pacific Northwest. While the characteristics and longevity of this stage depend on the forest type, it should not be ignored. As described in Chapter 3, early successional ecosystems are explicitly not young forests or plantations; rather, they are a highly diverse, preforest stage of plant and animal life that precedes development of a closed forest canopy. While trees are often present, they do not dominate the ecosystem. The preforest is an incredibly rich biological system as evidenced by the diversity of plant and animal species and numbers and complexity of food webs, as well as the structural remnants or legacies from the pre-disturbance forest (e.g., trees, snags, and logs).

Provision for early successional ecosystems on federal lands must be addressed during forest planning. Beyond their recognized contribution to biodiversity, maintaining early successional ecosystems as one of the stages of forest development helps provide a diverse set of stand conditions, which is one strategy for dealing with the uncertainties of coming climate change. Policies on early successional ecosystems need to integrate the active creation of such habitats with the early successional habitat that is created by natural disturbances.

Unfortunately, strong identification of any management that creates openings with clearcutting has generally caused a cessation of harvest activities that might provide for diverse early seral ecosystems on national forests. Ecological forestry can provide the mechanism to restore creation of openings to the mainstream of management activities, with its provision for sustaining critical structural legacies through retention harvesting approaches.

## Conserving Water Resources

An original reason for creation of the national forest systems was to secure favorable conditions of water flows. Impetus for additions to the national forest system by purchase of private lands was provided by the need to protect headwaters of rivers, primarily in the eastern United States; headwaters of many western rivers were already protected by the original national forests.

In the past few decades, concerns with protection of water resources on the national forests has focused primarily on maintaining and restoring water quality and providing habitat for fish and other aquatic organisms. Exemplary activities include provision of riparian buffers to shade streams and provide woody debris, preventing sediment from entering streams, and mitigating the effect of timber harvest on storm flows. Recently, though, there has been renewed interest in increasing total water flows for agriculture, protection of aquatic resources, domestic water use, and other uses. There is also concern that warming temperatures associated with climate change will reduce the area where snow accumulates and lead to earlier snow melt. Where snow is the major source of water resources, as in much of the western United States, earlier snow melt means earlier spring runoff and lower summer flows. Thus, there is interest in augmenting both the total amount and the timing of water running off of the national forests.

Trees transpire immense amounts of water and, as a generality, the more leaf area on an acre the greater the amount of transpiration, resulting in reduced inputs to groundwater and reduced streamflows (see Chapter 2). Ecological forest management practices can have significant positive effects on water yield, as suggested in these examples:

- Reducing forest densities in frequent-fire forests, using the restoration principles discussed in Chapter 4, can significantly reduce leaf area, transpiration and increase overall water yields (e.g., see Kirkman & Jack, 2017). In addition, creation of honeycomb patterns of forest openings in forests subject to winter snowpack accumulation can increase snow accumulation and slow spring melt and runoff.

- Deciduous hardwoods are more conservative of water than evergreen conifers, in part because the deciduous hardwoods have leaves for only a part of the year, thereby limiting transpiration. Increasing the percentage of hardwoods in mixed forests can increase water yields (as well as achieve other ecological benefits). Conversion of deciduous hardwood-dominated forests to conifers, on the other hand, is not advisable from the standpoint of water yields (e.g., Swank, Swift, & Douglas, 1988).

- Older trees are generally more conservative of water than younger trees, resulting in significantly less transpiration at comparable or even much greater leaf masses. Consequently, converting mature and old forests to dense young conifer plantations can significantly reduce stream flows, particularly during critical low flow periods (e.g., Perry & Jones, 2017). Maintaining older forests also provides other benefits to stream systems, such as in delivery of large and decay resistant coarse woody debris.

## Recognizing the Importance of Financial and Employment Benefits in Ecologically Grounded Actions

Experiences during the last 20 years have shown that management programs on federal forests need to provide a demonstrable ecological benefit to be broadly supported and successful, such as accelerating structural development in plantations or restoring resistance in frequent-fire forests. In general, commitments to ecological restoration have gone a long way toward helping the US Forest Service regain public trust and advance their new mission. As described above, the 2012 planning rule reinforces this approach with its call for an approach to forest management that restores and maintains ecological integrity. However, many of these activities will need to generate a financial return to be viable, and that need may affect the treatment proposed. Also, funds may be needed to do actions such as meadow or riparian restoration. In addition, there may be a need to provide wood to the local mill, whose purchases help support the restoration and who provides employment in the local community. Federal managers need to acknowledge these important financial and employment considerations in their proposals, where they exist, so they can avoid trying to justify activities solely on the basis of ecological benefits when they also have financial and employment goals.

This need to acknowledge economic considerations in management activities surfaces when a national forest identifies land suitable for timber production in forest planning, as required in the 2012 planning rule. It is hard to understand why lands would be classified as suitable for timber production without an economic goal. More generally, the planning rule calls for contributions to economic and social sustainability. Thus, tailoring restoration and other activities to provide these contributions, consistent with maintaining ecological integrity, is part of achieving the goals expressed in the 2012 planning rule. It is also the ecological forest management approach we have discussed throughout this book.

## A Role for Ecological Forest Management on Other Federal Forests

Our observations described here, regarding the applicability of ecological forest management principles to the national forests also apply to other federal forestlands. These include forests on the national wildlife refuges managed by the US Fish and Wildlife Service, on public domain and revested Oregon and California railroad lands (O&C lands) managed by the Bureau of Land Management, and even on some actively managed areas within national parks. In fact, some of the best current examples of ecological forest management are on federal wildlife refuges and O&C lands (see Chapter 4).

*Part V*
**Summary
and Conclusions**

*Long ago our livelihood and survival were placed in nature's hands and so we have lived by nature's laws. Nature to the best of its ability was our caretaker. Today nature remains our provider, but we must accept our obligations as caretakers of the land. [We] . . . need to care for and heal the land that has for so long cared for us* — JAMIE PINKHAM

# CHAPTER 21

# Potential Contributions of Ecological Forest Management

In this chapter we review some important principles of ecological forest management and consider potential contributions that this management philosophy can make toward resolving major 21st-century challenges to natural resource management. We also consider policy changes that could encourage adoption of ecologically based management approaches at scales ranging from the local to the global.

We remind the reader of our belief that ecological forest management is and must always be viewed as continuously evolving. We do not think any other perspective is credible in such a rapidly changing natural and social environment as well as a world in which new science and management experience are accumulating exponentially.

## Overall Goals and Philosophy of Ecological Forest Management (EFM)

In EFM, we seek to develop science-based ecological management strategies that integrate multiple environmental, economic, and social goals while sustaining the integrity of forest ecosystems and landscapes. Fundamental to the approach is the view of forests as complex and diverse ecosystems providing a broad array of valuable services, including various kinds of products, and not simply as collections of trees. All forests are viewed as *working forests*, including reserves, because all are providing important ecosystem services essential to human and other global life.

## Principles Underlying EFM

Consideration and integration of environmental, economic, and social goals is a basic premise of EFM. *However, given the great uncertainties in the 21st century, we simultaneously seek approaches and outcomes that will reduce risks to the forest resource and increase future management options.* Hence, forest conditions that increase resilience and adap-

tive capacity will be favored over those that expose forests to higher risks of vulnerability, such as to major disturbances and invasive species. Similarly, we will try to create forest conditions that increase future societal options rather than limiting them. An example of *increasing options* would be to develop forest stands and landscapes that offer a broader array of potential products, such as might be provided by a mixture of tree species and qualities. Another example of increasing options would be to create forest stands and landscapes that offer a diversity of management pathways. Developing forest stands and landscapes that have high levels of resilience and adaptive capacity can contribute importantly to the goals of reducing risk and increasing options.

*Management approaches in EFM are based on natural models and, as noted, have the overall goal of sustaining the ecological integrity or capacities of forest ecosystems.* Those capacities, current and potential, are measured by their biological richness, structural complexity, and functional capabilities, which also underpin the inherent resilience and adaptive capacity of forest ecosystems.

*Given the overarching goal of maintaining ecological integrity, plans or approaches that seek to optimize any single function or output generally are avoided in EFM.* Experience has shown that efforts to maximize a single good or service, such as timber production or carbon sequestration, inevitably result in marginalizing or eliminating other important ecosystem services.

*Economic concerns are an important consideration in EFM, as they ultimately must be for anyone that undertakes management of forest properties.* Acquisition and management of forests necessarily involves economics, even when dealing with forest properties created and managed as ecological preserves. However, basic economic assumptions of ecological forestry are different from those of production forestry, as we discussed in Chapter 9.

*Most fundamentally, approaches based on EFM challenge the economic paradigm that views the forest as capital that can be transformed into other forms of capital as needed to maintain a desired rate of return. Rather, some elements of the forest are viewed as critical natural capital needed to provide the ecosystem services people seek*

*Jerry Franklin and Norm Johnson defending their ecological forestry ideas on a field trip in southwest Oregon.*

*and, therefore, require conservation.* Examples include biological legacies that will be left at harvest and exceptional ecological and cultural areas.

In addition, the multiple, interconnected goals of most landowners are recognized, largely negating a role for net present value as the primary guide to decision making. *While managers using ecological approaches will typically seek financial returns as part of the management program, these returns generally will be most usefully measured by income rather than return on capital.*

The economic value (that is, value to humans) of the many types of ecosystem services from the forest is recognized in EFM, as is described in Chapter 10. *However, economic valuation in EFM is done with a variety of mechanisms, of which conventional appraisal is only one, and also recognizes the intrinsic value of ecosystems to exist in their own right.*

*Utilizing an adaptive process is important in EFM in which relevant new information is systematically gathered, assessed, and incorporated into management procedures and practices* (Chapter 11). This includes new scientific information, modifications in societal goals and tolerances, and changing forest conditions. Special attention also is paid to information and issues that could affect foundational premises underpinning the initial management approaches.

*Engagement with the diversity of interested and affected stakeholders is characteristic of EFM,* particularly—but not exclusively—on public lands. Negotiation is a fact of life in most forestry in the 21st century, whether it be with interested family members, company boards, or the public (Chapter 8). EFM benefits from a broad range of engagements including—but not confined to—participation in goal-setting processes (such as long-term planning efforts) and review of activities (such as specific timber sales). Effective EFM, especially on public lands, needs active engagement of interested stakeholders, including members of local communities, in monitoring and research activities, which will contribute to stewardship and provide experience, educational value, and employment.

*Forest planning helps landowners, managers, and stakeholders understand the possibilities and trade-offs associated with simultaneous pursuit of ecological, financial, and other goals (Chapters 18 and 19).* Planning models under EFM utilize an understanding of the natural history of the forest in developing management choices and favor outcomes that reduce risk and increase options. Quantitative planning generally simulates potential actions over a relatively short planning horizon, in recognition of a changing and uncertain future. Beyond conserving critical natural capital, sustainability criteria often include achieving a distribution of the forest among development stages and conserving economic productivity.

## Principles Underlying Silvicultural Activities in EFM

Silviculture is the human manipulation of forests to achieve specific outcomes, and in EFM silviculture begins with an ecosystem-based vision of the forest. The dynamic nature of forests is always recognized in EFM as are the relationships of functional capabilities to different forest conditions—such as levels of structural complexity and compositional richness. Silvicultural activities build upon the variability and dynamics of existing forest stands to create and maintain the complexity and diversity needed to sustain the ecological integrity of forest landscapes.

In EFM silvicultural treatments are based on knowledge of the natural and social history of the forest ecosystems and landscapes that are to be managed, including their constituent species. Silvicultural treatments in EFM consider many aspects of forest biota including herbs and shrubs as well as trees; dead as well as live tree structures; understory as well as overstory; and the spatial aspects of structural diversity. Most importantly, silvicultural treatments are based on a thorough knowledge of the stands and landscapes where management is being undertaken and build on the opportunities that those stands and landscapes provide.

**Silvicultural Principles at the Stand Level**    Four principles underpin silvicultural treatments at the stand level in EFM (Chapter 4). *The first principle is to provide for continuity between forest generations in biological richness, functional capabilities, and structure.* This is based on the natural model of biological legacies (Chapter 3) and involves leaving elements of pre-harvest forest to be incorporated into the post-harvest forest. The kind, amount, and distribution of the legacies depend on the nature of the forest and overall management goals. However, the underlying goal always is to provide for continuity in biota (plants, animals and other organisms), structure, and function in contrast to effectively creating discontinuities as a result of harvest.

*A second silvicultural principle is to manage established forests in ways that create, restore, and maintain forests that—appropriate to the forest type—are structurally complex and biologically rich.* Structural complexity relates to both diversity of structural features, such as live and dead tree structures of varying sizes and conditions, and to spatial patterns, such as clump-based and other nonuniform spatial distributions of structures.

*A third principle is to conduct silvicultural interventions at intervals that are ecologically grounded.* Ecological goals provide the beginning point in the analysis of appropriate intervals for intervention. For example, how frequently are interventions needed to create open conditions for regeneration of light-requiring species? How much time is needed to develop the desired levels of structural complexity? How frequently do prescribed burns need to be conducted to maintain desired understory conditions and fuel loadings? Economic and other social considerations also are important factors in selecting intervals for treatments. Importantly, the emphasis in EFM on creating and maintaining forests with multiple age classes and on developing and retaining larger, older living and dead structures (e.g., old trees and large well-decayed snags and logs) actually provides much more flexibility in terms of the timing of silvicultural interventions than exists under even-aged management regimes.

*A fourth principle is to plan and implement silvicultural activities in the context of larger (e.g., landscape) spatial scales.* Most forest goals are only fully achieved at spatial scales larger than individual stands (Chapter 5). For example, multiple stands differing in structural development may be needed to maintain the full array of forest-related biodiversity. As another example, achieving more fire-resistant and resilient landscapes cannot be accomplished by treating a single stand. Hence, it is necessary to manage individual stands in the context of an overall plan for the landscape as a whole, a topic that segues to the next section.

### Silvicultural Principles at Landscape and Larger Spatial Scales

Four additional principles provide the basis for silvicultural treatments at larger spatial scales (Chapter 5). *The first principle is to create and maintain the heterogeneity of larger landscapes so as to provide the diversity of preforest and forest conditions required to maintain larger spatial scale functionality and all components of forest biodiversity.*

*A second principle is to recognize areas within managed landscapes that have exceptional ecological or cultural value and manage them in ways that will protect and sustain those values* (Chapter 5). Aquatic environments are among the most common and important specialized ecological features in most forested landscapes. Other features include unique habitats (e.g., caves and cliffs), nonforested habitats (e.g., meadows), migration routes, remnant natural forests and old trees, and areas of cultural importance to both indigenous and modern cultures. Of course, such features also need to be recognized and given appropriate attention when they are embedded within a managed stand.

*A third principle is to understand and accommodate landscape threshold values for conditions that can have critical impacts on landscape-level ecosystem functions* (Chapter 5). Examples of threshold conditions to avoid might include such activities as concentrated timber harvesting or road construction, which could result in cumulative negative effects on hydrologic regimes and water quality. Alternatively, thresholds might involve having target or minimum levels for important structures (e.g., large well-decayed snags) or conditions (e.g., non-tree-dominated openings) that cannot be addressed at the stand level.

*A fourth principle is to seek to create landscapes that are shades-of-green, meaning landscapes in which essentially all constituent patches or stands contribute to the goal of maintaining the ecological functionality of the landscape* (Chapter 5). Typically some of the ecological content within a patch includes important structural features that provide critical habitat for organisms and facilitate their movement through the landscape.

## Principles Underlying Forest Management Planning in EFM

Forest management planning has traditionally been based on timber production models that emphasized sustained yield and movement toward a regulated forest, while assuming a stable and largely unchanging future. Nature would be controlled and natural processes were not a major concern. More recently, forest planning has generally been grounded in the language and concepts of economics, while still assuming a relatively stable future and with ecological considerations as constraints (see Chapters 17, 18, and 20 for more discussion).

With EFM, we rethought our approach to forest planning—one that is grounded in the principles of ecological silviculture, multiple goals, the concept of critical natural capital, the embedding of forest planning within a social process, and a view of the future as changing and uncertain (see Chapter 18 for the general approach and Chapter 19 for application to a family forest). Key planning principles are to:

- *Start with an understanding of the natural history of your forest.* Historical forest dynamics, species, and structures provide vital information on forest capabilities and possibilities.

- *Recognize the legal, economic, social, and land use context in which planning will occur, including the people and groups that have influence over your potential success.* Without such recognition, planning processes have little chance of success. A consideration of the larger landscape in which your forest sits should be included.

- *Develop an engagement strategy for the different people and groups that have influence and interest, tailored to your relationship with them. That engagement can vary from informing them to collaborating with them.*

- *Surface the variety of ecological, economic, and social goals for the forest being studied.* [1] Ignoring important

---

1 Under structured decision making, which we employed in Chapters 18 and 19, these goals are called either fundamental objectives or means objectives. See Chapter 18 for more explanation.

goals, even if they are difficult to consider, can derail the planning process.

- *Identify and conserve critical natural capital. This natural capital includes special places,* such as old-growth groves, riparian areas, biodiversity hot-spots, and other areas of ecological or cultural significance, and types of biota, such as rare tree or shrub species and old-growth trees. Walking the land to find and protect these resources is a vital step in planning the future of a forest. *In addition, the natural capital that should be conserved at harvest needs to be specified, including the type, amount, and distribution of biological legacies.*

- *Develop sustainability criteria that will guide and limit the actions that will be taken.* Beyond conserving critical natural capital as described above, sustainability criteria are needed to help develop and evaluate a proposed scenario, especially forest-wide criteria such as achieving a distribution of the forest among different development stages, maintaining options, and conserving the economic productivity of the forest.

- *Craft prescriptions for management of different forest types and conditions in the context of maintaining and restoring a complex, diverse forest.* These prescriptions are the building blocks of the alternatives that will be considered; they should provide a variety of choices utilizing the silvicultural principles discussed earlier in this chapter.

- *Utilize an inclusive social process for considering forest management alternatives.* Building and examining alternatives for achievement of the goals, utilizing different combinations of prescriptions, enables the social learning that helps individuals and groups understand possibilities and limitations as they move toward selecting a forest plan. This analysis can be done either informally (primarily using mental simulation and expert opinion) or formally (primarily using quantitative planning models). [2] (See Chapter 18 for a discussion of both naturalistic and structured decision making.) At its best, alternative development is a dynamic, improvisational brainstorming session with much interaction of experts and analysts with decision makers and collaboration partners.

- *Try to reduce trade-offs in achievement of different goals.* The trade-off between ecological and financial goals is a continuing issue in many forest planning problems. More broadly, consideration

of the trade-off in achievement of different goals is often at the heart of the negotiation among those involved in development of a forest plan. Efficiency analysis can help minimize those trade-offs, as shown in the examples in Chapters 18 and 19.

- *Limit detailed planning to the near future.* The classical approach of making detailed quantitative harvest projections for 100 years or more is not very useful in the context of our changing and uncertain world. Detailed planning should cover a small number of decades, as noted in Chapters 17–20, where projections can be made with some confidence and specified ending conditions can express a commitment to sustainability.

- *Set up a structure for continued learning and adaptation.* This process can be relatively simple or very elaborate as described in Chapter 11. However, creating a culture of learning, and social mechanisms to ensure that information counter to expectations can surface and be acted upon is a key to linking planning to successful management.

## Contributions of EFM to Major Issues

With its ecosystem-based perspective, EFM has great potential to contribute to resolution of some of the major challenges in forest resource management. This potential relates to the commitment in EFM to manage forests in ways that sustain multiple values and integrate environmental, economic, and social goals. Ecosystem-based approaches provide the opportunity for win-win outcomes, although compromises are typically required from all stakeholder interests since no single value or function is optimized. We discuss four challenges below: (1) maintaining biodiversity, including threatened and endangered species, in forest landscapes; (2) mitigating and adapting to climate change; (3) supporting rural and small-town communities; and (4) providing an alternative to the choice of reserves or plantations.

## Maintaining Biodiversity in Forest Landscapes

Maintaining biodiversity in forest landscapes is fundamentally about *keeping all the pieces.* As noted in earlier chapters, this is not just about maintaining individual species but also maintaining biotic processes, including important functionalities, such as pollination, and the linkages among species. Although preserves have been touted as the major strategy for sustaining biodiversity, the reality is that the goal of maintaining biodiversity can and must be incorporated into the majority of human-managed landscapes (Chapter 5) (Lindenmayer & Franklin, 2002). *One premise*

---

2  Our examples in Chapters 18 and 19 utilize quantitative decision models to help develop and evaluate forest planning alternatives. This can also be done much more informally using expert opinion and mental simulation, once people gain experience in this type of planning.

*of EFM is that the primary way for sustaining global forest biodiversity and associated ecological processes is to incorporate those objectives into the management of the majority of the world's forests!* As important as preserves are, they cannot be the primary means for sustaining global biodiversity, a fact that is increasingly apparent as this century progresses. One reason is that there are never preserves sufficient in area and representativeness to sustain most of the global biodiversity. *Even more fundamentally, however, the biota are the essential element—the creative agents—that need to be present on the managed lands to carry out the ecological services and create the products upon which human society depends!*

EFM provides the conditions that will sustain that essential biodiversity. It does this using three approaches: (1) recognizing and maintaining important specialized habitats in managed landscapes (Chapters 5 and 14); (2) providing for the full range of developmental stages in managed landscapes, including nonforested conditions (e.g., preforest stage) (Chapters 3, 5, and 14); and (3) creating and sustaining structurally complex and biologically rich managed stands (Chapters 4 and 14). All three of these approaches contribute significantly to sustaining the full array of flora and fauna as well as critical biotic processes, such as essential symbiotic relationships (e.g., mycorrhizae) and activities (e.g., pollination). Specialized habitats are the critical locales for sustaining many rarer species (e.g., cave and cliff habitat dwellers) and biotic processes (e.g., calving and spawning habitat). Loss or degradation of such habitats has major consequences for the affected species and processes. Providing for the full array of developmental stages is critical since each stage sustains an array of biota and functions that are wholly or partially dependent on it—*the entire sere is necessary*! For example, both preforest and old forest conditions, which are populated by very different arrays of habitat specialists, need to be present to sustain the complete array of regional forest-related biodiversity in the Douglas-fir–western hemlock forest landscapes of northwestern North America (Chapter 3). Maintaining structurally complex stands (the third approach) provides the niches (e.g., snags, logs, and old trees) needed to support the full array of forest species that could potentially be present in the stands.

Species that have legal protection, such as species listed as threatened and endangered under the Endangered Species Act (ESA) in the United States, are a special case. These species have been valuable indicators of endangered and degraded ecosystems, which was an original intent of the Act (see Chapter 7 and Skillen, 2015). For example, concerns over the northern spotted owl signaled the rapidly declining availability of older forest ecosystems within its range. The red-cockaded woodpecker played a similar role in highlighting the decline of the longleaf pine ecosystem.

Ecologically based forest management practices often can make major contributions to the restoration of threatened and endangered species. Such practices can integrate creation of additional critical habitat for these species with achievement of other environmental, economic, and social goals. There are many good examples of such outcomes, including activities related to the recovery of the red-cockaded woodpecker. To paraphrase one wildlife manager, "what is good for the ecosystem will be good for [constituent species x]."

Unfortunately, this is not true when threatened and endangered species management focuses on optimizing habitat for a single species of interest, without regard for the integrity of the ecosystem or landscape of which it is a part. In an earlier example (Chapter 4), we mentioned the potential for managing habitats for the Kirtland's warbler in ways that sustain other biota and ecosystem processes as well as the warbler. As another example, concerns over preserving habitat for the northern spotted owl are sometimes used as justification to oppose restoration of degraded frequent-fire forest ecosystems.

The goal in threatened and endangered species management should be accomplished in ways that are, indeed, *good for the ecosystem*. When this is not the case—when goals related to recovery of a single species become significant impediments to restoring or maintaining the integrity of the ecosystem of which they are a part—appreciable reconsideration of recovery goals should occur. If our goal is to comprehensively conserve biodiversity, threatened and endangered species should rarely be impediments to restoring or maintaining the integrity of ecosystems.

## Mitigating and Adapting to Climate Change

Adoption of EFM can help mitigate both the causes and the effects of climate change by (1) creating resistant and resilient conditions in both natural and managed forests (Chapter 4), and (2) increasing levels of carbon sequestered in managed forest landscapes (Chapter 15).

**Increased Forest Resilience** There is a broad consensus in the scientific community that the key to managing ecosystems in a changing world is to increase their resilience. As noted in one article, *"Many ecosystems are likely to experience abrupt changes and extreme conditions due to forces such as climate change. These events and . . . the loss of ecosystem services . . . may occur without warning . . . reinforcing the need to enhance resilience by managing ecosystems. . . . Enhancing ecosystem resilience can be achieved through management, governance, and integration of natural and human infrastructure"* (Pace et al., 2016, pp. 460–461; emphasis added). Biggs et al. (2012) describe principles for maintaining or enhancing resilience including management that maintains diversity, facilitates connectivity, and monitors slowly changing variables: diversity of species and ecosystem types increase the diversity of potential responses to disturbances or directional environmental changes. Mori, Furukawa, and Sasaki (2013) describe diversity in composition and structure as a keystone element in resilience-based management. Seidl (2014, p. 1159; emphasis added) describes resilience-based stewardship as the approach *"to fostering the ability [of ecosystems] to absorb perturbations and maintain desired properties."*

A key EFM principle is to manage forests to reduce risks and increase resilience by sustaining higher levels of species diversity and creating forest conditions that contribute to resilience under probable disturbance regimes. As noted above, higher levels of species diversity includes the variety of tree species within forest stands. A second principle is to develop more resilient structural conditions at the stand level, to which the incorporation of specific species may contribute. For example, incorporating hardwood trees into conifer forests can increase resistance to wildfire. Similarly, a third principle operating at the landscape level, is to provide for diverse forest conditions, such as stands of differing structure (e.g., different developmental stages) and composition. Creation of this diversity at stand and landscape levels is basically a risk-reducing and resilience-spreading strategy. For example, a stand that is composed of a diversity of species, perhaps including both conifers and hardwoods, is less likely to experience a stand-replacing event than a stand composed of a single species, and if it does experience such an event, it is likely to recover faster.

Resilience will take different forms in different forest types. In many deciduous hardwood forests (Chapter 3) much of the resilience comes from the diversity of tree species that are present as well as from their ability to regenerate vegetatively. In Douglas-fir–western hemlock forests, old Douglas-firs often survive intense wildfire (resistance) and then provide seed sources for regeneration of the new forest (resilience). In some highly simplified natural forest landscapes, such as those dominated by lodgepole pine, the primary way of creating resiliency may be by creating diverse age classes (landscape-level heterogeneity).

*Frequent-fire forests and landscapes offer unique opportunities as well as challenges.* Creating resistance and resilience in such systems is generally achieved through creating or restoring forests to relatively open (low tree density) conditions, composed dominantly of larger and older trees of fire-tolerant species, and having understory communities that provide appropriate fuels. Structure is a key to resistance, and adding tree species diversity actually can reduce resistance if they increase fuel loadings, provide ladder fuels, and increase potential flammability. Lower-density forests also reduce the potential for losses as a result of drought cycles or bark beetle epidemics. However,

when restoring resistance and resilience to frequent-fire landscapes it may also be necessary to provide for areas of denser forest (Chapter 5) as well as openings to provide for the needs of specific species and functions. Although denser forest patches in such landscapes will still have the potential to burn intensely, embedding them in a landscape that has been restored to a more resilient state is likely to increase their probability of persisting for longer periods or, as one fire scientist has put it, "increase their hang time."

To summarize, application of EFM principles, including the creation of biologically rich forest stands and heterogeneous forest landscapes, can greatly enhance the ability of forests to adapt to altered climatic conditions as well as the altered disturbance regimes that climate change is likely to bring (Chapter 3).

**Increased Carbon Sequestration**    Carbon sequestration within managed forests and landscapes can be increased by retaining trees and wood during harvest operations and by adopting longer periods between major harvest operations (in traditional terms, by lengthening rotations) (Chapters 4 and 15). We caution at the outset of this discussion that how much on-site carbon sequestration benefits global carbon balances depends, in part, on many off-site factors, including leakage (such as increased logging pressures on other sites) and substitution effects (such as where wood is less available to substitute for cement or steel in construction) (Chapter 15).

Timber harvesting under EFM principles will almost always involve significant retention of existing live trees as well as snags and logs (Chapter 4). Consequently, carbon levels on even recently harvested sites will be considerably greater than levels that are present following harvest, under even-aged management regimes, particularly clearcutting (Chapter 15). Following timber harvest, the on-site carbon loss rates will also be less on sites with retention than on clearcut sites, since the microclimates on partially harvested sites are cooler and moister because of the retained trees and intact forest patches. Hence, the on-site carbon debt created by harvest will be less under EFM than on sites managed under even-aged systems. Longer intervals between harvests (i.e., longer rotations) also will be more common in forests managed under EFM principles than on sites intensively managed for wood production.

*Growing forests longer between major timber harvests has several carbon storage benefits* (Chapter 15). First, major harvests result in on-site carbon losses associated with reduced forest cover. Less-frequent harvests mean that these on-site losses are experienced less frequently. Second, on many forest sites high levels of carbon accumulation continue for many decades in young and even mature forests—it is often well into the second century before accumulation rates undergo significant decline. Even when they begin to decline, accumulation of additional carbon continues—simply at a lower rate. In some western conifer forests, carbon accumulation continues (i.e., carbon stocks do not peak and begin to decline) for many centuries. For example, in an approximately 500-year-old Douglas-fir–western hemlock stand carbon stocks are still slowly accumulating over multiyear periods, although there is appreciable annual variability in net primary productivity (Field & Kaduk, 2004).

Finally, under EFM principles, a variety of ecologically important areas would be identified and managed to sustain their unique ecological values and would not be subject to regular timber harvest (Chapter 5). These are likely to include any older forests, which have large stocks of sequestered carbon. Many other special areas, such as those associated with aquatic ecosystems, are also likely to have higher levels of sequestered carbon.

## Supporting Rural and Small-Town Communities

Rural and small-town communities are sources of skilled workforces and contain manufacturing facilities that provide markets for timber harvest. These populations are important participants in developing a consensus regarding management goals for public lands because of their dependence upon—as well as their knowledge of—local forest conditions. Members of local communities are also potential participants in adaptive management activities, such as monitoring. Further, local communities represent influential segments of democratic societies and, in the longer view, have the potential to be some of the most engaged advocates for forests in an increasingly urbanized society. For all of these reasons, the health and viability of rural and small-town communities are important concerns in natural resource management. There is truth in the statement that it is necessary to have healthy communities in order to have healthy forests!

Local communities provide the workforces needed to carry out forest management activities, including restoration and other stewardship activities, as well as more traditional activities such as forest protection (e.g., for firefighting), timber harvesting, and planting. Much of this work involves the employment of individuals with specialized training and skills and an enthusiasm for working in the woods.

The manufacturing facilities located in many local towns and small cities are critical to facilitating management by providing a market for timber harvested from the forest. Even where forest management is focused primarily on restoration or other forms of stewardship, the presence of industrial plants is often critical because of the funds that they provide for these activities through their purchases of raw materials that come from the forest. Adequate finan-

cial support for forest stewardship is almost never available for public lands through legislative appropriations, and the financial return from selling merchantable products acquired through the restoration activities is often critical to making such activities possible.

EFM is an approach that provides for a broad array of economic and other societal benefits for local communities, including direct economic benefits from employment in management of the forest and provision of wood for local manufacturing facilities. Moreover, EFM is likely to be more stable than production forest management, which at the local or regional level can produce economic booms and busts. Forests managed under EFM principles can also sustain a broad array of forest values cherished by local communities, such as many types of forest products (e.g., mushrooms, florist greenery, and berries), habitat for game species, and a sense of naturalness.

EFM emphasizes engaging stakeholders in the development of plans and proposals for specific activities, such as timber harvest, particularly on public lands. Local populations have high stakes in the outcomes of such decision-making processes. They can also bring to the table historical knowledge and personal experience regarding these resources. There is great potential to utilize local citizens in follow-on adaptive management processes, such as monitoring, since they reside in the area. Such participation also provides local citizens with educational opportunities, allowing them to gain additional scientific knowledge and insight into their local forests.

Finally, citizens in local communities may be important advocates for the retention and stewardship of public forests. We have an increasingly urbanized society that tends to lose touch with the sources of many of its essential resources; how many children today are aware of the sources of their food and the activities that are required to provide it? In a future, even more urbanized world, a relatively small percentage of society may have the opportunity to experience forest environments and understand their importance. In such a world human populations living near and within forest environments may be among the most important advocates for retention and continued stewardship of public forestlands.

## Providing an Alternative to the Choice of Reserves or Plantations

EFM provides forest stakeholders, managers, and landowners with an alternative to the false dichotomy of either production forestry or preserves. While there has always been an array of approaches that could be used to manage forests for multiple goals, including ecological and economic benefits, these approaches have usually been highly idiosyncratic—relevant to a single ownership or region—

and rarely widely adopted or advocated. When a major forestry organization (the US Forest Service) adopted multiple use as a goal, its approach was more about allocating a landscape to different uses than to integrating multiple goals within forest stands or across a landscape. To be fair, at that time (the 1960s) there was neither adequate scientific knowledge nor credible real-world examples of management that truly integrated multiple goals to carry out a major program in management of forests for multiple values. Small forest landowners who valued their properties for the multiple benefits they provided also had few models or sources of technical forestry expertise to which they could turn; if they consulted their local extension foresters they were most likely advised to adopt some variation of even-aged management. Indeed, to propose such ideas as retaining old trees, snags, and down logs was to risk being judged as doing something that was the antithesis of credible forestry!

In the realm of public forestland management, stakeholders and policy makers have not been offered alternatives to the choices of either preserves or plantations (Bennett, 2015). Debates have occurred in almost every forest region of the world over whether natural (and often old) forests should be placed in reserves or converted to plantations. However, the protagonists on both sides of these debates have rarely, if ever, proposed alternatives that involved active but ecologically conservative management; rather proponents usually agree that the forest should be divided into preserves and plantations and differ mainly in the proportion of the public forest that should end up in one or the other state! Public agencies generally have been slow to bring forward credible alternatives to preserves or plantations, perhaps partially because the forestry profession has not provided them (Bennett, 2015).

EFM provides a generalizable philosophical and scientific basis for managing forests simultaneously for environmental, economic, and social benefits. It provides not just an alternative to the false dichotomy of either preserves or plantations but, in actuality, an infinite array of approaches that can be adapted to differing forest conditions, management goals, and legal structures.

Conversion of forests to other land uses is a major challenge in the United States as well as other countries. One way to combat this challenge is EFM, which offers the small-forest landowner economically and ecologically beneficial alternatives for the management of their properties, where they might otherwise be reluctant to harvest trees to produce income. Credible forest practices no longer require adherence to philosophies and forest practices that assume timber primacy. In fact, management using EFM principles can result in improved ecological conditions as well as generate income, as we discuss throughout this book. Hence, small landowners may be able to simul-

taneously enhance the habitat for their favored songbirds, improve the resilience of their forest property, and contribute to their children's college fund. When the kids inherit the woodland they can know that there are approaches that integrate ecological and economic goals, if so desired. As a result, the EFM strategy can help facilitate retention of private forests where landowners find that strategy enables them to integrate timber production with other values they hold dear. Other incentives also can be critical to this retention including tax breaks, conservation easements, and carbon credits. (See Boxes 6.1, 6.2, 10.4, and the appendix to Chapter 15.)

Use of EFM can have a similar positive influence on management of public lands. Once it is clear that there are credible, even desirable, alternatives to preserves or plantations, stakeholders can consider many more options, particularly in forests and landscapes that have been harvested before— i.e., where the harvest of natural older forests is not an issue. Such an approach could work for many of the stakeholders. A common attitude that we have found among citizens in forest-oriented rural communities is that most do not want to see 21st-century production forestry applied to public forests; on the other hand, they do not want to see all of the public lands *locked up*. Similarly, many conservation-oriented citizens understand that benefits can arise from management activities that incorporate restorative and other ecological goals. This understanding is going to be increasingly the case as more and more people become aware of the importance of resilience to forest ecosystems. EFM provides a credible alternative to preserves or plantations.

We end this section with a note about the concept of intensively managing some portion of the global forests to provide much of the world's wood supply so that the rest of these forests can be preserved. We would observe first that only a small percentage of global forests can and will be managed for capital-rewarding production forestry; most forest lands cannot grow wood fast enough to provide a globally-competitive return on capital.

This does not and should not mean that the remainder of the global forests can or should be put into reserves. Much of the remainder of the global forests are either going to be managed to provide some level of income for the owners or going to be converted to other land uses. This conversion would not be a good outcome because society is dependent on the bulk of global forests to provide a broad array of ecosystem services.

Furthermore, most of the global forests will require continued active management to restore and sustain the functionality of these forests in the 21st century. Many forests and forest landscapes are currently in a degraded condition, meaning one in which important elements (e.g., functional capacities and biota) have been lost. In such instances, major restoration efforts are needed to accelerate or make possible natural recovery processes. Climate change is certain to bring considerable and often novel change to forests and forest biota; active management will be critical in assisting in their adaptation to the new conditions.

Bennett (2015, p. 151; emphasis added) reaches a similar conclusion in his book *Plantations and Protected Areas: A Global History of Forest Management*, suggesting that

> *the public and forest experts should be wary of embracing policies that entirely decouple timber production from forest protection. These policies reinforce the extremes of forest management, rely too much on free-market forces, and encourage the belief that forests have not historically been modified by human action in the past. Moreover, it decouples the creation of revenue from protection, leaving large swaths of forests without adequate management in the face of climate change, invasive species, continued ecological fragmentation, and increased pressure on the world's wood resources. Decoupling production from protection will continue to devalue the cost of native forest timber, forcing governments to either harvest using controversial techniques, such as clear-felling and wood-chipping, or to shut down harvesting altogether in native forests.*

To sum up, EFM provides forest owners and managers of diverse interests with an approach to active management of their forests that is ecologically based and allows the integration of environmental, economic, and social goals. It also provides society with an alternative (in fact, an infinite variety of alternatives) to the preserve/plantation dichotomy that has dominated so much of the social dialogue with regard to the appropriate management of public lands (Bennett, 2015).

## A Policy Framework for EFM

The policy context for ecological forest management can greatly influence its application and success. Thus, it is important to have a policy framework that enables EFM to flourish. Some existing forest practice rules actually work to discourage EFM. As an example, much early forest practice regulation in the US and elsewhere tried to shorten the preforest stage by mandating the quick reestablishment of a stand of commercial species after a stand had been cut. Hence, an initial goal in facilitating adoption of EFM is to try to modify or eliminate policies that prevent application of natural forest models—that is, to remove policies that mandate simplification of forests and truncation of natural successional stages or discourage development of ecologically based landscape patterns.

Beyond dismantling policies that inhibit EFM, the next step would be to build a policy framework that encourages:

- Natural stand development processes as models;
- Continuity, not discontinuity, between forest generations;
- Complexity, not simplicity;
- Heterogeneity, not homogeneity at multiple spatial scales, including stands and landscape;
- Valuing understories as well as overstories; and
- Maintaining or restoring the complete suite of development stages—the entire sere—on landscapes.

How might this be done? *We suggest that a public policy framework for EFM would start by recognizing that maintaining and restoring ecosystem integrity is a primary goal of public forest policy.* We further suggest a set of specific policy goals to guide and constrain forest management that include:

- Identifying areas of high ecological and cultural significance, including streams, lakes, and other aquatic and semi-aquatic features and adoption of management approaches that sustain the integrity of those features;
- Retaining biological legacies in areas harvested for timber. This retention would be representative of the pre-harvest forest conditions and include structures such as mature trees, snags, and logs. Retention should be sufficient to be ecologically meaningful immediately following harvest and in the post-harvest stand. One measure of significance of the retention would be the additional biota accommodated over that accommodated in a clearcut;
- Encouraging harvest and reforestation policies that provide for the full range of biota and structural complexity in forest conditions at the landscape and regional level, including the preforest stage as appropriate to a specific forest type. Both diversity of developmental stages and mixed-age stand management would contribute to this;
- Considering disturbance history and the influence of biological legacies in setting maximum harvest patch sizes; and
- Assessing and controlling cumulative watershed effects.

For an example application of these ideas, we utilize the regulations, requirements, and plans for the Oregon Coast Range. The current state of this forest landscape is discussed in Chapter 5, including the shortage of preforest, mature and old-forest stages and the abundance of young simplified forest. Given those conditions, we suggest how private and federal policies might be modified to encourage EFM (Box 21.1). It is important to note that some of the shift to EFM in private forests in the Oregon Coast Range, can be achieved by *removing regulations*, such as the free-to-grow requirement. Such actions increase landowner freedom and lower landowner costs—two very desirable outcomes from the standpoint of private landowners. Also, such efforts will inherently increase the diversity of forest conditions on the landscape as landowners individually respond to these new freedoms. However, other suggested changes, such as the expansion of aquatic buffers, would be more challenging and probably need to use the variety of policy tools discussed in Chapter 6 and the next few pages.

## Increasing the Adoption of EFM Globally

Although elements of ecological forest management have emerged in all temperate forest regions, EFM has a relatively low profile in forest policies for temperate forests around the world. Existing forest policies and associated dialogue regarding forests often do not acknowledge alternatives in which forests are simultaneously managed for conservation of ecological processes and biota and for other economic and social values (Bennett, 2015). Why would this be? One

reason is the relatively recent emergence of the science and philosophy of EFM. Further, and related in part to its recent emergence, such integrative approaches have not been widely advocated, let alone demonstrated, by many in the forestry profession (Bennett, 2015). Another factor may be that some stakeholders do not see integrated approaches as serving their particular value set. Recognizing both the potential for conserving biodiversity in managed forest landscapes as well as the necessity for doing so can be viewed as a threat by those who favor forest preservation. Similarly, advocates for production forestry may view EFM as a threat, seeing EFM as limiting the forests available for intensive management or giving rise to further efforts to put ecological constraints on production forestry.

It is also true that many aspects of ecologically based forest management are, in fact, already being utilized, to at least some degree, in many countries. In fact, the extent to which such practices have emerged in most temperate forest regions might be surprising. For example, efforts to better integrate ecological concerns into traditional forest practices have led to wide-spread incorporation of structural retention at the time of timber harvest (see,

---

### Box 21.1  Shifting forest practices in the Oregon Coast Range toward EFM

To illustrate how forest policies could be shifted toward EFM, we will consider the current policy environment in the Oregon Coast Range. This is a multi-owner region (Color Plate 5.2) that we used earlier to illustrate landscape assessment and planning (see Chapter 5 for additional background on the region).

**Private Forests**

Corporate forests are the main source of timber volume and of openings created through harvest (Figures 5.23 and 16.5). Oregon's Forest Practice Rules (OFPRs) guide and restrict forestry on private and state lands within the state, with the general goal of encouraging commercial timber production while recognizing public values on private lands (Adams & Storm, 2011). These rules emphasize rapid regeneration after harvest of commercial species, reflecting the historical fear that timber supplies might decline because of inadequate conifer regeneration. Also, the rules mandate buffers along fish-bearing streams, limits on the size of clearcuts, and a number of other requirements.

Our discussion here relates to how the state might shift to a different view regarding some OFPR requirements in order to facilitate adoption of EFM approaches. This change would be particularly important in terms of allowing development of the ecologically important preforest stage following harvest. Some potential changes could include:

1. Modifying or removing policies that inhibit development of a structurally complex and biologically rich preforest stage. Examples include:

   a) Removing the free-to-grow requirement, which currently calls for a certain number of commercial seedlings per acre to be free of shrub competition by the sixth year after harvest. Efforts to meet this requirement can greatly reduce the native shrub community and other rich flora and fauna of the preforest stage.

   b) Modifying regeneration requirements to allow variability in the density of tree seedlings per acre that must be present, as long as the average number exceeds the requirement.

   c) Removing artificial regeneration requirements for landowners who leave sufficient seed source (legacy trees) in harvest units to provide for eventual reforestation and who commit to non-native invasive plant control.

   d) Recognizing diverse early successional conditions not as regeneration failures but as biodiversity successes, which provide public values on private lands, in descriptions of the goals of the forest practice rules, the enforcement of those rules, and in technical assistance and educational activities.

   Removing the free-to-grow requirement and other reforestation regulations would almost certainly result in

e.g., Gustafsson et al., 2012). Also, in Europe, numerous approaches have emerged that attempt to better incorporate ecological goals, such as continuous cover forestry, nature- or diversity-oriented silviculture, close-to-nature forestry, and near-natural forestry (O'Hara, 2014).

## Potential Impediments to Adoption of EFM

Puettmann et al. (2015) have provided a useful overview of the various cultural, economic, and professional issues that can constrain adoption of unconventional silvicultural practices, which would generally include EFM-based practices. Among the constraints or concerns that they identify are:

- Economics, because management using such methods is *unlikely to reach the short-term profitability of intensively managed short rotation plantations*;

- Poor fit of alternative silvicultural approaches with prominent economic ideas, such as those that emphasize control, efficiency, and net present value;

- Safety and efficiency of harvest;

- Staffing challenges and costs—alternative approaches generally require greater professional expertise as well as greater numbers of professionals. Related to this is a *search for simplicity* due to shortages of personnel, such as in public agencies lacking adequate budgets;

- Necessity for changes in contracting policies;

- Inadequate scientific information, including long-term responses of forests to these alternative approaches;

- Educational bias, referring to professionals who assert that only the dominant management model is acceptable;

- Perceptions by professionals, decision makers, and the public that some aspects of EFM (e.g., brush-dominated preforest conditions) are ugly and represent failures of responsible resource management;

- Lack of *willingness or readiness* on the part of professionals and management organizations to do something different or try a new approach;

---

development of more and better quality preforest habitat in the Oregon Coast Range. Corporate landowners, who create most of the openings, would be able to provide a more diverse preforest condition if they concluded it was in their financial interest. Family forest landowners, with their more varied interests (Chapter 6), would be freed to create preforest habitat as they wish; the removal of the free-to-grow requirement would also allow them to return to the less intensive management practices small owners often favor for both financial and philosophical reasons.

2. Add policies that encourage significant structural retention at harvest; currently very little structure is required for retention within harvest units (see Figure 5.23). Such policies could include:

    a) Providing technical assistance to private landowners about increasing structural retention at relatively low cost, highlighting trees with high value for wildlife but low value for wood products.

    b) Requiring tree buffers along non-fish-bearing streams within harvest units, as is done in adjacent states. This would provide a multitude of fish and wildlife benefits. A compensation fund also could be created for family forest landowners, as has been done elsewhere.

    c) Allowing for larger harvest units, which would be more consistent with historical patch sizes, provided landowners committed to leaving significant structural retention within the unit. The size of permitted harvest units could be keyed

to retention levels—the greater the amount of retention the larger the harvest unit allowed.

3. Undertake a highly-visual educational campaign about the importance of both preforest ecosystems and structural retention at harvest in sustaining forest ecosystems and the many fish and wildlife species that depend on them.

### Federal Forests

While the Northwest Forest Plan (NWFP) for federal forests emphasized the importance of mature and old forests in the underlying science assessment (FEMAT, 1993), there was little emphasis on the importance of preforest ecosystems or the policy direction regarding provision of such habitat.

The following changes in the NWFP would bring it into better alignment with EFM principles:

1. Acknowledge in plans and programs the importance of sustaining all forest developmental stages;

2. Initiate a systematic research program to better understand the ecology of early successional ecosystems and species and to study how biologically rich, structurally complex preforest ecosystems can be created by retention harvests in the abundant, existing, young, simplified stands; and

3. Develop and demonstrate improved approaches to thinning in young forests, which will better approximate developmental pathways and characteristics of natural forests.

- Lack of strong intellectual, political, and administrative leadership to adopt alternative forest management approaches;

- Lack of social or financial incentives to make changes; and

- Perceived or actual failures in previous attempts to adopt alternative approaches.

All of these represent potential impediments to the adoption of EFM whether they arise from valid objections or concerns or not.

## Overcoming Impediments to EFM

Raising the profile of EFM—broadening its recognition—appears to be one of the most important tasks in expanding its consideration and application at the global level. Clearly this involves education in the broadest sense—making more people aware of its existence and capabilities and working to incorporate its principles in policy. All of the policy tools discussed in Chapter 6 could be useful here, including:

- Helping people make connections between their values and EFM;

- Creating capacity for implementing EFM through education, including demonstration;

- Engaging policy makers, land owners, and the public in active learning about the success of different practices in achieving EFM;

- Providing incentives for adoption of EFM through social as well as financial mechanisms (e.g., recognition of social good); and

- Reconciling forest practice requirements with the principles of EFM.

Education of the broader public is a major challenge that must involve a diversity of media and arenas. The overarching goal would be to raise the societal profile of EFM and to gain a greatly broadened appreciation of alternatives to the plantation/preserve dichotomy (Bennett, 2015). Part of this effort should be directed to helping people appreciate the wonder and beauty of a natural forest in all its developmental stages. An important subtext would be an increased understanding of the importance of active management of forests, particularly in the face of environmental change. *An expanded appreciation of the dangers associated with leaving nature to restore conditions in a world that has been so profoundly changed by humans is an essential part of this activity.* Finally, an additional important goal is rebuilding societal trust in foresters and other natural resource professionals.

Education is a very broad need that includes professional education in natural resource management and public education in the principles and capabilities of EFM. Clearly EFM needs to have as much attention in academic programs in forest management and conservation biology as production forestry and preserves have traditionally received in their respective programs. Incorporating EFM concepts into extension forestry activities would be an another important outcome of increasing attention to EFM in professional university training.

An expanded knowledge base is essential for successful long-term application of EFM, which can come in part from monitoring and research programs as well as practical demonstrations and experiments. There are outstanding opportunities to actively engage stakeholders in learning, by involving them in monitoring programs and even research projects, including activities categorized as *citizen science*. These serve the dual values of providing and expanding stakeholder knowledge of forest ecosystems. Demonstration projects can be a particularly powerful tool in creating more familiarity and comfort among both stakeholders and professional resource managers in EFM approaches. Formal science activities need to include large-scale experimental treatments and projects involving long-term measurements of forest stands.

Adoption of EFM practices could be strongly encouraged if governments would provide incentives for such practices. Examples of this could include tax breaks or payments for providing habitat, particularly for threatened and endangered species. Incentives could also be provided by creating markets for such services as carbon sequestration or maintaining forest cover to protect water quality. Certification could provide market incentives if it results in additional value premiums or marketing opportunities; governments could assist by requiring certified wood for government-funded projects.

Eliminating legal requirements that prevent forest owners from implementing EFM goals and practices is important. We have already noted some obvious examples of this in our case study of the Oregon Coast Range (Box 21.1). Forest owners should be able to carry out ecologically beneficial activities on their own properties without being penalized. Policies requiring prompt tree regeneration to a defined standard—particularly the free-to-grow requirements—by design interfere with development of high-quality (biologically rich) early successional (preforest) communities in regions where such preforest conditions naturally persist for two or more decades. Similarly, landowners should be protected from penalties that could occur if they create habitat for endangered species; Safe Harbor agreements provide a mechanism for dealing with that within the United States (Chapter 7).

Creating legal requirements for environmentally beneficial practices, where there is broad public support, may be part of the policy mix. A current example of these requirements would be protection (such as buffers) along streams and rivers and around lakes and ponds. As noted in Chapter 5, aquatic networks are highly connected, and impacts in one location can be difficult or impossible to mitigate at other locations in the network. Hence, aquatic networks are features of forest landscapes where landowners are likely to have stewardship obligation or consideration of societal interests than in the uplands. Many national, state, and provincial governments have created legal restrictions on management activities adjacent to streams and rivers, albeit they vary greatly in their limitation on management (Chapter 7). Thus, there is the potential need to modify requirements to provide more comprehensive protection (Box 21.1) and to allow restorative management.

Adopting policies to insure retention of biological legacies at harvest may be the biggest challenge in many locales relative to embedding the principles of EFM into policy frameworks that guide and limit forest practices. Often, landowner retention of biological legacies means forgoing immediate revenue. Undoubtedly, all of the types of policy tools will be needed to encourage retention of these legacies.

## Conclusion

EFM holds great promise for providing the philosophical and technical basis for integrated management of the majority of temperate forestlands for environmental, eco-

nomic, and social values. It provides a broad and rich set of alternatives to the false dichotomy that forests must be either preserves or plantations. EFM offers unique and positive responses to such 21st-century challenges as climate change and invasives, support of local communities, and conversion of forestlands to other land uses. It has particular relevance to the goal of sustaining forest biodiversity, which in this century cannot be achieved primarily by preserves (Rosenzweig, 2003).

Although ecologically based forest management practices are being developed and applied in temperate forestlands all over the world, there are challenges to their broad acceptance and application. Keys to addressing these challenges include expanding professional and public education regarding EFM and expanding the science and management knowledge base of EFM. *The greatest tasks may be increasing broad societal recognition of EFM, gaining confidence in EFM as an alternative to plantations or preserves, and establishing trust in the ability of resource professionals to carry out such management.*

As Bennett (2015, p. 156–157) has put it in the conclusion to his book, *"In order to achieve the best possible future outcome, it is critical that policy makers, scientists, environmentalists, and all interested people understand that the world is undergoing a forest management divergence that is reshaping timber production and forest protection. Only once we recognize this historic process can we then begin to resolve the tensions."*

# Literature Cited

Abt, K. L., Abt, R. C., Galik, C. S., & Skog, K. E. (2014). Effect of policies on pellet production and forests in the U.S. South: A technical document supporting the Forest Service update of the 2010 RPA Assessment. *USDA Forest Service General Technical Report SRS-202*. Asheville, NC: Southern Research Station.

Adams, P. W., & Storm, R. (2011). *Oregon's forest protection laws* (2nd ed.). Portland, OR: Oregon Forest Resources Institute.

Adler, R. W. (2003). The two lost books in the water quality trilogy: The elusive objectives of physical and biological integrity. *Environmental Law, 33*, 29–77.

Adler, R. W. (2015). US Environmental Protection Agency's new Waters of the United States Rule: Connecting law and science. *Freshwater Science, 34*(4), 1595–1600.

Agee, J. K. (1993). *Fire ecology of Pacific Northwest forests.* Washington, DC: Island Press.

Agee, J. K., & Skinner, C. N. (2005). Basic principles of forest fuel reduction treatments. *Forest Ecology and Management, 211*, 83–96.

Ager, A. A., Finney, M. A., Kerns, B. K., & Maffei, H. (2007). Modeling wildfire risk to northern spotted owl (Strix occidentalis caurina) habitat in Central Oregon, USA. *Forest Ecology and Management, 246*, 45–56.

Ager, A. A., Vaillant, N. M., & Finney, M. A. (2010). A comparison of landscape fuel treatment strategies to mitigate wildland fire risk in the urban interface and preserve old forest structure. *Forest Ecology and Management, 259*, 1556–1570.

Ager, A. A., Vaillant, N. M., & McMahan, A. (2013). Restoration of fire in managed forests: A model to prioritize landscapes and analyze tradeoffs. *Ecosphere, 4*, 1–19.

Aguilar, F. X., & Vlosky, R. P. (2007). Consumer willingness to pay price premiums for environmentally certified Assessment wood products in the U.S. *Forest Policy and Economics, 9*(8), 1100–1112.

Alban, D. H. (1969). The influence of western hemlock and western redcedar on soil properties. *Soil Science. Soc. Amer. Proc., 33*, 453–459.

Alexander, R. R. (1964). Minimizing windfall around clear cuttings in spruce-fir forests. *Forest Science, 10*, 130–142.

Allen, C. D., Macalady, A. K., Chenchouni, H., Bachelet, D., McDowell, N., Vennetier, M., Kitzberger, T., et al. (2010). A global overview of drought and heat-induced tree mortality reveals emerging climate change risks for forests." *Forest Ecology and Management, 259*(4), 660–684.

Allen, G., & Gould, E. (1986). Complexity, wickedness and public forests. *Journal of Forestry, 84*(4): 20–23.

Álvarez-Farizo, B., & Hanley, N. (2006). Improving the process of valuing non-market benefits: Combining citizens' juries with choice modeling. *Land Economics, 82*(3), 465–478.

Anderson, C. M., Field, C. B., & Mach, K. J. (2017). Forest offsets partner climate change mitigation with conservation. *Frontiers in Ecology and the Environment, 15*(7), 359–365.

Anderson, J. E. (2015). Public Policy-Making (8th ed.). New York, NY: Holt, Rinehart, and Winston.

Anderson, R. C. & Hansen, E. N. (2004). Determining consumer preferences for ecolabeled forest products: An experimental approach. *Journal of Forestry, 102*(4), 28–32.

Anderson, R. C., Laband, D. N., Hansen, E. N., & Knowles, C. D. (2005). Price premiums in the mist. *Forest Products Journal, 55*(6), 19–22.

Anderson, R. G., Canadell, J. G., Randerson, J. T., et al. (2011). Biophysical considerations in forestry for climate protection. *Frontiers in Ecology and the Environment, 9*(3), 174–182.

Andreen, W. L. (2013). Success and backlash: The remarkable (continuing) story of the Clean Water Act. *George Washington Journal of Energy & Environmental Law, 4*, 25–37.

Andrews, P. L. (2014). Current status and future needs of the BehavePlus Fire Modeling System. *International Journal of Wildland Fire, 23*, 21–33.

Ang, F., & Van Passel, S. (2012). Beyond the environmentalist's paradox and the debate on weak versus strong sustainability. *BioScience, 62*(3), 251–259.

Ansell, C., & Gash, A. (2008). Collaborative governance in theory and practice. *Journal of Public Administration Research and Theory, 18*(4), 543–571.

Aplet, G., Brown, P., Briggs, J., Mayben, S., Edwards, D., & Cheng, T. (2014). *Collaborative implementation of forest landscape restoration in the Colorado Front Range.* Colorado Forest Restoration Institute. Fort Collins: Colorado State University.

Appell, D. (2001, January). The new uncertainty principle. *Scientific American*, pp. 47–52.

Appraisal Foundation. (2016–2017). Uniform Standards of Professional Appraisal Practice (USPAP), Washington, DC: Author. Retrieved from http://www.uspap.org/#1

Appraisal Institute. (2000). *Uniform Appraisal Standards for Federal Land Acquisition* ("Yellow Book"). Chicago, IL. Retrieved from www.justice.gov/enrd/land-ack/Uniform-Appraisal-Standards.pdf

Aronow, M. E., & Washburn, C., Binkley, C. S. (2004). Explaining timberland values in the United States. *Journal of Forestry, 102*(8), 14–18.

Arrow K., Solow, R., Portney, P. R., Leanmer, E. E., Raddner, R., & Schuman, H. (1993). Report of the NOAA panel on contingent valuation. *US Federal Register, 58*(10), 4602–4614.

Askins, Robert A. (2014). *Saving the world's deciduous forests.* New Haven, CT: Yale University Press.

Auld, G. (2014). *Constructing private governance: The rise and evolution of forest, coffee, and fisheries certification.* New Haven, CT: Yale University Press.

Aust, W. M., & Blinn, C. R. (2004). Forestry best management practices for timber harvesting and site preparation in the eastern United States: An overview of water quality and productivity research during the past 20 years (1982–2002). *Water, Air and Soil Pollution: Focus, 4*(1), 5–36.

Ayres, M. P., Hicke, J. A., Kerns, B. K., Mckenzie, D., et al. (2014). Disturbance regimes and stressors. In D. L. Peterson, J. N. Vose, & T. Patel-Weynand (Eds.), *Climate change and United States forests* (pp. 55–92). New York, NY: Springer.

*Babbitt v. Sweet Home Chapter of Communities for a Great Oregon,* 515 U.S. 687. Supreme Court of the United States. (1995). Retrieved from https://supreme.justia.com/cases/federal/us/515/687/case.html

Bailey, J., & Witham, T. G. (2002). Interactions among fire, aspen, and elk affect insect diversity: Reversal of a community response. *Ecology, 83*(6), 1701–1712.

Barnes, B. V., Zak, D. R., Denton, S. R., & Spurr, S. H. (1998). *Forest Ecology* (4th ed.). New York, NY: John Wiley & Sons.

Batker, D., Schwartz, A., Schmidt, R., Mackenzie, A., Smith, J., & Robins, J. (2014). *Healthy lands & healthy economies: Nature's value in Santa Clara County.* Earth Economics, Tacoma, WA & the Santa Clara Valley Open Space Authority, San Jose, CA. Retrieved from http://www.openspaceauthority.org/about/pdf/NaturesValue_SCC_int.pdf

Bean, M. J., & Wilcove, D. S. (1997). The private-land problem. *Conservation Biology, 11,* 1–2.

Beiler, K. J., Durall, D. M., Simard, S. W., Maxwell, S. A., & Kretzer, A. M. (2010). Architecture of the wood-wide web: *Rhizopogon* spp. genets link multiple Douglas-fir cohorts. *New Phytologist 185,* 543–553.

Bechara, A., Damasio H., Tranel, D., & Damasio, A. (1997). Deciding advantageously before knowing the advantageous strategy. *Science, 275,* 1293–1295.

Beckley, T. M., Martz, D., Nadeau, S., Wall, E., & Reimer, B. (2008). Multiple capacities, multiple outcomes: Delving deeper into the meaning of community capacity. *Journal of Rural and Community Development, 3,* 56–75.

Behan, R. W. (1966). The myth of the omnipotent forester. *Journal of Forestry, 64,* 398–407.

Bella, D. (1992). Ethics and the credibility of applied science. In G. Reeves, D. Bottom, & M. Brooks (Eds.), *Ethical questions for resource managers* (pp. 19–32). Portland, OR: *USDA Forest Service General Technical Report PNW GTR-288.* Portland, OR: U.S. Department of Agriculture, Forest Service

Benda, L. E., Poff, N. L., Miller, D., Dunne, T., Reeves, G., Pess, G., & Pollock, M. (2004). The network dynamics hypothesis: How channel networks structure riverine habitats. *BioScience, 54*(5), 413–427.

Bennett, B. (2015). *Plantations and protected areas: A global history of forest management.* Cambridge, MA: MIT Press.

Benson, M. H., & Garmestani, A. S. (2011). Embracing panarchy, building resilience and integrating adaptive management through a rebirth of the National Environmental Policy Act. *Journal of Environmental Management, 92,* 1420–1427.

Bentz, B., Logan, J., MacMahon, J., et al. (2005). Bark beetle outbreaks in western North America: Causes and consequences. *Proceedings: Bark beetle symposium, USDA Forest Service, Rocky Mountain Research Station, Snowbird, Utah.* Salt Lake City: University of Utah Press.

Bergman, R., Puettmann, M., Taylor, A. & Skog, K. E. (2014). The carbon impacts of wood products. *Forest Products Journal, 64*(7), 220–231.

Berner, R. A., & Lasaga, A. C. (1989). Modeling the geochemical carbon cycle. *Scientific American, 260*(3), 74–81.

Bettinger, P., Boston, K., & Sessions, J. (1999). Combinatorial optimization of elk habitat effectiveness and timber harvest volume. *Environmental Modeling and Assessment, 4,* 143–153.

Bettinger, P., Boston, K., Siry, J. P., & Grebner, D. L. (2017). *Forest management and planning* (2nd ed.). Burlington, MA: Academic Press.

Bettinger, P., Johnson, D. L., Johnson, K. N. (2003). Spatial forest plan development with ecological and economic goals. *Ecological Modeling, 169,* 215–236.

Bettinger, P., Sessions, J., & Boston, K. (1997). Using Tabu search to schedule timber harvests subject to spatial wildlife goals for big game. *Ecological Modeling, 94,* 111–123.

Biggs, R., Schluter, M., Biggs, D., et al. (2012). Toward principles for enhancing the resilience of ecosystem services. *Annual Review Environment and Resources, 37,* 421–448.

Binkley, C. S., Beebe, S. B., New, D. A., & von Hagen, B. (2006). *An ecosystem-based forestry investment strategy for the coastal temperate rainforests of North America.* (GreenWood Resources Research Note 2006-1). Portland, OR: GreenWood Resources. Retrieved from http://greenwoodresources.com/wp-content/uploads/2014/06/AnEcosystemBasedForestryInvestment.pdf

Binkley, C. S., Raper, C. F., & Washburn, C. L. (1996). Institutional ownership of U.S. timberland: History, rationale, and implications for forest management. *Journal of Forestry, 94*(9), 21–28.

Birch, T. W. (1996). Private forest land-owners of the United States, 1994. *USDA Forest Service Research Bulletin NE-134.* Radnor, PA: Northeastern Forest Experiment.

Birdsey, R. A. (1996). Carbon storage for major forest types and regions in the conterminous United States. In N. E. Sampson & D. Hair (Eds.), *Forests and global change* (Vol. 2) (pp. 1–25). Washington, DC: American Forests.

Birdsey, R. A., Jenkins, J. C., & Johnston, M. (2007). North American Forests. In A. W. King (Ed.), *The first state of the carbon cycle report (SOCCR)* (pp. 117–176). Washington, DC: U. S. Climate Change Science Program.

Birdsey, R. A., Pregitzer, K., & Lucier, A. (2006). Forest carbon management in the United States: 1600–2100. *Journal of Environmental Quality, 35,* 1461–1469.

Biswell, H. H. (1958). Prescribed burning in Georgia and California compared. Journal of *Range Management, 11*(6), 293–298.

Blackman, A., Raimondi, A., & Cubbage, F. (2014). *Does forest certification in developing countries have environmental benefits? Insights from Mexican corrective action requests.* Washington, DC: Resources for the Future.

Blackman, A., & Rivera, J. (2011). Producer-level benefits of sustainability certification. *Conservation Biology, 25*(6), 1176–1185.

Bliss, J. C. (2000). Public perceptions of clearcutting. *Journal of Forestry, 98*(12), 4–9.

Bliss, J. C., Aplet, G., Hartzell, C., Harwood, P., Jahnige, P., Kittridge, D., et al. (2001). Community-based ecosystem monitoring. *Journal of Sustainable Forestry, 12,* 143–168.

Bliss, J. C., Kelly, E. C., Abrams, J., Bailey, C., & Dyer, J. (2010). Disintegration of the US industrial forest estate: Dynamics, trajectories, and questions. *Small-Scale Forestry, 9*(1), 53–66.

Bliss, J. C., & McNabb, K. (1992). Landowners reveal some surprising attitudes toward regulation. *Forest Farmer, 52*(1), 14–15.

Blockstein, D. E., & Wiegman, L. (2010). The climate solutions consensus: What we know and what to do about it. *The National Council for Science and the Environment.* Washington, DC: Island Press.

Bockino, N. K., & Tinker, B. D. (2012). Interactions of white pine blister rust and mountain pine beetle in whitebark pine ecosystems in the Southern Greater Yellowstone area. *Natural Areas Journal, 32*(1), 31–40.

Bond, W. J., & Keeley, J. E. (2005). Fire as global "herbivore": The ecology and evolution of flammable ecosystems. *Trends in Ecology and Evolution, 20,* 387–394.

Bormann, B. T. (1999). *The promise of adaptive management.* Portland: USDA Forest Service.

Bormann, B. T., Haynes, R. W., & Martin, J. R. (2007). Adaptive management of forest ecosystems: Did some rubber hit the road? *Bioscience, 57,* 186–191.

Bormann, F. H., & Likens, G. E. (1994). *Pattern and process in a forested ecosystem.* (Vol. 1). New York, NY: Springer-Verlag.

Boston, K., & Bettinger, P. (2006). An economic and landscape evaluation of the green-up rules for California, Oregon, and Washington (USA). *Forest Policy and Economics, 8,* 251–266.

Boyd, R. (Ed). (1999). *Indians, fire and the land in the Pacific Northwest.* Corvallis, OR: Oregon State University Press. Corvallis.

Bradley, B. A., Wilcove, D. S., & Oppenheimer, M. (2010). Climate change increases risk of plant invasion in the Eastern United States. *Biological Invasions, 12*(6), 1855–1872.

Breshears, D. D., Cobb, N. S., Rich, P. M., Price, K. P., Allen, C. D., Balice, R. G., Romme, W. H. et al. (2005). Regional vegetation die-off in response to global-change-type drought. *Proceedings of the National Academy of Sciences of the United States of America, 102*(42), 15144–15148.

Brooks, J. R. (2015). Water, bound and mobile. *Science, 349*(6244), 138–139.

Brown, T. C., & Gregory, R. (1999). Why the WTA-WTP disparity matters. *Ecological Economics, 28*(3), 313–325.

Brundtland, G. H., Khalid, M., Agnelli, S., et al. (1987). *Our Common Future: Report of the World Commission on Environment and Development.* Oxford, UK: Oxford University Press.

Brunson, M. W. (1996). A definition of "social acceptability" in ecosystem management. In M. W. Brunson, L. E. Kruger, C. B. Tyler, & S. A. Schroeder (Eds.), *Defining social acceptability in ecosystem management: A workshop proceedings. USDA Forest Service General Technical Report PNW-GTR-369* (pp. 7–16). Portland, OR: Pacific Northwest Research Station, OR. Retrieved from http://www.fs.fed.us/pnw/pubs/pnw_gtr369.pdf

Brunson, M. W., & Shindler, B. A. (2004). Geographic Variation in Social Acceptability of wildland fuels management in the western United States. *Society & Natural Resources: An International Journal, 17,* 8, 661–678, doi: 10.1080/08941920490480688

Bunnell, F. L., & Dunsworth, G. B. (Eds.). (2010). *Forestry and biodiversity: Learning how to sustain biodiversity in managed forests.* Vancouver, BC, Canada: UBC Press.

Bunnell, F. L., & Houde, I. (2010). Down wood and biodiversity-implications to forest practices. *Environmental Reviews, 18,* 397–421.

Bunnell, F. L., Huggard, D. J., & Dunsworth, G. B. (2010). Effectiveness monitoring: An introduction. In F. L., Bunnell & G. B. Dunsworth (Eds.), *Forestry and biodiversity: Learning how to sustain biodiversity in managed forests* (pp. 75–82). Vancouver, BC, Canada: University of British Columbia Press.

Bunnell, F. L., Huggard, D. J., & Kremsater, L. L. (2010). Summary: Progress and lessons learned. In F. L. Bunnell & G. B. Dunsworth (Eds.), *Forestry and biodiversity: Learning how to sustain biodiversity in managed forests* (pp. 276–293). Vancouver, BC, Canada: University of British Columbia Press.

Butler, B. J. (2008). Family forest owners of the United States, 2006. *USDA Forest Service General Technical Report NRS-27.* Newtown Square, PA: Northern Research Station.

Butler, B. J. (2011). Family forest owners rule! *Forest History Today,* Spring/Fall, 87–91.

Butler, B. J., Hewes, J. H., Dickinson, B. J., Andrejczyk, K., Butler, S. M., & Markowski-Lindsay, M. (2016a). USDA Forest Service national woodland owner survey. *USDA Forest Service Resource Bulletin NRS-99.* Newton Square, PA: Northern Research Station.

Butler, B. J., Hewes, J. H., Dickinson, B. J., Andrejczyk, K., Butler, S. M., & Markowski-Lindsay, M. (2016b). Family forest ownerships of the United States, 2013: Findings from the USDA Forest Service's national woodland owner survey. *Journal of Forestry, 114.* Retrieved from http://www.fs.fed.us/nrs/pubs/jrnl/2016/nrs_2016_butler_001.pdf

Butler, W. H. (2013). Collaboration at arm's length: Navigating agency engagement in landscape-scale ecological restoration collaboratives. *Journal of Forestry, 111*(6), 395–403.

Butler, W. H., Monroe, A., & McCaffrey, S. (2015). Collaborative implementation for ecological restoration on US public lands: Implications for legal context, accountability, and adaptive management. *Environmental Management, 55,* 564–577.

California Air Resources Board. (2014, November 14). *Compliance offset protocols: U.S. forest projects.* Retrieved from http://www.arb.ca.gov/regact/2014/capandtrade14/ctusforestprojectsprotocol.pdf

Calkin, D. E., Cohen, J. D., Finney, M. A., & Thompson, M. P. (2014). How risk management can prevent future wildfire disasters in the wildland-urban interface. *Proceedings of the National Academy of Sciences, 111*(2), 746–751.

Calkin, D. E., Gebert K. M., Jones J. G., & Neilson R. P. (2005). Forest Service large fire area burned and suppression expenditure trends, 1970–2002. *Journal of Forestry, 103,* 179–183.

Calkin, D. E., Thompson, M. P., & Finney, M. A. (2015). Negative consequences of positive feedbacks in US wildfire management. *Forest Ecosystems, 2*(1), 1–10.

Campbell, J. L., Donato, D., Azuma, D., & Law, B. (2007). Pyrogenic carbon emission from a large wildfire in Oregon, United States. *Journal of Geophysical Research, 112,* 1–11.

Campbell, J. L., Harmon, M. E., & Mitchell, R. (2011). Can fuel-reduction treatments really increase forest carbon storage in the western US by reducing future fire emissions? *Frontiers in Ecology and the Environment, 10*(2), 83–90.

Carey, A. B. (2007). *AIMing for healthy forests: Active intentional management for multiple values. USDA Forest Service General Technical Report PNW-GTR-721.* Portland, OR: USDA Forest Service Pacific Northwest Research Station.

Carey, A. B. (2009). Maintaining biodiversity in managed forests. In T. A. Spies, & S. L. Duncan, *Old growth in a new world: A Pacific Northwest icon reexamined* (pp. 58–69). Washington, DC: Island Press.

Carey, A. B., & Curtis, R. O. (1996). Conservation of biodiversity: a useful paradigm for forest ecosystem management. *Wildlife Soc. Bull., 24,* 61–62.

Carey, A. B., Lippke, B. R., & Sessions, J. (1999). Intentional systems management: managing forests for biodiversity. *Journal of Sustainable Forestry, 9*(3–4), 83–125.

Carroll, M. S., Blatner, K. A., Cohn, P. J., & Morgan, T. (2007). Managing fire danger in the forests of the US Inland Northwest: A classic "wicked problem" in public land policy. *Journal of Forestry, 105*(5), 239–244.

Carson, R. L. (1962). *Silent spring.* Boston, MA: Houghton-Mifflin.

Carson, R. T. (2012). *Contingent valuation: a comprehensive bibliography and history.* Cheltenham, UK: Edward Elgar.

Carson, R. T., & Mitchell, R. C. (1993). The value of clean water: The public's willingness to pay for boatable, fishable, and swimmable quality water. *Water Resources Research, 29*(7), 2445–2454.

Carson, R. T., Flores, N. E., & Meade, N. F. (2001). Contingent valuation: Controversies and evidence. *Environmental and Resource Economics, 19,* 173–210.

Carson, R. T., Mitchell, R. C., Hanemann, W. M., Kopp, R. J., Presser, S., & Ruud, P. A. (1992). *A contingent valuation study of lost passive use values resulting from the* Exxon Valdez *oil spill: A report to the Attorney General of the State of Alaska.* San Diego, CA: Natural Resource Damage Assessment Inc.

Carson, R. T., Mitchell, R. C., Hanemann, W. M., Kopp, R. J., Presser, S., & Ruud, P. A. (2003). Contingent valuation and lost passive use: Damages from the *Exxon Valdez* oil spill. *Environmental and Resource Economics, 25,* 257–286.

Cashore, B. W. (1997). Governing forestry: Environmental group influence in British Columbia and the US Pacific Northwest. PhD Dissertation, Department of Political Science, University of Toronto.

Cashore, B. W., Auld, G., & Newsom, D. (2004). *Governing through markets: Forest certification and the emergence of non-state authority*. New Haven, CT: Yale University Press.

Cashore, B., & Howlett, M. (2006). Behavioural thresholds and institutional rigidities as explanations of punctuated equilibrium processes in Pacific Northwest forest policy dynamics. In Robert Repetto (Ed.), *By fits and starts: Punctuated equilibrium in US environmental policy*. New Haven, CT: Yale University Press.

Castle, E. N., & Berrens, R. P. (1993). Endangered species, economic analysis, and the Safe Minimum Standard. *Northwest Environmental Journal, 9*(1/2), 108–130.

Cathcart, J. F., & Delaney, M. (2006). Carbon accounting: Determining carbon offsets from forest projects. In M. Cloughesy (Ed.), *Forests carbon and climate change: A synthesis of findings* (pp. 156–174). Portland, OR: Oregon Forest Resources Institute.

Cathcart, J. F., Kline, J. D., Delaney, M., & Tilton, M. (2007). Carbon storage and Oregon's land-use planning program. *Journal of Forestry, 105*(4), 167–172.

Champ, P. A., Boyle, K. J., & Brown, T. C. (Eds.). (2014). *A primer on non-market valuation* (2nd ed.). Dordrecht, The Netherlands: Kluwer Academic Publishers.

Chapin III, F. S., Matson, P. A., & Mooney, H. A. (2011). *Principles of terrestrial ecosystem ecology* (2nd ed.). New York, NY: Springer.

Charnley, S., Long, J. W., & Lake, F. K. (2014). Collaboration in national forest management. In J. W. Long, L. N. Quinn-Davidson, & C. N. Skinner (Eds.), *Science Synthesis to Support Socioecological Resilience in the Sierra Nevada and Southern Cascade Range USDA Forest Service General Technical Report PSW-GTR-247*. Albany, CA: Pacific Southwest Research Station, Forest Service, US Department of Agriculture.

Chaskin, R. J. (2001). Building community capacity: A definitional framework and case studies from a comprehensive community initiative. *Urban Affairs Review, 36*, 291–323.

Chen, J., Franklin, J. F., & Spies, T. A. (1993). Contrasting microclimates among clearcut, edge, and interior of old-growth Douglas-fir forest. *Agricultural and Forest Meteorology, 63*, 219–237.

Chen, J., Franklin, J. F., & Spies, T. A. (1995). Growing season microclimatic gradients from clearcut edges into old-growth Douglas-fir forests. *Ecological Applications, 5*(1), 74–86.

Chen, J., Innes, J. L., & Tikina, A. (2010). Private cost-benefits of voluntary forest product certification. *International Forestry Review, 12*(1), 1–12.

Cheng, A. S. (2006). Build it and they will come? Mandating collaboration in public lands planning and management. *Natural Resource Journal, 46*, 841–858.

Cheng, A. S., & Sturtevant, V. E. (2012). A framework for assessing collaborative capacity in community-based public forest management. *Environmental Management, 49*(3), 675–689. Online version retrieved from https://warnercnr.colostate.edu/docs/frs/Weirdness/Cheng-Sturtevant_AssessingCollaborativeCapacity_2012EnvMgt.pdf

Chiesura, A., & de Groot, R. (2003). Critical natural capital: A socio-cultural perspective. *Ecological Economics, 44*, 219–231.

Christensen, N. L. (1981). Fire regimes in southeastern ecosystems. In H. A. Mooney, T. M. Bonnicksen, N. L. Christensen, J. E. Lotan, & W. A. Reiners (Eds.), *Proceedings of the Conference: Fire Regimes and Ecosystem Properties, Honolulu, Hawaii. General Technical Report WO-26* (pp. 112–136). Washington, DC, USA: US Department of Agriculture Forest Service.

Christensen, N. L. (1988). Vegetation of the southeastern coastal plain. In M. G. Barbour & W. D. Billings (Eds.), *North American terrestrial vegetation* (pp. 317–363). New York, NY: Cambridge University Press.

Christensen, N. L. (2000). Vegetation of the Southeastern Coastal Plain. In M. G. Barbour, & W. D. Billings (Eds.), *North American Terrestrial Vegation Second Edition* (pp. 397–448). Cambridge, UK: Cambridge University Press.

Christensen, N. L., Agee, J. K., Brussard, P. F., Hughes, J., Knight, D. H., Minshall, G. W., Peek, J. M., et al. (1989). Interpreting the Yellowstone fires of 1988. *BioScience, 39*, 678–685.

Chuenpagdee, R., Knetch, J. L., & Brown, T. C. (2001). Environmental damage schedules: Community judgements of importance and assessments of losses. *Land Economics, 77*, 1–11.

Churchill, D. J., Larson, A. J., Dahlgreen, M. C., Franklin, J. F., Hessburg, P. F., & Lutz, J. A. (2013). Restoring forest resilience: From reference spatial patterns to silvicultural prescriptions and monitoring. *Forest Ecology and Management, 291*, 442–457.

Cissel, J. H., Swanson, F. J., & Weisberg, P. J. (1999). Landscape management using historical fire regimes: Blue River, Oregon. *Ecological Applications, 9*(4), 1217–1231.

Cohen, J. (2010). The wildland-burn interface fire problem. *Fremontia, 38*(2/3), 16–22.

Cohen, M. J., Creed, I., F., Alexander, L., Basu, N. B., Calhoun, A. J. K., et al. (2016). Do geographically isolated wetlands influence landscape functions? *Proceedings of the National Academy of Sciences, 113*(8), 1978–1986.

Collins, B. M., Miller, J. A., Thode, A. E., Kelly, M., van Wagtendonk, J. W., & Stephens, S. L. (2009). Interactions among wildland fires in a long-established Sierra Nevada natural fire area. *Ecosystems, 12*, 114–128.

Colorado Coalition of Land Trusts. (2004/2010). *A Conservation easement appraisal guide*. Denver, CO: Author. Retrieved from http://www.uwyo.edu/law/rural-law-center/conservation-easement-conference/weston%20cclt%20appraisal%20guide%206-01-04%20updated%2020101.pdf

Committee of Scientists. (1999). *Sustaining the people's lands: Recommendations for stewardship of the national forests and grasslands into the next century*. Washington DC: USDA. Retrieved from http://www.fs.fed.us/emc/nfma/includes/cosreport/cosfrnt.pdf

Cooksey, R. A. (1994). *Conservation easements as a public good: Willingness to pay to protect forest land benefits with conservation easements in the northern forest lands of New Hampshire*. MS Thesis. University of New Hampshire, Durham.

Cooksey, R. A., & Howard, T. E. (1995). Willingness to pay to protect forest benefits with conservation easements. Abstracts of invited papers, IUFRO XXth World Congress, 6–12 August, Tampere, Finland.

Cooper, C. F. (1960). Changes in vegetation, structure, and growth of southwestern pine forest since white settlement. *Ecological Monographs, 30*(2), 129–164.

Corace, R. G., & Goebel, P. C. (2010). An ecological approach to forest management for wildlife: Integrating disturbance ecology patterns into silvicultural treatments. *The Wildlife Professional,* 38–40.

Corace, R. G., Goebel, P. C., Hix, D. M., Casselman, T., & Seefelt, N. E. (2009). Ecological forestry at National Wildlife Refuges: Experiences from Seney National Wildlife Refuge and Kirtland's Warbler Wildlife Management Area, USA. *Forestry Chronicle, 85*, 695–701.

Cortner, H., & Moote, M. A. (1998). *The politics of ecosystem management*. Washington, DC: Island Press.

Coumou, D., Petoukhov, V., Rahmstorf, S., Petri, S., & Schellnguber, H. J. (2014). Quasi-resonant circulation regimes and hemispheric synchronization of extreme weather in boreal summer. *Proceedings of the National Academy of Sciences, 111*(34), 12331–12336.

Council on Environmental Quality (CEQ). (2007). *A citizen's guide to the NEPA: Having your voice heard*. Washington, DC: Council on Environmental Quality, Executive Office of the President.

Covington, W. W. (2000). Helping western forests heal (commentary). *Nature, 408*, 135–136.

Covington, W. W., Everett, R. L., Steele, R. W., Irwin, L. I., Daer, T. A., & Auclair, A. N. D. (1994). Historical and anticipated changes in forest ecosystems of the Inland West of the United States. *Journal of Sustainable Forestry, 2*, 13–63.

Covington, W. W., Fulé, P. Z., Moore, M. M., Hart, S. C., Kolb, T. E., Mast, J. N., Sackett, S. S., & Wagner, M. R. (1997). Restoration of ecosystem health in southwestern ponderosa pine forests. *Journal of Forestry, 95*(4), 23–29.

Covington, W. W. & Moore, M. M. (1994). Post-settlement changes in natural fire regimes and forest structure: Ecological restoration of old-growth ponderosa pine forests. *Journal of Sustainable Forestry, 2*(2), 153–181.

Crowards, T. M. (1998). Safe Minimum Standards: Costs and opportunities. *Ecological Economics, 25*(3), 303–314.

Crutzen, P. J. (2006). The "Anthropocene." In E. Ehlers & T. Kraft (Eds.*), Earth system science in the Anthropocene: Emerging issues and problems* (pp. 13–18). Berlin/Heidelbert/New York: Springer.

Cubbage, F. W., Moore, S., Cox, J., Jervis, L., Edeburn, J., Richter, D., Boyette, W., Thompson, M., & Chestnutt, M. (2003). Forest certification of state and university lands in North Carolina. *Journal of Forestry, 101*(8), 26–31.

Cubbage, F., Moore, S., Henderson, T., & Araujo, M. (2009). Costs and benefits of forest certification in the Americas. In J. B. Paulding (Ed.), *Natural resources: Management, economic development and protection* (pp. 155–183). Hauppauge, NY: Nova Publishers.

Cubbage, F. W., O'Laughlin, J., & Bullock III, C. S. (1993). *Forest resource policy*. New York, NY: John Wiley.

Cubbage, F. W., O'Laughlin, J. & Peterson, M. N. (2017). *Natural resource policy*. Long Grove, IL: Waveland Press.

Cubbage, F. W., & Siegel, W. (1985). The law regulating private forest practices. *Journal of Forestry, 83*, 538–545.

Cubbage, F. W., Snider, A. G., Abt, K. L., & Moulton, R. J. (2003). Private forests: Management. In E. O. Sills & K. L. Abt (Eds.), *Forests in a market economy* (pp. 23–38). Boston, MA: Kluwer Academic Publishers.

Curtis, R. O. (1995). *Extended rotations and culmination age of coast Douglas-fir: old studies speak to current issues. Res. Pap. PNW-RP-485.* Portland, OR: U.S. Department of Agriculture, Forest Service, Pacific Northwest Research Station.

Curtis, R. O. (1997). The role of extended rotations. In K. A. Kohn & J. F. Franklin (Eds.), *Creating a forestry for the 21st century: The science of ecosystem management* (pp. 165–170). Washington, DC: Island Press.

D'Amato, A. W., Catanzaro, P., Damery, D. T., Kittredge, D. B., & Ferrare, K. A. (2010). Are family forest owners facing a future in which forest management is not enough? *Journal of Forestry, 108*, 32–38.

D'Amato, A. W., Palik, B. J., Franklin, J. F., & Foster, D. R. (2017). Exploring the origins of ecological forestry in North America. *Journal of Forestry, 115*, 126–127.

Daily, G. C. (Ed.). (1997). *Nature's services: Societal dependence on natural ecosystems*. Washington, DC: Island Press.

Dale, V. H., Swanson, F. J., & Crisafulli, C. M. (2005). *Disturbance, survival, and succession: understanding ecological responses to the 1980 eruption of Mount St. Helens*. New York, NY: Springer.

Dalton, M. M., Mote, P. W., & Snover, A. K. (Eds.). (2013). *Climate change in the Northwest: Implications for our landscapes, waters, and communities*. Washington, DC: Island Press.

Daly, H. E., & Farley, J. (2011). *Ecological economics: Principles and applications*. Washington, DC: Island Press.

Dana, S., & Fairfax, S. (1980). *Forest and range policy* (2nd ed.). New York, NY: McGraw Hill.

Daniels, S. E., & Walker, G. B. (2001). *Working through environmental conflict: The collaborative learning approach*. Westport, CT: Praeger.

Davis, L. S. (1954). *Forest management*. New York, NY: McGraw Hill.

Davis, L. S. (1966). *Forest management* (2nd ed.). New York, NY: McGraw Hill.

Davis, L. S., & Johnson, K. N. (1987). *Forest management* (3rd ed.). New York, NY: McGraw-Hill.

Davis, L. S., Johnson K. N., Bettinger, P., & Howard, T. (2001). *Forest management* (4th ed.). Long Grove, IL: Waveland Press.

Davis, L. S., & Liu, G. (1998). Integrated forest planning across multiple ownerships and decision makers. *Forest Science, 39*, 152–165.

Dayton, P. K. (1972). Toward an understanding of community resilience and the potential effects of enrichments to the benthos at McMurdo Sound, Antarctica. In B. C. Parker (Ed.), *Proceedings of the colloquium on conservation problems in Antarctica*. Lawrence, KS: Allen Press.

de Groot, R. S., Wilson, M. A., & Boumans, R. M. J. (2002). A typology for the classification, description and valuation of ecosystem functions, goods and services. *Ecological Economics, 41*(3), 393–408.

De Valck, J., Vlaeminck, P., Broekx, S., Liekens, I., Aertsens, J., Chen, W., & Vranken, L. (2014). Benefits of clearing forest plantations to restore nature? Evidence from a discrete choice experiment in Flanders, Belgium. *Landscape and Urban Planning, 125*, 65–75.

DellaSala, D. A. (Ed.). (2011). *Temperate and boreal rainforests of the world*. Washington, DC: Island Press.

Deluca, T. H., Aplet, G. H., Wilmer, B., & Burchfield, J. (2010). The unknown trajectory of forest restoration: A call for ecosystem monitoring. *Journal of Forestry, 108*(9), 288–295.

Díaz, S., Fargione, J., Chapin III, F. S., & Tilman, D. (2006). Biodiversity loss threatens human well-being. *PLoS biology, 4*(8), e277.

Dickens, D. E., Sunday, J., & Moorhead, D. J. (2014). *Economics of growing loblolly, longleaf, and slash pine to a 33 year rotation with three stumpage price sets, four establishment costs sets, with and without pine straw: Net revenue and rate or return.* Series Paper 5, Warnell School of Forestry and Natural Resources, University of Georgia.

Dilkina, B., Houtman, R., Gomes, C. P., Montgomery, C. A., McKelvey, K. S., Kendall, K. Graves, T. A., Bernstein, R., & Schwartz, M. K. (2017). Trade-offs and efficiencies in optimal budget-constrained multispecies corridor networks. *Conservation Biology 31*(1), 192–202.

Dobson, A., Lodge, D., Alder, J., Cumming, G., Keymer, J., McGlade, J., Monney, H., et al. (2006). Habitat loss, trophic cascade, and the decline of ecosystem services. *Ecology, 87*(8), 1915–1924.

Donato, D. C., Fontaine, J. B., Campbell, J. L., Robinson, W. D., Kauffman, J. B., & Law, B. E. (2009). Conifer regeneration in stand-replacement portions of a large mixed-severity wildfire in the Klamath-Siskiyou Mountains. *Canadian Journal of Forest Research 39*, 823–838.

Donato, D. C., Kauffman, J. B., Murdiyarso, D., Kurnianto, S., Stidham, M., & Kanninen, M. (2011). Mangroves among the most carbon-rich forests in the tropics. *Nature Geoscience, 4*, 293–297.

Duerr, W. A. (1960). *Forest economics*. New York, NY: McGraw Hill.

Duerr, W. A., & Duerr, J. B. (1975). The role of faith in forest resource management. In F. Rumsey, & W. A. Duerr (Eds.), *Social Sciences in Forestry: A Book of Readings* (pp. 30–41). Philadelphia, PA: W. B. Saunders Company.

Dunlap, T. R. (1988). *Saving America's Wildlife: Ecology and the American mind, 1850–1990*. Princeton, NJ: Princeton University Press.

Durst, P. B., McKenzie, P. J., Brown, C. L., & Appanah, S. (2006). Challenges facing certification and eco-labelling of forest products in developing countries. *International Forestry Review, 8*(2), 193–200.

Dwyer, G., Dushoff, J., & Yee, S. H. (2004). The combined effects of pathogens and predators on insect outbreaks. *Nature, 430*(6997), 341–345.

Earth Observatory. (n.d.). NASA Goddard Institute for Space Studies. Retrieved from http://earthobservatory.nasa.gov/Features/WorldOfChange/decadaltemp.php

Ebeling, J., & Yasue, M. (2009). The effectiveness of market-based conservation in the tropics: Forest certification in Ecuador and Bolivia. *Journal of Environmental Management, 90*, 1145–1153.

Edmonds, R. L., Agee, J. K., & Gara R. I. (2011). *Forest health and protection*. Long Grove, IL: Waveland Press.

Egan, T. (2009). *The big burn: Teddy Roosevelt and the fire that saved America*. Boston: Mariner Books.

Eichner, T., & Pethig, R. (2011). Carbon leakage, the green paradox, and perfect future markets. *International Economic Review, 52*(3), 767–805.

Eisenberg, C. (2010). *The wolf's tooth: Keystone predators, trophic cascades, and biodiversity*. Washington, DC: Island Press.

Eisenberg, C. (2014). *The carnivore way: Coexisting with and conserving North America's predators*. Washington, DC: Island Press.

Eisenberg, C., Hibbs, D. E., Ripple, W. J., & Salwasser, H. (2014). Context dependence of elk vigilance and wolf predation risk. *Canadian Journal of Zoology, 92*, 727–736.

Eisenberg, C., Seager, S. T., & Hibbs, D. E. (2013). Wolf, elk, and aspen food web relationships: Context and complexity. *Forest Ecology and Management, 299*, 70–80.

Ekins, P., Simon, S., Deutsch, L., Folke, C., & de Groot, R. (2003). A framework for the practical application of the concepts of critical natural capital and strong sustainability. *Ecological Economics, 44*(2–3), 165–185.

Ellefson, P. (2000). Has Gifford Pinchot's regulatory vision been realized? *Journal of Forestry, 92*(5), 15–22.

Ellis, W. E., & Barton, N. P. (2012). Characterizing the North Pacific jet stream for understanding historical variability in western United States winter precipitation. *Physical Geography, 33*, 105–128.

Ellison, A. M., Bank, M. S., Clinton, B. D., Colburn, E. A., Elliott, K., Ford, C. R., Foster, D. R., Kloeppel, B. D., et al. (2005). Loss of foundation species: Consequences for the structure and dynamics of forested ecosystems. *Frontiers in Ecology and the Environment, 3*(9), 479–486.

Endangered Species Act of 1973 (P.L. 93-205), 87 Stat. 884 (1988) (codified at 16 U.S.C. §§ 1531-1544).

Enright, N. J., Fontaine, J. B., Bowman, D. M., Bradstock, R. A., & Williams, R. J. (2015). Interval squeeze: Altered fire regimes and demographic responses interact to threaten woody species persistence as climate changes. *Frontiers in Ecology and Environment, 13*(5), 265–272.

Environmental Commissioner of Ontario. (2014). *Managing new challenges, annual report, 2013/2014* (pp. 93–103). Retrieved from http://docs.assets.eco.on.ca/reports/environmental-protection/2013-2014/2013-14-AR.pdf

EPA (Environmental Protection Agency). (2015). Technical update of the social cost of carbon for regulatory impact analysis. Retrieved from https://www3.epa.gov/climatechange/EPAactivities/economics/scc.html

EPA (Environmental Protection Agency). (2016a). Polluted runoff: Nonpoint-source pollution. Retrieved from http://water.epa.gov/polwaste/nps/whatis.cfm

EPA (Environmental Protection Agency). (2016b). Portland Harbor superfund site. Retrieved from http://yosemite.epa.gov/R10/CLEANUP.NSF/ph/Portland+Harbor+Superfund+Site

Estes, J. A., Tinker, M. T., & Bodkin, J. L. (2010). Using ecological function to develop recovery criteria for depleted species: Sea otters and kelp forests in the Aleutian archipelago. *Conservation Biology, 24*(3), 852–860.

Fairfax, S., & Achterman, G. (1977). The Monongahela controversy and the political process. *Journal of Forestry, 7*, 485–487.

FAO. (2001). *State of the world's forests.* Food and Agriculture Organization of the United Nations. Retrieved from http://www.fao.org/docrep/003/Y0900E/y0900e00.htm

Farber, S., Costanza, R., Childers, D. L., Erickson, J., Gross, K., Grove, M., Hopkinson, C. S., Kahn, J., et al. (2006). Linking ecology and economics for ecosystem management. *Bioscience, 56*, 121–133.

Farley, J. (2012). Ecosystem services: The economics debate. *Ecosystem Services, 1*(1), 40–49.

Farley, J., Schmitt, A., Burke, M., & Farr, M. (2014). Extending market allocation to ecosystem services: Moral and practical implications on a full and unequal planet. *Ecological Economics, 117*, 244–252.

Fausch, K. D. (2015). *For the love of rivers: A scientist's journey.* Corvallis: Oregon State University Press.

Fedrowitz, K., Koricheva, J., Baker, S. C., Lindenmayer, D. B., Palik, B., Rosenvald, R., et al. (2014). Can retention forestry help conserve biodiversity? A meta-analysis. *Journal of Applied Ecology, 51*, 1669–1679.

FEMAT (Report of the Forest Ecosystem Management and Assessment Team). (1993). *Forest ecosystem management: An ecological, economic, and social assessment.* Excerpts retrieved from http://www.blm.gov/or/plans/nwfpnepa/FEMAT-1993/1993_%20FEMAT-ExecSum.pdf

Ferrey, S. (2013). *Environmental law: Examples and explanation* (6th ed.). New York, NY: Wolters Kluwer.

Feynman, R. P. (1986). Personal observations on the reliability of the shuttle. NASA. Retrieved from http://history.nasa.gov/rogersrep/v2appf.htm

Field, C. B., & Kaduk, J. (2004). The carbon balance of an old-growth forest: Building across approaches. *Ecosystems, 7*, 525–533.

Finney, M. A. (2004). FARSITE: Fire Area Simulator–model development and evaluation. *USDA Forest Service Research Paper RMRS-RP-4 Revised.* Ogden, UT: Rocky Mountain Research Station.

Finney, M. A. (2006). An overview of FlamMap fire modeling capabilities. *USDA Forest Service Proceedings RMRS-P-41.* Fort Collins, CO: Rocky Mountain Research Station.

Finney, M. A. (2007). A computational method for optimizing fuel treatment locations. *International Journal of Wildland Fire, 16*(6), 702–711 .

Finney, M. A., & Cohen, J. D. (2003). Expectation and evaluation of fuel management objectives. *USDA Forest Service Proceedings RMRS-P-29.* Fort Collins, CO: Rocky Mountain Research Station.

Finney, M. A., Cohen, J. D., Forthofer, J. M., McAllister, S. S., Gollner, M. J., et al. (2015). Role of buoyant flame dynamics in wildfire spread. *Proceedings of the National Academy of Sciences, 112*(32), 9833–9838.

Finney, M. A., Grenfell, I. C., & McHugh, C. W. (2009). Modeling large fire containment using generalized linear mixed model analysis. *Forest Science, 55*, 249–255.

Finney, M. A., Grenfell, I. C., McHugh, C. W., Seli, R. C., Trethewey, D., Stratton, R. D., & Brittain, S. (2011). A method for ensemble wildland fire simulation. *Environmental Modeling and Assessment, 16*, 153–167.

Finney, M. A., McHugh, C. W., & Grenfell, I. C. (2005). Stand- and landscape-level effects of prescribed burning on two Arizona wildfires. *Canadian Journal of Forest Research, 35*, 1714–1722.

Finney, M. A., Seli, R. C., McHugh, C. W., Ager, A. A., Bahro, B., & Agee, J. K. (2007). Simulation of long-term landscape-level fuel treatments effects on large wildfires. *International Journal of Wildland Fire, 16*, 712–727.

Firey, W. (1960). *Man, mind, and land.* Glencoe, IL: The Free Press.

Fischer, A. P., & Bliss, J. C. (2008). Behavioral assumptions of conservation policy: Conserving oak habitat on family-forest land in the Willamette Valley, Oregon. *Conservation Biology, 22*(2), 275–283.

Fisher, R., & Ury, W. (1991). *Getting to yes: Negotiating agreement without giving in.* New York, NY: Penguin Books.

Fisher, R., Ury, W., & Patton, B. (2011). *Getting to yes: Negotiating agreement without giving in* (Rev. ed.). New York, NY: Penguin Books.

Forman, R. T. (1995). *Land mosaics: The ecology of landscapes and regions.* Cambridge, UK: Cambridge University Press.

Foster, D. R. (Ed.). (2014). *Hemlock: A forest giant on the edge.* New Haven, CT: Yale University Press.

Foster, D. R., Donahue, B. M., Kittredge, D. B., Lambert, K. F., Hunter, M. L., Hall, B. R., et al. (2010). *Wildlands and woodlands: A vision for the New England landscape.* Petersham, MA: Harvard University Forest.

Fowlie, M., Greenstone, M., & Wolfram, C. (2015, June). *Do energy efficiency investments deliver? Evidence from the Weatherization Assistance Program.* Retrieved from https://nature.berkeley.edu/~fowlie/WAP.pdf

Franklin, J. F. (1993). Preserving biodiversity: Species, ecosystems, or landscapes? *Ecological Applications, 3*(2), 202–205.

Franklin, J. F., & Agee, J. K. (2003). Forging a science-based national forest fire policy. *Issues in Science and Technology, 20*, 59–66.

Franklin, J. F., Berg, D. R., Thornburg, D. A., & Tappeiner, J. C. (1997). Alternative silvicultural approaches to timber harvesting: Variable retention harvest systems. In *Creating a forestry for the 21st century: the science of ecosystem management* (pp. 111–139). Washington, DC: Island Press.

Franklin, J. F., Cromack, K., Denison, W., McKee, A., Maser, C., Sedell, J., Swanson, F., & Juday, G. (1981). Ecological characteristics of old-growth Douglas-fir forests. *USDA Forest Service General Technical Report, PNW-118.* Portland, OR: Pacific Northwest Research Station.

Franklin, J. F., & DeBell, D. S. (1988). Thirty-six years of tree population change in an old-growth Pseudotsuga-Tsuga forest. *Canadian Journal of Forest Research, 18*, 633–639.

Franklin, J. F., & Fites-Kaufmann, J. A. (1996). Assessment of late-successional forests of the Sierra Nevada. *Sierra Nevada ecosystem project: Final report to Congress, 2*, 627–662.

Franklin, J. F., & Forman, R. T. T. (1987). Creating landscape patterns by forest cutting: Ecological consequences and principles. *Landscape Ecology, 1*(1), 5–18.

Franklin, J. F., Hagmann, R. K., & Urgenson, L. S. (2014). Interactions between societal goals and restoration of dry forest landscapes in western North America. *Landscape Ecology, 29*(10), 1645–1655.

Franklin, J. F., & Halpern, C. B. (1989). Influence of biological legacies on succession. In D. E. Ferguson, P. Morgan, & F. D. Johnson (Eds.), *Proceedings—land classifications based on vegetation: Applications for resource management. USDA Forest Service Gen. Tech. Rep. INT-257* (pp. 54–55). Washington, DC: U.S. Department of Agriculture, Forest Service.

Franklin, J. F., Harmon, M. E., & Swanson, F. J. (1999). Complementary roles of research and monitoring: Lessons from the US LTER Program and Tierra del Fuego. In C. Aguirre-Bravo & C. R. Franco (Ed.), *North American science symposium toward a unified framework for inventorying and monitoring forest ecosystem resources. RMRS-P-12* (pp. 284–291). Fort Collins: USDA Forest Service Rocky Mountain Research Station.

Franklin, J. F., & Johnson, K. N. (2012). A restoration framework for federal forests in the Pacific Northwest. *Journal of Forestry, 110*(8), 429–439.

Franklin, J. F., & Johnson, K. N. (2013). Ecologically based management: A future for federal forestry in the Pacific Northwest. *Journal of Forestry, 111*(6), 429–432.

Franklin, J. F., Johnson, K. N., Churchill, D. J., Hagmann, K., Johnson, D., & Johnston, J. (2013). *Restoration of dry forests in eastern Oregon: A field guide*. Portland, OR: The Nature Conservancy.

Franklin, J. F., Lindenmayer, D., MacMahon, J. A., McKee, A., Magnuson, J., Perry, D. A., Waide, R., & Foster, D. (2000). Threads of continuity. *Conservation Biology in Practice, 1*(1), 9–16.

Franklin, J. F., & MacMahon, J. A. (2000). Messages from a mountain. *Science, 288*(5469), 1183–1184.

Franklin, J. F., Mitchell, R. J., & Palik, B. J. (2007). *Natural disturbance and stand development principles for ecological forestry. Gen. Tech. Rep. NRS-19*. Newton Square, PA: U.S. Department of Agriculture, Forest Service, Northern Research.

Franklin, J. F., Shugart, H. H., & Harmon, M. E. (1987). Tree death as an ecological process. *BioScience, 17,* 550–557.

Franklin, J. F., & Spies, T. A. (1991). Composition, function, and structure of old-growth Douglas-fir forests: Wildlife and vegetation of unmanaged Douglas-fir forests. *USDA Forest Service General Technical Report PNW-GTR-285*, 71–80. Station, 44.

Franklin, J. F., Spies, T. A., Van Pelt, R., Carey, A. B., Thornburgh, D. A., Berg, D. R., Lindenmayer, D. B., et al. (2002). Disturbances and structural development of natural forest ecosystems with silvicultural implications, using Douglas-fir forests as an example. *Forest Ecology and Management, 155,* 399–423.

Franklin, J. F., Swanson, F. J., Harmon, M. E., Perry, D. A., Spies, T. A., Dale, V. H., et al. (1991). Effects of global climatic change on forests in northwestern North America. *The Northwest Environmental Journal, 7,* 233–254.

Franklin, J. F., & Van Pelt, R. (2004). Spatial aspects of structural complexity in old-growth forests. *Journal of Forestry, 102*(3), 22–28.

Frelich, L. E. (2002). *Forest dynamics and disturbance regimes: Studies from temperate evergreen-deciduous forests*. Cambridge, UK: Cambridge University Press.

Freund, J. A., Franklin, J. F., Larson, A. J., & Lutz, J. A. (2014). Multi-decadal establishment for single-cohort Douglas-fir forests. *Canadian Journal of Forest Research, 44*(9), 1068–1078.

Frey, S. J. K., Hadley, A. S. & Betts, M. G. (2016a). Microclimate predicts within-season distribution dynamics of montane forest birds. *Diversity and Distributions*, 1–16.

Frey, S. J. K., Hadley, A. S., Johnson, S. L., Schulze, M., Jones, J. A., & Betts, M. G. (2016b). Spatial models reveal the microclimatic buffering capacity of old-growth forests. *Science Advances, 2*(4), e1501392.

FSC (Forest Stewardship Council). (2010). *Forest management certification*. Retrieved from https://us.fsc.org/download-box.188.htm

FSC (Forest Stewardship Council). (2011). *Costs and benefits of forest certification*. Retrieved from https://us.fsc.org/preview.costs-and-benefits-of-forest-certification.a-317.pdf

FSC (Forest Stewardship Council). (2014). *Global FSC certificates: Type and distribution*. Bonn: Forest Stewardship Council, FSC International Center GmbH. Retrieved from https://ic.fsc.org/preview.facts-and-figures-november-2014.a-3810.pdf

FSC (Forest Stewardship Council). (2015, July). FSC Principles and Criteria for Forest Stewardship FSC-STD-01-001 V5-2 EN_web_version. Retrieved from https://ic.fsc.org/en/certification/principles-and-criteria

FSCC (Forest Sector Carbon Calculator—Version 2.0). (2014). Retrieved from http://landcarb.forestry.oregonstate.edu/default.aspx

Gilliam, F. S., & Roberts, M. R. (Eds.). (2003). *The herbaceous layer in forests of eastern North America*. New York, NY: Oxford University Press.

Gladwell, M. (2005). *Blink: The power of thinking without thinking*. New York, NY: Little Brown.

Glitzenstein, J. S., Platt, W. J., & Streng, D. R. (1995). Effects of fire regime and habitat on tree dynamics in north Florida longleaf pine savannas. *Ecological Monographs, 65*(4), 441–476.

Glover, F., & Kochenberger, G. (Eds.). (2003). *Handbook of metaheuristics*. Dordrecht, Netherlands: Kluwer Academic Publishers.

Gordon, J., Berry, J., Ferrucci, M., Franklin, J., Johnson, K. N., Mukumoto, C., Patton, D., & Sessions, J. (2003). *An assessment of Indian forests and forest management in the United States*. Second Indian Forest Management Assessment Team. Portland, OR: Intertribal Timber Council.

Gordon, J., Franklin, J. F., Johnson, K. N., Patton, D., Sedell, J., Sessions, J., & Williston, E. (1993). *An assessment of Indian forests and forest management in the United States*. Rep. Indian For. Mgt. Team. Portland, OR: Intertribal Timber Council.

Gordon, J., Sessions, J., Bailey, J., Cleaves, D., Corrao, V., Leighton, A., Mason, L., Rasmussen, M., Salwasser, H., & Sterner, M. (2013). *Assessment of Indian forests and forest management in the United States: Final Report* (Vol. I). Report prepared for the Intertribal Timber Council, Portland, OR.

Gordon, S. (2006). *Decision support systems for forest biodiversity management: A review of tools and an analytical-deliberative framework for understanding their successful application*. PhD Thesis, Oregon State University.

Gordon, S. (2007). Appendix A—Case study briefs. In K. N. Johnson, S. Gordon, S. Duncan, D. Lach, B. McComb, & K. Reynolds (Eds.), *Conserving creatures of the forest: A guide to decision making and decision models for forest biodiversity*. Report to the National Commission on Science for Sustainable Forestry. Retrieved from http://ncseonline.org/sites/default/files/A10%20(II)%20Final%20Report%20ConservingCreatures%208.21.07.pdf

Graham, R., Finney, M., McHugh, C., Cohen, J., Calkin, D., Stratton, R., Bradshaw, L., & Nikolov, N. (2012). Fourmile Canyon Fire Findings. *USDA Forest Service General Technical Report RMRS-GTR-289*. Fort Collins, CO: Rocky Mountain Research Station.

Gratkowski, H. J. (1956). Windthrow around staggered settings in old-growth Douglas-fir. *Forest Science, 2,* 60–74.

Green, O. O., & Garmestani, A. S. (2012). Adaptive management to protect biodiversity: Best available science and the Endangered Species Act. *Diversity, 3,* 164–178.

Greenberg, C. H., Collins, B. S., & Thompson, III, F. R. (2011). *Sustaining young forest communities: Ecology and management of early successional habitats in the central hardwood region, USA*. (Vol. 21). New York, NY: Springer Science & Business Media.

Gregg F., Born, S. M., Lord, W. B., & Waterstone, M. (1991). *Institutional response to a changing water policy environment* (USGS Grant #14-08-0001-G1639). Tucson, AZ: Water Resources Research Center, University of Arizona.

Gregory, R., Failing, L., Harstone, M., Long, G., McDaniels, T., & Ohlson, D. (2012). *Structured decision making: A practical guide to environmental management choices*. New York, NY: Wiley-Blackwell.

Gucinski, H., Furniss, M. J., Ziemer, R. R., & Brookes, M. H. (2001). Forest roads: A synthesis of scientific information. *USDA Forest Service General Technical Report PNW-GTR-509*. Portland, OR: Pacific Northwest Research Station, Portland, OR.

Gulbrandsen, L. H. (2005). The effectiveness of non-state governance schemes: A comparative study of forest certification in Norway and Sweden. *International Environmental Agreements, 5,* 125–149.

Guldin, J. M., Iffrig, G. F., & Flader, S. L. (2008). Pioneer forest—a half century of sustainable uneven-aged forest management in the Missouri Ozarks. *USDS Forest Service General Technical Report SRS–108.* Asheville, NC: Southern Research Station.

Gunderson, L. H. (1999). Stepping back: Assessing for understanding in complex regional systems. In K. N. Johnson, F. Swanson, M. Herring, & S. Greene (Eds.), *Bioregional assessments: Science at the crossroads of management and policy.* Washington, DC: Island Press.

Gunderson, L. H., & Holling, C. S. (Eds.). (2002). *Panarchy: Understanding transformations in human and natural systems.* Washington, DC: Island Press.

Gunderson, L. H., Holling, C. S., & Light, S. S. (1995). Barriers broken and bridges built: A synthesis. In L. H. Gunderson, C. S. Holling, & S. S. Light (Eds.), *Barriers and bridges to the renewal of ecosystems and institutions* (pp. 489–532). New York, NY: Columbia University Press.

Gunnoe, A., & Gellert, P. K. (2011). Financialization, shareholder value, and the transformation of timberland ownership in the US. *Critical Sociology, 37*(3), 265–284.

Gustafsson, L., Baker, S. C., Bauhus, J., et al. (2012). Retention forestry to maintain multifunctional forests: A world perspective. *Bioscience, 62*(7), 633–645.

Hagen, D. A., Vincent, J. W., & Welle, P. G. (1992). Benefits of preserving old-growth forests and the northern spotted owl. *Contemporary Economic Policy, 10*(2), 13–26.

Hagmann, R. K., Franklin, J. F., & Johnson, K. N. (2013). Historical structure and composition of ponderosa pine and mixed-conifer forests in south-central Oregon. *Forest Ecology and Management, 304,* 492–504.

Hagmann, R. K., Franklin, J. F., & Johnson, K. N. (2014). Historical conditions in mixed-conifer forests on the eastern slopes of the northern Oregon Cascade Range, USA. *Forest Ecology and Management, 330,* 158–170.

Hagmann, R. K., Johnson, D. L., & Johnson, K. N. (2017). Historical and current forest structure and northern spotted owl habitat in south central Oregon. *Forest Ecology Management, 389,* 374–385.

Hairston, N. G., Smith, F. E., & Slobodkin, L. B. (1960). Community structure, population control, and competition. *The American Naturalist, 94,* 421–425.

Halaj, J., & Wise, D. H. (2001). Terrestrial trophic cascades: How much do they trickle? *The American Naturalist, 57*(3), 262–281.

Hammack, J., & Brown, G. M. (1974). *Waterfowl and wetlands: Toward bioeconomic analysis.* Baltimore, MD: Johns Hopkins University Press.

Hammond, G., & Jones C. (2008). *Inventory of carbon & energy (ICE) Version 1.6a.* University of Bath, UK. Retrieved from http://www.appropedia.org/images/5/56/ICE_Version_1.6a.pdf

Hampton, H. M., Sesnie, S. E., Bailey, J. D., & Snider, G. B. (2011). Estimating regional wood supply based on stakeholder consensus for forest restoration in northern Arizona. *Journal of Forestry, 109*(1), 15–26.

Hanley, N., Mourato, S., & Wright, R. E. (2001). Choice modeling approaches: A superior alternative for environmental valuation? *Journal of Economic Surveys, 15*(3), 435–462.

Hann, W. J., & Bunnell, D. L. (2001). Fire and land management planning and implementation across multiple scales. *International Journal of Wildland Fire, 10,* 389–403.

Hansen, A. J., Spies, T. A., Swanson, F. J., & Öhmann, J. L. (1991). Conserving biodiversity in managed forests. *BioScience, 41*(6), 382–392.

Hardin, G. (1968). The tragedy of the commons. *Science, 162,* 1243–1248.

Harmon, M. E. (2009). Effects of partial harvest on the carbon stores in Douglas-fir/western hemlock forests. *Ecosystems, 12,* 777–791.

Harmon, M. E. (2016). Have product substitution carbon benefits been overestimated? In preparation.

Harmon, M. E., & Campbell, J. L. (2017). Carbon in the forest sector. In D. H. Olsen & B. V. Horn (Eds.), *People, forests, and change: Lessons from the Pacific Northwest*, pp. 161–173. Washington, DC: Island Press.

Harmon, M. E., Ferrell, W. K., & Franklin, J. F. (1990). Effect on carbon storage of conversion of old-growth forests to young forests. *Science, 247,* 699–702.

Harmon, M. E., Franklin, J. F., Swanson, F. J., Sollins, P., Gregory, S. V., Lattin, J. D., Anderson, N. H., et al. (1986). Ecology of coarse woody debris in temperate ecosystems. *Advances in Ecological Research, 15,* 133–302.

Harmon, M. E., & Marks, B. (2002). Effects of silvicultural practices on carbon stores in Douglas-fir–western hemlock forests in the Pacific Northwest USA: Results from a simulation model. *Canadian Journal of Forest Research, 32,* 863–877.

Harr, R. D. (1982). Fog drip in the Bull Run Municipal Watershed, Oregon. *Journal of the American Water Resources Association, 18*(5), 785–789.

Hart, S. (2016, April 5). Local collaborative awarded $4 million in federal forest restoration funding. *Blue Mountain Eagle.* Retrieved from http://www.bluemountaineagle.com/Local_News/20160405/local-collaborative-awarded-4-million-in-federal-forest-restoration-funding

Hartsfield, A., & Ostermeier, D. (2003). The view from FSC-certified land managers. *Journal of Forestry, 101,* 32–36.

Haugo, R., Zanger, C., DeMeo, T., Ringo, C., Shlisky, A., Blankenship, K., et al. (2015). A new approach to evaluate forest structure restoration needs across Oregon and Washington, USA. *Forest Ecology and Management, 335,* 37–50.

Hausman, J. (2012). Contingent valuation: From dubious to hopeless. *Journal of Economic Perspectives, 26*(4), 43–56.

Hayhoe, K., Kheshgi, H. S., Jain, A. K., & Wuebbles, D. J. (2002). Substitution of natural gas for coal: climatic effects of utility sector emissions. Climatic Change 54(1-2): 107–139.

Healey P. (1997). *Collaborative planning.* Vancouver, Canada: University of British Columbia Press.

Heikkila, T., & Gerlak, A. K. (2005). The formation of large-scale collaborative resource management institutions: Clarifying the roles of stakeholders, science, and institutions. *Policy Studies Journal, 33*(4), 583–612.

Heilmayr, R., & Lambin, E. F. (2016). Impacts of nonstate, market driven governance on Chilean forests. *PNAS, 13*(11): 2910–2915.

Helms, J. A. (1998). *The dictionary of forestry.* Bethesda, MD: Society of American Foresters.

Henken, L. (2013). Sarah Deumling at Zena Forest. In R. H. Reinhard (Ed.), *Finding a sense of place: An environmental history of Zena* (pp. 95–105). Salem, OR: Polebridge Press.

Hennon, P. E., D'Amore, D. V., Schaberg, P. G., Wittwer, D. T., & Shanley, C. S. (2012). Shifting climate, altered niche, and a dynamic conservation strategy for yellow-cedar in the North Pacific coastal rainforest. *BioScience, 62*(2), 147–158.

Hessburg, P. F., Salter, R. B., & James, K. M. (2007). Re-examining fire severity relations in premanagement era mixed conifer forests: Inferences from landscape patterns of forest structure. *Landscape Ecology, 22,* 5–24.

Heyerdahl, E. K., Loehman, R. A., & Falk, D. A. (2014). Mixed-severity fire in lodgepole-dominated forests: Are historical regimes sustainable on Oregon's Pumice Plateau, USA? *Canadian Journal of Forest Research, 44*(6), 593–603.

Hobbs, N. T., & Cooper, D. J. (2013). Have wolves restored riparian willows in northern Yellowstone? In P. J. White, R. A. Garrott, & G. E. Plumb (Eds.), *Yellowstone's wildlife in transition* (pp. 179–194). Cambridge, MA: Harvard University Press.

Hobbs, R. J., Higgs, E., & Harris, J. A. (2009). Novel ecosystems: Implications for conservation and restoration. *Trends in Ecology & Evolution, 24*(11), 599–605.

Hoffman, C., Morgan, P., Mell, W., Parsons, R., Strand, E. K., Cook, S. (2012). Numerical simulation of crown fire hazard immediately after bark beetle-caused mortality in lodgepole pine forests. *Forest Science, 58*(2), 178–188.

Holden, Z. A., Morgan, P., & Hudak, A. T. (2010). Burn severity of areas reburned by wildfires in the Gila National Forest, New Mexico, USA. *Fire Ecology, 6,* 77–85.

Holiday, S., & Wagner, C. (2010). Wisconsin's forestry best management practices for water quality (field manual). Madison, WI: Wisconsin Department of Natural Resources, Department of Forestry.

Holling, C. S. (1973). Resilience and stability of ecological systems. *Annual Review of Ecology and Systematics, 4,* 1–23.

Holling, C. S. (1986). Resilience of ecosystems: Local surprised and global change. In W. C. Clark & R. E. Munn (Eds.), *Sustainable development of the biosphere.* Cambridge: Cambridge University Press.

Holling, C. S. (1992). Cross-scale morphology, geometry and dynamics of ecosystems. *Ecological Monographs, 62*(4), 447–502.

Holling, C. S., & Meffe, G. K. (1996). Command and control and the pathology of natural resource 344 management. *Conservation Biology, 10,* 328–337.

Hood, S. M. (2010). *Mitigating old tree mortality in long-unburned, fire dependent forests: A synthesis.* Fort Collins: USDA Forest Service, Rocky Mountain Research Station.

Hooper, D. U., Chapin III, F. S., Ewel, J. J., Hector, A., Inchausti, P., Lavorel, S., et al. (2005). Effects of biodiversity on ecosystem functioning: a consensus of current knowledge. *Ecological Monographs, 75*(1), 3–35.

Hoover, C., Birdsey, R., Goines, B., et al. (2014). Quantifying greenhouse gas sources and sinks in managed forest systems. In M. Eve et al. (Eds), *Quantifying greenhouse gas fluxes in agriculture and forestry: Methods for entity-scale inventory. Technical Bulletin Number 1939* (pp. 6-2–6-14). Washington, DC: Office of the Chief Economist, US Department of Agriculture.

Hoyos, D. (2010). The state of the art of environmental valuation with discrete choice experiments. *Ecological Economics, 69*(8), 1595–1603.

Hudiburg, T. W., Law, B. E., Wirth, C. & Luyssaert, S. (2011). Regional carbon dioxide implications of forest bioenergy production. *Nature Climate Change, 1,* 419–423.

Huhtala, A. (2004). What price recreation in Finland?—A contingent valuation study of non-market benefits of public outdoor recreation areas. *Journal of Leisure Research, 36*(1), 23–44.

Hunter, J. M., & Schmiegelow, F. K. (2011). *Wildlife, forests, and forestry. Principles of managing forests for biological diversity* (2nd ed.). Boston, MA: Prentice Hall.

Hunter, M. D., & Price, P. W. (1992). Playing chutes and ladders: Heterogeneity and the relative roles of bottom-up and top-down forces in natural communities. *Ecology, 73*(3), 724–732.

Hunter, M. L. (1990). *Wildlife, forests, and forestry. Principles of managing forests for biological diversity.* Englewood Cliffs, NJ: Prentice-Hall.

Hunter, M. L. (1999). Biological diversity. In M. L. Hunter (Ed.), *Maintaining biodiversity in forest ecosystems* (pp, 3–21). Cambridge, UK: Cambridge University Press.

Hunter, M. L., & Schmiegelow, F. (2011). *Wildlife, forests and forestry: Principles of managing forests for biological diversity* (2nd ed.). New York: Pearson.

Hunter, M. L. (2005). A mesofilter conservation strategy to complement fine and coarse filters. *Conservation Biology, 19*(4), 1025–1029.

Hurteau, M., & North, M. (2009). Fuel treatment effects on tree-based carbon storage under modeled wildfire scenarios. *Frontiers in Ecology and the Environment, 7,* 409–414.

Hutchinson, G. E. (1959). Homage to Santa Rosalia, or: Why are there so many kinds of animals? *American Naturalist, 93,* 145–59.

Hutto, R., & Belote, R. T. (2013). Distinguishing four types of monitoring based on the questions they address. *Forest Ecology and Management, 289,* 183–189.

Industrial Economics, Inc. (2007). *Plum Creek financial model, discussion paper #2.* Retrieved from http://www.osiny.org/site/DocServer/PLUM_CREEK_No2_9_07.pdf?docID=762

Innes, J. E., & Booher, D. E. (1999). Consensus building and complex adaptive systems: A framework for evaluating collaborative planning. *Journal of the American Planning Association, 65*(4), 412–423.

International Tropical Timber Organization (ITTO). (2012). Annual review and assessment of the world timber situation. Yokohama: International Tropical Timber Organization. Retrieved from http://www.itto.int/annual_review/

Ip, G. (2015, June 23). Energy-efficiency programs 'nudge' consumers in the wrong direction. *The Wall Street Journal.* Retrieved from http://www.wsj.com/articles/energy-efficiency-program-nudges-consumers-in-the-wrong-direction-1435088808

IPCC. (2014). *Climate change 2014: Synthesis report. Contribution of working groups I, II and III to the Fifth Assessment Report of the Intergovernmental Panel on Climate Change* (Core writing team, R. K. Pachauri & L. A. Meyer [Eds.]). Geneva, Switzerland: IPCC. Retrieved from https://www.ipcc.ch/pdf/assessment-report/ar5/syr/SYR_AR5_FINAL_full_wcover.pdf

Isaacson, W. (2008). *Einstein: His live and universe.* New York, NY: Simon and Schuster.

Ives, A. R. (2007). Diversity and stability in ecological communities. In R. May & A. McLean (Eds.), *Theoretical ecology: Principles and applications* (pp. 98–110). Oxford, UK: Oxford University Press.

Jain, T. B., Battaglia, M. A., Han, H., Graham, R. T., Keyes, C. R., Fried, J. S., & Sandquist, J. E. (2012). A comprehensive guide to fuel management practices for dry mixed conifer forests in the northwestern United States. *USDA Forest Service General Technical Report RMRS-GTR-292.* Fort Collins, CO: Rocky Mountain Research Station.

Janssen, Marco. (2002). A future of surprises. In L. H. Gunderson & C. S. Holling (Eds.), *Panarchy: Understanding transformations in human and natural systems* (pp. 241–260). Washington DC: Island Press.

Jaramillo, P., Griffin, W. M., & Matthews, H. S. (2007). Comparative life-cycle air emissions of coal, domestic natural gas, LNG, and SNG for electricity generation. *Environmental Science & Technology, 1*(17), 6290–6296.

Jenkins, J. C., Chojnacky, D. C., Heath, L. S., & Birdsey, R. A. (2003). National-scale biomass estimators for United States tree species. *Forest Science, 49*(1), 12–35.

Johnson, D. H., & O'Neil, T. A. (2001). *Wildlife-habitat relationships in Oregon and Washington.* Corvallis, OR: Oregon State University Press.

Johnson, K. N. (2007, February). Will linking science to policy lead to sustainable forestry? Lessons from the federal forests of the United States. In Reynolds, et al. (Eds.), *Sustainable Forestry: From Monitoring and Modelling to Knowledge Management and Policy Science* (pp. 15–29). New York: Oxford University Press.

Johnson, K. N., Agee, J., Beschta, R., Dale, V., Hardesty, L., Long, J., et al. (1999a). Sustaining the people's lands: Recommendations for stewardship of the national forests into the next century. *Report of the Committee of Scientists to the Secretary of Agriculture.* Washington, DC: US Department of Agriculture. Retrieved from http://www.fs.fed.us/emc/nfma/includes/cosreport/Committee%20of%20Scientists%20Report.htm

Johnson, K. N., Agee, J., Beschta, R., Dale, V., Hardesty, L., Long, J., et al. (1999b). Sustaining the people's lands. *Journal of Forestry, 97*(5), 7–12.

Johnson, K. N., Bettinger, P., Kline, J. D., Spies, T. A., Lennette, M., Lettman, G., Garber-Yonts, B., & Larsen, T. (2007). Simulating forest structure, timber production, and socioeconomic effects in a multi-owner province. *Ecological Applications, 88*(1), 34–47.

Johnson, K. N. & Duncan, S. (2007). Introduction. In K. N. Johnson, S. Gordon, S. Duncan, D. Lach, B. McComb, & K. Reynolds (Eds.), *Conserving creatures of the forest: A guide to decision making and decision models for forest biodiversity* (pp. 9–11). Corvallis: Oregon State University Press.

Johnson, K. N., Franklin, J. F., Thomas, J. W., & Gordon, J. (1991). *Alternatives for management of late-successional forests of the Pacific Northwest. A Report to the Agricultural Committee and the Merchant Marine and Fisheries Committee of the U.S. House of Representatives by the Scientific Panel on Late-successional Forest Ecosystems.* Washington, DC: US Government.

Johnson, K. N., Franklin, J. F., & Johnson, D. L. (2008). *A plan for the Klamath Tribes' management of the Klamath Reservation Forest.* Retrieved from www.klamathtribes.org/background/documents/Klamath_Plan_Final_May_2008.pdf

Johnson, K. N., & Gordon, S. (2007). DSS: How might they help? How might they hurt? In K. N. Johnson, S. Gordon, S. Duncan, D. Lach, B. McComb, & K. Reynolds (Eds.), *Conserving creatures of the forest: A guide to decision making and decision models for forest biodiversity* (pp. 35–46). Report to the National Commission on Science for Sustainable Forestry.

Johnson, K. N., Gordon, S., Duncan, S., Lach, D., McComb, B., Reynolds, K. (Eds.). (2007). *Conserving creatures of the forest: a guide to decision making and decision models for forest biodiversity.* Report to the National Commission on Science for Sustainable Forestry.

Johnson, M. L., Bell, K. P., Teisl, M. F. (2016). Does reading scenarios of future land use changes affect willingness to participate in land use planning? *Land Use Policy, 57,* 44–52.

Johnston, R., Rolfe, J., Rosenberger, R. & Brouwer, R. (Eds.). (2015). *Benefit transfer of environmental and resource values: A handbook for researchers and practitioners.* New York: Springer.

Johnstone, J. F., Allen, C. D., Franklin, J. F., Frelich, L. E., Harvey, B. J., Higuera, P. E., et al. (2016). Changing disturbance regimes, ecological memory, and forest resilience. *Frontiers in Ecology and the Environment, 14*(7), 369–378.

Jones, C. O. (1984). *An introduction to the study of public policy* (3rd ed.). Monterey, CA: Brooks/Cole.

Jose, S., Cox, J., Miller, D. L., Donn, G. S., & Merritt, S. (2002). Alien plant invasions: The story of cogongrass in southeastern forests. *Journal of Forestry, 100*(1), 41–44.

Kalen, S. (2010). Ecology comes of age: NEPA's lost mandate. *Duke Environmental Law & Policy Forum, 21*(1), 113–163.

Kauffman, J. B., Arifanti, V. B., Trejo, H. H., del Carmen Jesús Garcia, M., Norfolk, J., et al. (2017). The jumbo carbon footprint of a shrimp: Carbon losses from mangrove deforestation. *Frontiers in Ecology and the Environment.* In press.

Kauffman, M., Brodie, J. F., & Jules, E. S. (2010). Are wolves saving Yellowstone's aspen? A landscape-level test of a behaviorally mediated trophic cascade. *Ecology, 91*(9), 2742–2755.

Kaufmann, M. R. (1985). Annual transpiration in subalpine forests: Large differences among four tree species. *Forest ecology and Management, 13*(3-4), 235–246.

Keane, R. E., Hessburg, P. F., Landres, P. B., & Swanson, F. J. (2009). The use of historical range and variability (HRV) in landscape management. *Forest Ecology and Management, 258,* 1025–1037.

Keane, R. E., Tomback, D. F., Aubry, C. A., Bower, A. D., Campbell, E. M., Cripps, C. L., Jenkins, M. B., et al. (2012). A range-wide restoration strategy for whitebark pine (*Pinus albicaulis*). *Gen. Tech. Rep. RMRS-GTR-279.* Fort Collins, CO: U.S. Department of Agriculture, Forest Service, Rocky Mountain Research Station.

Keeley, J. E. (2009). Fire intensity, fire severity and burn severity: a brief review and suggested usage. *International Journal of Wildland Fire, 18,* 116–126.

Keenan, R. J., Reams, G. A., Achard, F., de Freitas, J. V., Grainger, A., & Lindquist, E. (2015). Dynamics of global forest area: Results from the FAO global forest resources assessment 2015. *Forest Ecology and Management, 352,* 9–20.

Keith, H., Lindenmayer, D., Mackey, B., Blair, D., Carter, L., McBurney, L., Okada, S., & Konishi-Nagano, T. (2014). Managing temperate forests for carbon storage: impacts of logging versus forest protection on carbon stocks. *Ecosphere, 5*(6), 1–34.

Kendall, K. C., Stetz, J. B., Boulanger, J., Macleod, A. C., Paetkau, D., & White, G. C. (2009). Demography and genetic structure of a recovering grizzly bear population. *Journal of Wildlife Management, 73*(1), 3–17.

Kendall, K. C., Stetz, J. B., Roon, D. A., Waits, L. P., Boulanger, J. B., & Paetkau, D. P. (2008). Grizzly bear density in Glacier National Park, Montana. *Journal of Wildlife Management, 72*(8), 1693–1705.

Kim, Y., Bettinger, P. & Finney, M. (2009). Spatial optimization of the pattern of fuel management activities and subsequent effects on simulated wildfires. *European Journal of Operational Research, 197,* 253–265.

Kimmins, J. P. (2004). *Forest ecology* (3rd ed.). Upper Saddle River, NJ: Pearson Prentice-Hall.

Kirkman, K., & Jack, S. (2017). *Ecological restoration and management of longleaf pine forests.* Boca Raton, FL: CRC Press.

Kirkman, L. K., Mitchell, R. J., Kaeser, M. J., Pecot, S. D., & Coffey, K. L. (2007). The perpetual forest: using undesirable species to bridge restoration. *Jour. Ecology, 44,* 604–614.

Kittredge, D. B. (2009). The fire in the East. *Journal of Forestry, 107*(3), 162–163.

Klein, G. (1999). *Sources of power: How people make decisions.* Cambridge, MA: MIT Press.

Klemperer, W. D. (1996). *Forest resource economics and finance.* New York, NY: McGraw Hill.

Klemperer, W. D., Cathcart, J. F., Haring, T., & Alig, R. J. (1994). Risk and the discount rate in forestry. *Canadian Journal of Forest Research, 24*(2), 390–397.

Kliejunas, J. T., Geils, B. W., Glaeser, J. M., Goheen, E. M., Hennon, P., Kim, M. S., et al. (2009). Review of literature on climate change and forest diseases of western North America. *Gen. Tech. Rep. PSW-GTR-225.* Albany, CA: U.S. Department of Agriculture, Forest Service, Pacific Southwest Research Station, 54.

Kline, J. D. Azuma, D. L., & Alig, R. J. (2004). Population growth, urban expansion, and private forestry in western Oregon. *Forest Science, 50*(1), 33–43.

Kling, C. L., Phaneuf, D. J., & Zhao, J. (2012). From Exxon to BP: Has some number become better than no number? *Journal of Economic Perspectives, 26*(4), 3–26.

Koontz, T. M., & Thomas, C. W. (2006). What do we know and need to know about environmental outcomes of collaborative management? *Public Administration Review, 66*(Supplement s1), 111–121.

Koontz, T. M., Steelman, T. A., Carmin, J., Korfmacher, K. S., Moseley, C., & Thomas, C. W. (2004). *Collaborative environmental management: What roles for government?* Washington, DC: Resources for the Future.

Kruckeberg, A. R. (1967). Ecotypic response to ultramafic soils by some plant species of northwestern United States. *Brittonia, 19*(2), 133–151.

Kuhn, T. (1996). *The structure of scientific revolutions* (3rd ed.). Chicago, IL: University of Chicago Press.

Kukkonen, M., Rita, H., Hohnwald, S., & Nygren, A. (2008). Treefall gaps of certified, conventionally managed and natural forests as regeneration sites for neotropical timber trees in northern Honduras. *Forest Ecology and Management, 255,* 2163–2176.

Lach, D., & Duncan, S. (2007). How do we make decisions? In K. N. Johnson, S. Gordon, S. Duncan, D. Lach, B. McComb, & K. Reynolds (Eds.), *Conserving creatures of the forest: A guide to decision making and decision models for forest biodiversity* (pp. 12–20). Report to the National Commission on Science for Sustainable Forestry.

Lachapelle, P. R., McCool, S. F., & Patterson, M. E. (2003). Barriers to effective natural resource planning in a "messy" world. *Society and Natural Resources, 16*(6): 473–490.

Landres, P. B., Morgan, P., Swanson, F. J. (1999). Overview and use of natural variability concepts in managing ecological systems. *Ecological Applications, 9,* 1179–1188.

Larson, A. J., Belote, R. T., Cansler, C. A., Parks, S. A., & Dietz, M. S. (2013). Latent resilience in ponderosa pine forest: Effects of resumed frequent fire. *Ecological Applications, 23*(6), 1243–1249.

Larson, A. J., Belote, R. T., Williamson, M. A., & Aplet, G. H. (2013). Making monitoring count: Project design for active adaptive management. *Journal of Forestry, 111*(5), 348–356.

Larson, A. J., & Churchill, D. (2008). Spatial patterns of overstory trees in late-successional conifer forests. *Canadian Journal of Forest Research, 38,* 2814–2825.

Larson, A. J., & Churchill, D. (2012). Tree spatial patterns in fire-frequent forests of western North America, including mechanisms of pattern formation and implications for designing fuel reduction and restoration treatments. *Forest Ecology and Management, 267,* 74–92.

Larson, A. J., & Franklin, J. F. (2005). Patterns of conifer tree regeneration following an autumn wildfire event in the western Oregon Cascade Range. *Forest Ecology & Management, 218,* 25–36.

Larson, A. J., & Franklin, J. F. (2006). Structural segregation and scales of spatial dependency in Abies amabilis forests. *Journal of Vegetation Science, 17,* 489–498.

Larson, A. J., Lutz, J. A., Donato, D. C., Freund, J. A., Swanson, M. E., Hille Ris Lambers, J., Sprugel, D. G., & Franklin, J. F. (2015). Spatial aspects of tree mortality strongly differ between young and old-growth forests. *Ecology, 996*(11), 2855–2861.

Larson, A. J., Lutz, J. A., Gersonde, R. F., Franklin, J. F., & Hietpas, F. F. (2008). Potential site productivity influences the rate of forest structural development. *Ecological Applications, 18,* 899–910.

Lassoie, J., Oglesby, R., & Smallidge, P. (1998). Roots of American forestry education: trials and tribulations at Cornell University. *Forest History Today,* pp. 21–25. Retrieved from http://www.foresthistory.org/publications/FHT/FHT1998/cornell.pdf

Laundré, J. W., Hernandez, L., & Ripple, W. J. (2010). The landscape of fear: Ecological implications of being afraid. *The Open Ecology Journal, 3,* 1–7.

Le Quéré, C., Moriarty, R., Andrew, R. M., et al. (2015). The global carbon budget 2014. *Earth System Science Data, 7,* 47–85.

Leach, W. D., & Sabatier, P. A. (2005). Are trust and social capital the keys to success? Watershed partnerships in California and Washington. In P. Sabatier, W. Focht, M. Lubell, A. Trachtenberg, A. Vedlitz, & M. Madock (Eds.), *Swimming upstream: Collaborative approaches to watershed Management* (pp. 233–258). Cambridge, MA: MIT Press.

Lee, K. N. (1999). Appraising adaptive management. *Conservation Ecology, 3*(3). Retrieved from http://www.consecol.org/vol3/iss2/art3/

Lee, R., & D. Field. (2005). Community complexity: Postmodern challenges to forest and natural resource management. In R. Lee & D, Field (Eds.), *Communities and forests: Where people meet the land,* pp. 291–303. Corvallis: Oregon State University Press.

Lenart, M. (2006). Collaborative stewardship to prevent wildfires. *Environment, 48*(7), 9–20.

Leopold, A. (1949). *A Sand County Almanac: And sketches here and there.* Oxford, UK: Oxford University Press.

Leopold, A. (1993). *Round River: From the Journals of Aldo Leopold,* L. B. Leopold (Ed.). Oxford, UK: Oxford University Press.

Leopold, A., Sowls, L. K., & Spencer, D. L. (1947). A survey of over-populated deer ranges in the United States. *Journal of Wildlife Management, 11*(2), 162–183.

Lettman, G. (coordinator). (2013). *Land use change on non-federal land in Oregon and Washington.* Salem, OR: Oregon Department of Forestry. Retrieved from https://olis.leg.state.or.us/liz/2016R1/Downloads/CommitteeMeetingDocument/86552

Likens, G. E. (1992). *The ecosystem approach: Its use and abuse. Excellence in Ecology No. 3.* (O. Kinne, Ed.) Oldendorf, Germany: Ecology Institute.

Lindblom, C. (1959). The science of muddling through. *Public Administration Review, 19,* 79–99.

Lindeman, R. L. (1942). The trophic-dynamic aspect of ecology. *Ecology, 23*(4), 399–417.

Lindenmayer, D. B. (2009). *Forest pattern and ecological process: A synthesis of 25 years of research.* Collingwood, Australia: CSIRO Publishing.

Lindenmayer, D. B., Blair, D., McBurney, L., & Banks, S. (2015). *Mountain ash: Fire, logging and the future of Victoria's giant forests.* Clayton South, Victoria, Australia: CSIRO Publishing.

Lindenmayer, D. B., Burton, P., & Franklin, J. F. (2008). *Salvage logging and its ecological consequences.* Washington, DC: Island Press.

Lindenmayer, D. B., & Franklin, J. F. (2002). *Conserving forest biodiversity. A comprehensive multiscaled approach.* Washington, DC: Island Press.

Lindenmayer, D. B., & Franklin, J. F. (2003). *Towards forest sustainability.* Clayton, Victoria, Australia: CSIRO Publishing.

Lindenmayer, D. B., Franklin, J. F., Lõhmus, A., Baker, S. C., Bauhus, J., Beese, W., Brodie, A., et al. (2012). A major shift to the retention approach for forestry can help resolve some global forest sustainability issues. *Conservation Letters, 5*(6), 421–431.

Lindenmayer, D. B., & Laurance, W. F. (2016). The ecology, distribution, conservation and management of large old trees. *Biological Reviews,* doi: 10:1111/brv.12290

Lindenmayer, D. B., & Likens, G. E. (2009). Improving ecological modeling. *Trends in Ecology and Evolution, 25*(4), 200–201.

Lippke, B., Oneil, E., Harrison, R., Skog, K., Gustavsson, L., & Sathre, R. (2011). Life cycle impacts of forest management and wood utilization on carbon mitigation: Knowns and unknowns. *Carbon Management, 2*(3), 303–333. Retrieved from http://www.corrim.org/pubs/articles/2011/fsg_review_carbon_synthesis.pdf

Littell, J. S., McKenzie, D., Peterson, D. L., Westerling, A. L. (2009). Climate and wildfire area burned in the western U.S. ecoprovinces, 1916–2003. *Ecological Applications, 19*(4), 1003–1021.

Littell, J. S., Oneil E. E., McKenzie D., Hicke J. A., Lutz J. A., Norheim R. A., & Elsner M. M. (2010). Forest ecosystems, disturbance, and climatic change in Washington State, USA. *Climatic Change, 102*(1), 129–158.

Lober, D. J. & Eisen, M. D. (1995). The greening of retailing: Certification and the home improvement industry. *Journal of Forestry, 93*(4), 38–41.

Logan, J. A., Macfarlane, W. W., & Wilcox, L. (2010). Whitebark pine vulnerability to climate-driven mountain pine beetle disturbance in the Greater Yellowstone Ecosystem. *Ecological Applications, 20*(4), 895–902.

Loomis, J. B. (1987). Balancing public trust resources of Mono Lake and Los Angeles' water right: An economic approach. *Water Resources Research, 23*(8), 1449–1456.

Loomis, J. B., González-Cabán, A., & Gregory, R. S. (1996). A contingent valuation study of the value of reducing fire hazards to old-growth forests in the Pacific Northwest. *USDA Forest Service Research Paper PSW-RP-229.* Albany, CA: Pacific Southwest Research Station. Retrieved from http://www.fs.fed.us/psw/publications/documents/psw_rp229/psw_rp229.pdf

Loreau, M., Naeem, S., Inchausti, P., Bengtsson, J., Grime, J. P., Hector, A., et al. (2001). Biodiversity and ecosystem functioning: Current knowledge and future challenges. *Science, 294*(5543), 804–808.

Lubell, M. (2005). Do watershed partnerships enhance beliefs conducive to collective action? In P. Sabatier, W. Focht, M. Lubell, A. Trachtenberg, A. Vedlitz, & M. Madock (Eds.), *Swimming Upstream: Collaborative Approaches to Watershed Management* (pp. 201–232). Cambridge, MA: MIT Press.

Lubowski, R. N., Plantinga, A. J., & Stavins, R. N. (2008). What drives land-use change in the United States? A national analysis of landowner decisions. *Land Economics, 84,* 529–550.

Luckert, M. K. (2006). Has the myth of the omnipotent forester become the reality of the impotent forester? *Journal of Forestry, 104*(6), 299–306.

Lunch, W. (n.d.). The legal system and the courts. In *Inside the Beltway: Class notes for Political Science Class, OSU,* pp. 70–73.

Lüthi, D., Le Floch, M., Bereiter, B., et al. (2008). High resolution carbon dioxide concentration record 650,000–800,000 years before present. *Nature, 453,* 379–382.

Lutz, J. A., & Halpern, C. B. (2006). Tree mortality during early forest development: A long-term study of rates, causes, and consequences. *Ecological Monographs, 76,* 257–275.

Lutz, J. A., Larson, A. J., Furniss, T. J., Donato, D. C., Freund, J. A., Swanson, et al. (2014). Spatially non-random tree mortality and ingrowth maintain equilibrium pattern in an old-growth Pseudotsuga-Tsuga forest. *Ecology, 95,* 2047–2054.

Luyssaert, S., Detlef Schulze, E., Börner, A., Knohl, A., Hessenmöller, D., Law, B. E., Ciais, P., & Grace, J. (2008). Old-growth forests as global carbon sinks. *Nature, 455,* 213–215.

Lyderson, J. M., North, M. P., & Collins, B. M. (2014). Severity of an uncharacteristically large wildfire, the Rim Fire, in forests with relatively restored frequent fire regimes. *Forest Ecology and Management, 328,* 326–334.

Mack, R. N. (1981). Invasion of *Bromus tectorum* L. into western North America: An ecological chronicle. *Agro-Ecosystems, 7,* 145–165.

Mackey, B., Prentice, I. C., Steffen, W., House, J. I., Lindenmayer, D., Keith, H., & Berry, S. (2013). Untangling the confusion around land carbon science and climate change mitigation policy. *Nature Climate Change, 3*(6), 552–557.

MacLaurin, J., & Sternley, K. (2008). What Is Biodiversity? Chicago, IL: University of Chicago Press.

MacLean, D. A., Seymour, R. S., Montigny, M. K., & Messier, C. (2009). Allocation of conservation efforts over the landscape: The TRIAD approach. P. 283–303 In M. A. Villard & B. G. Jonsson (Eds.), *Setting conservation targets for managed forest landscapes* (pp. 283–303). New York, NY: Cambridge University Press.

Marcot, B. G., Thompson, M. P., Runge, M. C., Thompson, F. R., McNulty, S., Cleaves, D., Tomosy, M., Fisher, L. A., & Bliss, A. (2012). Recent advances in applying decision science to managing national forests. *Forest Ecology and Management, 285,* 123–132.

Margerum, R. D. (2008). A typology of collaboration efforts in environmental management. *Environmental Management, 41,* 487–500.

Marshall, K. N., Hobbs, N. T., & Cooper, D. J. (2012). Stream hydrology limits recovery of riparian ecosystems after wolf reintroduction. *Proceedings of the Royal Society B: Biological Sciences, 280*(1756), 2012–2977.

Marshall, R. (1925). Recreational limitations to silviculture in the Adirondacks. *Journal of Forestry, 23,* 173–178.

Maser, C., Claridge, A. W., & Trappe, J. M. (2008). *Trees, truffles, and beasts: How forests function.* New Brunswick, NJ: Rutgers University Press.

Maser, C., Tarrant, R. F., Trappe, J. M., &. Franklin, J. F. (Tech. Eds.). (1988). From the forest to the sea: A story of fallen trees. *Gen. Tech. Rep. PNW-GTR-229.* Portland, OR: U. S. Department of Agriculture, Forest Service, Pacific Northwest Research Station, 153.

Matonis, M. S., Binkley, D., Franklin, J. F., & Johnson, K. N. (2016). Benefits of an "undesirable" approach to natural resource management. *Journal of Forestry.* In press.

Mausel, D. L., Waupochick, Jr., A., & Pecore, M. (2017). Menominee forestry: Past, present, and future. *Journal of Forestry, 115*(5), 366–369.

McClosky, M. (1999). Local communities and the management of public forests. *Ecology Law Quarterly, 25*(4), 624–629.

McCreary, S. T., Gamman, J. K., & Brooks, B. (2001). Refining and testing joint fact-finding for environmental dispute resolution: Ten years of success. *Mediation Quarterly, 18*(4), 329–348.

McDermott, C. L., Cashore, B., & Kanowski, P. (2010). *Global environmental forest policies: An international comparison.* London, UK: Earthscan.

McGinley, K. (2017). Natural resource, participation, collaboration, and partnerships. In F. Cubbage, J. O'Laughlin, & M. N. Peterson, *Natural resource policy* (pp. 459–485). Long Grove, IL: Waveland Press.

McKelvey, K. S., Buskirk, S. W., & Krebs, C. J. (1999). Theoretical insights into the population viability of lynx. In L. F. Ruggiero, K. B. Aubry, S. W. Buskirk, G. M. Koehler, C. J. Krebs, K. S. McKelvey, & J. R. Squires (Eds.), *Ecology and conservation of lynx in the US* (pp. 21–38). *USDA Forest Service General Technical Report RMRS-GTR-30WWW.* Missoula, MT: Rocky Mountain Research Station.

McKibben, B. (2015). Coda. In B. A. Minteer, & S. J. Pyne (Eds.), *After Preservation: Saving American Nature in the Age of Humans* (pp. 194–197). Chicago: University of Chicago Press.

McKillop, W. (1991). A critique of the use of nonmarket values in the U.S. Fish and Wildlife Service's August 1991 report "Economic analysis of designation of critical habitat for the northern spotted owl." *Forest Resources Technical Bulletin, TB91-12.* Washington, DC: American Forest Resource Alliance.

Meidinger, E., Elliott, C., & Oesten, G. (Eds.). (2003). *Social and political dimensions of forest certification.* Remagen, Germany: Forstbuch.

Meigs, G. W., Donato, D. C., Campbell, J. L., Martin, J. G., & Law, B. E. (2009). Forest fire impacts on carbon uptake, storage, and emission: The role of burn severity in the Eastern Cascades, Oregon. *Ecosystems, 12,* 1246–1267.

Melton, P. (2016). *LEED pilots legal wood, expansion of certified wood.* Brattleboro, VT: BuildingGreen, Inc. Retrieved from https://www.buildinggreen.com/news-analysis/leed-pilots-legal-wood-expansion-certified-wood.

Mendell, B., & Lang, A. (2013). Comparing forest certification standards in the United States: Economic analysis and practical considerations. *EconoStats,* George Mason University, Fairfax, Virginia. Retrieved from http://econostats.org/wp/wp-content/uploads/2013/06/EconoSTATS-ComparingForest-Certification-Standards-in-the-U-S-Final.pdf

Merschel, A. G., Spies, T. A., & Heyerdahl, E. K. (2014). Mixed-conifer forests of central Oregon: Effects of logging and fire exclusion vary with environment. *Ecological Applications, 24,* 1670–1688.

Messier, C., Tittler, R., Kneeshaw, D. D., Gelinas, N., Paquette, A., Berninger, K., et al. (2009). TRIAD zoning in Quebec: experiences and results after 5 years. *Forestry Chronicle, 85*(8), 885–896.

Meyer, H. A., & Stevenson, D. D. (1943). The structure and growth of virgin beech-birch-maple-hemlock forests in northern Pennsylvania. *Journal of Agricultural Research, 67,* 465–484.

Meyer, M. D., Roberts, S. L., Wills, R., Brooks, M., & Winford, E. M. (2015). Principles of effective USA federal fire management plans. *Fire Ecology, 11*(2), 59–83.

Meyer, W. H. (1942). Yield of even-aged stands of loblolly pine in northern Louisiana. *Yale University School of Forestry Bulletin, 51.*

Michel, A. K., & Winter, S. (2009). Tree microhabitat structures as indicators of biodiversity in Douglas-fir forests of different stand ages and management histories in the Pacific Northwest, U.S.A. *Forest Ecology and Management, 257,* 1453–1464.

Millar, C. I., Stephenson, N. L., & Stephens, S. L. (2007). Climate change and forests of the future: Managing in the face of uncertainty. *Ecological Applications, 17*(8), 2145–2151.

Millennium Ecosystem Assessment (MEA). (2003). Concepts of ecosystem value and valuation approaches. In *Ecosystems and human well-being: A framework for assessment* (pp. 127–147). Washington, DC: Island Press.

Millennium Ecosystem Assessment (MEA). (2005). *Ecosystems and human well-being: Current state and trends* (Vol. 1). Washington, DC: Island Press.

Miller, B., Reading, R., Trittholt, J. S., Carroll, C., Noss, R., Soulé, M., Sanchez, O., et al. (1999). Using focal species in the design of nature reserve networks. *Wild Earth, 8*(4), 81–92.

Miller, J. D., & Lindsay, B. E. (1993). Willingness to pay for a state gypsy moth control program in New Hampshire: A contingent valuation case study. *Journal of Economic Entomology, 86*(3), 828–837.

Miller, J. D., Safford, H. D., Crimmins, M., & Thode, A. E. (2009). Quantitative evidence for increasing forest fire severity in the Sierra Nevada and Southern Cascade Mountains, California and Nevada, USA. *Ecosystems, 12,* 16–35.

Mills, L. S., Soulé, M. E., & Doak, D. F. (1993). The keystone species concept in ecology and conservation. *BioScience, 43*(4), 219–224.

Milota, M. (2015). *CORRIM REPORT: Module B. Life cycle assessment for the production of Pacific Northwest softwood lumber.* Corvallis, OR: Consortium for Research on Renewable Industrial Materials (CORRIM). Retrieved from: https://corrim.org/wp-content/uploads/Module-B-PNW-Lumber.pdf

Milota, M. R., West, C. D., Hartley, I. D. (2005). Gate-to-gate life cycle inventory of softwood lumber production. *Wood and Fiber Science, 37,* 47–57.

Miner, R. A., Abt, R. C., Bowyer, J. L., Buford, M. A., Malmsheimer, R. W., O'Laughlin, J., Oneil, E. E., Sedjo, R. A., & Skog K. E. (2014). Forest carbon accounting considerations in US bioenergy policy. *Journal of Forestry, 112*(6), 591–606.

Mitchell, R. J., Hiers, J. K., O'Brien, J., & Starr, G. (2009). Ecological forestry in the Southeast: Understanding the ecology of fuels. *Journal of Forestry, 107*(8), 391–397.

Mitchell, S. R., Harmon, M. E., & O'Connell, K. E. B. (2009). Forest fuel reduction alters fire severity and long-term carbon storage in three Pacific Northwest ecosystems. *Ecological Applications, 19,* 643–655.

Miteva, D. A., Loucks, C. J., & Pattanayak, S. K. (2015). Social and environmental impacts of forest management certification in Indonesia. *PLoS ONE, 10*(7): e0129675. doi:10.1371/journal.pone.0129675

Molina, M., McCarthy, J., Wall, D., et al. (2013). *What we know: The reality, risk and response to climate change.* The AAAS Climate Science Panel. Retrieved from http://whatweknow.aaas.org/wp-content/uploads/2014/07/whatweknow_website.pdf

Montgomery, C. A., Brown, G. M., & Adams, D. M. (1994). The marginal cost of species preservation: The northern spotted owl. *Journal of Environmental Economics and Management, 26,* 111–128.

Mooney, H. A., Cushman, J. H., Medina, E., Sala, O. E., & Schulze, E. D. (1996). What we have learned about the ecosystem functioning of biodiversity. In H. A. Mooney (Ed.), *Functional roles of biodiversity: A global perspective* (pp. 476–484). Hoboken, NJ: John Wiley.

Moore, S., Cubbage, F., & Eicheldinger, C. (2012). Impacts of Forest Stewardship Council (FSC) and Sustainable Forestry Initiative (SFI) forest certification in North America. *Journal of Forestry, 110*(2), 79–88.

Moote, A. (2013, May). *Closing the feedback loop: Evaluation and adaptation in collaborative resource management.* Retrieved from http://willametteinitiative.org/sites/default/files/resources/Closing%20the%20feedback%20loop.pdf

Moote, M. A., Jakes, P., & Cheng, A. S. (2005). Social science to improve fuels management: A synthesis of research on collaboration. *USDA Forest Service General Technical Report NC-257.* St. Paul, MN: Northern Research Station.

Morgan, P. M., Aplet, G. H., Haufler, J. B., Humphries, H. C., Moore, M. M., Wilson, W. D. (1994). Historical range of variability: A useful tool for evaluating ecosystem change. *Journal of Sustainable Forestry, 2,* 87–111.

Morgan, P. M., Hardy, C. C., Swetnam, T. W., Rollins, M. G., & Long, D. G. (2001). Mapping fire regimes across time and space: Understanding coarse and fine-scale fire patterns. *International Journal of Wildland Fire, 10,* 329–342.

Mori, A. S., Furukawa, & T. Sasaki, T. (2013). Response diversity determines the resilience of ecosystems to environmental change. *Biological Reviews, 88,* 349–364.

Mori, A. S., & Kitagawa, R. (2014). Retention forestry as a major paradigm for safeguarding forest biodiversity in productive landscapes: A global meta analysis. *Biological Conservation, 175,* 65–73.

Mote, P. W., Hamlet, A. F., Clark, M. P., & Lettenmaier, D. P. (2005). Declining mountain snowpack in western North America. *Bull. Ameri. Meteorological Society, 86*(1), 39–49.

MTBS. (2014). *Monitoring trends in burn severity.* http://www.mtbs.gov

Mueller, T. (2005, December 12). Your move. *New Yorker,* p. 62.

Murdoch, W. W. (1966). Community structure, population control, and competition—A critique. *The American Naturalist, 100*(912), 219–226.

Murray, B. C., McCarl, B. A., & Lee, H. (2004). Estimating leakage from forest carbon sequestration programs. *Land Economics, 80,* 109–124.

Nabuurs, G. L., Masera, O., Andrasko, K., Benitez-Ponce, P., Boer, R., Dutschke, M., & Elsiddig, E. (2007). Forestry. In B. Metz, O. R. Davidson, P. R. Bosch, R. Dave, & L. A. Meyer (Eds.), *Climate change 2007: Mitigation of climate Change* (pp. 541–583). Cambridge, UK: Cambridge University Press.

Naeem, S., Thompson, L. J., Lawler, S. P., & Lawton, J. H. (1994). Declining biodiversity can alter the performance of ecosystems. *Nature, 368,* 734–737.

Naiman, R. J., & Bilby, R. E. (Eds.). (1998). *River ecology and management: Lessons from the Pacific Coastal Ecoregion.* New York, NY: Springer-Verlag.

Naiman, R. J., Decamps, H., & McClain, M. E. (2010). *Riparia: ecology, conservation, and management of streamside communities.* Cambridge, MA: Academic Press.

Nalle, D. J., Arthur, J. L., & Sessions, J. (2002). Designing compact and contiguous reserve networks with a hybrid heuristic algorithm. *Forest Science, 48*(1), 59–68.

Nalle, D. J., Montgomery, C. A., Arthur, J. L., Polasky, S., & Schumaker, N. H. (2004). Modeling joint production of wildlife and timber. *Journal of Environmental Economics and Management, 48*(3): 997–1017.

National Board of Forestry (Sweden). (1992). *A richer forest.* Jönköping, Sweden: Author.

NOAA. (2017). *National Centers for Environmental Information.* Retrieved from: http://cpo.noaa.gov/Who-We-Are/About-CPO/Glossary

National Environmental Policy Act. (1969). 42 U.S.C. §§4321-4370h.

National Research Council. (2005). *Valuing ecosystem services: Toward better environmental decision-making.* Washington, DC: The National Academies Press.

Nature Conservancy of Maine. (2012, May 15). 363,000 acres of Moosehead Lake Region conserved. Retrieved from: http://www.nature.org/ourinitiatives/regions/northamerica/unitedstates/maine/newsroom/363000-acres-of-moosehead-lake-region-conserved.xml

Nebel, G. L., Quevedo, J., Bredahl Jacobsen, J., & Helles, F. (2005). Development and economic significance of forest certification: The case of FSC in Bolivia. *Forest Policy and Economics, 7,* 175–186.

Neel, L. (2010). *The art of managing longleaf. A personal history of the Stoddard-Neel approach.* Athens, GA: University of Georgia Press.

Neumayer, E. (2013). *Weak versus strong sustainability: Exploring the limits of two opposing paradigms* (2nd ed.). Northampton, MA: Edward Elgar.

Newell, R. G., Sanchirico, J. N., & Kerr, S. (2005). Fishing quota markets. *Journal of Environmental Economics and Management, 49,* 437–462.

Newsom, D., Bahn, V., & Cashore, B. (2006). Does forest certification matter? An analysis of operation-level changes required during the SmartWood certification process in the United States. *Forest Policy and Economics, 9,* 197–208.

Newsom, D., & Hewitt, D. (2005). *The global impacts of SmartWood certification.* New York, NY: Rainforest Alliance.

Nie, M. (2008). *The governance of western public lands.* Lawrence, KS: University Press of Kansas.

Nielsen, A. B., Olsen, S. B., & Lundhede, T. (2007). An economic valuation of the recreational benefits associated with nature-based forest management practices. *Landscape and Urban Planning, 80*(1), 63–71.

North, M. (2012). Managing Sierra Nevada forests. *USDA Forest Service General Technical Report PSW-GTR-237.* Albany, CA: Pacific Southwest Research Station.

North, M., Stephens, S. L., Collins, B. M., Agee, J. K., Aplet, G., Franklin, J. F., & Fule, P. Z. (2015a). Reform forest fire management: Agency incentives undermine policy effectiveness. *Science, 349*(6254), 1280–1281.

North, M., Brough, A., Long, J., Collins, B., Bowden, P., Yasudsa, D., Miller, J., & Sugihara, N. (2015b). Constraints on mechanized treatment significantly limit mechanical fuels reduction extent in the Sierra Nevada. *Journal of Forestry, 113*(1), 40–48.

North, M., Collins, B. M., & Stephens, S. (2012). Using fire to increase the scale, benefits, and future maintenance of fuels treatments. *Journal of Forestry, 110*(7), 392–401.

North, M., & Hurteau M. (2011). High-severity wildfire effects on carbon stocks and emissions in fuels treated and untreated forest. *Forest Ecology and Management, 261,* 1115–1120.

Northcote, T. G., & Hartman, G. F. (Eds.). (2008). *Fishes and forestry: Worldwide watershed interactions and management.* Hoboken, NJ: John Wiley & Sons.

Noss, R. F. (1990). Indicators for monitoring biodiversity: A hierarchical approach. *Conservation Biology, 4*(4), 355–364.

Noss, R. F., & Cooperrider, A. Y. (1994). *Saving nature's legacy: Protecting and restoring biodiversity.* Washington, DC: Island Press.

Noss, R. F., Franklin, J. F., Baker, W. L., Schoennagel, T., & Moyle, P. B. (2006). Managing fire-prone forests in the western United States. *Frontiers in Ecology and the Environment, 4,* 481–487.

Nunery, J. S., & Keeton, W. S. (2010). Forest carbon storage in the northeastern United States: Net effects of harvesting frequency, post-harvest retention, and wood products. *Forest Ecology and Management, 259*(8), 1363–1375.

Nyland, R. D. (2016). *Silviculture: Concepts and applications* (3rd ed.). Long Grove, IL: Waveland Press.

O'Brien, J. J., Hiers, J. K., Callaham, M. A. Jr., Michell, R. J., & Jack, S. B. (2008). Interactions among overstory structure, seedling life-history traits, and fire in frequently burned neotropical pine forests. *Ambio 37*, 542–547.

O'Hara, K. L. (2014). *Multiaged silviculture.* Oxford, United Kingdom: Oxford University Press.

Odum, E. P. (1969). The strategy of ecosystem development. *Science, 164*(3877), 262–270.

Öhman, K. (2000). Creating continuous areas of old forest in long-term forest planning. *Canadian Journal of Forest Research, 30*, 1817–1823.

Öhmann, J. L., & Gregory, M. J. (2002). Predictive mapping of forest composition and structure with direct gradient analysis and nearest neighbor imputation in coastal Oregon, USA. *Canadian Journal of Forest Research, 32*, 725–741.

Oksanen, L., Fretwell, S. D., Arruda, J., & Niemela, P. (1981). Exploitation ecosystems in gradients of primary productivity. *American Naturalist, 118*(2), 240–261.

Oliver, C. D., & Larson, B. C. (1996). *Forest stand dynamics.* Update. New York, NY: John Wiley & Sons.

Oliver, C. D., Nassar, N. T., Lippke, B. R., & McCarter, J. B. (2014). Carbon, fossil fuel, and biodiversity mitigation with wood and forests. *Journal of Sustainable Forestry, 33*, 248–275.

Ontario Government. (2011). Crown Forest Sustainability Act, 1994. As amended. Retrieved from https://www.ontario.ca/laws/statute/94c25

Oregon Department of Environmental Quality (DEQ). (2010). *Cost estimate to restore riparian forest buffers and improve stream habitat in the Willamette Basin, Oregon.* Retrieved from www.deq.state.or.us/wq/tmdls/docs/WillametteRipCost030310.pdf

Oregon Department of Environmental Quality (DEQ). (2014). *Willamette Basin TMDLs Five Year Review: Designated Management Agency Implementation 2008–2013.* Retrieved from http://www.deq.state.or.us/wq/tmdls/docs/FiveYearDMAReport_Feb2014.pdf

Oregonians say they want more land and water protections. (2013, May 21). *The PEW Charitable Trusts.* Retrieved from http://www.pewtrusts.org/en/research-and-analysis/analysis/2013/05/21/oregonians-say-they-want-more-land-and-water-protections

Orr, J. C., Fabry, V. J., Aumont, O., et al. (2005). Anthropogenic ocean acidification over the twenty-first century and its impact on calcifying organisms. *Nature, 437*(29), 681–686.

Ostrom, E. (1986). A method of institutional analysis. In F. X. Kaufmann, G. Majone, & V. Ostrom (Eds.), *Guidance, control, and evaluation in the public sector* (pp. 501–523). New York, NY: Walter de Gruyter.

Ostrom, E. (1998). A behavioral approach to rational choice theory of collective action. *The American Political Science Review, 92*(1), 1–22.

Oswalt, S. N., Smith, W. B., Miles, P. D., & Pugh, S. A. (2014). Forest resources of the United States, 2012: A technical document supporting the Forest Service 2010 update of the RPA assessment. *USDA Forest Service General Technical Report WO-91.* Washington, DC: US Department of Agriculture, Forest Service, Washington Office. Retrieved from http://www.treesearch.fs.fed.us/pubs/47322

Ozanne, L. K., & Vlosky, R. P. (1996). Wood products environmental certification: The United States perspective. *The Forestry Chronicle, 72*(2), 157–165.

Ozanne, L. K., & Vlosky, R. P. (2003). Certification from the U.S. consumer perspective: A comparison from 1995 and 2000. *Forest Products Journal, 53*(3), 13–21.

Pace, M. I., Carpenter, S. R., & Cole, J. J. (2016). With and without warning: Managing ecosystems in a changing world. *Frontiers in Ecology and the Environment, 13*, 460–467.

Pahl-Wostl, C., & Hare, M. (2004). Processes of social learning in integrated resources management. *Journal of Community and Applied Social Psychology, 14*, 193–206.

Paine, R. T. (1980). Food webs: Linkage, interaction strength and community infrastructure. *Journal of Animal Ecology, 49*, 667–685.

Paine, R. T. (1969). A note on trophic complexity and species diversity. *The American Naturalist, 103*, 91–93.

Palomares, F. (2001). Vegetation structure and prey abundance requirements of the Iberian lynx: Implications for the design of reserves and corridors. *Journal of Applied Ecology, 38*(1), 9–18.

Parisien, M. A., Junor, D. R., & Kafka, V. G. (2007). Comparing landscape-based decision rules for placement of fuel treatments in the boreal mixed wood of western Canada. *International Journal of Wildland Fire, 16*(6), 664–672

Parker, G. G. (1997). Canopy structure and light environment of an old-growth Douglas-fir/western hemlock forest. *Northwest Science, 71*(4), 261–270.

Parkins, J. R. (2010). The Problem with trust: Insights from advisory committees in the forest sector of Alberta. *Society & Natural Resources, 23*(9), 822–836.

Parks, S. A., Miller, C., Nelson, C. R., & Holden, Z. A. (2013). Previous fires moderate burn severity of subsequent wildland fires in two large western US wilderness areas. *Ecosystems, 17*, 29–42.

Pattberg, P. H. (2005). The Forest Stewardship Council: Risk and potential of private forest governance. *The Journal of Environment & Development, 14*(3), 356–374.

Pausas, J. G., & Keeley, J. E. (2009). A burning story: The role of fire in the history of life. *Bioscience, 59*(7), 593–601.

Pearce, D. W., & Turner, R. K. (1990). *Economics of natural resources and the environment.* Baltimore, MD: Johns Hopkins University Press.

Peat, F. D. (2002). *From certainty to uncertainty: The story of science and ideas in the 20th century.* Washington, DC: Joseph Henry Press.

Peet, R. K., & Allard, D. J. (1993). Longleaf pine vegetation of the southern Atlantic and eastern Gulf Coast regions: A preliminary classification. *Proceedings of the Tall Timbers fire ecology conference.* 45–81.

Pendleton L., Donato D. C., Murray, B. C., et al. (2012). Estimating global "blue carbon" emissions from conversion and degradation of vegetated coastal ecosystems. *PLoS ONE, 7*(9), e43542.

Perakis, S. S., Sinkhorn, E. R., & Compton, J. E. (2011). δ15N constraints on long-term nitrogen balances in temperate forests. *Oecologia, 167,* 793–807.

Perara, P., & Vlosky, R. (2006). A history of forest certification. Louisiana Forest Products Development Center. Louisiana State University Agricultural Center, Baton Rouge.

Perera, P., Vlosky, R., Dunn, M., & Hughes, G. (2008). US home-center retailer attitudes, perceptions, and behaviors regarding forest certification. *Forest Products Journal, 58*(3), 21–25.

Perez-Garcia, J., Lippke, B., Comnick, J., & Manriquez, C. (2005). An assessment of carbon pools, storage, and products market substitution using life-cycle results. *Wood Fiber Science, 37,* 140–148.

Perry D. A., Hessburg P. F., Skinner C. N., Spies T. A., Stephens S. L., Taylor A. H., Franklin J. F., McComb B., & Riegel G. (2011). The ecology of mixed severity fire regimes in Washington, Oregon, and northern California. *Forest Ecology and Management, 262*, 703–717.

Perry, D. A., Oren, R., & Hart, S. C. (2008). *Forest ecosystems* (2nd ed.). Baltimore, MD: The John Hopkins University Press.

Perry, T. D., & Jones, J. A. (2017). Summer streamflow deficits from regenerating Douglas-fir forest in the Pacific Northwest, USA. *Ecohydrology, 10*(2), e1790.

Peterson, D. L., Evers, L., Gravenmier, B., Eberhardt, E. (2007). A consumer guide: tools to manage vegetation and fuels. *USDA Forest Service General Technical Report PNW-GTR-690.* Portland, OR: Pacific Northwest Research Station.

Peterson, G., Allen, C. R., & Holling, C. S. (1998). Ecological resilience, biodiversity, and scale. *Ecosystems, 1*(1), 6–18.

Petrolia, D. R. (2014). What have we learned from the Deepwater Horizon disaster? An economist's perspective. *Journal of Ocean and Coastal Economics, 2014*, 1–30.

Pickett, S. T., & White, P. S. (1985). *The ecology of natural disturbance and patch dynamics.* New York, NY: Academic Press.

Pilkey, O. H., & Pilkey-Jarvis, L. (2007). *Useless arithmetic: Why environmental scientists can't predict the future.* New York, NY: Columbia University Press.

Pimm, S. L., Davis, G. E., Loope, L., Roman, C. T., Smith, T. J., & Tilmant, J. T. (1994). Hurricane Andrew. *BioScience, 44,* 224–229.

Plotkin, A. B., Foster D., & Carlson, J. (2013). Survivors, not invaders, control forest development following simulated hurricane. *Ecology, 94,* 414–423.

Post, W. M., Peng, T., Emanuel, W. R., King, A. W., Dale, V. H., & DeAngelis, D. L. (1990). The global carbon cycle. *American Scientist, 78,* 310–326.

Power, M. E. (1990). Effects of fish in river food webs. *Science, 250*(4982), 811–814.

Proctor, M. F., Paetkau, D., McLellan, B. N., Stenhouse, G. B., Kendall, K. C., Mace, R. D., & Kasworm, W. F. (2012). Population fragmentation and inter-ecosystem movements of grizzly bears in Western Canada and the Northern United States. *Wildlife Monographs 180,* 1–46.

Programme for the Endorsement of Forest Certification (PEFC). (2014). PEFC global statistics: SFM and CoC certification. Geneva, Switzerland: PEFC. Retrieved from http://www.pefc.org/images/documents/PEFC_Global_Certificates_-_December_2014.pdf

Provis, C. (1996). Interests vs. positions: A Critique of the Distinction. *Negotiation Journal, 12*(4), 305–323.

Prugh, L. R., Hodges, K. E., Sinclair, A. R., & Brashares, J. S. (2008). Effect of habitat area and isolation on fragmented animal populations. *Proceedings of the National Academy of Sciences, 105*(52), 20770–20775.

Puettmann, K. J., Coates, K. D., & Messier, C. (2009). *A critique of silviculture.* Washington, DC: Island Press.

Puettmann, K. J., Wilson, S. M., Baker, S. C., Donoso, P. J., Drössler, L., Amente, G., Harvey, B. D., Knoke, T., et al. (2015). Silvicultural alternatives to conventional even-aged forest management—what limits global adoption? *Forest Ecosystems, 2*(8), 1–16.

Pyne, S. J. (2010). *America's fires: A historical context for policy and practice.* Durham, NC: Forest History Society.

Pyne, S. J. (2015). *Between two fires: A fire history of contemporary America.* Tucson, AZ: University of Arizona Press.

Raffa, K. F., Aukema, B. H., Bentz, B. J., Carroll, A. L., Hicke, J. A., Turner, M. G., & Romme, W. H. (2008). Cross-scale drivers of natural disturbances prone to anthropogenic amplification: The dynamics of bark beetle eruptions. *BioScience, 58*(6), 501–517.

Randall, A. (1981). *Resource economics.* Columbus, OH: Grid Publishing.

Rapp, V., & Spies, T. A. (2003). *New findings about old-growth forests. Science Update 4.* Portland, OR: U.S. Department of Agriculture, Forest Service, Pacific Northwest Research Station, 12.

Raymond, C. L., & Peterson, D. L. (2005). Fuel treatments alter the effects of wildfire in a mixed-evergreen forest, Oregon, USA. *Canadian Journal of Forest Research, 35*(12), 2981–2995.

Rebertus, A. J., Kitzberger, T., Veblen, T. T., & Roovers, L. M. (1997). Blowdown history and landscape patterns in the Andes of Tierra del Fuego, Argentina. *Ecology, 78*(3), 678–692.

Redford, K., & Richter, B. D. (1999). Conservation of biodiversity in a world of use. *Conservation biology, 13*(6), 1246–1256.

Reeves, G. H., Benda, L. E., Burnett, K. M., Bisson, P. A., & Sedell, J. R. (1995). A disturbance-based ecosystem approach to maintaining and restoring freshwater habitats of evolutionarily significant units of anadromous salmonids in the Pacific Northwest. *American Fisheries Society Symposium, 17,* 334–349.

Reeves, G. H., Burnett, K. M., & McGarry, E. V. (2003). Sources of large woody debris in the main stem of a fourth-order watershed in coastal Oregon. *Canadian Journal of Forest Research, 33,* 1363–1370. Retrieved from http://www.fsl.orst.edu/clams/download/pubs/Reeves_et_al_CJFR.pdf

Reeves, G. H., Pickard, B. R., & Johnson, K. N. (2016). An initial evaluation of potential options for managing riparian reserves of the aquatic conservation strategy of the northwest forest plan. *USDA Forest Service General Technical Report PNW-GTR-937.* Portland, OR: Pacific Northwest Research Station.

Reeves, G. H., & Spies, T. A. (2017). Watersheds and landscapes, in D. H. Olson & B. Van Horne (Eds.), *People, forests and change—Lessons from the Pacific Northwest* (pp. 207–222). Washington, DC: Island Press.

Reich, R. B. (1985). Public administration and public deliberation: An interpretive essay. *Yale Law Journal, 94*(7), 1617–1641.

Reid, L. M. (2010). Understanding and evaluating cumulative watershed impacts. In W. J. Elliot, I. S. Miller, & L. Audin (Eds.), *Cumulative watershed effects of fuel management in the western United States USDA Forest Service General Technical Report RMRS-GTR-231,* pp. 277–298. Fort Collins, CO: Rocky Mountain Research Station.

Reinhardt, B. H. (Ed.). (2013). *Finding a sense of place: An environmental history of Zena.* Salem, OR: Polebridge Press.

Reynolds, R. T., Sánchez Meador, A. J., Youtz, J. A., Nicolet, T., Matonis, M. S., Jackson, P. L., DeLorenzo, D. G., & Graves, A. D. (2013). Restoring composition and structure in southwestern frequent-fire forests: A science-based framework for improving ecosystem resiliency. *USDA Forest Service General Technical Report RMRS-GTR-310.* Fort Collins, CO. Rocky Mountain Research Station.

Richards, R. T., & Alexander, S. J. (2006). A social history of wild huckleberry harvesting in the Pacific Northwest. *USDA Forest Service General Technical Report PNW-GTR-657.* Portland, OR: Pacific Northwest Research Station.

Rickenbach, M., & Overdevest, C. (2006). More than markets: Assessing Forest Stewardship Council (FSC) certification as a policy tool. *Journal of Forestry, 104,* 143–147.

Ripple, W. J., & Beschta, R. L. (2006). Linking wolves to willows via risk-sensitive foraging by ungulates in the northern Yellowstone ecosystem. *Forest Ecology and Management, 230*(1), 96–106.

Rittel, H. W., & Webber, M. W. (1973). Dilemmas in the general theory of planning. *Policy Sciences, 4*(2), 155–169.

Robles, M. D., Flather, C. H., Stein, S. M., Nelson, M. D., & Cutko, A. (2008). The geography of private forests that support at-risk species in the conterminous United States. *Frontiers in Ecology and the Environment, 6*(6), 301–307.

Roling, N. G., & Wagemakers, M. A. E. (1998). *Facilitating sustainable agriculture: Participatory learning and adaptive management in times of environmental uncertainty.* Cambridge, UK: Cambridge University Press.

Rolston, H., III. (1994). *Conserving natural value.* New York, NY: Columbia University Press.

Romero, F., & Menakis, J. P. (2013). Fire season 2012: The impact of fuel treatments on wildfire outcomes. *Fire Management Today, 73*(2), 15–24.

Romme, W. H., Boyce, M. S., Gresswell, R., Merrill, E. H., Minshall, G. W., Whitlock, C., & Turner, M. G. (2011). Twenty years after the 1988 Yellowstone fires: Lessons about disturbance and ecosystems. *Ecosystems, 14*(7), 1196–1215.

Romme, W. H., Turner, M. G., Wallace, L. L., & Walker, J. S. (1995). Aspen, elk, and fire in northern Yellowstone Park. *Ecology, 76*(7), 2097–2106.

Rosenberger, R. S., Collins, A. R., & Svetlik, J. B. (2004). Private provision of a public good: Willingness to pay for privately stocked trout. *Society and Natural Resources, 18*(1), 75–87.

Rosenberger, R. S., & Johnston, R. J. (2013). Benefit transfer. In J. F. Shogren (Ed.), *Encyclopedia of energy, natural resource and environmental economics* (Vol. 3) (pp. 327–333). Amsterdam, Netherlands: Elsevier.

Rosenberger, R. S., & Johnston, R. J. (2014). Benefit transfer. In T. C. Habb & J. C. Whithead (Eds.), *Environmental and natural resource economics: An encyclopedia* (pp. 30–33). Santa Barbara, CA: Greenwood

Rosenberger, R. S., & Loomis, J. B. (2016). Benefit transfer. In P. A. Champ, K. J. Boyle, & T. C. Brown (Eds.), *A primer on non-market valuation* (2nd ed.). Dordrecht, Netherlands: Kluwer Academic Publishers.

Rosenberger, R. S., Peterson, G. L., Clarke, A., & Brown, T. C. (2003). Measuring dispositions for lexicographic preferences of environmental goods: Integrating economics, psychology and ethics. *Ecological Economics, 44*(1), 63–76.

Rosenzweig, M. L. (2003). *Win-win ecology: How the earth's species can survive in the midst of human enterprise.* New York: Oxford University Press.

Roth, F. (1925). *Forest regulation* (2nd ed.). Ann Arbor, MI: George Wahr.

Rothermel, R. C. (1983). How to predict the spread and intensity of forest and range fires. *USDA Forest Service General Technical Report INT-143.* Ogden, UT: Intermountain Forest and Range Experiment Station, Ogden.

Row, C., Kaiser, F., & Sessions, J. (1981). Discount rate for long-term forest service investments. *Journal of Forestry, 79*(6), 367–369.

Rubin, J., Helfand, G., & Loomis, J. (1991). A benefit-cost analysis of the northern spotted owl. *Journal of Forestry, 89*(12), 25–30.

Ruggierro, L. F., Aubry, K., Carey, A. B., & Huff, M. H. (Eds.). (1991). Wildlife and vegetation of unmanaged Douglas-fir forests. *USDA Forest Service General Technical Report PNW-GTR-285.* Portland OR: US Forest Service.

Ryan, M. G., Harmon, M. E., Birdsey, R. A., et al. (2010). A synthesis of the science on forests and carbon for U.S. forests. *Issues in Ecology, 13.* Washington, DC: Ecological Society of America. Retrieved from http://www.fs.fed.us/rm/pubs_other/rmrs_2010_ryan_m002.pdf

Ryan, M. G., Vose, J. M., Hanson, P. J., Iverson, L. R., Miniat, C. F., Luce, C. H., Band, L. E., et al. (2014). In D. L. Peterson, J. M. Vose, & R. Patel-Weynand (Eds.), *Climate change and United States Forests* (pp. 25–54). New York, NY: Springer.

Saatchi, S. S., Harris, N. L., Brown, S., Lefsky, M., Mitchard, E. T. A., Salas, W., et al. (2011). Benchmark map of forest carbon stocks in tropical regions across three continents. *Proceedings of the National Academy of Sciences USA, 108,* 9899–9904.

Sagoff, M. (2008). *The economy of the earth: Philosophy, law, and the environment* (2nd ed.). New York, NY: Cambridge University Press.

Salati, E. (1987). The forest and the hydrological cycle. In R. E. Dickinson (Ed.), *The geophysiology of Amazonia.* New York, NY: John Wiley & Sons.

Sample, V. A., Birdsey, R. A., Houghton, R. A., Swanston, C., Hollinger, D., Dockry, M., & Bettinger. P. (2015). *Forest carbon conservation and management: Integration with sustainable forest management for multiple resource values and ecosystem services.* Washington, DC: Pinchot Institute for Conservation.

Sathre, R., & O'Connor, J. (2010). Meta-analysis of greenhouse gas displacement factors of wood product substitution. *Environmental Science & Policy, 13*(2), 104–114.

Schmitz, O. J., Beckerman, A. P., & O'Brien, K. M. (1997). Behaviorally mediated trophic cascades: Effects of predation risk on food web interactions. *Ecology, 78*(5), 1388–1399.

Schmitz, O. J., Hambäck, P. A., & Beckerman, A. P. (2000). Trophic cascades in terrestrial systems: A review of the effects of carnivore removals on plants. *The American Naturalist, 155*(2), 141–153.

Schmutzenhofer, H. (1992). IUFRO's birthday. *IUFRO News, 21*(1&2), 3.

Schneider, A., & Ingram, H. (1990). Behavioral assumptions of policy tools. *The Journal of Politics, 52*(02), 510–529.

Schoennagel, T., Veblen, T. T., & Romme, W. H. (2004). The interaction of fire, fuels and climate across Rocky Mountain forests. *Bioscience, 54*(7), 661–676.

Schroeder, M., & Buck, C. (1970). Fire weather: A guide for application of meteorological information to forest fire control operations. *USDA Forest Service Agriculture Handbook 360.* Washington, DC: US Department of Agriculture, Forest Service. Retrieved from http://gacc.nifc.gov/nwcc/content/products/intelligence/Fire_Weather_Agriculture_Handbook_360.pdf

Schultz, C. A. (2010). Challenges in connecting cumulative effects analysis to effective wildlife conservation planning. *Bioscience, 60*(7), 545–551.

Schultz, C. A., Coelho, D. L., & Beam, R. D. (2014). Design and governance of multiparty monitoring under the USDA Forest Service's Collaborative Forest Landscape Restoration Program. *Journal of Forestry, 112*(2), 198–206.

Schultz, C. A., Jedd, T., & Beam, R. D. (2012). The Collaborative Forest Landscape Restoration Program: A history and overview of the first projects. *Journal of Forestry, 110*(7), 381–391.

Schusler, T. M., Decker, D. J., & Pfeffer, M. J. (2003). Social learning for collaborative natural resource management. *Society and Natural Resources, 16*(4), 309–326.

Schweitzer, D. L. Sassman, R. W., Schallau, C. H. (1972). Allowable cut effect: Some physical and economic implications. *Journal of Forestry, 70*(7), 415–418.

Scientific Panel for Sustainable Forest Practices in Clayoquot Sound. (1995). *Sustainable ecosystem management in Clayoquot Sound: Planning and practice*s. Victoria, BC, Canada: Cortex Consultants, Inc.

Scott, J. H. & R. E. Burgan. (2005). Standard fire behavior fuel models: A comprehensive set for use with Rothermel's surface fire spread model. *USDA Forest Service. General Technical Report RMRS-GTR-153.* Fort Collins, CO: Rocky Mountain Research Station.

Scott, J. H., Thompson, M. P., & Calkin, D. E. (2013). A wildfire risk assessment framework for land and resource management. *USDA Forest Service General Technical Report RMRS-GTR-315.* Fort Collins, CO: Rocky Mountain Research Station.

Seager, S. T., Eisenberg, C., & St. Clair, S. B. (2013). Patterns and consequences of ungulate herbivory on aspen in western North America. *Forest Ecology and Management, 299,* 81–90.

Sedjo, R. A., & Botkin, D. (1997). Using forest plantations to spare natural forests. *Environment, 39*(10), 15–20.

Seidl, R. (2014). The shape of ecosystem management to come: Anticipating risks and fostering resilience. *BioScience, 64,* 1159–1169.

Selin, S., & Chavez D. (1995). Developing a collaborative model for environmental planning and management. *Environmental Management, 19*(2), 189–195.

Seymour, R., & Hunter, M. (1999). Principles of ecological forestry. In M. Hunter (Ed.), *Managing biodiversity in forest ecosystems* (pp. 22–65). Cambridge: Cambridge University Press.

SFI (Sustainable Forestry Initiative). (2015). *SFI 2015–2019 Standards and Rules.* Retrieved from http://www.sfiprogram.org/sfi-standard/

Sharp, E. A., Thwaites, R., Curtis, R., & Millar, J. (2012). Trust and trustworthiness: Conceptual distinctions and their implications for natural resources management. *Journal of Environmental Planning and Management, 56*(8), 1246–1265.

Shindler, B. (2000). Landscape-level management: It's all about context. *Journal of Forestry, 98*(12), 10–14.

Shindler, B., & Aldred-Cheek, K. (1999). Integrating citizens in adaptive management: A propositional analysis. *Journal of Conservation Ecology, 3*(1), 13.

Shindler, B., Brunson, M., & Stankey, G. H. (2002). Social acceptability of forest conditions and management practices: A problem analysis. *USDA Forest Service General Technical Report PNW-GTR-537.* Portland, OR: Pacific Northwest Research Station.

Shindler, B., & Mallon, A. (2009). Public acceptance of disturbance-based forest management—a study of the Blue River landscape strategy in the Central Cascades Adaptive Management Area. *USDA Forest Service Research Paper PNW-RP-581.* Portland, OR: Pacific Northwest Research Station.

Shindler, B., & Neburka, J. (1997). Public participation in forest planning: Eight attributes of success. *Journal of Forestry, 91*(7), 17–19.

Shindler, B., Olsen, C., McCaffrey, S., McFarlane, B., Christianson, A., McGee, T., Curtis, A., & Sharp, E. (2014). Trust: A planning guide for wildfire agencies and practitioners—An international collaboration drawing on research and management experience in Australia, Canada, and the United States. *A Joint Fire Science Program Research Publication.* Corvallis, OR: Oregon State University.

Shindler, B., Peters, J., & Kruger, L. (1994). *Social values and acceptability of alternative harvest practices on the Tongass National Forest.* Corvallis, OR: Oregon State University Press.

Short, K. C. (2014). *Spatial wildfire occurrence data for the United States, 1992–2012 [FPA_FOD_20140428]* (2nd ed.). Fort Collins, CO: Forest

Service Research Data Archive. http://dx.doi.org/10.2737/RDS-2013-0009.2

Sillett, S. C., Van Pelt, R., Carroll, A. L., Kramer, R. D., Ambrose, A. R., & Trask, D. (2015). How do tree structure and old age affect growth potential of California redwoods? *Ecological Monographs, 85*(2), 181–212.

Simon, H. (1957). *Models of man: Social and rational.* New York, NY: Wiley.

Simons, R., Seo, Y., & Robinson, S. (2014). The effect of a large hog barn operation on residential sales prices in Marshall County, KY. *Journal of Sustainable Real Estate, 6*(2), 93–111.

Sinton, D. S., Jones, J. A., Öhmann, J. L., & Swanson, F. J. (2000). Windthrow disturbance, forest composition, and structure in the Bull Run Basin, Oregon. *Ecology, 81,* 2539–2556.

Skillen, J. R. (2015). *Federal ecosystem management: Its rise, fall, and afterlife.* Lawrence, KS: University of Kansas Press.

Skog, K. E. (2008). Sequestration of carbon in harvested wood products for the United States. *Forest Products Journal, 58,* 56–72.

Skolstad, E. (2012). *The carbon footprint of a shrimp cocktail.* American Association for the Advancement of Science. Retrieved from http://news.sciencemag.org/earth/2012/02/carbon-footprint-shrimp-cocktail

Smith, D. M. (1969). Adapting forestry to Megalopolitan Southern New England. *Journal of Forestry, 67*(6), 372–377.

Smith, D. M., Larson, B. C., Kelty, M. J., & Ashton, P. S. (1997). *The practice of silviculture: Applied forest ecology* (9th ed.). New York, NY: John Wiley & Sons.

Smith, J. E., Heath, L. S., Skog K. E., & Birdsey R. A. (2006). Methods for calculating forest ecosystem and harvested carbon with standard estimates for forest types of the United States. *USDA Forest Service General Technical Report NE-343.* Newton Square, PA: Northeastern Research Station.

Soberón, J., Rodríguez, P., & Vázquez-Domínguez, E. (2000). Implications of the hierarchical structure of biodiversity for the development of ecological indicators of sustainable use. *AMBIO: A Journal of the Human Environment, 29*(3), 136–142.

Souder, J., & Fairfax, S. (1996). *State trust lands: History, management, and sustainable use.* Lawrence, KS: University of Kansas Press.

Soulé, M. E., Estes, J. A., Berger, J., & Martinez Del Rio, C. (2003). Ecological effectiveness: Conservation goals for interactive species. *Conservation Biology, 17*(5), 1238–1250.

Soulé, M. E., Estes, J. A., Miller, B., & Honnold, D. L. (2005). Strongly interacting species: Conservation policy, management, and ethics. *BioScience, 55*(2), 168–176.

Spash, C. V. (2008). Deliberative monetary valuation and the evidence for a new value theory. *Land Economics, 84*(3), 469–488.

Spies, T. A. (2009). Science of old growth, or a journey into wonderland. In T. A. Spies & S. L. Duncan (Eds.), *Old growth in a new world: A Pacific Northwest icon reexamined* (pp. 31–43). Washington, DC: Island Press.

Spies, T. A., & Cline, S. P. (1988). Coarse woody debris in forests and plantations of coastal Oregon. *From the forest to the sea: A story of fallen trees. Gen. Tech. Rep. PNW-GTR-229,* 5–23. Portland, OR: Pacific Northwest Research Station, Forest Service, US Department of Agriculture.

Spies, T. A., & Franklin, J. F. (1988). Old-growth and forest dynamics in the Douglas-fir region of western Oregon and Washington. *Natural Areas Journal, 8,* 190–201.

Spies, T. A., & Franklin, J. F. (1996). The diversity and maintenance of old-growth forests. In R. C. Szaro & D. W. Johnson (Eds.), *Biodiversity in Managed Landscapes* (pp. 296–314). New York, NY: Oxford University Press.

Spies, T. A., Franklin, J. F., & Thomas, T. B. (1988). Coarse woody debris in Douglas-fir forests of western Oregon and Washington. *Ecology, 69*(6), 1689–1702.

Spies, T. A., Giesen, T. W., Swanson, F. J., Franklin, J. F., Lach, D., & Johnson, K. N. (2010). Climate change adaptation strategies for federal forests of the Pacific Northwest, USA: Ecological, policy, and socio-economic perspectives. *Landscape Ecology, 25*(8), 1185–1199.

Spies, T. A., Johnson, K. N., Burnett, K. M., Öhmann, J. L., McComb, B. C., Reeves, G. W., Bettinger P., Kline, J. D., & Garber-Yonts, B. (2007). Cumulative ecological and socioeconomic effects of forest policies in Coastal Oregon. *Ecological Applications, 88*(1), 5–17.

Spurr, S. H., & Cline, A. C. (1942). Ecological forestry in central New England. *Journal of Forestry, 40*(5), 418–420.

Stankey, G. H. (2001, April). Too early to tell, or too late to rescue? Adaptive management under scrutiny. *Science Findings.* Portland OR: US Department of Agriculture: Pacific Northwest Research Station.

Stankey, G. H., Bormann, B., Ryan, C., Shindler, B., Sturtevant, V., Clark, R. N., & Philpot, C. (2003). Adaptive management and the northwest forest plan: Rhetoric and reality. *Journal of Forestry, 101,* 40–46.

Steel, B. S. (2009). Common sense versus symbolism: The case for public involvement in the old-growth debate. In T. A. Spies & S. L. Duncan (Eds.), *Old growth in a new world: A Pacific Northwest icon reexamined* (pp. 116–126). Washington, DC: Island Press.

Steel, B. S., Shindler, B., & Brunson, M. (1998). Social acceptability of ecosystem management in the Pacific Northwest. In B. Lamb, D. Soden, & J. Tennert (Eds.), *Ecosystem management: A social science perspective.* Dubuque, IA: Kendall-Hunt.

Steel, Z. L., Safford, H. D., & Viers, J. H. (2015). The fire frequency-severity relationship and the legacy of fires suppression in California forests. *Ecosphere, 6*(1), 1–23.

Stein, S. M., McFoberts, R. E., Mahal, L. G., Carr, M. A., Alig, R. J., Comas, S. J., Theobald, D. M., & Cundiff, A. (2009). Private forests, public benefits: Increased housing density and other pressures on private forest contributions. *USDA Forest Service General Technical Report PNW-GTR-795.* Portland, OR: Pacific Northwest Research Station.

Stephens, S. L., McIver, J. D., Boerner, R. E. J., Fettig, C. J., Fontaine, J. B., Hartsough, B. R., Kennedy, P. L., & Schwilk, D. W. (2012). The effects of forest fuel-reduction treatments in the United States. *Bioscience, 62,* 549–560.

Stern, M. J., & Coleman, K. J. (2015). The multidimensionality of trust: Applications in collaborative natural resource management. *Society & Natural Resources, 28*(2), 117–132. doi 10.1080/08941920.2014.945062

Stetler, K. M., Venn, T. J., & Calkin, D. E. (2010). The effects of wildfire and environmental amenities on property values in northwest Montana, USA. *Ecological Economics, 69*(11), 2233–2243.

Stevens, J., Ahmad, M., & Ruddell, S. (1998). Forest products certification: A survey of manufacturers. *Forest Products Journal, 48*(6), 43–48.

Stine, P., Hessburg, P., Spies, T., Kramer, M., Fettig, C. J., Hansen, A., et al. (2014).The ecology and management of moist mixed-conifer forests in eastern Oregon and Washington: A synthesis of the relevant biophysical science and implications for future land management. *USDA Forest Service General Technical Report PNW-GTR-897.* Portland, OR: Pacific Northwest Research Station.

Stohr, W. G. (2013). Belowground ecosystems: The foundation for forest health, restoration, and sustainable management. *Jour. Environmental Assessment Policy and Management, 15*(4).

Stone, J. K., Coop, L. B., & Manger, D. K. (2008). Predicting effects of climate change on Swiss needle cast disease severity in Pacific Northwest forests. *Canadian Journal Plant Pathology, 30*(2), 169–176.

Strong, D. (1992). Are trophic cascades all wet? Differentiation and donor control in speciose systems. *Ecology, 73*(3), 745–754.

Stroup, R. L., & Baden, J. A. (1973). Externality, property rights, and the management of our national forests. *The Journal of Law and Economics, 16*(2), 303–312.

Sugihara, N. G., van Wagtendonk, J., Shaffer, K. E., Fites-Kaufman, J., & Thode, A. E. (Eds.). (2006). *Fire in California's ecosystems.* Berkeley, CA: University of California Press.

Surowiecki, J. (2004). *The wisdom of crowds.* New York, NY: Doubleday.

Swain, D. S., Tsiang, M., Haugen, M., et al. (2014, September). The extraordinary California drought of 2013/2014: Character, context, and the role of climate change (pp. 53–57). *Bulletin of the American Meteorological Society.* Retrieved from http://stanford.edu/~dlswain/Swain_et_al_2014.pdf

Swank, W. T., Swift, J. L., & Douglass, J. E. (1988). Streamflow changes associated with forest cutting, species conversions, and natural disturbances. In W. T. Swank & D. A. Crossley, Jr. (Eds.), *Forest hydrology and ecology at Coweeta* (pp. 297–312). New York, NY: Springer-Verlag.

Swanson, M. E., Franklin, J. F., Beschta, R. L., Crisafulli, C. M., DellaSala, D. A., Hutto, R. L., Lindenmayer, D. B., & Swanson, F. J. (2010). The forgotten state of forest succession: Early successional ecosystems on forest sites. *Frontiers in Ecology and the Environment, 9*(2), 117–125.

Swetnam, T. W., Farella, J., Roos, C. I., Liebmann, M. J., Falk, D. A., & Allen, C. D. (2016). Multiscale perspectives of fire, climate and humans in western North America and the Jemez Mountains, USA. *Philosophical Transactions Royal Society B, 371*, 20150168. Retrieved from http://rstb.royalsocietypublishing.org/content/royptb/371/1696/20150168.full.pdf

Takeda, L. (2015). *Islands' spirit rising.* Vancouver, BC, Canada: University of British Columbia Press.

Tamura, M., & Tharayil, N. (2014). Plant litter chemistry and microbial priming regulate the accrual, composition and stability of soil carbon in invaded ecosystems. *New Phytologist, 203*(1), 110–124.

Taylor, A. H., Trouet, V., Skinner, C. N., & Stephens, S. (2016). Socio-Ecological transformations trigger fire regime shifts and modulate fire-climate interactions in the Sierra Nevada, USA 1600–2015 CE. *Proceedings of the National Academy of Science, 113*(48), 13684–13689.

Teeguarden, D. E. (1973). The allowable cut effect: A comment. *Journal of Forestry, 71*(4), 224–226.

Tepley, A. J., Swanson, F. J., & Spies, T. A. (2014). Post-fire tree establishment and early cohort development in conifer forests of the western Cascades of Oregon, USA. *Ecosphere, 5*(7), art80.

Teply, A. J., Swanson, F. J., & Spies, T. A. (2013). Fire-mediated pathways of stand development in Douglas-fir/western hemlock forests of the Pacific Northwest, USA. *Ecology, 94*(8), 1729–1743.

Tews, J., Brose, U., Grimm, V., Tielbörger, K., Wichmann, M. C., Schwager, M., & Jeltsch, F. (2004). Animal species diversity driven by habitat heterogeneity/diversity: The importance of keystone structures. *Journal of Biogeography, 31*(1), 79–92.

Theobold, D. M., & Romme, W. H. (2007). Expansion of the US wildland-urban interface. *Landscape and Urban Planning, 83*, 340–354.

Thomas, J. W. (Ed.) (1979). Wildlife habitats in managed forests the Blue Mountains of Oregon and Washington. *USDA Forest Service Agriculture Handbook No. 553.* Washington, DC: US Department of Agriculture, Forest Service.

Thomas, J. W., Forsman, E. D., Lint, J. B., Meslow, E. C., Noon, B. R., & Verner, J. (1990). *A conservation strategy for the northern spotted owl. Interagency committee to address the conservation of the northern spotted owl.* Washington, DC: USDA Forest, Service, USDI Bureau of Land Management, USDI Fish and Wildlife Service, and USDI National Park Service.

Thomas, J. W., Franklin, J. F., Gordon, J., Johnson, K. N. (2006). The Northwest Forest Plan: Origins, components, implementation experience, and suggestions for change. *Conservation Biology, 20*, 277–287.

Thompson, J. R., Anderson, M. A. & Johnson, K. N. (2004). Ecosystem management across ownerships: The potential for collision with Antitrust Laws. *Conserv. Biol. 18*, 1475–1481.

Thompson, M. P. (2014). Social, institutional, and psychological factors affecting wildfire incident decision making. *Society and Natural Resources, 27*(6), 636–644.

Thompson, M. P., Adams, D., & Johnson, K. N. (2009). The albedo effect and forest carbon offset design. *Journal of Forestry, 107*(8), 425–431.

Thompson, M. P., Bowden, P., Brough, A., Scott, J. H., Gilbertson-Day, J., Taylor, A., Anderson, J., & Haas, J. R. (2016). Application of wildfire risk assessment results to wildfire response planning in the southern Sierra Nevada, USA. *Forests, 7*(64), 1–22.

Thompson, M. P., Marcot, B. G., Thompson, F. R., McNutty, S., Fisher, L. A., Runge, M. C., Cleaves, D., & Tomosy, M. (2013a). The science of decision making: Applications for sustainable forest and grassland management in the national forest system. *USDA Forest Service General Technical Report WO-GTR-88.* Washington, DC: US Department of Agriculture, Forest Service.

Thompson, M. P., Vaillant, N. M., Haas, J. R., Gebert, K. M., & Stockmann, K. D. (2013b). Quantifying the potential impacts of fuel treatments on wildfire suppression costs. *Journal of Forestry, 111*(1), 49–58.

Tormark, C. (2002). A low energy building in a life cycle—its embodied energy, energy need for operation and recycling potential. *Building and Environment, 3*, 429–435.

Toth, S. F., & McDill, M. E. (2008). Promoting large, compact mature forest patches in harvest scheduling models. *Environmental Modeling and Assessment, 13*(1), 1–15.

Treverton, G. F. (2007, June). Risks and riddles: The Soviet Union was a puzzle. Al Qaeda is a mystery. Why we need to know the difference. *Smithsonian.* Retrieved from http://www.smithsonianmag.com/people-places/risks-and-riddles-154744750/

Trombulak, S. C., & Frissell, C. A. (2000). Review of ecological effects of roads on terrestrial and aquatic communities. *Conservation Biology, 14*(1), 18–30.

Tucker, M. M., Corace III, R. G., Cleland, D. T., & Kashian, D. M. (2016). Long-term effects of managing for an endangered songbird on the heterogeneity of a fire-prone landscape. *Landscape Ecology, 31*, 2445–2458.

Turner, D. P., &. Franz, E. H. (1985). The influence of western hemlock and western redcedar on microbial numbers, nitrogen mineralization, and nitrification. *Plant and Soil, 88*, 259–267.

Turner, M. G. (2010). Disturbance and landscape dynamics in a changing world. *Ecology 91*(10), 2833–2849.

Turner, M. G., Gardner, R. H., & O'Neill, R. V. (2001). *Landscape ecology in theory and practice* (Vol. 401). New York, NY: Springer-Verlag.

Turner, R. K. (1992). *Speculations on weak and strong sustainability.* (CSERGE working paper GEC 92-26). London: Center for Social and Economic Research on the Global Environment (CSERGE).

United Nations. (1987). *Report of the World Commission on Environment and Development.* Retrieved from http://www.un-documents.net/ocf-ov.htm

United Nations. (1992). *Rio declaration on environment and development.* Retrieved from www.unesco.org/education/nfsunesco/pdf/RIO_E.PDF

Upton B., Miner R., Spinny, M., & Heath, L. S. (2008). The greenhouse gas and energy impacts of using wood instead of alternative in residential construction in the United States. *Biomass & Bioenergy, 32*, 1–10.

Urban, D. L., O'Neill, R. V., & Shugart, H. H. (1987). Landscape ecology. *BioScience, 37*, 119–127.

Ury, W. (1993). *Getting past no: Negotiating in difficult situations.* New York, NY: Bantam Books.

USDA. (1976). National Forest Management Act of 1976. (16 U.S.C. 1600).

USDA. (1982). National forest system land management planning. *Federal Register, 47*, 43037-43061.

USDA. (2010). Wood handbook: Wood as an engineering material. *USDA Forest Service General Technical Report FPL-GTR-190.* Madison, WI: Forest Products Laboratory.

USDA. (2012). National forest system land management planning. *Federal Register, 77*(68), 21162–21276.

USDA Forest Service, Pacific Northwest Region. (1984, May). *Regional guide for the Pacific Northwest Region.* Retrieved from: https://babel.hathitrust.org/cgi/pt?id=umn.31951p009254479;view=1up;seq=1

USDA Forest Service. (2010). Environmental assessments and related documents. *US Forest Service Handbook 1909.15*, Chapter 40. Retrieved from http://www.fs.fed.us/im/directives/fsh/1909.15/wo_1909.15_40.doc

USDA Forest Service. (2011). *National report on sustainable forests—2010.* Retrieved from http://www.fs.fed.us/research/sustain/docs/national-reports/2010/2010-sustainability-report.pdf

USDA Forest Service. (2012a). National forest system land management planning. *Federal Register, 77*(68), 21162–21276. Retrieved from http://www.fs.usda.gov/Internet/FSE_DOCUMENTS/stelprdb5362536.pdf

USDA Forest Service. (2012b). Future of America's forest and rangelands: Forest Service 2010 Resources Planning Act assessment. *USDA For. Serv., Gen. Tech. Rep. WO-87.* Washington, DC: USDA.

USDA Forest Service. (2012c). *Increasing the pace of restoration and job creation on our national forests.* Washington, DC: United States Department of Agriculture, Forest Service. Retrieved from http://www.fs.fed.us/sites/default/files/media/types/publication/field_pdf/increasing-pace-restoration-job-creation-2012.pdf

USDA Forest Service. (2014). Accelerated restoration: New landscape tools to prioritize projects and analyze tradeoffs. *Science Findings Issue, 159.* Portland, OR: Pacific Northwest Research Station.

USDA Forest Service. (2015, January). *FSH 1909.12 - Land management planning handbook.* Retrieved from http://www.fs.usda.gov/detail/planningrule/home/?cid=stelprd3828310

USDA Forest Service. (2016a, June). A citizen's guide to national forest planning (prepared by the Federal Advisory Committee on implementation of the 2012 land management planning rule). Version 1.0. Retrieved from http://www.fs.usda.gov/main/planningrule/committee

USDA Forest Service. (2016b, May). *Draft revised forest plan for the Flathead National Forest.* Retrieved from: http://www.fs.usda.gov/detailfull/flathead/home/?cid=stelprdb5422786&width=full

US Department of the Interior (USDI). (2015, September 22). Press Release. Historic conservation campaign protects greater sage-grouse. Retrieved from https://www.doi.gov/pressreleases/historic-conservation-campaign-protects-greater-sage-grouse

USDA-USDI. (1994). *Record of decision for amendments for Forest Service and Bureau of Land Management planning documents within the range of the northern spotted owl.* Portland, OR: USDA Forest Service Pacific Northwest Region.

USDA-USDI. (2014, April). The national strategy: The final phase in the development of the *National Cohesive Wildland Fire Management Strategy.* Retrieved from https://www.forestsandrangelands.gov/strategy/documents/strategy/CSPhaseIIINationalStrategyApr2014.pdf

USDI BLM. (2012a). *Environmental assessment for Trout Creek Rock Climbing Area access and trail plan.* Prineville, OR: US Department of the Interior, Bureau of Land Management. Retrieved from http://www.blm.gov/or/districts/prineville/plans/files/Trout_Cr_EA_Final.pdf

USDI BLM. (2012b). *Decision record: Trout Creek Rock Climbing Area.* Prineville, OR: US Department of the Interior, Bureau of Land Management. Retrieved from http://www.blm.gov/or/districts/prineville/plans/files/2012-0028-EA_decision_1842form_fonsi_BLMResponse_11_08_2012.pdf

USEPA. (2005). *National management measures to control nonpoint-source pollution from foestry.* Retrieved from: https://www.epa.gov/nps/national-management-measures-control-nonpoint-source-pollution-forestry

USEPA. (2014). *Inventory of US Greenhouse Gas Emissions and Sinks: 1990–2012.* Washington, DC: US Environmental Protection Agency.

USEPA. (2016). *Allowance markets.* Retrieved from https://www.epa.gov/airmarkets/allowance-markets

US Federal Reserve. (2015). Selected interest rates and historical data. Board of Governors of the Federal Reserve System. Retrieved from http://www.federalreserve.gov/releases/h15/data.htm#fn10

US Fish and Wildlife Service (USFWS). (2011). *Revised recovery plan for the northern spotted owl* (Strix occidentalis caurina). Portland, OR: Author. Retrieved from https://www.fws.gov/wafwo/pdf/NSO%20Revised%20Recovery%20Plan%202011.pdf

US Fish and Wildlife Service (USFWS). (2015, February 17). News Release: Endangered Species Act scores another success as Oregon chub becomes first fish delisted due to recovery. Retrieved from http://www.fws.gov/pacific/news/news.cfm?id=2144375359

US Fish and Wildlife Service (USFWS). (2016). Listed species summary. Retrieved from http://ecos.fws.gov/tess_public/reports/box-score-report

U.S.G.B.C. (U.S. Green Building Council). (2017). *Guide to LEED Certification.* Washington, DC: U.S. Green Building Council. Retrieved from https://www.usgbc.org/cert-guide

US Presidential Commission. (1986). Report to the president on the space shuttle *Challenger* accident. Retrieved from http://history.nasa.gov/rogersrep/genindex.htm

Vaillant, N. M., Ager, A. A., Anderson, J., & Miller, L. (2013). ArcFuels user guide and tutorial: For use with ArcGIS 9. *USDA Forest Service General Technical Report PNWGTR-877.* Portland, OR: Pacific Northwest Research Station.

van Andel, J., & Aronson, J. (2005). *Restoration ecology: The new frontier.* Oxford, UK: Blackwell.

Van der Heijden. K. (2005). *Scenarios: The art of strategic conversation* (2nd ed.). West Sussex, UK: John Wiley.

van Mantgem, P. J., Stephenson, N. L., Byrne, J. C., Daniels, L. D., Franklin, J. F., Fule, P. Z., et al. (2009). Widespread increase of tree mortality rates in the western United States. *Science, 323,* 521–524.

van Mantgem, P. J., Stephenson, N. L., Mutch, L. S., Johnson, V. G., Esperanza, A. M., & Parsons, D. J. (2003). Growth rate predicts mortality of *Abies concolor* in both burned and unburned stands. *Canadian Journal of Forest Research, 33*(6), 1029–1038.

Van Pelt, R., & Nadkarni, N. M. (2004). Development of canopy structure in Pseudotsuga menziesii forests in the southern Washington Cascades. *Forest Science, 50,* 326–341.

Van Pelt, R., & Sillett, S. C. (2008). Crown development of coastal *Pseudotsuga menziesii,* including a conceptual model for tall conifers. *Ecological Monographs, 78,* 283–311.

Van Pelt, R., Sillett, S. C., Kruse, W. A., Freund, J. A., & Kramer, R. D. (2016). Emergent crowns and light-use complimentarity lead to global maximum biomass and leaf area in *Sequoia sempervirens* forests. *Forest Ecology and Management, 375,* 275–308.

van Wagtendonk, J. W. (2007). The history and evolution of wildland fire use. *Fire Ecology, 3*(2), 3–17.

Vucetich, J. A., Bruskotter, J. T., & Nelson, M. P. (2015). Evaluating whether nature's intrinsic value is an axiom of or anathema to conservation. *Conservation Biology, 29*(2), 321–332.

Walker, J. F. (1977). Economic efficiency and the National Forest Management Act of 1976. *Journal of Forestry, 75*(11), 715–718.

Walker, L. R., Lodge, D. J., Brokaw, N. V. L., & Waide, R. B. (1991). Special Issue: Ecosystem, plant, and animal responses to hurricanes in the Caribbean. *Biotropica, 23*(4), 313–521.

Walker, T., Cardellichio, P. Gunn, J. S., Saahd, D. S., & Hagan, J. M. (2013). Carbon accounting for woody biomass from Massachusetts (USA) managed forests: A framework for determining the temporal impacts of woody biomass energy on atmospheric greenhouse gas levels. *Journal of Sustainable Forestry, 32,* 130–158.

Wallace, L. L. (2004). *After the fires: The ecology of change in Yellowstone National Park.* New Haven, CT: Yale University Press.

Wallinger, S. (1995). A commitment to the future: AF&PA's Sustainable Forestry Initiative. *Journal of Forestry. 93*(1), 16–19.

Walters, C. J. (1986). *Adaptive management of renewable resources.* Caldwell, NJ: Blackburn Press.

Walters, C. J. (1997). Challenges in adaptive management of riparian and coastal ecosystems. *Conservation Ecology.* Retrieved from http://www.consecol.org/vol1/iss2/art1

Walters, C. J., & Holling, C. S. (1990). Large-scale management experiments and learning by doing. *Ecology, 71,* 2060–2068.

Waples, R. S., Beechie, T., & Pess, G. R. (2009). Evolutionary history, habitat disturbance regimes, and anthropogenic changes: What do these mean for resilience of Pacific salmon populations? *Ecology and Society, 14*(1), 3. Retrieved from http://www.ecologyandsociety.org/vol14/iss1/art3/

Ware, S., Frost, C., & Doerr, P. D. (1993). Southern mixed hardwood forest: The former longleaf pine forest. In W. H. Martin, S. G. Boyce, & A. C. Echternacht (Eds.), *Biodiversity of the southeastern United States: Lowland terrestrial communities* (pp. 447–493). New York, NY: John Wiley and Sons.

Watts, C., Kobziar, L. N., & Snyder, J. R. (2012). Fire reinforces structure of pondcypress (*Taxodium distichum var. imbricarium*) domes in a wetland landscape. *Wetlands 32*(3), 439–448.

Way, A. G. (2011). *Conserving southern longleaf. Herbert Stoddard and the rise of ecological land management.* Athens, GA: University of Georgia Press.

Wear, D. N., & Coulston, J. W. (2015). From sink to source: Regional variation in U.S. forest carbon futures. *Scientific Reports, 5,* 16518.

Wear, D. N., Liu, R., Foreman, J. M., & Sheffield, R. M. (1999). The effects of population growth on timber management and inventories in Virginia. *Forest Ecology and Management, 118,* 107–115.

Wear, D. N., & Murray, B. C. (2004). Federal timber restrictions, interregional spillovers, and the impact on U.S. softwood markets. *Journal of Environmental Economics and Management, 47,* 307–330.

Weaver, H. (1943). Fire as an ecological and silvicultural factor in the ponderosa pine region of the Pacific slope. *Journal of Forestry, 41,* 7–14.

Weber, E. P. (2003). *Bringing society back in: Grassroots ecosystem management, accountability, and sustainable communities.* Cambridge, MA: MIT Press.

Welsh, H. H., & Droege, S. (2001). The case for using plethodontid salamanders for monitoring biodiversity and ecosystem integrity of North American forests. *Conservation Biology, 15*(3), 558–569.

West, N. E. (1968). Rodent-influenced establishment of ponderosa pine and bitterbrush seedlings in central Oregon. *Ecology, 49*(5), 1009–1011.

Westerling, A. L., Hidalgo H. G., Cayan, D. R., & Swetnam T. W. (2006). Warming and earlier spring increase western U.S. forest wildfire activity. *Science, 313*(5789), 940–943.

Westerling, A., Brown, T., Schoennagel, T., Swetnam, T., Turner, M., & Veblen, T. (2014). Briefing: Climate and wildfire in western U.S. forests. In V. Alaric & R. P. Bixler (Eds.), *Forest conservation and management in the Anthropocene: Conference proceedings.* Proceedings RMRS-P-71 (pp. 81–102). Fort Collins, CO: US Department of Agriculture, Forest Service. Rocky Mountain Research Station.

Westoby, J. (1989). *Introduction to world forestry: People and their trees.* Oxford, UK: Blackwell.

Wheeler, A. (2012). Case Study: Roseburg District Pilot Project. *Journal of Forestry, 110*(8), 439–441.

Wiersum, K. F. (1995). 200 years of sustainability in forestry: Lessons from history. *Environmental Management, 19*(3), 321–329.

Wilent, S. (2017). BMPs: Standard operating procedures in the south. *The Forestry Source, 22*(8), 6–7. Retrieved from http://www.nxtbook.com/nxtbooks/saf/forestrysource_201708/index.php

Wilcove, D. S., Rothstein, D., Dubow, J., Phillips, A., & Lasos, E. (2000). Leading threats to biodiversity: What's imperiling US species? In B. A. Stein, L. S. Kutner, & J. S. Adams (Eds.), *Precious heritage* (pp. 239–254). Oxford, UK: Oxford University Press.

Willig, R. D. (1976). Consumer surplus without apology. *American Economic Review, 66,* 345–356.

Wilson, D., Timmel, J., Miller, R. (2004). Cognitive cooperation: When the going gets tough, think as a group. Human Nature 15(3):225–250.

Wilson, E. O. (1999). *The diversity of life* (2nd ed.). New York, NY: W. W. Norton & Company.

Wilson, E. O., & Peter, F. M. (Eds.). (1988). *Biodiversity: Papers from the 1st National Forum on Biodiversity, September 1986.* Washington, DC: National Academy of Sciences.

Wimberly, M. C. (2002). Spatial simulation of historical landscape patterns in coastal forests of the Pacific Northwest. *Canadian Journal of Forest Research, 32,* 1316–1328.

Wimberly, M. C., Cochrane M. A., Baer A., & Pabst, K. (2009). Assessing fuel treatment effectiveness using satellite imagery and spatial statistics. *Ecological Applications, 19,* 1377–1384.

Wondolleck, J. M. (1988). *Public lands conflict and resolution: Managing national forest disputes.* New York, NY: Plenum.

Wondolleck, J. M., & Yaffee S. L. (2000). *Making collaboration work: Lessons from innovation in natural resource management.* Washington, DC: Island Press.

World Commission on Environment and Development (WCED). (1987). *Our Common Future.* Oxford, UK: Oxford University Press.

Worrell, A. C. (1970). *Principles of forest policy.* New York, NY: McGraw Hill.

Yaffee, S. (1994). *The wisdom of the northern spotted owl: Policy lessons for a new century.* Washington, DC: Island Press.

Yamamoto, Y., Skinkuma, T., & Takeuchi, K. (2014). Is there a price premium for certified wood? Empirical evidence from log auction data in Japan. *Forest Policy and Economics, 38,* 168–172.

Zald, H. S., Spies, T. A., Harmon, M. E., & Twery, M. J. (2015). Forest carbon calculators: A Review for managers, policymakers, and educators. *Journal of Forestry, 114,* 134–143.

Zhang, D., & Mehmood, S. R. (2002). Safe harbor for the red-cockaded woodpecker: Private forest landowners share their views. *Journal of Forestry, 100*(5), 24–29.

Zhao, K., & Jackson, B. (2014). Biophysical forcings of land-use changes from potential forestry activities in North America. *Ecological Monographs, 82*(2), 329–353.

Zinke, P. J. (1962). The pattern of influence of individual forest trees on soil properties. *Ecology, 43*(1), 130–133.

Zinke, P. J., & Crocker, R. L. (1962). The influence of Giant Sequoia on soil properties. *Forest Science, 8*(1), 2–11.

Zsambok, C. E., & Klein, G. (Eds.). (1997). *Naturalistic decision making.* Mahwah, NJ: Lawarence Erlbaum.

# Index